Plant Pests of Importance to North American Agriculture

Index of Plant Virus Diseases

Agriculture Handbook No. 307

Agricultural Research Service

U.S. DEPARTMENT OF AGRICULTURE

Washington, D.C.

Issued May 1966

For sale by the Superintendent of Documents, U.S. Government Printing Office, Washington, D.C., 20402 - Price $2.50

FOREWORD

This "Index of Plant Virus Diseases" complements the "Index of Plant Diseases in the United States," Agriculture Handbook No. 165, published in 1960. The content of the present index is subject to two limitations. First, it takes into account only records published in the English language. Second, the cutoff date is 1958, since funds allotted were not sufficient to continue it further.

In spite of these restrictions, the index should be useful from both research and practical standpoints.

The background material provided will aid virologists in planning research, in identifying and classifying viruses, and in predicting the reaction to a given virus of additional plants outside the known host range.

Regulatory programs will have many uses for the index. It will aid quarantine inspectors at ports of importation in the diagnosis of visible, and the detection of latent, virus infections. It will provide an authoritative basis for quarantine legislation against any particular virus and its hosts.

The information on distribution of plant viruses will be particularly useful in assessing the probable danger from introducing destructive viruses hitherto absent from this country. A feature of particular significance in times of national emergency is the provision of a basis for judging the likelihood of the synthesis of new viruses or of new strains of existing viruses that might severely damage vulnerable important crops.

PAUL R. MILLER,
Crops Research Division,
Beltsville, Md.

PREFACE

This "Index of Plant Virus Diseases" is the out-growth of a compilation started 24 years ago with technical assistance by the Rev. C. L. Bliss, 1941–42, and supported by a Public Works Administration (PWA) project to prepare lists of names of hosts of plant viruses for quick reference. The names of host plants and viruses in K. M. Smith's book, "A Textbook of Plant Virus Diseases" (1937), were rearranged to provide the desired lists; that is, alphabetical lists of plants susceptible to some common viruses. These lists proved to be timesaving and helpful in various searches for information on known hosts of viruses. In 1958, R. E. Fitzpatrick and others in their "Index of Hosts and Vectors of Plant Viruses" compiled some lists from the second edition of K. M. Smith's book (1957). This "Index of Plant Virus Diseases" enlarges these lists and serves as a companion handbook to "Index of Plant Diseases in the United States," Agriculture Handbook No. 165.

From my World War II experience in the use of coded cards (Soldier Qualification Card) it seemed worthwhile to use coded cards in compiling from the literature the names of flowering plants susceptible or insusceptible to viruses, provided financial support for technical assistance could be found. A 2-year grant in 1956 provided services of a technical compiler who retrieved a part of the desired information from research articles and typed this information on approximately 25,000 coded cards. Description of the system was published by the National Science Foundation in "Nonconventional Technical Information Systems in Current Use," No. 2 (NSF–59–49), pp. 61–63, September 1959; and No. 3 (NSF–62–34), pp. 40–41, October 1962. A second grant in March 1964 permitted the organization of the material for the Index—Subindices I through VII, inclusive.

The indices were prepared by assembling data on the coded cards and photographing these data. The manner of presenting the data is sometimes inconsistent with regular usage. For example, for the sake of clearness and convenience of typing, scientific names of plants and viruses have not been italicized or underlined. Also, a comma has been inserted between Latin and authority names. This comma is omitted in regular usage.

Responsibility for the designation of plant susceptibility or insusceptibility is solely with the authors of the original publications, cited here by authors and year of publication. Decision to include the information in the index was based upon the evidence for susceptibility or insusceptibility in the original article. In some cases a plant name will appear in both the susceptible and the insusceptible list. This double listing is unavoidable since cultivars within a plant species, or *varietas* (smallest taxon considered), sometimes differ in their susceptibility to a virus. Journal name and page citation of the original article are not given, to conserve space and to exclude reference material that would tend to distract the reader's attention from primary information. With the name of the authors and year of publication, one can quickly find the full citation in indices of comprehensive abstracting journals or in private collections of reprints if available and filed or cross-referenced by the author.

Sole authorship of the compendium is taken for three reasons: (1) To indicate the originator of the plan and the maker of decisions relative to undertaking the program, obtaining support, compiling the information, and preparing the manuscript; (2) to simplify author citation; and (3) to center responsibility for the index and the work done by those giving technical assistance to the project.

CONTENTS

	Page
Scope	V
Nomenclature	V
Binomials of plant species	V
Names of viruses	V
Scientific names: plant viruses	V
Scientific names: families and genera	VI
Biovectors of viruses	VI
Subindex I: Plants susceptible—viruses	1
Subindex II: Plants insusceptible—viruses	135
Subindex III: Virus—plants susceptible	217
Subindex IV: Virus—plants insusceptible	337
Subindex V: Scientific names—plant viruses	407
Subindex VI: Scientific names—plant families	437
Subindex VII: Scientific names—plant genera	439

Plant Pests of Importance to North American Agriculture
INDEX OF PLANT VIRUS DISEASES

By H. H. Thornberry, plant pathologist, University of Illinois

SCOPE

The purpose of this index is to provide checklists in the form of a readily accessible and quick-reference handbook of published information on plants susceptible or insusceptible to viruses in order that the results of research can be more fully utilized.

Coverage of information is incomplete since the retrieval aspects of the program terminated in 1958. Original articles, not abstract journals, were reviewed. Publications in modern languages other than English were not examined.

NOMENCLATURE

Binomials of Plant Species

Binomials of plant species in the index have been edited to conform to the nomenclature of species in Agriculture Handbook 165. For names of species not given in the handbook, the binomial and authority are those given by the author publishing the information. Where binominal authority was not given in the original article (or not copied on the "work" card), authority found in "Index Kewensis," Gray's "Manual of Botany," or Britton and Brown's "Illustrated Flora of the Northern States and Canada" (in this order) was given. Binomials for which authority was not found in the taxonomic references are designated by an asterisk. Authority and year for plant binomials are included in Subindices I and II but not in Subindices III and IV.

Names of Viruses

The virus names taken from the literature for the index have been edited to conform to the names in "Common Names of Virus Diseases Used in the Review of Applied Mycology," Review of Applied Mycology Supplement (35: 1–78. 1957). Authority for the virus names is not included in Subindices I and II in order to confine the virus name to one line. This arrangement conserves space and permits easy reading since each line has its specific information. Authority for the names is included in Subindices III and IV.

For virus names not given in the Review of Applied Mycology Supplement, the names are those used by the authors; these are designated by an asterisk. In cases where the virus name used by the author did not contain a plant name (common or Latin binomial), the plant name (in parentheses) has been added.

Word order of the virus names was changed in order to comply with a logical sequence in a systematic word order indicating subordination or subdivision from left to right. The substantive (virus) of the name was placed first (left), followed by the qualifying epithets, a plant name (common or Latin binomial), and a letter or word (or words) designating further description. In addition to the logical sequence, the word order permits an economy of space since the abbreviation for virus (V.) allows the name to be confined to one line. The word order also prevents any momentary confusion of a virus name with the Latin genus name of a plant in cases where the first element in the virus name in the Review of Applied Mycology Supplement is a plant genus name; for example, chrysanthemum stunt virus.

Translated names of viruses or viral diseases by V. Bojnansky may provide aid to users of the index. (Bojnansky, V. 1961. Virus Diseases Terminology, "Rostlinna vyroba," Sbornik Cesko-slovenske Akademie Zemedelskych Ved, Praha 34 (Rocnik 7): 1437–1462.)

Scientific Names: Plant Viruses

Latin binomials (scientific names) of viruses were not used in the checklists herein because the list of names compiled by F. A. Barkley for inclusion in "Index Bergeyana" was omitted from that publication. To make these viral binomials accessible, they are included here, with Barkley's consent, in Subindex V. The material was supplied by R. E. Buchanan, November 18, 1963, and June 8, 1964.

Scientific Names: Families and Genera

Scientific names of families of flowering plants treated in the index are given in alphabetical order in Subindex VI; scientific names of plant genera are in Subindex VII.

BIOVECTORS OF VIRUSES

Retrieved information in the coded-card file on biovectors was not included in this index as originally planned because the information, incomplete in the card file, is largely available in some other compendia readily accessible to most virologists or other scientists and technical personnel having need for the information. Some of these publications are:

Carter, W. Insects in relation to plant diseases. 705 pp. Interscience Publishers, A division of John Wiley and Sons, New York. 1962.

Entomological Society of America. Common names of insects. Bul. Ent. Soc. Amer. 6(4): 173–211. 1960.

Heinze, Kurt. Phytopathogene viren und ihre uberträger. 290 pp. Ducker und Humblot, Berlin, Germany. 1959.

Kennedy, J. S., Day, M. F., and Eastop, V. F. A conspectus of aphids as vectors of plant viruses. 114 pp. Commonwealth Institute of Entomology. London. 1962.

Nielson, M. W. A synonymical list of leafhopper vectors of plant viruses (Homoptera, Cicadellidae). U.S. Dept. Agr., Agr. Res. Serv. ARS 33–74, 12 pp. 1962.

ABROMA Jacq. 1776 (Sterculiaceae)
A. augusta, L. f.
   V. cacao swollen shoot
      Tinsley, T.W. and A.L. Wharton, 1958

ABUTILON Tourn. ex Adans. 1763 (Malvaceae)
A. mulleri friderici, Gurke & K. Schum.
   V. abutilon infectious variegation
      Keur, John Y., 1933
A. regnellii, Miq. in Linnaea
   V. abutilon infectious variegation
      Keur, John Y., 1933
A. spp.
   V. cotton leaf curl
      (K.M. Smith, 1957) R.E. Fitzpatrick, et al., 1958
A. striatum, Dicks., clone thompsonii, Veitch
   V. abutilon infectious variegation
      Keur, John Y., 1933, 1934
A. theophrasti, Medic.
   V. tobacco streak
      Fulton, Robert W., 1948
   V. turnip mosaic
      Walker, J.C., Francis J. LeBeau and Glenn S.
      Pound, 1945

ACACIA ((Tourn.)) L. 1737 (Leguminosae)
A. longifolia, Willd.
   V. lucerne dwarf
      Freitag, J.H., 1951

ACALYPHA L. 1737 (Euphorbiaceae)
A. virginica, L.
   V. tobacco broad ring spot
      Johnson, James and Robert W. Fulton, 1942

ACANTHOSPERMUM Schrank 1819 (Compositae)
A. hispidum, DC.
   V. beet curly top
      Bennett, C.W. and A.S. Costa, 1949

ACER ((Tourn.)) L. 1735 (Aceraceae)
A. ginnala, Maxim.
   V. tobacco ring spot
      Wilkinson, R.E., 1952
A. negundo, L.
   V. tobacco ring spot
      Wilkinson, R.E., 1952

ACHILLEA L. 1735 (Compositae)
A. millefolium, L.
   V. chrysanthemum stunt
      Brierley, Philip, 1953
A. ptarmica, L.
   V. chrysanthemum stunt
      Brierley, Philip, 1950, 1953
      Keller, John R., 1953

ACHYRANTHES L. 1737 (Amaranthaceae)
A. aspera, L.
   V. beet yellows
      Roland, G. and J. Tahon, 1961

ADANSONIA L. 1753 (Bombacaceae)
A. digitata, L.
   V. cacao swollen shoot
      Attafuah, A. and T.W. Tinsley, 1958
      Posnette, A.F., N.F. Robertson and J. McA.
      Todd, 1950
      Tinsley, T.W. and A.L. Wharton, 1958

ADENIA Forsk. 1775 (Passifloraceae)
A. spp.
   V. cucumber mosaic
      Nattrass, R.M., 1944

ADLUMIA Raf. 1808 (Papaveraceae)
A. fungosa, Greene
   V. tobacco mosaic
      Holmes, Francis O., 1946

ADONIS Dill. ex L. 1735 (Ranunculaceae)
A. aestivalis, L.
   V. aster yellows
      (K.M. Smith, 1957) R.E. Fitzpatrick, et al., 1958

AEGILOPS L. 1737 (Gramineae)
A. crassa, Boiss.
   V. wheat streak mosaic
      McKinney, H.H. and Hurley Fellows, 1951
A. cylindrica, Host
   V. wheat streak mosaic
      McKinney, H.H. and Hurley Fellows, 1951
A. ovata, L.
   V. wheat streak mosaic
      McKinney, H.H. and Hurley Fellows, 1951
A. triuncialis, L.
   V. barley yellow dwarf
      Oswald, John W. and Byron R. Houston, 1953
   V. wheat streak mosaic
      McKinney, H.H. and Hurley Fellows, 1951
A. ventricosa, Tausch
   V. wheat streak mosaic
      McKinney, H.H. and Hurley Fellows, 1951

AEGLOPSIS Swingle 1911 (Rutaceae)
A. chevalieri, Swingle
   V. citrus tristeza
      Hughes, W.A. and C.A. Lister, 1953
      Knorr, L.C., 1956

AESCHYNOMENE L. 1737 (Leguminosae)
A. falcata, (Poir.) DC.
   V. (legume) little leaf disease *
      Hutton, E.M. and N.E. Grylls, 1956
A. indica, L.
   V. tobacco streak
      Fulton, Robert W., 1948

AFRAEGLE Stapf 1906 (Rutaceae)
A. paniculata, (Schum.) Engl.
   V. citrus tristeza
      Hughes, W.A. and C.A. Lister, 1953
      Knorr, L.C., 1956

AGERATUM L. 1737 (Compositae)
A. conyzoides, L.
   V. anemone mosaic *
      Hollings, M., 1957
   V. tobacco leaf curl
      Pruthi, Hem Singh and C.K. Samuel, 1939
A. spp.
   V. tobacco necrosis
      Price, W.C., 1940

AGROPYRON J. Gaertn. 1770 (Gramineae)
A. elongatum, (Host) Beauv.
   V. agropyron mosaic
      Slykhuis, J.T., 1952
   V. wheat streak mosaic
      McKinney, H.H. and W.J. Sando, 1951
A. hybrid
   V. barley stripe mosaic
      Sill, W.H., Jr., 1956
   V. brome mosaic
      Sill, W.H., Jr., 1956
   V. wheat streak mosaic
      Sill, W.H., Jr., 1956
A. inerme, (Scribn. & Sm.) Rydb.
   V. agropyron mosaic
      Slykhuis, J.T., 1952
   V. barley yellow dwarf
      Bruehl, G.W. and H.V. Toko, 1957
A. intermedium, (Host) Beauv.
   V. agropyron mosaic
      Slykhuis, J.T., 1952
   V. barley yellow dwarf
      Bruehl, G.W. and H.V. Toko, 1957
   V. wheat streak mosaic
      McKinney, H.H. and W.J. Sando, 1951
A. junceum, (L.) Beauv.
   V. agropyron mosaic
      Slykhuis, J.T., 1952
A. lasianthum, Boiss.
   V. wheat streak mosaic
      McKinney, H.H. and W.J. Sando, 1951
A. pertenue, (Mey.) Nevski
   V. agropyron mosaic
      Slykhuis, J.T., 1952

A. pungens, (Pers.) Roem. & Schult.
   V. wheat streak mosaic
      McKinney, H.H. and W.J. Sando, 1951
A. repens, L.
   V. agropyron mosaic
      Slykhuis, J.T., 1952
   V. oat pseudo-rosette
      (K.M. Smith, 1957) R.E. Fitzpatrick, et al., 1958
A. rigidum, Beauv.
   V. agropyron mosaic
      Slykhuis, J.T., 1952
A. trachycaulum, (Link) Malte
   V. barley yellow dwarf
      Oswald, John W. and Byron R. Houston, 1953
   V. wheat streak mosaic
      McKinney, H.H. and W.J. Sando, 1951
A. ugamicum, Drobov
   V. wheat streak mosaic
      McKinney, H.H. and W.J. Sando, 1951

AIZOON L. 1737 (Aizoaceae)
A. spp.
   V. beet yellows
      Roland, G. and J. Tahon, 1961

ALEURITES Forst. 1776 (Euphorbiaceae)
A. fordii, Hemsl.
   V. (tung) rough bark *
      Large, John R., 1949

ALLIUM ((Tourn.)) L. 1735 (Liliaceae)
A. ascalonicum, L.
   V. aster yellows
      Smith, Floyd F. and Philip Brierley, 1948
   V. onion yellow dwarf
      Henderson, D.M., 1953
      Henderson, W.J., 1935
A. canadense, L.
   V. onion mosaic
      McKinney, H.H., 1928
A. cepa, L.
   V. aster yellows
      Brierley, Philip and Floyd F. Smith, 1944
      Severin, Henry H.P. and Julius H. Freitag, 1945
   V. bayberry yellows
      Raychaudhuri, S.P., 1953
   V. cucumber mosaic
      Wellman, F.L., 1935
   V. onion mosaic
      Brierley, Philip and Floyd F. Smith, 1944
   V. onion yellow dwarf
      Brierley, Philip and Floyd F. Smith, 1946
      Henderson, D.M., 1953
      Henderson, W.J., 1932, 1935
      Melhus, I.E. and W.J. Henderson, 1929
      Melhus, I.E., C.S. Reddy, W.J. Henderson and
      E. Vestal, 1929
A. cepa var. solaninum, Alef.
   V. onion yellow dwarf
      Brierley, Philip and Floyd F. Smith, 1944
A. cepa var. viviparum, Metz.
   V. onion yellow dwarf
      Brierley, Philip and Floyd F. Smith, 1944
A. neopolitanum, Cyr.
   V. onion mosaic
      Brierley, Philip and Floyd F. Smith, 1944
A. porrum, L.
   V. onion yellow dwarf
      (K.M. Smith, 1957) R.E. Fitzpatrick, et al., 1958
A. sativum, L.
   V. onion mosaic
      Brierley, Philip and Floyd F. Smith, 1944
   V. onion yellow dwarf
      (K.M. Smith, 1957) R.E. Fitzpatrick, et al., 1958
A. vineale, L.
   V. onion mosaic
      Brierley, Philip and Floyd F. Smith, 1944
   V. onion yellow dwarf
      Brierley, Philip and Floyd F. Smith, 1944

ALONSOA Ruiz & Pav. 1798 (Scrophulariaceae)
A. warscewicizii, Regel
   V. anemone mosaic *
      Hollings, M., 1957

A. warscewiczii, Regel (cont.)
   V. cabbage black ring spot
      Hollings, M., 1957

ALOPECURUS L. 1735 (Gramineae)
A. fulvus, Small
   V. rice dwarf
      (K.M. Smith, 1957) R.E. Fitzpatrick, et al., 1958

ALTERNANTHERA Forsk. 1775 (Amaranthaceae)
A. ficoidea, (L.) R. Br.
   V. cucumber mosaic
      Dale, W.T., 1954

ALTHAEA ((Tourn.)) L. 1735 (Malvaceae)
A. rosea, (L.) Cav.
   V. abutilon infectious variegation
      Bird, Julio, 1958
   V. carnation ring spot
      Brierley, Philip and Floyd F. Smith, 1957
   V. cotton leaf curl
      (K.M. Smith, 1957) R.E. Fitzpatrick, et al., 1958
   V. hibiscus yellow vein mosaic
      Capoor, S.P. and P.M. Varma, 1950
   V. hollyhock mosaic
      (K.M. Smith, 1957) R.E. Fitzpatrick, et al., 1958
   V. tobacco leaf curl
      (K.M. Smith, 1957) R.E. Fitzpatrick, et al., 1958
   V. tobacco ring spot no. 2
      Wilkinson, R.E., 1952a
   V. tobacco streak
      Fulton, Robert W., 1948

ALYSSUM Tourn. ex L. 1735 (Cruciferae)
A. compactum var. procumbens *
   V. aster yellows
      Kunkel, L.O., 1926
A. maritimum, Lam.
   V. turnip mosaic
      Tompkins, C.M., 1939

AMARANTHUS L. 1735 (Amaranthaceae)
A. albus, L.
   V. beet yellows
      Roland, G. and J. Tahon, 1961
A. aureus, F.G. Dietr.
   V. beet yellows
      Roland, G. and J. Tahon, 1961
A. auroro or aurora *
   V. aster yellows
      Kunkel, L.O., 1926
   V. beet curly top
      Freitag, Julius H. and Henry H.P. Severin, 1936
A. caracu, Zucc. ex Steud.
   V. beet yellows
      Roland, G. and J. Tahon, 1961
A. carneus, Hort. ex Moq. in DC.
   V. beet yellows
      Roland, G. and J. Tahon, 1961
A. caudatus, L.
   V. anemone brown ring *
      Hollings, M., 1958
   V. anemone mosaic *
      Hollings, M., 1957
   V. aster yellows
      Kunkel, L.O., 1926
   V. beet curly top
      Freitag, Julius H. and Henry H.P. Severin, 1936
   V. beet mosaic
      (K.M. Smith, 1957) R.E. Fitzpatrick, et al., 1958
   V. beet yellows
      Roland, G. and J. Tahon, 1961
   V. cabbage black ring spot
      Hollings, M., 1957
   V. chrysanthemum latent *
      Hollings, M., 1957
   V. cucumber mosaic
      Fulton, Joseph P., 1950
      Pound, Glenn S. and J.C. Walker, 1948
      Price, W.C., 1940
   V. lucerne mosaic
      Price, W.C., 1940
   V. potato leaf rolling mosaic
      (K.M. Smith, 1957) R.E. Fitzpatrick, et al., 1958

A. caudatus, L. (cont.)
    V. tobacco necrosis
        Price, W.C., 1940
    V. tobacco ring spot
        Fulton, Robert W., 1941
        Price, W.C., 1940
    V. tobacco ring spot no. 2
        Hildebrand, E.M., 1942
        Price, W.C., 1940
    V. tomato bushy stunt
        (K.M. Smith, 1957) R.E. Fitzpatrick, et al., 1958
    V. turnip mosaic
        Pound, Glenn S., 1948
A. cruentus, L.
    V. beet yellows
        Roland, G. and J. Tahon, 1961
A. deflexus, L.
    V. beet curly top
        Severin, Henry H.P., 1934
    V. beet yellows
        Roland, G. and J. Tahon, 1961
A. gangeticus, L.
    V. beet curly top
        Freitag, Julius H. and Henry H.P. Severin, 1936
    V. beet yellows
        Roland, G. and J. Tahon, 1961
    V. potato X
        Hutton, E.M., 1949
A. graecizans, L.
    V. beet curly top
        Carsner, E., 1919
        Severin, Henry H.P., 1934
    V. beet yellows
        Roland, G. and J. Tahon, 1961
    V. potato leaf roll
        (K.M. Smith, 1957) R.E. Fitzpatrick, et al., 1958
    V. tobacco mosaic
        Holmes, Francis O., 1938
A. hybridus, L.
    V. tobacco mosaic
        Holmes, Francis O., 1938
A. palmeri, S. Wats.
    V. beet yellows
        Roland, G. and J. Tahon, 1961
A. paniculatus, L.
    V. beet yellows
        Roland, G. and J. Tahon, 1961
    V. tobacco broad ring spot
        (K.M. Smith, 1957) R.E. Fitzpatrick, et al., 1958
    V. tobacco ring spot
        Wingard, S.A., 1928
A. patulus, Bert.
    V. beet yellows
        Roland, G. and J. Tahon, 1961
A. retroflexus, L.
    V. aster yellows
        Frazier, Norman W. and Henry H.P. Severin, 1945
    V. beet curly top
        Severin, Henry H.P., 1934
    V. beet mosaic
        Bennett, C.W., 1949
        Pound, Glenn S., 1947
    V. beet yellows
        Roland, G. and J. Tahon, 1961
    V. cucurbit mosaic *
        Doolittle, S.P., 1921
        Doolittle, S.P. and M.N. Walker, 1925
    V. hydrangea ring spot
        Brierley, Philip and Paul Lorentz, 1956, 1957
    V. iris ring spot *
        Travis, R.V., 1957
    V. potato leaf roll
        (K.M. Smith, 1957) R.E. Fitzpatrick, et al., 1958
    V. potato X
        Dykstra, T.P., 1939
        Larson, R.H., 1944
    V. tobacco broad ring spot
        Johnson, James and Robert W. Fulton, 1942
    V. tomato ring spot
        Samson, R.W. and E.P. Imle, 1942
    V. tomato spotted wilt
        Milbrath, J.A., 1939

A. tricolor, L.
    V. cucumber mosaic
        Price, W.C., 1940
    V. red currant ring spot
        Klesser, P.J., 1951
    V. tobacco mosaic
        Holmes, Francis O., 1946
    V. tomato ring spot
        Samson, R.W. and E.P. Imle, 1942
    V. turnip mosaic
        Walker, J.C., Francis J. LeBeau and Glenn S. Pound, 1945

AMARYLLIS L. 1735 (Amaryllidaceae)
(HIPPEASTRUM) Herb. 1821
A. hybrid
    V. tomato spotted wilt
        Gardner, M.W., C.M. Tompkins and O.C. Whipple, 1935
(H. spp.)
    V. tomato spotted wilt
        (K.M. Smith, 1957) R.E. Fitzpatrick, et al., 1958

AMBROSIA L. 1737 (Compositae)
A. artemisiifolia, L.
    V. aster yellows
        Kunkel, L.O., 1926
        Younkin, S.G., 1943
    V. beet leaf curl
        (K.M. Smith, 1957) R.E. Fitzpatrick, et al., 1958
    V. tobacco mosaic
        Boyle, John S. and David C. Wharton, 1957
        Holmes, Francis O., 1938
    V. tobacco ring spot
        Wingard, S.A., 1928
    V. tobacco streak
        Fulton, Robert W., 1948
A. artemisiifolia var. elatior, (L.) Descourtils
    V. cucumber mosaic
        Wellman, F.L., 1935
A. trifida, L.
    V. aster yellows
        Kunkel, L.O., 1926
    V. chrysanthemum stunt
        Brierley, Philip, 1953
    V. tobacco mosaic
        Holmes, Francis O., 1938, 1946
    V. tobacco ring spot
        Wingard, S.A., 1928
    V. tobacco streak
        Fulton, Robert W., 1948

AMELANCHIER Medic. 1789 (Rosaceae)
A. spp.
    V. apple *
        Millikan, D.F. and H.W. Guengerich, 1956

AMMOBIUM R. Br. 1824 (Compositae)
A. alatum, R. Br.
    V. aster yellows
        Kunkel, L.O., 1926

AMSINCKIA Lehm. 1831 (Boraginaceae)
A. douglasiana, DC.
    V. lucerne dwarf
        Freitag, J.H., 1951

ANAGALLIS ((Tourn.)) L. 1735 (Primulaceae)
A. arvensis, L.
    V. aster yellows
        Frazier, Norman W. and Henry H.P. Severin, 1945
    V. beet curly top
        Severin, Henry H.P., 1934
    V. raspberry yellow dwarf *
        Harrison, B.D., 1958
    V. strawberry green petal
        Frazier, N.W. and A.F. Posnette, 1957
    V. tobacco mosaic
        Holmes, Francis O., 1946
A. linifolia, L.
    V. clover big vein
        Black, L.M., 1945

ANANAS Tourn. ex L. 1735 (Bromeliaceae)
A. comosus, (L.) Merr.
 V. cucumber mosaic
  Carter, W., 1935
 V. tomato spotted wilt
  Carter, W., 1935
  Illingworth, J.F., 1931
  Linford, M.B., 1931, 1932, 1943
  Sakimura, K., 1940

ANCHUSA L. 1735 (Boraginaceae)
A. azurea, Mill.
 V. beet curly top
  Freitag, Julius H. and Henry H.P. Severin, 1936
 V. tobacco mosaic
  Holmes, Francis O., 1946
A. capensis, Thunb.
 V. cabbage black ring spot
  (K.M. Smith, 1957) R.E. Fitzpatrick, et al., 1958
 V. tobacco mosaic
  Holmes, Francis O., 1946
A. spp.
 V. cucumber mosaic
  (K.M. Smith, 1957) R.E. Fitzpatrick, et al., 1958

ANDROCERA Nutt. 1818 (Solanaceae)
A. rostrata, Rydb.
 V. tomato ring spot
  Samson, R.W. and E.P. Imle, 1942

ANDROPOGON L. 1753 (Gramineae)
A. barbinodis, Lag.
 V. barley yellow dwarf
  Oswald, John W. and Byron R. Houston, 1953
A. sorghum, (L.) Brot.
 V. sugarcane mosaic
  Lawas, Orencio M. and William L. Fernandez,
  1949
A. sorghum var. virgatus *
 V. sugarcane mosaic
  (K.M. Smith, 1957) R.E. Fitzpatrick, et al., 1958

ANEMONE L. 1735 (Ranunculaceae)
A. coronaria, L.
 V. anemone brown ring *
  Hollings, M., 1958
 V. anemone mosaic *
  Hollings, M., 1957
 V. aster yellows
  Severin, Henry H.P. and Julius H. Freitag, 1945
 V. beet curly top
  Freitag, Julius H. and Henry H.P. Severin, 1936
A. nemorosa, L.
 V. anemone mosaic *
  Hollings, M., 1957
 V. cabbage black ring spot
  Hollings, M., 1957
A. spp.
 V. tomato spotted wilt
  (K.M. Smith, 1957) R.E. Fitzpatrick, et al., 1958

ANETHUM Tourn. ex L. 1737 (Umbelliferae)
A. graveolens, L.
 V. aster yellows
  Kunkel, L.O., 1926
 V. beet curly top
  Severin, Henry H.P., 1929
 V. celery mosaic
  Freitag, Julius H. and Henry H.P. Severin, 1945
  Severin, Henry H.P. and Julius H. Freitag, 1938
 V. cucumber mosaic
  Wellman, F.L., 1935
 V. poison hemlock ring spot
  Freitag, Julius H. and Henry H.P. Severin, 1945

ANGRAECUM Bory 1804 (Orchidaceae)
A. eburneum, Lindl.
 V. orchid (cymbidium) mosaic
  Jensen, D.D. and A.H. Gold, 1955

ANTHEMIS Mich. ex L. 1735 (Compositae)
A. cotula, L.
 V. aster yellows
  Frazier, Norman W. and Henry H.P. Severin, 1945

A. cotula, L. (cont.)
 V. beet curly top
  Severin, Henry H.P., 1934
 V. clover big vein
  Black, L.M., 1945
 V. clover witches' broom *
  Frazier, N.W. and A.F. Posnette, 1957
 V. cucumber mosaic
  Burnett, G., 1934
 V. strawberry green petal
  Frazier, N.W. and A.F. Posnette, 1957
A. tinctoria, L.
 V. chrysanthemum stunt
  Brierley, Philip, 1950, 1953

ANTHOXANTHUM L. 1737 (Gramineae)
A. odoratum, L.
 V. barley yellow dwarf
  Oswald, John W. and Byron R. Houston, 1953

ANTHRISCUS Bernh. 1800 (Umbelliferae)
A. cerefolium, Hoffm.
 V. beet curly top
  Severin, Henry H.P., 1929
 V. celery mosaic
  Freitag, Julius H. and Henry H.P. Severin, 1945
  Severin, Henry H.P. and Julius H. Freitag, 1938
 V. cucumber mosaic
  Price, W.C., 1940
 V. lucerne mosaic
  Price, W.C., 1940
 V. poison hemlock ring spot
  Freitag, Julius H. and Henry H.P. Severin, 1945
 V. squash mosaic
  Freitag, J.H., 1956
 V. tobacco necrosis
  Price, W.C., 1940
 V. tobacco ring spot
  Price, W.C., 1940
 V. tobacco ring spot no. 2
  Price, W.C., 1940

ANTIRRHINUM Tourn. ex L. 1735 (Scrophulariaceae)
A. majus, L.
 V. carnation ring spot
  Brierley, Philip and Floyd F. Smith, 1957
 V. chrysanthemum latent *
  Hollings, M., 1957
 V. cucumber mosaic
  Berkeley, G.H., 1951, 1953
  Brierley, Philip, 1952
  Doolittle, S.P. and W.J. Zaumeyer, 1953
  Hollings, M., 1955
  Nienow, Inez, 1948
  Pound, Glenn S. and J.C. Walker, 1948
  Wellman, F.L., 1935
 V. hydrangea ring spot
  Brierley, Philip and Paul Lorentz, 1956, 1957
 V. lucerne mosaic
  Berkeley, G.H., 1947
  Kreitlow, K.W., and W.C. Price, 1948, 1949
  Price, W.C., 1940
  Zaumeyer, W.J., 1953
 V. pea mottle
  Johnson, Folke, 1942
 V. pelargonium leaf curl
  McWhorter, Frank P., 1957
 V. prunus A *
  Fulton, Robert W., 1957
 V. prunus B *
  Fulton, Robert W., 1957
 V. prunus E *
  Fulton, Robert W., 1957
 V. prunus G *
  Fulton, Robert W., 1957
 V. tobacco broad ring spot
  Johnson, James and Robert W. Fulton, 1942
 V. tobacco mosaic
  Berkeley, G.H., 1951
  Grant, T.J., 1934
  Holmes, Francis O., 1946
 V. tobacco necrosis
  Price, W.C., 1940

A. majus, L. (cont.)
  V. tobacco ring spot
    Berkeley, G.H., 1951, 1953
    Brierley, Philip, 1952
    Brierley, Philip and Floyd F. Smith, 1954
    Travis, R.V. and Philip Brierley, 1957
    Wingard, S.A., 1928
  V. tobacco ring spot no. 2
    Brierley, Philip, 1954
  V. tomato aspermy
    Brierley, Philip, Floyd F. Smith and S.P.
    Doolittle, 1955
    Hollings, M., 1955
A. spp.
  V. chrysanthemum Q
    (K.M. Smith, 1957) R.E. Fitzpatrick, et al., 1958
  V. tobacco streak
    (K.M. Smith, 1957) R.E. Fitzpatrick, et al., 1958
  V. tomato black ring
    (K.M. Smith, 1957) R.E. Fitzpatrick, et al., 1958
  V. tomato spotted wilt
    (K.M. Smith, 1957) R.E. Fitzpatrick, et al., 1958

APIUM ((Tourn.)) L. 1735 (Umbelliferae)
A. graveolens, L.
  V. aster yellows
    George, J.A. and J.K. Richardson, 1957
    Raymer, W.B. and Clark R. Amen, 1954
  V. bayberry yellows
    (K.M. Smith, 1957) R.E. Fitzpatrick, et al., 1958
  V. celery mosaic
    Doolittle, S.P. and F.L. Wellman, 1934
  V. clover witches' broom
    Frazier, N.W. and A.F. Posnette, 1957
  V. cucumber mosaic
    Anderson, C.W., 1955
    Bhargava, K.S., 1951
    Doolittle, S.P. and F.L. Wellman, 1934
    Doolittle, S.P. and W.J. Zaumeyer, 1953
    Fulton, Robert W., 1941
    Wellman, F.L., 1935
  V. dodder latent mosaic
    Bennett, C.W., 1944, 1949
  V. lucerne mosaic
    Berkeley, G.H., 1947
    Houston, Byron R. and John W. Oswald, 1953
    Richardson, D.E. and T.W. Tinsley, 1956
    Snyder, William C. and Saul Rich, 1942
  V. tobacco broad ring spot
    Johnson, James and Robert W. Fulton, 1942
  V. tobacco mosaic
    Holmes, Francis O., 1946
  V. tobacco ring spot
    Anderson, C.W., 1954
  V. tobacco streak
    Fulton, Robert W., 1948
  V. tomato big bud
    Helms, Katie, 1957
  V. vaccinium false blossom
    Kunkel, L.O., 1945
A. graveolens var. dulce, DC.
  V. aster yellows
    Freitag, J.H., 1956
    Magie, R.O., Floyd F. Smith and Philip
    Brierley, 1952
    Raymer, W.B., 1956
    Severin, Henry H.P., 1928, 1929, 1930, 1932,
    1934
    Severin, Henry H.P. and Julius H. Freitag, 1945
    Severin, Henry H.P. and Sidney J. Oliver, 1939
    Smith, Floyd F. and Philip Brierley, 1953
  V. beet curly top
    Severin, Henry H.P., 1928, 1929
  V. celery mosaic
    Bardin, Roy, 1947
    Freitag, Julius H. and Henry H.P. Severin, 1939
    Freitag, Julius H. and Henry H.P. Severin, 1945
    Poole, R.F., 1922
    Severin, Henry H.P. and Julius H. Freitag, 1935,
    1938
  V. (celery) pseudo-calico
    Freitag, Julius H. and Henry H.P. Severin, 1939
  V. celery yellow spot
    Freitag, Julius H. and Henry H.P. Severin, 1939

A. graveolens var. dulce, DC. (cont.)
  V. celery yellow spot
    Freitag, Julius H. and Henry H.P. Severin, 1945
  V. cucumber mosaic
    Anderson, C.W., 1951
    Severin, Henry H.P., 1950
    Simons, John N., 1955, 1957
    Wellman, F.L., 1934
    Whipple, O.C. and J.C. Walker, 1941
  V. lucerne mosaic
    Houston, Byron R. and John W. Oswald, 1951
    Oswald, John W., 1950
    Severin, Henry H.P., 1950
    Severin, Henry H.P. and Julius H. Freitag, 1935
    Swenson, K.G., 1952
  V. peach western X disease
    Jensen, D.D., 1955, 1957
  V. poison hemlock ring spot
    Freitag, Julius H. and Henry H.P. Severin, 1939,
    1945
  V. tobacco ring spot
    Severin, Henry H.P., 1950
  V. tomato spotted wilt
    Gardner, M.W., C.M. Tompkins and O.C.
    Whipple, 1935
    Sakimura, K., 1940
  V. cucumber western mosaic *
    Severin, Henry H.P., 1950
    Severin, Henry H.P. and Julius H. Freitag, 1948
A. graveolens var. rapaceum, DC.
  V. aster yellows
    Severin, Henry H.P., 1929, 1932
    Severin, Henry H.P. and Julius H. Freitag, 1945
  V. celery mosaic
    Freitag, Julius H. and Henry H.P. Severin, 1945
    Severin, Henry H.P. and Julius H. Freitag, 1938
  V. cucumber mosaic
    Wellman, F.L., 1935
  V. poison hemlock ring spot
    Freitag, Julius H. and Henry H.P. Severin, 1945
A. leptophyllum, (DC.) F. Muell. ex Benth.
  V. carrot motley dwarf
    Stubbs, L.L., 1955

APOCYNUM ((Tourn.)) L. 1735 (Apocynaceae)
A. androsaemifolium, L.
  V. prunus A *
    Fulton, Robert W., 1957
  V. prunus B *
    Fulton, Robert W., 1957
  V. prunus E *
    Fulton, Robert W., 1957
  V. prunus G *
    Fulton, Robert W., 1957

AQUILEGIA ((Tourn.)) L. 1735 (Ranunculaceae)
A. caerulea, James
  V. anemone brown ring *
    Hollings, M., 1958
  V. anemone mosaic *
    Hollings, M., 1957
  V. lucerne mosaic
    Price, W.C., 1940
  V. tobacco ring spot
    Price, W.C., 1940
A. vulgaris, L.
  V. cucumber mosaic
    (K.M. Smith, 1957) R.E. Fitzpatrick, et al., 1958
  V. tomato spotted wilt
    (K.M. Smith, 1957) R.E. Fitzpatrick, et al., 1958

ARABIS L. 1737 (Cruciferae)
A. hirsuta, (L.) Scop.
  V. arabis mosaic
    Smith, Kenneth M. and Roy Markham, 1944
  V. lovage mosaic
    Smith, Kenneth M. and Roy Markham, 1944

ARACHIS L. 1735 (Leguminosae)
A. hypogaea, L.
  V. groundnut mosaic
    Cooper, W.E., 1950
  V. groundnut rosette
    Evans, A.C., 1954

A. hypogeae, L. (cont.)
  V. groundnut rosette
    McKinney, H.H., 1929
    Storey, H.H. and A.M. Bottomley, 1928
    Storey, H.H. and Audrie K. Ryland, 1955, 1957
  V. groundnut witches' broom
    (K.M. Smith, 1957) R.E. Fitzpatrick, et al., 1958
  V. tobacco necrosis
    Fulton, Robert W., 1950

ARANDA * (Orchidaceae)
A. spp. (Arachnis hookeriana x Vanda sanderiana)
  V. orchid (vanda) mosaic
    Murakishi, Harry H., 1952

ARCTIUM L. 1735 (Compositae)
A. lappa, L.
  V. tobacco mosaic
    Holmes, Francis O., 1946
  V. tobacco ring spot no. 2
    Wilkinson, R.E., 1952a
A. minus, Bernh.
  V. tobacco streak
    Fulton, Robert W., 1948

ARCTOTIS L. 1737 (Compositae)
A. stoechadifolia, Berg.
  V. beet curly top
    Freitag, Julius H. and Henry H.P. Severin, 1936

ARENARIA Rupp. ex L. 1735 (Caryophyllaceae)
A. montana, L.
  V. carnation ring spot
    Brierley, Philip and Floyd F. Smith, 1957

ARISTIDA L. 1753 (Gramineae)
A. oligantha, Michx.
  V. barley yellow dwarf
    Oswald, John W. and Byron R. Houston, 1953

ARMORACIA Gaertn., Mey. & Scherb. 1800 (Cruci-
A. rusticana, Gaertn., Mey. & Scherb.   ferae)
  V. beet curly top
    Severin, Henry H.P., 1929
  V. turnip mosaic
    Dana, B.F. and F.P. McWhorter, 1932
    Hoggan, I.A. and J. Johnson, 1935
    Pound, Glenn S., 1948, 1949

ARRACACIA Bancroft. 1826 (Umbelliferae)
(ARRACACHA) DC. 1829
A. esculenta, DC.
  V. citrus tristeza
    Costa, A.S. and T.J. Grant, 1951

ARTEMISIA L. 1735 (Compositae)
A. vulgaris, L., var. heterophylla, Jepson
  V. lucerne dwarf
    Freitag, Julius H., 1951

ARUM ((Tourn.)) L. 1735 (Araceae)
A. palaestinum, Boiss.
  V. tomato spotted wilt
    Tompkins, C.M. and Henry H.P. Severin, 1950

ASCLEPIAS L. 1737 (Asclepiadaceae)
A. curassavica, L.
  V. cucumber mosaic
    Silberschmidt, K., 1955
A. nivea, L.
  V. aster yellows
    Kunkel, L.O., 1926
A. syriaca, L.
  V. asclepias yellows *
    Kunkel, L.O., 1950
  V. carnation mosaic
    Gasiorkiewicz, E.C., 1954
  V. cucurbit mosaic *
    Doolittle, S.P., 1921
    Doolittle, S.P. and M.N. Walker, 1922, 1924, 1925
  V. milkweed mosaic *
    Newhall, A.G., 1923

A. syriaca, L. (cont.)
  V. prunus A *
    Fulton, Robert W., 1957
  V. prunus G *
    Fulton, Robert W., 1957
  V. strawberry mottle
    Smith, Harlan E. and J. Duain Moore, 1952
  V. tobacco streak
    Fulton, Robert W., 1948

ASPERULA L. 1735 (Rubiaceae)
A. odorata, L.
  V. tobacco ring spot no. 2
    Price, W.C., 1940

ASTER Tourn. ex L. 1735 (Compositae)
A. amellus, L.
  V. beet mosaic
    Pound, Glenn S., 1947
  V. chrysanthemum B (mild mosaic) *
    Hollings, M., 1957
  V. cucumber mosaic
    Pound, Glenn S. and J.C. Walker, 1948
  V. tobacco ring spot
    Pound, Glenn S., 1949
A. chilensis, Nees
  V. aster yellows
    Frazier, Norman W. and Henry H.P. Severin, 1945
A. dumosus, L.
  V. tobacco mosaic
    Holmes, Francis O., 1938
A. laevis, L.
  V. tobacco ring spot
    Fulton, Robert W., 1941
    Wingard, S.A., 1928
A. novae-angliae, L.
  V. aster yellows
    George, J.A. and J.K. Richardson, 1957
A. spp.
  V. tobacco ring spot
    (K.M. Smith, 1957) R.E. Fitzpatrick et al., 1958
  V. tomato bushy stunt
    (K.M. Smith, 1957) R.E. Fitzpatrick et al., 1958
  V. tomato spotted wilt
    (K.M. Smith, 1957) R.E. Fitzpatrick et al., 1958

ASTRAGALUS Tourn. ex L. 1737 (Leguminosae)
A. chinensis, L.
  V. lucerne witches' broom
    Klostermeyer, E.C. and J.D. Menzies, 1951
A. falcatus, Lam.
  V. lucerne witches' broom
    Klostermeyer, E.C. and J.D. Menzies, 1951
A. glycyphyllus, L.
  V. (legume) little leaf disease *
    Hutton, E.M. and N.E. Grylls, 1956
A. mortoni, Nutt.
  V. lucerne witches' broom
    Klostermeyer, E.C. and J.D. Menzies, 1951
A. rubyi, Greene & Morris
  V. pea enation mosaic
    Hagedorn, D.J., 1957
  V. prunus A *
    Fulton, Robert W., 1957
  V. prunus B *
    Fulton, Robert W., 1957

ATRIPLEX ((Tourn.)) L. 1735 (Chenopodiaceae)
A. argentea, Nutt. subsp. expansa, Hall & Clements
  V. beet curly top
    Severin, Henry H.P., 1934
    Severin, Henry H.P. and Charles F. Henderson, 1928
    Severin, Henry H.P. and Byron R. Houston, 1945
A. argentea var. hillmanii, Jones
  V. beet curly top
    Severin, Henry H.P., 1934
A. bracteosa, S. Wats.
  V. beet curly top
    Severin, Henry H.P., 1934
    Severin, Henry H.P. and Charles F. Henderson, 1928

A. bracteosa, S. Wats. (cont.)
  V. beet curly top
    Severin, Henry H.P. and Byron R. Houston, 1945
  V. beet mosaic
    Severin, Henry H.P. and Roger M. Drake, 1947
  V. beet yellows
    Roland, G. and J. Tahon, 1961
A. canescens, (Pursh) Nutt.
  V. beet yellows
    Roland, G. and J. Tahon, 1961
A. cordulata, Jepson
  V. beet curly top
    Severin, Henry H.P., 1934
    Severin, Henry H.P. and Charles F. Henderson,
    1928
A. coronata, S. Wats.
  V. beet curly top
    Severin, Henry H.P., 1934
    Severin, Henry H.P. and Charles F. Henderson,
    1928
  V. beet yellows
    Roland, G. and J. Tahon, 1961
A. coulteri, D. Dietr.
  V. beet yellows
    Roland, G. and J. Tahon, 1961
A. elegans, (Moq.) D. Dietr.
  V. beet yellows
    Roland, G. and J. Tahon, 1961
A. expansa, (Det. H) S. Wats.
  V. beet yellows
    Roland, G. and J. Tahon, 1961
A. fruticulosa, Jepson
  V. beet curly top
    Severin, Henry H.P., 1934
    Severin, Henry H.P. and Charles F. Henderson,
    1928
A. hortensis, L.
  V. beet mosaic
    Pound, Glenn S., 1947
  V. beet yellows
    Roland, G. and J. Tahon, 1961
A. hortensis var. rubra, L. *
  V. beet curly top
    Severin, Henry H.P., 1934
A. lentiformis, (Torr.) S. Wats.
  V. beet curly top
    Severin, Henry H.P., 1934
    Severin, Henry H.P. and Charles F. Henderson,
    1928
A. microcarpa, D. Dietr.
  V. beet yellows
    Roland, G. and J. Tahon, 1961
A. nitens, Schkuhr
  V. beet yellows
    (K.M. Smith, 1957) R.E. Fitzpatrick, et al., 1958
    Roland, G. and J. Tahon, 1961
A. parishii, S. Wats.
  V. beet curly top
    Severin, Henry H.P., 1934
    Severin, Henry H.P. and Charles F. Henderson,
    1928
A. patula, L.
  V. beet yellows
    Roland, G. and J. Tahon, 1961
A. patula var. hastata, A. Gray
  V. beet curly top
    Severin, Henry H.P., 1934
    Severin, Henry H.P. and Charles F. Henderson,
    1928
  V. beet mosaic
    Severin, Henry H.P. and Roger M. Drake, 1947
  V. beet yellows
    Roland, G. and J. Tahon, 1961
A. phyllostegia, S. Wats.
  V. beet curly top
    Severin, Henry H.P., 1934
    Severin, Henry H.P. and Charles F. Henderson,
    1928
A. rosea, L.
  V. beet curly top
    Severin, Henry H.P., 1934
    Severin, Henry H.P. and Charles F. Henderson,
    1928

A. rosea, L. (cont.)
  V. beet mosaic
    Severin, Henry H.P. and Roger M. Drake, 1947
  V. beet yellows
    Roland, G. and J. Tahon, 1961
A. semibaccata, R. Br.
  V. beet curly top
    Severin, Henry H.P., 1934
    Severin, Henry H.P. and Charles F. Henderson,
    1928
  V. beet yellows
    Roland, G. and J. Tahon, 1961
A. siberica, L.
  V. beet yellows
    Roland, G. and J. Tahon, 1961
A. spongiosa, F. Muell.
  V. beet yellows
    Roland, G. and J. Tahon, 1961
A. tularensis, Coult.
  V. beet curly top
    Severin, Henry H.P., 1934
    Severin, Henry H.P. and Charles F. Henderson,
    1928

ATROPA L. 1737 (Solanaceae)
A. belladonna, L.
  V. atropa belladonna mosaic
    R.A.M. 22: 451, 1943
  V. cucumber mosaic
    Wellman, F.L., 1935
  V. henbane mosaic
    (K.M. Smith, 1957) R.E. Fitzpatrick, et al., 1958
  V. potato X
    Larson, R.H., 1944
  V. tomato black ring
    (K.M. Smith, 1957) R.E. Fitzpatrick, et al., 1958
  V. tomato spotted wilt
    Smith, Kenneth M., 1932

AVENA L. 1735 (Gramineae)
A. barbata, Brot.
  V. barley yellow dwarf
    Oswald, John W. and Byron R. Houston, 1953
A. byzantina, C. Koch.
  V. brome mosaic
    (K.M. Smith, 1957) R.E. Fitzpatrick, et al., 1958
  V. oat pseudo-rosette
    (K.M. Smith, 1957) R.E. Fitzpatrick, et al., 1958
  V. soil-borne oat mosaic
    McKinney, H.H., 1946
  V. wheat streak mosaic
    McKinney, H.H., 1949
A. fatua, L.
  V. barley yellow dwarf
    Bruehl, G.W. and H.V. Toko, 1957
    Oswald, John W. and Byron R. Houston, 1952,
    1953
  V. lucerne dwarf
    Freitag, Julius H., 1951
  V. ryegrass mosaic *
    Bruehl, G.W., H. Toko and H.H. McKinney,
    1957
  V. wheat streak mosaic
    Slykhuis, John T., 1955
A. festuca *
  V. oat pseudo-rosette
    (K.M. Smith, 1957) R.E. Fitzpatrick, et al., 1958
A. sativa, L.
  V. barley stripe mosaic
    McKinney, H.H., 1953
    Sill, W.H., Jr. and E.D. Hansing, 1955
  V. barley yellow dwarf
    Allen, Thomas C., Jr., 1956, 1957
    Allen, Thomas C., Jr. and Byron R. Houston,
    1956
    Bruehl, G.W. and H. Toko, 1955, 1957
    Endo, R.M., 1957
    Moore, M.B., 1952
    Oswald, John W. and Byron R. Houston, 1951,
    1952, 1953
    Oswald, John W. and T.H. Thung, 1955
    Takeshita, R.M., 1956
    Toko, H.V. and G.W. Bruehl, 1957

A. sativa, L. (cont.)
   V. barley yellow dwarf
      Watson, Marion A. and T. Mulligan, 1957
      Wilson, V.E. and H.C. Murphy, 1953
   V. beet ring spot *
      Harrison, B.D., 1957
   V. brome mosaic
      McKinney, H.H., 1944, 1953
      McKinney, H.H., H. Fellows and C.O. Johnston,
      1942
   V. grass orchard mosaic *
      McKinney, H.H., 1956
   V. maize streak
      (K.M. Smith, 1957) R.E. Fitzpatrick, et al., 1958
   V. (oat) blue dwarf *
      Moore, M.B., 1952
   V. oat pseudo-rosette
      (K.M. Smith, 1957) R.E. Fitzpatrick, et al., 1958
   V. rice dwarf
      (K.M. Smith, 1957) R.E. Fitzpatrick, et al., 1958
   V. soil-borne oat mosaic
      Hadden, S.J. and H.F. Harrison, 1955
      McKinney, H.H., 1946
      Moseman, J.G., U.R. Gore and H.H. McKinney,
      1953
   V. tobacco necrosis
      Fulton, J.P., 1952
   V. wheat streak mosaic
      Finley, A.M., 1957
      Houston, Byron R. and John W. Oswald, 1952
      McKinney, H.H., 1949
      Slykhuis, J.T., 1952, 1955
   V. wheat striate mosaic
      Slykhuis, J.T., 1953
      Slykhuis, John T. and Marion A. Watson, 1958
A. sativa var. orientalis (Schreb.) Richter
   V. wheat streak mosaic
      McKinney, H.H., 1949
A. spp.
   V. wheat streak mosaic
      Sill, W.H., Jr. and Patrick C. Agusiobo, 1955
A. sterilis, L.
   V. oat pseudo-rosette
      (K.M. Smith, 1957) R.E. Fitzpatrick, et al., 1958
A. strigosa, Schreb.
   V. barley yellow dwarf
      Endo, R.M., 1957
   V. oat pseudo-rosette
      (K.M. Smith, 1957) R.E. Fitzpatrick, et al., 1958

BABIANA Ker-Gawl. 1802 (Iridaceae)
B. spp.
   V. babiana mosaic
      Smith, Floyd F. and Philip Brierley, 1944

BACCHARIS L. 1737 (Compositae)
B. pilularis, DC.
   V. lucerne dwarf
      Freitag, J.H., 1951

BAERIA Fisch. & Mey. 1835 (Compositae)
B. uliginosa, (Nutt.) A. Gray
   V. beet curly top
      Severin, Henry H.P., 1934

BARBAREA R. Br. 1812 (Cruciferae)
B. barbarea, MacMill.
   V. tobacco ring spot
      Wingard, S.A., 1928
·B. verna, Asch.
   V. cauliflower mosaic
      (K.M. Smith, 1957) R.E. Fitzpatrick, et al., 1958
B. vulgaris, R. Br.
   V. beet curly top
      Severin, Henry H.P., 1929
   V. cabbage black ring spot
      (K.M. Smith, 1957) R.E. Fitzpatrick, et al., 1958
   V. cauliflower mosaic
      (K.M. Smith, 1957) R.E. Fitzpatrick, et al., 1958
   V. clover big vein
      Black, L.M., 1945
   V. cucumber mosaic
      Pound, Glenn S. and J.C. Walker, 1948

B. vulgaris, R. Br. (cont.)
   V. potato yellow dwarf
      Hansing, E.D., 1942
   V. turnip crinkle
      Broadbent, L. and G.D. Heathcote, 1958
   V. turnip mosaic
      Pound, Glenn S., 1948
   V. turnip rosette *
      Broadbent, L. and G.D. Heathcote, 1958
   V. turnip yellow mosaic
      Broadbent, L. and G.D. Heathcote, 1958

BASSIA All. 1766 (Chenopodiaceae)
B. hyssopifolia, (Pall.) Ktze.
   V. beet yellows
      Roland, G. and J. Tahon, 1961

BECKMANNIA Host 1805 (Gramineae)
B. syzigachne, (Steud.) Fern.
   V. barley yellow dwarf
      Bruehl, G.W. and H.V. Toko, 1957

BEGONIA ((Tourn.)) L. 1742 (Begoniaceae)
B. semperflorens, Link & Otto
   V. aster yellows
      Kunkel, L.O., 1926
   V. cabbage black ring spot
      Tompkins, C.M., M.W. Gardner and H. Rex
      Thomas, 1938
   V. tobacco ring spot
      Price, W.C., 1940
   V. tobacco ring spot no. 2
      Price, W.C., 1940
   V. tomato spotted wilt
      Gardner, M.W., C.M. Tompkins and O.C.
      Whipple, 1935
   V. turnip mosaic
      Tompkins, C.M., 1938

BELAMCANDA Adans. 1763 (Iridaceae)
B. chinensis, (L.) DC.
   V. iris bearded mosaic *
      Brierley, Philip and Floyd F. Smith, 1948
      Travis, R.V., 1957
   V. iris beardless mosaic *
      Travis, R.V., 1957
   V. iris fulva mosaic *
      Travis, R.V., 1957
   V. iris spuria mosaic *
      Brierley, Philip and Floyd F. Smith, 1948

BELLIS ((Tourn.)) L. 1737 (Compositae)
B. perennis, L.
   V. aster yellows
      Kunkel, L.O., 1926
   V. beet curly top
      Freitag, Julius H. and Henry H.P. Severin, 1936
   V. tobacco mosaic
      Holmes, Francis O., 1946

BENINCASA Savi 1818 (Cucurbitaceae)
B. cerifera, Savi
   V. cucurbit mosaic *
      Doolittle, S.P. and M.N. Walker, 1925
B. hispida, Cogn.
   V. cucumber mosaic
      Jagger, I.C., 1918
   V. cucurbit mosaic *
      Doolittle, S.P. and M.N. Walker, 1925
   V. prunus B *
      Fulton, Robert W., 1957
   V. prunus G *
      Fulton, Robert W., 1957

BERBERIS ((Tourn.)) L. 1737 (Berberidaceae)
B. thunbergii, DC.
   V. cucumber mosaic
      Wilkinson, R.E., 1953

BERTEROA DC. 1821 (Cruciferae)
B. incana, (L.) DC.
   V. cabbage ring necrosis
      Larson, R.H. and J.C. Walker, 1941

B. incana, (L.) DC. (cont.)
  V. turnip mosaic
    Walker, J.C., Francis J. LeBeau and Glenn S.
    Pound, 1945

BETA ((Tourn.)) L. 1735 (Chenopodiaceae)
B. atriplicifolia, Rouy.
  V. beet yellows
    Roland, G. and J. Tahon, 1961
B. cicla viridis, L. *
  V. beet yellows
    Roland, G. and J. Tahon, 1961
B. hybrida, Andrz. ex Trautv.
  V. beet yellows
    Roland, G. and J. Tahon, 1961
B. lomatogona, Fish. & Mey.
  V. beet yellows
    Roland, G. and J. Tahon, 1961
B. macrocarpa, Guss.
  V. beet curly top
    Bennett, C.W. and Aziz Tanrisever, 1957
    Costa, A.S., 1952
    Giddings, N.J., 1944
  V. beet yellows
    Costa, A.S. and C.W. Bennett, 1955
    Roland, G. and J. Tahon, 1961
B. maritima, L.
  V. beet curly top
    Severin, Henry H.P. and Charles F. Henderson,
    1928
  V. beet mosaic
    Severin, Henry H.P. and Roger M. Drake, 1948
  V. beet yellows
    Costa, A.S. and C.W. Bennett, 1955
    Roland, G. and J. Tahon, 1961
B. patellaris, Moq.
  V. beet curly top
    Costa, A.S., 1952
    Giddings, N. J., 1944
  V. beet mosaic
    Bennett, C.W., 1949
  V. beet yellows
    Roland, G. and J. Tahon, 1961
  V. tobacco streak
    Costa, A.S., 1952
B. patula, ((Soland. in) Ait. Hort. Kew.
  V. beet curly top
    Costa, A.S., 1952
  V. beet yellows
    Roland, G. and J. Tahon, 1961
B. procumbens, Chr. Sm.
  V. beet yellows
    Costa, A.S. and C.W. Bennett, 1955
    Roland, G. and J. Tahon, 1961
B. trigyna, Waldst. & Kit.
  V. beet curly top
    Giddings, N.J., 1944
  V. beet yellows
    Roland, G. and J. Tahon, 1961
B. vulgaris, L.
  V. bayberry yellows
    Raychaudhuri, S.P., 1953
  V. beet curly top
    Bennett, C.W., 1934, 1937, 1944, 1951, 1955
    Bennett, C.W., Eubanks Carsner, G.H. Coons
    and E.W. Brandes, 1946
    Bennett, C.W. and A.S. Costa, 1949
    Bennett, C.W. and Aziz Tanrisever, 1957
    Carsner, Eubanks, 1919, 1926, 1938
    Carsner, Eubanks and C.F. Stahl, 1924
    Costa, A.S., 1952
    Esau, Katherine, 1930
    Fawcett, G.L., 1927
    Giddings, N.J., 1938, 1940, 1941, 1944, 1946,
    1952, 1954
    Johnson, Folke, 1941
    Jones, Leon K., 1931
    Lackey, C.F., 1932, 1937, 1941, 1942, 1951
    Menzies, J.D. and N.J. Giddings, 1953
    Mumford, Edward Philpott, 1930
    Owen, F.V., Albert M. Murphy and Bion Tolman,
    1942
    Severin, Henry H.P. and Charles F. Henderson,
    1928

B. vulgaris, L. (cont.)
  V. beet curly top
    Severin, Henry H.P. and Byron R. Houston, 1945
    Smith, R.E. and P.A. Boncquet, 1915
    Thornberry, H.H. and R.M. Takeshita, 1954
  V. beet leaf curl
    Boncquet, P.A., 1923
    Coons, G.H., J.E. Kotila and D. Stewart, 1937
    Hildebrand, A.A. and L.W. Koch, 1942
    Severin, Henry H.P., 1924
  V. beet mosaic
    Bawden, F.C., Brenda M.G. Hamlyn and
    Marion A. Watson, 1954
    Bennett, C.W., 1944
    Doncaster, J.P. and B. Kassanis, 1946
    Hale, J.B., Marion A. Watson and R. Hull, 1946
    Hoggan, I.A., 1933
    Jones, Leon K., 1931
    McLean, D.M., 1952
    Pound, Glenn S., 1947
    Robbins, W.W., 1921
    Severin, Henry H.P. and Roger M. Drake, 1948
    Sylvester, Edward S., 1947, 1949, 1950, 1952
    Watson, Marion A., R. Hull, J.W. Blencowe
    and Brenda M.F. Hamlyn, 1951
  V. beet ring spot *
    Harrison, B.D., 1957
  V. beet rosette *
    Bennett, C.W. and James E. Duffus, 1957
  V. beet yellow net
    Bennett, C.W., 1944, 1956
    McLean, D.M., 1952
    Sylvester, Edward S., 1948, 1949, 1950
  V. beet yellow wilt
    Bennett, C.W. and Carlos Munck, 1946
  V. beet yellows
    Bawden, F.C., Brenda M.G. Hamlyn and
    Marion A. Watson, 1954
    Coons, G.H., 1952
    Costa, A.S. and C.W. Bennett, 1955
    Doncaster, J.P. and B. Kassanis, 1946
    Dufrenoy, Jean, 1940
    Hale, J.B., Marion A. Watson and R. Hull, 1946
    Kassanis, B., 1949
    McLean, D.M., 1952, 1953
    Roland, G. and J. Tahon, 1961
    Watson, Marion A., 1942
    Watson, Marion A., R. Hull, J.W. Blencowe
    and Brenda M.F. Hamlyn, 1951
    Watson, Marion A. and G.E. Russell, 1956
  V. brome mosaic
    McKinney, H.H., 1953
  V. cabbage ring necrosis
    Larson, R.H. and J.C. Walker, 1940, 1941
  V. carnation mosaic
    Brierley, Philip and Floyd F. Smith, 1957
  V. carnation ring spot
    Brierley, Philip and Floyd F. Smith, 1957
  V. cucumber mosaic
    Anderson, C.W., 1951
    Bennett, C.W., 1944
    Berkeley, G.H. and J.H. Tremaine, 1954
    Bhargava, K.S., 1951
    Fulton, Joseph P., 1950
    Harrison, B.D., 1958
    Hoggan, I.A., 1933
    Johnson, E.M., 1930
    Severin, Henry H.P., 1948
    Wellman, F.L., 1934, 1935
  V. cucumber western mosaic *
    Severin, Henry H.P. and Julius H. Freitag, 1948
  V. delphinium ring spot
    Severin, Henry H.P. and R.C. Dickson, 1942
  V. dodder latent mosaic
    Bennett, C.W., 1944, 1949
  V. hydrangea ring spot
    Brierley, Philip and Paul Lorentz, 1956, 1957
  V. lucerne mosaic
    Price, W.C., 1940
    Richardson, D.E. and T.W. Tinsley, 1956
    Severin, Henry H.P., 1948
  V. potato paracrinkle
    Kassanis, B., 1955

B. vulgaris, L. (cont.)
  V. potato X
    Johnson, E.M., 1930
  V. raspberry Scottish leaf curl
    Harrison, B.D., 1958
  V. raspberry yellow dwarf *
    Harrison, B.D., 1958
  V. tobacco mosaic
    Grant, T.J., 1934
    Holmes, Francis O., 1946
  V. tobacco ring spot
    Cheo, Pen Ching and W.J. Zaumeyer, 1952
    Grogan, R.G. and W.C. Schnathorst, 1955
    Priode, C.N., 1928
    Wingard, S.A., 1928
  V. tobacco ring spot no. 2
    Hildebrand, E.M., 1942
    Price, W.C., 1940
  V. tobacco streak
    Fulton, Robert W., 1948
  V. tomato aspermy
    Brierley, Philip, Floyd F. Smith and S.P.
    Doolittle, 1955
    Hollings, M., 1955
  V. tomato big bud
    Helms, Katie, 1957
    Hill, A.V. and M. Mandryk, 1954
  V. turnip mosaic
    LeBeau, Francis J. and J.C. Walker, 1945
    Walker, J.C., Francis J. LeBeau and Glenn S.
    Pound, 1945
B. vulgaris var. cicla, (L.) Moq.
  V. beet curly top
    Bennett, C.W., Eubanks Carsner, F.H. Coons
    and E.W. Brandes, 1946
    Severin, Henry H.P. and Charles F. Henderson,
    1928
  V. beet mosaic
    McLean, D.M., 1952
    Pound, Glenn S., 1947
    Severin, Henry H.P. and Roger M. Drake, 1948
  V. beet yellow net
    McLean, D.M., 1952
    Sylvester, Edward S., 1948
  V. beet yellow wilt
    (K.M. Smith, 1957) R.E. Fitzpatrick, et al., 1958
  V. beet yellows
    McLean, D.M., 1953
  V. brome mosaic
    McKinney, H.H., 1953
  V. cabbage ring necrosis
    Larson, R.H. and J.C. Walker, 1940, 1941
  V. cucumber mosaic
    Berkeley, G.H. and J.H. Tremaine, 1954
    Bhargava, K.S., 1951
    Fulton, Joseph P., 1950
    Nienow, Inez, 1948
    Simons, John N., 1955, 1957
    Wellman, F.L., 1935
  V. cucumber western mosaic *
    Severin, Henry H.P. and Julius H. Freitag, 1948
  V. tobacco mosaic
    Grant, T.J., 1934
  V. tobacco ring spot
    Wingard, S.A., 1928
  V. turnip mosaic
    LeBeau, Francis J. and J.C. Walker, 1945
    Walker, J.C., Francis J. LeBeau and Glenn S.
    Pound, 1945
B. vulgaris var. macrorhiza *
  V. beet curly top
    Bennett, C.W., Eubanks Carsner, G.H. Coons
    and E.W. Brandes, 1946
    Severin, Henry H.P. and Charles F. Henderson,
    1928
  V. beet mosaic
    Severin, Henry H.P. and Roger M. Drake, 1948
  V. cabbage ring necrosis
    Larson, R.H. and J.C. Walker, 1941
B. webbiana, Moq.
  V. beet yellows
    Roland, G. and J. Tahon, 1961

BIDENS ((Tourn.)) L. 1737 (Compositae)
B. discoidea, (Torr. & Gray) Brit.
  V. tobacco ring spot
    Wingard, S.A., 1928
B. frondosa, L.
  V. aster yellows
    Frazier, Norman W. and Henry H.P. Severin,
    1945
  V. tobacco mosaic
    Holmes, Francis O., 1938, 1946
B. pilosa, L.
  V. aster yellows
    Frazier, Norman W. and Henry H.P. Severin,
    1945

BIGNONIA ((Tourn.)) L. 1735 (Bignoniaceae)
B. capreolata, L.
  V. tobacco necrosis
    Price, W.C., 1940

BOLTONIA L'Herit. 1788 (Compositae)
B. latisquama, A. Gray
  V. prunus B *
    Fulton, Robert W., 1957

BOMBAX L. 1753 (Bombacaceae)
B. buonopozense, Beauv.
  V. cacao swollen shoot
    Attafuah, A. and T.W. Tinsley, 1958
    Posnette, A.F., N.F. Robertson and J. McA.
    Todd, 1950
    Tinsley, T.W. and A.L. Wharton, 1958
B. malabaricum, DC.
  V. cacao swollen shoot
    Tinsley, T.W. and A.L. Wharton, 1958

BORAGO L. 1753 (Boraginaceae)
B. officinalis, L.
  V. beet curly top
    Severin, Henry H.P., 1929

BOUTELOUA Lag. 1805 (Gramineae)
B. curtipendula, (Michx.) Torr.
  V. barley yellow dwarf
    Oswald, John W. and Byron R. Houston, 1953
B. hirsuta, Lag.
  V. wheat streak mosaic
    McKinney, H.H. and Hurley Fellows, 1951

BRACHIARIA Griseb. 1853 (Gramineae)
B. platyphylla, Nash
  V. sugarcane mosaic
    Brandes, E.W. and Peter J. Klaphaak, 1923

BRACHYCOMBE
(BRACHYCOME) Cass. 1825 (Compositae)
B. iberidifolia, Benth.
  V. aster yellows
    Kunkel, L.O., 1926
    Severin, Henry H.P. and Julius H. Freitag, 1945
  V. beet curly top
    Freitag, Julius H. and Henry H.P. Severin, 1936
  V. clover big vein
    Black, L.M., 1945
  V. tobacco etch
    Holmes, Francis O., 1946
  V. tobacco mosaic
    Holmes, Francis O., 1946
  V. vaccinium false blossom
    Kunkel, L.O., 1945

BRACHYSTEGIA Benth. 1865 (Leguminosae)
B. burttii, Hoyle ex C.H.N. Jackson
  V. groundnut rosette
    Evans, A.C., 1954

BRASSICA ((Tourn.)) L. 1735 (Cruciferae)
(SINAPIS) L. 1735
B. adpressa, Boiss.
  V. cabbage black ring spot
    Tompkins, C.M., M.W. Gardner and H. Rex
    Thomas, 1938

B. adpressa, Boiss. (cont.)
  V. cauliflower mosaic
    Tompkins, C.M., 1937
    Tompkins, C.M. and H. Rex Thomas, 1938
  V. dodder latent mosaic
    Bennett, C.W., 1949
  V. radish mosaic
    Tompkins, C.M., 1939
  V. tobacco yellow dwarf
    Helson, G.A.H., 1950
  V. turnip mosaic
    Bennett, C.W., 1944
    Tompkins, C.M., 1938, 1939
B. campestris, L.
  V. aster yellows
    Frazier, Norman W. and Henry H.P. Severin, 1945
  V. cauliflower mosaic
    Tompkins, C.M., 1937
    Walker, J.C., Francis J. LeBeau and Glenn S. Pound, 1945
  V. radish mosaic
    Raychaudhuri, S.P. and P.S. Pathanian, 1955
  V. turnip mosaic
    LeBeau, Francis J. and J.C. Walker, 1945
    Sylvester, Edward S., 1953
    Tompkins, C.M., 1938
    Walker, J.C., Francis J. LeBeau and Glenn S. Pound, 1945
B. campestris var. napobrassica, (L.) DC.
  V. beet ring spot *
    Harrison, B.D., 1957
  V. cabbage black ring spot
    Tompkins, C.M., M.W. Gardner, and H. Rex Thomas, 1937, 1938
  V. cabbage ring necrosis
    Larson, R.H. and J.C. Walker, 1941
  V. cauliflower mosaic
    Alvarez-Garcia, L.A., 1951
    Berkeley, G.H. and J.H. Tremaine, 1954
    Caldwell, John and Ian W. Prentice, 1942
    Tompkins, C.M., 1937
  V. cucumber mosaic
    Berkeley, G.H. and J.H. Tremaine, 1954
  V. tobacco mosaic
    Holmes, Francis O., 1946
  V. turnip mosaic
    Berkeley, G.H. and J.H. Tremaine, 1954
    Berkeley, G.H. and M. Weintraub, 1952
    Clayton, E.E., 1930
    LeBeau, Francis J. and J.C. Walker, 1945
    Sylvester, Edward S., 1953
    Tompkins, C.M., 1938
B. carinata, A. Braun
  V. turnip mosaic
    Takahashi, William N., 1949
  V. turnip yellow mosaic
    (K.M. Smith, 1957) R.E. Fitzpatrick, et al., 1958
B. chinensis, L.
  V. cabbage black ring spot
    Hamlyn, Brenda M.G., 1953
  V. rape savoy
    Ling, Lee and Juhwa Y. Yang, 1940
  V. turnip mosaic
    Clayton, E.E., 1930
    Dale, W.T., 1948
    Sylvester, Edward S., 1953
    Sylvester, Edward S. and John N. Simons, 1951
    Takahashi, William N., 1949
B. hirta, Moench, (B. alba, (L.) Rabh.)
  V. anemone mosaic *
    Hollings, M., 1957
  V. aster yellows
    Severin, Henry H.P., 1934
  V. beet curly top
    Severin, Henry H.P., 1929
  V. cabbage black ring spot
    Hamlyn, Brenda M.G., 1953
    Hollings, M., 1957
    Tompkins, C.M., M.W. Gardner and H. Rex Thomas, 1938
  V. cabbage ring necrosis
    Larson, R.H. and J.C. Walker, 1941

B. hirta, Moench, (B. alba, (L.) Rabh.) (cont.)
  V. cauliflower mosaic
    Tompkins, C.M., 1937
    Walker, J.C., Francis J. LeBeau and Glenn S. Pound, 1945
  V. radish mosaic
    Raychaudhuri, S.P. and P.S. Pathanian, 1955
    Tompkins, C.M., 1939
  V. tobacco mosaic
    Grant, T.J., 1934
  V. turnip mosaic
    Clayton, E.E., 1930
    LeBeau, Francis J. and J.C. Walker, 1945
    Sylvester, Edward S., 1953
    Takahashi, William N., 1949
    Tompkins, C.M., 1939
    Walker, J.C., Francis J. LeBeau and Glenn S. Pound, 1945
(S. alba, L.)
  V. turnip crinkle
    Broadbent, L. and G.D. Heathcote, 1958
  V. turnip mosaic
    Berkeley, G.H. and M. Weintraub, 1952
  V. turnip yellow mosaic
    Broadbent, L. and G.D. Heathcote, 1958
B. incana, (L.) F.W. Schultz *
  V. dodder latent mosaic
    Bennett, C.W., 1944
B. juncea (L.) Coss (B. japonica, Hort.)
  V. cabbage black ring spot
    Tompkins, C.M., M.W. Gardner and H. Rex Thomas, 1938
  V. cabbage ring necrosis
    Larson, R.H. and J.C. Walker, 1941
  V. cauliflower mosaic
    Tompkins, C.M., 1937
    Walker, J.C., Francis J. LeBeau and Glenn S. Pound, 1945
  V. cucumber mosaic
    Pound, Glenn S. and J.C. Walker, 1948
  V. radish mosaic
    Raychaudhuri, S.P. and P.S. Pathanian, 1955
    Takahashi, William N., 1952
    Tompkins, C.M., 1939
  V. rape savoy
    Ling, Lee and Juhwa Y. Yang, 1940
  V. turnip mosaic
    Dale, W.T., 1948
    LeBeau, Francis J. and J.C. Walker, 1945
    Pound, Glenn S., 1948
    Schultz, E.S., 1921
    Sylvester, Edward S., 1950, 1953, 1954
    Sylvester, Edward S. and John N. Simons, 1951
    Takahashi, William N., 1949
    Tompkins, C.M., 1938, 1939
    Walker, J.C., Francis J. LeBeau and Glenn S. Pound, 1945
  V. turnip yellow mosaic
    Broadbent, L. and G.D. Heathcote, 1958
B. kaber, (DC.) L.C. Wheeler (B. arvensis (L.) Rabh.)
  V. beet curly top
    Severin, Henry H.P., 1929, 1934
  V. cabbage black ring spot
    Tompkins, C.M., M.W. Gardner, and H. Rex Thomas, 1937, 1938
  V. cauliflower mosaic
    Tompkins, C.M., 1937
  V. cucumber mosaic
    Pound, Glenn S. and J.C. Walker, 1948
  V. radish mosaic
    Tompkins, C.M., 1939
  V. tobacco broad ring spot
    Johnson, James and Robert W. Fulton, 1942
  V. tobacco streak
    Fulton, Robert W., 1948
  V. turnip crinkle
    (K.M. Smith, 1957) R.E. Fitzpatrick, et al., 1958
  V. turnip mosaic
    Takahashi, William N., 1949
    Tompkins, C.M., 1939
    Tompkins, C.M. and H. Rex Thomas, 1938
  V. turnip yellow mosaic
    (K.M. Smith, 1957) R.E. Fitzpatrick, et al., 1958

B. kaber, (DC.) L.C. Wheeler (B. arvensis (L.) Rabh.)
(Cont.)
(S. arvensis, L.)
   V. cauliflower mosaic
      Caldwell, John and Ian W. Prentice, 1942
   V. turnip crinkle
      Broadbent, L. and G.D. Heathcote, 1958
   V. turnip rosette *
      Broadbent, L. and G.D. Heathcote, 1958
   V. turnip yellow mosaic
      Broadbent, L. and G.D. Heathcote, 1958
B. kaber var. pinnatifida (Stokes), L.C. Wheeler
   V. cauliflower mosaic
      Walker, J.C., Francis J. LeBeau and Glenn S.
      Pound, 1945
   V. turnip mosaic
      Walker, J.C., Francis J. LeBeau and Glenn S.
      Pound, 1945
B. muralis, Huds.
   V. cabbage black ring spot
      Hamlyn, Brenda M.G., 1953
   V. cauliflower mosaic
      (K.M. Smith, 1957) R.E. Fitzpatrick, et al., 1958
B. napus, L.
   V. anemone mosaic *
      Hollings, M., 1957
   V. cabbage black ring spot
      Hollings, M., 1957
      Tompkins, C.M., M.W. Gardner and H. Rex
      Thomas, 1938
   V. cabbage ring necrosis
      Larson, R.H. and J.C. Walker, 1941
   V. cauliflower mosaic
      Berkeley, G.H. and J.H. Tremaine, 1954
      Caldwell, John and Ian W. Prentice, 1942
      Tompkins, C.M., 1937
      Tompkins, C.M. and H. Rex Thomas, 1938
      Walker, J.C., Francis J. LeBeau and Glenn S.
      Pound, 1945
   V. cucumber mosaic
      Berkeley, G.H. and J.H. Tremaine, 1954
      Pound, Glenn S. and J.C. Walker, 1948
   V. rape savoy
      Ling, Lee and Juhwa Y. Yang, 1940
   V. turnip crinkle
      Broadbent, L. and G.D. Heathcote, 1958
      Lister, R.M., 1958
   V. turnip mosaic
      Berkeley, G.H. and J.H. Tremaine, 1954
      Berkeley, G.H. and M. Weintraub, 1952
      Clayton, E.E., 1930
      Dale, W.T., 1948
      LeBeau, Francis J. and J.C. Walker, 1945
      Pound, Glenn S., 1949
      Takahashi, William N., 1949
      Walker, J.C., Francis J. LeBeau and Glenn S.
      Pound, 1945
   V. turnip rosette *
      Broadbent, L. and G.D. Heathcote, 1958
      Lister, R.M., 1958
   V. turnip yellow mosaic
      Broadbent, L. and G.D. Heathcote, 1958
      Lister, R.M., 1958
B. napus var. biennis, (Schubl. & Mart.) Reichb. *
   V. turnip mosaic
      Sylvester, Edward S., 1953
B. nigra, (L.) Koch
   V. cabbage ring necrosis
      Larson, R.H. and J.C. Walker, 1941
   V. cauliflower mosaic
      Tompkins, C.M., 1937
      Walker, J.C., Francis J. LeBeau and Glenn S.
      Pound, 1945
   V. cucumber mosaic
      Pound, Glenn S. and J.C. Walker, 1948
   V. radish mosaic
      Raychaudhuri, S.P. and P.S. Pathanian, 1955
      Tompkins, C.M., 1939
   V. tobacco broad ring spot
      Johnson, James and Robert W. Fulton, 1942
   V. turnip crinkle
      Broadbent, L. and G.D. Heathcote, 1958

B. nigra, (L.) Koch
   V. turnip mosaic
      Berkeley, G.H. and M. Weintraub, 1952
      Clayton, E.E., 1930
      Dana, B.F. and F.P. McWhorter, 1932
      Hoggan, I.A. and J. Johnson, 1935
      LeBeau, Francis J. and J.C. Walker, 1945
      Sylvester, Edward S., 1953
      Takahashi, William N., 1949
      Tompkins, C.M., 1939
      Walker, J.C., Francis J. LeBeau and Glenn S.
      Pound, 1945
   V. turnip yellow mosaic
      Broadbent, L. and G.D. Heathcote, 1958
B. oleracea, L.
   V. radish mosaic
      Raychaudhure, S.P. and P.S. Pathanian, 1955
   V. tobacco broad ring spot
      Johnson, James and Robert W. Fulton, 1942
   V. turnip mosaic
      Takahashi, William N., 1949
B. oleracea var. acephala, DC.
   V. beet curly top
      Severin, Henry H.P., 1929
   V. cabbage black ring spot
      Broadbent, L., 1954
      Hamlyn, Brenda M.G., 1953
      Tompkins, C.M., M.W. Gardner and H. Rex
      Thomas, 1938
   V. cauliflower mosaic
      Alvarez-Garcia, L.A., 1951
      Caldwell, John and Ian W. Prentice, 1942
      Tompkins, C.M., 1934, 1937
   V. crucifer ring spot *
      Smith, Kenneth M., 1935
   V. cucumber mosaic
      Pound, Glenn S. and J.C. Walker, 1948
   V. radish mosaic
      Tompkins, C.M., 1939
B. oleracea var. botrytis, L.
   V. aster yellows
      Severin, Henry H.P. and Julius H. Freitag, 1945
   V. beet curly top
      Severin, Henry H.P., 1929
   V. cabbage black ring spot
      Broadbent, L., 1954
      Broadbent, L. and T.W. Tinsley, 1953
      Hamlyn, Brenda M.G., 1953
      Tompkins, C.M., M.W. Gardner, and H. Rex
      Thomas, 1937, 1938
   V. cabbage ring necrosis
      Larson, R.H. and J.C. Walker, 1941
   V. cauliflower mosaic
      Alvarez-Garcia, L.A., 1951
      Berkeley, G.H. and J.H. Tremaine, 1954
      Broadbent, L., 1954
      Broadbent, L. and T.W. Tinsley, 1953
      Caldwell, John and Ian W. Prentice, 1942
      Jenkinson, J.G., 1955
      Severin, Henry H.P. and C.M. Tompkins, 1948
      Tompkins, C.M., 1934, 1937
      Walker, J.C., Francis J. LeBeau and Glenn S.
      Pound, 1945
   V. cucumber mosaic
      Pound, Glenn S. and J.C. Walker, 1948
   V. radish mosaic
      Raychaudhuri, S.P. and P.S. Pathanian, 1955
      Tompkins, C.M., 1939
   V. tomato spotted wilt
      Gardner, M.W., C.M. Tompkins and O.C.
      Whipple, 1935
   V. turnip crinkle
      Broadbent, L. and G.D. Heathcote, 1958
   V. turnip mosaic
      Berkeley, G.H. and J.H. Tremaine, 1954
      Berkeley, G.H. and M. Weintraub, 1952
      Clayton, E.E., 1930
      LeBeau, Francis J. and J.C. Walker, 1945
      Pound, Glenn S., 1948
      Tompkins, C.M., 1939
      Tompkins, C.M. and H. Rex Thomas, 1938
      Walker, J.C., Francis J. LeBeau and Glenn S.
      Pound, 1945

B. oleracea var. botrytis, L. (cont.)
  V. turnip rosette *
    Broadbent, L. and G.D. Heathcote, 1958
  V. turnip yellow mosaic
    Broadbent, L. and G.D. Heathcote, 1958
    Croxall, H.E., D.C. Gwynne and L. Broadbent, 1953
B. oleracea var. bullata, L. *
  V. cabbage black ring spot
    Hamlyn, Brenda M.G., 1953
B. oleracea var. capitata, L.
  V. anemone mosaic *
    Hollings, M., 1957
  V. aster yellows
    Severin, Henry H.P. and Julius H. Freitag, 1945
  V. beet curly top
    Severin, Henry H.P., 1929
  V. cabbage black ring spot
    Hamlyn, Brenda M.G., 1953
    Hollings, M., 1957
    Pound, Glenn S., 1952
    Pound, Glenn S. and J.C. Walker, 1951
    Tompkins, C.M., M.W. Gardner, and H. Rex Thomas, 1937, 1938
  V. cabbage ring necrosis
    Larson, R.H. and J.C. Walker, 1940, 1941
  V. cauliflower mosaic
    Alvarez-Garcia, L.A., 1951
    Berkeley, G.H. and J.H. Tremaine, 1954
    Caldwell, John and Ian W. Prentice, 1942
    Natti, J.J., 1956
    Pound, Glenn S., 1946, 1947, 1952
    Pound, Glenn S. and J.C. Walker, 1951
    Tompkins, C.M., 1934, 1937
    Walker, J.C., Francis J. LeBeau and Glenn S. Pound, 1945
  V. crucifer ring spot *
    Smith, Kenneth M., 1935
  V. cucumber mosaic
    Pound, Glenn S. and J.C. Walker, 1948
  V. radish mosaic
    Raychaudhuri, S.P. and P.S. Pathanian, 1955
    Tompkins, C.M., 1939
  V. tobacco broad ring spot
    (K.M. Smith, 1957) R.E. Fitzpatrick, et al., 1958
  V. tobacco necrosis
    Fulton, Robert W., 1950
  V. turnip crinkle
    Broadbent, L. and G.D. Heathcote, 1958
  V. turnip mosaic
    Berkeley, G.H. and J.H. Tremaine, 1954
    Berkeley, G.H. and M. Weintraub, 1952
    Hoggan, I.A. and J. Johnson, 1935
    LeBeau, Francis J. and J.C. Walker, 1945
    Natti, J.J., 1956
    Pound, Glenn S., 1946, 1947, 1948
    Tompkins, C.M., 1938
    Tompkins, C.M. and H. Rex Thomas, 1938
    Walker, J.C., Francis J. LeBeau and Glenn S. Pound, 1945
  V. turnip rosette *
    Broadbent, L. and G.D. Heathcote, 1958
  V. turnip yellow mosaic
    Broadbent, L. and G.D. Heathcote, 1958
B. oleracea var. caulorapa, DC.
  V. cabbage black ring spot
    Hamlyn, Brenda M.G., 1953
    Tompkins, C.M., M.W. Gardner and H. Rex Thomas, 1938
  V. cauliflower mosaic
    Caldwell, John and Ian W. Prentice, 1942
    Tompkins, C.M., 1937
  V. radish mosaic
    Tompkins, C.M., 1939
  V. turnip yellow mosaic
    (K.M. Smith, 1957) R.E. Fitzpatrick, et al., 1958
B. oleracea var. gemmifera, DC.
  V. cabbage black ring spot
    Broadbent, L., 1954
    Hamlyn, Brenda M.G., 1953
    Tompkins, C.M., M.W. Gardner and H. Rex Thomas, 1937, 1938
  V. cabbage ring necrosis
    Larson, R.H. and J.C. Walker, 1941

B. oleracea var. gemmifera, DC. (cont.)
  V. cauliflower mosaic
    Alvarez-Garcia, L.A., 1951
    Berkeley, G.H. and J.H. Tremaine, 1954
    Caldwell, John and Ian W. Prentice, 1942
    Severin, Henry H.P. and C.M. Tompkins, 1948
    Tompkins, C.M., 1937
    Walker, J.C., Francis J. LeBeau and Glenn S. Pound, 1945
  V. crucifer ring spot *
    Smith, Kenneth M., 1935
  V. cucumber mosaic
    Pound, Glenn S. and J.C. Walker, 1948
  V. radish mosaic
    Tompkins, C.M., 1939
  V. turnip crinkle
    Broadbent, L. and G.D. Heathcote, 1958
  V. turn ip mosaic
    Berkeley, G.H. and J.H. Tremaine, 1954
    Clayton, E.E., 1930
    LeBeau, Francis J. and J.C. Walker, 1945
    Pound, Glenn S., 1948
    Walker, J.C., Francis J. LeBeau and Glenn S. Pound, 1945
  V. turnip rosette *
    Broadbent, L. and G.D. Heathcote, 1958
  V. turnip yellow mosaic
    Broadbent, L. and G.D. Heathcote, 1958
    Croxall, H.E., D.C. Gwynne and L. Broadbent, 1953
B. oleracea var. gongylodes, L.
  V. cabbage black ring spot
    Tompkins, C.M., M.W. Gardner and H. Rex Thomas, 1937
  V. cabbage ring necrosis
    Larson, R.H. and J.C. Walker, 1941
  V. cauliflower mosaic
    Alvarez-Garcia, L.A., 1951
    Berkeley, G.H. and J.H. Tremaine, 1954
    Walker, J.C., Francis J. LeBeau and Glenn S. Pound, 1945
  V. cucumber mosaic
    Pound, Glenn S. and J.C. Walker, 1948
  V. turnip mosaic
    Berkeley, G.H. and J.H. Tremaine, 1954
    LeBeau, Francis J. and J.C. Walker, 1945
    Walker, J.C., Francis J. LeBeau and Glenn S. Pound, 1945
B. oleracea var. italica, Plenck. *
  V. aster yellows
    Severin, Henry H.P. and Julius H. Freitag, 1945
  V. cabbage black ring spot
    Hamlyn, Brenda M.G., 1953
  V. cauliflower mosaic
    (K.M. Smith, 1957) R.E. Fitzpatrick, et al., 1958
  V. turnip yellow mosaic
    (K.M. Smith, 1957) R.E. Fitzpatrick, et al., 1958
B. oleracea var. subauda, L. *
  V. cauliflower mosaic
    Caldwell, John and Ian W. Prentice, 1942
B. oleracea var. viridis, L.
  V. cabbage black ring spot
    Tompkins, C.M., M.W. Gardner and H. Rex Thomas, 1937
  V. cabbage ring necrosis
    Larson, R.H. and J.C. Walker, 1941
  V. cauliflower mosaic
    Berkeley, G.H. and J.H. Tremaine, 1954
    Walker, J.C., Francis J. LeBeau and Glenn S. Pound, 1945
  V. turnip mosaic
    Berkeley, G.H. and J.H. Tremaine, 1954
    LeBeau, Francis J. and J.C. Walker, 1945
    Walker, J.C., Francis J. LeBeau and Glenn S. Pound, 1945
B. pekinensis, (Lour.) Rupr.
  V. anemone mosaic *
    Hollings, M., 1957
  V. beet curly top
    Costa, A.S., 1952
  V. cabbage black ring spot
    Hamlyn, Brenda M.G., 1953
    Hollings, M., 1957

B. pekinensis, (Lour.) Rupr. (cont.)
V. cabbage black ring spot
  Tompkins, C.M., M.W. Gardner and H. Rex
  Thomas, 1938
V. cabbage ring necrosis
  Larson, R.H. and J.C. Walker, 1941
V. cauliflower mosaic
  Alvarez-Garcia, L.A., 1951
  Berkeley, G.H. and J.H. Tremaine, 1954
  Tompkins, C.M., 1937
  Walker, J.C., Francis J. LeBeau and Glenn S.
  Pound, 1945
V. cucumber mosaic
  Pound, Glenn S. and J.C. Walker, 1948
V. radish mosaic
  Tompkins, C.M., 1939
V. rape savoy
  Ling, Lee and Juhwa Y. Yang, 1940
V. raspberry yellow dwarf *
  Harrison, B.D., 1958
V. turnip crinkle
  Broadbent, L. and G.D. Heathcote, 1958
V. turnip mosaic
  Berkeley, G.H. and J.H. Tremaine, 1954
  Berkeley, G.H. and M. Weintraub, 1952
  LeBeau, Francis J. and J.C. Walker, 1945
  Schultz, E.S., 1921
  Sylvester, Edward S., 1953
  Takahashi, William N., 1949
  Tompkins, C.M., 1938, 1939
  Tompkins, C.M. and H. Rex Thomas, 1938
  Walker, J.C., Francis J. LeBeau and Glenn S.
  Pound, 1945
V. turnip rosette *
  Broadbent, L. and G.D. Heathcote, 1958
  Lister, R.M., 1958
V. turnip yellow mosaic
  Broadbent, L. and G.D. Heathcote, 1958
  Lister, R.M., 1958
B. rapa, L.
V. anemone mosaic *
  Hollings, M., 1957
V. beet curly top
  Severin, Henry H.P., 1929
V. beet ring spot *
  Harrison, B.D., 1957
V. cabbage black ring spot
  Bawden, F.C., Brenda M.G. Hamlyn and Marion
  A. Watson, 1954
  Hamlyn, Brenda M.G., 1953
  Hollings, M., 1957
  Tompkins, C.M., M.W. Gardner and H. Rex
  Thomas, 1937, 1938
V. cabbage ring necrosis
  Larson, R.H. and J.C. Walker, 1941
V. cauliflower mosaic
  Alvarez-Garcia, L.A., 1951
  Hamlyn, Brenda M.G., 1955
  Tompkins, C.M., 1937
  Walker, J.C., Francis J. LeBeau and Glenn S.
  Pound, 1945
V. cucumber mosaic
  Wellman, F.L., 1935
V. radish mosaic
  Raychaudhuri, S.P. and P.S. Pathanian, 1955
  Takahashi, William N., 1952
  Tompkins, C.M., 1939
V. rape savoy
  Ling, Lee and Juhwa Y. Yang, 1940
V. raspberry yellow dwarf *
  Harrison, B.D., 1958
V. tobacco mosaic
  Grant, T.J., 1934
V. turnip crinkle
  Broadbent, L. and G.D. Heathcote, 1958
  Lister, R.M., 1958
V. turnip mosaic
  Berkeley, G.H. and M. Weintraub, 1952
  Clayton, E.E., 1930
  Dale, W.T., 1948
  Dana, B.F. and F.P. McWhorter, 1932
  (K.M. Smith, 1957) R.E. Fitzpatrick, et al., 1958
  Gardner, Max W. and James B. Kendrick, 1921
  Hoggan, I.A. and J. Johnson, 1935

B. rapa, L. (cont.)
V. turnip mosaic
  LeBeau, Francis J. and J.C. Walker, 1945
  Schultz, E.S., 1921
  Sylvester, Edward S., 1953
  Tompkins, C.M., 1938, 1939
  Tompkins, C.M. and H. Rex Thomas, 1938
  Walker, J.C., Francis J. LeBeau and Glenn S.
  Pound, 1945
V. turnip rosette *
  Broadbent, L. and G.D. Heathcote, 1958
  Lister, R.M., 1958
V. turnip yellow mosaic
  Broadbent, L. and G.D. Heathcote, 1958
  Lister, R.M., 1958
B. spp.
V. cabbage ring necrosis
  (K.M. Smith, 1957) R.E. Fitzpatrick, et al., 1958
V. mustard (black) ring spot *
  (K.M. Smith, 1957) R.E. Fitzpatrick, et al., 1958

BRASSOCATTLEYA X, Rolfe 1889 (Orchidaceae)
B. dietrichiana *
V. orchid (cymbidium) mosaic
  Jensen, D.D. and A.H. Gold, 1955

BROMUS Dill. ex L. 1735 (Gramineae)
B. brizaeformis, Fisch. & Mey.
V. barley yellow dwarf
  Bruehl, G.W. and H.V. Toko, 1957
B. carinatus, Hook. & Arn.
V. barley yellow dwarf
  Bruehl, G.W. and H.V. Toko, 1957
B. catharticus, Vahl
V. barley yellow dwarf
  Bruehl, G.W. and H.V. Toko, 1957
  Oswald, John W. and Byron R. Houston, 1953
V. lucerne dwarf
  Freitag, J.H., 1951
B. commutatus, Schrad.
V. barley yellow dwarf
  Bruehl, G.W. and H.V. Toko, 1957
V. ryegrass mosaic *
  Bruehl, G.W., H.V. Toko and H.H. McKinney,
  1957
B. erectus, Huds.
V. barley yellow dwarf
  Bruehl, G.W. and H.V. Toko, 1957
B. inermis, Leyss
V. barley stripe mosaic
  McKinney, H.H., 1951, 1953
V. barley yellow dwarf
  Oswald, John W. and Byron R. Houston, 1953
V. brome mosaic
  McKinney, H.H., 1953
  McKinney, H.H., H. Fellows and C.O. Johnston,
  1942
V. oat pseudo-rosette
  (K.M. Smith, 1957) R.E. Fitzpatrick, et al., 1958
B. japonicus, Thunb.
V. barley stripe mosaic
  Slykhuis, J.T., 1952
V. barley yellow dwarf
  Bruehl, G.W. and H.V. Toko, 1957
V. wheat streak mosaic
  McKinney, H.H. and Hurley Fellows, 1951
  Slykhuis, J.T., 1952, 1955
B. mollis, L.
V. barley yellow dwarf
  Bruehl, G.W. and H.V. Toko, 1957
  Oswald, John W. and Byron R. Houston, 1953
V. ryegrass mosaic *
  Bruehl, G.W., H.V. Toko and H.H. McKinney,
  1957
B. racemosus, L.
V. barley yellow dwarf
  Bruehl, G.W. and H.V. Toko, 1957
V. ryegrass mosaic *
  Bruehl, G.W., H.V. Toko and H.H. McKinney,
  1957
B. rigidus, Roth.
V. barley yellow dwarf
  Allen, Thomas C., Jr. and Byron R. Houston,
  1956

B. rigidus, Roth (cont.)
   V. barley yellow dwarf
      Bruehl, G.W. and H.V. Toko, 1957
      Oswald, John W. and Byron R. Houston, 1953
   V. lucerne dwarf
      Freitag, Julius H., 1951
B. rubens, L.
   V. barley yellow dwarf
      Oswald, John W. and Byron R. Houston, 1953
B. secalinus, L.
   V. barley stripe mosaic
      Slykhuis, J.T., 1952
   V. barley yellow dwarf
      Bruehl, G.W. and H.V. Toko, 1957
   V. ryegrass mosaic *
      Bruehl, G.W., H.V. Toko and H.H. McKinney, 1957
   V. wheat streak mosaic
      Slykhuis, J.T., 1952, 1955
B. spp.
   V. barley yellow dwarf
      Oswald, John W. and Byron R. Houston, 1952
   V. lucerne dwarf
      Freitag, Julius H., 1951
B. sterilis, L.
   V. barley yellow dwarf
      Bruehl, G.W. and H.V. Toko, 1957
B. tectorum, L.
   V. barley stripe mosaic
      Slykhuis, J.T., 1952
   V. barley yellow dwarf
      Bruehl, G.W. and H.V. Toko, 1957
      Oswald, John W. and Byron R. Houston, 1953
   V. ryegrass mosaic *
      Bruehl, G.W., H.V. Toko and H.H. McKinney, 1957
   V. wheat streak mosaic
      Slykhuis, J.T., 1952, 1955
B. tomentellus, Boiss.
   V. barley yellow dwarf
      Bruehl, G.W. and H.V. Toko, 1957

BROWALLIA L. 1737 (Solanaceae)
B. americana, L. (B. demissa, L.)
   V. aster yellows
      (K.M. Smith, 1957) R.E. Fitzpatrick, et al., 1958
   V. tobacco mosaic
      Holmes, Francis O., 1946
   V. tomato spotted wilt
      Gardner, M.W., C.M. Tompkins and O.C. Whipple, 1935
B. elata, L.
   V. potato M *
      Bagnall, R.H., R.H. Larson and J.C. Walker, 1956
   V. potato paracrinkle
      Bagnall, R.H., R.H. Larson and J.C. Walker, 1956
   V. prunus B *
      Fulton, Robert W., 1957
B. speciosa, Hook.
   V. beet curly top
      Freitag, Julius H. and Henry H.P. Severin, 1936
   V. beet mosaic
      Bennett, C.W., 1949
   V. cucumber mosaic
      Price, W.C., 1940
   V. potato X
      Dennis, R.W.G., 1939
   V. tobacco etch
      Holmes, Francis O., 1946
   V. tobacco mosaic
      Holmes, Francis O., 1946
   V. tomato spotted wilt
      (K.M. Smith, 1957) R.E. Fitzpatrick, et al., 1958
B. speciosa var. major, Hort.
   V. tobacco mosaic
      Holmes, Francis O., 1938

BRYONIA L. 1735 (Cucurbitaceae)
B. dioica, Jacq.
   V. cucumber mosaic
      Ainsworth, G.C., 1935

BRYONOPSIS Arn. 1841 (Cucurbitaceae)
B. laciniosa, Naud.
   V. cucurbit mosaic *
      Doolittle, S.P. and M.N. Walker, 1925

BUDDLEIA Houst. ex L. 1737 (Loganiaceae)
B. spp.
   V. cucumber mosaic
      (K.M. Smith, 1957) R.E. Fitzpatrick, et al., 1958

CAJANUS DC. 1813 (Leguminosae)
C. cajan, (L.) Millsp.
   V. groundnut rosette
      Evans, A.C., 1954
   V. (legume) little leaf disease *
      Hutton, E.M. and N.E. Grylls, 1956
   V. pigeon pea sterility mosaic
      Capoor, S.P., 1952
C. indicus, Spreng.
   V. bean yellow mosaic
      Zaumeyer, W.J. and B.L. Wade, 1935
   V. cucumber mosaic
      Dale, W.T., 1949

CALANDRINIA H.B. & K. 1823 (Portulacaceae)
C. grandiflora, Lindl.
   V. aster yellows
      Kunkel, L.O., 1926
   V. beet curly top
      Freitag, Julius H. and Henry H.P. Severin, 1936
C. menziesii, Torr. & Gray
   V. beet curly top
      Carsner, Eubanks and C.F. Stahl, 1924

CALCEOLARIA L. 1771 (Scrophulariaceae)
C. crenatiflora, Cav.
   V. aster yellows
      Kunkel, L.O., 1926
C. spp.
   V. tomato spotted wilt
      (K.M. Smith, 1957) R.E. Fitzpatrick, et al., 1958

CALENDULA L. 1735 (Compositae)
C. officinalis, L.
   V. aster yellows
      Kunkel, L.O., 1926
      Severin, Henry H.P. and Julius H. Freitag, 1945
   V. beet curly top
      Freitag, Julius H. and Henry H.P. Severin, 1936
   V. cabbage ring necrosis
      Larson, R.H. and J.C. Walker, 1940, 1941
   V. carnation ring spot
      Brierley, Philip and Floyd F. Smith, 1957
   V. chrysanthemum Q
      (K.M. Smith, 1957) R.E. Fitzpatrick et al., 1958
   V. cucumber mosaic
      Nienow, Inez, 1948
      Pound, Glenn S. and J.C. Walker, 1948
      Price, W.C., 1940
   V. lucerne mosaic
      Richardson, D.E. and T.W. Tinsley, 1956
   V. lucerne witches' broom
      Helms, Katie, 1957
   V. tobacco broad ring spot
      Johnson, James and Robert W. Fulton, 1942
   V. tobacco mosaic
      Holmes, Francis O., 1946
   V. tobacco ring spot
      Fulton, Robert W., 1941
      Pound, Glenn S., 1949
      Wingard, S.A., 1928
   V. tomato aspermy
      Brierley, Philip, Floyd F. Smith and S.P. Doolittle, 1955
      Hollings, M., 1955
   V. tomato big bud
      Helms, Katie, 1957
   V. turnip mosaic
      Walker, J.C., Francis J. LeBeau and Glenn S. Pound, 1945
   V. vaccinium false blossom
      Kunkel, L.O., 1945

C. spp.
  V. aster yellows
    Severin, Henry H.P., 1934

CALLISTEPHUS Cass. 1825 (Compositae)
C. chinensis, (L.) Nees
  V. aster yellows
    Black, L.M., 1941
    Brierley, Philip and Floyd F. Smith, 1957
    Freitag, Julius H., 1956
    Johnson, Folke, 1941
    Kunkel, L.O., 1924, 1926
    Magie, R.O., Floyd F. Smith and Philip Brierley, 1952
    Maramorosch, Karl, 1952, 1955
    Raymer, W.B., 1956
    Raymer, W.B. and Clark R. Amen, 1954
    Severin, Henry H.P., 1929, 1932, 1934, 1940
    Severin, Henry H.P. and Julius H. Freitag, 1945
    Smith, Floyd F. and Philip Brierley, 1948, 1951, 1953
    Younkin, S.G., 1943
  V. carnation ring spot
    Brierley, Philip and Floyd F. Smith, 1955, 1957
  V. chrysanthemum Q
    (K.M. Smith, 1957) R.E. Fitzpatrick, et al., 1958
  V. hydrangea ring spot
    Brierley, Philip and Floyd F. Smith, 1952
  V. lucerne dwarf
    Freitag, Julius H., 1951
  V. potato stem mottle
    Van der Want, J.P.H., 1955
  V. potato yellow dwarf
    Black, L.M., 1938
  V. prunus B *
    Fulton, Robert W., 1957
  V. strawberry green petal
    Frazier, N.W. and A.F. Posnette, 1957
  V. tobacco broad ring spot
    Johnson, James and Robert W. Fulton, 1942
  V. tobacco etch
    Holmes, Francis O., 1946
  V. tobacco mosaic
    Holmes, Francis O., 1946
  V. tobacco necrosis
    (K.M. Smith, 1957) R.E. Fitzpatrick, et al., 1958
  V. tobacco ring spot
    Anderson, C.W., 1954
    Cheo, Pen Ching and W.J. Zaumeyer, 1952
    Wingard, S.A., 1928
  V. tobacco ring spot no. 2
    Brierley, Philip, 1954
    Hildebrand, E.M., 1942
    Price, W.C., 1940
  V. tobacco streak
    Fulton, Robert W., 1948
  V. tobacco yellow dwarf
    Helson, G.A.H., 1950
  V. tomato aspermy
    Brierley, Philip, Floyd F. Smith and S.P. Doolittle, 1953, 1955
    Hollings, M., 1955
  V. tomato bushy stunt
    Smith, Kenneth M., 1935
  V. tomato spotted wilt
    Black, L.M., M.K. Brakke and A.E. Vatter, 1952
    Gardner, M.W. and O.C. Whipple, 1934
    Smith, Kenneth M., 1932
    Tompkins, C.M. and M.W. Gardner, 1934
    Whipple, O.C., 1936
  V. vaccinium false blossom
    (K.M. Smith, 1957) R.E. Fitzpatrick, et al., 1958
C. hortensis, Cass.
  V. cucumber mosaic
    Govier, D.A., 1957

CALOCHORTUS Pursh 1814 (Liliaceae)
C. spp.
  V. cucumber mosaic
    Brierley, Philip and Floyd F. Smith, 1944
  V. tulip breaking
    Brierley, Philip and Floyd F. Smith, 1944

CALONYCTION Choisy 1833 (Convolvulaceae)
C. aculeatum, (L.) House
  V. sweet potato feathery mottle
    Webb, Raymon E., 1954
  V. sweet potato foliage spotting disease *
    Holmes, Francis O., 1956
  V. tobacco mosaic
    Holmes, Francis O., 1946

CAMELINA Crantz 1762 (Cruciferae)
C. sativa, (L.) Crantz
  V. cabbage black ring spot
    (K.M. Smith, 1957) R.E. Fitzpatrick, et al., 1958
  V. cauliflower mosaic
    (K.M. Smith, 1957) R.E. Fitzpatrick, et al., 1958
  V. turnip crinkle
    Broadbent, L. and G.D. Heathcote, 1958
  V. turnip rosette *
    Broadbent, L. and G.D. Heathcote, 1958

CAMELLIA L. 1735 (Theaceae)
C. japonica, L.
  V. camellia yellow mottle leaf
    Milbrath, J.A. and F.P. McWhorter, 1940
    Plakidas, A.G., 1953, 1954
C. sasanqua, Thunb.
  V. camellia yellow mottle leaf
    Plakidas, A.G., 1953, 1954
C. thea, Link. *
  V. tea phloem necrosis
    Bond, T.E.T., 1944

CAMPANULA ((Tourn.)) L. 1735 (Campanulaceae)
C. americana, L.
  V. tomato spotted wilt
    Gardner, M.W., C.M. Tompkins and O.C. Whipple, 1935
C. drabifolia, Sibth. & Sm.
  V. tobacco etch
    Holmes, Francis O., 1946
  V. tobacco mosaic
    Holmes, Francis O., 1946
C. medium, L.
  V. tobacco necrosis
    Price, W.C., 1940
  V. tobacco ring spot
    Price, W.C., 1940
  V. tobacco ring spot no. 2
    Price, W.C., 1940
C. pyramidalis, L.
  V. tomato spotted wilt
    (K.M. Smith, 1957) R.E. Fitzpatrick, et al., 1958

CANAVALIA DC. 1825 (Leguminosae)
C. ensiformis, (L.) DC.
  V. bean yellow mosaic
    Thomas, H. Rex and W.J. Zaumeyer, 1953
  V. cowpea mosaic
    Anderson, C.W., 1955
    Capoor, S.P. and P.M. Varma, 1956
    Dale, W.T., 1949
  V. tobacco ring spot
    Cheo, Pen Ching and W.J. Zaumeyer, 1952
C. gladiata, (Jacq.) DC.
  V. cowpea mosaic
    Anderson, C.W., 1955

CANNA L. 1735 (Cannaceae)
C. edulis, Ker-Gawl.
  V. canna mosaic
    Celino, M.S. and G.O. Ocfemia, 1941
C. generalis, Bailey
  V. aster yellows
    Smith, Floyd F. and Philip Brierley, 1951
  V. canna mosaic
    Brierley, Philip and Floyd F. Smith, 1948
    Castillo, B.S., C.E. Yarwood and A.H. Gold, 1956
C. glauca, L.
  V. canna mosaic
    Brierley, Philip and Floyd F. Smith, 1948
    Castillo, B.S., C.E. Yarwook and A.H. Gold, 1956

C. indica, L.
    V. cabbage black ring spot
        Hollings, M., 1957
    V. canna mosaic
        Brierley, Philip and Floyd F. Smith, 1948
        Castillo, B.S., C.E. Yarwood and A.H. Gold, 1956
        Ocfemia, G.O., Isidro S. Macaspac and Hsieh
        Feng Yuan, 1941
    V. cucumber mosaic
        Celino, Martin S., 1940
        Celino, M.S. and Aureo L. Martinez, 1956
        Magee, C.J.P., 1940
    V. tomato aspermy
        Ocfemia, G.O., 1956
C. spp.
    V. cucumber mosaic
        Ocfemia, G.O. and Martin S. Celino, 1938
    V. lucerne dwarf
        Freitag, Julius H., 1951

CAPSELLA Medic. 1792 (Cruciferae)
(Bursa) Weber 1780
C. bursa-pastoris, (L.) Medik.
    V. anemone mosaic *
        Hollings, M., 1957
    V. aster yellows
        Frazier, Norman W. and Henry H.P. Severin, 1945
    V. beet curly top
        Severin, Henry H.P., 1929, 1934
    V. beet mosaic
        Pound, Glenn S., 1947
    V. beet ring spot *
        Harrison, B.D., 1957
    V. beet yellows
        (K.M. Smith, 1957) R.E. Fitzpatrick, et al., 1958
        Roland, G. and J. Tahon, 1961
    V. cabbage black ring spot
        Hamlyn, Brenda M.G., 1953
        Hollings, M., 1957
        Tompkins, C.M., M.W. Gardner and H. Rex
        Thomas, 1938
    V. cabbage ring necrosis
        Larson, R.H. and J.C. Walker, 1941
    V. cauliflower mosaic
        Tompkins, C.M., 1937
        Walker, J.C., Francis J. LeBeau and Glenn S.
        Pound, 1945
    V. clover big vein
        Black, L.M., 1945
        Lee, C.L., 1956
    V. cucumber mosaic
        Burnett, G., 1934
        Pound, Glenn S. and J.C. Walker, 1948
    V. potato yellow dwarf
        Hansing, E.D., 1942
    V. radish mosaic
        Tompkins, C.M., 1939
    V. tobacco broad ring spot
        (K.M. Smith, 1957) R.E. Fitzpatrick, et al., 1958
    V. tobacco mosaic
        Holmes, Francis O., 1938, 1946
    V. tobacco ring spot
        Pound, Glenn S., 1949
    V. turnip crinkle
        Broadbent, L. and G.D. Heathcote, 1958
    V. turnip mosaic
        Berkeley, G.H. and M. Weintraub, 1952
        Pound, Glenn S., 1948
        Tompkins, C.M., 1938, 1939
        Tompkins, C.M. and H. Rex Thomas, 1938
        Walker, J.C., Francis J. LeBeau and Glenn S.
        Pound, 1945
    V. turnip yellow mosaic
        Broadbent, L. and G.D. Heathcote, 1958
(B. bursa-pastoris), Shafer
    V. tobacco broad ring spot
        Johnson, James and Robert W. Fulton, 1942

CAPSICUM ((Tourn.)) L. 1735 (Solanaceae)
C. cerasiforme, Mill.
    V. tobacco mosaic
        Allard, H.A., 1916

C. frutescens, L. (C. annuum, L.)
    V. beet curly top
        Costa, A.S., 1952
        Kendrick, J.B., Jr., L.D. Anderson and R.C.
        Dickson, 1951
        Severin, Henry H.P., 1929
    V. carrot motley dwarf
        (K.M. Smith, 1957) R.E. Fitzpatrick, et al., 1958
    V. chilli (pepper) mosaic
        Dale, W.T., 1954
        Ferguson, I.A.C., 1951
        Jha, Ashrafi and S.P. Raychaudhuri, 1956
    V. chilli veinbanding
        Simons, J.N., 1956, 1957
    V. cucumber mosaic
        Adsuar, Jose and A. Cruz Miret, 1950
        Anderson, C.W., 1951, 1955, 1957
        Anderson, C.W. and M.K. Corbett, 1957
        Berkeley, G.H., 1951, 1953
        Doolittle, S.P., 1931
        Doolittle, S.P. and W.J. Zaumeyer, 1952, 1953
        Fulton, Robert W., 1941
        Harter, L.L., 1938
        Hoggan, Isme A., 1927
        Hollings, M., 1955
        Johnson, E.M., 1930
        Johnson, J., 1926, 1927
        Nariani, T.K. and Nirmaljit Singh, 1952
        Simons, J.N., 1955, 1957
        Wellman, F.L., 1935
        Whipple, O.C. and J.C. Walker, 1941
    V. cucurbit mosaic *
        Doolittle, S.P., 1921
        Doolittle, S.P. and M.N. Walker, 1925
    V. datura distortion mosaic
        Capoor, S.P. and P.M. Varma, 1952
    V. eggplant mosaic
        Dale, W.T., 1954
        Ferguson, I.A.C., 1951
    V. lovage mosaic
        Smith, K.M. and Roy Markham, 1944
    V. lucerne mosaic
        Berkeley, G.H., 1947
        Dykstra, T.P., 1939
        Houston, Byron R. and John W. Oswald, 1953
        Johnson, E.M., 1946
        Kreitlow, K.W. and W.C. Price, 1948, 1949
        Oswald, John W., 1948, 1950
        Porter, D.R., 1935
        Price, W.C., 1940
        Swenson, K.G., 1952
    V. lupine disease *
        Weimer, J.L., 1950
    V. (physalis) mosaic *
        Melhus, I.E., 1922
    V. potato aucuba mosaic
        Bagnall, R.H., R.H. Larson and J.C. Walker,
        1956
        Dennis, R.W.G., 1939
    V. potato leaf roll
        Dykstra, T.P., 1930
    V. potato stunt
        (K.M. Smith, 1957) R.E. Fitzpatrick, et al., 1958
    V. potato X
        Bagnall, R.H., R.H. Larson and J.C. Walker,
        1956
        Blodgett, F.M., 1927
        Cockerham, George, 1943
        Dennis, R.W.G., 1939
        Hoggan, Isme A., 1927
        Hoyman, Wm. G., 1951
        Johnson, E.M., 1930
        Johnson, J., 1925, 1927
        Larson, R.H., 1947
        Smith, J. Henderson, 1928
        Vasudeva, R. Sahai and T.B. Lal, 1944
    V. potato Y
        Alvarez-Garcia, L.A. and Jose Adsuar, 1943
        Anderson, C.W. and M.K. Corbett, 1957
        Bald, J.G. and D.O. Norris, 1945
        Dennis, R.W.G., 1939
        Dykstra, T.P., 1939

C. frutescens, L. (C. annuum, L.) (cont.)
  V. potato Y
    Easton, G.D., R.H. Larson and R.W. Hougas,
      1958
    Hoggan, Isme A., 1927
    Hutton, E.M. and J.W. Peak, 1952
    Johnson, E.M., 1930
    Johnson, J., 1927
    Roque, Arturo and Jose Adsuar, 1941
    Sakimura, K., 1953
    Simons, J.N., Robert A. Conover and James M.
      Walter, 1956
  V. sweet potato mosaic
    Elmer, O.H., 1957
  V. tobacco etch
    Anderson, C.W., 1954
    Anderson, C.W. and M.K. Corbett, 1957
    Doolittle, S.P., 1946
    Greenleaf, W.H., 1953, 1956
    Holmes, Francis O., 1942, 1946
    Johnson, E.M., 1930
  V. tobacco green mosaic
    Peterson, Paul D. and H.H. McKinney, 1938
  V. tobacco mosaic
    Abbott, E.V., 1931
    Ainsworth, G.C., 1933
    Anderson, C.W. and M.K. Corbett, 1957
    Berkeley, G.H., 1951
    Cox, C.E. and L.O. Weaver, 1950
    Dale, W.T., 1954
    Desjardins, P.R., J.M. Wallace and R.J.
      Drake, 1954
    Doolittle, S.P. and F.S. Beecher, 1942
    Dykstra, T.P., 1939
    Greenleaf, W.H., 1953
    Heuberger, J.W., 1944
    Hoggan, Isme A., 1927
    Holmes, Francis O., 1934, 1937, 1946
    Jensen, D.D., 1949
    Johnson, J., 1926, 1927
    Kendrick, J.B., Jr., L.D. Anderson and R.C.
      Dickson, 1951
    McKinney, H.H., 1929, 1952
    Perez, J. Enrique, J. Adsuar and Orlando Sala,
      1956
    Schwarze, C.A., 1914
    Stover, W.G. and M.T. Vermillion, 1933
    Woods, M.W. and Richard V. Eck, 1948
  V. tobacco necrosis
    Price, W.C., 1940
  V. tobacco ring spot
    Anderson, C.W., 1954
    Berkeley, G.H., 1951
    Steere, Russell L., 1956
  V. tobacco streak
    Fulton, Robert W., 1948
  V. tomato aspermy
    Brierley, Philip, Floyd F. Smith and S.P.
      Doolittle, 1953, 1955
    Hollings, M., 1955
  V. tomato bunchy top
    (K.M. Smith, 1957) R.E. Fitzpatrick, et al., 1958
  V. tomato ring spot
    Samson, R.W. and E.P. Imle, 1942
  V. tomato spotted wilt
    Ferguson, I.A.C., 1951
    Gardner, M.W. and O.C. Whipple, 1934
    Kendrick, J.B., Jr., L.D. Anderson and R.C.
      Dickson, 1951
    Smith, Kenneth M., 1932
    Tompkins, C.M. and M.W. Gardner, 1934
    Yu, T.F., 1947
  V. tomato twisted leaf
    Ferguson, I.A.C., 1951
  V. yam mosaic *
    Adsuar, J., 1955
C. frutescens (C. annuum, L.) var. cerasiforme,
  V. cucumber mosaic   Bailey
    Pound, Glenn S. and J.C. Walker, 1948
C. frutescens (C. annuum, L.) var. conoides, Irish
  V. cucumber mosaic
    Wellman, F.L., 1934

C. frutescens (C. annuum, L.) var. Golden Dawn x (var.
Golden Dawn x var. minimum
  V. tobacco mosaic
    Holmes, Francis O., 1934
C. frutescens (C. annuum, L.) var. Golden Dawn x
var. minimum
  V. tobacco mosaic
    Holmes, Francis O., 1934
C. frutescens (C. annuum, L.) var. grossum, Bailey
  V. beet curly top
    Costa, A.S., 1952
  V. chilli (pepper) mosaic
    Dale, W.T., 1954
    Ferguson, I.A.C., 1951
  V. cucumber mosaic
    Wellman, F.L., 1934, 1935
  V. tomato spotted wilt
    Sakimura, K., 1940
C. frutescens (C. annuum, L.) var. longum, Bailey
  V. chilli veinbanding
    Simons, J.N., 1956
C. frutescens (C. annuum, L.) var. minimum *
  V. chilli (pepper) mosaic
    Dale, W.T., 1954
    Ferguson, I.A.C., 1951
C. frutescens (C. annuum, L.) var. Tabasco x
var. Ruby King
  V. tobacco mosaic
    Holmes, Francis O., 1934
C. microcarpum, Cav.
  V. tobacco etch
    Greenleaf, W.H., 1953
  V. tobacco mosaic
    Greenleaf, W.H., 1953
C. pendulum, Willd.
  V. tobacco etch
    Greenleaf, W.H., 1953
C. spp.
  V. tobacco mosaic
    McKinney, H.H., 1928
  V. tomato spotted wilt
    Smith, K.M., 1931, 1932

CARDAMINE ((Tourn.)) L. 1735 (Cruciferae)
C. hirsuta, L.
  V. cabbage black ring spot
    (K.M. Smith, 1957) R.E. Fitzpatrick, et al., 1958

CARDIOSPERMUM L. 1735 (Sapindaceae)
C. halicacabum, L.
  V. beet curly top
    Freitag, Julius H. and Henry H.P. Severin, 1936
  V. tobacco ring spot
    Price, W.C., 1940

CARICA L. 1737 (Caricaceae)
C. papaya, L.
  V. papaw bunchy top
    Bird, Julio and Jose Adsuar, 1952
  V. papaw mosaic
    Adsuar, Jose, 1946, 1947
  V. papaw ring spot
    Holmes, Francis O., J.W. Hendrix, W. Ikeda,
      D.D. Jensen, R.C. Lindner, and W.B. Storey,
      1948
    Jensen, D.D., 1949
  V. tobacco leaf curl
    Goenaga, Alvaro, 1945
    Nariani, T.K., 1956
  V. tobacco mosaic
    Holmes, Francis O., 1946

CARTHAMUS ((Tourn.)) L. 1735 (Compositae)
C. tinctorius, L.
  V. chilli (pepper) mosaic
    Jha, Ashrafi and S.P. Raychaudhuri, 1956
  V. prunus A *
    Fulton, Robert W., 1957
  V. prunus B *
    Fulton, Robert W., 1957
  V. prunus E *
    Fulton, Robert W., 1957

C. tinctorius, L. (cont.)
    V. prunus G *
        Fulton, Robert W., 1957

CARUM Rupp. ex L. 1735 (Umbelliferae)
C. carvi, L.
    V. celery mosaic
        Freitag, Julius H. and Henry H.P. Severin, 1945
        Severin, Henry H.P. and Julius H. Freitag, 1938

CARYA Nutt. 1818 (Juglandaceae)
(HICORIA) Rafin. 1838
C. illinoensis, (Wang.) K. Koch
    V. (pecan) bunch *
        Cole, J.R., 1937
(H. aquatica), (Michx. f.) Nutt.
    V. (pecan) bunch *
        Cole, J.R., 1937

CASSIA Tourn. ex L. 1735 (Leguminosae)
C. absus, L.
    V. groundnut rosette
        Evans, A.C., 1954
C. marilandica, L.
    V. prunus E *
        Fulton, Robert W., 1957
C. tora, L.
    V. bean yellow mosaic
        Corbett, M.K., 1957
    V. cowpea mosaic
        Anderson, C.W., 1954, 1955
    V. potato Y
        Anderson, C.W., 1954
    V. prunus A *
        Fulton, Robert W., 1957
    V. prunus E *
        Fulton, Robert W., 1957
    V. prunus G *
        Fulton, Robert W., 1957
    V. tobacco etch
        Anderson, C.W., 1954

CATHARANTHUS G. Don 1836 (Apocynaceae)
C. roseus, (L.) Don
    V. cucumber mosaic
        Adsuar, Jose and A. Cruz Miret, 1950

CATTLEYA Lindl. 1824 (Orchidaceae)
C. mossiae, Hook.
    V. orchid (cattleya) mosaic
        Jensen, D.D., 1949
C. spp.
    V. orchid (cattleya) mosaic
        Murakishi, Harry H., 1952
    V. orchid (cymbidium) mosaic
        Murakishi, Harry H. and M. Ishii, 1954
    V. orchid (odontoglossum) ring spot
        Jensen, D.D. and A. Herbert Gold, 1952
    V. tobacco mosaic
        Perez, J. Enrique, J. Adsuar and Orlando Sala, 1956
C. trianaei, Lind. & Reichb. f.
    V. orchid (cattleya) mosaic
        Jensen, D.D., 1949
    V. orchid (cymbidium) mosaic
        Jensen, D.D. and A. Herbert Gold, 1955
C. waltersiana *
    V. orchid (cymbidium) mosaic
        Jensen, D.D. and A. Herbert Gold, 1955

CEIBA Gaertn. (Bombacaceae)
C. cordifolia *
    V. cacao swollen shoot
        (K.M. Smith, 1957) R.E. Fitzpatrick, et al., 1958
C. pentandra, Gaertn.
    V. cacao swollen shoot
        Attafuah, A. and T.W. Tinsley, 1958
        Posnette, A.F., N.F. Robertson and J. McA. Todd, 1950
        Tinsley, T.W. and A.L. Wharton, 1958

CELERI Adans. 1763 (Umbelliferae)
C. graveolens, Britton
    V. cucumber mosaic
        Adsuar, Jose and A. Cruz Miret, 1950

CELOSIA L. 1737 (Amaranthaceae)
C. argentea, L.
    V. beet curly top
        Freitag, Julius H. and Henry H.P. Severin, 1936
    V. beet yellows
        Roland, G. and J. Tahon, 1961
    Y. chrysanthemum latent *
        Hollings, M., 1957
    V. tobacco etch
        Holmes, Francis O., 1946
    V. tobacco mosaic
        Holmes, Francis O., 1946
C. argentea var. cristata, Kuntze
    V. beet curly top
        (K.M. Smith, 1957) R.E. Fitzpatrick, et al., 1958
        Severin, Henry H.P. and Julius H. Freitag, 1934
    V. beet yellows
        Roland, G. and J. Tahon, 1961
    V. carnation ring spot
        Brierley, Philip and Floyd F. Smith, 1957
    V. cucumber mosaic
        Price, W.C., 1940
    V. lucerne mosaic
        Kreitlow, K.W. and W.C. Price, 1949
    V. potato leaf roll
        (K.M. Smith, 1957) R.E. Fitzpatrick, et al., 1958
    V. tomato aspermy
        Brierley, Philip, Floyd F. Smith and S.P. Doolittle, 1955
    V. turnip mosaic
        Pound, Glenn S., 1948
        Walker, J.C., Francis J. LeBeau and Glenn S. Pound, 1945
C. argentea var. plumosa *
    V. turnip crinkle
        Broadbent, L. and G.D. Heathcote, 1958

CENTAUREA L. 1737 (Compositae)
C. americana, Nutt.
    V. aster yellows
        Severin, Henry H.P. and Julius H. Freitag, 1945
    V. beet curly top
        Freitag, Julius H. and Henry H.P. Severin, 1936
    V. tobacco mosaic
        Holmes, Francis O., 1946
C. cyanus, L.
    V. aster yellows
        Frazier, Norman W. and Henry H.P. Severin, 1945
        Severin, Henry H.P. and Julius H. Freitag, 1945
    V. beet curly top
        Freitag, Julius H. and Henry H.P. Severin, 1936
    V. chrysanthemum stunt
        Brierley, Philip, 1950, 1953
        Keller, John R., 1953
    V. cynarus curly dwarf
        Morton, Donald J., 1957
C. imperialis, Hort.
    V. aster yellows
        Kunkel, L.O., 1926, 1928
    V. prunus A *
        Fulton, Robert W., 1957
    V. prunus B *
        Fulton, Robert W., 1957
    V. prunus E *
        Fulton, Robert W., 1957
    V. prunus G *
        Fulton, Robert W., 1957
    V. vaccinium false blossom
        Kunkel, L.O., 1945
C. margaritacea, Ten.
    V. aster yellows
        Kunkel, L.O., 1926
C. melitensis, L.
    V. aster yellows
        Frazier, Norman W. and Henry H.P. Severin, 1945

C. montana, L.
  V. tobacco mosaic
    Holmes, Grancis O., 1946
C. moschata, L.
  V. beet curly top
    Freitag, Julius H. and Henry H.P. Severin, 1936
  V. cucumber mosaic
    Price, W.C., 1940
  V. tobacco ring spot
    Price, W.C., 1940
  V. turnip mosaic
    Walker, J.C., Francis J. LeBeau and Glenn S. Pound, 1945

CERASTIUM ((Dill.)) L. 1735 (Caryophyllaceae)
C. spp.
  V. raspberry yellow dwarf *
    Harrison, B.D., 1958
C. viscosum, L.
  V. beet yellows
    Roland, G. and J. Tahon, 1961
C. vulgatum, L.
  V. anemone mosaic *
    Hollings, M., 1957
  V. tobacco mosaic
    Holmes, Francis O., 1938
  V. tobacco streak
    Fulton, Robert W., 1948

CHARIEIS Cass. 1817 (Compositae)
C. heterophylla, Cass.
  V. tobacco etch
    Holmes, Francis O., 1946
  V. tobacco mosaic
    Holmes, Francis O., 1946

CHAYOTA Jacq. 1780 (Cucurbitaceae)
C. edulis, Jacq.
  V. cucumber mosaic
    Wellman, F.L., 1935

CHEIRANTHUS L. 1737 (Cruciferae)
C. allionii, Hort.
  V. aster yellows
    (K.M. Smith, 1957) R.E. Fitzpatrick, et al., 1958
  V. cabbage ring necrosis
    Larson, R.H. and J.C. Walker, 1941
  V. cucumber mosaic
    Pound, Glenn S. and J.C. Walker, 1948
  V. tobacco mosaic
    Holmes, Francis O., 1946
  V. turnip mosaic
    Pound, Glenn S., 1948
C. cheiri, L.
  V. aster yellows
    Severin, Henry H.P. and Julius H. Freitag, 1945
  V. cabbage black ring spot
    (K.M. Smith, 1957) R.E. Fitzpatrick, et al., 1958
    Hollings, M., 1957
    Tompkins, C.M., M.W. Gardner, and H. Rex Thomas, 1937, 1938
  V. cauliflower mosaic
    Berkeley, G.H. and J.H. Tremaine, 1954
  V. cucumber mosaic
    Berkeley, G.H. and J.H. Tremaine, 1954
  V. tobacco mosaic
    Holmes, Francis O., 1946
  V. tomato black ring
    (K.M. Smith, 1957) R.E. Fitzpatrick, et al., 1958
  V. tomato spotted wilt
    Gardner, M.W., C.M. Tompkins and O.C. Whipple, 1935
  V. turnip crinkle
    Broadbent, L. and G.D. Heathcote, 1958
  V. turnip mosaic
    Berkeley, G.H. and J.H. Tremaine, 1954
    Berkeley, G.H. and M. Weintraub, 1952
    Pound, Glenn S., 1948
    Tompkins, C.M., 1939
    Walker, J.C., Francis J. LeBeau and Glenn S. Pound, 1945
  V. turnip rosette *
    Broadbent, L. and G.D. Heathcote, 1958

C. cheiri, L. (cont.)
  V. turnip yellow mosaic
    Broadbent, L. and G.D. Heathcote, 1958
C. spp.
  V. tomato spotted wilt
    (K.M. Smith, 1957) R.E. Fitzpatrick, et al., 1958

CHELIDONIUM Tourn. ex L. 1735 (Papaveraceae)
C. majus, L.
  V. tobacco mosaic
    Holmes, Francis O., 1938, 1946

CHENOPODIUM ((Tourn.)) L. 1735 (Chenopodiaceae)
C. album, L.
  V. anemone mosaic *
    Hollings, M., 1957
  V. barley stripe mosaic
    Sill, W.H., Jr. and E.D. Hansing, 1955
  V. beet curly top
    Bennett, C.W. and Aziz Tanrisever, 1957
    Carsner, E., 1919
    Lackey, C.F., 1929
    Severin, Henry H.P., 1934
    Severin, Henry H.P. and Charles F. Henderson, 1928
  V. beet leaf curl
    (K.M. Smith, 1957) R.E. Fitzpatrick, et al., 1958
  V. beet mosaic
    Pound, Glenn S., 1947
    Severin, Henry H.P. and Roger M. Drake, 1947
  V. beet yellows
    (K.M. Smith, 1957) R.E. Fitzpatrick, et al., 1958
    Roland, G. and J. Tahon, 1961
  V. brome mosaic
    McKinney, H.H., 1953
  V. cabbage black ring spot
    Hollings, M., 1957
    Tompkins, C.M., M.W. Gardner and H. Rex Thomas, 1937, 1938
  V. carnation mosaic
    Brierley, Philip and Floyd F. Smith, 1957
    Gasiorkiewicz, E.C., 1956
  V. carnation ring spot
    Brierley, Philip and Floyd F. Smith, 1957
  V. cucumber mosaic
    Fulton, Joseph P., 1950
  V. dodder latent mosaic
    Bennett, C.W., 1944
  V. hydrangea ring spot
    Brierley, Philip and Paul Lorentz, 1957
  V. potato M *
    Bagnall, R.H., R.H. Larson and J.C. Walker, 1956
  V. potato paracrinkle
    Bagnall, R.H. and R.H. Larson, 1957
    Bagnall, R.H., R.H. Larson and J.C. Walker, 1956
  V. potato X
    Thompson, A.D., 1956
  V. radish mosaic
    Tompkins, C.M., 1939
  V. tobacco broad ring spot
    Johnson, James and Robert W. Fulton, 1942
  V. tobacco etch
    Greenleaf, W.H., 1953
  V. tobacco mosaic
    Holmes, Francis O., 1938, 1946
  V. tobacco ring spot
    Wingard, S.A., 1928
  V. tobacco streak
    Fulton, Robert W., 1948
  V. turnip crinkle
    Broadbent, L. and G.D. Heathcote, 1958
  V. turnip mosaic
    Pound, Glenn S., 1948
    Tompkins, C.M., 1938, 1939
    Walker, J.C., Francis J. LeBeau and Glenn S. Pound, 1945
C. album var. viride, (L.) Pursh
  V. beet curly top
    Lackey, C.F., 1929
C. amaranticolor, Coste & Reyn.
  V. anemone brown ring *
    Hollings, M., 1957, 1958

C. amaranticolor, Coste & Reyn. (cont.)
  V. anemone latent *
    (K.M. Smith, 1957) R.E. Fitzpatrick, et al., 1958
  V. anemone mosaic *
    Hollings, M., 1956, 1957
  V. barley stripe mosaic
    Hollings, M., 1957
  V. bean yellow mosaic
    Hollings, M., 1957
  V. beet curly top
    Bennett, C.W. and Aziz Tanrisever, 1957
  V. beet mosaic
    Hollings, M., 1957
  V. beet ring spot *
    Harrison, B.D., 1957
  V. beet yellows
    Roland, G. and J. Tahon, 1961
  V. broad bean mottle
    Hollings, M., 1957
  V. cabbage black ring spot
    Hollings, M., 1956, 1957
  V. carnation mosaic
    Brierley, Philip and Floyd F. Smith, 1957
  V. carnation mottle
    Brierley, Philip and Floyd F. Smith, 1957
    Hollings, M., 1956
  V. carnation ring spot
    Brierley, Philip and Floyd F. Smith, 1957
    Hollings, M., 1956
  V. carnation vein mottle
    Hollings, M., 1956
  V. chrysanthemum D *
    Hollings, M., 1956
  V. chrysanthemum latent *
    Hollings, M., 1957
  V. cucumber mosaic
    Harrison, B.D., 1958
    Hollings, M., 1955, 1956
  V. dandelion yellow mosaic
    Hollings, M., 1956
  V. dock mosaic
    Hollings, M., 1956
  V. henbane mosaic
    Hollings, M., 1956
  V. hydrangea ring spot
    Brierley, Philip and Paul Lorentz, 1956, 1957
    Hollings, M., 1957
  V. iris mosaic
    Hollings, M., 1956
  V. irisring spot *
    Travis, R.V., 1957
  V. lettuce mosaic
    Hollings, M., 1957
  V. lucerne mosaic
    Hollings, M., 1957
  V. narcissus stripe *
    Hollings, M., 1957
  V. orchid (cymbidium) mosaic
    Hollings, M., 1956
  V. pea mosaic
    Hollings, M., 1957
  V. pelargonium leaf curl
    Hollings, M., 1956
  V. potato aucuba mosaic
    Hollings, M., 1957
  V. potato paracrinkle
    Hollings, M., 1956
  V. potato X
    Hollings, M., 1956
  V. potato Y
    Hollings, M., 1956
  V. privet mosaic *
    Hollings, M., 1956
  V. raspberry Scottish leaf curl
    Harrison, B.D., 1958
    Lister, R.M., 1958
  V. raspberry yellow dwarf *
    Harrison, B.D., 1958
    Lister, R.M., 1958
  V. tobacco etch
    Hollings, M., 1956
  V. tobacco mosaic
    Hollings, M., 1956

C. amaranticolor, Coste & Reyn. (cont.)
  V. tobacco necrosis
    Hollings, M., 1957
  V. tobacco ring spot
    Hollings, M., 1956, 1957
  V. tomato aspermy
    Hollings, M., 1955, 1956
  V. tomato black fleck *
    Hollings, M., 1957
  V. tomato black ring
    Harrison, B.D., 1958
    Hollings, M., 1956
  V. tomato spotted wilt
    Hollings, M., 1956
  V. turnip crinkle
    Broadbent, L. and G.D. Heathcote, 1958
    Hollings, M., 1957
    Lister, R.M., 1958
C. ambrosioides, L.
  V. beet curly top
    (K.M. Smith, 1957) R.E. Fitzpatrick, et al., 1958
    Severin, Henry H.P., 1934
    Severin, Henry H.P. and Charles F. Henderson,
     1928
  V. beet yellows
    Roland, G. and J. Tahon, 1961
  V. lucerne dwarf
    Freitag, J.H., 1951
  V. tobacco mosaic
    Holmes, Francis O., 1938, 1946
C. ambrosioides var. anthelminticum, (L.) A. Gray
  V. cowpea mosaic
    Anderson, C.W., 1955
C. bonus-henricus, L.
  V. beet yellows
    Roland, G. and J. Tahon, 1961
C. botrys, L.
  V. beet yellows
    Roland, G. and J. Tahon, 1961
C. californicum, S. Wats.
  V. beet curly top
    Severin, Henry H.P., 1934
    Severin, Henry H.P. and Charles F. Henderson,
     1928
C. capitatum, (L.) Asch.
  V. beet yellows
    Roland, G. and J. Tahon, 1961
C. ficifolium, Sm.
  V. beet yellows
    Roland, G. and J. Tahon, 1961
C. foliosum, (Moench) Asch.
  V. beet yellows
    Roland, G. and J. Tahon, 1961
C. giganteum, D. Don
  V. beet yellows
    Roland, G. and J. Tahon, 1961
C. glaucum, L.
  V. beet yellows
    Roland, G. and J. Tahon, 1961
  V. tobacco mosaic
    Holmes, Francis O., 1946
C. hybridum, L.
  V. beet yellows
    Roland, G. and J. Tahon, 1961
  V. cucumber mosaic
    Roberts, Daniel A., 1952
    Roberts, Daniel A., R.E. Wilkinson and A.
    Frank Ross, 1951
  V. eggplant mosaic
    Dale, W.T., 1954
  V. tobacco ring spot
    Benedict, W.G., 1955
C. leptophyllum, Nutt. ex S. Wats.
  V. beet curly top
    Severin, Henry H.P., 1934
    Severin, Henry H.P. and Charles F. Henderson,
     1928
  V. beet yellows
    Roland, G. and J. Tahon, 1961
C. murale, L.
  V. beet curly top
    Bennett, C.W. and Aziz Tanrisever, 1957
    Carsner, E., 1925

C. murale, L. (cont.)
  V. beet curly top
      Carsner, E. and C.F. Stahl, 1924
      Giddings, N.J., 1944
      Lackey, C.F., 1932, 1937
      Severin, Henry H.P., 1934
      Severin, Henry H.P. and Charles F. Henderson,
      1928
  V. beet mosaic
      Severin, Henry H.P. and Roger M. Drake, 1947
  V. beet yellows
      Costa, A.S. and C.W. Bennett, 1955
      Roland, G. and J. Tahon, 1961
  V. cabbage black ring spot
      Tompkins, C.M., M.W. Gardner and H. Rex
      Thomas, 1937, 1938
  V. cucumber mosaic
      Wellman, F.L., 1935
  V. dodder latent mosaic
      Bennett, C.W., 1944
  V. radish mosaic
      Tompkins, C.M., 1939
  V. turnip mosaic
      Tompkins, C.M., 1939
C. opulifolium, Schrad.
  V. beet yellows
      Roland, G. and J. Tahon, 1961
C. polyspermum, L.
  V. beet yellows
      Roland, G. and J. Tahon, 1961
C. quinoa, Willd.
  V. beet yellows
      Roland, G. and J. Tahon, 1961
C. rubrum, L.
  V. beet yellows
      Roland, G. and J. Tahon, 1961
  V. tobacco mosaic
      Holmes, Francis O., 1946
C. spp.
  V. beet yellows
      (K.M. Smith, 1957) R.E. Fitzpatrick, et al., 1958
  V. potato X
      (K.M. Smith, 1957) R.E. Fitzpatrick, et al., 1958
  V. tobacco broad ring spot
      (K.M. Smith, 1957) R.E. Fitzpatrick, et al., 1958
  V. tobacco mosaic
      (K.M. Smith, 1957) R.E. Fitzpatrick, et al., 1958
  V. tobacco ring spot
      (K.M. Smith, 1957) R.E. Fitzpatrick, et al., 1958
      Travis, R.V. and Philip Brierley, 1957
  V. tobacco streak
      (K.M. Smith, 1957) R.E. Fitzpatrick, et al., 1958
C. suecicum, Murr. *
  V. beet yellows
      Roland, G. and J. Tahon, 1961
C. urbicum, L.
  V. beet yellows
      Roland, G. and J. Tahon, 1961
  V. lettuce mosaic
      Wilkinson, R.E. and Ursula Hirsch, 1952
  V. potato Y
      Darby, J.F., R.H. Larson and J.C. Walker, 1951
      Ross, A. Frank, 1948
C. vulvaria, L. - foetidum *
  V. beet yellows
      Roland, G. and J. Tahon, 1961
C. watsoni, A. Nels.
  V. beet yellows
      Roland, G. and J. Tahon, 1961

CHLORIS Sw. 1788 (Gramineae)
C. gayana, Kunth.
  V. barley yellow dwarf
      Oswald, John W. and Byron R. Houston, 1953
C. virgata, Swartz
  V. maize streak
      (K.M. Smith, 1957) R.E. Fitzpatrick, et al., 1958

CHRYSANTHEMUM ((Tourn.)) L. 1735 (Compositae)
C. carinatum, L.
  V. anemone mosaic *
      Hollings, M., 1957
  V. aster yellows
      Severin, Henry H.P. and Julius H. Freitag, 1945

C. carinatum, L. (cont.)
  V. cabbage black ring spot
      Hollings, M., 1957
  V. chrysanthemum Q
      Hollings, M., 1957
  V. chrysanthemum stunt
      Brierley, Philip, 1950, 1953
  V. cucumber mosaic
      Govier, D.A., 1957
  V. tomato aspermy
      Hollings, M., 1955
C. cinerariifolium (Trev.) Vis.
  V. chrysanthemum stunt
      Brierley, Philip, 1953
C. coccineum, Willd.
  V. chrysanthemum stunt
      Brierley, Philip, 1950, 1953
  V. tomato aspermy
      Hollings, M., 1955
C. coronarium, L.
  V. aster yellows
      Kunkel, L.O., 1926
  V. beet curly top
      Freitag, Julius H. and Henry H.P. Severin, 1936
  V. cabbage black ring spot
      Tompkins, C.M., M.W. Gardner and H. Rex
      Thomas, 1938
  V. chrysanthemum stunt
      Brierley, Philip, 1950, 1953
C. corymbosum, L.
  V. chrysanthemum stunt
      Brierley, Philip, 1953
C. frutescens, L.
  V. aster yellows
      Kunkel, L.O., 1926
      Severin, Henry H.P. and Julius H. Freitag, 1945
  V. beet curly top
      Freitag, Julius H. and Henry H.P. Severin, 1936
  V. chrysanthemum stunt
      Brierley, Philip, 1953
  V. tomato aspermy
      Brierley, Philip, Floyd F. Smith and S.P.
      Doolittle, 1955
C. hortorum, Bailey
  V. aster yellows
      Smith, Floyd F. and Philip Brierley, 1948
  V. chrysanthemum Q
      Graham, D.C., 1957
  V. chrysanthemum stunt
      Brierley, Philip, 1950
  V. cucumber mosaic
      Graham, D.C., 1957
  V. tomato aspermy
      Graham, D.C., 1957
C. indicum, L.
  V. chrysanthemum Q
      (K.M. Smith, 1957) R.E. Fitzpatrick, et al., 1958
  V. chrysanthemum ring spot
      (K.M. Smith, 1957) R.E. Fitzpatrick, et al., 1958
  V. chrysanthemum rosette
      (K.M. Smith, 1957) R.E. Fitzpatrick, et al., 1958
  V. chrysanthemum stunt
      (K.M. Smith, 1957) R.E. Fitzpatrick, et al., 1958
  V. tomato aspermy
      (K.M. Smith, 1957) R.E. Fitzpatrick, et al., 1958
      Hollings, M., 1955
C. lacustre, Brot.
  V. chrysanthemum stunt
      Brierley, Philip, 1953
C. leucanthemum, L.
  V. aster yellows
      Kunkel, L.O., 1926
  V. chrysanthemum stunt
      Brierley, Philip, 1953
  V. tomato aspermy
      Brierley, Philip, Floyd F. Smith and S.P.
      Doolittle, 1955
C. leucanthemum var. maximum *
  V. aster yellows
      Kunkel, L.O., 1926
C. leucanthemum var. pinnatifidum, Lecoq. & Lamotte
  V. clover big vein
      Black, L.M., 1945

C. majus, (Desf.) Asch.
  V. chrysanthemum stunt
    Brierley, Philip, 1953
C. maximum, Ramond
  V. aster yellows
    Kunkel, L.O., 1926
  V. chrysanthemum stunt
    Brierley, Philip, 1953
C. morifolium, (Ramat.) Hemsl.
  V. aster yellows
    Brierley, Philip and Floyd F. Smith, 1957
    Smith, Floyd F. and Philip Brierley, 1953
  V. chrysanthemum latent *
    Hollings, M., 1957
  V. chrysanthemum Q
    Brierley, Philip, 1955
    Brierley, Philip and Floyd F. Smith, 1953
    Hollings, M., 1957
    Holmes, Francis O., 1956
    Keller, John R., 1951, 1953
  V. chrysanthemum ring spot
    Brierley, Philip and Floyd F. Smith, 1955
  V. chrysanthemum stunt
    Brierley, Philip, 1953
    Brierley, Philip and Floyd F. Smith, 1949, 1955
    Keller, John R., 1951, 1953
    Welsh, Maurice F., 1948
  V. chrysanthemum vein mottle *
    Hollings, M., 1957
  V. cucumber mosaic
    Hollings, M., 1955
    Whipple, O.C. and J.C. Walker, 1941
  V. tomato aspermy
    Blencowe, J.W. and John Caldwell, 1949
    Brierley, Philip, 1955
    Brierley, Philip and Floyd F. Smith, 1953, 1957
    Brierley, Philip, Floyd F. Smith and S.P.
    Doolittle, 1953, 1955
    Hollings, M., 1955
    Holmes, Francis O., 1956
    Ocfemia, G.O., 1956
  V. tomato spotted wilt
    Gardner, M.W. and O.C. Whipple, 1934
C. myconis, L.
  V. chrysanthemum stunt
    Brierley, Philip, 1953
C. nivellei, Braun-Blanq. & Maire
  V. chrysanthemum stunt
    Brierley, Philip, 1953
C. parthenium, (L.) Bernh.
  V. beet curly top
    Freitag, Julius H. and Henry H.P. Severin, 1936
  V. chrysanthemum stunt
    Brierley, Philip, 1953
C. parthenium f. flosculosum, (DC.) Beck *
  V. chrysanthemum stunt
    Brierley, Philip, 1953
  V. tomato aspermy
    Brierley, Philip, Floyd F. Smith and S.P.
    Doolittle, 1955
C. praealtum, Vent.
  V. chrysanthemum stunt
    Brierley, Philip, 1950, 1953
C. segetum, L.
  V. aster yellows
    Severin, Henry H.P. and Julius H. Freitag, 1934,
    1945
  V. cucumber mosaic
    Govier, D.A., 1957
C. segetum x C. carinatum, L.
  V. aster yellows
    Severin, Henry H.P. and Julius H. Freitag, 1945
C. spp.
  V. aster yellows
    Kunkel, L.O., 1926
  V. chrysanthemum stunt
    Brierley, Philip, 1953
  V. cucumber mosaic
    Govier, D.A., 1957
    Price, W.C., 1940
  V. lucerne mosaic
    Price, W.C., 1940
  V. tobacco ring spot
    Price, W.C., 1940

C. spp. (cont.)
  V. tomato spotted wilt
    (K.M. Smith, 1957) R.E. Fitzpatrick, et al., 1958
C. viscosum, Desf.
  V. chrysanthemum stunt
    Brierley, Philip, 1953

CICER ((Tourn.)) L. 1735 (Leguminosae)
C. arietinum, L.
  V. bean yellow mosaic
    Snyder, William C., A.O. Paulus and A. Herbert
    Gold, 1956
    Zaumeyer, W.J. and B.L. Wade, 1935
  V. beet curly top
    Severin, Henry H.P. and Charles F. Henderson,
    1928
  V. lucerne mosaic
    Zaumeyer, W.J., 1938
  V. pea enation mosaic
    Hagedorn, D.J., 1957
  V. pea mosaic
    Murphy, D.M. and W.H. Pierce, 1937
    Zaumeyer, W.J. and B.L. Wade, 1935
  V. pea streak
    Zaumeyer, W.J., 1938
  V. red clover mosaic *
    Zaumeyer, W.J. and B.L. Wade, 1935

CICHORIUM ((Tourn.)) L. 1735 (Compositae)
C. endivia, L.
  V. aster yellows
    Linn, M.B., 1940
    Severin, Henry H.P. and Julius H. Freitag, 1945
  V. cabbage black ring spot
    Hamlyn, Brenda M.G., 1953
  V. cucumber mosaic
    Price, W.C., 1940
  V. lucerne mosaic
    Price, W.C., 1940
  V. tobacco mosaic
    Holmes, Francis O., 1946
  V. tobacco necrosis
    Price, W.C., 1940
  V. tobacco ring spot
    Price, W.C., 1940
  V. tobacco streak
    Fulton, Robert W., 1948
  V. tomato spotted wilt
    Sakimura, K., 1940
C. intybus, L.
  V. aster yellows
    Severin, Henry H.P. and Julius H. Freitag, 1945
  V. lettuce mosaic
    Grogan, R.G., J.E. Welch and Roy Bardin, 1952
  V. tomato spotted wilt
    Sakimura, K., 1940

CINERARIA L. p.p. 1763 (Compositae)
C. cruenta, Mass.
  V. cineraria mosaic
    Jones, Leon K., 1944
  V. tomato spotted wilt
    Jones, Leon K., 1944

CIRSIUM ((Tourn.)) Adans. 1763 (Compositae)
C. arvense, (L.) Scop.
  V. raspberry Scottish leaf curl
    Harrison, B.D., 1958
  V. tobacco mosaic
    Boyle, John S. and David C. Wharton, 1956

CITROPSIS Swingle & Kellerman 1913 (Rutaceae)
C. articulata, Swingle & Kellerman
  V. citrus tristeza
    Hughes, W.A. and C.A. Lister, 1953

CITRULLUS Forsk. 1775 (Cucurbitaceae)
C. citrullus, Small
  V. cucumber mosaic
    Adsuar, Jose and A. Cruz Miret, 1950
C. colocynthis, Schrad.
  V. prunus A *
    Fulton, Robert W., 1957

C. colocynthis, Schrad. (cont.)
  V. prunus B *
    Fulton, Robert W., 1957
C. vulgaris, Schrad.
  V. beet curly top
    Lackey, C.F., 1929
    Severin, Henry H.P. and Charles F. Henderson, 1928
  V. cucumber green mottle mosaic
    Ainsworth, G.C., 1935
  V. cucumber mosaic
    Anderson, C.W., 1951
    Aycock, Robert, 1951
    Bhargava, K.S., 1951
    Jagger, I.C., 1918
    Lindberg, G.D., D.H. Hall and J.C. Walker, 1956
    Porter, R.H., 1930
    Pound, Glenn S. and J.C. Walker, 1948
    Vasudeva, R. Sahai and T.B. Lal, 1943
    Wellman, F.L., 1934, 1935
    Whipple, O.C. and J.C. Walker, 1941
  V. cucurbit mosaic *
    Doolittle, S.P. and M.N. Walker, 1925
  V. muskmelon mosaic
    Anderson, C.W., 1954
    Lindberg, G.D., D.H. Hall and J.C. Walker, 1956
  V. prunus A *
    Ehlers, Clifford G. and J. Duain Moore, 1957
    Fulton, Robert W., 1957
  V. prunus B *
    Ehlers, Clifford G. and J. Duain Moore, 1957
    Fulton, Robert W., 1957
  V. prunus E *
    Ehlers, Clifford G. and J. Duain Moore, 1957
  V. rose mosaic
    Fulton, Robert W., 1952
  V. squash mosaic
    Lindberg, G.D., D.H. Hall and J.C. Walker, 1956
  V. squash mosaic (southern)
    Anderson, C.W., 1951
  V. tobacco mosaic
    McKinney, H.H. and Robert W. Fulton, 1949
  V. tobacco necrosis
    Fulton, Robert W., 1950
  V. tobacco ring spot
    Anderson, C.W., 1954
    Bridgmon, G.H. and J.C. Walker, 1952
    Grogan, R.G. and W.C. Schnathorst, 1955
    McKeen, C.D., 1957
    Pound, Glenn S., 1949
    Rosberg, David W., 1953
    Sheperd, Robert J. and F. Ben Struble, 1956
    Steere, Russell L., 1956
    Wingard, S.A., 1928
  V. tobacco streak
    Fulton, Robert W., 1948
  V. watermelon mosaic
    Anderson, C.W., 1952, 1954
    Lindberg, G.D., D.H. Hall and J.C. Walker, 1956
    Pound, Glenn S., 1949
    Walker, M.N., 1933
  V. western watermelon mosaic
    Freitag, J.H., 1952
C. vulgaris var. citroides
  V. beet curly top
    Severin, Henry H.P. and Charles F. Henderson, 1928
  V. muskmelon mosaic
    Anderson, C.W., 1954
  V. prunus A *
    Fulton, Robert W., 1957
  V. prunus B *
    Fulton, Robert W., 1957
  V. squash mosaic
    Freitag, J.H., 1956
  V. tobacco ring spot
    Anderson, C.W., 1954
  V. watermelon mosaic
    Anderson, C.W., 1954

CITRUS L. 1735 (Rutaceae)
C. aurantifolia, (Christm.) Swingle
  V. citrus psorosis
    Wallace, J.M., 1951

C. aurantifolia, (Christm.) Swingle (cont.)
  V. citrus psorosis
    Weathers, L.G., E.C. Calavan and J.M. Wallace, 1956
  V. citrus tristeza
    Dickson, R.C., Metta McD. Johnson, R.A. Flock and Edward F. Laird, Jr., 1956
    Grant, Theodore J. and Henry Schneider, 1953
    Hughes, W.A. and C.A. Lister, 1953
    Knorr, L.C., 1956
    Olson, Edward O., 1956
    Wallace, J.M., 1951, 1957
    Wallace, J.M., P.C.J. Oberholzer and J.D.J. Hofmeyer, 1956
    Wallace, J.M., I. Reichert, A. Bental and E. Winocour, 1956
  V. citrus vein-yellowing disease *
    Weathers, L.G., 1957
  V. citrus xyloporosis
    Childs, J.F.L., 1956
C. aurantifolia x Fortunella margarita, (Lour.) Swingle
  V. citrus vein-yellowing disease *
    Weathers, L.G., 1957
C. aurantium, L.
  V. citrus tristeza
    Costa, A.S. and T.J. Grant, 1951
    Grant, T.J. and A.S. Costa, 1951
    Hughes, W.A. and C.A. Lister, 1953
    Olson, Edward O., 1956
C. combara, Raf.
  V. citrus tristeza
    Knorr, L.C., 1956
C. grandis, (L.) Osbeck
  V. citrus tristeza
    Carpenter, J.B., 1957
    Wallace, James M., 1957
C. grandis on C. aurantium, L.
  V. citrus tristeza
    Bennett, C.W. and A.S. Costa, 1949
C. hystrix, DC.
  V. citrus tristeza
    Knorr, L.C., 1956
C. limon, (L.) Burm. f.
  V. citrus growth-retarding *
    Calavan, E.C., J.M. Wallace and L.G. Weathers, 1954
  V. citrus psorosis
    Fawcett, H.S. and A.A. Bitancourt, 1943
    Weathers, L.G., E.C. Calavan and J.M. Wallace, 1956
  V. citrus tristeza
    Bennett, C.W. and A.S. Costa, 1949
    Carpenter, J.B., 1956, 1957
    Grant, T.J. and Richard P. Higgins, 1957
    Hughes, W.A. and C.A. Lister, 1953
    Olson, Edward O. and James R. McDonald, 1954
    Schneider, Henry, 1957
    Wallace, James M., 1957
    Wallace, J.M., P.C.J. Oberholzer and J.D.J. Hofmeyer, 1956
    Wallace, J.M., I. Reichert, A. Bental and E. Winocour, 1956
  V. citrus vein-yellowing disease *
    Weathers, L.G., 1957
  V. lemon wood pocket *
    Fawcett, H.S. and E.C. Calavan, 1947
C. limon on C. aurantium, L.
  V. citrus tristeza
    Bennett, C.W. and A.S. Costa, 1949
C. limon x C. sinensis, (L.) Osbeck
  V. citrus tristeza
    Olson, Edward O., 1956
C. limon on Poncirus trifoliata, (L.) Raf.
  V. citrus tristeza
    Olson, Edward O. and James R. McDonald, 1954
C. maxima, Merr.
  V. citrus psorosis
    Weathers, L.G., E.C. Calavan and J.M. Wallace, 1956
C. medica, L.
  V. citrus tristeza
    Hughes, W.A. and C.A. Lister, 1953
  V. cucumber mosaic
    Porter, R.H., 1930

C. mitis, Blanco
  V. citrus vein-yellowing disease *
    Weathers, L.G., 1957
C. nobilis, Lour., var. unshiu, Swingle
  V. citrus tristeza
    Hughes, W.A. and C.A. Lister, 1953
    Olson, Edward O. and James R. McDonald, 1954
    Wallace, James M., 1957
C. nobilis var. unshiu on C. paradisi, Macf. x
Poncirus trifoliata, (L.) Raf.
  V. citrus tristeza
    Olson, Edward O. and James R. McDonald, 1954
C. nobilis var. unshiu on C. sinensis, (L.) Osbeck x
Poncirus trifoliata, (L.) Raf.
  V. citrus tristeza
    Olson, Edward O. and James R. McDonald, 1954
C. nobilis var. unshiu on Poncirus trifoliata, (L.) Raf.
  V. citrus tristeza
    Olson, Edward O. and James R. McDonald, 1954
C. paradisi, Macf.
  V. citrus psorosis
    Fawcett, H.S., 1938
    Weathers, L.G., E.C. Calavan and J.M.
    Wallace, 1956
  V. citrus tristeza
    Carpenter, J.B., 1957
    Hughes, W.A. and C.A. Lister, 1953
    Knorr, L.C., 1956
    Olson, Edward O., 1956
    Wallace, James M., 1957
    Wallace, James M., P.C.J. Oberholzer and
    J.D.J. Hofmeyer, 1956
C. paradisi on C. aurantifolia, (Christm.) Swingle
  V. citrus exocortis
    Olson, E.O. and A.V. Shull, 1956
  V. citrus xyloporosis
    Olson, E.O. and A.V. Shull, 1956
C. paradisi on C. aurantium, L.
  V. citrus tristeza
    Bennett, C.W. and A.S. Costa, 1949
C. paradisi on (C. paradisi x C. reticulata, Blanco)
  V. citrus xyloporosis
    Olson, E.O. and A.V. Shull, 1956
C. paradisi x C. reticulata, Blanco
  V. citrus tristeza
    Costa, A.S. and T.J. Grant, 1951
    Hughes, W.A. and C.A. Lister, 1953
  V. citrus vein-yellowing disease *
    Weathers, L.G., 1957
  V. citrus xyloporosis
    Childs, J.F.L., 1956
C. paradisi x C. reticulata, Blanco on C. aurantium, L.
  V. citrus tristeza
    Bennett, C.W. and A.S. Costa, 1949
C. paradisi on (C. sinensis, (L.) Osbeck x Poncirus
trifoliata, (L.) Raf.)
  V. citrus exocortis
    Olson, E.O. and A.V. Shull, 1956
C. reticulata, Blanco
  V. citrus psorosis
    Fawcett, H.S., 1938
  V. citrus tristeza
    Bennett, C.W. and A.S. Costa, 1949
    Carpenter, J.B., 1957
    Hughes, W.A. and C.A. Lister, 1953
    Olson, Edward O., 1956
    Wallace, James M., 1957
C. reticulata on C. aurantium, L.
  V. citrus tristeza
    Bennett, C.W. and A.S. Costa, 1949
C. sinensis, (L.) Osbeck
  V. citrus psorosis
    Fawcett, H.S., 1933, 1934, 1938
    Fawcett, H.S. and A.A. Bitancourt, 1943
    Fawcett, H.S. and L.C. Cochra, 1941, 1942
    Rhoads, Authur S., 1942
    Wallace, James M., 1945
  V. citrus stubborn disease
    Fawcett, H.S., 1946
  V. citrus tristeza
    Carpenter, J.B., 1957
    Costa, A.S. and T.J. Grant, 1951
    Dickson, R.C., Metta McD. Johnson, R.A. Flock,
    and Edward F. Laird, Jr., 1956

C. sinensis, (L.) Osbeck (cont.)
  V. citrus tristeza
    Grant, T.J. and A.S. Costa, 1951
    Grant, T.J. and Henry Schneider, 1953
    Hughes, W.A. and C.A. Lister, 1953
    Knorr, L.C., 1956
    Schneider, Henry, J.M. Wallace and J.E.
    Dimitman, 1950
    Wallace, J.M., 1949, 1957
  V. citrus xyloporosis
    Childs, J.F.L., 1956
C. sinensis on C. aurantifolia, (Christm.) Swingle
  V. citrus exocortis
    Olson, E.O. and A.V. Shull, 1956
  V. citrus tristeza
    Bennett, C.W. and A.S. Costa, 1949
C. sinensis on C. aurantium, L.
  V. citrus tristeza
    Bennett, C.W. and A.S. Costa, 1949
    Schneider, Henry, 1954
C. sinensis on C. paradisi, Macf.
  V. citrus tristeza
    Bennett, C.W. and A.S. Costa, 1949
C. sinensis x C. reticulata, Blanco
  V. citrus xyloporosis
    Childs, J.F.L., 1956
C. spp.
  V. citrus convex gum *
    (K.M. Smith, 1957) R.E. Fitzpatrick, et al., 1958
  V. citrus psorosis
    Bennett, C.W., 1944
  V. citrus vein enation
    (K.M. Smith, 1957) R.E. Fitzpatrick, et al., 1958

CLARKIA Pursh 1814 (Onagraceae)
C. elegans, Dougl.
  V. aster yellows
    Severin, Henry H.P. and Julius H. Freitag, 1945
  V. beet curly top
    Freitag, Julius H. and Henry H.P. Severin, 1936
  V. cucumber mosaic
    Price, W.C., 1940
  V. tobacco necrosis
    Price, W.C., 1940
  V. tobacco ring spot
    Price, W.C., 1940
  V. tobacco ring spot no. 2
    Price, W.C., 1940

CLAUSENA Burm. f. 1768 (Rutaceae)
C. anisata, (Willd.) Hook. f.
  V. citrus tristeza
    Hughes, W.A. and C.A. Lister, 1953

CLAYTONIA Gronov. ex L. 1737 (Portulacaceae)
C. perfoliata, Donn.
  V. beet yellows
    Roland, G. and J. Tahon, 1961

CLEOME L. 1735 (Capparidaceae)
C. spinosa, L.
  V. beet curly top
    Freitag, Julius H. and Henry H.P. Severin, 1936
  V. cucumber mosaic
    Adsuar, Jose and A. Cruz Miret, 1950
    Faan, Hwei Chung and James Johnson, 1951
    Price, W.C., 1940
  V. lucerne mosaic
    Price, W.C., 1940
  V. tobacco mosaic
    Holmes, Francis O., 1946
  V. tobacco necrosis
    Price, W.C., 1940
  V. tobacco ring spot
    Price, W.C., 1940
  V. tobacco ring spot no. 2
    Price, W.C., 1940
  V. turnip crinkle
    Broadbent, L. and G.D. Heathcote, 1958

COBAEA Cav. 1791 (Polemoniaceae)
C. scandens, Cav.
  V. beet curly top
    Freitag, Julius H. and Henry H.P. Severin, 1936

COCHLEARIA Tourn. ex L. 1735 (Cruciferae)
C. armoracia, L.
    V. cabbage black ring spot
        (K.M. Smith, 1957) R.E. Fitzpatrick, et al., 1958
    V. cauliflower mosaic
        (K.M. Smith, 1957) R.E. Fitzpatrick, et al., 1958

COCOS L. 1753 (Palmaceae)
C. nucifera, L.
    V. (coconut) cadang-cadang disease *
        Celino, M.S., 1947

COFFEA L. 1735 (Rubiaceae)
C. arabica, L.
    V. coffee hot and cold disease *
        (K.M. Smith, 1957) R.E. Fitzpatrick, et al., 1958
    V. coffee ring spot *
        (K.M. Smith, 1957) R.E. Fitzpatrick, et al., 1958

COIX L. 1737 (Gramineae)
C. lachyrma-jobi, L.
    V. rice and corn leaf-gall *
        Agati, Julian A. and Carlos A. Calica, 1950

COLA Schott & Endl. 1832 (Sterculiaceae)
C. chlamydantha, K. Schum.
    V. cacao swollen shoot
        Tinsley, T.W. and A.L. Wharton, 1958
C. cordifolia, R. Br.
    V. cacao swollen shoot
        Posnette, A.F., N.F. Robertson and J. McA.
        Todd, 1950
C. gigantea, A. Chev., var. glabrescens, Brenan &
    V. cacao swollen shoot   Keay *
        Tinsley, T.W. and A.L. Wharton, 1958
C. lateritia, K. Schum., var. maclaudi (A. Chev.)
    V. cacao swollen shoot   Brenan & Keay *
        Tinsley, T.W. and A.L. Wharton, 1958

COLCHICUM L. 1735 (Liliaceae)
C. autumnale, L.
    V. cucumber mosaic
        Brierley, Philip and Floyd F. Smith, 1944

COLEUS Lour. 1790 (Labiatae)
C. blumei, Benth.
    V. coleus mosaic
        Creager, D.B., 1945
    V. cucumber mosaic
        Price, W.C., 1940
    V. lucerne mosaic
        Price, W.C., 1940
    V. prunus B *
        Fulton, Robert W., 1957
    V. prunus E *
        Fulton, Robert W., 1957
    V. tobacco mosaic
        Holmes, Francis O., 1946
    V. tobacco necrosis
        Price, W.C., 1940
        Price, W.C., Frank P. McWhorter and Betty H.
        Steranka, 1950
    V. tobacco ring spot
        Price, W.C., 1940
    V. tobacco ring spot no. 2
        Hildebrand, E.M., 1942
        Price, W.C., 1940
C. lanuginosus, Hochst. ex Benth.
    V. cucumber mosaic
        Adsuar, Jose and A. Cruz Miret, 1950

COLLINSIA Nutt. 1817 (Scrophulariaceae)
C. bicolor, Benth.
    V. clover big vein
        Black, L.M., 1945
    V. tobacco etch
        Holmes, Francis O., 1946
    V. tobacco mosaic
        Holmes, Francis O., 1946

COLOCYNTHIS ((Tourn.)) L. 1735 (Cucurbitaceae)
C. vulgaris, Schrad.
    V. cucumber green mottle mosaic
        Vasudeva, R.S., S.P. Raychaudhuri and
        Jagannath Singh, 1949

COMMELINA Plum. ex L. 1735 (Commelinaceae)
C. communis, L.
    V. celery mosaic
        Price, W.C., 1935
    V. cucumber mosaic
        Price, W.C., 1935
        Wellman, F.L., 1935
C. diffusa, Burm. f.
    V. cucumber mosaic
        Dale, W.T., 1954
C. elegans, H. B. & K.
    V. cucumber mosaic
        Anderson, C.W., 1952
        Dale, W.T., 1954
C. erecta, L.
    V. cucumber mosaic
        Wellman, F.L., 1935
C. gigas, Small
    V. cucumber mosaic
        Anderson, C.W., 1951, 1952
C. nudiflora, L.
    V. celery mosaic
        Doolittle, S.P., 1931
        Doolittle, S.P. and F.L. Wellman, 1934
    V. cucumber mosaic
        Anderson, C.W., 1952
        Price, W.C., 1941
        Wellman, F.L., 1934, 1935
C. spp.
    V. cucumber mosaic
        Simons, John N., 1957

CONIUM L. 1735 (Umbelliferae)
C. maculatum, L.
    V. celery yellow spot
        Freitag, Julius H. and Henry H.P. Severin, 1945
    V. poison hemlock ring spot
        Freitag, Julius H. and Henry H.P. Severin, 1945

CONRINGIA Heist. ex L. 1735 (Cruciferae)
C. orientalis, (L.) Dimort.
    V. turnip yellow mosaic
        Broadbent, L. and G.D. Heathcote, 1958

CONVOLVULUS ((Tourn.)) L. 1735 (Convolvulaceae)
C. arvensis, L.
    V. tobacco streak
        Fulton, Robert W., 1948
    V. tomato spotted wilt
        Sherf, A.F., 1948
    V. vaccinium false blossom
        (K.M. Smith, 1957) R.E. Fitzpatrick, et al., 1958
C. occidentalis, A. Gray
    V. beet yellows
        Roland, G. and J. Tahon, 1961
C. spp.
    V. cucumber mosaic
        Wellman, F.L., 1935
    V. tobacco streak
        Fulton, Robert W., 1948
C. tricolor, L.
    V. anemone mosaic *
        Hollings, M., 1957
    V. beet yellows
        Roland, G. and J. Tahon, 1961
    V. rose mosaic
        Fulton, Robert W., 1952
    V. tobacco necrosis
        Price, W.C., 1940
    V. tobacco ring spot
        Price, W.C., 1940
    V. tobacco ring spot no. 2
        Price, W.C., 1940

C. tricolor, L. (cont.)
  V. tomato aspermy
    Brierley, Philip, Floyd F. Smith and S.P.
    Doolittle, 1955

COPROSMA Forst. 1776 (Rubiaceae)
C. baueri, Endl.
  V. lucerne dwarf
    Freitag, Julius H., 1951

CORCHORUS ((Tourn.)) L. 1735 (Tiliaceae)
C. aestuans, L.
  V. cacao swollen shoot
    Tinsley, T.W. and A.L. Wharton, 1958
C. olitorius, L.
  V. cacao swollen choot
    Tinsley, T.W. and A.L. Wharton, 1958
C. tridens, L.
  V. cacao swollen shoot
    Tinsley, T.W. and A.L. Wharton, 1958
C. trilocularis, L.
  V. cacao swollen shoot
    Tinsley, T.W. and A.L. Wharton, 1958

COREOPSIS L. 1737 (Compositae)
C. douglasii, Hall
  V. dahlia mosaic
    Brierley, Philip and Floyd F. Smith, 1950
C. drummondii, Torr. & Gray
  V. aster yellows
    Severin, Henry H.P. and Julius H. Freitag, 1945
  V. tomato spotted wilt
    (K.M. Smith, 1957) R.E. Fitzpatrick, et al., 1958
C. grandiflora, Nutt.
  V. aster yellows
    Severin, Henry H.P. and Julius H. Freitag, 1945
  V. tobacco mosaic
    Holmes, Francis O., 1946
C. tinctoria, Nutt.
  V. aster yellows
    Kunkel, L.O., 1926
  V. beet curly top
    Freitag, Julius H. and Henry H.P. Severin, 1936
    Severin, Henry H.P. and Julius H. Freitag, 1934

CORIANDRUM ((Tourn.)) L. 1735 (Umbelliferae)
C. sativum, L.
  V. beet curly top
    Severin, Henry H.P., 1929
  V. celery mosaic
    Freitag, Julius H. and Henry H.P. Severin, 1945
    Severin, Henry H.P. and Julius H. Freitag, 1938
  V. poison hemlock ring spot
    Freitag, Julius H. and Henry H.P. Severin, 1945
  V. squash mosaic
    Freitag, Julius H., 1956

COSMIDIUM Nutt. 1841 (Compositae)
C. burridgeanum, X, Hort. ex Regel
  V. aster yellows
    Kunkel, L.O., 1926

COSMOS Cav. 1791 (Compositae)
C. bipinnatus, Cav.
  V. aster yellows
    Severin, Henry H.P. and Julius H. Freitag, 1945
  V. beet curly top
    Freitag, Julius H. and Henry H.P. Severin, 1936
    Severin, Henry H.P. and Julius H. Freitag, 1934
  V. tomato spotted wilt
    (K.M. Smith, 1957) R.E. Fitzpatrick, et al., 1958
C. hybridus, Hort. ex Gard. & For. i
  V. beet curly top
    Freitag, Julius H. and Henry H.P. Severin, 1936

COTONEASTER Rupp. 1745 (Rosaceae)
C. rotundifolia, Wall., var. lanata, Schneid.
  V. lucerne dwarf
    Freitag, Julius H., 1951
C. spp.
  V. apple mosaic
    (K.M. Smith, 1957) R.E. Fitzpatrick, et al., 1958

COTULA ((Tourn.)) L. 1735 (Compositae)
C. australis, Hook.
  V. aster yellows
    Frazier, Norman W. and Henry H.P. Severin,
    1945

CRAMBE Tourn. ex L. 1735 (Cruciferae)
C. maritima, L.
  V. cauliflower mosaic
    (K.M. Smith, 1957) R.E. Fitzpatrick, et al., 1958

CRASSINA Scepin 1758 (Compositae)
C. elegans, Kuntze
  V. cucumber mosaic
    Adsuar, Jose and A. Cruz Miret, 1950

CROTALARIA Dill. ex L. 1737 (Leguminosae)
C. capensis, Jacq.
  V. prunus B *
    Fulton, Robert W., 1957
C. fwamboensis, E.G. Baker
  V. groundnut rosette
    Evans, A.C., 1954
C. goreensis, Guill. & Perr.
  V. (legume) little leaf disease *
    Hutton, E.M. and N.E. Grylls, 1956
  V. lucerne witches' broom
    Helms, Katie, 1957
  V. tomato big bud
    Helms, Katie, 1957
C. grahamiana, Wight & Arn.
  V. (legume) little leaf disease *
    Hutton, E.M. and N.E. Grylls, 1956
C. incana, L.
  V. crotalaria mosaic
    Jensen, D.D., 1949, 1950
    Johnson, H.W. and C.L. Lefebvre, 1938
C. intermedia, Kotschy
  V. crotalaria mosaic
    Johnson, H.W. and C.L. Lefebvre, 1938
  V. cucumber mosaic
    Price, W.C., 1940
  V. groundnut rosette
    Evans, A.C., 1954
  V. (legume) little leaf disease *
    Hutton, E.M. and N.E. Grylls, 1956
  V. lucerne dwarf
    Price, W.C., 1940
  V. prunus A *
    Fulton, Robert W., 1957
  V. prunus E *
    Fulton, Robert W., 1957
  V. prunus G *
    Fulton, Robert W., 1957
  V. rose mosaic
    Fulton, Robert W., 1952
  V. tobacco necrosis
    Price, W.C., 1940
  V. tobacco ring spot
    LeBeau, F.J., 1947
  V. tobacco streak
    Fulton, Robert W., 1948
C. juncea, L.
  V. cowpea mosaic
    Capoor, S.P. and P.M. Varma, 1956
    Dale, W.T., 1949
  V. crotalaria mosaic
    (K.M. Smith, 1957) R.E. Fitzpatrick, et al., 1958
  V. (legume) little leaf disease *
    Hutton, E.M. and N.E. Grylls, 1956
  V. strawberry green petal
    Rose, B.D. and S.D. Misra, 1938
  V. tobacco leaf curl
    Pruthi, Hem Singh and C.K. Samuel, 1937, 1939
C. kirkii, Baker
  V. groundnut rosette
    Evans, A.C., 1954
C. lanceolata, E. Mey.
  V. crotalaria mosaic
    Johnson, H.W. and C.L. Lefebvre, 1938
C. maxillaris, Klotzsch
  V. crotalaria mosaic
    Johnson, H.W. and C.L. Lefebvre, 1938

C. mucronata, Desv.
  V. cowpea mosaic
    Anderson, C.W , 1955
  V. crotalaria mosaic
    Jensen, D.D., 1949
  V. cucumber mosaic
    Anderson, C.W., 1955
  V. prunus E *
    Fulton, Robert W., 1957
  V. prunus G *
    Fulton, Robert W., 1957
C. orixensis, Willd.
  V. (legume) little leaf disease *
    Hutton, E.M. and N.E. Grylls, 1956
C. pumila, Ortega
  V. (legume) little leaf disease *
    Hutton, E.M. and N.E. Grylls, 1956
C. retusa, L.
  V. bean yellow mosaic
    Zaumeyer, W.J., 1940
  V. crotalaria mosaic
    Johnson, H.W. and C.L. Lefebvre, 1938
  V. (legume) little leaf disease *
    Hutton, E.M. and N.E. Grylls, 1956
C. sericea, Retz.
  V. (legume) little leaf disease *
    Hutton, E.M. and N.E. Grylls, 1956
C. spectabilis, Roth
  V. alsike clover mosaic
    Zaumeyer, W.J., 1940
  V. bean yellow mosaic
    Corbett, M.K., 1957
    Hungerford, C.W. and Irvin G. Hillyer, 1954
    Zaumeyer, W.J., 1940
  V. cowpea mosaic
    Anderson, C.W., 1955
  V. crotalaria mosaic
    Johnson, H.W. and C.L. Lefebvre, 1938
  V. lucerne mosaic
    Thomas, H. Rex, 1951
  V. prunus B *
    Fulton, Robert W., 1957
  V. tobacco ring spot
    Corbett, M.K., 1957
    LeBeau, F.J., 1947
  V. tobacco streak
    Thomas, H. Rex and W.J. Zaumeyer, 1950
C. spp.
  V. datura rugose leaf curl
    (K.M. Smith, 1957) R.E. Fitzpatrick, et al., 1958
  V. kaimi clover disease *
    Murakishi, Harry H., 1952
C. striata, DC.
  V. alsike clover mosaic
    Zaumeyer, W.J., 1940
  V. bean yellow mosaic
    Zaumeyer, W.J., 1940
  V. crotalaria mosaic
    Cook, Melville T., 1931
    Johnson, H.W. and C.L. Lefebvre, 1938
C. usaramoensis, E.G. Baker
  V. crotalaria mosaic
    Johnson, H.W. and C.L. Lefebvre, 1938
  V. tobacco leaf curl
    (K.M. Smith, 1957) R.E. Fitzpatrick, et al., 1958

CRYPTOSTEMMA R. Br. 1813 (Compositae)
C. calendulaceum, (L.) R. Br.
  V. tobacco yellow dwarf
    Helson, G.A.H., 1950
    Hill, A.V., 1950
  V. vaccinium false blossom
    (K.M. Smith, 1957) R.E. Fitzpatrick, et al., 1958

CUCUMIS ((Tourn.)) L. 1735 (Cucurbitaceae)
C. anguria, L.
  V. beet curly top
    Severin, Henry H.P. and Charles F. Henderson, 1928
  V. cucumber green mottle mosaic
    Ainsworth, G.C., 1935
  V. cucumber mosaic
    Jagger, I.C., 1918

C. anguria, L. (cont.)
  V. cucumber mosaic
    Rader, Wm.E., Hugh F. Fitzpatrick and E.M. Hildebrand, 1947
    Wellman, F.L., 1935
  V. cucumber western mosaic *
    Severin, Henry H.P. and Julius H. Freitag, 1948
  V. cucurbit mosaic *
    Doolittle, S.P. and M.N. Walker, 1925
  V. muskmelon mosaic
    Rader, Wm.E., Hugh F. Fitzpatrick and E.M. Hildebrank, 1947
  V. prunus A *
    Fulton, Robert W., 1957
  V. prunus B *
    Fulton, Robert W., 1957
  V. prunus E *
    Fulton, Robert W., 1957
  V. prunus G *
    Fulton, Robert W., 1957
  V. squash mosaic
    Freitag, Julius H., 1956
C. dipsaceus, Ehr.
  V. prunus A *
    Fulton, Robert W., 1957
  V. prunus B *
    Fulton, Robert W., 1957
  V. prunus E *
    Fulton, Robert W., 1957
  V. prunus G *
    Fulton, Robert W., 1957
C. ficifolius, Bouche
  V. cucurbit mosaic *
    Doolittle, S.P. and M.N. Walker, 1925
C. grossulariaeformis, Hort. *
  V. cucurbit mosaic *
    Doolittle, S.P. and M.N. Walker, 1925
C. maderaspatanus, Roxbg.
  V. cucumber green mottle mosaic
    Ainsworth, G.C., 1935
C. melo, L.
  V. aster yellows
    Freitag, Julius H., 1956
  V. beet curly top
    Giddings, N.J., 1948
  V. cucumber green mottle mosaic
    Ainsworth, G.C., 1935
    Azad, R.N., 1956
  V. cucumber mosaic
    Adsuar, Jose, 1955
    Adsuar, Jose and A. Cruz Miret, 1950
    Doolittle, S.P., 1916
    Jagger, I.C., 1918
    Lindberg, G.D., D.H. Hall and J.C. Walker, 1956
    Pound, Glenn S. and J.C. Walker, 1948
    Vasudeva, R. Sahai and T.B. Lal, 1943
    Wellman, F.L., 1934, 1935
  V. cucurbit mosaic *
    Doolittle, S.P. and M.N. Walker, 1925
    Kendrick, J.B., 1934
  V. dodder latent mosaic
    Bennett, C.W., 1949
  V. muskmelon mosaic
    Anderson, C.W., 1954
    Freitag, Julius H., 1952
    Lindberg, G.D., D.H. Hall and J.C. Walker, 1956
  V. muskmelon vein necrosis
    Freitag, Julius H., 1952
  V. prunus A *
    Fulton, Robert W., 1957
  V. prunus B *
    Fulton, Robert W., 1957
  V. prunus E *
    Fulton, Robert W., 1957
  V. prunus G *
    Fulton, Robert W., 1957
  V. squash mosaic
    Freitag, Julius H., 1956
    Lindberg, G.D., D.H. Hall and J.C. Walker, 1956
  V. tobacco mosaic
    McKinney, H.H. and Robert W. Fulton, 1949

C. melo, L. (cont.)
V. tobacco necrosis
Fulton, Robert W., 1950
V. tobacco ring spot
Bridgmon, G.H. and J.C. Walker, 1952
Cheo, Pen Ching and W.J. Zaumeyer, 1952
Henderson, R.G. and S.A. Wingard, 1931
Pound, Glenn S., 1949
V. tobacco streak
Fulton, Robert W., 1948
V. watermelon mosaic
Anderson, C.W., 1954
Lindberg, G.D., D.H. Hall and J.C. Walker, 1956
Pound, Glenn S., 1949
C. melo var. cantalupensis, Naud.
V. beet curly top
Severin, Henry H.P. and Charles F. Henderson, 1928
V. tobacco ring spot
Wingard, S.A., 1928
C. melo var. chito, Naud.
V. cucumber mosaic
Rader, Wm.E., Hugh F. Fitzpatrick and E.M. Hildebrand, 1947
V. muskmelon mosaic
Rader, Wm.E., Hugh F. Fitzpatrick and E.M. Hildebrand, 1947
C. melo var. conomon, (Thunb.) Makino *
V. cucumber mosaic
Rader, Wm.E., Hugh F. Fitzpatrick and E.M. Hildebrand, 1947
Whitaker, Thomas W. and G.W. Bohn, 1954
V. muskmelon mosaic
Rader, Wm.E., Hugh F. Fitzpatrick and E.M. Hildebrand, 1947
C. melo var. dudaim, Naud.
V. cucurbit mosaic *
Doolittle, S.P. and M.N. Walker, 1925
C. melo var. flexuosus, Naud.
V. cucumber mosaic
Rader, Wm.E., Hugh F. Fitzpatrick and E.M. Hildebrand, 1947
V. cucurbit mosaic *
Doolittle, S.P. and M.N. Walker, 1925
V. muskmelon mosaic
(K.M. Smith, 1957) R.E. Fitzpatrick, et al., 1958
Rader, Wm.E., Hugh F. Fitzpatrick and E.M. Hildebrand, 1947
C. melo var. inodorus, Naud.
V. beet curly top
Severin, Henry H.P. and Charles F. Henderson, 1928
V. cucumber mosaic
Rader, Wm.E., Hugh F. Fitzpatrick and E.M. Hildebrand, 1947
Whipple, O.C. and J.C. Walker, 1941
V. cucumber western mosaic *
Severin, Henry H.P. and Julius H. Freitag, 1948
V. muskmelon mosaic
Rader, Wm.E., Hugh F. Fitzpatrick and E.M. Hildebrand, 1947
C. melo var. reticulatus, Naud.
V. beet curly top
Severin, Henry H.P. and Charles F. Henderson, 1928
V. cucumber mosaic
Anderson, C.W., 1952
Aycock, Robert, 1951
Freitag, Julius H., 1952
Rader, Wm.E., Hugh F. Fitzpatrick and E.M. Hildebrand, 1947
Whipple, O.C. and J.C. Walker, 1941
V. muskmelon mosaic
Rader, Wm.E., Hugh F. Fitzpatrick and E.M. Hildebrand, 1947
V. tobacco necrosis
Fulton, J.P., 1952
V. tobacco ring spot
McKeen, C.D., 1957
V. watermelon mosaic
Anderson, C.W., 1952

C. melo var. rockyford *
V. dodder latent mosaic
Bennett, C.W., 1944
C. melo var. utilissimus *
V. chilli (pepper) mosaic
Jha, Ashrafi and S.P. Raychaudhuri, 1956
V. cucumber green mottle mosaic
Azad, R.N., 1956
V. cucurbit mosaic *
Doolittle, S.P. and M.N. Walker, 1925
C. metuliferus, E. Mey. ex Schrad.
V. cucurbit mosaic *
Doolittle, S.P. and M.N. Walker, 1925
C. odoratissimus, Moench
V. cucurbit mosaic *
Doolittle, S.P. and M.N. Walker, 1925
C. prophetarum, L.
V. prunus A *
Fulton, Robert W., 1957
V. prunus E *
Fulton, Robert W., 1957
V. prunus G *
Fulton, Robert W., 1957
C. sativus, L.
V. apple mosaic
Yarwood, C.E., 1955
Yarwood, C.E. and H.E. Thomas, 1954
V. arabis mosaic
Smith, K.M. and Roy Markham, 1944
V. aster yellows
Freitag, Julius H., 1956
V. beet curly top
Severin, Henry H.P. and Charles F. Henderson, 1928
V. beet ring spot *
Harrison, B.D., 1957
V. brome mosaic
McKinney, H.H., 1944, 1953
V. cabbage ring necrosis
Larson, R.H. and J.C. Walker, 1940, 1941
V. carnation ring spot
Brierley, Philip and Floyd F. Smith, 1955, 1957
V. celery mosaic
Doolittle, S.P., 1931
Doolittle, S.P. and F.L. Wellman, 1934
V. (sour) cherry yellows
Gilmer, R.M., K.D. Brase and K.G. Parker, 1957
Willison, R.S., 1951
V. chilli (pepper) mosaic
Jha, Ashrafi and S.P. Raychaudhuri, 1956
V. cucumber green mottle mosaic
Ainsworth, G.C., 1935
Fulton, Robert W., 1950
Johnson, Folke, 1941
Vasudeva, R.S. and T.K. Nariani, 1952
Vasudeva, R.S., S.P. Raychaudhuri and Jagannath Singh, 1949
V. cucumber mosaic
Adsuar, Jose and A. Cruz Miret, 1950
Ainsworth, G.C., 1938, 1940
Anderson, C.W., 1951, 1952, 1955
Aycock, Robert, 1951
Berkeley, G.H., 1951, 1953
Bhargava, K.S., 1951
Brierley, Philip, 1939
Burnett, G., 1934
Cook, M.T., 1937
Dale, W.T., 1954
Diachun, Stephen, 1952
Doolittle, S.P., 1916
Doolittle, S.P. and M.N. Walker, 1928
Doolittle, S.P. and W.J. Zaumeyer, 1952, 1953
Elmer, O.H., 1927
Freitag, Julius H., 1952
Fulton, Joseph P., 1950
Fulton, Robert W., 1941
Govier, D.A., 1957
Hagedorn, D.J. and J.C. Walker, 1954
Harrison, B.D., 1958
Harter, L.L., 1936, 1938
Hoggan, Isme A., 1933, 1935

C. sativus, L. (cont.)
V. cucumber mosaic
  Hollings, M., 1955
  Jagger, I.C., 1916, 1918
  Johnson, E.M., 1930
  Larsh, Howard W. and J.R. Shay, 1945
  Lindberg, G.D., D.H. Hall and J.C. Walker, 1956
  Magee, C.J.P., 1940
  Milbrath, J.A. and Roy A. Young, 1956
  Nariani, T.K. and Nirmaljit Singh, 1952
  Nienow, Inez, 1948
  Porter, Clark A., 1954
  Porter, R.H., 1928, 1929, 1930
  Pound, Glenn S. and J.C. Walker, 1948
  Price, W.C., 1934, 1937, 1941
  Rader, Wm.E., Hugh F. Fitzpatrick and E.M. Hildebrand, 1947
  Shifriss, Oved, C.H. Myers and Charles Chupp, 1942
  Silberschmidt, K., 1955
  Sill, Webster H., Jr., 1951
  Sill, Webster H., Jr. and J.C. Walker, 1952
  Simons, John N., 1955, 1957
  Sinclair, J.B. and J.C. Walker, 1956
  Smith, Floyd F. and Philip Brierley, 1944
  Storey, I.F., 1939
  Valleau, W.D., 1932
  Varney, E.H. and J. Duain Moore, 1951
  Vasudeva, R. Sahai and T.B. Lal, 1943
  Walker, M.N., 1926
  Wellman, F.L., 1934, 1935
  Whipple, O.C. and J.C. Walker, 1938, 1941
V. (cucumber) O.S.C. isolate 606 *
  Porter, Clark A. and Frank P. McWhorter, 1951
V. cucumber western mosaic *
  Severin, Henry H.P. and Julius H. Freitag, 1948
V. cucurbit mosaic *
  Doolittle, S.P. and M.N. Walker, 1925
V. delphinium ring spot
  Severin, Henry H.P. and R.C. Dickson, 1942
V. eggplant mosaic
  Dale, W.T., 1954
V. elm mosaic
  Varney, E.H. and J. Duain Moore, 1952
V. hydrangea ring spot
  Brierley, Philip and Paul Lorentz, 1957
  Brierley, Philip and Floyd F. Smith, 1952
V. lovage mosaic
  Smith, K.M. and Roy Markham, 1944
V. lucerne mosaic
  Berkeley, G.H., 1947
  Black, L.M. and W.C. Price, 1940
  Johnson, E.M., 1946
  Oswald, John W., 1950
  Richardson, D.E. and T.W. Tinsley, 1956
  Severin, Henry H.P., 1942
  Thomas, H. Rex, 1951, 1953
  Zaumeyer, W.J., 1938
V. lupine disease *
  Weimer, J.L., 1950
V. muskmelon mosaic
  Anderson, C.W., 1954
  Lindberg, G.D., D.H. Hall and J.C. Walker, 1956
  Rader, Wm.E., Hugh F. Fitzpatrick and E.M. Hildebrand, 1947
V. pea die back *
  Zaumeyer, W.J., 1939
V. pea mottle
  Johnson, Folke, 1942
V. pea stem streak *
  Zaumeyer, W.J., 1939
V. peach ring spot
  Boyle, J.S., J. Duain Moore and G.W. Keitt, 1949
  Fulton, Robert W., 1956
  Gilmer, R.M., 1955
  Gilmer, R.M., K.D. Brase and K.G. Parker, 1957
  Hobbs, Gordon A., 1951
  Milbrath, J.A., 1953
  Tomlinson, N., 1955
  Willison, R.S., 1951
V. peach yellow bud mosaic
  Yarwood, C.E., 1956
V. (physalis) mosaic *
  Walker, M.N., 1925, 1926

C. sativus, L. (cont.)
V. physalis subglabrata mosaic *
  Walker, M.N., 1925
V. potato X
  Matthews, R.E.F., 1949
V. prune diamond canker
  Yarwood, C.E. and H. Rex Thomas, 1954
V. prune dwarf
  Willison, R.S., 1951
V. prunus A *
  Fulton, Robert W., 1957
V. prunus B *
  Fulton, Robert W., 1957
V. prunus E *
  Fulton, Robert W., 1957
V. prunus G *
  Fulton, Robert W., 1957
V. ranunculus mosaic
  (K.M. Smith, 1957) R.E. Fitzpatrick, et al., 1958
V. raspberry Scottish leaf curl
  Harrison, B.D., 1958
  Lister, R.M., 1958
V. raspberry yellow dwarf *
  Harrison, B.D., 1958
V. red currant ring spot
  Klesser, P.J., 1951
V. rhubarb ring spot *
  Vaughan, Edward K. and John W. Yale, Jr., 1953
  Yale, John W., Jr. and Edward K. Vaughan, 1954
V. rose mosaic
  Fulton, Robert W., 1952
V. squash mosaic
  Freitag, Julius H., 1956
  Lindberg, G.D., D.H. Hall and J.C. Walker, 1956
V. squash mosaic (southern)
  Anderson, C.W., 1951
V. stone fruit *
  Boyle, J.S., J. Duain Moore and G.W. Keitt, 1954
  Lindner, R.C., Hugh C. Kirkpatrick and T.E. Weeks, 1955
V. stone fruit necrotic ring spot *
  Gilmer, R.M., 1956
V. stone fruit ring spot *
  Heinis, Julius L., 1956
  Heinis, Julius L. and J.A. Milbrath, 1954
V. tobacco broad ring spot
  Johnson, James and Robert W. Fulton, 1940, 1942
V. tobacco broken ring spot
  Smith, K.M. and Roy Markham, 1944
V. tobacco mosaic
  Berkeley, G.H., 1951
  Cox, C.E. and L.O. Weaver, 1950
  Fulton, Robert W., 1950
  McKinney, H.H., 1952
  McKinney, H.H. and Robert W. Fulton, 1949
  Walker, M.N., 1924, 1926
V. tobacco necrosis
  Fulton, Joseph P., 1952
  Price, W.C., Frank P. McWhorter and Betty H. Steranka, 1950
  Price, W.C. and Ralph W.G. Wyckoff, 1939
V. tobacco ring spot
  Allington, William B., 1946
  Anderson, C.W., 1954
  Berkeley, G.H., 1951, 1953
  Bridgmon, G.H. and J.C. Walker, 1952
  Brierley, Philip and Floyd F. Smith, 1954
  Cheo, Pen Ching and W.J. Zaumeyer, 1952
  Fulton, Robert W., 1941
  Ivanoff, S.S., 1942
  Johnson, E.M., 1930
  LeBeau, F.J., 1947
  McKeen, C.D., 1957
  McKinney, H.H. and E.E. Clayton, 1944
  Pound, Glenn S., 1949
  Rosberg, David W., 1953
  Shepherd, Robert J. and F. Ben Struble, 1956
  Steere, Russell L., 1956
  Wingard, S.A., 1928
V. tobacco ring spot no. 2
  Brierley, Philip, 1954
  Hildebrand, E.M., 1942
  Price, W.C., 1940

C. sativus, L. (cont.)
  V. tobacco streak
    Fulton, Robert W., 1948
    Thomas, H. Rex and W.J. Zaumeyer, 1950
  V. tomato aspermy
    Brierley, Philip, Floyd F. Smith and S.P.
    Doolittle, 1953, 1955
    Hollings, M., 1955
  V. tomato black ring
    (K.M. Smith, 1957) R.E. Fitzpatrick, et al., 1958
  V. tomato bushy stunt
    (K.M. Smith, 1957) R.E. Fitzpatrick, et al., 1958
  V. turnip crinkle
    Broadbent, L. and G.D. Heathcote, 1958
    Lister, R.M., 1958
  V. watermelon mosaic
    Anderson, C.W., 1952, 1954
    Lindberg, G.D., D.H. Hall and J.C. Walker, 1956
  V. yam mosaic *
    Adsuar, Jose, 1955

CUCURBITA ((Tourn.)) L. 1735 (Cucurbitaceae)
(PEPO) ((Tourn.)) L. 1735
C. ficifolia, Bouche
  V. prunus A *
    Fulton, Robert W., 1957
  V. prunus B *
    Fulton, Robert W., 1957
  V. prunus E *
    Fulton, Robert W., 1957
  V. prunus G *
    Fulton, Robert W., 1957
C. lagenaria, L.
  V. cucumber mosaic
    Adsuar, Jose and A. Cruz Miret, 1950
C. maxima, Dcne.
  V. aster yellows
    Freitag, Julius H., 1956
  V. beet curly top
    Bennett, C.W., 1934
    Dana, B.F., 1938
    Lackey, C.F., 1929
    McKay, M.B. and T.P. Dykstra, 1927
    Severin, Henry H.P. and Charles F. Henderson,
    1928
  V. (sour) cherry yellows
    Milbrath, J.A., 1956
  V. cucumber mosaic
    Anderson, C.W., 1952
    Aycock, Robert, 1951
    Jagger, I.C., 1918
    Lindberg, G.D., D.H. Hall and J.C. Walker, 1956
    Magee, C.J.P., 1940
    Pound, Glenn S. and J.C. Walker, 1948
    Rader, Wm.E., Hugh F. Fitzpatrick and E.M.
    Hildebrand, 1947
    Wellman, F.L., 1935
  V. cucumber western mosaic *
    Freitag, Julius H., 1941
  V. cucurbit mosaic *
    Doolittle, S.P. and M.N. Walker, 1925
  V. cucurbit ring mosaic *
    Freitag, Julius H., 1941
  V. muskmelon mosaic
    Lindberg, G.D., D.H. Hall and J.C. Walker, 1956
    Rader, Wm.E., Hugh F. Fitzpatrick and E.M.
    Hildebrand, 1947
  V. peach ring spot
    Milbrath, J.A., 1957
  V. peach stunt *
    Milbrath, J.A., 1956
  V. prune dwarf
    Milbrath, J.A., 1956
    Willison, R.S., 1951
  V. prunus A *
    Fulton, Robert W., 1957
  V. prunus B *
    Fulton, Robert W., 1957
  V. prunus E *
    Fulton, Robert W., 1957
  V. prunus G *
    Fulton, Robert W., 1957
  V. rose mosaic
    Fulton, Robert W., 1952

C. maxima, Dcne. (cont.)
  V. squash mosaic
    Freitag, Julius H., 1941, 1952, 1956
    Lindberg, G.D., D.H. Hall and J.C. Walker, 1956
  V. stone fruit *
    Boyle, J.S., J. Duain Moore and G.W. Keitt, 1954
  V. stone fruit ring spot *
    Milbrath, J.A., 1956
  V. tobacco broad ring spot
    Johnson, James and Robert W. Fulton, 1942
  V. tobacco necrosis
    Fulton, Joseph P., 1952
    Fulton, Robert W., 1950
  V. tobacco ring spot
    McKeen, C.D., 1957
    Pound, Glenn S., 1949
  V. tobacco ring spot no. 2
    Steere, Russell L., 1956
    Wilkinson, R.E., 1952
  V. tobacco streak
    Fulton, Robert W., 1948
  V. watermelon mosaic
    Anderson, C.W., 1952, 1954
    Lindberg, G.D., D.H. Hall and J.C. Walker, 1956
  V. wild cucumber mosaic *
    Freitag, Julius H., 1941
C. mixta, Pang.
  V. aster yellows
    Freitag, Julius H., 1956
  V. squash mosaic
    Freitag, Julius H., 1956
C. moschata, Dcne.
  V. aster yellows
    Freitag, Julius H., 1956
  V. beet curly top
    Dana, B.F., 1941
    Severin, Henry H.P. and Charles F. Henderson,
    1928
  V. cucumber green mottle mosaic
    Vasudeva, R.S. and T.K. Nariani, 1952
    Vasudeva, R.S., S.P. Raychaudhuri and
    Jagannath Singh, 1949
  V. cucumber mosaic
    Adsuar, Jose and A. Cruz Miret, 1950
    Jagger, I.C., 1918
    Lindberg, G.D., D.H. Hall and J.C. Walker, 1956
    Rader, Wm.E., Hugh F. Fitzpatrick and E.M.
    Hildebrand, 1947
  V. cucurbit mosaic *
    Doolittle, S.P. and M.N. Walker, 1925
  V. muskmelon mosaic
    Anderson, C.W., 1954
    Lindberg, G.D., D.H. Hall and J.C. Walker, 1956
    Rader, Wm.E., Hugh F. Fitzpatrick and E.M.
    Hildebrand, 1947
  V. prunus A *
    Fulton, Robert W., 1957
  V. prunus B *
    Fulton, Robert W., 1957
  V. prunus E *
    Fulton, Robert W., 1957
  V. prunus G *
    Fulton, Robert W., 1957
  V. squash mosaic
    Freitag, Julius H., 1956
    Lindberg, G.D., D.H. Hall and J.C. Walker, 1956
  V. squash mosaic (southern)
    Anderson, C.W., 1951
  V. tobacco ring spot
    Bridgmon, G.H. and J.C. Walker, 1952
    Wingard, S.A., 1928
  V. tobacco ring spot no. 2
    Steere, Russell L., 1956
  V. watermelon mosaic
    Anderson, C.W., 1954
    Lindberg, G.D., D.H. Hall and J.C. Walker, 1956
C. okeechobeensis, Bailey
  V. muskmelon mosaic
    Anderson, C.W., 1954
  V. prunus A *
    Fulton, Robert W., 1957
  V. prunus B *
    Fulton, Robert W., 1957

C. okeechobeensis, Bailey (cont.)
V. prunus E *
Fulton, Robert W., 1957
V. prunus G *
Fulton, Robert W., 1957
V. watermelon mosaic
Anderson, C.W., 1954
C. pepo, L.
V. aster yellows
Freitag, Julius H., 1956
V. beet curly top
Dana, B.F., 1941
Severin, Henry H.P. and Charles F. Henderson, 1928
V. cucumber green mottle mosaic
Ainsworth, G.C., 1935
Storey, I.F., 1939
V. cucumber mosaic
Adsuar, Jose and A. Cruz Miret, 1950
Jagger, I.C., 1916, 1918
Lindberg, G.D., D.H. Hall and J.C. Walker, 1956
Pound, Glenn S. and J.C. Walker, 1948
Rader, Wm.E., Hugh F. Fitzpatrick and E.M. Hildebrand, 1947
Vasudeva, R. Sahai and T.B. Lal, 1943
Wellman, F.L., 1935
Whipple, O.C. and J.C. Walker, 1941
V. cucurbit mosaic *
Doolittle, S.P. and M.N. Walker, 1925
V. muskmelon mosaic
Lindberg, G.D., D.H. Hall and J.C. Walker, 1956
Rader, Wm.E., Hugh F. Fitzpatrick and E.M. Hildebrand, 1947
V. peach ring spot
Hobbs, Gordon A., 1951
V. prunus A *
Fulton, Robert W., 1957
V. prunus B *
Fulton, Robert W., 1957
V. prunus E *
Fulton, Robert W., 1957
V. rose mosaic
Fulton, Robert W., 1952
V. squash mosaic
Freitag, Julius H., 1956
Lindberg, G.D., D.H. Hall and J.C. Walker, 1956
Middleton, John T., 1944
V. stone fruit necrotic ring spot *
Willison, R.S., 1951
V. tobacco mosaic
McKinney, H.H. and Robert W. Fulton, 1949
V. tobacco ring spot
Bridgmon, G.H. and J.C. Walker, 1952
Cheo, Pen Ching and W.J. Zaumeyer, 1952
Pound, Glenn S., 1949
Steere, Russell L., 1956
Wingard, S.A., 1928
V. tobacco streak
Fulton, Robert W., 1948
V. tomato black ring
(K.M. Smith, 1957) R.E. Fitzpatrick, et al., 1958
V. watermelon mosaic
Lindberg, G.D., D.H. Hall and J.C. Walker, 1956
C. pepo var. medullosa, Alef. *
V. muskmelon mosaic
Anderson, C.W., 1954
C. pepo var. melopepo, (L.) Alef. (condensa, Bailey)
V. cucumber mosaic
Anderson, C.W., 1951
Jagger, I.C., 1916
Wellman, F.L., 1934, 1935
V. cucurbit mosaic *
Doolittle, S.P. and M.N. Walker, 1925
Kendrick, J.B., 1934
V. muskmelon mosaic
Anderson, C.W., 1954
V. squash mosaic
Freitag, Julius H., 1956
V. tobacco necrosis
Frazier, Norman W., 1955
V. tobacco ring spot
Anderson, C.W., 1954
Henderson, R.G. and S.A. Wingard, 1931
Rosberg, David W., 1953

C. pepo var. melopepo, (L.) Alef. (condensa, Bailey) (cont.)
V. tobacco ring spot
Wingard, S.A., 1928
V. watermelon mosaic
Anderson, C.W., 1954
C. pepo var. ovifera, (L.) Alef.
V. beet curly top
Freitag, Julius H. and Henry H.P. Severin, 1936
V. cucumber mosaic
Jagger, I.C., 1916
V. cucurbit mosaic *
Doolittle, S.P. and M.N. Walker, 1925
V. tobacco ring spot
Wingard, S.A., 1928

CUSCUTA ((Tourn.)) L. 1735 (Convolvulaceae)
C. californica, Choisy
V. beet yellows
Roland, G. and J. Tahon, 1961
V. dodder latent mosaic
Bennett, C.W., 1944, 1949
V. tobacco etch
(K.M. Smith, 1957) R.E. Fitzpatrick, et al., 1958
C. campestris, Yuncker
V. bayberry yellows
(K.M. Smith, 1957) R.E. Fitzpatrick, et al., 1958
V. beet yellows
Roland, G. and J. Tahon, 1961
V. cucumber mosaic
Costa, A.S., 1944
V. dodder latent mosaic
Bennett, C.W., 1944, 1949
V. potato stem mottle
Van der Want, J.P.H., 1955
V. vaccinium false blossom
Costa, A.S., 1944
C. gronovii, Willd.
V. beet yellows
Roland, G. and J. Tahon, 1961
C. subinclusa, Dur. & Hilg.
V. bayberry yellows
(K.M. Smith, 1957) R.E. Fitzpatrick, et al., 1958
V. cucumber mosaic
Bennett, C.W., 1940
V. dodder latent mosaic
Bennett, C.W., 1944
V. raspberry streak
(K.M. Smith, 1957) R.E. Fitzpatrick, et al., 1958

CYAMOPSIS DC. 1825 (Leguminosae)
C. psoraloides, DC.
V. tobacco ring spot
Cooper, W.E., 1949
LeBeau, F.J., 1947
Starr, Chester K. and W.E. Cooper, 1944
C. tetragonoloba, (L.) Taub.
V. apple mosaic
Yarwood, C.E., 1955
V. bean yellow mosaic
Thomas, H. Rex and W.J. Zaumeyer, 1953
V. bean yellow stipple
Zaumeyer, W.J. and H. Rex Thomas, 1950
V. cowpea mosaic
Capoor, S.P. and P.M. Varma, 1956
V. iris ring spot *
Travis, R.V., 1957
V. lucerne mosaic
Thomas, H. Rex, 1951
V. peach ring spot
Fulton, Robert W., 1956
V. peach yellow bud mosaic
Yarwood, C.E., 1956
V. potato M *
Bagnall, R.H. and R.H. Larson, 1957
Bagnall, R.H., R.H. Larson and J.C. Walker, 1956
V. potato paracrinkle
Bagnall, R.H. and R.H. Larson, 1957
Bagnall, R.H., R.H. Larson and J.C. Walker, 1956
Yarwood, C.E. and A.H. Gold, 1955
V. prunus A *
Ehlers, Clifford G. and J. Duain Moore, 1957
Fulton, Robert W., 1957

C. tetragonoloba, (L.) Taub. (cont.)
  V. prunus B *
    Ehlers, Clifford G. and J. Duain Moore, 1957
  V. prunus E *
    Ehlers, Clifford G. and J. Duain Moore, 1957
    Fulton, Robert W., 1957
  V. prunus G *
    Fulton, Robert W., 1957
  V. prunus isolates A, E, G *
    Fulton, Robert W., 1957
  V. rose mosaic
    Fulton, Robert W., 1952
  V. tobacco necrosis
    Fulton, Robert W., 1950
  V. tobacco ring spot
    Cheo, Pen Ching and W.J. Zaumeyer, 1952
  V. tobacco streak
    Fulton, Robert W., 1948
    Thomas, H. Rex and W.J. Zaumeyer, 1950

CYCLANTHERA Schrad. 1831 (Cucurbitaceae)
C. pedata, Schrad.
  V. muskmelon mosaic
    Anderson, C.W., 1954
  V. prunus A *
    Fulton, Robert W., 1957
  V. prunus B *
    Fulton, Robert W., 1957
  V. prunus E *
    Fulton, Robert W., 1957
  V. prunus G *
    Fulton, Robert W., 1957
  V. watermelon mosaic
    Anderson, C.W., 1954

CYCLOLOMA Moq. 1840 (Chenopodiaceae)
C. atriplicifolium, (Spreng.) Coult.
  V. beet yellows
    Roland, G. and J. Tahon, 1961

CYDONIA Tourn. ex Mill. 1752 (Rosaceae)
C. oblonga, Mill.
  V. pear mosaic
    Posnette, A.F., 1957
  V. pear red mottle *
    Posnette, A.F., 1957
  V. quince sooty ring spot *
    Posnette, A.F., 1957
  V. quince stunt *
    Posnette, A.F., 1957

CYMBALARIA Medic. 1791 (Scrophulariaceae)
C. muralis, Gaertn., Mey. & Scherb.
  V. beet curly top
    Freitag, Julius H. and Henry H.P. Severin, 1936
  V. cucumber mosaic
    Price, W.C., 1940
  V. lucerne mosaic
    Price, W.C., 1940
  V. tobacco etch
    Holmes, Francis O., 1946
  V. tobacco necrosis
    Price, W.C., 1940
  V. tobacco ring spot
    Price, W.C., 1940
  V. tobacco ring spot no. 2
    Hildebrand, E.M., 1942
    Price, W.C., 1940

CYMBIDIUM Sw. 1799 (Orchidaceae)
C. insigne, Rolfe
  V. orchid (cymbidium) mosaic
    Jensen, D.D., 1951
C. lowianum, Reichb. f.
  V. orchid (cymbidium) mosaic
    Jensen, D.D., 1951
C. spp.
  V. orchid (cymbidium) mosaic
    Jensen, D.D., 1950
    Jensen, D.D. and A.H. Gold, 1955
    Murakishi, H. and M. Ishii, 1954
    White, N.H. and D.J. Goodchild, 1955
  V. orchid (laelia anceps) *
    Jensen, D.D. and A.H. Gold, 1952

C. spp. (cont.)
  V. orchid (odontoglossum ring spot
    Jensen, D.D. and A.H. Gold, 1952
  V. orchid (oncidium rogers) *
    Jensen, D.D. and A.H. Gold, 1952

CYMBOPOGON Spreng. 1815 (Gramineae)
C. nardus, (L.) Rendle
  V. sugarcane mosaic
    Costa, A.S. and M.P. Penteado, 1951
    Lawas, Orencio M. and William L. Fernandez, 1949

CYNARA Vaill. ex L. 1737 (Compositae)
C. cardunculus, L.
  V. cynarus curly dwarf
    Leach, L.D. and J.W. Oswald, 1950
  V. rose mosaic
    Fulton, Robert W., 1952
C. scolymus, L.
  V. cynarus curly dwarf
    Leach, L.D. and J.W. Oswald, 1950
    Morton, Donald J., 1957

CYNODON Rich. 1805 (Gramineae)
C. dactylon, (L.) Pers.
  V. barley yellow dwarf
    Oswald, John W. and Byron R. Houston, 1953
  V. lucerne dwarf
    Freitag, Julius H., 1951

CYNOGLOSSUM ((Tourn.)) L. 1735 (Boraginaceae)
C. amabile, Stapf & Drum.
  V. beet curly top
    Freitag, Julius H. and Henry H.P. Severin, 1936
  V. cucumber mosaic
    Fulton, Robert W., 1941
    Wellman, F.L., 1935
  V. lucerne mosaic
    Price, W.C., 1940
  V. prunus A *
    Fulton, Robert W., 1957
  V. prunus B *
    Fulton, Robert W., 1957
  V. tobacco broad ring spot
    Johnson, James and Robert W. Fulton, 1942
  V. tobacco mosaic
    Fulton, Robert W., 1941
    Grant, T.J., 1934
    Holmes, Francis O., 1946
  V. tobacco ring spot
    Fulton, Robert W., 1941
    Price, W.C., 1940

CYNOSURUS L. 1737 (Gramineae)
C. echinatus, L.
  V. barley yellow dwarf
    Oswald, John W. and Byron R. Houston, 1953

CYPERUS ((Mich.)) L. 1735 (Cyperaceae)
C. esculentus, L.
  V. lucerne dwarf
    Freitag, Julius H., 1951

CYPHOMANDRA Mart. ex Sendtn. 1845 (Solanaceae)
C. betacea, (Cav.) Sendt.
  V. potato X
    Larson, R.H., 1947
    Matthews, R.E.F., 1949
    Thompson, A.D., 1956
  V. potato Y
    (K.M. Smith, 1957) R.E. Fitzpatrick, et al., 1958

CYTISUS L. 1735 (Leguminosae)
C. scoparius, (L.) Link
  V. lucerne dwarf
    Freitag, Julius H., 1951

DACTYLIS L. 1742 (Gramineae)
D. glomerata, L.
  V. barley yellow dwarf
    Bruehl, G.W. and H.V. Toko, 1957
    Oswald, John W. and Byron R. Houston, 1953

D. glomerata, L. (cont.)
  V. cocksfoot streak
    Smith, K.M., 1952
  V. grass orchard mosaic *
    McKinney, H.H., 1956
  V. ryegrass mosaic *
    Bruehl, G.W., H.V. Toko and H.H. McKinney, 1957

DACTYLOCTENIUM Willd. 1809 (Gramineae)
D. aegyptium, (L.) Richt.
  V. rice and corn leaf-gall *
    Agati, Julian A. and Carlos A. Calica, 1950
  V. sugarcane mosaic
    Lawas, Orencio M. and William L. Fernandez, 1949

DAHLIA Cav. 1791 (Compositae)
D. pinnata, Cav.
  V. chrysanthemum stunt
    Brierley, Philip, 1953
  V. cucumber mosaic
    Pound, Glenn S. and J.C. Walker, 1948
  V. tomato spotted wilt
    Holmes, Francis O., 1948, 1955
    Smith, K.M., 1932
D. spp.
  V. chrysanthemum stunt
    Keller, John R., 1953
  V. potato Y
    (K.M. Smith, 1957) R.E. Fitzpatrick, et al., 1958
D. variabilis, (Willd.) Desf.
  V. aster yellows
    Smith, Floyd F. and Philip Brierley, 1953
  V. chrysanthemum stunt
    Brierley, Philip, 1950
  V. cucumber mosaic
    Brierley, Philip, 1951
  V. dahlia mosaic
    Brierley, Philip, 1933, 1951
    Brierley, Philip and Floyd F. Smith, 1950
  V. tomato spotted wilt
    Brierley, Philip, 1933
    (K.M. Smith, 1957) R.E. Fitzpatrick, et al., 1958
    Gardner, M.W. and O.C. Whipple, 1934

DALBERGIA L. f. 1781 (Leguminosae)
D. melanoxylon, Guill. & Perr.
  V. groundnut rosette
    Evans, A.C., 1954

DAPHNE Tourn. ex L. 1735 (Thymeleaceae)
D. mezereum, L.
  V. cucumber mosaic
    (K.M. Smith, 1957) R.E. Fitzpatrick, et al., 1958
D. odora, Thunb.
  V. cucumber mosaic
    Milbrath, J.A. and Roy A. Young, 1956
  V. lucerne mosaic
    Milbrath, J.A. and Roy A. Young, 1956

DATURA L. 1735 (Solanaceae)
D. aegyptiaca, Vesl.
  V. potato leaf roll
    Webb, R.E., R.H. Larson and J.C. Walker, 1952
D. bernhardii, Lund.
  V. potato M *
    Bagnall, R.H., R.H. Larson and J.C. Walker, 1956
  V. potato paracrinkle
    Bagnall, R.H., R.H. Larson and J.C. Walker, 1956
D. chlorantha, Hook.
  V. datura distortion mosaic
    Capoor, S.P. and P.M. Varma, 1952
  V. potato leaf roll
    Webb, R.E., R.H. Larson and J.C. Walker, 1952
D. fastuosa, L.
  V. nicotiana glutinosa mosaic *
    Allard, H.A., 1916
  V. potato leaf roll
    Webb, R.E., R.H. Larson and J.C. Walker, 1952
  V. vaccinium false blossom
    (K.M. Smith, 1957) R.E. Fitzpatrick, et al., 1958

D. ferox, L.
  V. cabbage black ring spot
    (K.M. Smith, 1957) R.E. Fitzpatrick, et al., 1958
  V. tobacco etch
    Greenleaf, W.H., 1956
D. inoxia, Mill.
  V. apple *
    Hilborn, M.T. and Reiner Bonde, 1956
  V. carnation ring spot
    Brierley, Philip and Floyd F. Smith, 1957
  V. datura distortion mosaic
    Capoor, S.P. and P.M. Varma, 1952
  V. tomato aspermy
    Brierley, Philip, Floyd F. Smith and S.P. Doolittle, 1955
D. metel, L.
  V. cucumber mosaic
    Pound, Glenn S. and J.C. Walker, 1948
  V. datura distortion mosaic
    Capoor, S.P. and P.M. Varma, 1952
  V. potato leaf roll
    Webb, R.E., R.H. Larson and J.C. Walker, 1952
  V. potato M *
    Bagnall, R.H. and R.H. Larson, 1957
    Bagnall, R.H., R.H. Larson and J.C. Walker, 1956
  V. potato paracrinkle
    Bagnall, R.H. and R.H. Larson, 1957
    Bagnall, R.H., R.H. Larson and J.C. Walker, 1956
  V. potato X
    Larson, R.H., 1947
  V. potato Y
    Darby, J.F., R.H. Larson and J.C. Walker, 1951
    Easton, G.D., R.H. Larson and R.W. Hougas, 1958
  V. tobacco mosaic
    Perez, J. Enrique, J. Adsuar and Orlando Sala, 1956
  V. tobacco ring spot
    Price, W.C., 1940
  V. tobacco streak
    Fulton, Robert W., 1948
  V. turnip mosaic
    Walker, J.C., Francis J. LeBeau and Glenn S. Pound, 1945
D. metel var. fastuosa, L. *
  V. datura distortion mosaic
    Capoor, S.P. and P.M. Varma, 1952
D. meteloides, DC.
  V. cucumber mosaic
    Wellman, F.L., 1935
  V. jimsonweed mosaic *
    Fernow, Karl Hermann, 1925
  V. potato X
    Fernow, Karl Hermann, 1925
  V. tobacco etch
    Bennett, C.W., 1944
  V. tobacco mosaic
    Keener, Paul D., 1954
  V. tomato bushy stunt
    Steere, Russell L., 1953
  V. turnip mosaic
    Walker, J.C., Francis J. LeBeau and Glenn S. Pound, 1945
D. spp.
  V. tobacco ring spot
    Smith, Kenneth M., 1929
  V. tomato ring spot
    Samson, R.W. and E.P. Imle, 1942
D. stramonium, L.
  V. aster yellows
    Frazier, Norman W. and Henry H.P. Severin, 1945
    Raymer, W.B., 1956
  V. atropa belladonna mosaic
    (K.M. Smith, 1957) R.E. Fitzpatrick, et al., 1958
  V. beet curly top
    Adsuar, Jose, 1955
    Bennett, C.W. and A.S. Costa, 1949
    Bennett, C.W. and Aziz Tanrisever, 1957
    Costa, A.S., 1952
    Fulton, Robert W., 1955
    Giddings, N.J., 1944, 1954

D. stramonium, L. (cont.)
  V. beet curly top
    Giddings, N.J., C.W. Bennett and A.L. Harrison, 1951
    Severin, Henry H.P., 1929, 1934
  V. beet ring spot *
    Harrison, B.D., 1957
  V. cabbage black ring spot
    (K.M. Smith, 1957) R.E. Fitzpatrick, et al., 1958
  V. carnation ring spot
    Brierley, Philip and Floyd F. Smith, 1957
  V. carrot motley dwarf
    (K.M. Smith, 1957) R.E. Fitzpatrick, et al., 1958
  V. chilli (pepper) mosaic
    Jha, Ashrafi and S.P. Raychaudhuri, 1956
  V. cucumber green mottle mosaic
    Ainsworth, G.C., 1935
    Vasudeva, R.S. and T.K. Nariani, 1952
    Vasudeva, R.S., S.P. Raychaudhuri and Jagannath Singh, 1949
  V. cucumber mosaic
    Berkeley, G.H., 1951, 1953
    Bhargava, K.S., 1951
    Doolittle, S.P. and W.J. Zaumeyer, 1953
    Govier, D.A., 1957
    Hagedorn, D.J. and J.C. Walker, 1954
    Harrison, B.D., 1958
    Hollings, M., 1955
    Johnson, E.M., 1930
    Lindberg, G.D., D.H. Hall and J.C. Walker, 1956
    Nariani, T.K. and Nirmaljit Singh, 1952
    Nienow, Inez, 1948
    Smith, Kenneth M., 1935
    Wellman, F.L., 1934, 1935
    Whipple, O.C. and J.C. Walker, 1941
  V. datura distortion mosaic
    Capoor, S.P. and P.M. Varma, 1952
  V. datura rugose leaf curl
    (K.M. Smith, 1957) R.E. Fitzpatrick, et al., 1958
  V. delphinium ring spot
    Severin, Henry H.P. and R.C. Dickson, 1942
  V. euphorbia mosaic
    Costa, A.S. and C.W. Bennett, 1950
  V. henbane mosaic
    Bradley, R.H.E., 1952
    Hamilton, Marion A., 1932
  V. jimsonweed mosaic *
    Fernow, Karl Hermann, 1925
  V. (legume) little leaf disease *
    Hutton, E.M. and N.E. Grylls, 1956
  V. lovage mosaic
    Smith, K.M. and Roy Markham, 1944
  V. lucerne mosaic
    Berkeley, G.H., 1947
    Oswald, John W., 1950
    Porter, D.R., 1935
    Richardson, D.E. and T.W. Tinsley, 1956
    Thomas, H. Rex, 1951, 1953
    Zaumeyer, W.J., 1938, 1953
  V. lucerne witches' broom
    Helms, Katie, 1957
  V. orchid (cymbidium) mosaic
    Jensen, D.D. and A.H. Gold, 1955
    White, N.H. and D.J. Goodchild, 1955
  V. peach X disease
    Slack, Derald A., 1952
  V. physalis floridana yellow net
    Webb, R.E., 1955
  V. potato A
    Vasudeva, R. Sahai and C.S. Ramamoorthy, 1946
  V. potato aucuba mosaic
    Bagnall, R.H., R.H. Larson and J.C. Walker, 1956
    Dennis, R.W.G., 1939
  V. potato leaf roll
    Dykstra, T.P., 1930, 1933
    Kassanis, B., 1952
    Kirkpatrick, Hugh C. and A. Frank Ross, 1952
    Webb, R.E., 1956
    Williams, W. Llewelyn and A. Frank Ross, 1957
  V. potato necrotic *
    Schultz, E.S. and W.P. Raleigh, 1933
  V. potato X
    Ainsworth, G.C., 1933, 1934

D. stramonium, L. (cont.)
  V. potato X
    Ainsworth, G.C., G.H. Berkeley and J. Caldwell, 1934
    Bagnall, R.H., R.H. Larson and J.C. Walker, 1956
    Bawden, F.C., 1936
    Bawden, F.C. and F.M.L. Sheffield, 1944
    Cockerham, George, 1943
    Dennis, R.W.G., 1939
    Dykstra, T.P., 1933, 1939
    Fernow, Karl Hermann, 1925
    Folsom, Donald and Reiner Bonde, 1937
    Goss, R.W., 1931
    Hutton, E.M., 1949
    Jarrett, Phyllis H., 1930
    Johnson, E.M., 1930
    Johnson, James, 1925
    Roberts, F.M., 1948
    Samson, R.W., 1930
    Schultz, E.S., C.F. Clark, W.P. Raleigh, F.J. Stevenson, R. Bonde and J.H. Beaumont, 1937
    Schultz, E.S. and W.P. Raleigh, 1936
    Smith, J. Henderson, 1928
    Thompson, A.D., 1956
    Vasudeva, R. Sahai and T.B. Lal, 1944
  V. potato Y
    Bawden, F.C., 1936
    Bawden, F.C. and B. Kassanis, 1947
    Samson, R.W., 1930
  V. potato yellow dwarf
    Hougas, R.W., 1951
  V. prunus B *
    Fulton, Robert W., 1957
  V. raspberry Scottish leaf curl
    Cadman, C.H., 1956
    Harrison, B.D., 1958
    Lister, R.M., 1958
  V. raspberry yellow dwarf *
    Harrison, B.D., 1958
  V. red currant ring spot
    Klesser, P.J., 1951
  V. tobacco bergerac ring spot
    (K.M. Smith, 1957) R.E. Fitzpatrick, et al., 1958
  V. tobacco broad ring spot
    Johnson, James and Robert W. Fulton, 1942
  V. tobacco coarse etch
    Johnson, E.M., 1930
  V. tobacco etch
    Anderson, C.W. and M.K. Corbett, 1957
    Bawden, F.C. and B. Kassanis, 1941
    Bennett, C.W., 1944
    Fulton, Robert W., 1941
    Greenleaf, W.H., 1956
    Holmes, Francis O., 1942, 1946
    Johnson, E.M., 1930
  V. tobacco leaf curl
    Vasudeva, R.S. and J. Sam Raj, 1948
  V. tobacco mosaic
    Ainsworth, G.C., 1933, 1937
    Ainsworth, G.C., G.H. Berkeley and J. Caldwell, 1934
    Allard, H.A., 1916
    Anderson, C.W. and M.K. Corbett, 1957
    Berkeley, G.H., 1951
    Caldwell, John, 1932
    Crawford, R.F., 1921
    Das, C.R. and S.P. Raychaudhuri, 1953
    Doolittle, S.P. and F.S. Beecher, 1942
    Holmes, F.O., 1934, 1946
    Jarrett, Phyllis H., 1930
    Johnson, E.M., 1930
    McKinney, H.H., 1952
    McKinney, H.H. and Robert W. Fulton, 1949
    Samson, R.W., 1930
  V. tobacco mottle
    (K.M. Smith, 1957) R.E. Fitzpatrick, et al., 1958
  V. tobacco ring spot
    Berkeley, G.H., 1951, 1953
    Bridgmon, G.H. and J.C. Walker, 1952
    Cheo, Pen Ching and W.J. Zaumeyer, 1952
    Cooper, W.E., 1949
    (K.M. Smith, 1957) R.E. Fitzpatrick, et al., 1958
    Fulton, Robert W., 1941

D. stramonium, L. (cont.)
  V. tobacco ring spot
    Henderson, R.G. and S.A. Wingard, 1931
    Johnson, E.M., 1930
    Steere, Russell L., 1956
    Thomas, H. Rex and W.J. Zaumeyer, 1950
    Wingard, S.A., 1928
  V. tobacco ring spot no. 2
    Brierley, Philip, 1954
  V. tobacco streak
    Fulton, Robert W., 1941, 1948
    Johnson, J., 1936
    Thomas, H. Rex and W.J. Zaumeyer, 1950
  V. tobacco vein distorting
    (K.M. Smith, 1957) R.E. Fitzpatrick, et al., 1958
  V. tobacco yellow dwarf
    Helson, G.A.H., 1950
    Hill, A.V., 1950
    Hill, A.V. and M. Mandryk, 1954
  V. tomato aspermy
    Brierley, Philip, Floyd F. Smith and S.P. Doolittle, 1955
    Hollings, M., 1955
  V. tomato big bud
    Helms, Katie, 1957
    Hill, A.V. and M. Mandryk, 1954
    Norris, D.O., 1954
  V. tomato black ring
    (K.M. Smith, 1957) R.E. Fitzpatrick, et al., 1958
  V. tomato bushy stunt
    Steere, Russell L., 1953
  V. tomato ring spot
    Imle, E.P. and R.W. Samson, 1937
    Samson, R.W. and E.P. Imle, 1942
  V. tomato spotted wilt
    Ainsworth, G.C., 1933
    Ainsworth, G.C., G.H. Berkeley and J. Caldwell, 1934
    Gardner, M.W., C.M. Tompkins and O.C. Whipple, 1935
    Gardner, M.W. and O.C. Whipple, 1934
    Milbrath, J.A., 1939
    Norris, D.O., 1951
    Sakimura, K., 1940
    Shapovalov, M., 1934
    Smith, Kenneth M., 1931, 1932, 1935
    Snyder, W.C. and H. Rex Thomas, 1936
    Whipple, O.C., 1936
  V. tomato V-52-1
    Miller, Patrick M., 1953
  V. turnip crinkle
    Broadbent, L. and G.D. Heathcote, 1958
  V. turnip rosette *
    Broadbent, L. and G.D. Heathcote, 1958
  V. vaccinium ring spot
    Hilborn, M.T. and Reiner Bonde, 1956
D. stramonium var. tatula, (L.) Torr.
  V. datura rugose leaf curl
    (K.M. Smith, 1957) R.E. Fitzpatrick, et al., 1958
  V. lucerne witches' broom
    Helms, Katie, 1957
  V. potato A
    MacLachlan, D.S., R.H. Larson and J.C. Walker, 1953
  V. potato aucuba mosaic
    Bagnall, R.H., R.H. Larson and J.C. Walker, 1956
  V. potato leaf roll
    Dykstra, T.P., 1930, 1933
    Kassanis, B., 1952
    Webb, R.E., R.H. Larson and J.C. Walker, 1952
  V. potato X
    Dykstra, T.P., 1933
    Larson, R.H., 1947
    Matthews, R.E.F., 1949
    Timian, Roland G., W.J. Hooker and C.E. Peterson, 1955
  V. tobacco yellow dwarf
    Helson, G.A.H., 1950
  V. tomato big bud
    Helms, Katie, 1957
  V. tomato ring spot
    Samson, R.W. and E.P. Imle, 1942

D. wrightii, Hort. ex Regel
  V. tomato spotted wilt
    (K.M. Smith, 1957) R.E. Fitzpatrick, et al., 1958

DAUCUS ((Tourn.)) L. 1735 (Umbelliferae)
D. carota, L.
  V. aster yellows
    George, J.A. and J.K. Richardson, 1957
  V. bayberry yellows
    Raychaudhuri, S.P., 1953
  V. clover witches' broom *
    Frazier, N.W. and A.F. Posnette, 1957
  V. cucumber mosaic
    Wellman, F.L., 1935
  V. (legume) little leaf disease *
    Hutton, E.M. and N.E. Grylls, 1956
  V. lucerne witches' broom
    Helms, Katie, 1957
  V. tobacco mosaic
    Holmes, Francis O., 1938, 1946
  V. tomato big bud
    Helms, Katie, 1957
  V. vaccinium false blossom
    Kunkel, L.O., 1945
  V. vinca yellows *
    Maramorosch, Karl, 1956
D. carota var. sativa, DC.
  V. asclepias yellows *
    Kunkel, L.O., 1950
  V. aster yellows
    Hervey, G.E.R. and W.T. Schroeder, 1949
    Severin, Henry H.P., 1930, 1932, 1934
    Severin, Henry H.P. and Julius H. Freitag, 1945
  V. bayberry yellows
    Raychaudhuri, S.P., 1952
  V. carrot motley dwarf
    Stubbs, L.L., 1956
  V. celery mosaic
    Freitag, Julius H. and Henry H.P. Severin, 1945
    Severin, Henry H.P. and Julius H. Freitag, 1938
  V. datura rugose leaf curl
    (K.M. Smith, 1957) R.E. Fitzpatrick, et al., 1958
  V. lucerne dwarf
    Freitag, Julius H., 1951
  V. lucerne mosaic
    Price, W.C., 1940
  V. lucerne witches' broom
    Kunkel, L.O., 1952
  V. peach western X disease
    Weathers, Lewis G. and George W. Cochran, 1950
  V. peach X disease
    Kunkel, L.O., 1944
    Slack, Derald A., 1952
  V. poison hemlock ring spot
    Freitag, Julius H. and Henry H.P. Severin, 1945
  V. tobacco mosaic
    Grant, T.J., 1934
  V. tomato big bud
    Kunkel, L.O., 1951
  V. vinca yellows *
    Maramorosch, Karl, 1957

DELPHINIUM Tourn. ex L. 1735 (Ranunculaceae)
D. ajacis, L.
  V. aster yellows
    Severin, Henry H.P. and Julius H. Freitag, 1945
  V. cucumber mosaic
    Nienow, Inez, 1948
  V. radish mosaic
    Tompkins, C.M., 1939
  V. tomato aspermy
    Brierley, Philip, Floyd F. Smith and S.P. Doolittle, 1955
  V. turnip mosaic
    Walker, J.C., Francis J. LeBeau and Glenn S. Pound, 1945
D. cardinale, Hook.
  V. cucumber western mosaic *
    Severin, Henry H.P., 1942
D. consolida, L.
  V. cucumber mosaic
    Wellman, F.L., 1935
  V. tobacco mosaic
    Grant, T.J., 1934

D. cultorum, Voss
  V. aster yellows
    Severin, Henry H.P. and Julius H. Freitag, 1945
    Severin, Henry H.P. and Sidney J. Oliver, 1939
  V. cucumber mosaic
    Valleau, W.D., 1932
  V. lucerne mosaic
    Price, W.C., 1940
  V. tomato spotted wilt
    Gardner, M.W., C.M. Tompkins and O.C.
    Whipple, 1935
D. formosum, Boiss. & Huet.
  V. cucumber mosaic
    Severin, Henry H.P., 1942
  V. cucumber western mosaic *
    Severin, Henry H.P., 1942
  V. lucerne mosaic
    Severin, Henry H.P., 1942
D. grandiflorum, L.
  V. anemone mosaic *
    Hollings, M., 1957
D. grandiflorum var. album, Hort.
  V. aster yellows
    Severin, Henry H.P., 1942
  V. cucumber western mosaic *
    Severin, Henry H.P., 1942
  V. lucerne mosaic
    Severin, Henry H.P., 1942
D. hybrid
  V. aster yellows
    Severin, Henry H.P., 1942
  V. cucumber mosaic
    Severin, Henry H.P., 1942
  V. cucumber western mosaic *
    Severin, Henry H.P., 1942
  V. delphinium ring spot
    Severin, Henry H.P. and R.C. Dickson, 1942
  V. lucerne mosaic
    Severin, Henry H.P., 1942
  V. tobacco mosaic
    Severin, Henry H.P., 1942
  V. tobacco ring spot
    Severin, Henry H.P., 1942
  V. tomato spotted wilt
    Severin, Henry H.P., 1942
D. nudicaule, Torr. & Gray
  V. beet curly top
    Freitag, Julius H. and Henry H.P. Severin, 1936
    Severin, Henry H.P., 1942
D. parryi, Gray, var. maritimum, Davidson
  V. cucumber mosaic
    Severin, Henry H.P., 1942
  V. lucerne mosaic
    Severin, Henry H.P., 1942
D. spp.
  V. anemone latent *
    (K.M. Smith, 1957) R.E. Fitzpatrick, et al., 1958
  V. aster yellows
    Severin, Henry H.P., 1942
  V. beet curly top
    Severin, Hnnry H.P., 1942
  V. cucumber mosaic
    Burnett, G., 1934
  V. cucumber western mosaic *
    Severin, Henry H.P., 1942
  V. lucerne mosaic
    Severin, Henry H.P., 1942
  V. tobacco broad ring spot
    Johnson, James and Robert W. Fulton, 1942
D. zalil, Aitch. & Hemsl.
  V. cucumber western mosaic *
    Severin, Henry H.P., 1942
  V. lucerne mosaic
    Severin, Henry H.P., 1942

DENDROBIUM Sw. 1799 (Orchidaceae)
D. superbum, Reichb. f.
  V. orchid (dendrobium) mosaic *
    Murakishi, Harry H., 1952
    Murakishi, Harry H. and M. Ishii, 1954

DESCHAMPSIA Beauv. 1812 (Gramineae)
D. caespitosa, (L.) Beauv.
  V. barley yellow dwarf
    Bruehl, G.W. and H.V. Toko, 1957
D. danthonioides, (Trin.) Munro
  V. barley yellow dwarf
    Bruehl, G.W. and H.V. Toko, 1957

DESMODIUM Desv. 1813 (Leguminosae)
D. batocaulon, A. Gray
  V. (legume) little leaf disease *
    Hutton, E.M. and N.E. Grylls, 1956
D. canadense, (L.) DC.
  V. pea mosaic
    Murphy, D.M. and W.H. Pierce, 1937
D. canum, Schinz & Thell.
  V. kaimi clover disease *
    Murakishi, Harry H., 1952
  V. (legume) little leaf disease *
    Hutton, E.M. and N.E. Grylls, 1956
D. frutescens, Schindl.
  V. cowpea mosaic
    Dale, W.T., 1949
D. gangeticum, (L.) DC.
  V. (legume) little leaf disease *
    Hutton, E.M. and N.E. Grylls, 1956
D. incanum, DC.
  V. cowpea mosaic
    Anderson, C.W., 1955
D. scorpiurus, (Sw.) Desv.
  V. (legume) little leaf disease *
    Hutton, E.M. and N.E. Grylls, 1956
D. uncinatum, (Jacq.) DC.
  V. (legume) little leaf disease *
    Hutton, E.M. and N.E. Grylls, 1956

DIANTHUS L. 1735 (Caryophyllaceae)
D. arenarius, L.
  V. carnation ring spot
    Brierley, Philip and Floyd F. Smith, 1957
D. armeria, L.
  V. clover big vein
    Black, L.M., 1945
D. barbatus, L.
  V. aster yellows
    Kunkel, L.O., 1926
    Severin, Henry H.P. and Julius H. Freitag, 1945
  V. beet curly top
    Freitag, Julius H. and Henry H.P. Severin, 1936
  V. carnation mosaic
    Ames, Ralph W. and H.H. Thornberry, 1952
    Ames, Ralph W., A.E. Vatter, John J. Scholz
    and H.H. Thornberry, 1951
    Brierley, Philip and Floyd F. Smith, 1955, 1957
    Gasiorkiewicz, E.C., 1954, 1956
    Rumley, Gail E. and W.D. Thomas, Jr., 1951
    Thomas, W.D., Jr. and R.R. Baker, 1952
    Wright, Charles M., 1951
  V. carnation mottle
    Brierley, Philip and Floyd F. Smith, 1957
    Kassanis, B., 1955
  V. carnation ring spot
    Brierley, Philip and Floyd F. Smith, 1957
    Kassanis, B., 1955
  V. carnation vein mottle
    Kassanis, B., 1955
  V. clover big vein
    Black, L.M., 1945
  V. hydrangea ring spot
    Brierley, Philip and Paul Lorentz, 1956, 1957
  V. potato paracrinkle
    Kassanis, B., 1955
  V. rhubarb ring spot *
    Vaughan, Edward K. and John W. Yale, Jr., 1953
    Yale, John W., Jr. and Edward K. Vaughan, 1954
D. caesius, Smith
  V. carnation ring spot.
    Brierley, Philip and Floyd F. Smith, 1957
D. caryophyllus, L.
  V. aster yellows
    Brierley, Philip and Floyd F. Smith, 1957

D. caryophyllus, L. (cont.)
  V. aster yellows
    Jones, Leon K., 1945
    Thomas, W.D., Jr., 1953
  V. beet curly top
    Freitag, Julius H. and Henry H.P. Severin, 1936
    Severin, Henry H.P. and Julius H. Freitag, 1934
  V. carnation mosaic
    Ames, Ralph W. and H.H. Thornberry, 1952
    Ames, Ralph W., A.E. Vatter, John J. Scholz
    and H.H. Thornberry, 1951
    Brierley, Philip and Floyd F. Smith, 1955, 1957
    Creager, D.B., 1943
    Gasiorkiewicz, E.C., 1954, 1956
    Jones, Leon K., 1945
    Rumley, Gail E. and W.D. Thomas, Jr., 1951
    Thomas, W.D. Jr. and R.R. Baker, 1952
    Wright, Charles M., 1951
  V. carnation mottle
    Brierley, Philip and Floyd F. Smith, 1957
    Kassanis, B., 1955
  V. carnation ring spot
    Brierley, Philip and Floyd F. Smith, 1955, 1957
    Kassanis, B., 1955
  V. carnation vein mottle
    Kassanis, B., 1955
  V. potato paracrinkle
    Kassanis, B., 1955
D. chinensis, L.
  V. beet curly top
    Freitag, Julius H. and Henry H.P. Severin, 1936
  V. carnation mosaic
    Brierley, Philip and Floyd F. Smith, 1957
D. chinensis var. heddewigii, Regel
  V. beet curly top
    Freitag, Julius H. and Henry H.P. Severin, 1936
D. deltoides, L.
  V. beet yellows
    Roland, G. and J. Tahon, 1961
  V. carnation mosaic
    Brierley, Philip and Floyd F. Smith, 1957
  V. carnation ring spot
    Brierley, Philip and Floyd F. Smith, 1957
D. giganteus, Urv.
  V. carnation mosaic
    Brierley, Philip and Floyd F. Smith, 1957
D. latifolius, Willd.
  V. carnation mosaic
    Brierley, Philip and Floyd F. Smith, 1957
D. plumarius, L.
  V. beet curly top
    Freitag, Julius H. and Henry H.P. Severin, 1936
    Severin, Henry H.P., 1939
    Severin, Henry H.P. and Julius H. Freitag, 1934
  V. carnation mosaic
    Brierley, Philip and Floyd F. Smith, 1957
  V. carnation ring spot
    Brierley, Philip and Floyd F. Smith, 1957
  V. tobacco ring spot
    Price, W.C., 1940
D. spp.
  V. vaccinium false blossom
    Kunkel, L.O., 1945
D. superbus, L.
  V. carnation mosaic
    Brierley, Philip and Floyd F. Smith, 1957
  V. carnation mottle
    Brierley, Philip and Floyd F. Smith, 1957
  V. carnation ring spot
    Brierley, Philip and Floyd F. Smith, 1957

DICHROSTACHYS Wight & Arn. 1834 (Leguminosae)
D. nyassana, Taub.
  V. groundnut rosette
    Evans, A.C., 1954

DIDISCUS DC. 1828 (Umbelliferae)
D. caeruleus, DC.
  V. aster yellows
    Kunkel, L.O., 1926

DIGITALIS ((Tourn.)) L. 1735 (Scrophulariaceae)
D. ambigua, Murr.
  V. beet curly top
    Freitag, Julius H. and Henry H.P. Severin, 1936
D. lanata, Ehrh.
  V. potato X
    Larson, R.H., 1944
D. purpurea, L.
  V. tobacco mosaic
    Grant, T.J., 1934
    Holmes, Francis O., 1946
  V. turnip mosaic
    Walker, J.C., Francis J. LeBeau and Glenn S.
    Pound, 1945

DIGITARIA Heist. ex Adans. 1763 (Gramineae)
D. corymbosa, Merr.
  V. sugarcane mosaic
    Lawas, Orencio M. and William L. Fernandez,
    1949
D. horizontalis, Willd.
  V. maize streak
    Storey, H.H. and A.P.D. McClean, 1930
D. ischaemum, (Schreb.) Muhl.
  V. barley stripe mosaic
    McKinney, H.H., 1951, 1953
  V. brome mosaic
    McKinney, H.H., 1953
  V. wheat streak mosaic
    McKinney, H.H. and Hurley Fellows, 1951
    Meiners, Jack P. and H.H. McKinney, 1954
D. sanguinalis, (L.) Scop.
  V. barley stripe mosaic
    Slykhuis, J.T., 1952
  V. lucerne dwarf
    Freitag, Julius H., 1951
  V. panicum mosaic *
    Sill, W.H., Jr., 1957
    Sill, W.H., Jr. and R.C. Pickett, 1957
  V. sugarcane mosaic
    Ingram, J.W. and E.M. Summers, 1938
  V. wheat streak mosaic
    Slykhuis, J.T., 1952, 1955

DIMORPHOTHECA Vaill. ex L. 1735 (Compositae)
D. aurantiaca, DC.
  V. aster yellows
    Kunkel, L.O., 1926
  V. beet curly top
    Freitag, Julius H. and Henry H.P. Severin, 1936
  V. cabbage black ring spot
    Tompkins, C.M., M.W. Gardner and H. Rex
    Thomas, 1938
  V. tobacco etch
    Holmes, Francis O., 1946
  V. tobacco mosaic
    Grant, T.J., 1934
    Holmes, Francis O., 1946
  V. turnip mosaic
    Walker, J.C., Francis J. LeBeau and Glenn S.
    Pound, 1945
  V. vaccinium false blossom
    Kunkel, L.O., 1945

DIOSCOREA Plum. ex L. 1737 (Dioscoreaceae)
D. rotundata, Poir.
  V. yam mosaic *
    Adsuar, Jose, 1955

DIPLACUS Nutt. 1838 (Scrophulariaceae)
D. aurantiacus, Hort. ex Vilmorin's Blumeng
  V. aster yellows
    Frazier, Norman W. and Henry H.P. Severin,
    1945

DIPLOTAXIS DC. 1821 (Cruciferae)
D. tenuifolia, (L.) DC.
  V. cauliflower mosaic
    (K.M. Smith, 1957) R.E. Fitzpatrick, et al., 1958
  V. turnip yellow mosaic
    Broadbent, L. and G.D. Heathcote, 1958

DIPSACUS L. 1735 (Dipsaceae)
D. fullonum, L.
 V. aster yellows
  Frazier, Norman W. and Henry H.P. Severin,
  1945
 V. teasel mosaic
  Stoner, Warren N., 1951
D. spp.
 V. cucumber mosaic
  (K.M. Smith, 1957) R.E. Fitzpatrick, et al., 1958
D. sylvestris, Mill.
 V. tomato black ring
  (K.M. Smith, 1957) R.E. Fitzpatrick, et al., 1958
DODONAEA L. 1737 (Sapindaceae)
D. viscosa, Jacq.
 V. sandal spike
  (K.M. Smith, 1957) R.E. Fitzpatrick, et al., 1958

DOLICHOS L. 1737 (Leguminosae)
D. biflorus, L.
 V. bean yellow mosaic
  (K.M. Smith, 1957) R.E. Fitzpatrick, et al., 1958
 V. rose mosaic
  Fulton, Robert W., 1952
 V. tobacco streak
  Fulton, Robert W., 1948
D. fulcatus *
 V. groundnut rosette
  Evans, A.C., 1954
D. lablab, L.
 V. cowpea mosaic
  Anderson, C.W., 1955
  Dale, W.T., 1949
 V. cucumber mosaic
  Anderson, C.W., 1955
 V. lucerne mosaic
  Pierce, W.H., 1934
  Zaumeyer, W.J., 1953
 V. tobacco broad ring spot
  Johnson, James and Robert W. Fulton, 1942
 V. tobacco ring spot
  Cheo, Pen Ching and W.J. Zaumeyer, 1952
  Fulton, Robert W., 1941
  Pierce, W.H., 1934
  Wingard, S.A., 1928
D. malosanus, Baker
 V. groundnut rosette
  Evans, A.C., 1954
D. striatus, Steud.
 V. (legume) little leaf disease *
  Hutton, E.M. and N.E. Grylls, 1956

DUCHESNEA Smith 1811 (Rosaceae)
D. indica, (Andr.) Focke
 V. clover witches' broom *
  Frazier, N.W. and A.F. Posnette, 1957
 V. strawberry green petal
  Frazier, N.W. and A.F. Posnette, 1957

ECBALLIUM A. Rich. 1824 (Cucurbitaceae)
E. elaterium, A. Rich.
 V. cucurbit mosaic *
  Doolittle, S.P. and M.N. Walker, 1925

ECHINACEA Moench 1794 (Compositae)
E. purpurea, (L.) Moench
 V. chrysanthemum stunt
  Brierley, Philip, 1950, 1953
  Keller, John R., 1953

ECHINOCHLOA Beauv. 1812 (Gramineae)
E. colonum, (L.) Link
 V. sugarcane mosaic
  Chardon, C.E. and R.A. Veve, 1923
E. crus-galli, (L.) Beauv.
 V. barley stripe mosaic
  Slykhuis, J.T., 1952
 V. lucerne dwarf
  Freitag, Julius H., 1951
 V. oat pseudo-rosette
  (K.M. Smith, 1957) R.E. Fitzpatrick, et al., 1958
 V. panicum mosaic *
  Sill, W.H., Jr., 1957
  Sill, W.H., Jr. and R.C. Pickett, 1957

E. crus-galli, (L.) Beauv. (cont.)
 V. sugarcane mosaic
  Brandes, E.W. and Peter J. Klaphaak, 1923
 V. wheat streak mosaic
  Sill, W.H., Jr. and Patrick C. Agusiobo, 1955
  Slykhuis, J.T., 1952, 1955
E. crus-galli var. edulis, Hitchc.
 V. rice dwarf
  (K.M. Smith, 1957) R.E. Fitzpatrick, et al., 1958

ECHINOCYSTIS Torr. & Gray 1840 (Cucurbitaceae)
(MICRAMPELIS) Raf. 1808
E. lobata, (Michx.) Torr. & Gray (M. lobata, Greene)
 V. cucumber mosaic
  Doolittle, S.P. and W.W. Gilbert, 1918
 V. cucurbit mosaic *
  Doolittle, S.P., 1921
  Doolittle, S.P. and W.W. Gilbert, 1919
  Doolittle, S.P. and M.N. Walker, 1924, 1925
 V. prunus A *
  Fulton, Robert W., 1957
 V. prunus B *
  Fulton, Robert W., 1957
 V. prunus E *
  Fulton, Robert W., 1957
 V. prunus G *
  Fulton, Robert W., 1957
 V. wild cucumber mosaic *
  Fernow, Karl Hermann, 1925
E. oregana, (Torr. & Gray) Cogn.
 V. (cucumber) O.S.C. isolate 606 *
  Porter, Clark A. and Frank P. McWhorter, 1951

ECHIUM Tourn. ex L. 1737 (Boraginaceae)
E. vulgare, L.
 V. cabbage black ring spot
  Hollings, M., 1957
 V. tobacco mosaic
  Holmes, Francis O., 1946

ELETTARIA Maton 1811 (Zingiberaceae)
E. cardamomum, Maton
 V. cardamom mosaic
  (K.M. Smith, 1957) R.E. Fitzpatrick, et al., 1958

ELEUSINE Gaertn. 1788 (Gramineae)
E. indica, (L.) Gaertn.
 V. maize streak
  Storey, H.H. and A.P.D. McClean, 1930
 V. rice and corn leaf-gall *
  Agati, Julian A. and Carlos A. Calica, 1950
 V. sugarcane mosaic
  Chardon, C.E. and R.A. Veve, 1923
  Lawas, Orencio M. and William L. Fernandez,
  1949
 V. sugarcane streak
  Storey, H.H. and A.P.D. McClean, 1930

ELYMUS L. 1748 (Gramineae)
E. canadensis, L.
 V. wheat streak mosaic
  McKinney, H.H. and Hurley Fellows, 1951
  Slykhuis, J.T., 1955
E. caput-medusae, L.
 V. barley yellow dwarf
  Bruehl, G.W. and H.V. Toko, 1957
  Oswald, John W. and Byron R. Houston, 1953
E. condensatus, Presl
 V. barley yellow dwarf
  Bruehl, G.W. and H.V. Toko, 1957
 V. wheat streak mosaic
  McKinney, H.H. and Hurley Fellows, 1951
E. giganteus, Vahl
 V. wheat streak mosaic
  McKinney, H.H. and Hurley Fellows, 1951
E. triticoides, Buckl.
 V. barley yellow dwarf
  Oswald, John W. and Byron R. Houston, 1953
E. virginicus, L.
 V. wheat streak mosaic
  McKinney, H.H. and Hurley Fellows, 1951

EMILIA Cass. 1817 (Compositae)
E. flammea, Cass.
    V. tobacco mosaic
        Holmes, Francis O., 1946
E. sagittata, DC.
    V. chrysanthemum stunt
        Brierley, Philip, 1950, 1953
        Keller, John R., 1953
    V. cucumber mosaic
        Wellman, F.L., 1934, 1935
    V. tobacco mosaic
        Grant, T.J., 1934
    V. tomato aspermy
        Brierley, Philip, Floyd F. Smith and S.P.
        Doolittle, 1955
    V. tomato spotted wilt
        Gardner, M.W., C.M. Tompkins and O.C.
        Whipple, 1935
        Linford, M.B., 1931, 1932
        Whipple, O.C., 1936
E. sonchifolia, Hort.
    V. tomato spotted wilt
        Norris, D.O., 1951
        Parris, G.K., 1940
        Sakimura, K., 1940

EMMENANTHE Benth. 1835 (Hydrophyllaceae)
E. penduliflora, Benth.
    V. tobacco etch
        Holmes, Francis O., 1946
    V. tobacco mosaic
        Holmes, Francis O., 1946

ENSETE Bruce 1862 (Musaceae)
E. glaucum, (Roxb.) Cheesman
    V. cucumber mosaic
        Bernardo, Fernando A. and Dioscoro L. Umali,
        1956

EPIDENDRUM L. 1737 (Orchidaceae)
E. spp.
    V. orchid (cymbidium) mosaic
        Jensen, D.D. and A.H. Gold, 1955

EPILOBIUM Dill. ex L. 1735 (Onagraceae)
E. californicum, Hausskn.
    V. aster yellows
        Frazier, Norman W. and Henry H.P. Severin,
        1945
    V. lucerne dwarf
        Freitag, Julius H., 1951
E. paniculatum, Nutt.
    V. aster yellows
        Frazier, Norman W. and Henry H.P. Severin, 1945
    V. lucerne dwarf
        Freitag, Julius H., 1951

ERAGROSTIS Host 1809 (Gramineae)
E. abyssinica, Link
    V. maize streak
        (K.M. Smith, 1957) R.E. Fitzpatrick, et al., 1958
E. amabilis, (L.) Wight & Arn.
    V. sugarcane mosaic
        Lawas, Orencio M. and William L. Fernandez,
        1949
E. aspera, Nees
    V. maize streak
        (K.M. Smith, 1957) R.E. Fitzpatrick, et al., 1958
E. cilianensis, (All.) Link (E. major, Host)
    V. barley stripe mosaic
        Slykhuis, J.T., 1952
    V. wheat spot mosaic *
        Slykhuis, J.T., 1956
    V. wheat streak mosaic
        Slykhuis, J.T., 1952, 1955
    V. wheat striate mosaic
        Slykhuis, J.T., 1952, 1953
E. curvula, (Schrad.) Nees
    V. maize streak
        (K.M. Smith, 1957) R.E. Fitzpatrick, et al., 1958
E. diffusa, Buckl.
    V. lucerne dwarf
        Freitag, Julius H., 1951

E. trichodes, (Nutt.) Wood
    V. wheat streak mosaic
        McKinney, H.H. and Hurley Fellows, 1951

ERIGERON L. 1737 (Compositae)
E. annuus, (L.) Pers.
    V. aster yellows
        Kunkel, L.O., 1926
    V. tobacco mosaic
        Holmes, Francis O., 1938, 1946
E. canadensis, L.
    V. aster yellows
        Frazier, Norman W. and Henry H.P. Severin, 1945
        Kunkel, L.O., 1926
        McClintock, J.A., 1931
    V. tobacco mosaic
        Holmes, Francis O., 1938
    V. tobacco ring spot
        Wingard, S.A., 1928
E. linifolius, Willd.
    V. aster yellows
        Frazier, Norman W. and Henry H.P. Severin, 1945

ERIOBOTRYA Lindl. 1822 (Rosaceae)
E. spp.
    V. apple mosaic
        (K.M. Smith, 1957) R.E. Fitzpatrick, et al., 1958

ERODIUM L'Herit. 1787 (Geraniaceae)
E. botrys, Bertol.
    V. beet curly top
        Severin, Henry H.P., 1934
    V. filaree red leaf
        Frazier, Norman W., 1951
E. chamaefryoides, L'Herit., var. roseum *
    V. filaree red leaf
        Anderson, Chris W., 1952
E. cicutarium, (L.) L'Herit.
    V. aster yellows
        Frazier, Norman W. and Henry H.P. Severin, 1945
    V. beet curly top
        Carsner, E., 1919
        Carsner, E. and C.F. Stahl, 1924
        Giddings, N.J., 1944
        Lackey, C.F., 1937
        Severin, Henry H.P., 1934
    V. filaree red leaf
        Anderson, Chris W., 1951
        Frazier, Norman W., 1951
    V. lucerne dwarf
        Freitag, Julius H., 1951
    V. peach yellow bud mosaic
        Karle, Harry P., 1957
    V. strawberry green petal
        Frazier, N.W. and A.F. Posnette, 1957
    V. tobacco yellow dwarf
        Helson, G.A.H., 1950
        Hill, A.V., 1950
    V. vaccinium false blossom
        (K.M. Smith, 1957) R.E. Fitzpatrick, et al., 1958
E. cygnorum, Nees
    V. tobacco yellow dwarf
        Helson, G.A.H., 1950
    V. vaccinium false blossom
        (K.M. Smith, 1957) R.E. Fitzpatrick, et al., 1958
E. macrophyllum, Hook. & Arn.
    V. beet curly top
        Severin, Henry H.P., 1934
E. moschatum, L'Herit.
    V. aster yellows
        Frazier, Norman W. and Henry H.P. Severin, 1945
    V. beet curly top
        Carsner, E., 1919
        Severin, Henry H.P., 1934
    V. filaree red leaf
        Anderson, Chris W., 1951
        Frazier, Norman W., 1951

ERYNGIUM ((Tourn.)) L. 1735 (Umbelliferae)
E. aquaticum, L.
    V. cucumber mosaic
        Johnson, James, 1946
        Johnson, James and Edith M. Hein, 1948

E. aquaticum, L. (cont.)
V. eryngium yellow mosaic *
Johnson, James, 1946
Johnson, James and Edith M. Hein, 1948
V. tobacco mosaic
Johnson, James, 1946

ERYSIMUM ((Tourn.)) L. 1735 (Cruciferae)
E. cheiranthoides, L.
V. cucumber mosaic
Pound, Glenn S. and J.C. Walker, 1948
V. turnip crinkle
Broadbent, L. and G.D. Heathcote, 1958
V. turnip rosette *
Broadbent, L. and G.D. Heathcote, 1958
V. turnip yellow mosaic
Broadbent, L. and G.D. Heathcote, 1958
E. repandum, L.
V. beet curly top
Giddings, N.J., 1944

ERYTHROPSIS Endl. * (Sterculiaceae)
E. barteri, (Mast.) Ridley
V. cacao swollen shoot
Posnette, A.F., N.F. Robertson and J. McA.
Todd, 1950

ESCALLONIA Mutis, ex L. f. 1781 (Saxifragaceae)
E. montevidensis, DC.
V. lucerne dwarf
Freitag, Julius H., 1951

ESCHSCHOLTZIA Cham. 1820 (Papaveraceae)
(ESCHSCHOLZIA) Cham. 1820
E. californica, Cham.
V. aster yellows
Kunkel, L.O., 1926
Severin, Henry H.P. and Julius H. Freitag, 1934,
1945
V. beet curly top
Giddings, N.J., 1944
V. lucerne mosaic
Price, W.C., 1940
V. tobacco necrosis
Price, W.C., 1940
V. tobacco ring spot
Price, W.C., 1940
V. tobacco ring spot no. 2
Brierley, Philip, 1954
V. vaccinium false blossom
Kunkel, L.O., 1945

EUCHLAENA Schrad. 1832 (Gramineae)
E. mexicana, Schrad.
V. brome mosaic
McKinney, H.H., 1944
V. cucumber mosaic
Wellman, F.L., 1934, 1935
V. maize streak
(K.M. Smith, 1957) R.E. Fitzpatrick, et al., 1958
V. sugarcane mosaic
Chona, B.L. and S.A. Rafay, 1950
V. wheat streak mosaic
Sill, W.H., Jr. and Patrick C. Agusiobo, 1955
E. perennis, Hitchc.
V. brome mosaic
(K.M. Smith, 1957) R.E. Fitzpatrick, et al., 1958

EUCOMIS L'Herit. 1788 (Liliaceae)
E. spp.
V. ornithogalum mosaic
(K.M. Smith, 1957) R.E. Fitzpatrick, et al., 1958

EUGENIA Mich. ex L. 1735 (Myrtaceae)
E. caryophyllata, Thunb.
V. clove sudden death disease *
Nutman, F.J. and F.M.L. Sheffield, 1949
E. myrtifolia, Sims
V. lucerne dwarf
Freitag, Julius H., 1951

EUONYMUS L. 1737 (Celastraceae)
E. fortunei (Turcz.) Hand.-Mazz., var. radicans (Miq.)
V. euonymus infectious variegation   Rehd.
Woods, M.W. and H.G. DuBuy, 1943

EUPATORIUM ((Tourn.)) L. 1735 (Compositae)
E. lasseauxii, Carr.
V. tobacco etch
Holmes, Francis O., 1946
V. tobacco mosaic
Holmes, Francis O., 1946

EUPHORBIA L. 1737 (Euphorbiaceae)
E. corollata, L.
V. cucumber mosaic
Faan, Hwei-Chung and James Johnson, 1951
E. hirta, L.
V. tobacco leaf curl
Pruthi, Hem Singh and C.K. Samuel, 1941
E. marginata, Pursh
V. beet curly top
Freitag, Julius H. and Henry H.P. Severin, 1936
E. peplus, L.
V. beet curly top
Severin, Henry H.P., 1934
E. prunifolia, Jacq.
V. beet curly top
Bennett, C.W. and A.S. Costa, 1949
Costa, A.S., 1952
V. euphorbia mosaic
Costa, A.S. and C.W. Bennett, 1950
E. splendens, Bojer
V. cucumber mosaic
(K.M. Smith, 1957) R.E. Fitzpatrick, et al., 1958

FAGOPYRUM Tourn. ex Hall. 1742 (Polygonaceae)
F. esculentum, Moench
V. aster yellows
Kunkel, L.O., 1926
V. beet curly top
Bennett, C.W. and A.S. Costa, 1949
Carsner, E., 1919
Costa, A.S., 1952
Severin, Henry H.P., 1929
V. cucumber mosaic
Fulton, Robert W., 1941
Wellman, F.L., 1935
V. dodder latent mosaic
Bennett, C.W., 1944
V. euphorbia mosaic
Costa, A.S. and C.W. Bennett, 1950
V. rhubarb ring spot *
Vaughan, Edward K. and John W. Yale, Jr., 1953
Yale, John W., Jr. and Edward K. Vaughan, 1954
V. tobacco broad ring spot
Johnson, James and Robert W. Fulton, 1942
V. tobacco mosaic
Fulton, Robert W., 1941
Grant, T.J., 1934
Holmes, Francis O., 1946
V. tobacco streak
Fulton, Robert W., 1948

FESTUCA ((Tourn.)) L. 1735 (Gramineae)
F. arundinacea, Schreb.
V. barley yellow dwarf
Bruehl, G.W. and H.V. Toko, 1957
Oswald, John W. and Byron R. Houston, 1953
F. elatior, L.
V. barley yellow dwarf
Bruehl, G.W. and H.V. Toko, 1957
V. ryegrass mosaic *
Bruehl, G.W., H.V. Toko and H.H. McKinney,
1957
F. idahoensis, Elmer
V. barley yellow dwarf
Bruehl, G.W. and H.V. Toko, 1957
F. megalura, Nutt.
V. lucerne dwarf
Freitag, Julius H., 1951

F. myuros, L.
  V. barley yellow dwarf
    Oswald, John W. and Byron R. Houston, 1953
F. ovina, L.
  V. barley yellow dwarf
    Bruehl, G.W. and H.V. Toko, 1957
F. reflexa, Buckl.
  V. barley yellow dwarf
    Bruehl, G.W. and H.V. Toko, 1957
    Oswald, John W. and Byron R. Houston, 1953
F. rubra, L.
  V. agropyron mosaic
    Slykhuis, J.T., 1952
  V. barley yellow dwarf
    Bruehl, G.W. and H.V. Toko, 1957
F. spp.
  V. barley yellow dwarf
    Oswald, John W. and Byron R. Houston, 1952

FICUS Tourn. ex L. 1735 (Moraceae)
F. altissima, Blume
  V. fig mosaic
    (K.M. Smith, 1957) R.E. Fitzpatrick, et al., 1958
F. carica, L.
  V. fig mosaic
    Condit, I.J. and W.T. Horne, 1933, 1941, 1943
    Flock, R.A. and J.M. Wallace, 1955
F. carica var. sylvestris *
  V. fig mosaic
    Condit, I.J. and W.T. Horne, 1943
F. krishna, DC.
  V. fig mosaic
    (K.M. Smith, 1957) R.E. Fitzpatrick, et al., 1958
F. pseudocarica, Miq.
  V. fig mosaic
    Condit, I.J. and W.T. Horne, 1933
F. tsida *
  V. fig mosaic
    (K.M. Smith, 1957) R.E. Fitzpatrick, et al., 1958

FOENICULUM Tourn. ex L. 1735 (Umbelliferae)
F. vulgare, Mill.
  V. cucumber mosaic
    Wellman, F.L., 1935
F. vulgare var. dulce, (Mill.) Fiori
  V. beet curly top
    Severin, Henry H.P., 1929

FORTUNELLA Swingle 1915 (Rutaceae)
F. margarita, (Lour.) Swingle
  V. citrus vein yellowing disease *
    Weathers, L.G., 1957

FRAGARIA ((Tourn.)) L. 1735 (Rosaceae)
F. bracteata, Heller
  V. aster yellows
    Frazier, Norman W. and Harold E. Thomas, 1953
  V. filaree red leaf
    Anderson, Chris W., 1952
  V. strawberry crinkle
    Frazier, Norman W., 1951
  V. strawberry latent
    Frazier, Norman W., 1953
F. californica, Cham. & Schlecht.
  V. aster yellows
    Frazier, Norman W. and Henry H.P. Severin,
    1945
  V. strawberry veinbanding
    Frazier, Norman W., 1955
  V. tobacco necrosis
    Frazier, Norman W., 1955
F. chiloensis, Dcne.
  V. strawberry crinkle
    Harris, R.V. and Mary E. King, 1942
    Miller, P.W., 1951
    Zeller, S.M., 1933
  V. strawberry latent
    Miller, P.W., 1951
F. chiloensis var. ananassa, Bailey
  V. aster yellows
    Frazier, Norman W. and Harold E. Thomas, 1953
    Fulton, J.P., 1957

F. chiloensis var. ananassa, Bailey (cont.)
  V. strawberry crinkle
    Beaumont, A. and L.N. Staniland, 1945
    Miller, P.W., 1952
    Prentice, I.W., 1949, 1952
    Vaughan, E.K., 1933
    Zeller, S.M., 1933
  V. strawberry green petal
    Posnette, A.F., 1953
  V. strawberry, isolate I, mild mottle *
    Rorie, Forest Gay, 1957
  V. strawberry, isolate II *
    Rorie, Forest Gay, 1957
  V. strawberry latent
    McGrew, J.R., 1956
  V. strawberry mild mottle *
    McGrew, J.R., 1956
  V. strawberry mild yellow edge
    Prentice, I.W., 1952
  V. strawberry mottle
    Mellor, Frances C. and R.E. Fitzpatrick, 1952
    Prentice, Ian W., 1948, 1952
    Scott, D.H., D.P. Ink, George M. Darrow and
    C.P. Marcus, 1952
  V. strawberry stunt
    Skiles, R.L. and T.H. King, 1952
    Zeller, S.M. and L.E. Weaver, 1941
  V. strawberry, type 2 *
    Braun, Alvin J., 1955
    Fulton, R.H., 1954
  V. strawberry veinbanding
    Frazier, Norman W., 1955
  V. strawberry vein chlorosis
    Prentice, I.W., 1952
  V. strawberry witches' broom
    Mellor, Frances C. and R.E. Fitzpatrick, 1952
    Prentice, Ian W., 1948
    Zeller, S.M., 1927
  V. tobacco necrosis
    Fulton, J.P., 1952
F. cuneifolia, Nutt. ex Howell
  V. strawberry crinkle
    Zeller, S.M., 1933
F. ovalis, Rydb.
  V. strawberry crinkle
    Miller, P.W., 1951
  V. strawberry latent
    Miller, P.W., 1951
F. spp.
  V. rose mosaic
    Fulton, Robert W., 1952
  V. strawberry crinkle
    Harris, R.V. and Mary E. King, 1942
    Massee, A.M., 1942
  V. strawberry leaf burn *
    (K.M. Smith, 1957) R.E. Fitzpatrick, et al., 1958
  V. strawberry mosaic
    (K.M. Smith, 1957) R.E. Fitzpatrick, et al., 1958
F. vesca, L.
  V. aster yellows
    Fulton, J.P., 1957
  V. beet ring spot *
    Harrison, B.D., 1957
  V. clover witches' broom
    Frazier, Norman W. and A.F. Posnette, 1957
  V. peach X disease
    Slack, Derald A., 1952
  V. raspberry Scottish leaf curl
    Lister, R.M., 1958
    Vaughan, Edward K. and Harold W. Wiedman, 1955
  V. raspberry yellow blotch curl
    Vaughan, Edward K. and Harold W. Wiedman, 1955
  V. raspberry yellow dwarf *
    Harrison, B.D., 1958
    Lister, R.M., 1958
  V. rose mosaic
    Fulton, Robert W., 1952
  V. strawberry crinkle
    Demaree, J.B. and C.P. Marcus, 1951
    Harris, R.V. and Mary E. King, 1942
    Massee, A.M., 1942
    Miller, P.W., 1951, 1952

F. vesca, L. (cont.)
  V. strawberry crinkle
    Prentice, I.W., 1949, 1952
    Prentice, I.W. and Tamsyn M. Woollcombe, 1951
    Smith, Harlan E., 1952
    Smith, Harlan E. and J. Duain Moore, 1952
  V. strawberry green petal
    Frazier, N.W. and A.F. Posnette, 1957
  V. strawberry, isolate I, mild mottle *
    Rorie, Forest Gay, 1957
  V. strawberry, isolate II *
    Rorie, Forest Gay, 1957
  V. strawberry latent
    Frazier, Norman W., 1953
    McGrew, J.R., 1956
  V. strawberry mild mottle *
    McGrew, J.R., 1956
  V. strawberry mild yellow edge
    Prentice, I.W., 1952
  V. strawberry mottle
    Demaree, J.B. and C.P. Marcus, 1951
    Prentice, I.W., 1948, 1952
    Scott, D.H., D.P. Ink, George M. Darrow and
    C.P. Marcus, 1952
    Smith, Harlan E., 1952
    Smith, Harlan E. and J. Duain Moore, 1952
    Stubbs, L.L., 1957
  V. strawberry stunt
    Skiles, R.L. and T.H. King, 1952
  V. strawberry, type 2 *
    Braun, Alvin J., 1955
    Demaree, J.B. and C.P. Marcus, 1951
    Fulton, R.H., 1954
    Smith, Harlan E., 1952
    Smith, Harlan E. and J. Duain Moore, 1952
  V. strawberry veinbanding
    Frazier, Norman W., 1955
  V. strawberry vein chlorosis
    Prentice, I.W., 1952
  V. strawberry witches' broom
    Prentice, I.W., 1948
  V. tobacco necrosis
    Frazier, Norman W., 1955
    Fulton, J.P., 1952
F. vesca var. alpina *
  V. apple mosaic
    Yarwood, C.E., 1955
  V. strawberry crinkle
    Miller, P.W., 1951
F. vesca var. americana, Porter
  V. aster yellows
    Frazier, Norman W. and Harold E. Thomas, 1953
F. vesca, subsp. californica, (Cham. & Schlechtd.)
  V. strawberry mottle   Staudt
    Thomas, Harold E., 1949
  V. strawberry, type 2 *
    Thomas, Harold E., 1949
F. virginiana, Dcne.
  V. strawberry leaf roll
    Berkeley, G.H. and A.G. Plakidas, 1942
  V. tobacco streak
    Fulton, Robert W., 1948

FRANSERIA Cav. 1793 (Compositae)
F. acanthicarpa, (Hook.) Cov.
  V. lucerne dwarf
    Freitag, Julius H., 1951

FRAXINUS Tourn. ex L. 1735 (Oleaceae)
F. berlandieriana, A. DC.
  V. ash witches' broom
    Plakidas, A.G., 1949
F. dipetala, Hook. & Arn.
  V. lucerne dwarf
    Freitag, Julius H., 1951
F. pennsylvanica, Marsh.
  V. tobacco ring spot
    Wilkinson, R.E., 1952

FREESIA Klatt 1865-66 (Iridaceae)
F. spp.
  V. bean yellow mosaic
    (K.M. Smith, 1957) R.E. Fitzpatrick, et al., 1958

F. spp. (cont.)
  V. freesia mosaic
    (K.M. Smith, 1957) R.E. Fitzpatrick, et al., 1958

FRITILLARIA ((Tourn.)) L. 1735 (Liliaceae)
F. pudica, Spreng.
  V. cucumber mosaic
    Brierley, Philip and Floyd F. Smith, 1944
  V. tulip breaking
    Brierley, Philip and Floyd F. Smith, 1944

FUCHSIA ((Plum.)) L. 1735 (Onagraceae)
F. magellanica, Lam.
  V. lucerne dwarf
    Freitag, Julius H., 1951

FUMARIA Tourn. ex L. 1735 (Papaveraceae)
F. officinalis, L.
  V. anemone mosaic *
    Hollings, M., 1957

GAILLARDIA Fouger. 1788 (Compositae)
G. aristata, Pursh
  V. aster yellows
    Kunkel, L.O., 1926
  V. tomato spotted wilt
    Gardner, M.W., C.M. Tompkins and O.C.
    Whipple, 1935
  V. vaccinium false blossom
    Kunkel, L.O., 1945
G. pulchella, Foug. var. picta, Gray
  V. aster yellows
    Severin, Henry H.P. and Julius H. Freitag, 1945
  V. tomato aspermy
    Brierley, Philip, Floyd F. Smith and S.P.
    Doolittle, 1955

GALINSOGA Ruiz & Pav. 1794 (Compositae)
G. parviflora, Cav.
  V. tobacco mosaic
    Holmes, Francis O., 1938, 1946
  V. tomato aspermy
    Brierley, Philip, Floyd F. Smith and S.P.
    Doolittle, 1955

GALIUM L. 1737 (Rubiaceae)
G. aparine, L.
  V. anemone mosaic *
    Hollings, M., 1957
G. triflorum, Michx.
  V. tobacco mosaic
    Holmes, Francis O., 1938

GAMOLEPIS Less. 1832 (Compositae)
G. tagetes, DC.
  V. tobacco etch
    Holmes, Francis O., 1946
  V. tobacco mosaic
    Holmes, Francis O., 1946

GASTRIDIUM Beauv. 1812 (Gramineae)
G. ventricosum, (Gouan) Shinz & Thell.
  V. barley yellow dwarf
    Oswald, John W. and Byron R. Houston, 1953

GAURA L. 1751 (Onagraceae)
G. lindheimeri, Engelm. & Gray
  V. aster yellows
    Severin, Henry H.P. and Julius H. Freitag, 1945

GERANIUM ((Tourn.)) L. 1735 (Geraniaceae)
G. carolinianum, L.
  V. cucumber mosaic
    Wellman, F.L., 1935
  V. tobacco mosaic
    Holmes, Francis O., 1938, 1946
G. dissectum, L.
  V. aster yellows
    Frazier, Norman W. and Henry H.P. Severin, 1945
  V. filaree red leaf
    Frazier, Norman W., 1951
G. molle, L.
  V. filaree red leaf
    Anderson, Chris W., 1952

GESNERIA L. 1737 (Gesneriaceae)
G. spp.
  V. tobacco mosaic
    (K.M. Smith, 1957) R.E. Fitzpatrick, et al., 1958

GEUM L. 1735 (Rosaceae)
G. chiloense, Balb.
  V. anemone mosaic *
    Hollings, M., 1957
  V. aster yellows
    Severin, Henry H.P. and Julius H. Freitag, 1945
G. spp.
  V. tobacco streak
    Fulton, Robert W., 1948

GILIA Ruiz & Pav. 1794 (Polemoniaceae)
G. capitata, Dougl.
  V. cucumber mosaic
    Wellman, F.L., 1935
  V. tobacco mosaic
    Holmes, Francis O., 1946
  V. tobacco necrosis
    Price, W.C., 1940
  V. tobacco ring spot
    Price, W.C., 1940
  V. tobacco ring spot no. 2
    Brierley, Philip, 1954
G. capitata var. achilleaefolia, (Benth.) Mason *
  V. aster yellows
    Severin, Henry H.P. and Julius H. Freitag, 1945
G. liniflora, Benth.
  V. cucumber mosaic
    Price, W.C., 1940
  V. lucerne mosaic
    Price, W.C., 1940
  V. tobacco mosaic
    Holmes, Francis O., 1946
  V. tobacco necrosis
    Price, W.C., 1940
  V. tobacco ring spot
    Price, W.C., 1940
  V. tobacco ring spot no. 2
    Price, W.C., 1940

GLADIOLUS ((Tourn.)) L. 1735 (Iridaceae)
G. gandavensis, Van Houtte
  V. bean yellow mosaic
    McWhorter, Frank P., 1949
G. hortulanus, Bailey
  V. aster yellows
    Magie, R.O., Floyd F. Smith and Philip Brierley, 1952
    Smith, Floyd F. and Philip Brierley, 1953
  V. bean yellow mosaic
    Berkeley, G.H., 1953
    Bridgmon, G.H., 1951
    Bridgmon, G.H. and J.C. Walker, 1952
    Brierley, Philip, 1952
    Brierley, Philip and Floyd F. Smith, 1948
    Dosdall, Louise, 1928
  V. cucumber mosaic
    Berkeley, G.H., 1951, 1953
    Bridgmon, G.H., 1951
    Brierley, Philip, 1952
  V. gladiolus *
    Snow, Gordon F., 1955
  V. iris bearded mosaic *
    Brierley, Philip and Floyd F. Smith, 1948
  V. iris mosaic
    Brierley, Philip and Floyd F. Smith, 1948
  V. laburnum vein mosaic *
    Brierley, Philip and Floyd F. Smith, 1954
  V. tobacco mosaic
    Berkeley, G.H., 1951
  V. tobacco ring spot
    Berkeley, G.H., 1951, 1953
    Bridgmon, G.H., 1951
    Bridgmon, G.H. and J.C. Walker, 1952
    Brierley, Philip, 1952
    Smith, Floyd F. and Philip Brierley, 1955
G. spp.
  V. aster yellows
    Smith, Floyd F. and Philip Brierley, 1948

G. spp. (cont.)
  V. bean yellow mosaic
    Smith, Floyd F. and Philip Brierley, 1944
  V. cucumber mosaic
    Faan, Hwei Chung and James Johnson, 1951
  V. tomato spotted wilt
    (K.M. Smith, 1957) R.E. Fitzpatrick, et al., 1958

GLEDITSIA L. 1742 (Leguminosae)
G. triacanthos, L.
  V. prunus B *
    Fulton, Robert W., 1957

GLORIOSA L. 1735 (Liliaceae)
G. rothschildiana, O'Brien
  V. cucumber mosaic
    Brierley, Philip and Floyd F. Smith, 1944

GLOXINIA L'Herit. 1785 (Gesneriaceae)
G. spp.
  V. tomato black ring
    (K.M. Smith, 1957) R.E. Fitzpatrick, et al., 1958

GLYCINE L. 1737 (Leguminosae)
(SOJA) Moench 1794
(SOYA) Benth. 1838
G. max, (L.) Merr.
  V. bean pod mottle
    Zaumeyer, W.J. and H. Rex Thomas, 1948
  V. bean southern mosaic
    Zaumeyer, W.J. and L.L. Harter, 1943
    Zaumeyer, W.J. and H. Rex Thomas, 1948
  V. bean yellow mosaic
    Afanasiev, M.M. and H.E. Morris, 1952
    Conover, Robert A., 1948
    Grogan, Raymond G. and J.C. Walker, 1948
    Hagedorn, D.J., 1952
    Hagedorn, D.J. and J.C. Walker, 1949, 1950, 1954
    Pierce, W.H., 1934, 1935
    Thomas, H. Rex and W.J. Zaumeyer, 1953
    Zaumeyer, W.J. and H.H. Fisher, 1953
  V. bean yellow stipple
    Zaumeyer, W.J. and H. Rex Thomas, 1950
  V. broad bean mottle
    Bawden, F.C., R.P. Chaudhuri and B. Kassanis, 1951
  V. carnation ring spot
    Brierley, Philip and Floyd F. Smith, 1957
  V. cowpea mosaic
    Anderson, C.W., 1955
    Capoor, S.P. and P.M. Varma, 1956
    Dale, W.T., 1949
  V. cucumber mosaic
    Hagedorn, D.J., 1950, 1952
    Hagedorn, D.J. and J.C. Walker, 1954
  V. kaimi clover disease *
    Murakishi, Harry H., 1952
  V. lucerne mosaic
    Berkeley, G.H., 1947
    Kreitlow, K.W. and W.C. Price, 1948, 1949
    Pierce, W.H., 1934
    Snyder, William C. and Saul Rich, 1942
    Thomas, H. Rex, 1951
    Zaumeyer, W.J., 1938, 1953
  V. pea enation mosaic
    Chaudhuri, R.P., 1950
    Hagedorn, D.J., 1952
    Hagedorn, D.J. and J.C. Walker, 1954
    Pierce, W.H., 1935
    Simons, John N., 1954
    Stubbs, M.W., 1936, 1937
  V. pea streak
    Kim, Woon S. and D.J. Hagedorn, 1957
    Zaumeyer, W.J., 1938
  V. pea wilt
    Pierce, W.H., 1935
  V. red clover vein mosaic
    Hagedorn, D.J., 1952
  V. soybean mosaic
    Conover, Robert A., 1948
    Gardner, Max W. and James B. Kendrick, 1921
    Kendrick, James B. and Max W. Gardner, 1924

G. max, (L.) Merr. (cont.)
 V. soybean mosaic
  Pierce, W.H., 1935
 V. soybean new disease *
  Dunleavy, John, 1957
 V. subterranean clover mosaic
  Aitken, Y. and B.J. Grieve, 1943
 V. tobacco leaf curl
  (K.M. Smith, 1957) R.E. Fitzpatrick, et al., 1958
 V. tobacco necrosis
  Price, W.C., 1940
 V. tobacco ring spot
  Allington, William B., 1946
  Bridgmon, G.H. and J.C. Walker, 1952
  Cheo, Pen Ching and W.J. Zaumeyer, 1952
  Cooper, W.E., 1949
  Desjardins, P.R., R.L. Latterell and J.E.
  Mitchell, 1954
  Dunleavy, John M., 1957
  Kahn, Robert P., 1956
  Kahn, Robert P. and Frances M. Latterell, 1955
  LeBeau, F.J., 1947
  Pierce, W.H., 1934
  Starr, Chester K. and W.E. Cooper, 1944
  Stubbs, M.W., 1937
 V. tobacco streak
  Fulton, Robert W., 1948
  Thomas, H. Rex and W.J. Zaumeyer, 1950
 V. tomato aspermy
  (K.M. Smith, 1957) R.E. Fitzpatrick, et al., 1958
 V. tomato ring spot
  Kahn, Robert P., 1956
  Kahn, Robert P. and Frances M. Latterell, 1955
 V. Wisconsin pea streak
  Hagedorn, D.J., 1952
  Hagedorn, D.J. and J.C. Walker, 1949, 1954

GNAPHALIUM L. 1737 (Compositae)
G. chilense, Spreng.
 V. beet curly top
  Severin, Henry H.P., 1934
G. decurrens, Ives., var. californicum, Gray *
 V. aster yellows
  Frazier, Norman W. and Henry H.P. Severin,
  1945
G. ramosissimum, Nutt.
 V. aster yellows
  Frazier, Norman W. and Henry H.P. Severin,
  1945

GODETIA Spach 1835 (Onagraceae)
G. amoena, G. Don
 V. cucumber mosaic
  Price, W.C., 1940
 V. lucerne mosaic
  Price, W.C., 1940
 V. tobacco necrosis
  Price, W.C., 1940
 V. tobacco ring spot
  Price, W.C., 1940
 V. tobacco ring spot no. 2
  Price, W.C., 1940
 V. turnip mosaic
  Walker, J.C., Francis J. LeBeau and Glenn S.
  Pound, 1945
G. grandiflora, Lindl.
 V. aster yellows
  Severin, Henry H.P. and Julius H. Freitag, 1934,
  1945
 V. lucerne dwarf
  Freitag, Julius H., 1951
 V. tomato spotted wilt
  Gardner, M.W., C.M. Tompkins and O.C.
  Whipple, 1935

GOMPHRENA L. 1737 (Amaranthaceae)
G. globosa, L.
 V. anemone brown ring *
  Hollings, M., 1958
 V. anemone mosaic *
  Hollings, M., 1957
 V. apple mosaic
  Yarwood, C.E., 1955

G. globosa, L. (cont.)
 V. beet curly top
  Freitag, Julius H. and Henry H.P. Severin, 1936
 V. beet yellows
  Roland, G. and J. Tahon, 1961
 V. cabbage black ring spot
  Hollings, M., 1957
 V. carnation mosaic
  Brierley, Philip and Floyd F. Smith, 1957
  Gasiorkiewicz, E.C., 1954
  Wright, Charles M., 1951
 V. carnation mottle
  Brierley, Philip and Floyd F. Smith, 1957
 V. carnation ring spot
  Brierley, Philip and Floyd F. Smith, 1955, 1957
  Kassanis, B., 1955
 V. chrysanthemum latent *
  Hollings, M., 1957
 V. cucumber mosaic
  Berkeley, G.H. and J.H. Tremaine, 1954
  Doolittle, S.P. and W.J. Zaumeyer, 1953
 V. hydrangea ring spot
  Brierley, Philip and Paul Lorentz, 1956, 1957
 V. iris ring spot *
  Travis, R.V., 1957
 V. lettuce mosaic
  Couch, Houston B., 1954, 1955
  Wilkinson, R.E. and Ursula Hirsch, 1952
  Richardson, D.E. and T.W. Tinsley, 1956
  Thomas, H. Rex, 1951
 V. potato leaf roll
  (K.M. Smith, 1957) R.E. Fitzpatrick, et al., 1958
 V. potato X
  Bagnall, R.H., R.H. Larson and J.C. Walker,
  1956
  Hoyman, Wm. G., 1951
  Roberts, Daniel A., 1952
  Thompson, A.D., 1956
  Timian, Roland G., W.J. Hooker and C.E.
  Peterson, 1955
  Wilkinson, R.E. and F.M. Blodgett, 1948
  Wilkinson, R.E. and A. Frank Ross, 1949
 V. prunus A *
  Fulton, Robert W., 1957
 V. prunus G *
  Fulton, Robert W., 1957
 V. ranunculus mosaic
  (K.M. Smith, 1957) R.E. Fitzpatrick, et al., 1958
 V. raspberry yellow dwarf *
  Harrison, B.D., 1958
 V. sweet potato mosaic
  Elmer, O.H., 1957
 V. tobacco etch
  Greenleaf, W.H., 1953
 V. tobacco mosaic
  Desjardins, P.R., J.M. Wallace and R.J. Drake,
  1954
 V. tobacco necrosis
  Kassanis, B., 1955
 V. tobacco ring spot
  Berkeley, G.H., 1953
 V. tomato aspermy
  Hollings, M., 1955
 V. tomato ring spot
  Brierley, Philip, 1956
  Brierley, Philip and Paul Lorentz, 1956, 1957
 V. turnip crinkle
  Broadbent, L. and G.D. Heathcote, 1958
 V. turnip mosaic
  Berkeley, G.H. and J.H. Tremaine, 1954
G. spp.
 V. tobacco ring spot
  Travis, R.V. and Philip Brierley, 1957

GOSSYPIUM L. 1735 (Malvaceae)
G. arboreum, L., var. typicum, f. indica *
 V. cotton small leaf *
  (K.M. Smith, 1957) R.E. Fitzpatrick, et al., 1958
G. barbadense, L.
 V. cotton veinal mosaic *
  (K.M. Smith, 1957) R.E. Fitzpatrick, et al., 1958

G. hirsutum, L.
  V. cotton leaf crumple
    Dickson, R.C., M. McD. Johnson and Edward F.
    Laird, 1954
  V. cotton leaf curl
    (K.M. Smith, 1957) R.E. Fitzpatrick, et al., 1958
  V. cotton Texas *
    Rosberg, David W., 1957
  V. cotton veinal mosaic *
    (K.M. Smith, 1957) R.E. Fitzpatrick, et al., 1958
  V. delphinium ring spot
    Severin, Henry H.P. and R.C. Dickson, 1942
  V. prunus A *
    Fulton, Robert W., 1957
  V. prunus B *
    Fulton, Robert W., 1957
  V. prunus E *
    Fulton, Robert W., 1957
  V. tobacco streak
    Fulton, Robert W., 1948
G. klotzchianum, Anderss.
  V. cotton veinal mosaic *
    (K.M. Smith, 1957) R.E. Fitzpatrick, et al., 1958
G. peruvianum, Cav.
  V. cotton leaf curl
    (K.M. Smith, 1957) R.E. Fitzpatrick, et al., 1958
G. peruvianum x G. barbadense, L.
  V. cotton leaf curl
    (K.M. Smith, 1957) R.E. Fitzpatrick, et al., 1958
G. punctatum, Guill. & Perr.
  V. cotton veinal mosaic *
    (K.M. Smith, 1957) R.E. Fitzpatrick, et al., 1958
G. spp.
  V. abutilon infectious variegation
    Crandall, Bowen S., 1954
G. trilobum, (DC.) Kearney
  V. cotton veinal mosaic *
    (K.M. Smith, 1957) R.E. Fitzpatrick, et al., 1958
G. vitifolium, Lam.
  V. cotton leaf curl
    (K.M. Smith, 1957) R.E. Fitzpatrick, et al., 1958

GYNERIUM Humb. & Bonpl. 1809 (Gramineae)
G. sagittatum, Beauv.
  V. (sugarcane) mosaic
    Abbott, E.V., 1930

GYPSOPHILA L. 1751 (Caryophyllaceae)
G. elegans, Bieb.
  V. beet yellows
    Roland, G. and J. Tahon, 1961
  V. carnation ring spot
    Kassanis, B., 1955
  V. tobacco etch
    Holmes, Francis O., 1946
  V. tobacco mosaic
    Holmes, Francis O., 1946
  V. tobacco necrosis
    Kassanis, B., 1955
G. paniculata, L.
  V. aster yellows
    Kunkel, L.O., 1926
    Severin, Henry H.P. and Julius H. Freitag, 1945
  V. beet curly top
    Freitag, Julius H. and Henry H.P. Severin, 1936

HAYNALDIA Kanitz 1877 (Campanulaceae)
H. villosa *
  V. wheat streak mosaic
    McKinney, H.H. and Hurley Fellows, 1951

HEDEOMA Pers. 1807 (Labiatae)
H. pulegioides, (L.) Pers.
  V. tobacco mosaic
    Holmes, Francis O., 1938

HEDERA Tourn. ex L. 1737 (Araliaceae)
H. helix, L.
  V. lucerne dwarf
    Freitag, Julius H., 1951

HEDYSARUM ((Tourn.)) L. 1735 (Leguminosae)
H. coronarium, L.
  V. lucerne witches' broom
    Klostermeyer, E.C. and J.D. Menzies, 1951
  V. prunus A *
    Fulton, Robert W., 1957
  V. prunus G *
    Fulton, Robert W., 1957
  V. tobacco streak
    Fulton, Robert W., 1948

HELENIUM L. 1753 (Compositae)
H. puberulum, DC.
  V. aster yellows
    Frazier, Norman W. and Henry H.P. Severin,
    1945
H. spp.
  V. strawberry green petal
    Frazier, Norman W. and A.F. Posnette, 1957

HELIANTHUS L. 1735 (Compositae)
H. debilis, Nutt.
  V. beet curly top
    Freitag, Julius H. and Henry H.P. Severin, 1936
  V. cucumber mosaic
    Jagger, I.C., 1918
H. decapetalus, L., var. multiflorus, Hort.
  V. beet curly top
    Freitag, Julius H. and Henry H.P. Severin, 1936

HELICHRYSUM Vaill. ex L. 1737 (Compositae)
H. arenarium, DC.
  V. aster yellows
    Kunkel, L.O., 1926
H. bracteatum, Andr.
  V. aster yellows
    Severin, Henry H.P. and Julius H. Freitag, 1934,
    1945
  V. beet curly top
    Freitag, Julius H. and Henry H.P. Severin, 1936
    Severin, Henry H.P. and Julius H. Freitag, 1934
  V. carnation mosaic
    Gasiorkiewicz, E.D., 1954
  V. chrysanthemum latent *
    Hollings, M., 1957
  V. cucumber mosaic
    Govier, D.A., 1957
    Price, W.C., 1940
  V. tobacco mosaic
    Holmes, Francis O., 1946
  V. tobacco ring spot no. 2
    Brierley, Philip, 1954
  V. tomato aspermy
    Brierley, Philip, Floyd F. Smith and S.P.
    Doolittle, 1955
    Hollings, M., 1955

HELIOCARPUS L. 1740 (Tiliaceae)
H. popayanensis, H. B. & K.
  V. cacao swollen shoot
    Tinsley, T.W. and A.L. Wharton, 1958

HELIOPHILA Burm. f. ex L. 1763 (Cruciferae)
H. linearifolia, Burch. ex DC. Syst.
  V. clover big vein
    Black, L.M., 1945

HELIOPSIS Pers. 1807 (Compositae)
H. helianthoides, Sweet, var. pitcheriana, Hort.
  V. chrysanthemum stunt
    Brierley, Philip, 1953

HELIOTROPIUM ((Tourn.)) L. 1735 (Boraginaceae)
H. corymbosum, Ruiz. & Pav.
  V. cucumber mosaic
    Price, W.C., 1940
  V. tobacco mosaic
    Holmes, Francis O., 1946
  V. tobacco necrosis
    Price, W.C., 1940

H. corymbosum, Ruiz & Pav. (cont.)
  V. tobacco ring spot
    Price, W.C., 1940
  V. tobacco ring spot no. 2
    Price, W.C., 1940
H. peruvianum, L.
  V. beet curly top
    Freitag, Julius H. and Henry H.P. Severin, 1936
  V. clover big vein
    Black, L.M., 1945
  V. cucumber mosaic
    Price, W.C., 1940

HELIPTERUM DC. 1837 (Compositae)
H. humboldtianum, DC.
  V. tobacco etch
    Holmes, Francis O., 1946
  V. tobacco mosaic
    Holmes, Francis O., 1946
H. roseum, Benth.
  V. beet curly top
    Freitag, Julius H. and Henry H.P. Severin, 1936

HEMIZONIA DC. 1836 (Compositae)
H. corymbosa, (DC.) Torr. & Gray
  V. aster yellows
    Frazier, Norman W. and Henry H.P. Severin, 1945

HERACLEUM L. 1735 (Umbelliferae)
H. sphondylium, L.
  V. beet ring spot *
    Harrison, B.D., 1957

HERRANIA Goudot 1844 (Sterculiaceae)
H. balaensis, Preuss
  V. cacao swollen shoot
    Tinsley, T.W. and A.L. Wharton, 1958
H. spp.
  V. cacao swollen shoot
    Tinsley, T.W. and A.L. Wharton, 1958

HESPERIS L. 1735 (Cruciferae)
H. matronalis, L.
  V. beet curly top
    Freitag, Julius H. and Henry H.P. Severin, 1936
  V. cabbage black ring spot
    Tompkins, C.M., M.W. Gardner and H. Rex
    Thomas, 1937, 1938
  V. cabbage ring necrosis
    Larson, R.H. and J.C. Walker, 1941
  V. cucumber mosaic
    Berkeley, G.H. and J H. Tremaine, 1954
    Pound, Glenn S. and J.C. Walker, 1948
  V. tobacco ring spot
    Pound, Glenn S., 1949
  V. turnip mosaic
    Berkeley, G H. and J.H. Tremaine, 1954
    LeBeau, Francis J. and J.C. Walker, 1945
    Tompkins, C M., 1938, 1939
    Walker, J.C., Francis J LeBeau and Glenn S.
    Pound, 1945

HIBISCUS L. 1737 (Malvaceae)
H. abelmoschus, L.
  V. hibiscus yellow vein mosaic
    Capoor, S.P. and P.M. Varma, 1950
  V. hibiscus yellows *
    Hendrix, J. Walter, 1950
H. arnottianus, Gray
  V. hibiscus yellows *
    Hendrix, J. Walter, 1950
H. cannabinus, L.
  V. abutilon infectious variegation
    Crandall, Bowen S., 1954
  V. cotton leaf curl
    (K.M. Smith, 1957) R.E. Fitzpatrick, et al., 1958
  V. hibiscus yellow vein mosaic
    Capoor, S.P. and P.M. Varma, 1950
H. esculentus, L.
  V. beet curly top
    Severin, Henry H.P., 1929
  V. cotton leaf curl
    (K.M. Smith, 1957) R.E. Fitzpatrick, et al., 1958

H. esculentus, L. (cont.)
  V. cucumber mosaic
    Fulton, Robert W., 1941
  V. hibiscus yellow vein mosaic
    Capoor, S.P. and P.M. Varma, 1950
    Varma, P.M., 1952
  V. tobacco broad ring spot
    Johnson, James and Robert W. Fulton, 1942
  V. tobacco ring spot
    Fulton, Robert W., 1941
    Wingard, S.A., 1928
  V. tobacco streak
    Fulton, Robert W., 1948
H. manihot, L.
  V. cucumber mosaic
    Price, W.C., 1940
  V. tobacco necrosis
    Price, W.C., 1940
  V. tobacco ring spot no. 2
    Price, W.C., 1940
H. palustris, L. (moscheutos, L.)
  V. hibiscus yellow vein mosaic
    Capoor, S.P. and P.M. Varma, 1950
H. rosa-sinensis, L.
  V. hibiscus ring spot *
    Jensen, D.D., 1949
  V. hibiscus yellows *
    Hendrix, J. Walter, 1950
H. sabdariffa, L.
  V. cotton leaf curl
    (K.M. Smith, 1957) R.E. Fitzpatrick, et al., 1958
  V. hibiscus yellow vein mosaic
    Capoor, S.P. and P.M. Varma, 1950
H. spp.
  V. tobacco streak
    Fulton, Robert W., 1948
H. syriacus, L.
  V. tobacco ring spot
    Wilkinson, R.E., 1952
H. tetraphyllus, Roxb.
  V. hibiscus yellow vein mosaic
    Capoor, S.P. and P.M. Varma, 1950

HIERACIUM ((Tourn.)) L. 1735 (Compositae)
H. scabrum, Michx.
  V. tobacco mosaic
    Holmes, Francis O., 1938

HILDEGARDIA Schott & Endl. 1832 (Sterculiaceae)
H. barteri, (Mast.) Kosterm.
  V. cacao swollen shoot
    Tinsley, T.W. and A.L. Wharton, 1958

HOLCUS L. 1735 (Gramineae)
H. halepensis, L. (Andropogon halepensis, Brot.)
  V. lucerne dwarf
    Freitag, Julius H., 1951
  V. rice and corn leaf-gall *
    Agati, Julian A. and Carlos A. Calica, 1950
  V. sugarcane mosaic
    Lawas, Orencio M. and William L. Fernandez,
    1949
H. sorghum, L.
  V. cucumber mosaic
    Wellman, F.L., 1934, 1935
  V. sugarcane mosaic
    Adsuar, Jose, 1950, 1954
    Brandes, E.W. and Peter J. Klaphaak, 1923
H. sudanensis, Bailey
  V. lucerne dwarf
    Freitag, Julius H., 1951

HOLODISCUS Maxim. 1879 (Rosaceae)
H. discolor, (Pursh) Maxim.
  V. holodiscus witches' broom
    Zeller, S.M., 1931

HORDEUM ((Tourn.)) L. 1735 (Gramineae)
H. brachyantherum, Nevski
  V. barley yellow dwarf
    Oswald, John W. and Byron R. Houston, 1953
H. brevisubulatum, (Trin.) Link
  V. barley yellow dwarf
    Bruehl, G.W. and H.V. Toko, 1957

H. bulbosum, L.
  V. barley yellow dwarf
    Bruehl, G.W. and H.V. Toko, 1957
H. gussoneanum, Parl.
  V. wheat streak mosaic
    McKinney, H.H. and Hurley Fellows, 1951
H. hystrix, Roth.
  V. barley yellow dwarf
    Oswald, John W. and Byron R. Houston, 1953
H. jubatum, L.
  V. barley stripe mosaic
    Slykhuis, J.T., 1952
H. leporinum, Link
  V. barley yellow dwarf
    Bruehl, G.W. and H.V. Toko, 1957
    Oswald, John W. and Byron R. Houston, 1953
  V. ryegrass mosaic *
    Bruehl, G.W., H.V. Toko and H.H. McKinney,
    1957
H. murinum, L.
  V. lucerne dwarf
    Freitag, Julius H., 1951
  V. wheat streak mosaic
    McKinney, H.H. and Hurley Fellows, 1951
H. sativum, Pers.
  V. soil-borne wheat mosaic
    McKinney, H.H., 1930
H. spp.
  V. barley yellow dwarf
    Oswald, John W. and Byron R. Houston, 1952
  V. wheat streak mosaic
    McKinney, H.H. and Hurley Fellows, 1951
    Sill, W.H., Jr. and Patrick C. Agusiobo, 1955
H. vulgare, L.
  V. barley stripe mosaic
    Afanasiev, M.M., 1956
    Eslick, R.F. and M.M. Afanasiev, 1955
    Fitzgerald, Paul J., Harland Stevens and R.G.
    Timian, 1957
    Hagborg, W.A.F., 1954
    McKinney, H.H., 1951, 1953, 1954, 1956
    Sill, W.H., Jr. and E.D. Hansing, 1955
    Sisler, W.W. and R.G. Timian, 1956
    Slykhuis, J.T., 1952
    Timian, R.G. and W.W. Sisler, 1955
    Wadsworth, D.F., 1949
  V. barley yellow dwarf
    Allen, Thomas C., Jr., 1956, 1957
    Allen, Thomas C., Jr. and Byron R. Houston, 1956
    Bruehl, G.W. and H.V. Toko, 1955, 1957
    Oswald, John W. and Byron R. Houston, 1951, 1952,
    1953
    Oswald, John W. and T.H. Thung, 1955
    Takeshita, R.M., 1956
    Toko, H.V. and G.W. Bruehl, 1957
    Watson, Marion A. and T. Mulligan, 1957
  V. brome mosaic
    McKinney, H.H., 1944, 1953, 1956
  V. (cereal) California mosaic disease *
    Houston, Byron R. and John W. Oswald, 1952
  V. (cereal) enanismo disease *
    Gibler, John W., 1957
  V. corn new mosaic *
    Finley, A.M., 1954
  V. lucerne dwarf
    Freitag, Julius H., 1951
  V. maize streak
    (K.M. Smith, 1957) R.E. Fitzpatrick, et al., 1958
  V. oat pseudo-rosette
    (K.M. Smith, 1957) R.E. Fitzpatrick, et al., 1958
  V. soil-borne wheat mosaic
    McKinney, H.H., 1948
  V. tobacco necrosis
    Fulton, Robert W., 1950
  V. wheat spot mosaic *
    Slykhuis, J.T., 1956
  V. wheat streak mosaic
    Finley, A.M., 1957
    McKinney, H.H., 1949, 1956
    Slykhuis, J.T., 1952, 1954, 1955
  V. wheat striate mosaic
    Slykhuis, J.T., 1953
    Slykhuis, J.T. and Marion A. Watson, 1958

HOYA R. Br. 1809 (Asclepiadaceae)
H. carnosa, R. Br.
  V. tomato spotted wilt
    Prentice, I.W., 1952

HUMULUS L. 1735 (Moraceae)
H. japonicus, Sieb. & Zucc.
  V. beet curly top
    Freitag, Julius H. and Henry H.P. Severin, 1936
H. lupulus, L.
  V. hop chlorotic disease
    Salmon, E.S. and W.M. Ware, 1930, 1932, 1935
  V. hop mosaic
    Cheal, W.F., 1929
    Mackenzie, D., E.S. Salmon, W.M. Ware and
    R. Williams, 1929
    Salmon, E.S. and W.M. Ware, 1928, 1932
    Thrupp, T.C., 1927
  V. hop nettle head
    Blattny, C. and V. Vukolov, 1935
    Keyworth, W.G. and D.L.G. Davies, 1946
  V. hop split leaf blotch
    Keyworth, W.G., 1951

HYACINTHUS ((Tourn.)) L. 1735 (Liliaceae)
H. orientalis, L.
  V. cucumber mosaic
    Ainsworth, G.C., 1938

HYDRANGEA Gronov. ex L. 1737 (Saxifragaceae)
H. macrophylla, Ser.
  V. aster yellows
    Brierley, Philip and Floyd F. Smith, 1954
  V. hydrangea *
    Brierley, Philip, 1954
  V. hydrangea die back *
    Brierley, Philip and Floyd F. Smith, 1952
  V. hydrangea ring spot
    Brierley, Philip, 1957
    Brierley, Philip and Paul Lorentz, 1956, 1957
    Brierley, Philip and Floyd F. Smith, 1952
  V. tobacco ring spot no. 2
    Brierley, Philip, 1954
  V. tomato ring spot
    Brierley, Philip and Paul Lorentz, 1956
    Brierley, Philip and Floyd F. Smith, 1953
H. paniculata, Sieb.
  V. lucerne dwarf
    Freitag, Julius H., 1951

HYOSCYAMUS ((Tourn.)) L. 1735 (Solanaceae)
H. albus, L.
  V. lucerne mosaic
    Price, W.C., 1940
  V. tobacco necrosis
    Price, W.C., 1940
  V. tobacco ring spot
    Price, W.C., 1940
H. niger, L.
  V. atropa belladonna mosaic
    (K.M. Smith, 1957) R.E. Fitzpatrick, et al., 1958
  V. cucumber mosaic
    Govier, D.A., 1957
    Hoggan, Isme A., 1927
    Johnson, James, 1927
  V. henbane mosaic
    Hamilton, Marion A., 1932
    Watson (Hamilton), Marion A., 1937
  V. lucerne mosaic
    Price, W.C., 1940
  V. potato X
    Cockerham, George, 1943
    Dennis, R.W.G., 1939
    Hamilton, Marion A., 1932
    Hoggan, Isme A., 1927
    Johnson, James, 1927
    Smith, J. Henderson, 1928
  V. potato Y
    Cockerham, George, 1943
    Hamilton, Marion A., 1932
    Hoggan, Isme A., 1927
    Johnson, James, 1927
    Larson, R.H., 1947

H. niger, L. (cont.)
  V. potato Y
    Smith, Kenneth M. and R. W. G. Dennis, 1940
    Watson (Hamilton), Marion A., 1937
  V. potato yellow dwarf
    Black, L. M., 1937, 1938
  V. raspberry Scottish leaf curl
    Cadman, C. H., 1956
  V. tobacco etch
    Bawden, F. C. and B. Kassanis, 1941
  V. tobacco mosaic
    Allard, H. A., 1916
    Hoggan, Isme A., 1927
    Jarrett, Phyllis H., 1930
    Johnson, James, 1927
    Sheffield, F. M. L., 1931, 1936
  V. tobacco necrosis
    Price, W. C., 1940
  V. tobacco ring spot
    Price, W. C., 1940
  V. tomato aspermy
    Hollings, M., 1955
  V. tomato ring spot
    Samson, R. W. and E. P. Imle, 1942
  V. tomato spotted wilt
    Smith, Kenneth M., 1932

HYPOCHOERIS L. 1737 (Compositae)
H. radicata, L.
  V. tobacco yellow dwarf
    Helson, G. A. H., 1950

IBERIS Dill. ex L. 1735 (Cruciferae)
I. amara, L.
  V. cauliflower mosaic
    Tompkins, C. M., 1937
  V. turnip mosaic
    Walker, J. C., Francis J. LeBeau and Glenn S.
    Pound, 1945
I. gibraltarica, L.
  V. tobacco mosaic
    Holmes, Francis O., 1946
I. umbellata, L.
  V. beet curly top
    Freitag, Julius H. and Henry H. P. Severin, 1936
  V. tobacco mosaic
    Holmes, Francis O., 1946

ILYSANTHES Rafin. 1820 (Scrophulariaceae)
I. dubia, Barnh.
  V. aster yellows
    Frazier, Norman W. and Henry H. P. Severin,
    1945

IMPATIENS Riv. ex L. 1735 (Balsaminaceae)
I. balsamina, L.
  V. cucumber mosaic
    Price, W. C., 1940
  V. lucerne mosaic
    Price, W. C., 1940
  V. tobacco ring spot
    Price, W. C., 1940
  V. tobacco ring spot no. 2
    Price, W. C., 1940
  V. tomato aspermy
    Brierley, Philip, Floyd F. Smith and S. P.
    Doolittle,
I. sultanii, Hook. f. (I. holstii, Engler & Warb.)
  V. cucumber mosaic
    Adsuar, Jose, 1955
  V. lucerne mosaic
    Kreitlow, K. W. and W. C. Price, 1949
    Zaumeyer, W. J., 1953
  V. tobacco mosaic
    Holmes, Francis O., 1946

INCARVILLEA Juss. 1789 (Bignoniaceae)
I. delavayi, Bur. & Franch.
  V. tobacco necrosis
    Price, W. C., 1940
  V. tobacco ring spot
    Price, W. C., 1940

I. variabilis, Batalin
  V. tobacco mosaic
    Holmes, Francis O., 1946

INDIGOFERA L. 1737 (Leguminosae)
I. endecaphylla, Jacq.
  V. (legume) little leaf disease *
    Hutton, E. M. and N. E. Grylls, 1956
I. hirsuta, L.
  V. potato Y
    Anderson, C. W. and M. K. Corbett, 1957
  V. prunus G *
    Fulton, Robert W., 1957
  V. tobacco etch
    Anderson, C. W. and M. K. Corbett, 1957
I. retroflexa, Baill.
  V. (legume) little leaf disease *
    Hutton, E. M. and N. E. Grylls, 1956
I. rhynchocarpa, Welw. ex Bak.
  V. groundnut rosette
    Evans, A. C., 1954
I. spp.
  V. (legume) little leaf disease *
    Hutton, E. M. and N. E. Grylls, 1956
I. subulata, Vahl.
  V. (legume) little leaf disease *
    Hutton, E. M. and N. E. Grylls, 1956
I. tettensis, Klotzsch
  V. (legume) little leaf disease *
    Hutton, E. M. and N. E. Grylls, 1956

IODANTHUS Torr. & Gray 1838 (Cruciferae)
I. pinnatifidus, (Michx.) Steud.
  V. beet mosaic
    Pound, Glenn S., 1947
  V. tobacco streak
    Fulton, Robert W., 1948

IPOMOEA L. 1735 (Convolvulaceae)
I. batata, (L.) Lam.
  V. cucumber mosaic
    Wellman, F. L., 1935
  V. sweet potato A *
    Sheffield, F. M. L., 1957
  V. sweet potato B, strains 1, 2, 3, 4, and 5 *
    Sheffield, F. M. L., 1957
  V. sweet potato feathery mottle
    Webb, R. E., 1954
    Webb, R. E. and R. H. Larson, 1954
  V. sweet potato foliage spotting disease *
    Holmes, Francis O., 1956
  V. sweet potato internal cork
    Aycock, Robert and Morris B. Hughes, 1952
    Feazell, George D., 1953
    Hildebrand, E. M., 1956, 1957
    Hildebrand, E. M. and F. F. Smith, 1956
    Martin, W. J., 1950, 1955
    Nielsen, L. W., 1956
    Nielsen, L. W. and L. H. Person, 1954
    Nusbaum, C. J., 1947, 1950
    Rankin, H. W., 1950
    Williams, A. S., 1954
  V. sweet potato mosaic
    Adsuar, Jose, 1955
    Borders, H. I. and T. J. Ratcliff, 1954
    Elmer, O. H., 1957
    Rosen, H. R., 1926
I. hederacea, (L.) Jacq.
  V. sweet potato internal cork
    Hildebrand, E. M. and H. A. Borthwick, 1956
I. nil, (L.) Roth
  V. (ipomoea) mosaic *
    Cook, Melville T., 1931
  V. tobacco mosaic
    Holmes, Francis O., 1946
I. purpurea, (L.) Lam.
  V. cucumber mosaic
    Pound, Glenn S. and J. C. Walker, 1948
    Wellman, F. L., 1935
  V. prunus A *
    Fulton, Robert W., 1957
  V. prunus B *
    Fulton, Robert W., 1957

I. purpurea, (L.) Lam. (cont.)
  V. prunus E *
    Fulton, Robert W., 1957
  V. prunus G *
    Fulton, Robert W., 1957
  V. sweet potato feathery mottle
    Webb, R.E., 1954
  V. sweet potato internal cork
    Hildebrand, E.M., 1956
    Hildebrand, E.M. and H.A. Borthwick, 1956
    Hildebrand, E.M. and F.F. Smith, 1956
  V. tobacco ring spot
    Wingard, S.A., 1928
  V. tomato aspermy
    Brierley, Philip, Floyd F. Smith and S.P.
    Doolittle, 1955
I. rubra, Murr.
  V. sweet potato mosaic
    Adsuar, Jose, 1955
I. setosa, Ker.
  V. beet curly top
    Freitag, Julius H. and Henry H.P. Severin, 1936
  V. tobacco necrosis
    Price, W.C., 1940
  V. tobacco ring spot no. 2
    Price, W.C., 1940
I. spp.
  V. tobacco necrosis
    Price, W.C., 1940
I. tricolor, Cav.
  V. sweet potato foliage spotting disease *
    Holmes, Francis O., 1956
  V. tobacco mosaic
    Grant, T.J., 1934
    Holmes, Francis O., 1946

IRIS Tourn. ex L. 1735 (Iridaceae)
I. aurea, Lindl.
  V. iris spuria mosaic *
    Brierley, Philip and Floyd F. Smith, 1948
I. filifolia, Boiss.
  V. iris mosaic
    Brierley, Philip and Frank P. McWhorter, 1936
I. germanica, L.
  V. tobacco ring spot
    Travis, R.V. and Philip Brierley, 1957
I. ricardi, Hort. *
  V. iris mosaic
    Brierley, Philip and Frank P. McWhorter, 1936
I. spuria, L.
  V. iris spuria mosaic *
    Brierley, Philip and Floyd F. Smith, 1948
I. tingitana, Boiss. & Reut.
  V. iris mosaic
    Brierley, Philip and Frank P. McWhorter, 1936
I. unguicularis, Poir., var. alba, Hort.
  V. iris mosaic
    Brierley, Philip and Frank P. McWhorter, 1936
I. xiphioides, Ehrh.
  V. iris mosaic
    Brierley, P. and F.P. McWhorter, 1934
I. xiphium, L.
  V. iris mosaic
    Brierley, Philip and Frank P. McWhorter, 1936
I. xiphium praecox, Hort. *
  V. iris mosaic
    Brierley, Philip and Frank P. McWhorter, 1936

ISATIS Tourn. ex L. 1735 (Cruciferae)
I. tinctoria, L.
  V. cabbage black ring spot
    (K.M. Smith, 1957) R.E. Fitzpatrick, et al., 1958
  V. cauliflower mosaic
    (K.M. Smith, 1957) R.E. Fitzpatrick, et al., 1958

ISCHAEMUM L. 1742 (Gramineae)
I. rogusum, Salisb.
  V. rice and corn leaf-gall *
    Agati, Julian A. and Carlos A. Calica, 1950

IXIA L. 1737 (Iridaceae)
I. spp.
  V. ixia mosaic
    Smith, Floyd F. and Philip Brierley, 1944

JATROPHA L. 1735 (Euphorbiaceae)
J. gossypifolia, L.
  V. jatropha mosaic *
    Bird, Julio, 1957
J. multifida, L.
  V. jatropha mosaic *
    Bird, Julio, 1957

JUGLANS L. 1737 (Juglandaceae)
J. cinerea, L.
  V. walnut brooming disease *
    Hutchins, Lee M. and Horace V. Wester, 1947
J. cordiformis, Maxim., var. ailantifolia, (Carr.) Rend.
  V. walnut brooming disease *
    Hutchins, Lee M. and Horace V. Wester, 1947
J. nigra, L.
  V. walnut brooming disease *
    Hutchins, Lee M. and Horace V. Wester, 1947

KALANCHOE Adans. 1763 (Crassulaceae)
K. daigremontiana, Hamet. & Perrier
  V. potato yellow dwarf
    Hansing, E.D., 1942
  V. tobacco mosaic
    Holmes, Francis O., 1946

KERRIA DC. 1817 (Rosaceae)
K. japonica, (L.) DC.
  V. peach yellow bud mosaic
    Thomas, H. Earl and T.E. Rawlins, 1939

KICKXIA Blume 1828 (Apocynaceae)
K. spuria, (L.) Dum.
  V. raspberry yellow dwarf *
    Harrison, B.D., 1958

KOCHIA Roth 1801 (Chenopodiaceae)
K. childsii, Hort. ex Mollers
  V. beet yellows
    Roland, G. and J. Tahon, 1961
K. scoparia, (L.) Schrad.
  V. beet yellows
    Roland, G. and J. Tahon, 1961
  V. tobacco mosaic
    Holmes, Francis O., 1946
K. scoparia var. trichophylla, Bailey
  V. beet curly top
    Freitag, Julius H. and Henry H.P. Severin, 1936
    Severin, Henry H.P. and Julius H. Freitag, 1934
  V. beet mosaic
    Severin, Henry H.P. and Roger M. Drake, 1948
  V. clover big vein
    Black, L.M., 1945

KOELERIA Pers. 1805 (Gramineae)
K. cristata, (L.) Pers.
  V. barley yellow dwarf
    Bruehl, G.W. and H.V. Toko, 1957

LABURNUM L. 1735 (Leguminosae)
L. alpinum, J. Presl
  V. laburnum vein mosaic *
    Brierley, Philip and Floyd F. Smith, 1954
L. anagyroides, Med.
  V. laburnum infectious variegation
    (K.M. Smith, 1957) R.E. Fitzpatrick, et al., 1958
L. vosii *
  V. laburnum infectious variegation
    (K.M. Smith, 1957) R.E. Fitzpatrick, et al., 1958
L. vulgare, Bercht. & Presl
  V. laburnum infectious variegation
    (K.M. Smith, 1957) R.E. Fitzpatrick, et al., 1958
L. watereri, Dipp.
  V. laburnum vein mosaic *
    Brierley, Philip and Floyd F. Smith, 1954

LACTUCA ((Tourn.)) L. 1735 (Compositae)
L. altaica, Fisch. & Mey.
  V. aster yellows
    Tompson, Ross C., 1944
L. canadensis, L.
  V. aster yellows
    Tompson, Ross C., 1944

L. floridana, (L.) Gaertn.
    V. aster yellows
        Tompson, Ross C., 1944
L. graminifolia, Michx.
    V. aster yellows
        Tompson, Ross C., 1944
L. indica, L.
    V. aster yellows
        Tompson, Ross C., 1944
L. laciniata, Roth
    V. aster yellows
        Tompson, Ross C., 1944
L. muralis, (L.) Gaertn.
    V. anemone mosaic *
        Hollings, M., 1957
    V. aster yellows
        Tompson, Ross C., 1944
L. perennis, L.
    V. aster yellows
        Tompson, Ross C., 1944
L. raddeana, Maxim.
    V. aster yellows
        Tompson, Ross C., 1944
L. saligna, L.
    V. aster yellows
        Tompson, Ross C., 1944
L. sativa, L.
    V. aster yellows
        Brierley, Philip and Floyd F. Smith, 1944
        Kunkel, L.O., 1926
        Lee, P.E. and A.G. Robinson, 1958
        Linn, M.B., 1940
        Raymer, W.B. and Clark R. Amen, 1954
        Severin, H.H.P., 1928, 1929
        Severin, Henry H.P. and Julius H. Freitag, 1945
        Smith, Floyd F. and Philip Brierley, 1951
        Tompson, Ross C., 1944
    V. beet curly top
        Giddings, N.J., 1944
    V. cucumber mosaic
        Anderson, C.W., 1955
        Hollings, M., 1955
        Kassanis, B., 1947
        Price, W.C., 1940
    V. cucumber western mosaic *
        Severin, Henry H.P. and Julius H. Freitag, 1948
    V. dandelion yellow mosaic
        Doncaster, J.P. and B. Kassanis, 1946, 1947
    V. lettuce big vein
        Allen, M.W., 1948
        Doolittle, S.P. and Ross C. Tompson, 1945
        Pryor, Dean E., 1946
        Thompson, Ross C., S.P. Doolittle and Floyd F.
        Smith, 1944
    V. lettuce mosaic
        Ainsworth, G.C. and L. Ogilvie, 1939
        Broadbent, L., T.W. Tinsley, W. Buddin and
        E.T. Roberts, 1951
        Couch, Houston B., 1954, 1955
        Doncaster, J.P. and B. Kassanis, 1946
        Grogan, R.G., J.E. Welch and Roy Bardin, 1952
        Jagger, Ivan C., 1920-21
        Jones, Leon K., 1944
        Kassanis, B., 1947
        Newhall, A.G., 1923
        Selman, Ireson W., 1945
        Sylvester, Edward S., 1954, 1955
    V. lucerne witches' broom
        Helms, Katie, 1957
    V. prunus A *
        Fulton, Robert W., 1957
    V. prunus B *
        Fulton, Robert W., 1957
    V. tobacco necrosis
        (K.M. Smith, 1957) R.E. Fitzpatrick, et al., 1958
    V. tobacco ring spot
        Grogan, R.G., Roy Bardin and W.C. Schnathorst,
        1954
        Grogan, R.G. and W.C. Schnathorst, 1955
    V. tobacco streak
        Fulton, Robert W., 1948
    V. tomato aspermy
        Brierley, Philip, Floyd F. Smith and S.P.
        Doolittle, 1953, 1955

L. sativa, L. (cont.)
    V. tomato aspermy
        Hollings, M., 1955
    V. tomato big bud
        Helms, Katie, 1957
    V. tomato spotted wilt
        Gardner, M.W. and O.C. Whipple, 1934
        Milbrath, J.A., 1939
        Sakimura, K., 1940
        Tompkins, C.M. and M.W. Gardner, 1934
L. sativa var. capitata, L.
    V. lettuce mosaic
        Ainsworth, G.C., 1940
        Ainsworth, G.C. and L. Ogilvie, 1939
    V. tobacco ring spot
        Wingard, S.A., 1928
    V. tomato spotted wilt
        Ainsworth, G.C., 1940
        Snyder, W.C. and H. Rex Thomas, 1936
    V. turnip crinkle
        Broadbent, L. and G.D. Heathcote, 1958
    V. turnip rosette *
        Broadbent, L. and G.D. Heathcote, 1958
L. sativa var. longifolia, Lam.
    V. aster yellows
        Severin, Henry H.P. and Julius H. Freitag, 1945
    V. tomato spotted wilt
        Snyder, W.C. and H. Rex Thomas, 1936
        Tompkins, C.M. and M.W. Gardner, 1934
L. sativa var. romana, Hort.
    V. lettuce mosaic
        Ainsworth, G.C. and L. Ogilvie, 1939
L. scariola, L.
    V. cucumber mosaic
        Burnett, G., 1934
    V. lucerne dwarf
        Freitag, Julius H., 1951
    V. tobacco ring spot
        Wingard, S.A., 1928
    V. tomato spotted wilt
        Milbrath, J.A., 1939
L. scariola var. integrata, Gren. & Godr.
    V. aster yellows
        Frazier, Norman W. and Henry H.P. Severin,
        1945
L. serriola, L.
    V. aster yellows
        Tompson, Ross C., 1944
    V. dandelion yellow mosaic
        Kassanis, B., 1947
    V. lettuce mosaic
        Grogan, R.G., J.E. Welch and Roy Bardin, 1952
        Kassanis, B., 1947
    V. tobacco ring spot
        Grogan, R.G. and W.C. Schnathorst, 1955
L. spicata, (Lam.) Hitchc.
    V. aster yellows
        Tompson, Ross C., 1944
L. squarrosa, (Thunb.) Miq.
    V. aster yellows
        Tompson, Ross C., 1944
L. virosa, Rydb.
    V. aster yellows
        Tompson, Ross C., 1944
    V. dandelion yellow mosaic
        Kassanis, B., 1947
    V. lettuce mosaic
        Kassanis, B., 1947
    V. peach yellow bud mosaic
        Karle, Harry P., 1957

LAELIA Lindl. 1831 (Orchidaceae)
L. anceps, Lindl.
    V. orchid (cymbidium) mosaic
        Jensen, D.D. and A.H. Gold, 1955
    V. orchid (laelia anceps) *
        Jensen, D.D. and A.H. Gold, 1952

LAELIOCATTLEYA X, Rolfe 1887 (Orchidaceae)
L. lustre plumosa *
    V. orchid (cymbidium) mosaic
        Jensen, D.D. and A.H. Gold, 1955

L. pasadena *
  V. orchid (cymbidium) mosaic
    Jensen, D.D. and A.H. Gold, 1955
L. proca *
  V. orchid (cymbidium) mosaic
    Jensen, D.D. and A.H. Gold, 1955
L. sargon *
  V. orchid (cymbidium) mosaic
    Jensen, D.D. and A.H. Gold, 1955
L. shoshone *
  V. orchid (cymbidium) mosaic
    Jensen, D.D. and A.H. Gold, 1955

LAGENARIA Ser. 1825 (Cucurbitaceae)
L. siceraria (Mol.) Standl. (L. leucantha, Rusby)
  V. beet curly top
    Freitag, Julius H. and Henry H.P. Severin, 1936
  V. cucumber green mottle mosaic
    Azad, R.N., 1956
    Vasudeva, R.S. and T.K. Nariani, 1952
    Vasudeva, R.S., S.P. Raychaudhuri and
    Jagannath Singh, 1949
  V. cucurbit mosaic *
    Doolittle, S.P. and M.N. Walker, 1925
  V. muskmelon mosaic
    Anderson, C.W., 1954
  V. prunus B *
    Fulton, Robert W., 1957
  V. squash mosaic
    Freitag, Julius H., 1956
  V. tobacco ring spot
    Wingard, S.A., 1928
  V. watermelon mosaic
    Anderson, C.W., 1954
L. vulgaris, Ser.
  V. cucumber mosaic
    Jagger, I.C., 1918
    Vasudeva, R. Sahai and T.B. Lal, 1943
  V. cucurbit mosaic *
    Doolittle, S.P. and M.N. Walker, 1925

LAMIUM ((Tourn.)) L. 1735 (Labiatae)
L. amplexicaule, L.
  V. aster yellows
    Frazier, Norman W. and Henry H.P. Severin,
    1945
  V. tobacco etch
    Holmes, Francis O., 1946
  V. tobacco mosaic
    Holmes, Francis O., 1938, 1946
L. hybridum, Vill.
  V. potato X
    Larson, R.H., 1947
L. purpureum, L.
  V. potato X
    (K.M. Smith, 1957) R.E. Fitzpatrick, et al., 1958

LAPSANA L. 1737 (Compositae)
L. communis, L.
  V. tomato black ring
    (K.M. Smith, 1957) R.E. Fitzpatrick, et al., 1958

LATHYRUS ((Tourn.)) L. 1735 (Leguminosae)
L. cicera, L.
  V. lucerne dwarf
    Freitag, Julius H., 1951
  V. pea enation mosaic
    Hagedorn, D.J., 1957
L. clymenum, L.
  V. lucerne dwarf
    Freitag, Julius H., 1951
L. hirsutus, L.
  V. bean yellow mosaic
    Hagedorn, D.J. and J.C. Walker, 1950, 1954
  V. pea enation mosaic
    Johnson, Folke and Leon K. Jones, 1937
    McEwen, F.L. and W.T. Schroeder, 1956
  V. pea mosaic
    Hagedorn, D.J., 1948
  V. pea streak
    Hagedorn, D.J., 1948
  V. red clover vein mosaic
    Hagedorn, D.J. and J.C. Walker, 1954

L. hirsutus, L. (cont.)
  V. Wisconsin pea streak
    Hagedorn, D.J. and J.C. Walker, 1949, 1954
  V. Wisconsin pea stunt
    Hagedorn, D.J. and J.C. Walker, 1949
L. latifolius, L.
  V. lucerne witches' broom
    Klostermeyer, E.C. and J.D. Menzies, 1951
  V. pea mottle
    Johnson, Folke and Leon K. Jones, 1937
L. odoratus, L.
  V. anemone brown ring *
    Hollings, M., 1958
  V. bean yellow mosaic
    Ainsworth, G.C., 1940
    Hagedorn, D.J. and J.C. Walker, 1950, 1954
    Zaumeyer, W.J. and B.L. Wade, 1933, 1935
  V. beet curly top
    Giddings, N.J., 1944
  V. broad bean mottle
    Bawden, F.C., R.P. Chaudhuri and B. Kassanis,
    1951
    Yu, T.F., 1939
  V. carnation ring spot
    Brierley, Philip and Floyd F. Smith, 1957
  V. cucumber mosaic
    Ainsworth, G.C., 1940
    Doolittle, S.P. and W.J. Zaumeyer, 1952, 1953
  V. lettuce mosaic
    Ainsworth, G.C., 1940
    Ainsworth, G.C. and L. Ogilvie, 1939
  V. lucerne mosaic
    Berkeley, G.H., 1947
    Kreitlow, K.W. and W.C. Price, 1949
    Snyder, William C. and Saul Rich, 1942
    Zaumeyer, W.J., 1938
    Zaumeyer, W.J. and B.L. Wade, 1935
  V. pea enation mosaic
    Ainsworth, G.C., 1940
    Chaudhuri, R.P., 1950
    Hagedorn, D.J. and J.C. Walker, 1954
    Johnson, Folke and Leon K. Jones, 1937
    Osborn, H.T., 1938
    Simons, John N., 1954
    Stubbs, M.W., 1936, 1937
  V. pea mosaic
    Ainsworth, G.C., 1940
    Chaudhuri, R.P., 1950
    Doolittle, S.P. and F.R. Jones, 1925
    Hagedorn, D.J. and J.C. Walker, 1954
    Murphy, D.M. and W.H. Pierce, 1937
    Osborn, H.T., 1934, 1935
    Stubbs, M.W., 1936, 1937
  V. pea mottle
    Johnson, Folke, 1942
    Johnson, Folke and Leon K. Jones, 1937
  V. pea wilt
    Johnson, Folke, 1942
  V. pea yellow mosaic *
    Ainsworth, G.C., 1940
  V. red clover mosaic *
    Doolittle, S.P. and F.R. Jones, 1925
    Zaumeyer, W.J. and B.L. Wade, 1935
  V. red clover vein mosaic
    Hagedorn, D.J. and E.W. Hanson, 1951
    Hagedorn, D.J. and J.C. Walker, 1949, 1954
    Osborn, H.T., 1937
    Roberts, D.A., 1957
  V. squash mosaic
    Freitag, Julius H., 1956
  V. subterranean clover mosaic
    Aitken, Y. and B.J. Grieve, 1943
  V. sweet pea mosaic *
    Zaumeyer, W.J. and B.L. Wade, 1935
  V. tobacco necrosis
    Price, W.C., 1940
  V. tobacco ring spot
    Stubbs, M.W., 1937
  V. tomato spotted wilt
    Ainsworth, G.C., 1940
    Snyder, W.C. and H. Rex Thomas, 1936
  V. Wisconsin pea streak
    Hagedorn, D.J. and J.C. Walker, 1949, 1954

L. pusillus, Ell.
    V. bean leaf wilt
        Johnson, James, 1942
L. sativus, L.
    V. lucerne dwarf
        Freitag, Julius H., 1951
    V. pea mosaic
        Murphy, D.M. and W.H. Pierce, 1937
L. sylvestris, L.
    V. (legume) little leaf disease *
        Hutton, E.M. and N.E. Grylls, 1956
L. tingitanus, L.
    V. pea enation mosaic
        Hagedorn, D.J., 1957

LAUNEA Endl. 1841 (Compositae)
L. asplenifolia, Hook. f.
    V. tobacco leaf curl
        Pruthi, Hem Singh and C.K. Samuel, 1941

LAVANDULA Tourn. ex L. 1740 (Labiatae)
L. officinalis, L.
    V. aster yellows
        Kunkel, L.O., 1926

LAVATERA L. 1737 (Malvaceae)
L. assurgentiflora, Kell.
    V. malva yellow vein mosaic *
        Costa, A.S. and James E. Duffus, 1957
L. trimestris, L.
    V. anemone mosaic *
        Hollings, M., 1957
    V. beet curly top
        Freitag, Julius H. and Henry H.P. Severin, 1936
    V. cucumber mosaic
        Price, W.C., 1940
    V. lovage mosaic
        Smith, Kenneth M. and Roy Markham, 1944
    V. lucerne mosaic
        Price, W.C., 1940
    V. tobacco necrosis
        Price, W.C., 1940
    V. tobacco ring spot
        Price, W.C., 1940

LAYIA Hook. & Arn. 1833 (Compositae)
L. elegans, Torr. & Gray
    V. tomato spotted wilt
        Gardner, M.W., C.M. Tompkins and O.C. Whipple, 1935

LENS ((Tourn.)) L. 1735 (Leguminosae)
L. culinaris, Medik.
    V. pea mottle
        Johnson, F. and L.K. Jones, 1936
L. esculenta, Moench
    V. bean yellow mosaic
        Zaumeyer, W.J. and B.L. Wade, 1935
    V. lucerne mosaic
        Zaumeyer, W.J., 1938
    V. pea mottle
        Johnson, Folke, 1942
        Johnson, Folke and Leon K. Jones, 1937
    V. pea streak
        Zaumeyer, W.J., 1938
    V. pea wilt
        Johnson, Folke, 1942
    V. red clover mosaic *
        Zaumeyer, W.J. and B.L. Wade, 1935

LEONURUS L. 1735 (Labiatae)
L. cardiaca, L.
    V. cucumber mosaic
        Faan, Hwei-Chung and James Johnson, 1951

LEPIDIUM L. 1735 (Cruciferae)
L. campestre, (L.) R. Br.
    V. cabbage black ring spot
        (K.M. Smith, 1957) R.E. Fitzpatrick, et al., 1958
    V. cauliflower mosaic
        (K.M. Smith, 1957) R.E. Fitzpatrick, et al., 1958
    V. clover big vein
        Black, L.M., 1945

L. campestre, (L.) R. Br.
    V. tobacco mosaic
        Holmes, Francis O., 1938
    V. turnip crinkle
        Broadbent, L. and G.D. Heathcote, 1958
    V. turnip rosette *
        Broadbent, L. and G.D. Heathcote, 1958
    V. turnip yellow mosaic
        Broadbent, L. and G.D. Heathcote, 1958
L. lasiocarpum, Nutt. ex Torr. & Gray
    V. beet curly top
        Giddings, N.J., 1944
L. nitidum, Nutt. ex Torr. & Gray
    V. beet curly top
        Giddings, N.J., 1938, 1944
        Lackey, C.F., 1937
        Severin, Henry H.P., 1934
L. ruderale, L.
    V. tobacco mosaic
        Holmes, Francis O., 1938
L. sativum, L.
    V. cabbage ring necrosis
        Larson, R.H. and J.C. Walker, 1941
    V. cauliflower mosaic
        Tompkins, C.M., 1937
        Walker, J.C., Francis J. LeBeau and Glenn S. Pound, 1945
    V. turnip mosaic
        Berkeley, G.H. and M. Weintraub, 1952
        Walker, J.C., Francis J. LeBeau and Glenn S. Pound, 1945
L. virginicum, L.
    V. cabbage ring necrosis
        Larson, R.H. and J.C. Walker, 1941
    V. cauliflower mosaic
        Walker, J.C., Francis J. LeBeau and Glenn S. Pound, 1945
    V. clover big vein
        Black, L.M., 1945
    V. turnip mosaic
        Dale, W.T., 1948
        Pound, Glenn S., 1948
        Walker, J.C., Francis J. LeBeau and Glenn S. Pound, 1945

LEPTOSYNE DC. 1836 (Compositae)
L. maritima, (Hook. f.) A. Gray
    V. tobacco mosaic
        Holmes, Francis O., 1946

LESPEDEZA Michx. 1803 (Leguminosae)
L. formosa, Koehne
    V. laburnum infectious variegation
        (K.M. Smith, 1957) R.E. Fitzpatrick, et al., 1958
L. striata, (Thunb.) Hook. & Arn.
    V. bean common mosaic
        Pierce, W.H., 1934
    V. bean yellow mosaic
        Pierce, W.H., 1934
    V. lucerne mosaic
        Zaumeyer, W.J., 1938

LIATRIS Schreb. 1791 (Compositae)
L. pycnostachya, Michx.
    V. chrysanthemum stunt
        Brierley, Philip, 1953
L. spicata, (L.) Willd.
    V. chrysanthemum stunt
        Brierley, Philip, 1950
        Keller, John R., 1953

LIGUSTICUM L. 1737 (Umbelliferae)
L. scothicum, L.
    V. lovage mosaic
        Smith, Kenneth M. and Roy Markham, 1944

LIGUSTRUM ((Tourn.)) L. 1735 (Oleaceae)
L. obtusifolium, Sieb. & Zucc., var. regelianum
    V. lilac witches' broom   (Koehne) Rehd.
        Lorentz, Paul and Philip Brierley, 1953
L. spp.
    V. cucumber mosaic
        (K.M. Smith, 1957) R.E. Fitzpatrick, et al., 1958

LILIUM Tourn. ex L. 1737 (Liliaceae)
L. amabile luteum *
    V. tulip breaking
        Brierley, Philip, 1940
L. auratum, Lindl.
    V. cucumber mosaic
        Brierley, Philip, 1940
        Guterman, C.E.F., 1928
        Wellman, F.L., 1935
    V. tulip breaking
        Brierley, Philip, 1940
L. batemaniae, (Hort.) Wallace
    V. lily rosette
        (K.M. Smith, 1957) R.E. Fitzpatrick, et al., 1958
L. brownii, Poit.
    V. cucumber mosaic
        Brierley, Philip, 1940
L. brownii var. leucanthemum, Hort.
    V. lily rosette
        Brierley, Philip and Floyd F. Smith, 1945
    V. tulip breaking
        Brierley, Philip, 1940
        Brierley, Philip and Floyd F. Smith, 1944
L. canadense, L.
    V. cucumber mosaic
        Brierley, Philip, 1940
    V. tulip breaking
        Brierley, Philip, 1940
L. candidum, L.
    V. cucumber mosaic
        Brierley, Philip, 1940
    V. tulip breaking
        Brierley, Philip, 1940
        Brierley, Philip and Floyd F. Smith, 1944
L. cernuum, Kom.
    V. tulip breaking
        Brierley, Philip, 1940
L. chalcedonicum, L.
    V. tulip breaking
        Brierley, Philip, 1940
L. croceum, Chaix
    V. cucumber mosaic
        Brierley, Philip, 1940
    V. tulip breaking
        Brierley, Philip, 1940
L. dauricum, Ker-Gawl.
    V. lily rosette
        Brierley, Philip and Floyd F. Smith, 1945
    V. tulip breaking
        Brierley, Philip and Floyd F. Smith, 1944
L. dauricum var. luteum, Hort.
    V. tulip breaking
        Brierley, Philip, 1940
L. davidi, Duch.
    V. lily rosette
        Brierley, Philip and Floyd F. Smith, 1945
L. davidi var. willmottiae, Cotton & Grove *
    V. lily rosette
        Brierley, Philip and Floyd F. Smith, 1945
    V. tulip breaking
        Brierley, Philip and Floyd F. Smith, 1944
L. davmottiae *
    V. tulip breaking
        Brierley, Philip, 1940
L. elegans, Thunb.
    V. lily rosette
        Brierley, Philip and Floyd F. Smith, 1945
    V. tulip breaking
        Brierley, Philip, 1940
        Brierley, Philip and Floyd F. Smith, 1944
L. formosanum, (Baker) Wallace or Stapf. *
    V. cucumber mosaic
        Brierley, Philip, 1939
        Brierley, Philip and S.P. Doolittle, 1940
        Brierley, Philip and Floyd F. Smith, 1944
    V. lily rosette
        Brierley, Philip and Floyd F. Smith, 1945
    V. lily symptomless
        Brierley, Philip, 1940
    V. tulip breaking
        Brierley, Philip, 1939, 1940
        Brierley, Philip and S.P. Doolittle, 1940
        Brierley, Philip and Floyd F. Smith, 1944
        Smith, Floyd F. and Philip Brierley, 1948

L. giganteum, Wall.
    V. tulip breaking
        Brierley, Philip, 1940
L. harrisi (L. longiflorum var. eximium, Nichols), Carr.
    V. cucumber mosaic
        Ainsworth, G.C., 1938
        Ogilvie, L. and C.E.F. Guterman, 1929
    V. lily rosette
        Ogilvie, Lawrence, 1928
L. henryi, Baker
    V. lily rosette
        Brierley, Philip and Floyd F. Smith, 1945
    V. tulip breaking
        Brierley, Philip, 1940
L. henryi x L. myriophyllum, Hort., var. superbum
    V. lily color adding *   (Baker) *
        McWhorter, Frank P., 1956
    V. lily color removing *
        McWhorter, Frank P., 1956
L. longiflorum, Thunb.
    V. celery mosaic
        Price, W.C., 1937
    V. cucumber mosaic
        Brierley, Philip, 1939
        Brierley, Philip and S.P. Doolittle, 1940
        McWhorter, F.P. and H.H. Millsap, 1954
        Porter, Clark A., 1954
        Price, W.C., 1937
        Smith, Floyd F. and Philip Brierley, 1948
        Wellman, F.L., 1935
    V. (cucumber) O.S.C. isolate 606 *
        Porter, Clark A. and Frank P. McWhorter, 1951
    V. lily rosette
        Brierley, Philip and Floyd F. Smith, 1944, 1945, 1954
        Smith, Floyd F. and Philip Brierley, 1948
    V. lily symptomless
        Brierley, Philip, 1940
        Brierley, Philip and S.P. Doolittle, 1940
        Brierley, Philip and Floyd F. Smith, 1944
        Porter, Clark A., 1954
    V. tobacco ring spot
        Travis, R.V. and Philip Brierley, 1957
    V. tomato aspermy
        Brierley, Philip, Floyd F. Smith and S.P. Doolittle, 1955
    V. tulip breaking
        Brierley, Philip, 1939
        Brierley, Philip and S.P. Doolittle, 1940
        Brierley, Philip and Floyd F. Smith, 1944
        Smith, Floyd F. and Philip Brierley, 1948
L. longiflorum var. formosum, Hort.
    V. cucumber mosaic
        Ainsworth, G.C., 1938
L. longiflorum var. takesima, Duchartie
    V. lily rosette
        Ogilvie, Lawrence, 1928
L. monadelphum, Marsh & Bieb.
    V. cucumber mosaic
        Brierley, Philip, 1940
L. myriophyllum, Hort., var. superbum, (Baker)
    V. lily rosette   Wilson *
        Brierley, Philip and Floyd F. Smith, 1945
    V. tulip breaking
        Brierley, Philip, 1940
L. princeps, E.H. Wilson
    V. tulip breaking
        Brierley, Philip, 1940
L. pumilum, DC.
    V. tulip breaking
        Brierley, Philip, 1940
L. regale, Wilson
    V. cucumber mosaic
        Brierley, Philip, 1940
    V. lily ring spot
        (K.M. Smith, 1957) R.E. Fitzpatrick, et al., 1958
    V. lily rosette
        Brierley, Philip and Floyd F. Smith, 1945
    V. tulip breaking
        Brierley, Philip, 1940
L. sargentiae, Wilson
    V. cucumber mosaic
        Brierley, Philip, 1940

L. sargentiae, Wilson
   V. lily rosette
      Brierley, philip and Floyd F. Smith, 1945
   V. tulip breaking
      Brierley, Philip, 1940
L. speciosum, Thunb.
   V. cucumber mosaic
      Brierley, Philip, 1940
      Brierley, Philip and S.P. Doolittle, 1940
   V. lily rosette
      Brierley, Philip and Floyd F. Smith, 1945
   V. tulip breaking
      Brierley, Philip, 1940
L. speciosum var. rubrum, Hort.
   V. cucumber mosaic
      McWhorter, F.P. and H.H. Millsap, 1954
L. spp.
   V. cucumber mosaic
      (K.M. Smith, 1957) R.E. Fitzpatrick, et al., 1958
L. superbum, L.
   V. cucumber mosaic
      Brierley, Philip, 1940
   V. tulip breaking
      Brierley, Philip, 1940
      Brierley, Philip and Floyd F. Smith, 1944
L. testaceum, Lindl.
   V. tulip breaking
      Brierley, Philip, 1940
L. tigrinum, Ker-Gawl.
   V. cucumber mosaic
      Brierley, Philip, 1940
      Brierley, Philip and Floyd F. Smith, 1944
   V. lily ring spot
      (K.M. Smith, 1957) R.E. Fitzpatrick, et al., 1958
   V. tulip breaking
      Brierley, Philip, 1940
      Brierley, Philip and Floyd F. Smith, 1944
L. umbellatum, Hort.
   V. cucumber mosaic
      Brierley, Philip, 1940
   V. lily rosette
      Brierley, Philip and Floyd F. Smith, 1945
   V. tulip breaking
      Brierley, Philip, 1940
      Brierley, Philip and Floyd F. Smith, 1944
L. wallacei, Wallace
   V. cucumber mosaic
      Brierley, Philip, 1940
   V. tulip breaking
      Brierley, Philip, 1940

LIMONIUM Tourn. ex Mill. 1752 (Plumbaginaceae)
L. bonduelli, (Lest.) Kuntze
   V. tobacco mosaic
      Holmes, Francis O., 1946
L. sinuatum, (L.) Mill.
   V. aster yellows
      Severin, Henry H.P. and Julius H. Freitag, 1945
   V. beet curly top
      Freitag, Julius H. and Henry H.P. Severin, 1936
   V. lucerne mosaic
      Price, W.C., 1940
   V. tobacco mosaic
      Holmes, Francis O., 1946
   V. tobacco necrosis
      Price, W.C., 1940

LINARIA Tourn. ex Mill. 1752 (Scrophulariaceae)
L. bipartita, Willd.
   V. aster yellows
      Severin, Henry H.P. and Julius H. Freitag, 1945
L. canadensis, (L.) Dumort.
   V. aster yellows
      Frazier, Norman W. and Henry H.P. Severin, 1945
L. cymbalaria, (L.) Mill.
   V. tobacco mosaic
      Grant, T.J., 1934
L. macedonica, Griseb.
   V. lucerne mosaic
      Price, W.C., 1940
   V. tobacco necrosis
      Price, W.C., 1940

L. macedonica, Griseb. (cont.)
   V. tobacco ring spot
      Price, W.C., 1940
   V. tobacco ring spot no. 2
      Price, W.C., 1940
L. maroccana, Hook. f.
   V. clover big vein
      Black, L.M., 1945
   V. tobacco etch
      Holmes, Francis O., 1946
   V. tobacco mosaic
      Holmes, Francis O., 1946
L. vulgaris, Mill.
   V. tobacco mosaic
      Holmes, Francis O., 1938, 1946

LINUM Tourn. ex L. 1735 (Linaceae)
L. flavum, L.
   V. beet curly top
      Giddings, N.J., 1947, 1948
L. grandiflorum, Desf.
   V. clover big vein
      Black, L.M., 1945
L. grandiflorum var. rubrum, Hort. *
   V. beet curly top
      Giddings, N.J., 1947, 1948
L. lewisii, Pursh
   V. beet curly top
      Bennett, C.W. and A.S. Costa, 1949
      Giddings, N.J., 1947, 1948
L. perenne, L.
   V. beet curly top
      Giddings, N.J., 1947, 1948
L. usitatissimum, L.
   V. aster yellows
      Severin, Henry H.P. and Byron R. Houston, 1945
   V. beet curly top
      Atkins, I.M., M.C. Futrell and O.G. Merkle, 1957
      Bennett, C.W. and A.S. Costa, 1949
      Giddings, N.J., 1948
      Severin, Henry H.P., 1929
      Severin, Henry H.P. and Byron R. Houston, 1945

LOBELIA Plum. ex L. 1737 (Lobeliaceae)
L. cardinalis, L.
   V. beet curly top
      Freitag, Julius H. and Henry H.P. Severin, 1936
L. erinus, L.
   V. clover big vein
      Black, L.M., 1945
   V. tobacco mosaic
      Holmes, Francis O., 1946
   V. tomato aspermy
      Hollings, M., 1955
L. erinus var. speciosa *
   V. beet curly top
      Freitag, Julius H. and Henry H.P. Severin, 1936
L. gracilis, Andr.
   V. cucumber mosaic
      Jagger, I.C., 1918
   V. tobacco etch
      Holmes, Francis O., 1946
   V. tobacco mosaic
      Holmes, Francis O., 1946
L. inflata, L.
   V. tobacco etch
      Holmes, Francis O., 1946
   V. tobacco mosaic
      Holmes, Francis O., 1938, 1946
L. spp.
   V. tomato spotted wilt
      (K.M. Smith, 1957) R.E. Fitzpatrick, et al., 1958
L. tenuior, R. Br.
   V. cucumber mosaic
      Price, W.C., 1940
   V. lucerne mosaic
      Price, W.C., 1940
   V. tobacco etch
      Holmes, Francis O., 1946
   V. tobacco mosaic
      Holmes, Francis O., 1946
   V. tobacco necrosis
      Price, W.C., 1940

L. tenuior, R. Br. (cont.)
  V. tobacco ring spot
    Price, W.C., 1940

LOBULARIA Desv. 1814 (Cruciferae)
L. maritima, (L.) Desv.
  V. cucumber mosaic
    Pound, Glenn S. and J.C. Walker, 1948
    Price, W.C., 1940
  V. tobacco mosaic
    Holmes, Francis O., 1946
  V. tobacco ring spot
    Price, W.C., 1940
  V. tobacco ring spot no. 2
    Hildebrand, E.M., 1942
    Price, W.C., 1940
  V. turnip mosaic
    Pound, Glenn S., 1948

LOLIUM L. 1735 (Gramineae)
L. multiflorum, Lam.
  V. barley yellow dwarf
    Bruehl, G.W. and H.V. Toko, 1957
    Oswald, John W. and Byron R. Houston, 1953
  V. lucerne dwarf
    Freitag, Julius H., 1951
  V. ryegrass mosaic *
    Bruehl, G.W., H.V. Toko and H.H. McKinney,
    1957
  V. wheat striate mosaic
    Slykhuis, John T. and Marion A. Watson, 1958
L. perenne, L.
  V. barley yellow dwarf
    Bruehl, G.W. and H.V. Toko, 1957
    Watson, Marion A. and T. Mulligan, 1957
  V. ryegrass mosaic *
    Bruehl, G.W., H.V. Toko and H.H. McKinney,
    1957
  V. wheat striate mosaic
    Slykhuis, John T. and Marion A. Watson, 1958
L. remotum, Schrank
  V. barley yellow dwarf
    Bruehl, G.W. and H.V. Toko, 1957
  V. ryegrass mosaic *
    Bruehl, G.W., H.V. Toko and H.H. McKinney,
    1957
L. subulatum, Vis.
  V. maize streak
    (K.M. Smith, 1957) R.E. Fitzpatrick, et al., 1958
L. temulentum, L.
  V. barley yellow dwarf
    Bruehl, G.W. and H.V. Toko, 1957
  V. lucerne dwarf
    Freitag, Julius H., 1951
  V. ryegrass mosaic *
    Bruehl, G.W., H.V. Toko and H.H. McKinney,
    1957

LONICERA L. 1737 (Caprifoliaceae)
L. brachypoda var. foliis aureo-reticulatis, Hort. *
  V. (honeysuckle) mottle *
    Corp, V.H., 1949
L. japonica, Thunb.
  V. (honeysuckle) mottle *
    Corp, V.H., 1949
  V. lucerne dwarf
    Freitag, Julius H., 1951

LOTONONIS Eckl. & Zeyh. 1836 (Leguminosae)
L. bainesii, R.T. Bak.
  V. (legume) little leaf disease *
    Hutton, E.M. and N.E. Grylls, 1956

LOTUS ((Tourn.)) L. 1735 (Leguminosae)
L. americanus, (Nutt.) Bisch.
  V. beet curly top
    Severin, Henry H.P., 1934
L. corniculatus, L.
  V. lucerne witches' broom
    Klostermeyer, E.C. and J.D. Menzies, 1951
L. salsuginosus, Greene
  V. aster yellows
    Frazier, Norman W. and Henry H.P. Severin,
    1945

L. strigosus, Greene
  V. beet curly top
    Severin, Henry H.P., 1934

LUFFA ((Tourn.)) L. 1735 (Cucurbitaceae)
L. acutangula, Roxb.
  V. cucumber green mottle mosaic
    Vasudeva, R.S., S.P. Raychaudhuri and
    Jagannath Singh, 1949
  V. cucumber mosaic
    Adsuar, Jose and A. Cruz Miret, 1950
  V. cucurbit mosaic *
    Doolittle, S.P. and M.N. Walker, 1925
L. aegyptiaca, Mill. (L. cylindrica, Roem.)
  V. beet curly top
    Freitag, Julius H. and Henry H.P. Severin, 1936
  V. cucurbit mosaic *
    Doolittle, S.P. and M.N. Walker, 1925
  V. muskmelon mosaic
    Anderson, C.W., 1954
  V. tobacco ring spot
    Wingard, S.A., 1928
  V. watermelon mosaic
    Anderson, C.W., 1954
L. spp.
  V. cucumber mosaic
    Jagger, I.C., 1918

LUNARIA Tourn. ex L. 1735 (Cruciferae)
L. annua, L.
  V. beet curly top
    Freitag, Julius H. and Henry H.P. Severin, 1936
  V. cabbage black ring spot
    Tompkins, C.M., M.W. Gardner and H. Rex
    Thomas, 1937, 1938
  V. cauliflower mosaic
    Tompkins, C.M., 1937
  V. tobacco mosaic
    Holmes, Francis O., 1946
  V. turnip crinkle
    Broadbent, L. and G.D. Heathcote, 1958
  V. turnip mosaic
    Tompkins, C.M., 1938, 1939
    Tompkins, C.M. and H. Rex Thomas, 1938
  V. turnip rosette *
    Broadbent, L. and G.D. Heathcote, 1958
  V. turnip yellow mosaic
    Broadbent, L. and G.D. Heathcote, 1958

LUPINUS ((Tourn.)) L. 1735 (Leguminosae)
L. albus, L.
  V. alsike clover mosaic
    Zaumeyer, W.J., 1940
  V. bean yellow mosaic
    Pierce, W.H., 1934
    Zaumeyer, W.J., 1940
  V. lucerne mosaic
    Thomas, H. Rex, 1951
    Zaumeyer, W.J., 1938, 1953
  V. pea enation mosaic
    Hagedorn, D.J., 1957
  V. pea mosaic
    Hagedorn, D.J. and J.C. Walker, 1954
    Murphy, D.M. and W.H. Pierce, 1937
    Pierce, W.H., 1937
    Stubbs, M.W., 1936, 1937
  V. pea mottle
    Johnson, Folke, 1942
  V. pea wilt
    Johnson, Folke, 1942
  V. tobacco ring spot
    Cheo, Pen Ching and W.J. Zaumeyer, 1952
    LeBeau, F.J., 1947
    Pierce, W.H., 1934
    Stubbs, M.W., 1937
  V. tobacco streak
    Thomas, H. Rex and W.J. Zaumeyer, 1950
  V. tomato spotted wilt
    Gardner, M.W. and O.C. Whipple, 1934
L. angustifolius, L.
  V. alsike clover mosaic
    Zaumeyer, W.J., 1940
  V. bean yellow mosaic
    Hagedorn, D.J. and J.C. Walker, 1950, 1954

L. angustifolius, L. (cont.)
  V. bean yellow mosaic
    Zaumeyer, W.J., 1940
  V. cucumber mosaic
    Whipple, O.C. and J.C. Walker, 1941
  V. lupine disease *
    Weimer, J.L., 1950
  V. pea enation mosaic
    Hagedorn, D.J., 1957
  V. pea mosaic
    Murphy, D.M. and W.H. Pierce, 1937
  V. red clover vein mosaic
    Hagedorn, D.J. and J.C. Walker, 1949, 1954
  V. subterranean clover mosaic
    Aitken, Y. and B.J. Grieve, 1943
  V. tobacco streak
    Thomas, H. Rex and W.J. Zaumeyer, 1950
  V. tomato spotted wilt
    Smith, Kenneth M., 1932
L. densiflorus, Benth.
  V. bean yellow mosaic
    Hungerford, C.W. and Irvin G. Hillyer, 1954
  V. pea mosaic
    Murphy, D.M. and W.H. Pierce, 1937
L. hartwegii, Lindl.
  V. cucumber mosaic
    Whipple, O.C. and J.C. Walker, 1941
  V. pea mosaic
    Murphy, D.M. and W.H. Pierce, 1937
L. hirsutus, L.
  V. pea mottle
    Johnson, Folke, 1942
  V. subterranean clover mosaic
    Aitken, Y. and B.J. Grieve, 1943
L. leucophyllus, Dougl. ex Lindl.
  V. tomato spotted wilt
    (K.M. Smith, 1957) R.E. Fitzpatrick, et al., 1958
L. luteus, L.
  V. lucerne mosaic
    Zaumeyer, W.J., 1938
  V. pea mosaic
    Steveninck, R.F.M. Van, 1957
  V. subterranean clover mosaic
    Aitken, Y. and B.J. Grieve, 1943
L. nanus, Dougl.
  V. pea mosaic
    Murphy, D.M. and W.H. Pierce, 1937
L. varius, L.
  V. subterranean clover mosaic
    Aitken, Y. and B.J. Grieve, 1943

LYCHNIS ((Tourn.)) L. 1735 (Caryophyllaceae)
L. alba, Mill.
  V. carnation ring spot
    Kassanis, B., 1955
  V. clover big vein
    Black, L.M., 1945
  V. cucumber mosaic
    Faan, Hwei-Chung and James Johnson, 1951
    Price, W.C., 1940
  V. tobacco necrosis
    Kassanis, B., 1955
  V. tobacco ring spot
    Price, W.C., 1940
  V. tobacco streak
    Fulton, Robert W., 1948
L. chalcedonica, L.
  V. beet curly top
    Freitag, Julius H. and Henry H.P. Severin, 1936
  V. cucumber mosaic
    Price, W.C., 1940
  V. tobacco ring spot
    Price, W.C., 1940
  V. tobacco ring spot no. 2
    Hildebrand, E.M., 1942
    Price, W.C., 1940
L. coeli-rosa, (L.) Desr.
  V. tobacco mosaic
    Holmes, Francis O., 1946
L. coronaria, (L.) Desr.
  V. beet yellows
    Roland, G. and J. Tahon, 1961

L. haageana, Lem.
  V. beet curly top
    Freitag, Julius H. and Henry H.P. Severin, 1936
L. viscaria, L.
  V. cucumber mosaic
    Wellman, F.L., 1935

LYCIUM L. 1735 (Solanaceae)
L. barbarum, L.
  V. potato A
    MacLachlan, D.S. and R.H. Larson, 1953
    MacLachlan, D.S., R.H. Larson and J.C.
    Walker, 1953
  V. potato X
    Dennis, R.W.G., 1939
  V. potato Y
    Darby, J.F., R.H. Larson and J.C. Walker,
    1951
    Smith, Kenneth M. and R.W.G. Dennis, 1940
L. chinense, Mill.
  V. potato Y
    Ross, A. Frank, 1948
  V. tobacco etch
    Holmes, Francis O., 1946
  V. tobacco mosaic
    Holmes, Francis O., 1946
L. ferocissimum, Miers
  V. tobacco mosaic
    (K.M. Smith, 1957) R.E. Fitzpatrick, et al., 1958
  V. tomato spotted wilt
    (K.M. Smith, 1957) R.E. Fitzpatrick, et al., 1958
L. halimifolium, Mill.
  V. cabbage black ring spot
    Hamlyn, Brenda M.G., 1953
  V. potato A
    MacLachlan, D.S. and R.H. Larson, 1953
    MacLachlan, D.S., R.H. Larson and J.C.
    Walker, 1953
  V. potato Y
    Hutton, E.M. and J.W. Peak, 1952
    Larson, R.H. and J.F. Darby, 1951
    Ross, A. Frank, 1948
  V. tobacco streak
    Fulton, Robert W., 1948
  V. turnip mosaic
    Walker, J.C., Francis J. LeBeau and Glenn S.
    Pound, 1945
L. rhombifolium, Dipp.
  V. potato A
    MacLachlan, D.S. and R.H. Larson, 1953
    MacLachlan, D.S., R.H. Larson and J.C.
    Walker, 1953
  V. potato Y
    Darby, J.F., R.H. Larson and J.C. Walker, 1951
    Hutton, E.M. and J.W. Peak, 1952
    Larson, R.H. and J.F. Darby, 1951

LYCOPERSICON Tourn. ex Rupp. 1745 (Solanaceae)
(LYCOPERSICUM) Hill 1765
L. chilense, Dun.
  V. tobacco mosaic
    Holmes, Francis O., 1943, 1946
L. esculentum, Mill. (Solanum lycopersicum, L.)
  V. anemone brown ring *
    Hollings, M., 1958
  V. apple mosaic
    Yarwood, C.E., 1955
    Yarwood, C.E. and H.E. Thomas, 1954
  V. asclepias yellows *
    Kunkel, L.O., 1950
  V. aster ring spot
    Anderson, C.W., 1954
  V. aster yellows
    Kunkel, L.O., 1930
    Raymer, W.B., 1956
  V. bean yellow mosaic
    Osborn, H.T., 1938
  V. beet curly top
    Adsuar, Jose, 1955
    Bennett, C.W., 1944, 1951
    Bennett, C.W. and A.S. Costa, 1949
    Bennett, C.W. and Aziz Tanrisever, 1957

L. esculentum, Mill. (cont.)
    V. beet curly top
        Carsner, Eubanks and C.F. Stahl, 1924
        Costa, A.S., 1952
        Fulton, Robert W., 1955
        Giddings, N.J., 1938, 1944, 1952, 1954
        Giddings, N.J., C.W. Bennett and A.L.
        Harrison, 1951
        Lackey, C.F., 1929
        Lesley, J.W., 1931
        Lesley, J.W. and J.M. Wallace, 1938
        McKay, M.B. and T.P. Dykstra, 1927
        Menzies, J.D. and N.J. Giddings, 1952, 1953
        Severin, Henry H.P., 1928
        Shapovalov, M., 1927, 1931
        Virgin, Walter J., 1940
        Wallace, J.M. and J.W. Lesley, 1944
        Watson, R.D. and J.E. Kraus, 1949
    V. beet ring spot *
        Harrison, B.D., 1957
    V. carnation mosaic
        Wright, Charles M., 1951
    V. celery mosaic
        Doolittle, S.P., 1931
        Doolittle, S.P. and F.L. Wellman, 1934
    V. chilli veinbanding
        Simons, John N., 1956
    V. clover witches' broom *
        Frazier, N.W. and A.F. Posnette, 1957
    V. cucumber green mottle mosaic
        Ainsworth, G.C., 1935
    V. cucumber mosaic
        Ainsworth, G.C., 1940
        Anderson, C.W., 1951, 1955
        Berkeley, G.H., 1951, 1953
        Bhargava, K.S., 1951
        Bridgmon, G.H. and J.C. Walker, 1952
        Burnett, G., 1934
        Doolittle, S.P. and L.J. Alexander, 1936, 1951
        Doolittle, S.P. and W.J. Zaumeyer, 1953
        Fulton, Joseph P., 1950
        Fulton, Robert W., 1941
        Govier, D.A., 1957
        Harrison, B.D., 1958
        Harter, L.L., 1938
        Heuberger, J.W. and J.B.S. Norton, 1933
        Hoggan, Isme A., 1927, 1935
        Hollings, M., 1955
        Johnson, E.M., 1930
        Johnson, J., 1926, 1927
        Johnson, James and Edith M. Hein, 1948
        Larsh, Howard W. and J.R. Shay, 1945
        Magee, C.J.P., 1940
        Mogendorff, N., 1930
        Nariani, T.K. and Nirmaljit Singh, 1952
        Nienow, Inez, 1948
        Pound, Glenn S. and J.C. Walker, 1948
        Price, W.C., 1934
        Selman, Ireson W., 1941
        Severin, Henry H.P., 1950
        Simons, John N., 1955
        Storey, I.F., 1939
        Valleau, W.D., 1932
        Valleau, W.D. and E.M. Johnson, 1930
        Wellman, F.L., 1934, 1935
        Whipple, O.C. and J.C. Walker, 1941
    V. cucumber western mosaic *
        Severin, Henry H.P., 1950
        Severin, Henry H.P. and Julius H. Freitag, 1948
    V. datura distortion mosaic
        Capoor, S.P. and P.M. Varma, 1952
    V. datura rugose leaf curl
        (K.M. Smith, 1957) R.E. Fitzpatrick, et al., 1958
    V. dodder latent mosaic
        Bennett, C.W., 1944, 1949
    V. eggplant mosaic
        Dale, W.T., 1954
        Ferguson, I.A.C., 1951
    V. henbane mosaic
        Hamilton, Marion A., 1932
    V. (legume) little leaf disease *
        Hutton, E.M. and N.E. Grylls, 1956

L. esculentum, Mill. (cont.)
    V. lucerne mosaic
        Berkeley, G.H., 1947
        Johnson, E.M., 1946
        Milbrath, J.A. and F.P. McWhorter, 1953
        Porter, D.R., 1935
        Severin, Henry H.P., 1942, 1950
    V. lucerne witches' broom
        Helms, Katie, 1957
        Kunkel, L.O., 1952
    V. lovage mosaic
        Smith, Kenneth M. and Roy Markham, 1944
    V. nicotiana glutinosa mosaic *
        Walker, M.N., 1925
    V. peach X disease
        Hildebrand, E.M., 1953
        Kunkel, L.O., 1944
    V. petunia mosaic
        Johnson, J., 1926, 1927
    V. (physalis) mosaic *
        Melhus, I.E., 1922
        Walker, M.N., 1926
    V. potato A
        Doolittle, S.P., 1928
        Jarrett, Phyllis H., 1930
        Krantz, F.A. and G.R. Bisby, 1921
        Quanjer, H.M., 1920
        Schultz, E.S. and Donald Folsom, 1923
        Smith, J. Henderson, 1928
        Stover, W.G., 1928
    V. potato aucuba mosaic
        (K.M. Smith, 1957) R.E. Fitzpatrick, et al., 1958
    V. potato bunch top disease *
        Menzies, J.D., 1950
    V. potato leaf roll
        Burnett, Grover and Leon K. Jones, 1931
        Dykstra, T.P., 1930, 1933
        MacCarthy, H.R., 1954
        Natti, John J., 1953
        Stover, W.G., 1928
    V. potato M *
        Bagnall, R.H. and R.H. Larson, 1957
        Bagnall, R.H., R.H. Larson and J.C. Walker, 1956
    V. potato necrotic *
        Schultz, E.S. and W.P. Raleigh, 1933
    V. potato paracrinkle
        Dykstra, T.P., 1939
    V. potato rosette
        Hutton, E.M. and C.E.W. oldaker, 1949
    V. potato spindle tuber
        Stover, W.G., 1928
    V. potato stunt
        (K.M. Smith, 1957) R.E. Fitzpatrick, et al., 1958
    V. potato witches' broom
        Young, P.A. and H.E. Morris, 1928
    V. potato X
        Ainsworth, G.C., 1933, 1934
        Ainsworth, G.C., G.H. Berkeley and J. Caldwell, 1934
        Bawden, F.C. and F.M.L. Sheffield, 1944
        Burnett, Grover and Leon K. Jones, 1931
        Cockerham, George, 1943
        Dennis, R.W.G., 1939
        Dykstra, T.P., 1933, 1935
        Fernow, Karl Hermann, 1925
        Folsom, Donald and Reiner Bonde, 1937
        Fulton, Robert W., 1941
        Goss, R.W., 1931
        Hamilton, Marion A., 1932
        Hoggan, Isme A., 1927
        Johnson, E.M., 1930
        Johnson, James, 1925, 1927
        Jones, Leon K. and Grover Burnett, 1935
        MacNeill, Blair H., 1955
        Matthews, R.E.F., 1949
        Samson, R.W., 1930
        Smith, Kenneth M., 1929
        Valleau, W.D. and E.M. Johnson, 1930
        Vasudeva, R. Sahai and T.B. Lal, 1944
    V. potato Y
        Alvarez-Garcia, L.A. and Jose Adsuar, 1943

L. esculentum, Mill. (cont.)
V. potato Y
Bawden, F.C. and B. Kassanis, 1951
Bawden, F.C. and F.M.L. Sheffield, 1944
Burnett, Grover and Leon K. Jones, 1931
Cockerham, George, 1943
Conover, Robert A. and Robert W. Fulton, 1953
Dykstra, T.P., 1933, 1939
Hoggan, Isme A., 1927
Johnson, E.M., 1930
Johnson, James, 1927
Jones, Leon K. and C.L. Vincent, 1937
Koch, K.L., 1933
MacNeill, Blair H., 1955
Roque, Arturo and Jose Adsuar, 1941
Sakimura, K., 1953
Samson, R.W., 1930
Schultz, E.S. and Donald Folsom, 1923
Simons, J.N., Robert A. Conover and James M.
Walter, 1956
Smith, Kenneth M. and R.W.G. Dennis, 1940
V. potato yellow dwarf
Black, L.M., 1937
Hougas, R.W., 1951
V. raspberry yellow dwarf *
Harrison, B.D., 1958
V. red current ring spot
Klesser, P.J., 1951
V. sweet potato mosaic
Elmer, O.H., 1957
V. tobacco bergerac ring spot
(K.M. Smith, 1957) R.E. Fitzpatrick, et al., 1958
V. tobacco broad ring spot
Johnson, James and Robert W. Fulton, 1942
V. tobacco etch
Anderson, C.W., 1954
Bawden, F.C. and B. Kassanis, 1941
Bennett, C.W., 1944
Doolittle, S.P. and L.J. Alexander, 1951
Fulton, Robert W., 1941
Holmes, Francis O., 1942, 1946
Johnson, E.M., 1930
MacNeill, Blair H., 1955
Valleau, W.D. and E.M. Johnson, 1930
V. tobacco green mosaic
McKinney, H.H., 1929
V. tobacco leaf curl
Bird, Julio, 1957
Nariani, T.K., 1956
Pal, B.P. and R.K. Tandon, 1937
Pruthi, Hem Singh and C.K. Samuel, 1941
Vasudeva, R.S. and J. Sam Raj, 1948
V. tobacco leaf roll disease *
Goenaga, Alvaro, 1945
V. tobacco mosaic
Abbott, E.V., 1929, 1931
Ainsworth, G.C., 1933, 1937
Ainsworth, G.C., G.H. Berkeley and J. Caldwell,
1934
Ainsworth, G.C. and I.W. Selman, 1936
Allard, H.A., 1916
Berkeley, G.H., 1927, 1951
Berkeley, G.H. and G.O. Madden, 1932, 1933
Boyle, John S., 1956
Boyle, John S. and David C. Wharton, 1956, 1957
Brierley, W.B., 1916
Burnett, Grover and Leon K. Jones, 1931
Caldwell, John, 1932
Cochran, G.W., 1946
Conover, Robert A. and Robert W. Fulton, 1953
Costa, A.S., 1944
Cox, C.E. and L.O. Weaver, 1950
Dale, W.T., 1954
Das, C.R. and S.P. Raychaudhuri, 1953
Desai, S.V., 1933
Desjardins, P.R., J.M. Wallace and R.J. Drake,
1954
Doering, G.R., W.C. Price and S.B. Fenne, 1957
Doolittle, S.P., 1928
Doolittle, S.P. and L.J. Alexander, 1936, 1951
Doolittle, S.P. and F.S. Beecher, 1942
Doolittle, S.P. and W.S. Porte, 1949
Eckerson, Sophia H. and H.R. Kraybill, 1927
Fernow, Karl Hermann, 1925

L. esculentum, Mill. (cont.)
V. tobacco mosaic
Fulton, Robert W., 1941
Gardner, Max W., 1925
Gardner, Max W. and James B. Kendrick, 1922
Heuberger, J.W. and J.B.S. Norton, 1933
Hoggan, Isme A., 1927
Holmes, Francis O., 1941, 1943, 1946, 1950
Jarrett, Phyllis H., 1930
Jensen, J.H., 1933, 1936
Johnson, E.M., 1930
Johnson, J., 1926, 1927
Jones, Leon K., 1940
Jones, Leon K. and Grover Burnett, 1935
Kunkel, L.O., 1932
MacNeill, Blair H., 1955
McKinney, H.H., 1929, 1952
McRitchie, John J., 1957
McRitchie, John J. and Leonard J. Alexander,
1957
Mogendorff, N., 1930
Norval, I.P., 1938
Perez, J. Enrique, J. Adsuar and Orlando Sala,
1956
Peterson, Paul D. and H.H. McKinney, 1938
Price, W.C. and S.B. Fenne, 1951
Quanjer, H.M., 1920
Raychaudhuri, S.P., 1952
Schultz, E.S. and Donald Folsom, 1923
Selman, Ireson W., 1941, 1943
Severin, Henry H.P., 1950
Sheffield, F.M.L., 1931, 1936
Smith, J. Henderson, 1928, 1933
Smith, Kenneth M., 1935
Stover, W.G., 1928
Stover, W.G. and M.T. Vermillion, 1933
Valleau, W.D. and E.M. Johnson, 1930, 1943
Vanterpool, T.C., 1926
Verwoerd, Len, 1929
Walker, M.N., 1926
Watson, R.D., E.C. Heinrich and W.R. Harvey,
1954
Woods, M.W. and Richard V. Eck, 1948
V. tobacco mottle
(K.M. Smith, 1957) R.E. Fitzpatrick, et al., 1958
V. tobacco necrosis
(K.M. Smith, 1957) R.E. Fitzpatrick, et al., 1958
V. tobacco ring spot
Henderson, R.G. and S.A. Wingard, 1931
Steere, Russell L., 1956
V. tobacco ring spot no. 2
Brierley, Philip, 1954
Hildebrand, E.M., 1942
Price, W.C., 1936
Thomas, H. Rex and W.J. Zaumeyer, 1950
V. tobacco streak
Fulton, Robert W., 1948
V. tobacco vein distorting
(K.M. Smith, 1957) R.E. Fitzpatrick, et al., 1958
V. tobacco yellow dwarf
Hill, A.V., 1950
Hill, A.V. and M. Mandryk, 1954
V. tomato aspermy
Blencowe, J.W. and John Caldwell, 1949
Brierley, Philip and Floyd F. Smith, 1953
Brierley, Philip, Floyd F. Smith and S.P.
Doolittle, 1953, 1955
Hollings, M., 1955
V. tomato big bud
Alvarez-Garcia, L.A. and Jose Adsuar, 1950
Dana, B.F., 1940
Helms, Katie, 1957
Hill, A.V. and M. Mandryk, 1954
Hutton, E.M. and D.C. Work, 1947
Menzies, J.D., 1950
Norris, D.O., 1954
Samuel, G., J.G. Bald and C.M. Eardley, 1933
Vasudeva, R. Sahai and T.B. Lal, 1944
V. tomato black ring
(K.M. Smith, 1957) R.E. Fitzpatrick, et al., 1958
V. tomato bushy stunt
Johnson, Folke, 1941
Smith, Kenneth M., 1935
Steere, Russell L., 1953

L. esculentum, Mill. (cont.)
　V. tomato ring spot
　　Imle, E.P. and R.W. Samson, 1937
　　Samson, R.W. and E.P. Imle, 1942
　　Varney, E.H. and J. Duain Moore, 1952
　V. tomato shoestring *
　　Doering, G.R., W.C. Price and S.B. Fenne, 1957
　V. tomato spotted wilt
　　Ainsworth, G.C., 1933, 1940
　　Ainsworth, G.C., G.H. Berkeley and J. Caldwell, 1934
　　Bennett, C.W., 1944
　　Berkeley, G.H., 1935
　　Best, Rupert J. and Geoffrey Samuel, 1936
　　Black, L.M., M.K. Brakke and A.E. Vatter, 1952
　　Doolittle, S.P. and C.B. Sumner, 1931, 1934
　　Ferguson, I.A.C., 1951
　　Gardner, M.W., C.M. Tompkins and O.C. Whipple, 1935
　　Gardner, M.W. and O.C. Whipple, 1934
　　Holmes, Francis O., 1948
　　Hutton, E.M. and A.R. Peak, 1949, 1953
　　Jones, Leon K., 1944
　　MacNeill, Blair H., 1955
　　McWhorter, F.P., 1935
　　McWhorter, F.P. and J.A. Milbrath, 1935
　　Milbrath, J.A., 1939
　　Norris, D.O., 1951
　　Parris, G.K., 1940
　　Sakimura, K., 1940
　　Shapovalov, M., 1934
　　Sherf, A.F., 1948
　　Smith, Kenneth M., 1931, 1932, 1935
　　Smith, Paul G., 1944
　　Smith, Paul G. and M.W. Gardner, 1948, 1951
　　Snyder, W.C. and H. Rex Thomas, 1936
　　Tompkins, C.M. and M.W. Gardner, 1934
　　Whipple, O.C., 1936
　　Yu, T.F., 1947
　V. tomato twisted leaf
　　Ferguson, I.A.C., 1951
　V. tomato V-52-1
　　Miller, Patrick M., 1953
　V. tomato yellow net
　　Sylvester, Edward S., 1954
　V. tomato yellow top·
　　(K.M. Smith, 1957) R.E. Fitzpatrick, et al., 1958
　V. turnip crinkle
　　Broadbent, L. and G.D. Heathcote, 1958
　V. vaccinium false blossom
　　Costa, A.S., 1944
　　Kunkel, L.O., 1943, 1945
L. esculentum var. cerasiforme, (Dun.) A. Gray
　V. chilli veinbanding
　　Simons, John N., 1956
　V. tobacco mosaic
　　Gardner, Max W. and James B. Kendrick, 1922
L. esculentum var. grandifolium, Bailey
　V. cucumber mosaic
　　Mogendorff, N., 1930
L. esculentum var. Sioux x L. hirsutum, H. B. & K.
　V. tobacco mosaic
　　Watson, R.D. and E.C. Heinrich, 1951
L. esculentum f. pyriforme, (Dun.) C.H. Mull.
　V. potato X
　　Dennis, R.W.G., 1939
L. esculentum x L. chilense, Dun.
　V. tobacco mosaic
　　Holmes, Francis O., 1943
L. esculentum x L. hirsutum, H. B. & K.
　V. tobacco mosaic
　　Watson, R.D., E.C. Heinrich and W.R. Harvey, 1954
L. esculentum x L. pimpinellifolium, (Jusl.) Mill.
　V. tomato twisted leaf
　　Ferguson, I.A.C., 1951
L. glandulosum, C.H. Mull.
　V. tobacco mosaic
　　Doolittle, S.P. and F.S. Beecher, 1942
L. hirsutum, H. B. & K.
　V. beet curly top
　　Giddings, N.J., C.W. Bennett and A.L. Harrison, 1951

L. hirsutum, H. B. & K. (cont.)
　V. tobacco etch
　　Holmes, Francis O., 1946
　V. tobacco mosaic
　　Doolittle, S.P. and F.S. Beecher, 1942
　　Doolittle, S.P., W.S. Porte and F.S. Beecher, 1946
　　Holmes, Francis O., 1946
　　Porte, W.S., S.P. Doolittle and F.L. Wellman, 1939
　　Watson, R.D., E.C. Heinrich and W.R. Harvey, 1954
　V. tomato big bud
　　Hutton, E.M. and D.C. Work, 1947
　V. tomato spotted wilt
　　Smith, Paul G., 1944
L. hirsutum f. glabratum, C.H. Mull. *
　V. tobacco mosaic
　　Doolittle, S.P. and F.S. Beecher, 1942
L. hirsutum x L. esculentum, Mill.
　V. tobacco mosaic
　　Doolittle, S.P. and W.S. Porte, 1949
L. hybrids
　V. tomato spotted wilt
　　Hutton, E.M. and A.R. Peak, 1949
L. lycopersicon, (L.) Karst. *
　V. cucumber mosaic
　　Adsuar, Jose and A. Cruz Miret, 1950
L. peruvianum, (L.) Mill.
　V. tobacco etch
　　Holmes, Francis O., 1946
　V. tobacco mosaic
　　Doolittle, S.P. and F.S. Beecher, 1942
　　Holmes, Francis O., 1946
　　Nagaich, B.B. and H.H. Thornberry, 1957
　V. tomato big bud
　　Hutton, E.M. and D.C. Work, 1947
　V. tomato spotted wilt
　　Hutton, E.M. and A.R. Peak, 1949, 1953
L. peruvianum subsp. dentatum, (Dun.) Luckwill.
　V. tobacco mosaic
　　Doolittle, S.P. and F.S. Beecher, 1942
L. pimpinellifolium, (Jusl.) Mill.
　V. beet curly top
　　Costa, A.S., 1952
　　Lesley, J.W. and J.M. Wallace, 1938
　V. eggplant mosaic
　　Dale, W.T., 1954
　　Ferguson, I.A.C., 1951
　V. potato A
　　MacLachlan, D.S. and R.H. Larson, 1953
　　MacLachlan, D.S., R.H. Larson and J.C. Walker, 1953
　V. potato leaf roll
　　MacCarthy, H.R., 1954
　V. tobacco etch
　　Holmes, Francis O., 1946
　V. tobacco mosaic
　　Doolittle, S.P. and F.S. Beecher, 1942
　　Gardner, Max W. and James B. Kendrick, 1922
　　Holmes, Francis O., 1946
　V. tomato big bud
　　Hutton, E.M. and D.C. Work, 1947
　V. tomato ring spot
　　Samson, R.W. and E.P. Imle, 1942
　V. tomato spotted wilt
　　Hutton, E.M. and A.R. Peak, 1949, 1953
　　Sakimura, K., 1940
　　Smith, Paul G., 1944
　　Smith, Paul G. and M.W. Gardner, 1948, 1951
　V. tomato yellow net
　　Sylvester, Edward S., 1954
　V. turnip mosaic
　　Hoggan, I.A. and J. Johnson, 1935
L. pimpinellifolium No. 381-1 x No. 548
　V. beet curly top
　　Lesley, J.W. and J.M. Wallace, 1938
L. pimpinellifolium No. 503 x F.P.I. 79532
　V. beet curly top
　　Lesley, J.W. and J.M. Wallace, 1938
L. pimpinellifolium No. 573 x No. 548
　V. beet curly top
　　Lesley, J.W. and J.M. Wallace, 1938

L. pimpinellifolium, (Jusl.) Mill. No. 573 x F.P.I.
  V. beet curly top   79532
    L3sley, J.W. and J.M. Wallace, 1938
L. pimpinellifolium x L. esculentum, Mill.
  V. tomato spotted wilt
    Smith, Paul G. and M.W. Gardner, 1948
L. racemigerum, Lange
  V. potato X
    Dennis, R.W.G., 1939
  V. potato Y
    Smith, Kenneth M. and R.W.G. Dennis, 1940
L. spp. (South America)
  V. tomato big bud
    Dana, B.F., 1940

LYCOPSIS L. 1735 (Boraginaceae)
L. arvensis, L.
  V. beet ring spot *
    Harrison, B.D., 1957

LYCOPUS Tourn. ex L. 1735 (Labiatae)
L. rubellus, Moench
  V. tobacco mosaic
    Holmes, Francis O., 1938, 1946
L. virginicus, L.
  V. tobacco mosaic
    Holmes, Francis O., 1938

LYTHRUM L. 1735 (Lythraceae)
L. salicaria, L.
  V. cucumber mosaic
    Price, W.C., 1940

MADIA Molina 1782 (Compositae)
M. sativa, Mol.
  V. aster yellows
    Frazier, Norman W. and Henry H.P. Severin,
    1945

MAJORANA ((Tourn.)) Rupp. 1745 (Labiatae)
M. hortensis, Moench
  V. lucerne dwarf
    Freitag, Julius H., 1951

MALCOMIA ((R. Br. in)) Ait. Hort. Kew. 1812
(MALCOLMIA) Spreng. 1818 (Cruciferae)
M. maritima, R. Br.
  V. anemone mosaic *
    Hollings, M., 1957
  V. aster yellows
    (K.M. Smith, 1957) R.E. Fitzpatrick, et al., 1958
  V. beet curly top
    Giddings, N.J., 1944
  V. cabbage black ring spot
    Hollings, M., 1957
    Tompkins, C.M., M.W. Gardner and H. Rex
    Thomas, 1937, 1938
  V. radish mosaic
    Tompkins, C.M., 1939
  V. turnip mosaic
    Pound, Glenn S., 1948
    Tompkins, C.M., 1938, 1939
    Tompkins, C.M. and H. Rex Thomas, 1938
    Walker, J.C., Francis J. LeBeau and Glenn S.
    Pound, 1945

MALUS Tourn. ex L. 1737 (Rosaceae)
M. baccata, (L.) Borkh.
  V. apple mosaic
    Hockey, J.F., 1943
M. coronaria, (L.) Mill.
  V. apple dwarf fruit
    Cation, Donald and Roy E. Gibson, 1952
M. spectabilis, (Ait.) Borkh.
  V. apple mosaic
    Thomas, H. Earl and L.M. Massey, 1939
M. spp.
  V. apple false sting
    (K.M. Smith, 1957) R.E. Fitzpatrick, et al., 1958
  V. apple mosaic
    (K.M. Smith, 1957) R.E. Fitzpatrick, et al., 1958
  V. apple ring spot
    (K.M. Smith, 1957) R.E. Fitzpatrick, et al., 1958

M. spp. (cont.)
  V. apple rosette
    (K.M. Smith, 1957) R.E. Fitzpatrick, et al., 1958
  V. apple rough skin
    (K.M. Smith, 1957) R.E. Fitzpatrick, et al., 1958
  V. apple rubbery wood
    (K.M. Smith, 1957) R.E. Fitzpatrick, et al., 1958
  V. apple witches' broom
    (K.M. Smith, 1957) R.E. Fitzpatrick, et al., 1958
M. sylvestris, Mill.
  V. apple *
    Hilborn, M.T. and Reiner Bonde, 1956
    Millikan, D.F. and H.W. Guengerich, 1956
  V. apple dwarf fruit
    Cation, Donald and Roy E. Gibson, 1952
  V. apple false sting
    Hockey, J.F., 1941, 1943
  V. apple green mottle
    Palmiter, D.H. and K.G. Parker, 1955
  V. apple mosaic
    Blodgett, F.M., 1938
    Fulton, Robert W., 1956
    Gilmer, R.M., 1956
    Hockey, J.F., 1943
    Hunter, J.A., E.E. Chamberlain and J.D.
    Atkinson, 1958
    Kirkpatrick, Hugh C., 1955
    Posnette, A.F. and R. Cropley, 1956
    Posnette, A.F. and Christina E. Ellenberger,
    1957
    Yarwood, C.E., 1955, 1957
    Yarwood, C.E. and H.E. Thomas, 1954
  V. peach ring spot
    Cochran, L.C., 1950
M. sylvestris on M. angustifolia, (Ait.) Michx.
  V. apple stem pitting *
    Guengerich, H.W. and D.F. Millikan, 1956

MALVA ((Tourn.)) L. 1735 (Malvaceae)
M. nicaeensis, All.
  V. aster yellows
    Frazier, Norman W. and Henry H.P. Severin,
    1945
M. parviflora, L.
  V. aster yellows
    Frazier, Norman W. and Henry H.P. Severin,
    1945
  V. beet curly top
    Bennett, C.W. and Aziz Tanrisever, 1957
    Carsner, E., 1919
    Severin, Henry H.P., 1929, 1934
  V. datura rugose leaf curl
    Grylls, N.E., 1955
  V. (legume) little leaf disease *
    Hutton, E.M. and N.E. Grylls, 1956
  V. malva yellow vein mosaic *
    Costa, A.S. and James E. Duffus, 1957
  V. tobacco yellow dwarf
    Helson, G.A.H., 1950
M. rotundifolia, L.
  V. aster yellows
    Frazier, Norman W. and Henry H.P. Severin,
    1945
  V. beet curly top
    Severin, Henry H.P., 1929, 1934
  V. malva yellow vein mosaic *
    Costa, A.S. and James E. Duffus, 1957
  V. tobacco streak
    Fulton, Robert W., 1948
  V. tomato spotted wilt
    Milbrath, J.A., 1939
M. spp.
  V. hollyhock mosaic
    (K.M. Smith, 1957) R.E. Fitzpatrick, et al., 1958
M. sylvestris, L.
  V. malva yellow vein mosaic *
    Costa, A.S. and James E. Duffus, 1957

MALVASTRUM A. Gray 1849 (Malvaceae)
M. coromandelianum, Garcke
  V. abutilon infectious variegation
    Crandall, Bowen S., 1954

MANIHOT Tourn. ex Adans. 1763 (Euphorbiaceae)
M. esculenta, Crantz (M. utilissima, Pohl)
   V. cassava brown streak
      (K.M. Smith, 1957) R.E. Fitzpatrick, et al., 1958
   V. cassava mosaic
      Chant, S.R., 1958
      McKinney, H.H., 1928
      Storey, H.H. and R.F.W. Nichols, 1938
M. palmata, Muell. Arg.
   V. cassava mosaic
      (K.M. Smith, 1957) R.E. Fitzpatrick, et al., 1958
M. spp.
   V. (cassava) green mosaic *
      McKinney, H.H., 1929

MARANTA Plum. ex L. 1737 (Marantaceae)
M. arundinaceae, L.
   V. cucumber mosaic
      Celino, M.S. and Aureo L. Martinez, 1956

MARRUBIUM Tourn. ex L. 1735 (Labiatae)
M. vulgare, L.
   V. cucumber mosaic
      Burnett, G., 1934
   V. tobacco mosaic
      Holmes, Francis O., 1946

MARTYNIA Houst. ex L. 1735 (Martyniaceae)
M. annua, L.
   V. tomato spotted wilt
      Gardner, M.W. and O.C. Whipple, 1934
M. louisiana, Mill.
   V. aster yellows
      Kunkel, L.O., 1926
   V. cucurbit mosaic *
      Doolittle, S.P., 1921
      Doolittle, S.P. and M.N. Walker, 1925
   V. tobacco mosaic
      Fernow, Karl Hermann, 1925
      Grant, T.J., 1934
   V. tomato ring spot
      Samson, R.W. and E.P. Imle, 1942

MATRICARIA ((Tourn.)) L. 1735 (Compositae)
M. alba, Hort. ex Vilmorin's Blumeng.
   V. aster yellows
      Kunkel, L.O., 1926
M. inodora, L.
   V. beet curly top
      Freitag, Julius H. and Henry H.P. Severin, 1936
M. matricarioides, (Less.) Porter
   V. raspberry Scottish leaf curl
      Harrison, B.D., 1958
M. suaveolens, (Pursh) Buch.
   V. aster yellows
      Frazier, Norman W. and Henry H.P. Severin,
      1945

MATTHIOLA R. Br. 1812 (Cruciferae)
M. bicornis, (Sibth. & Sm.) DC.
   V. cabbage black ring spot
      Tompkins, C.M., M.W. Gardner and H. Rex
      Thomas, 1938
   V. clover big vein
      Black, L.M., 1945
   V. radish mosaic
      Tompkins, C.M., 1939
   V. tobacco mosaic
      Holmes, Francis O., 1946
   V. turnip mosaic
      Tompkins, C.M., 1939
      Tompkins, C.M. and H. Rex Thomas, 1938
      Walker, J.C., Francis J. LeBeau and Glenn S.
      Pound, 1945
M. incana, (L.) R. Br.
   V. beet curly top
      Severin, Henry H.P. and Julius H. Freitag, 1934
   V. cabbage black ring spot
      (K.M. Smith, 1957) R.E. Fitzpatrick, et al., 1958
      Tompkins, C.M., M.W. Gardner and H. Rex
      Thomas, 1938
   V. cauliflower mosaic
      Berkeley, G.H. and J.H. Tremaine, 1954
      Tompkins, C.M., 1934

M. incana, (L.) R. Br. (cont.)
   V. cucumber mosaic
      Berkeley, G.H. and J.H. Tremaine, 1954
   V. radish mosaic
      (K.M. Smith, 1957) R.E. Fitzpatrick, et al., 1958
   V. stock mosaic
      Tompkins, C.M., 1934
   V. turnip mosaic
      Berkeley, G.H. and J.H. Tremaine, 1954
      Berkeley, G.H. and M. Weintraub, 1952
M. incana var. annua, (L.) Voss
   V. anemone mosaic *
      Hollings, M., 1957
   V. beet curly top
      Freitag, Julius H. and Henry H.P. Severin, 1936
      Severin, Henry H.P. and Julius H. Freitag, 1934
   V. cabbage black ring spot
      Hamlyn, Brenda M.G., 1953
      Hollings, M., 1957
      Tompkins, C.M., M.W. Gardner and H. Rex
      Thomas, 1937, 1938
   V. cabbage ring necrosis
      Larson, R.H. and J.C. Walker, 1941
   V. cauliflower mosaic
      Severin, Henry H.P. and C.M. Tompkins, 1948
      Tompkins, C.M., 1937
      Walker, J.C., Francis J. LeBeau and Glenn S.
      Pound, 1945
   V. cucumber mosaic
      Pound, Glenn S. and J.C. Walker, 1948
   V. turnip mosaic
      LeBeau, Francis J. and J.C. Walker, 1945
      Pound, Glenn S., 1948
      Severin, Henry H.P. and C.M. Tompkins, 1950
      Tompkins, C.M., 1938, 1939
      Tompkins, C.M. and H. Rex Thomas, 1938
      Walker, J.C., Francis J. LeBeau and Glenn S.
      Pound, 1945

MEDICAGO Tourn. ex L. 1737 (Leguminosae)
M. arabica, (L.) All.
   V. bean yellow mosaic
      Elliott, J.A., 1921
   V. lucerne mosaic
      Kreitlow, K.W. and W.C. Price, 1949
   V. pea enation mosaic
      Simons, John N., 1954
   V. pea mosaic
      Murphy, D.M. and W.H. Pierce, 1937
   V. red clover mosaic *
      Elliott, J.A., 1921
   V. subterranean clover mosaic
      Aitken, Y. and B.J. Grieve, 1943
M. denticulata, Willd.
   V. tobacco yellow dwarf
      Helson, G.A.H., 1950
      Hill, A.V., 1950
M. falcata, L.
   V. lucerne dwarf
      Houston, Byron R. and Ernest H. Stanford, 1954
   V. lucerne witches' broom
      Klostermeyer, E.C. and J.D. Menzies, 1951
M. glutinosa, Bieb.
   V. lucerne dwarf
      Houston, Byron R. and Ernest H. Stanford, 1954
M. hispida, Gaertn.
   V. aster yellows
      Frazier, Norman W. and Henry H.P. Severin,
      1945
   V. beet curly top
      Carsner, E., 1919
      Giddings, N.J., 1944
      Severin, Henry H.P., 1934
      Severin, Henry H.P. and Charles F. Henderson,
      1928
   V. lucerne dwarf
      Freitag, Julius H., 1951
   V. lucerne mosaic
      Kreitlow, K.W. and W.C. Price, 1949
   V. lucerne witches' broom
      Klostermeyer, E.C. and J.D. Menzies, 1951
      Menzies, J.D., 1944, 1946
   V. pea enation mosaic
      Simons, John N., 1954

M. hispida, Gaertn. (cont.)
V. pea mosaic
Murphy, D.M. and W.H. Pierce, 1937
M. hispida var. denticulata *
V. subterranean clover mosaic
Aitken, Y. and B.J. Grieve, 1943
M. lupulina, L.
V. bean yellow mosaic
Hungerford, C.W. and Irvin G. Hillyer, 1954
V. datura rugose leaf curl
(K.M. Smith, 1957) R.E. Fitzpatrick, et al., 1958
V. lucerne witches' broom
Klostermeyer, E.C. and J.D. Menzies, 1951
Menzies, J.D., 1944, 1946
V. pea mottle
Johnson, Folke, 1942
Johnson, Folke and Leon K. Jones, 1937
V. pea wilt
Johnson, Folke, 1942
V. potato yellow dwarf
Hansing, E.D., 1942
V. red clover mosaic *
Dickson, B.T., 1922
V. red clover vein mosaic
Graves, Clinton H., Jr. and D.J. Hagedorn, 1956
V. subterranean clover mosaic
Aitken, Y. and B.J. Grieve, 1943
M. obscura, Retz.
V. lucerne mosaic
Kreitlow, K.W. and W.C. Price, 1949
M. orbicularis, All.
V. bean yellow mosaic
Hagedorn, D.J. and J.C. Walker, 1950, 1954
V. lucerne mosaic
Kreitlow, K.W. and W.C. Price, 1949
V. Wisconsin pea streak
Hagedorn, D.J. and J.C. Walker, 1949, 1954
M. ruthenica, Trautv.
V. lucerne witches' broom
Klostermeyer, E.C. and J.D. Menzies, 1951
M. sativa, L.
V. alsike clover mosaic
(K.M. Smith, 1957) R.E. Fitzpatrick, et al., 1958
Zaumeyer, W.J., 1940.
V. bean yellow mosaic
McWhorter, Frank P., 1949
Zaumeyer, W.J., 1940
V. beet curly top
Severin, Henry H.P. and Charles F. Henderson, 1928
V. broad bean mottle
Yu, T.F., 1939
V. datura rugose leaf curl
(K.M. Smith, 1957) R.E. Fitzpatrick, et al., 1958
V. (legume) little leaf disease *
Hutton, E.M. and N.E. Grylls, 1956
V. lucerne dwarf
Frazier, Norman W. and J.H. Freitag, 1946
Freitag, J.H., 1951
Freitag, J.H. and Norman W. Frazier, 1954
Freitag, J.H., N.W. Frazier and R.A. Flock, 1952
Hewitt, Wm.B., Byron R. Houston, Norman W. Frazier and J.H. Freitag, 1946
Houston, Byron R., Katherine Esau and Wm.B. Hewitt, 1946
Houston, Byron R., N.W. Frazier and Wm.B. Hewitt, 1942
Houston, Byron R. and Ernest H. Stanford, 1954
Severin, Henry H.P., 1949
Stoner, Warren N., 1953
Weimer, J.L., 1936
V. lucerne mosaic
Diachun, Stephen and Lawrence Henson, 1957
Henson, Lawrence and Stephen Diachun, 1957
Houston, Byron R. and John W. Oswald, 1951, 1953
Johnson, E.M., 1946
McWhorter, Frank P., 1949
Oswald, John W., 1950
Pierce, W.H., 1934, 1937
Snyder, William C. and Saul Rich, 1942
Swenson, K.G., 1952
Thomas, H. Rex, 1951

M. sativa, L. (cont.)
V. lucerne mosaic
Weimer, J.L., 1931, 1934
Zaumeyer, W.J., 1938, 1953
Zaumeyer, W.J. and B.L. Wade, 1935
V. lucerne witches' broom
Helms, Katie, 1957
Kunkel, L.O., 1952
Menzies, J.D., 1944, 1946
Menzies, J.D. and F.D. Heald, 1942
V. pea enation mosaic
Johnson, Folke and Leon K. Jones, 1937
McEwen, F.L. and W.T. Schroeder, 1956
V. pea leaf roll
(K.M. Smith, 1957) R.E. Fitzpatrick, et al., 1958
V. pea mosaic
Johnson, F. and L.K. Jones, 1936
V. pea mottle
Johnson, Folke, 1942
Johnson, F. and L.K. Jones, 1936, 1937
V. pea streak
Zaumeyer, W.J., 1938
V. tobacco ring spot
(K.M. Smith, 1957) R.E. Fitzpatrick, et al., 1958
V. tobacco yellow dwarf
Helson, G.A.H., 1950
V. tomato big bud
Helms, Katie, 1957
M. tribuloides, Desr.
V. subterranean clover mosaic
Aitken, Y. and B.J. Grieve, 1943

MELILOTUS Tourn. ex Hall. 1742 (Leguminosae)
M. alba, Desr.
V. alsike clover mosaic
Zaumeyer, W.J., 1940
V. aster yellows
Frazier, Norman W. and Henry H.P. Severin, 1945
V. bean common mosaic
Harrison, Arthur L., 1935
V. bean Montana *
Afanasiev, M.M. and H.E. Morris, 1946
V. bean yellow mosaic
Afanasiev, M.M. and H.E. Morris, 1952
Conover, Robert A., 1948
Diachun, Stephen and Lawrence Henson, 1956
Elliott, J.A., 1921
Grogan, Raymond G. and J.C. Walker, 1948
Hagedorn, D.J. and J.C. Walker, 1950, 1954
Hanson, E.W. and D.J. Hagedorn, 1954, 1956
Hungerford, C.W. and Irvin G. Hillyer, 1954
McWhorter, Frank P., 1949
Pierce, W.H., 1934, 1937
Thomas, H. Rex and W.J. Zaumeyer, 1953
Zaumeyer, W.J., 1940, 1952
Zaumeyer, W.J. and H.H. Fisher, 1953
Zaumeyer, W.J. and B.L. Wade, 1935
V. beet curly top
Severin, Henry H.P. and Charles F. Henderson, 1928
V. broad bean mottle
Yu, T.F., 1939
V. clover big vein
Black, L.M., 1945, 1951
V. cucumber mosaic
Doolittle, S.P. and W.J. Zaumeyer, 1952, 1953
V. lucerne dwarf
Freitag, J.H., 1951
V. lucerne mosaic
Hanson, E.W. and D.J. Hagedorn, 1954, 1956
Kreitlow, K.W. and W.C. Price, 1949
Pierce, W.H., 1934, 1937
Thomas, H. Rex, 1951
Zaumeyer, W.J., 1938, 1953
Zaumeyer, W.J. and B.L. Wade, 1935
V. lucerne witches' broom
Klostermeyer, E.C. and J.D. Menzies, 1951
V. pea enation mosaic
McEwen, F.L. and W.T. Schroeder, 1956
V. pea mosaic
Hagedorn, D.J., 1948
Murphy, D.M. and W.H. Pierce, 1937
Osborn, H.T., 1937

M. alba, Desr. (cont.)
   V. pea mosaic
      Pierce, W.H., 1937
      Zaumeyer, W.J. and B.L. Wade, 1935
   V. pea mottle
      Johnson, Folke, 1942
      Johnson, F. and L.K. Jones, 1936
   V. pea streak
      Hagedorn, D.J., 1948
      Zaumeyer, W.J., 1938
   V. pea wilt
      Johnson, Folke, 1942
   V. prunus A *
      Fulton, Robert W., 1957
   V. prunus B *
      Fulton, Robert W., 1957
   V. prunus G *
      Fulton, Robert W., 1957
   V. red clover mosaic *
      Elliott, J.A., 1921
   V. red clover vein mosaic
      Graves, Clinton H., Jr. and D.J. Hagedorn, 1956
      Hagedorn, D.J. and E.W. Hanson, 1951
      Hagedorn, D.J. and J.C. Walker, 1949, 1954
      Hanson, E.W. and D.J. Hagedorn, 1954, 1956
      Osborn, H.T., 1937
   V. soybean new disease *
      Dunleavy, John, 1957
   V. subterranean clover mosaic
      Aitken, Y. and B.J. Grieve, 1943
   V. tobacco ring spot
      Fenne, S.B., 1931
      Henderson, R.G., 1934
      Pierce, W.H., 1934
      Pound, Glenn S., 1949
      Rich, Saul, 1940
      Stubbs, M.W., 1937
   V. tobacco streak
      Fulton, Robert W., 1948
      Thomas, H. Rex and W.J. Zaumeyer, 1950
   V. Wisconsin pea streak
      Hagedorn, D.J. and J.C. Walker, 1949, 1954
M. alba var. annua, Coe
   V. lucerne dwarf
      Freitag, J.H., 1951
   V. pea mosaic
      Murphy, D.M. and W.H. Pierce, 1937
M. altissima, Thuill.
   V. clover big vein
      Black, L.M., 1951
M. dentata, (Waldst. & Kit.) Pers.
   V. clover big vein
      Black, L.M., 1951
M. indica, (L.) All.
   V. bean yellow mosaic
      Hagedorn, D.J. and E.W. Hanson, 1953
   V. beet curly top
      Giddings, N.J., 1944
      Severin, Henry H.P. and Charles F. Henderson, 1928
   V. beet mosaic
      Bennett, C.W., 1949
   V. beet yellows
      Roland, G. and J. Tahon, 1961
   V. clover big vein
      Black, L.M., 1951
   V. lucerne dwarf
      Freitag, J.H., 1951
   V. lucerne mosaic
      Hagedorn, D.J. and E.W. Hanson, 1953
      Kreitlow, K.W. and W.C. Price, 1949
      Snyder, William C. and Saul Rich, 1942
   V. pea mosaic
      Murphy, D.M. and W.H. Pierce, 1937
   V. prunus B *
      Fulton, Robert W., 1957
   V. red clover vein mosaic
      Hagedorn, D.J. and E.W. Hanson, 1953
   V. subterranean clover mosaic
      Aitken, Y. and B.J. Grieve, 1943
   V. tobacco ring spot
      LeBeau, F.J., 1947
      Pound, Glenn S., 1949

M. indica, (L.) All. (cont.)
   V. tobacco streak
      Diachun, Stephen and W.D. Valleau, 1950
M. officinalis, (L.) Lam.
   V. bean Montana *
      Afanasiev, M.M. and H.E. Morris, 1946
   V. bean yellow mosaic
      Afanasiev, M.M. and H.E. Morris, 1952
      Baggett, James R., 1957
      Conover, Robert A., 1948
      Grogan, Raymond G. and J.C. Walker, 1948
      Hagedorn, D.J. and E.W. Hanson, 1957
      Hagedorn, D.J. and J.C. Walker, 1950, 1954
      Pierce, W.H., 1935
      Zaumeyer, W.J. and B.L. Wade, 1935
   V. clover big vein
      Black, L.M., 1951
   V. cucumber mosaic
      Hagedorn, D.J., 1950, 1954
      Whipple, O.C. and J.C. Walker, 1941
   V. lucerne dwarf
      Freitag, J.H., 1951
      Hagedorn, D.J. and E.W. Hanson, 1957
   V. lucerne mosaic
      Kreitlow, K.W. and W.C. Price, 1949
   V. pea enation mosaic
      Hagedorn, D.J. and J.C. Walker, 1954
      McEwen, F.L. and W.T. Schroeder, 1956
      Stubbs, M.W., 1936, 1937
   V. pea mosaic
      Hagedorn, D.J., 1948
      Hagedorn, D.J. and J.C. Walker, 1954
   V. pea mottle
      Johnson, Folke and Leon K. Jones, 1937
   V. pea mosaic
      Murphy, D.M. and W.H. Pierce, 1937
      Pierce, W.H., 1935
      Stubbs, M.W., 1936, 1937
   V. prunus B *
      Fulton, Robert W., 1957
   V. red clover vein mosaic
      Graves, Clinton H., Jr. and D.J. Hagedorn, 1956
      Hagedorn, D.J. and E.W. Hanson, 1957
      Hagedorn, D.J. and J.C. Walker, 1949, 1954
   V. tobacco mosaic
      Holmes, Francis O., 1946
   V. tobacco ring spot
      Henderson, R.G., 1934
      Henderson, R.G. and S.A. Wingard, 1931
      Stubbs, M.W., 1937
      Wingard, S.A., 1928
   V. tobacco streak
      Fulton, Robert W., 1948
   V. Wisconsin pea streak
      Hagedorn, D.J. and J.C. Walker, 1949, 1954
      Skotland, C.B., 1953
      Skotland, C.B. and D.J. Hagedorn, 1954
M. polonica, Pers.
   V. clover big vein
      Black, L.M., 1951
M. spp.
   V. bean yellow mosaic
      McLarty, H.R., 1920
   V. lucerne mosaic
      Kreitlow, K.W. and W.C. Price, 1948
   V. tobacco streak
      (K.M. Smith, 1957) R.E. Fitzpatrick, et al., 1958
M. suaveolens, Ledeb.
   V. clover big vein
      Black, L.M., 1951
   V. lucerne mosaic
      Kreitlow, K.W. and W.C. Price, 1949
M. taurica, (Bieb.) Ser.
   V. clover big vein
      Black, L.M., 1951
M. tommasinii, Jord.
   V. clover big vein
      Black, L.M., 1951
M. wolgica, Poir.
   V. clover big vein
      Black, L.M., 1951

MELOTHRIA L. 1737 (Cucurbitaceae)
M. guadalupensis, (Spreng.) Cogn.
 V. cucumber mosaic
  Adsuar, Jose and A. Cruz Miret, 1950
 V. papaw mosaic
  Adsuar, Jose, 1950
 V. prunus B *
  Fulton, Robert W., 1957
 V. prunus E *
  Fulton, Robert W., 1957
 V. prunus G *
  Fulton, Robert W., 1957
M. pendula, L.
 V. muskmelon mosaic
  Anderson, C.W., 1954
 V. prunus A *
  Fulton, Robert W., 1957
 V. prunus B *
  Fulton, Robert W., 1957
 V. prunus E *
  Fulton, Robert W., 1957
 V. watermelon mosaic
  Anderson, C.W., 1954
M. scabra, Naud.
 V. cucumber mosaic
  Jagger, I.C., 1918
M. spp.
 V. watermelon mosaic
  Anderson, C.W., 1952

MENTHA ((Tourn.)) L. 1735 (Labiatae)
M. spicata, L.
 V. tobacco mosaic
  Holmes, Francis O., 1946
M. spp.
 V. lucerne dwarf
  Freitag, J.H., 1951

MERREMIA Dennst. 1818 (Convolvulaceae)
M. sibirica, (Pers.) Hall. f.
 V. sweet potato feathery mottle
  Webb, Raymon E., 1954

MERTENSIA Roth 1797 (Boraginaceae)
M. virginica, (L.) DC.
 V. cucumber mosaic
  Nienow, Inez, 1948

MESEMBRYANTHEMUM Dill. ex L. 1735 (Aizoaceae)
M. crystallinum, L.
 V. beet yellows
  Roland, G. and J. Tahon, 1961
 V. cucumber mosaic
  Wellman, F.L., 1935
 V. tobacco mosaic
  Holmes, Francis O., 1946
M. lineare, Thunb.
 V. tobacco mosaic
  Holmes, Francis O., 1946

MICROSERIS D. Don 1832 (Compositae)
M. douglasii, Sch.
 V. beet curly top
  Severin, Henry H.P., 1934

MILLETTIA Wight & Arn. 1834 (Leguminosae)
M. makondensis, Harms
 V. groundnut rosette
  Evans, A.C., 1954

MIMULUS L. 1741 (Scrophulariaceae)
M. cardinalis, Dougl.
 V. aster yellows
  Severin, Henry H.P. and Julius H. Freitag, 1945
M. guttatus, DC.
 V. aster yellows
  Frazier, Norman W. and Henry H.P. Severin, 1945
  Severin, Henry H.P. and Julius H. Freitag, 1945
 V. tomato bushy stunt
  Smith, Kenneth M., 1935
M. luteus, L.
 V. anemone mosaic *
  Hollings, M., 1957

M. luteus, L. (cont.)
 V. aster yellows
  Kunkel, L.O., 1926
 V. beet curly top
  Freitag, Julius H. and Henry H.P. Severin, 1936
 V. cabbage black ring spot
  Hollings, M., 1957
 V. tomato bushy stunt
  (K.M. Smith, 1957) R.E. Fitzpatrick, et al., 1958
M. moschatus, Dougl.
 V. cucumber mosaic
  Price, W.C., 1940
 V. tobacco mosaic
  Holmes, Francis O., 1946
 V. tobacco necrosis
  Price, W.C., 1940
 V. tobacco ring spot
  Price, W.C., 1940
 V. tobacco ring spot no. 2
  Price, W.C., 1940
M. tigrinus, Hort. ex Vilmorin
 V. tobacco mosaic
  Holmes, Francis O., 1946

MIRABILIS Riv. ex L. 1735 (Nyctaginaceae)
M. jalapa, L.
 V. beet curly top
  Freitag, Julius H. and Henry H.P. Severin, 1936
  Severin, Henry H.P. and Julius H. Freitag, 1934
 V. lucerne mosaic
  Price, W.C., 1940
 V. tobacco necrosis
  Price, W.C., 1940
 V. tobacco ring spot
  Price, W.C., 1940
 V. tobacco ring spot no. 2
  Price, W.C., 1940
 V. tobacco streak
  Fulton, Robert W., 1948

MISCANTHUS Anderss. 1855 (Gramineae)
M. sinensis, Anders.
 V. sugarcane mosaic
  Brandes, E.W. and Peter J. Klaphaak, 1923

MODIOLA Moench 1794 (Malvaceae)
M. caroliniana, (L.) G. Don
 V. beet curly top
  Severin, Henry H.P., 1934, 1939
 V. tobacco yellow dwarf
  Helson, G.A.H., 1950

MOLLUGO L. 1737 (Aizoaceae)
M. verticillata, L.
 V. cucumber mosaic
  Faan, Hwei-Chung and James Johnson, 1951
 V. tobacco etch
  Holmes, Francis O., 1946
 V. tobacco mosaic
  Holmes, Francis O., 1938, 1946

MOMORDICA ((Tourn.)) L. .1735 (Cucurbitaceae)
M. balsamina, L.
 V. cucumber mosaic
  Jagger, I.C., 1918
 V. prunus A *
  Fulton, Robert W., 1957
 V. prunus B *
  Fulton, Robert W., 1957
 V. prunus E *
  Fulton, Robert W., 1957
 V. prunus G *
  Fulton, Robert W., 1957
 V. prunus isolates A,E,G *
  Fulton, Robert W., 1957
M. charantia, L.
 V. cucumber green mottle mosaic
  Vasudeva, R.S., S.P. Raychaudhuri and Jagannath Singh, 1949
 V. cucumber mosaic
  Simons, John N., 1957
  Vasudeva, R. Sahai and T.B. Lal, 1943
 V. cucurbit mosaic *
  Doolittle, S.P. and M.N. Walker, 1925

M. charantia, L. (cont.)
  V. muskmelon mosaic
    Anderson, C.W., 1954
  V. prunus B *
    Fulton, Robert W., 1957
  V. squash mosaic
    Freitag, J.H., 1956
M. involucrata, E. Meyer
  V. cucurbit mosaic *
    Doolittle, S.P. and M.N. Walker, 1925

MONOLEPIS Schrad. 1830 (Chenopodiaceae)
M. nuttalliana, (R. & S.) Greene
  V. beet curly top
    Severin, Henry H.P., 1934
  V. beet yellows
    Roland, G. and J. Tahon, 1961
M. trifida, Schrad.
  V. beet yellows
    Roland, G. and J. Tahon, 1961

MUCUNA Adans. 1763 (Leguminosae)
(STIZOLOBIUM) P. Br. 1756
M. pruriens, (L.) DC.
  V. abutilon infectious variegation
    Crandall, Bowen S., 1954
(S. spp.)
  V. abutilon infectious variegation
    Crandall, Bowen S., 1954
  V. tobacco ring spot
    Pierce, W.H., 1934

MUSA L. 1736 (Musaceae)
M. banksii, F. Muell.
  V. cucumber mosaic
    Bernardo, Fernando A. and Dioscoro L. Umali,
    1956
M. cavendishii, Lamb.
  V. cucumber mosaic
    Magee, C.J.P., 1940
    Wellman, F.L., 1934, 1935
M. ensete, Gmel.
  V. cucumber mosaic
    Magee, C.J.P., 1940
M. fehi, Vieill.
  V. banana bunchy top
    (K.M. Smith, 1957) R.E. Fitzpatrick, et al., 1958
M. paradisiaca, L., subsp. sapientum, (L.) Kuntze
  V. cucumber mosaic
    Castillo, Bernardo S., 1952
    Magee, C.J.P., 1940
    Wellman, F.L., 1934, 1935
M. paradisiaca var. cinerea, Blanco
  V. abaca bunchy top
    Ocfemia, Gerardo Offimaria, 1930
M. paradisiaca var. lacatan, Blanco
  V. abaca bunchy top
    Ocfemia, Gerardo Offimaria, 1930
M. paradisiaca var. suaveolens, Blanco
  V. abaca bunchy top
    Ocfemia, Gerardo Offimaria, 1930
M. spp.
  V. banana bunchy top
    Magee, C.J.P., 1940, 1948
M. textilis, Nee
  V. abaca bunchy top
    Calinisan, Melanio R., 1931
    Calinisan, Melanio R. and Crispiniano C.
    Hernandez, 1936
    Ocfemia, G.O., 1926, 1930
    Ocfemia, G.O. and Gabino G. Buhay, 1934
    Ocfemia, G.O., Martin S. Celino and Feliciano J.
    Garcia, 1947
  V. canna mosaic
    Juliano, Jorge P., 1951
    Ocfemia, G.O., Isidro S. Macaspac and Hsieh
    Feng Yuan, 1941
  V. cucumber mosaic
    Bernardo, Fernando A. and Dioscoro L. Umali,
    1956
    Calinisan, Melanio R., 1938
    Celino, Martin S., 1940
    Celino, M.S. and Aureo L. Martinez, 1955, 1956

M. textilis, Nee (cont.)
  V. cucumber mosaic
    Lawas, Orencio M. and William L. Fernandez,
    1949
    Magee, C.J.P., 1940
    Ocfemia, G.O. and Martin S. Celino, 1938
    Ocfemia, G.O., Martin S. Celino and Feliciano
    J. Garcia, 1947
  V. maize mosaic
    Juliano, Jorge P., 1951
  V. sugarcane mosaic
    Lawas, Orencio M. and William L. Fernandez,
    1949
M. textilis x M. balbisiana, Colla.
  V. abaca bunchy top
    Bernardo, Fernando A. and Dioscoro L. Umali,
    1956
  V. cucumber mosaic
    Bernardo, Fernando A. and Dioscoro L. Umali,
    1956
M. textilis x M. banksii, F. Muell.
  V. cucumber mosaic
    Bernardo, Fernando A. and Dioscoro L. Umali,
    1956

MYOSOTIS ((Tourn.)) Dill. ex L. 1735 (Boraginaceae)
M. alpestris, Schmidt
  V. cabbage black ring spot
    Tompkins, C.M., M.W. Gardner and H. Rex
    Thomas, 1938
M. arvensis, Lam.
  V. beet ring spot *
    Harrison, B.D., 1957
  V. raspberry Scottish leaf curl
    Harrison, B.D., 1958
M. scorpioides, L.
  V. aster yellows
    Kunkel, L.O., 1926
    Severin, Henry H.P. and Julius H. Freitag, 1945
  V. beet curly top
    Freitag, Julius H. and Henry H.P. Severin, 1936
  V. tobacco mosaic
    Holmes, Francis O., 1946
M. sylvatica, Hoffm.
  V. cucumber mosaic
    Price, W.C., 1940
  V. tobacco mosaic
    Holmes, Francis O., 1946

MYRICA L. 1735 (Myricaceae)
M. carolinensis, Mill.
  V. bayberry yellows
    Raychaudhuri, S.P., 1952, 1953

NARCISSUS ((Tourn.)) L. 1735 (Amaryllidaceae)
N. jonquilla, L.
  V. onion yellow dwarf
    Henderson, W.J., 1935
N. pallida praecox, Hort. *
  V. narcissus stripe *
    Caldwell, John and Ian W. Prentice, 1943
N. poeticus, L.
  V. (lily) color adding *
    McWhorter, F.P., 1932
  V. (lily) color removing *
    McWhorter, F.P., 1932
  V. tulip breaking
    McWhorter, F.P., 1932
N. pseudo-narcissus, L.
  V. narcissus mosaic
    Haasis, Frank A., 1939
N. spp.
  V. narcissus mosaic
    Blanton, F.S. and F.A. Haasis, 1942
    Haasis, Frank A., 1939
    McWhorter, Frank P. and Freeman Weiss, 1932
  V. narcissus stripe *
    Caldwell, John and Ian W. Prentice, 1943
    Hawker, Lilian E., 1943
N. tazetta, L.
  V. onion yellow dwarf
    Henderson, W.J., 1935

N. triandrus, L.
   V. narcissus stripe *
      Caldwell, John and Ian W. Prentice, 1943

NASTURTIUM L. 1735 (Cruciferae)
N. officinale, R. Br. (Rorippa nasturtium-aquaticum,
(L.) Schinz & Thell.)
   V. cabbage black ring
      Tompkins, C.M., M.W. Gardner and H. Rex
      Thomas, 1937
   V. cucumber mosaic
      (K.M. Smith, 1957) R.E. Fitzpatrick, et al., 1958
   V. turnip yellow mosaic
      (K.M. Smith, 1957) R.E. Fitzpatrick, et al., 1958

NEMESIA Vent. 1803 (Scrophulariaceae)
N. spp.
   V. carrot motley dwarf
      (K.M. Smith, 1957) R.E. Fitzpatrick, et al., 1958
N. strumosa, Benth.
   V. aster yellows
      Kunkel, L.O., 1926
   V. beet curly top
      Freitag, Julius H. and Henry H.P. Severin, 1936
   V. cucumber mosaic
      Price, W.C., 1940
   V. lucerne mosaic
      Price, W.C., 1940
   V. tobacco mosaic
      Holmes, Francis O., 1946
   V. tobacco necrosis
      Price, W.C., 1940
   V. tobacco ring spot
      Price, W.C., 1940
   V. tobacco ring spot no. 2
      Price, W.C., 1940

NEMOPHILA Nutt. ex Barton 1882 (Hydrophyllaceae)
N. maculata, Benth.
   V. aster yellows
      Kunkel, L.O., 1926
   V. beet curly top
      Freitag, Julius H. and Henry H.P. Severin, 1936
      Giddings, N.J., 1944
   V. tobacco etch
      Holmes, Francis O., 1946
   V. tobacco mosaic
      Holmes, Francis O., 1946
N. menziesii, Hook. & Arn., subsp. insignis, Brand.
   V. lucerne mosaic
      Price, W.C., 1940
   V. tobacco etch
      Holmes, Francis O., 1946
   V. tobacco mosaic
      Holmes, Francis O., 1946
   V. tobacco necrosis
      Price, W.C., 1940
   V. tobacco ring spot
      Price, W.C., 1940
   V. tobacco ring spot no. 2
      Hildebrand, E.M., 1942
      Price, W.C., 1940

NEPETA Riv. ex L. 1737 (Labiatae)
N. cataria, L.
   V. cucurbit mosaic *
      Doolittle, S.P. and M.N. Walker, 1925
   V. elm mosaic
      Varney, E.H. and J. Duain Moore, 1952
   V. prunus B *
      Fulton, Robert W., 1957
   V. tobacco mosaic
      Holmes, Francis O., 1946
   V. tobacco streak
      Fulton, Robert W., 1948
   V. tomato spotted wilt
      Milbrath, J.A., 1939
N. mussini, Spreng.
   V. tobacco mosaic
      Holmes, Francis O., 1946

NERIUM L. 1735 (Apocynaceae)
N. oleander, L.
   V. rose mosaic
      Fulton, Robert W., 1952

NESLIA Desv. 1814 (Cruciferae)
N. paniculata, (L.) Desv.
   V. cabbage ring necrosis
      Larson, R.H. and J.C. Walker, 1941
   V. cauliflower mosaic
      Walker, J.C., Francis J. LeBeau and Glenn S.
      Pound, 1945
   V. turnip crinkle
      Broadbent, L. and G.D. Heathcote, 1958
   V. turnip mosaic
      Walker, J.C., Francis J. LeBeau and Glenn S.
      Pound, 1945
   V. turnip yellow mosaic
      Broadbent, L. and G.D. Heathcote, 1958

NICANDRA Adans. 1763 (Solanaceae)
N. physalodes, (L.) Gaertn.
   V. abutilon infectious variegation
      Silberschmidt, K. and L.R. Tommasi, 1956
   V. cucumber mosaic
      Burnett, G., 1934
      Hoggan, Isme A., 1927
      Johnson, E.M., 1930
      Pound, Glenn S. and J.C. Walker, 1948
      Wellman, F.L., 1935
   V. datura rugose leaf curl
      (K.M. Smith, 1957) R.E. Fitzpatrick, et al., 1958
   V. euphorbia mosaic
      Costa, A.S. and C.W. Bennett, 1950
   V. lucerne mosaic
      Price, W.C., 1940
   V. (physalis) mosaic *
      Fernow, K.H., 1923
   V. potato A
      Bagnall, R.H., R.H. Larson and J.C. Walker,
      1956
      MacLachlan, D.S. and R.H. Larson, 1953
      MacLachlan, D.S., R.H. Larson and J.C. Walker,
      1953
   V. potato leaf roll
      Webb, R.E., R.H. Larson and J.C. Walker, 1952
   V. potato X
      Dennis, R.W.G., 1939
      Fernow, K.H., 1923, 1925
      Folsom, Donald and Reiner Bonde, 1937
      Goss, R.W., 1931
      Hoggan, Isme A., 1927
      Johnson, E.M., 1930
      Larson, R.H., 1947
      Smith, J. Henderson, 1928
   V. potato Y
      Bagnall, R.H., R.H. Larson and J.C. Walker,
      1956
      Hoggan, Isme A., 1927
      Koch, K.L., 1933
      Sakimura, K., 1953
   V. red currant ring spot
      Klesser, P.J., 1951
   V. tobacco broad ring spot
      Johnson, James and Robert W. Fulton, 1942
   V. tobacco coarse etch
      Johnson, E.M., 1930
   V. tobacco etch
      Fulton, Robert W., 1941
      Holmes, Francis O., 1946
      Johnson, E.M., 1930
   V. tobacco mosaic
      Crawford, R.F., 1921
      Fulton, Robert W., 1941
      Hoggan, Isme A., 1927
      Holmes, Francis O., 1946
      Jarrett, Phyllis H., 1930
      Johnson, E.M., 1930
   V. tobacco necrosis
      Price, W.C., 1940

N. physalodes, (L.) Gaertn. (cont.)
  V. tobacco ring spot
    Fulton, Robert W., 1941
    Johnson, E.M., 1930
    Wingard, S.A., 1928
  V. tobacco streak
    Fulton, Robert W., 1948
    Johnson, J., 1936
  V. tomato bunchy top
    (K.M. Smith, 1957) R.E. Fitzpatrick, et al., 1958
  V. tomato ring spot
    Samson, R.W. and E.P. Imle, 1942
  V. tomato spotted wilt
    Gardner, M.W. and O.C. Whipple, 1934
  V. turnip mosaic
    Walker, J.C., Francis J. LeBeau and Glenn S.
    Pound, 1945
  V. wild cucumber mosaic *
    Fernow, Karl Hermann, 1925

NICOTIANA L. 1735 (Solanaceae)
N. acuminata, Hook.
  V. tobacco etch
    Holmes, Francis O., 1946
  V. tobacco mosaic
    Adsuar, J. and L. Lopez Matos, 1955
    Caldwell, John, 1932
    Diachun, Stephen and W.D. Valleau, 1954
    Holmes, Francis O., 1929, 1934, 1946
    Jensen, J.H., 1933
    Kunkel, L.O., 1932
  V. tobacco ring spot
    Wingard, S.A., 1928
  V. tobacco streak
    Diachun, Stephen and W.D. Valleau, 1954
  V. tomato spotted wilt
    Gardner, M.W. and O.C. Whipple, 1934
  V. turnip mosaic
    Walker, J.C., Francis J. LeBeau and Glenn S.
    Pound, 1945
N. affinis, T. Moore
  V. chrysanthemum B (mild mosaic) *
    Hollings, M., 1957
  V. cucumber mosaic
    Govier, D.A., 1957
  V. potato X
    Smith, J. Henderson, 1928
  V. tobacco mosaic
    Jarrett, Phyllis H., 1930
    McKinney, H.H., 1935
  V. tomato ring spot
    Samson, R.W. and E.P. Imle, 1942
N. alata, Link & Otto
  V. cucumber mosaic
    Price, W.C., 1941
  V. lucerne mosaic
    Price, W.C., 1940
  V. potato X
    Dennis, R.W.G., 1939
  V. potato Y
    Smith, Kenneth M. and R.W.G. Dennis, 1940
  V. tobacco etch
    Holmes, Francis O., 1946
  V. tobacco mosaic
    Diachun, Stephen and W.D. Valleau, 1954
    Holmes, F.O., 1934, 1946
    Kunkel, L.O., 1932
    Weber, Paul V.V., 1951
  V. tobacco ring spot
    Steere, Russell L., 1956
  V. tobacco ring spot no. 2
    Wilkinson, R.E., 1952
  V. tobacco streak
    Diachun, Stephen and W.D. Valleau, 1954
  V. tomato spotted wilt
    Gardner, M.W. and O.C. Whipple, 1934
N. alata var. grandiflora, Comes
  V. beet curly top
    Freitag, Julius H. and Henry H.P. Severin, 1936
  V. chilli (pepper) mosaic
    Dale, W.T., 1954
  V. delphinium ring spot
    Severin, Henry H.P. and R.C. Dickson, 1942

N. alata var. grandiflora, Comes (cont.)
  V. turnip mosaic
    Walker, J.C., Francis J. LeBeau and Glenn S.
    Pound, 1945
N. arentsii, Goodspeed
  V. tobacco mosaic
    Diachun, Stephen and W.D. Valleau, 1954
  V. tobacco streak
    Diachun, Stephen and W.D. Valleau, 1954
N. atropurpureum, Hort. *
  V. tomato spotted wilt
    (K.M. Smith, 1957) R.E. Fitzpatrick, et al., 1958
N. attenuata, Torr. ex S. Wats.
  V. tobacco mosaic
    Diachun, Stephen and W.D. Valleau, 1954
  V. tobacco streak
    Diachun, Stephen and W.D. Valleau, 1954
N. australasiae, R. Br.
  V. tobacco yellow dwarf
    Hill, A.V. and M. Mandryk, 1954
N. benavidesii, Goodspeed
  V. tobacco mosaic
    Diachun, Stephen and W.D. Valleau, 1954
  V. tobacco streak
    Diachun, Stephen and W.D. Valleau, 1954
N. benthamiana, Domin
  V. prunus A *
    Fulton, Robert W., 1957
  V. prunus B *
    Fulton, Robert W., 1957
  V. prunus E *
    Fulton, Robert W., 1957
  V. rose mosaic
    Fulton, Robert W., 1952
  V. tobacco mosaic
    Adsuar, J. and L. Lopez Matos, 1955
    Diachun, Stephen and W.D. Valleau, 1954
  V. tobacco streak
    Diachun, Stephen and W.D. Valleau, 1947, 1954
N. bigelovii, S. Wats.
  V. beet yellows
    Roland, G. and J. Tahon, 1961
  V. tobacco etch
    Holmes, Francis O., 1946
  V. tobacco mosaic
    Adsuar, J. and L. Lopez Matos, 1955
    Diachun, Stephen and W.D. Valleau, 1954
    Holmes, F.O., 1934, 1946
    Stover, R.H., 1951
  V. tobacco streak
    Diachun, Stephen and W.D. Valleau, 1954
  V. tomato spotted wilt
    (K.M. Smith, 1957) R.E. Fitzpatrick, et al., 1958
N. bigelovii var. multivalvis, Gray *
  V. potato Y
    Roque, Arturo and Jose Adsuar, 1941
  V. turnip crinkle
    Broadbent, L. and G.D. Heathcote, 1958
  V. turnip rosette *
    Broadbent, L. and G.D. Heathcote, 1958
N. bigelovii var. quadrivalvis, Pursh *
  V. cucumber mosaic
    Price, W.C., 1940, 1941
  V. potato Y
    Roque, Arturo and Jose Adsuar, 1941
N. bigelovii var. quadrivalvis x N. glutinosa, L.
  V. tobacco mosaic
    Holmes, F.O., 1934
N. bigelovii var. quadrivalvis x N. sanderae, W. Wats.
  V. tobacco mosaic
    Holmes, F.O., 1934
N. bigelovii var. quadrivalvis x N. tabacum, L.
  V. tobacco mosaic
    Holmes, F.O., 1934
N. bonariensis, Lehm.
  V. tobacco etch
    Holmes, Francis O., 1946
  V. tobacco mosaic
    Adsuar, J. and L. Lopez Matos, 1955
    Diachun, Stephen and W.D. Valleau, 1954
    Holmes, Francis O., 1946
  V. tobacco streak
    Diachun, Stephen and W.D. Valleau, 1954

N. calyciflora *
  V. tomato spotted wilt
    (K.M. Smith, 1957) R.E. Fitzpatrick, et al., 1958
N. caudigera, Phil.
  V. tobacco etch
    Holmes, Francis O., 1946
  V. tobacco mosaic
    Holmes, Francis O., 1946
N. caudigera x N. acuminata, Hook.
  V. tobacco mosaic
    Holmes, F.O., 1934
N. chinensis, Fisch.
  V. chilli (pepper) mosaic
    Dale, W.T., 1954
  V. tobacco mosaic
    Ferguson, I.A.C., 1951
  V. tomato spotted wilt
    (K.M. Smith, 1957) R.E. Fitzpatrick, et al., 1958
  V. vaccinium false blossom
    (K.M. Smith, 1957) R.E. Fitzpatrick, et al., 1958
N. clevelandi, A. Gray
  V. beet mosaic
    Bennett, C.W., 1949
  V. beet yellows
    Roland, G. and J. Tahon, 1961
  V. tobacco etch
    Holmes, Francis O., 1946
  V. tobacco mosaic
    Adsuar, J. and L. Lopez Matos, 1955
    Diachun, Stephen and W.D. Valleau, 1954
    Holmes, F.O., 1934, 1946
  V. tobacco ring spot
    Wingard, S.A., 1928
  V. tobacco streak
    Diachun, Stephen and W.D. Valleau, 1947, 1954
N. cordifolia, Phil.
  V. tobacco mosaic
    Diachun, Stephen and W.D. Valleau, 1954
  V. tobacco streak
    Diachun, Stephen and W.D. Valleau, 1954
N. corymbosa, Remy
  V. tobacco mosaic
    Diachun, Stephen and W.D. Valleau, 1954
  V. tobacco streak
    Diachun, Stephen and W.D. Valleau, 1954
N. debneyi, Domin
  V. potato M *
    Bagnall, R.H. and R.H. Larson, 1957
    Bagnall, R.H., R.H. Larson and J.C. Walker, 1956
  V. potato paracrinkle
    Bagnall, R.H. and R.H. Larson, 1957
    Bagnall, R.H., R.H. Larson and J.C. Walker, 1956
  V. tobacco mosaic
    Adsuar, J. and L. Lopez Matos, 1955
    Diachun, Stephen and W.D. Valleau, 1954
  V. tobacco streak
    Diachun, Stephen and W.D. Valleau, 1954
N. digluta, Clausen & Goodspeed *
  V. tobacco etch
    Holmes, Francis O., 1946
  V. tobacco mosaic
    Holmes, Francis O., 1938, 1946
N. digluta x N. tabacum, L.
  V. tobacco mosaic
    Holmes, Francis O., 1938
    Price, W.C. and S.B. Fenne, 1951
  V. tobacco necrosis
    Price, W.C., 1938
  V. tobacco ring spot
    Tall, M.G., W.C. Price and Kenneth Wertman, 1949
  V. tobacco ring spot no. 2
    Tall, M.G., W.C. Price and Kenneth Wertman, 1949
N. excelsior, Black
  V. tobacco yellow dwarf
    Hill, A.V. and M. Mandryk, 1954
N. exigua, Wheeler
  V. tobacco mosaic
    Diachun, Stephen and W.D. Valleau, 1954
  V. tobacco streak
    Diachun, Stephen and W.D. Valleau, 1954

N. forgetiana, Hort. Sand. ex Hemsl.
  V. rose mosaic
    Fulton, Robert W., 1952
N. fragrans, Hook.
  V. rose mosaic
    Fulton, Robert W., 1952
  V. tobacco mosaic
    Diachun, Stephen and W.D. Valleau, 1954
  V. tobacco streak
    Diachun, Stephen and W.D. Valleau, 1954
N. glauca, Graham
  V. beet curly top
    Bennett, C.W., 1934, 1937
    Bennett, C.W. and Aziz Tanrisever, 1957
    Costa, A.S., 1952
    Giddings, N.J., 1944
    Severin, Henry H.P., 1934, 1939
  V. cucumber mosaic
    Hoggan, Isme A., 1927
    Johnson, J., 1926, 1927
    Nariani, T.K. and Nirmaljit Singh, 1952
    Price, W.C., 1941
  V. datura distortion mosaic
    Capoor, S.P. and P.M. Varma, 1952
  V. dodder latent mosaic
    Bennett, C.W., 1944, 1949
  V. henbane mosaic
    Hamilton, Marion A., 1932
  V. nicotiana glauca light green mosaic *
    McKinney, H.H., 1929
  V. petunia mosaic
    Johnson, J., 1926, 1927
  V. potato stem mottle
    (K.M. Smith, 1957) R.E. Fitzpatrick, et al., 1958
  V. potato X
    Hoggan, Isme A., 1927
  V. potato Y
    Hoggan, Isme A., 1927
    Johnson, James, 1927
  V. potato yellow dwarf
    Black, L.M., 1938
  V. red currant ring spot
    Klesser, P.J., 1951
  V. tobacco etch
    Holmes, Francis O., 1946
  V. tobacco green mosaic
    McKinney, H.H., 1929
  V. tobacco leaf curl
    (K.M. Smith, 1957) R.E. Fitzpatrick, et al., 1958
  V. tobacco mosaic
    Allard, H.A., 1917
    Diachun, Stephen and W.D. Valleau, 1954
    Doolittle, S.P. and F.S. Beecher, 1942
    Hoggan, Isme A., 1927
    Holmes, F.O., 1934, 1946
    Jensen, J.H., 1933
    Johnson, J., 1926, 1927
    Keener, Paul D., 1954
    McKinney, H.H., 1928, 1929, 1935, 1943, 1952
  V. tobacco ring spot
    Grogan, R.G. and W.C. Schnathorst, 1955
    Smith, Kenneth M., 1931
  V. tobacco streak
    Diachun, Stephen and W.D. Valleau, 1947, 1954
  V. tobacco yellow dwarf
    Hill, A.V., 1950
    Hill, A.V. and M. Mandryk, 1954
  V. tomato big bud
    Hill, A.V. and M. Mandryk, 1954
  V. tomato spotted wilt
    Gardner, M.W., C.M. Tompkins and O.C. Whipple, 1935
    Smith, Kenneth M., 1932
N. glauca x N. langsdorffii, Weinm.
  V. tobacco mosaic
    Holmes, F.O., 1934
N. glutinosa, L.
  V. anemone mosaic *
    Hollings, M., 1957
  V. apple mosaic
    Yarwood, C.E., 1955
  V. arabis mosaic
    Smith, Kenneth M. and Roy Markham, 1944

Nicotiana glutinosa, L. (cont.)
V. atropa belladonna mosaic
(K.M. Smith, 1957) R.E. Fitzpatrick, et al., 1958
V. beet curly top
Bennett, C.W. and A.S. Costa, 1949
Bennett, C.W. and Aziz Tanrisever, 1957
Costa, A.S., 1952
Fulton, Robert W., 1955
Giddings, N.J., 1944, 1947, 1954
V. beet ring spot *
Harrison, B.D., 1957
V. cabbage black ring spot
Hamlyn, Brenda M.G., 1953
Hollings, M., 1957
Tompkins, C.M., M.W. Gardner and H. Rex
Thomas, 1937, 1938
V. cabbage ring necrosis
Larson, R.H. and J.C. Walker, 1940, 1941
V. carnation ring spot
Kassanis, B., 1955
V. chilli (pepper) mosaic
Dale, W.T., 1954
Jha, Ashrafi and S.P. Raychaudhuri, 1956
V. chilli veinbanding
Simons, John N., 1956
V. chrysanthemum B (mild mosaic) *
Hollings, M., 1957
V. chrysanthemum latent *
Hollings, M., 1957
V. crucifer ring spot *
Smith, Kenneth M., 1935
V. cucumber mosaic
Adsuar, Jose and A. Cruz Miret, 1950
Ainsworth, G.C., 1935, 1940
Anderson, C.W., 1951, 1955
Anderson, C.W. and M.K. Corbett, 1957
Berkeley, G.H., 1951, 1953
Berkeley, G.H. and J.H. Tremaine, 1954
Bhargava, K.S., 1951
Black, L.M. and W.C. Price, 1940
Bridgmon, G.H. and J.C. Walker, 1952
Costa, A.S., 1944
Doolittle, S.P. and W.J. Zaumeyer, 1953
Fulton, Robert W., 1941
Govier, D.A., 1957
Hagedorn, D.J. and J.C. Walker, 1954
Hoggan, Isme A., 1927, 1935
Johnson, J., 1926, 1927
Lindberg, G.D., D.H. Hall and J.C. Walker, 1956
Nariani, T.K. and Nirmaljit Singh, 1952
Nienow, Inez, 1948
Pound, Glenn S. and J.C. Walker, 1948
Price, W.C., 1934, 1941
Roberts, Daniel A., 1952
Silberschmidt, K., 1955
Sill, W.H., Jr. and J.C. Walker, 1952
Simons, John N., 1955, 1957
Smith, Kenneth M., 1935
Storey, I.F., 1939
Wellman, F.L., 1934, 1935
Whipple, O.C. and J.C. Walker, 1941
V. datura distortion mosaic
Capoor, S.P. and P.M. Varma, 1952
V. delphinium ring spot
Severin, Henry H.P. and R.C. Dickson, 1942
V. dodder latent mosaic
Bennett, C.W., 1949
V. eggplant mosaic
Dale, W.T., 1954
Ferguson, I.A.C., 1951
V. henbane mosaic
Hamilton, Marion A., 1932
Hollings, M., 1955
V. lily ring spot
(K.M. Smith, 1957) R.E. Fitzpatrick, et al., 1958
V. lovage mosaic
Smith, Kenneth M. and Roy Markham, 1944
V. lucerne mosaic
Berkeley, G.H., 1947
Black, L.M. and W.C. Price, 1940
Dykstra, T.P., 1939
Houston, Byron R. and John W. Oswald, 1953
Kreitlow, K.W. and W.C. Price, 1948, 1949
Oswald, John W., 1950

N. glutinosa, L. (cont.)
V. lucerne mosaic
Pierce, W.H., 1934
Severin, Henry H.P., 1942
Thomas, H. Rex, 1951
Zaumeyer, W.J., 1953
V. lucerne witches' broom
Helms, Katie, 1957
V. nicotiana glutinosa mosaic *
Allard, H.A., 1916
Fernow, Karl Hermann, 1925
V. nicotiana glutinosa root necrosis *
Cetas, Robert C. and A. Frank Ross, 1952
V. petunia mosaic
Johnson, J., 1926, 1927
V. physalis pubescens mosaic *
Walker, M.N., 1925
V. potato A
Vasudeva, R. Sahai and C.S. Ramamoorthy, 1946
V. potato aucuba mosaic
Bagnall, R.H., R.H. Larson and J.C. Walker,
1956
Black, L.M. and W.C. Price, 1940
Dykstra, T.P., 1939
V. potato leaf roll
Webb, R.E., R.H. Larson and J.C. Walker, 1952
V. potato stem mottle
(K.M. Smith, 1957) R.E. Fitzpatrick, et al., 1958
V. potato X
Ainsworth, G.C., 1933, 1934
Ainsworth, G.C., G.H. Berkeley and J. Caldwell,
1934
Black, L.M. and W.C. Price, 1940
Cockerham, George, 1943
Dennis, R.W.G., 1939
Fernow, Karl Hermann, 1925
Fulton, Robert W., 1941
Hoggan, Isme A., 1927
Johnson, James, 1927
Larson, R.H., 1944, 1947
Matthews, R.E.F., 1949
Roberts, Daniel A., 1952
Timian, Roland G., W.J. Hooker and C.E.
Peterson, 1955
Thompson, A.D., 1956
Vasudeva, R. Sahai and T.B. Lal, 1944
V. potato Y
Alvarez-Garcia, L.A. and Jose Adsuar, 1943
Bald, J.G. and D.O. Norris, 1945
Bawden, F.C. and B. Kassanis, 1951
Cockerham, George, 1943
Conover, Robert A. and Robert W. Fulton, 1953
Corbett, M.K., 1955
Darby, J.F., R.H. Larson and J.C. Walker, 1951
Hamilton, Marion A., 1932
Hoggan, Isme A., 1927
Hutton, E.M. and J.W. Peak, 1952
Johnson, James, 1927
Koch, K.L., 1933
Peterson, Paul D. and H.H. McKinney, 1938
Roque, Arturo and Jose Adsuar, 1941
Ross, A. Frank, 1948, 1949, 1950, 1953
Sakimura, K., 1953
Simons, J.N., Robert A. Conover and James M.
Walter, 1956
Smith, Kenneth M. and R.W.G. Dennis, 1940
Vasudeva, R. Sahai and T.B. Lal, 1945
Watson, Marion A., 1956
V. potato yellow dwarf
Black, L.M., 1938
V. radish mosaic
Tompkins, C.M., 1939
V. ranunculus mosaic
(K.M. Smith, 1957) R.E. Fitzpatrick, et al., 1958
V. raspberry Scottish leaf curl
Cadman, C.H., 1956
V. raspberry yellow dwarf *
Harrison, B.D., 1958
V. red currant ring spot
Klesser, P.J., 1951
V. rose mosaic
Fulton, Robert W., 1952
V. sweet potato mosaic
Elmer, O.H., 1957

Nicotiana glutinosa, L. (cont.)
V. tobacco bergerac ring spot
(K.M. Smith, 1957) R.E. Fitzpatrick, et al., 1958
V. tobacco broad ring spot
Johnson, James and Robert W. Fulton, 1942
V. tobacco broken ring spot
Smith, Kenneth M. and Roy Markham, 1944
V. tobacco etch
Anderson, C.W., 1954
Fulton, Robert W., 1941
Holmes, Francis O., 1942, 1946
V. tobacco leaf curl
Pal, B.P. and R.K. Tandon, 1937
Vasudeva, R.S. and J. Sam Raj, 1948
V. tobacco mosaic
Adsuar, J. and L. Lopez Matos, 1955
Ainsworth, G.C., 1933, 1937
Ainsworth, G.C., G.H. Berkeley and J. Caldwell, 1934
Anderson, C.W. and M.K. Corbett, 1957
Bawden, F.C. and F.M. Roberts, 1948
Berkeley, G.H., 1951
Best, Rupert J. and Geoffrey Samuel, 1936
Boyle, John S. and David C. Wharton, 1956, 1957
Caldwell, John, 1932
Conover, Robert A. and Robert W. Fulton, 1953
Costa, A.S., 1944
Cox, C.E. and L.O. Weaver, 1950
Desjardins, P.R., J.M. Wallace and R.J. Drake, 1954
Diachun, Stephen and W.D. Valleau, 1954
Doering, G.R., W.C. Price and S.B. Fenne, 1957
Doolittle, S.P. and F.S. Beecher, 1942
Dykstra, T.P., 1939
Hoggan, Isme A., 1927
Holmes, Francis O., 1929, 1934, 1936, 1941, 1946
Jensen, J.H., 1933, 1936, 1937
Johnson, J., 1926, 1927
Kendrick, J.B., Jr., L.D. Anderson and R.C. Dickson, 1951
Kunkel, L.O., 1932
McKinney, H.H., 1935, 1943, 1952
Nagaich, B.B. and H.H. Thornberry, 1957
Nolla, J.A.B., 1934
Norval, I.P., 1938
Peterson, Paul D. and H.H. McKinney, 1938
Pierce, W.H., 1934
Price, W.C. and S.B. Fenne, 1951
Raychaudhuri, S.P., 1952
Roberts, Daniel A., 1952
Sheffield, F.M.L., 1936
Siegel, Albert and Sam G. Wildman, 1954
Smith, Kenneth M., 1935
Spencer, E.L., 1935
Stover, R.H., 1951
Walker, M.N., 1924, 1925
Walters, H.J., 1952
Weber, Paul V.V., 1951
Woods, M.W. and Richard V. Eck, 1948
V. tobacco mottle
(K.M. Smith, 1957) R.E. Fitzpatrick, et al., 1958
V. tobacco necrosis
Bawden, F.C. and B. Kassanis, 1947
Kassanis, B., 1949, 1955
Price, W.C., 1938
Price, W.C., Frank P. McWhorter and Betty H. Steranka, 1950
Price, W.C. and Ralph W.G. Wyckoff, 1939
V. tobacco ring spot
Anderson, C.W., 1954
Benedict, W.G., 1955
Berkeley, G.H., 1951, 1953
Bridgmon, G.H. and J.C. Walker, 1952
Cheo, Pen Ching and W.J. Zaumeyer, 1952
Cooper, W.E., 1949
(K.M. Smith, 1957) R.E. Fitzpatrick, et al., 1958
Fromme, F.D., S.A. Wingard and C.N. Priode, 1927
Fulton, Robert W., 1941
Grogan, R.G., Roy Bardin and W.C. Schnathorst, 1954
Grogan, R.G. and W.C. Schnathorst, 1955
Pierce, W.H., 1934
Pound, Glenn S., 1949

N. glutinosa, L. (cont.)
V. tobacco ring spot
Wingard, S.A., 1928
V. tobacco ring spot no. 2
Hildebrand, E.M., 1942
Price, W.C., 1936
V. tobacco streak
Diachun, Stephen and W.D. Valleau, 1954
Fulton, Robert W., 1941
Johnson, J., 1936
Thomas, H. Rex and W.J. Zaumeyer, 1950
V. tobacco vein distorting
(K.M. Smith, 1957) R.E. Fitzpatrick, et al., 1958
V. tobacco yellow dwarf
Hill, A.V., 1950
Hill, A.V. and M. Mandryk, 1954
V. tomato aspermy
Blencowe, J.W. and John Caldwell, 1949
Brierley, Philip, Floyd F. Smith and S.P. Doolittle, 1955
Hollings, M., 1955
Ocfemia, G.O., 1956
Wilkinson, John, 1952
V. tomato big bud
Helms, Katie, 1957
Hill, A.V. and M. Mandryk, 1954
V. tomato black ring
(K.M. Smith, 1957) R.E. Fitzpatrick, et al., 1958
V. tomato bunchy top
(K.M. Smith, 1957) R.E. Fitzpatrick, et al., 1958
V. tomato bushy stunt
Bawden, F.C. and F.M. Roberts, 1948
Smith, Kenneth M., 1935
Steere, Russell L., 1953
V. tomato ring spot
Bennett, C.W., 1944
Varney, E.H. and J. Duain Moore, 1952
V. tomato shoestring *
Doering, G.R., W.C. Price and S.B. Fenne, 1957
V. tomato spotted wilt
Ainsworth, G.C., 1933
Ainsworth, G.C., G.H. Berkeley and J. Caldwell, 1934
Berkeley, G.H., 1935
Black, L.M., M.K. Brakke and A.E. Vatter, 1952
Ferguson, I.A.C., 1951
Gardner, M.W. and O.C. Whipple, 1934
Holmes, Francis O., 1948
Kendrick, J.B., Jr., L.D. Anderson and R.C. Dickson, 1951
Milbrath, J.A., 1939
Norris, D.O., 1951
Sakimura, K., 1940
Shapovalov, M., 1934
Smith, Kenneth M., 1932
Snyder, W.C. and H. Rex Thomas, 1936
Whipple, O.C., 1936
V. tomato V-52-1
Miller, Patrick M., 1953
V. tropaeolum mosaic
Silberschmidt, Karl, 1953
V. tropaeolum ring spot
(K.M. Smith, 1957) R.E. Fitzpatrick, et al., 1958
V. tulip white streak
(K.M. Smith, 1957) R.E. Fitzpatrick, et al., 1958
V. turnip mosaic
Bennett, C.W., 1944
Berkeley, G.H. and J.H. Tremaine, 1954
Berkeley, G.H. and M. Weintraub, 1952
Hoggan, I.A. and J. Johnson, 1935
LeBeau, Francis J. and J.C. Walker, 1945
Pound, Glenn S., 1948
Pound, Glenn S. and Lewis G. Weathers, 1953
Tompkins, C.M., 1938, 1939
Tompkins, C.M. and H. Rex Thomas, 1938
Walker, J.C., Francis J. LeBeau and Glenn S. Pound, 1945
V. vaccinium false blossom
Kunkel, L.O., 1945
V. wild cucumber mosaic *
Fernow, Karl Hermann, 1925
N. glutinosa x N. langsdorffii, Weinm.
V. tobacco mosaic
Holmes, F.O., 1934

Nicotiana glutinosa, L. x N. tabacum, L.
  V. tobacco mosaic
    Fulton, Robert W., 1941
N. goodspeedii, Wheeler
  V. tobacco mosaic
    Adsuar, J. and L. Lopez Matos, 1955
    Diachun, Stephen and W.D. Valleau, 1954
  V. tobacco streak
    Diachun, Stephen and W.D. Valleau, 1954
N. gossei, Domin
  V. tobacco mosaic
    Adsuar, J. and L. Lopez Matos, 1955
    Diachun, Stephen and W.D. Valleau, 1954
  V. tobacco streak
    Diachun, Stephen and W.D. Valleau, 1947, 1954
  V. tobacco yellow dwarf
    Hill, A.V. and M. Mandryk, 1954
N. knightiana, Goodspeed
  V. tobacco mosaic
    Diachun, Stephen and W.D. Valleau, 1954
  V. tobacco streak
    Diachun, Stephen and W.D. Valleau, 1954
N. langsdorffii, Weinm.
  V. cabbage black ring spot
    (K.M. Smith, 1957) R.E. Fitzpatrick, et al., 1958
    Tompkins, C.M., M.W. Gardner and H. Rex
    Thomas, 1938
  V. cabbage ring necrosis
    Larson, R.H. and J.C. Walker, 1940, 1941
  V. crucifer ring spot *
    Smith, Kenneth M., 1935
  V. cucumber mosaic
    Price, W.C., 1934
    Smith, Kenneth M., 1935
  V. lovage mosaic
    Smith, Kenneth M. and Roy Markham, 1944
  V. lucerne mosaic
    Price, W.C., 1940
    Severin, Henry H.P., 1942
  V. potato Y
    Peterson, Paul D. and H.H. McKinney, 1938
    Smith, Kenneth M. and R.W.G. Dennis, 1940
  V. potato yellow dwarf
    Black, L.M., 1938
  V. radish mosaic
    Tompkins, C.M., 1939
  V. tobacco etch
    Holmes, Francis O., 1946
  V. tobacco green mosaic
    Peterson, Paul D. and H.H. McKinney, 1938
  V. tobacco mosaic
    Ainsworth, G.C., 1937
    Diachun, Stephen and W.D. Valleau, 1954
    Holmes, F.O., 1929, 1934, 1936, 1946
    Jensen, J.H., 1933, 1936
    Kunkel, L.O., 1932, 1934
    Peterson, Paul D. and H.H. McKinney, 1938
    Stover, R.H., 1951
  V. tobacco necrosis
    Price, W.C., 1940
  V. tobacco ring spot
    Fromme, F.D., S.A. Wingard and C.N. Priode,
    1927
    Wingard, S.A., 1928
  V. tobacco ring spot no. 2
    Hildebrand, E.M., 1942
    Price, W.C., 1936
  V. tobacco streak
    Diachun, Stephen and W.D. Valleau, 1954
  V. tomato black ring
    (K.M. Smith, 1957) R.E. Fitzpatrick, et al., 1958
  V. tomato bushy stunt
    (K.M. Smith, 1957) R.E. Fitzpatrick, et al., 1958
    Smith, Kenneth M., 1935
  V. tomato spotted wilt
    Gardner, M.W. and O.C. Whipple, 1934
  V. turnip mosaic
    Tompkins, C.M., 1939
  V. vaccinium false blossom
    Kunkel, L.O., 1945
N. langsdorffii x N. sanderae, W. Wats.
  V. tobacco mosaic
    Holmes, F.O., 1934

N. linearis, Phil.
  V. tobacco streak
    Diachun, Stephen and W.D. Valleau, 1954
N. longiflora, Cav.
  V. lucerne mosaic
    Price, W.C., 1940
  V. tobacco etch
    Holmes, Francis O., 1946
  V. tobacco mosaic
    Adsuar, J. and L. Lopez Matos, 1955
    Diachun, Stephen and W.D. Valleau, 1954
    Holmes, F.O., 1934, 1946
    Stover, R.H., 1951
    Weber, Paul V.V., 1951
  V. tobacco ring spot
    Cheo, Pen Ching and W.J. Zaumeyer, 1952
    Wingard, S.A., 1928
  V. tobacco streak
    Diachun, Stephen and W.D. Valleau, 1954
  V. tomato spotted wilt
    (K.M. Smith, 1957) R.E. Fitzpatrick, et al., 1958
  V. turnip mosaic
    Walker, J.C., Francis J. LeBeau and Glenn S.
    Pound, 1945
N. longiflora x N. alata, Link & Otto
  V. tobacco mosaic
    Weber, Paul V.V., 1951
N. maritima, Wheeler
  V. tobacco mosaic
    Adsuar, J. and L. Lopez Matos, 1955
    Diachun, Stephen and W.D. Valleau, 1954
  V. tobacco streak
    Diachun, Stephen and W.D. Valleau, 1954
  V. tobacco yellow dwarf
    Hill, A.V. and M. Mandryk, 1954
N. megalosiphon, Heurck & Meull.
  V. tobacco mosaic
    Adsuar, J. and L. Lopez Matos, 1955
    Diachun, Stephen and W.D. Valleau, 1954
  V. tobacco streak
    Diachun, Stephen and W.D. Valleau, 1947, 1954
N. miersii, Remy
  V. tobacco streak
    Diachun, Stephen and W.D. Valleau, 1947, 1954
N. multivalvis, Lindl.
  V. beet mosaic
    Bennett, C.W., 1949
  V. tobacco mosaic
    (K.M. Smith, 1957) R.E. Fitzpatrick, et al., 1958
  V. tobacco ring spot
    (K.M. Smith, 1957) R.E. Fitzpatrick, et al., 1958
    Wingard, S.A., 1928
  V. turnip mosaic
    LeBeau, Francis J. and J.C. Walker, 1945
    Pound, Glenn S. and Lewis G. Weathers, 1953
    Walker, J.C., Francis J. LeBeau and Glenn S.
    Pound, 1945
N. nesophila, I.M. Johnston
  V. tobacco mosaic
    Diachun, Stephen and W.D. Valleau, 1954
  V. tobacco streak
    Diachun, Stephen and W.D. Valleau, 1954
N. noctiflora, Hook.
  V. potato Y
    Smith, Kenneth M. and R.W.G. Dennis, 1940
N. nudicaulis, S. Wats.
  V. tobacco etch
    Holmes, Francis O., 1946
  V. tobacco mosaic
    Diachun, Stephen and W.D. Valleau, 1954
    Holmes, Francis O., 1946
  V. tobacco streak
    Diachun, Stephen and W.D. Valleau, 1954
  V. turnip mosaic
    Walker, J.C., Francis J. LeBeau and Glenn S.
    Pound, 1945
N. occidentalis, Wheeler
  V. rose mosaic
    Fulton, Robert W., 1952
  V. tobacco mosaic
    Adsuar, J. and L. Lopez Matos, 1955
    Diachun, Stephen and W.D. Valleau, 1954
  V. tobacco streak
    Diachun, Stephen and W.D. Valleau, 1954

Nicotiana otophora, Griseb.
V. potato stem mottle
(K.M. Smith, 1957) R.E. Fitzpatrick, et al., 1958
V. tobacco mosaic
Adsuar, J. and L. Lopez Matos, 1955
Diachun, Stephen and W.D. Valleau, 1954
Holmes, Francis O., 1946
V. tobacco streak
Diachun, Stephen and W.D. Valleau, 1954
N. palmeri, A. Gray
V. dodder latent mosaic
Bennett, C.W., 1944
V. lucerne mosaic
Price, W.C., 1940
V. tobacco mosaic
Adsuar, J. and L. Lopez Matos, 1955
Diachun, Stephen and W.D. Valleau, 1954
Holmes, F.O., 1934, 1946
V. tobacco streak
Diachun, Stephen and W.D. Valleau, 1954
N. paniculata, L.
V. cucumber mosaic
Govier, D.A., 1957
V. lucerne mosaic
Price, W.C., 1940
V. potato yellow dwarf
Black, L.M., 1938
V. tobacco etch
Holmes, Francis O., 1946
V. tobacco mosaic
Adsuar, J. and L. Lopez Matos, 1955
Diachun, Stephen and W.D. Valleau, 1954
Doolittle, S.P. and F.S. Beecher, 1942
Holmes, F.O., 1934, 1946
Jensen, J.H., 1933
Kunkel, L.O., 1932
Woods, M.W. and Richard V. Eck, 1948
V. tobacco ring spot
Fromme, F.D., S.A. Wingard and C.N. Priode, 1927
Wingard, S.A., 1928
V. tobacco streak
Diachun, Stephen and W.D. Valleau, 1954
V. tomato black ring
(K.M. Smith, 1957) R.E. Fitzpatrick, et al., 1958
V. tomato spotted wilt
(K.M. Smith, 1957) R.E. Fitzpatrick, et al., 1958
V. turnip mosaic
Walker, J.C., Francis J. LeBeau and Glenn S.
Pound, 1945
N. paniculata x N. rustica, L.
V. tobacco mosaic
Holmes, F.O., 1934
N. pauciflora, Remy
V. tobacco mosaic
Diachun, Stephen and W.D. Valleau, 1954
V. tobacco streak
Diachun, Stephen and W.D. Valleau, 1954
N. plumbaginifolia, Viv.
V. tobacco etch
Holmes, Francis O., 1946
V. tobacco mosaic
Boyle, John S. and David C. Wharton, 1956, 1957
Diachun, Stephen and W.D. Valleau, 1954
Holmes, Francis O., 1946
V. tobacco ring spot
Cheo, Pen Ching and W.J. Zaumeyer, 1952
Wingard, S.A., 1928
V. tobacco streak
Diachun, Stephen and W.D. Valleau, 1954
N. purpurea *
V. vaccinium false blossom
(K.M. Smith, 1957) R.E. Fitzpatrick, et al., 1958
N. quadrivalvis, Pursh
V. beet mosaic
Bennett, C.W., 1949
V. tobacco mosaic
Doolittle, S.P. and F.S. Beecher, 1942
V. tobacco ring spot
Wingard, S.A., 1928
V. turnip mosaic
Walker, J.C., Francis J. LeBeau and Glenn S.
Pound, 1945

N. raimondii, Macbride
V. tobacco mosaic
Diachun, Stephen and W.D. Valleau, 1954
Holmes, Francis O., 1946
V. tobacco streak
Diachun, Stephen and W.D. Valleau, 1954
N. repanda, Willd.
V. cabbage ring necrosis
Larson, R.H. and J.C. Walker, 1940, 1941
V. cucumber mosaic
Nienow, Inez, 1948
V. nicotiana glutinosa root necrosis *
Cetas, Robert C. and A. Frank Ross, 1952
V. tobacco etch
Holmes, Francis O., 1946
V. tobacco mosaic
Adsuar, J. and L. Lopez Matos, 1955
Diachun, Stephen and W.D. Valleau, 1954
Holmes, Francis O., 1946
V. tobacco ring spot
Wingard, S.A., 1928
V. tobacco streak
Diachun, Stephen and W.D. Valleau, 1954
V. turnip mosaic
LeBeau, Francis J. and J.C. Walker, 1945
N. rotundifolia, Lindl.
V. tobacco mosaic
Diachun, Stephen and W.D. Valleau, 1954
V. tobacco streak
Diachun, Stephen and W.D. Valleau, 1954
N. rusbyi, Britton, ex Rusby
V. tobacco mosaic
Kunkel, L.O., 1932
N. rustica, L.
V. anemone mosaic *
Hollings, M., 1957
V. aster yellows
Johnson, Folke, 1941
Kunkel, L.O., 1930
Raymer, W.B., 1956
Self, R.L. and H.M. Darling, 1949
Younkin, S.G., 1943
V. bean yellow mosaic
Thomas, H. Rex and W.J. Zaumeyer, 1953
Zaumeyer, W.J., 1952
Zaumeyer, W.J. and H.H. Fisher, 1953
V. beet curly top
Fulton, Robert W., 1955
Lackey, C.F., 1929
Severin, Henry H.P., 1929
V. beet ring spot *
Harrison, B.D., 1957
V. cabbage black ring spot
Hamlyn, Brenda M.G., 1953
V. cabbage ring necrosis
Larson, R.H. and J.C. Walker, 1940, 1941
V. chilli (pepper) mosaic
Dale, W.T., 1954
V. chrysanthemum B (mild mosaic) *
Hollings, M., 1957
V. chrysanthemum latent *
Hollings, M., 1957
V. cucumber mosaic
Doolittle, S.P. and W.J. Zaumeyer, 1953
Govier, D.A., 1957
Johnson, E.M., 1930
Johnson, J., 1926, 1927
Lindberg, G.D., D.H. Hall and J.C. Walker, 1956
Pound, Glenn S. and J.C. Walker, 1948
V. datura distortion mosaic
Capoor, S.P. and P.M. Varma, 1952
V. dodder latent mosaic
Bennett, C.W., 1944, 1949
V. henbane mosaic
Bradley, R.H.E., 1952
V. lovage mosaic
Smith, Kenneth M. and Roy Markham, 1944
V. lucerne mosaic
Berkeley, G.H., 1947
Kreitlow, K.W. and W.C. Price, 1948, 1949
Oswald, John W., 1950
Price, W.C., 1940

Nicotiana rustica, L. (cont.)
V. lucerne mosaic
Thomas, H. Rex, 1951
Zaumeyer, W.J., 1953
V. lucerne witches' broom
Helms, Katie, 1957
V. petunia mosaic
Johnson, J., 1926, 1927
V. potato leaf roll
Webb, R.E., R.H. Larson and J.C. Walker, 1952
V. potato stunt
(K.M. Smith, 1957) R.E. Fitzpatrick, et al., 1958
V. potato X
Larson, R.H., 1943, 1944, 1947
Larson, R.H. and R.C. Ladeburg, 1949
Thompson, A.D., 1956
Timian, Roland G., W.J. Hooker and C.E.
Peterson, 1955
Vasudeva, R. Sahai and T.B. Lal, 1944
V. potato Y
Johnson, E.M., 1930
Johnson, James, 1927
Koch, K.L., 1933
Oswald, John W., 1948
Roque, Arturo and Jose Adsuar, 1941
Sakimura, K., 1953
Smith, Kenneth M. and R.W.G. Dennis, 1940
Vasudeva, R. Sahai and T.B. Lal, 1945
V. potato yellow dwarf
Black, L.M., 1938, 1940, 1943
Hougas, R.W., 1951
Price, W.C. an' L.M. Black, 1941
Younkin, S.G., 1943
V. raspberry Scottish leaf curl
Cadman, C.H., 1956
Harrison, B.D., 1958
Lister, R.M., 1958
V. raspberry yellow dwarf *
Harrison, B.D., 1958
Lister, R.M., 1958
V. red currant ring spot
Klesser, P.J., 1951
V. rose mosaic
Fulton, Robert W., 1952
V. sweet potato mosaic
Elmer, O.H., 1957
V. tobacco broad ring spot
Johnson, James and Robert W. Fulton, 1942
V. tobacco coarse etch
Johnson, E.M., 1930
V. tobacco etch
Holmes, Francis O., 1946
Johnson, E.M., 1930
V. tobacco green mosaic
Peterson, Paul D. and H.H. McKinney, 1938
V. tobacco leaf curl
Pal, B.P. and R.K. Tandon, 1937
V. tobacco mosaic
Allard, H.A., 1914-15, 1916
Boyle, John S. and David C. Wharton, 1956, 1957
Caldwell, John, 1932
Das, C.R. and S.P. Raychaudhuri, 1953
Diachun, Stephen and W.D. Valleau, 1954
Doolittle, S.P. and F.S. Beecher, 1942
Fernow, Karl Hermann, 1925
Holmes, Francis O., 1929, 1934, 1946
Jensen, J.H., 1933
Johnson, E.M., 1930
Johnson, J., 1926, 1927
Kunkel, L.O., 1932
McKinney, H.H., 1935
Peterson, Paul D. and H.H. McKinney, 1938
Stover, R.H., 1951
V. tobacco necrosis
Price, W.C., 1938
Price, W.C., Frank P. McWhorter and Betty H.
Steranka, 1950
V. tobacco ring spot
Grogan, R.G., Roy Bardin and W.C. Schnathorst,
1954
Grogan, R.G. and W.C. Schnathorst, 1955
Johnson, E.M., 1930
Pound, Glenn S., 1949
Wingard, S.A., 1928

N. rustica, L. (cont.)
V. tobacco ring spot no. 2
Hildebrand, E.M., 1941, 1942
V. tobacco streak
Diachun, Stephen, 1947
Diachun, Stephen and W.D. Valleau, 1950, 1954
Johnson, J., 1936
Price, W.C. and L.M. Black, 1941
Thomas, H. Rex and W.J. Zaumeyer, 1950
V. tobacco yellow dwarf
Hill, A.V. and M. Mandryk, 1954
V. tomato aspermy
Brierley, Philip, Floyd F. Smith and S.P.
Doolittle, 1955
Hollings, M., 1955
V. tomato big bud
Helms, Katie, 1957
V. tomato black ring
Harrison, B.D., 1958
V. tomato sheostring *
Doering, G.R., W.C. Price and S.B. Fenne, 1957
V. tomato spotted wilt
Black, L.M., M.K. Brakke and A.E. Vatter, 1952
Gardner, M.W. and O.C. Whipple, 1934
Smith, Kenneth M., 1932
Tompkins, C.M. and M.W. Gardner, 1934
V. turnip crinkle
Lister, R.M., 1958
V. turnip mosaic
LeBeau, Francis J. and J.C. Walker, 1945
Pound, Glenn S. and Lewis G. Weathers, 1953
Walker, J.C., Francis J. LeBeau and Glenn S.
Pound, 1945
V. vaccinium false blossom
Kunkel, L.O., 1945
N. rustica var. humulis, Schrank *
V. delphinium ring spot
Severin, Henry H.P. and R.C. Dickson, 1942
V. radish mosaic
Tompkins, C.M., 1939
N. rustica var. jamaicensis *
V. dodder latent mosaic
Bennett, C.W., 1944
V. potato yellow dwarf
Black, L.M., 1938
V. tobacco ring spot
Wingard, S.A., 1928
N. rustica var. pumila *
V. dodder latent mosaic
Bennett, C.W., 1944
V. potato yellow dwarf
Black, L.M., 1938
N. sanderae, W. Wats. (N. alata, Link & Otto x N.
forgetiana, Sander)
V. chilli (pepper) mosaic
Dale, W.T., 1954
V. cucumber mosaic
Wellman, F.L., 1935
V. lucerne mosaic
Price, W.C., 1940
V. potato X
Smith, J. Henderson, 1928
V. potato yellow dwarf
Black, L.M., 1938
V. tobacco etch
Holmes, Francis O., 1946
V. tobacco mosaic
Holmes, Francis O., 1929, 1934, 1946
Stover, R.H., 1951
V. tobacco ring spot
Wingard, S.A., 1928
V. tomato spotted wilt
Gardner, M.W. and O.C. Whipple, 1934
V. turnip mosaic
Walker, J.C., Francis J. LeBeau and Glenn S.
Pound, 1945
N. sanderae x N. langsdorffii, Weinm.
V. tobacco mosaic
Holmes, F.O., 1934
N. sanderae (mottling) x N. sanderae (necrotic)
V. tobacco mosaic
Holmes, F.O., 1934

Nicotiana setchellii, Goodspeed
  V. tobacco mosaic
    Diachun, Stephen and W.D. Valleau, 1954
  V. tobacco streak
    Diachun, Stephen and W.D. Valleau, 1954
N. solanifolia, Walp.
  V. tobacco etch
    Holmes, Francis O., 1946
  V. tobacco mosaic
    Holmes, Francis O., 1946
N. spp.
  V. prunus B *
    Fulton, Robert W., 1957
  V. tobacco etch
    Bawden, F.C. and B. Kassanis, 1941
  V. tobacco streak
    Fulton, Robert W., 1948
N. stocktoni, Brandegee, in Erythea
  V. tobacco mosaic
    Diachun, Stephen and W.D. Valleau, 1954
  V. tobacco streak
    Diachun, Stephen and W.D. Valleau, 1954
N. suaveolens, Lehm.
  V. tobacco mosaic
    Diachun, Stephen and W.D. Valleau, 1954
    Holmes, F.O., 1934
    Kunkel, L.O., 1932
  V. tobacco ring spot
    Wingard, S.A., 1928
  V. tobacco streak
    Diachun, Stephen and W.D. Valleau, 1954
  V. tobacco yellow dwarf
    Hill, A.V. and M. Mandryk, 1954
  V. tomato spotted wilt
    (K.M. Smith, 1957) R.E. Fitzpatrick, et al., 1958
N. sylvestris, Speg. & Comes
  V. bean yellow mosaic
    Thomas, H. Rex and W.J. Zaumeyer, 1953
  V. chilli (pepper) mosaic
    Dale, W.T., 1954
  V. cucumber mosaic
    Govier, D.A., 1957
    Nienow, Inez, 1948
    Wellman, F.L., 1935
  V. datura distortion mosaic
    Capoor, S.P. and P.M. Varma, 1952
  V. lovage mosaic
    Smith, Kenneth M. and Roy Markham, 1944
  V. lucerne mosaic
    Dykstra, T.P., 1939
    Price, W.C., 1940
  V. potato A
    Bagnall, R.H., R.H. Larson and J.C. Walker, 1956
    Dykstra, T.P., 1939
    MacLachlan, D.S., R.H. Larson and J.C. Walker, 1953
  V. potato aucuba mosaic
    Dykstra, T.P., 1939
  V. potato X
    Dennis, R.W.G., 1939
    Vasudeva, R. Sahai and T.B. Lal, 1944
  V. potato Y
    Dykstra, T.P., 1939
    Vasudeva, R. Sahai and T.B. Lal, 1945
  V. potato yellow dwarf
    Black, L.M., 1938
  V. red currant ring spot
    Klesser, P.J., 1951
  V. tobacco broad ring spot
    Johnson, James and Robert W. Fulton, 1942
  V. tobacco etch
    Holmes, Francis O., 1946
  V. tobacco green mosaic
    Peterson, Paul D. and H.H. McKinney, 1938
  V. tobacco green ring spot *
    Price, W.C., 1936
  V. tobacco leaf curl
    Vasudeva, R.S. and J. Sam Raj, 1948
  V. tobacco mosaic
    Boyle, John S. and David C. Wharton, 1956, 1957
    Conover, Robert A. and Robert W. Fulton, 1953
    Diachun, Stephen and W.D. Valleau, 1954
    Doolittle, S.P. and F.S. Beecher, 1942

N. sylvestris, Speg. & Comes (cont.)
  V. tobacco mosaic
    Dykstra, T.P., 1939
    Fulton, Robert W., 1951
    Holmes, F.O., 1934, 1941, 1946
    Jensen, J.H., 1933, 1936, 1937
    Kunkel, L.O., 1932, 1934
    McKinney, H.H., 1935, 1952
    Norval, I.P., 1938
    Peterson, Paul D. and H.H. McKinney, 1938
    Price, W.C. and S.B. Fenne, 1951
    Raychaudhuri, S.P., 1952
    Siegel, Albert and Sam G. Wildman, 1954
    Stover, R.H., 1951
    Weber, Paul V.V., 1951
  V. tobacco necrosis
    Price, W.C., 1940
    Price, W.C., Frank P. McWhorter and Betty H. Steranka, 1950
  V. tobacco ring spot
    Cheo, Pen Ching and W.J. Zaumeyer, 1952
    Fromme, F.D., S.A. Wingard and C.N. Priode, 1927
    Price, W.C., 1936
    Wingard, S.A., 1928
  V. tobacco ring spot no. 2
    Hildebrand, E.M., 1942
    Price, W.C., 1936
  V. tobacco streak
    Diachun, Stephen and W.D. Valleau, 1954
  V. tobacco vein distorting
    (K.M. Smith, 1957) R.E. Fitzpatrick, et al., 1958
  V. tobacco yellow mosaic
    McKinney, H.H., 1935
  V. tomato aspermy
    Brierley, Philip, Floyd F. Smith and S.P. Doolittle, 1955
  V. tomato black ring
    (K.M. Smith, 1957) R.E. Fitzpatrick, et al., 1958
  V. tomato shoestring *
    Doering, G.R., W.C. Price and S.B. Fenne, 1957
  V. tomato spotted wilt
    (K.M. Smith, 1957) R.E. Fitzpatrick, et al., 1958
  V. turnip mosaic
    LeBeau, Francis J. and J.C. Walker, 1945
    Walker, J.C., Francis J. LeBeau and Glenn S. Pound, 1945
N. tabacum, L.
  V. abutilon infectious variegation
    Bird, Julio, 1958
  V. anemone latent *
    (K.M. Smith, 1957) R.E. Fitzpatrick, et al., 1958
  V. anemone mosaic *
    Hollings, M., 1957
  V. apple mosaic
    Fulton, Robert W., 1956
    Yarwood, C.E., 1955, 1957
    Yarwood, C.E. and H.E. Thomas, 1954
  V. arabis mosaic
    Smith, Kenneth M. and Roy Markham, 1944
  V. atropa belladonna mosaic
    (K.M. Smith, 1957) R.E. Fitzpatrick, et al., 1958
  V. barley stripe mosaic
    McKinney, H.H., 1951
  V. bean yellow mosaic
    Thomas, H. Rex and W.J. Zaumeyer, 1953
    Zaumeyer, W.J., 1952
    Zaumeyer, W.J. and H.H. Fisher, 1953
  V. beet curly top
    Bennett, C.W., 1934, 1937, 1944, 1951
    Bennett, C.W. and A.S. Costa, 1949
    Bennett, C.W. and Aziz Tanrisever, 1957
    Costa, A.S., 1952
    Fulton, Robert W., 1955
    Giddings, N.J., 1938, 1944, 1947, 1954
    Lackey, C.F., 1941
    Price, W.C., 1943
    Severin, Henry H.P., 1929
  V. beet mosaic
    Hoggan, Isme A., 1934
    Severin, Henry H.P. and Roger M. Drake, 1948
  V. beet ring spot *
    Harrison, B.D., 1957

Nicotiana tabacum, L. (cont.)
  V. brome mosaic
    McKinney, H.H., 1944, 1953
  V. cabbage black ring spot
    Bawden, F.C., Brenda M.G. Hamlyn and Marion
    A. Watson, 1954
    Broadbent, L., 1954
    (K.M. Smith, 1957) R.E. Fitzpatrick, et al., 1958
    Hamlyn, Brenda M.G., 1953
    Hollings, M., 1957
    Pound, Glenn S., 1952
    Tompkins, C.M., M.W. Gardner and H. Rex
    Thomas, 1937, 1938
  V. cabbage ring necrosis
    Larson, R.H. and J.C. Walker, 1940, 1941
  V. carnation ring spot
    Brierley, Philip and Floyd F. Smith, 1955, 1957
    Kassanis, B., 1955
  V. carrot motley dwarf
    (K.M. Smith, 1957) R.E. Fitzpatrick, et al., 1958
  V. cauliflower mosaic
    Broadbent, L., 1954
    Pound, Glenn S., 1952
  V. celery mosaic
    Doolittle, S.P., 1931
    Doolittle, S.P. and F.L. Wellman, 1934
    Nolla, J.A.B., 1934
    Price, W.C., 1936
  V. chilli (pepper) mosaic
    Dale, W.T., 1954
    Ferguson, I.A.C., 1951
    Jha, Ashrafi and S.P. Raychaudhuri, 1956
  V. chilli veinbanding
    Simons, John N., 1956
  V. chrysanthemum latent *
    Hollings, M., 1957
  V. clover big vein
    (K.M. Smith, 1957) R.E. Fitzpatrick, et al., 1958
  V. crucifer ring spot *
    Smith, Kenneth M., 1935
  V. cucumber green mottle mosaic
    Ainsworth, G.C., 1935
    Storey, I.F., 1939
    Vasudeva, R.S. and T.K. Nariani, 1952
  V. cucumber mosaic
    Adsuar, Jose and A. Cruz Miret, 1950
    Ainsworth, G.C., 1938, 1940
    Anderson, C.W., 1951, 1955
    Bennett, C.W., 1944
    Berkeley, G.H., 1951, 1953
    Berkeley, G.H. and J.H. Tremaine, 1954
    Bhargava, K.S., 1951
    Black, L.M. and W.C. Price, 1940
    Bridgmon, G.H. and J.C. Walker, 1952
    Brierley, Philip, 1939, 1940, 1951
    Brierley, Philip and S.P. Doolittle, 1940
    Burnett, G., 1934
    Costa, A.S., 1944
    Diachun, Stephen, 1952
    Doncaster, J.P. and B. Kassanis, 1946
    Doolittle, S.P. and W.J. Zaumeyer, 1952, 1953
    Dykstra, T.P., 1939
    Fulton, Joseph P., 1950
    Fulton, Robert W., 1941, 1953
    Govier, D.A., 1957
    Hagedorn, D.J. and J.C. Walker, 1954
    Harrison, B.D., 1958
    Harter, L.L., 1936, 1938
    Hoggan, Isme A., 1927, 1930, 1933, 1934, 1935
    Johnson, E.M., 1930
    Johnson, J., 1926, 1927, 1933
    Kassanis, B., 1947
    Larsh, Howard W. and J.R. Shay, 1945
    Lindberg, G.D., D.H. Hall and J.C. Walker, 1956
    Magee, C.J.P., 1940
    McKinney, H.H., 1943
    Nariani, T.K. and Nirmaljit Singh, 1952
    Nienow, Inez, 1948
    Nolla, J.A.B., 1934
    Pound, Glenn S. and J.C. Walker, 1948
    Price, W.C., 1934, 1936, 1937, 1941
    Silberschmidt, K., 1955
    Sill, Webster H., Jr., 1951
    Sill, W.H., Jr. and J.C. Walker, 1952

N. tabacum, L. (cont.)
  V. cucumber mosaic
    Simons, John N., 1955, 1957
    Smith, Floyd F. and Philip Brierley, 1944
    Smith, Kenneth M., 1935
    Valleau, W.D., 1935
    Wellman, F.L., 1934, 1935
    Whipple, O.C. and J.C. Walker, 1938, 1941
    Wilkinson, R.E., 1953
  V. datura distortion mosaic
    Capoor, S.P. and P.M. Varma, 1952
  V. delphinium disease *
    Valleau, W.D., 1932
  V. delphinium ring spot
    Severin, Henry H.P. and R.C. Dickson, 1942
  V. dodder latent mosaic
    Bennett, C.W., 1944, 1949
  V. eggplant mosaic
    Dale, W.T., 1954
  V. elm mosaic
    Moore, J. Duain and E.H. Varney, 1954
    Varney, E.H. and J. Duain Moore, 1952
  V. eryngium chlorosis *
    Johnson, James, 1946
  V. eryngium yellow mosaic *
    Johnson, James and Edith M. Hein, 1948
  V. henbane mosaic
    Bawden, F.C., Brenda M.G. Hamlyn and Marion
    A. Watson, 1954
    Bradley, R.H.E., 1952
    Doncaster, J.P. and B. Kassanis, 1946
    Hamilton, Marion A., 1932
    Sheffield, F.M.L., 1936, 1938
    Watson (Hamilton), Marion A., 1937
  V. hydrangea ring spot
    Brierley, Philip and Floyd F. Smith, 1952
  V. iris ring spot *
    Travis, R.V., 1957
  V. jatropha mosaic *
    Bird, Julio, 1957
  V. laburnum vein mosaic *
    Brierley, Philip and Floyd F. Smith, 1954
  V. lovage mosaic
    Smith, Kenneth M. and Roy Markham, 1944
  V. lucerne mosaic
    Berkeley, G.H., 1947
    Black, L.M. and W.C. Price, 1940
    Houston, Byron R. and John W. Oswald, 1951,
    1953
    Johnson, E.M., 1946
    Kreitlow, K.W. and W.C. Price, 1948, 1949
    Oswald, John W., 1950
    Pierce, W.H., 1934
    Richardson, D.E. and T.W. Tinsley, 1956
    Severin, Henry H.P., 1942
    Swenson, K.G., 1952
    Thomas, H. Rex, 1951, 1953
    Thomas, H. Rex and W.J. Zaumeyer, 1950
    Zaumeyer, W.J., 1938, 1953
  V. lucerne witches' broom
    Helms, Katie, 1957
  V. nicotiana glauca light green mosaic *
    McKinney, H.H., 1929
  V. nicotiana glauca mild dark green mosaic *
    McKinney, H.H., 1929
  V. nicotiana glauca yellow mosaic *
    McKinney, H.H., 1929
  V. nicotiana glutinosa mosaic *
    Walker, M.N., 1925
  V. pea die back *
    Zaumeyer, W.J., 1939
  V. pea stem streak *
    Zaumeyer, W.J., 1939
  V. pea streak
    Kim, Woon S. and D.J. Hagedorn, 1957
  V. peach yellow bud mosaic
    Karle, Harry P., 1957
    Yarwood, C.E., 1956
  V. petunia mosaic
    Johnson, J., 1926, 1927
  V. plantago mosaic
    McKinney, H.H., 1943
  V. potato A
    Bagnall, R.H., R.H. Larson and J.C. Walker, 1956

Nicotiana tabacum, L. (cont.)
V. potato A
Bawden, F.C., 1936
Bawden, F.C. and F.M.L. Sheffield, 1944
Dykstra, T.P., 1936, 1939
Dykstra, T.P. and W.C. Whitaker, 1938
MacLachlan, D.S., R.H. Larson and J.C. Walker, 1953
Valleau, W.D. and E.M. Johnson, 1930
Vasudeva, R. Sahai and C.S. Ramamoorthy, 1946
V. potato aucuba mosaic
Bagnall, R.H., R.H. Larson and J.C. Walker, 1956
Black, L.M. and W.C. Price, 1940
Dennis, R.W.G., 1939
Dykstra, T.P., 1939
V. potato leaf roll
Webb, R.E., R.H. Larson and J.C. Walker, 1952
V. potato necrotic *
Schultz, E.S. and W.P. Raleigh, 1933
V. potato rosette
Hutton, E.M. and C.E.W. Oldaker, 1949
V. potato stem mottle
Harrison, B.D., 1957
Van der Want, J.P.H., 1955
V. potato stunt
(K.M. Smith, 1957) R.E. Fitzpatrick, et al., 1958
V. potato witches' broom
(K.M. Smith, 1957) R.E. Fitzpatrick, et al., 1958
Young, P.A., 1929
V. potato X
Ainsworth, G.C., 1933, 1934
Bagnall, R.H., R.H. Larson and J.C. Walker, 1956
Bawden, F.C., 1936
Bawden, F.C. and F.M.L. Sheffield, 1944
Black, L.M. and W.C. Price, 1940
Blodgett, F.M., 1927
Burnett, Grover and Leon K. Jones, 1931
Cockerham, George, 1943
Dennis, R.W.G., 1939
Dykstra, T.P., 1939
Folsom, Donald and Reiner Bonde, 1937
Fulton, Robert W., 1941
Hamilton, Marion A., 1932
Hoggan, Isme A., 1927
Hollings, M., 1955
Johnson, E.M., 1930
Johnson, James, 1925, 1926, 1927
Koch, K.L., 1933
Koch, Karl and James Johnson, 1935
Larson, R.H., 1943, 1944, 1947
Larson, R.H. and R.C. Ladeburg, 1949
Matthews, R.E.F., 1949
Nolla, J.A.B., 1934
Price, W.C., 1936
Quanjer, H.M., 1933
Roberts, Daniel A., 1952
Roberts, F.M., 1948
Smith, J. Henderson, 1928
Smith, Kenneth M., 1930
Thompson, A.D., 1956
Timian, Roland G., W.J. Hooker and C.E. Peterson, 1955
Valleau, W.D. and E.M. Johnson, 1930
Vasudeva, R. Sahai and T.B. Lal, 1944
Walters, H.J., 1952
V. potato Y
Alvarez-Garcia, L.A. and Jose Adsuar, 1943
Bagnall, R.H., R.H. Larson and J.C. Walker, 1956
Bald, J.G. and D.O. Norris, 1945
Bawden, F.C., 1936
Bawden, F.C. and B. Kassanis, 1946, 1947, 1951
Bawden, F.C. and F.M.L. Sheffield, 1944
Burnett, Grover and Leon K. Jones, 1931
Cockerham, George, 1943
Conover, Robert A. and Robert W. Fulton, 1953
Corbett, M.K., 1955
Darby, J.F., R.H. Larson and J.C. Walker, 1951
Doncaster, J.P. and B. Kassanis, 1946
Dykstra, T.P., 1936, 1939
Easton, G.D., R.H. Larson and R.W. Hougas, 1958

N. tabacum, L. (cont.)
V. potato Y
Hamilton, Marion A., 1932
Hoggan, Isme A., 1927
Johnson, E.M., 1930
Johnson, James, 1927
Jones, Leon K. and C.L. Vincent, 1937
Kassanis, B., 1942
Koch, K.L., 1933
Koch, Karl and James Johnson, 1935
Larson, R.H., 1947
Larson, R.H. and J.F. Darby, 1951
McKinney, H.H., 1943
Nolla, J.A.B., 1934
Oswald, John W., 1948
Peterson, Paul D. and H.H. McKinney, 1938
Price, W.C., 1936
Richardson, D.E., 1958
Roque, Arturo and Jose Adsuar, 1941
Ross, A. Frank, 1950, 1953
Sakimura, K., 1953
Simons, J.N., Robert A. Conover and James M. Walter, 1956
Smith, Kenneth M. and R.W.G. Dennis, 1940
Valleau, W.D. and E.M. Johnson, 1930
Vasudeva, R. Sahai and T.B. Lal, 1945
Watson (Hamilton), Marion A., 1937, 1956
V. potato yellow dwarf
Black, L.M., 1938
V. prunus *
Varney, E.H. and J. Duain Moore, 1954
V. prunus A *
Ehlers, Clifford G. and J. Duain Moore, 1957
Fulton, Robert W., 1957
V. prunus B *
Ehlers, Clifford G. and J. Duain Moore, 1957
Fulton, Robert W., 1956, 1957
V. prunus E *
Ehlers, Clifford G. and J. Duain Moore, 1957
V. prunus G *
Fulton, Robert W., 1957
V. radish mosaic
Tompkins, C.M., 1939
V. ranunculus mosaic
(K.M. Smith, 1957) R.E. Fitzpatrick, et al., 1958
V. raspberry Scottish leaf curl
Cadman, C.H., 1956
Harrison, B.D., 1957, 1958
Lister, R.M., 1958
V. raspberry yellow dwarf *
Harrison, B.D., 1958
Lister, R.M., 1958
V. red currant ring spot
Klesser, P.J., 1951
V. sunflower mosaic
(K.M. Smith, 1957) R.E. Fitzpatrick, et al., 1958
V. sweet clover new *
Henderson, R.G., 1934
V. sweet potato mosaic
Elmer, O.H., 1957
V. tobacco bergerac ring spot
(K.M. Smith, 1957) R.E. Fitzpatrick, et al., 1958
V. tobacco broad ring spot
Fulton, Robert W., 1941
Johnson, James and Robert W. Fulton, 1940, 1942
V. tobacco broken ring spot
(K.M. Smith, 1957) R.E. Fitzpatrick, et al., 1958
Smith, Kenneth M. and Roy Markham, 1944
V. tobacco coarse etch
Johnson, E.M., 1930
V. tobacco etch
Anderson, C.W., 1954
Bawden, F.C. and B. Kassanis, 1941
Bennett, C.W., 1944
Doncaster, J.P. and B. Kassanis, 1946
Fulton, Robert W., 1941
Holmes, Francis O., 1941, 1942, 1946
Johnson, E.M., 1930
Price, W.C., 1936
Stover, R.H., 1951
Valleau, W.D., 1935
V. tobacco green mosaic
Dufrenoy, J., 1933
Peterson, Paul D. and H.H. McKinney, 1938

Nicotiana tabacum, L. (cont.)

V. tobacco green ring spot *
Price, W.C., 1936
Valleau, W.D., 1935

V. tobacco leaf curl
Bird, Julio, 1957
Kerling, L.C.P., 1933
Nariani, T.K., 1956
Nariani, T.K. and P.S. Pathanian, 1953
Pal, B.P. and R.K. Tandon, 1937
Pruthi, Hem Singh and C.K. Samuel, 1937, 1939, 1941
Vasudeva, R.S. and J. Sam Raj, 1948

V. tobacco leaf curl-like disease *
Morgan, O.D. and H.H. McKinney, 1951

V. tobacco leaf roll disease *
Goenaga, Alvaro, 1945

V. tobacco mosaic
Ainsworth, G.C., 1933, 1937
Ainsworth, G.C., G.H. Berkeley and J. Caldwell, 1934
Allard, H.A., 1914-15, 1915, 1916, 1917
Bawden, F.C. and F.M. Roberts, 1948
Beale, Helen P., 1933
Bennett, C.W., 1944
Berkeley, G.H., 1927, 1951
Best, Rupert J. and Geoffrey Samuel, 1936
Boyle, John S. and David C. Wharton, 1956, 1957
Caldwell, John, 1932
Conover, Robert A. and Robert W. Fulton, 1953
Costa, A.S., 1944
Cox, C.E. and L.O. Weaver, 1950
Dale, W.T., 1954
Das, C.R. and S.P. Raychaudhuri, 1953
Diachun, Stephen and W.D. Valleau, 1954
Doolittle, S.P. and F.S. Beecher, 1942
Dufrenoy, J., 1933
Fernow, Karl Hermann, 1925
Fulton, Robert W., 1941
Gutierrez, Mariano E., 1954
Gutierrez, Mariano E., Julian Agati and Serapion Bayubay, 1950
Henderson, R.G., 1950
Hoggan, Isme A., 1927, 1934
Holmes, F.O., 1934, 1936, 1941, 1946, 1953
Jarrett, Phyllis H., 1930
Jensen, J.H., 1933, 1936, 1937
Johnson, E.M., 1930
Johnson, Folke, 1941
Johnson, J., 1926, 1927
Jones, Leon K., 1940
Kassanis, B. and Ireson W. Selman, 1947
Kunkel, L.O., 1932
McKinney, H.H., 1935, 1939, 1943, 1952
McMurtrey, J.E., Jr., 1928, 1929
Nagaich, B.B. and H.H. Thornberry, 1957
Nolla, J.A.B., 1934
Nollan, J.A.B., John Simon Guggenheim and Arturo Roque, 1933
Norval, I.P., 1938
Perez, J. Enrique, J. Adsuar and Orlando Sala, 1956
Peterson, Paul D. and H.H. McKinney, 1938
Pierce, W.H., 1934
Price, W.C., 1936
Price, W.C. and S.B. Fenne, 1951
Purdy, Helen A., 1927
Quanjer, H.M., 1920, 1933
Raychaudhuri, S.P., 1952
Roberts, Daniel A., 1952
Schwarze, C.A., 1914
Sheffield, F.M.L., 1931, 1936
Siegel, Albert and Sam G. Wildman, 1954
Smith, J. Henderson, 1933
Smith, Kenneth M., 1935
Spencer, E.L., 1935, 1937
Stover, R.H., 1951
Stover, W.G., 1928
Stover, W.G. and M.T. Vermillion, 1933
Valleau, W.D., 1935
Valleau, W.D. and E.M. Johnson, 1935, 1943
Vanterpool, T.C., 1926
Walker, M.N., 1926
Walters, H.J., 1952

N. tabacum, L. (cont.)

V. tobacco mosaic
Weber, Paul V.V., 1951
Woods, M.W. and Richard V. Eck, 1948

V. tobacco mottle
(K.M. Smith, 1957) R.E. Fitzpatrick, et al., 1958

V. tobacco necrosis
Bawden, F.C. and B. Kassanis, 1947
Bawden, F.C. and F.M. Roberts, 1948
Frazier, Norman W., 1955
Fulton, Robert W., 1950
Fulton, J.P., 1952
Kassanis, B., 1949, 1955
Price, W.C., 1938
Price, W.C., Frank P. McWhorter and Betty H. Steranka, 1950
Price, W.C. and Ralph W.G. Wyckoff, 1939

V. tobacco ring spot
Allington, William B., 1946
Anderson, C.W., 1954
Benedict, W.G., 1955
Berkeley, G.H., 1951, 1953
Bridgmon, G.H. and J.C. Walker, 1952
Brierley, Philip, 1952
Cheo, Pen Ching and W.J. Zaumeyer, 1952
Cook, A.A., 1956
Cooper, W.E., 1949
Dunleavy, John M., 1957
Fenne, S.B., 1931
(K.M. Smith, 1957) R.E. Fitzpatrick, et al., 1958
Fromme, F.D., S.A. Wingard and C.N. Priode, 1927
Fulton, Robert W., 1941
Grogan, R.G., Roy Bardin and W.C. Schnathorst, 1954
Grogan, R.G. and W.C. Schnathorst, 1955
Harrison, B.D., 1957
Henderson, R.G. and S.A. Wingard, 1931
Hoggan, I.A., 1933
Johnson, E.M., 1930
Kahn, Robert P. and Frances M. Latterell, 1955
LeBeau, F.J., 1947
McKinney, H.H., 1943
McKinney, H.H. and E.E. Clayton, 1944
Nolla, J.A.B., 1934
Pierce, W.H., 1934
Pound, Glenn S., 1949
Price, W.C., 1936
Roberts, Daniel A., 1952
Rosberg, David W., 1953
Shepherd, Robert J. and F. Ben Struble, 1956
Smith, Kenneth M., 1929, 1935
Starr, Chester K. and W.E. Cooper, 1944
Steere, Russell L., 1956
Stubbs, M.W., 1937
Tall, M.G., W.C. Price and Kenneth Wertman, 1949
Travis, R.V. and Philip Brierley, 1957
Valleau, W.D., 1932, 1935, 1941
Walters, H.J., 1952
Wingard, S.A., 1928

V. tobacco ring spot no. 2
Brierley, Philip, 1954
Hildebrand, E.M., 1941, 1942
Price, W.C., 1936
Tall, M.G., W.C. Price and Kenneth Wertman, 1949

V. tobacco streak
Costa, A.S., 1945, 1952
Diachun, Stephen, 1947
Diachun, Stephen and W.D. Valleau, 1950, 1954
Fulton, Robert W., 1941, 1956
Johnson, J., 1936
Thomas, H. Rex and W.J. Zaumeyer, 1950

V. tobacco stunt *
Hidaka, Zyun, Tetsuo Uozumi and Chuji Hiruki, 1956

V. tobacco vein distorting
(K.M. Smith, 1957) R.E. Fitzpatrick, et al., 1958

V. tobacco yellow dwarf
Hill, A.V., 1950
Hill, A.V. and M. Mandryk, 1954

V. tomato aspermy
Blencowe, J.W. and John Caldwell, 1949

Nicotiana tabacum, L. (cont.)
  V. tomato aspermy
    Brierley, Philip, 1955
    Brierley, Philip and Floyd F. Smith, 1953
    Brierley, Philip, Floyd F. Smith and S.P.
    Doolittle, 1953, 1955
    Hollings, M., 1955
    Ocfemia, G.O., 1956
  V. tomato big bud
    Helms, Katie, 1957
    Hill, A.V. and M. Mandryk, 1954
  V. tomato black ring
    Harrison, B.D., 1958
  V. tomato bunchy top
    (K.M. Smith, 1957) R.E. Fitzpatrick, et al., 1958
  V. tomato bushy stunt
    Smith, Kenneth M., 1935
  V. tomato filiform leaf disease *
    Schwarze, C.A., 1914
  V. tomato ring spot
    Bennett, C.W., 1944
    Brierley, Philip and Paul Lorentz, 1957
    Brierley, Philip and Floyd F. Smith, 1953
    Imle, E.P. and R.W. Samson, 1937
    Kahn, Robert P.and Frances M. Latterell, 1955
    Samson, R.W. and E.P. Imle, 1942
    Varney, E.H. and J. Duain Moore, 1952
  V. tomato sheostring *
    Doering, G.R., W.C. Price and S.B. Fenne, 1957
  V. tomato spotted wilt
    Ainsworth, G.C., 1933
    Ainsworth, G.C., G.H. Berkeley and J. Caldwell, 1934
    Bennett, C.W., 1944
    Berkeley, G.H., 1935
    Best, Rupert J. and Geoffrey Samuel, 1936
    Black, L.M., M.K. Barkke and A.E. Vatter, 1952
    Doolittle, S.P. and C.B. Summer, 1934
    Ferguson, I.A.C., 1951
    Gardner, M.W., C.M. Tompkins and O.C.
    Whipple, 1935
    Gardner, M.W. and O.C. Whipple, 1934
    Milbrath, J.A., 1939
    Price, W.C., 1936
    Sakimura, K., 1940
    Shapovalov, M., 1934
    Sherf, A.F., 1948
    Smith, Kenneth M., 1931, 1932
    Snyder, W.C. and H. Rex Thomas, 1936
    Whipple, O.C., 1936
    Yu, T.F., 1947
  V. tomato V-52-1
    Miller, Patrick M., 1953
  V. tropaeolum mosaic
    Silberschmidt, Karl, 1953
  V. tropaeolum ring spot
    (K.M. Smith, 1957) R.E. Fitzpatrick, et al., 1958
  V. tulip white streak
    (K.M. Smith, 1957) R.E. Fitzpatrick, et al., 1958
  V. turnip crinkle
    Broadbent, L. and G.D. Heathcote, 1958
    Lister, R.M., 1958
  V. turnip mosaic
    Bennett, C.W., 1944
    Berkeley, G.H. and J.H. Tremaine, 1954
    Berkeley, G.H. and M. Weintraub, 1952
    Dale, W.T., 1948
    Hoggan, Isme A., 1934
    Hoggan, I.A. and J. Johnson, 1935
    LeBeau, Francis J. and J.C. Walker, 1945
    Pound, Glenn S. and Lewis G. Weathers, 1953
    Tompkins, C.M., 1938, 1939
    Tompkins, C.M. and H. Rex Thomas, 1938
    Walker, J.C., Francis J. LeBeau and Glenn S.
    Pound, 1945
  V. vaccinium false blossom
    Kunkel, L.O., 1945
  V. watermelon mosaic
    Pound, Glenn S., 1949
  V. yam mosaic *
    Adsuar, J., 1955
N. tabacum var. angustifolia, Comes
  V. tobacco broad ring spot
    Johnson, James and Robert W. Fulton, 1942

N. tabacum var. angustifolia, Comes (cont.)
  V. tobacco mosaic
    Adsuar, J. and L. Lopez Matos, 1955
  V. tomato spotted wilt
    (K.M. Smith, 1957) R.E. Fitzpatrick, et al., 1958
N. tabacum var. atropurpurea, Hort. *
  V. lucerne witches' broom
    Helms, Katie, 1957
  V. tobacco mosaic
    Weber, Paul V.V., 1951
  V. tobacco ring spot
    Wingard, S.A., 1928
  V. tobacco yellow dwarf
    Hill, A.V. and M. Mandryk, 1954
  V. tomato big bud
    Helms, Katie, 1957
N. tabacum var. atropurpureum, Hort. *
  V. tomato spotted wilt
    Norris, D.O., 1951
N. tabacum var. auriculata *
  V. tobacco ring spot
    Wingard, S.A., 1928
N. tabacum var. brasiliensis, Comes
  V. tobacco ring spot
    Wingard, S.A., 1928
N. tabacum var. calyciflora, L. *
  V. tobacco ring spot
    Wingard, S.A., 1928
N. tabacum var. calycina *
  V. tobacco ring spot
    Wingard, S.A., 1928
N. tabacum var. cavala *
  V. tobacco ring spot
    Wingard, S.A., 1928
N. tabacum var. colossea *
  V. tobacco ring spot
    Wingard, S.A., 1928
N. tabacum var. gigantea *
  V. tobacco ring spot
    Wingard, S.A., 1928
N. tabacum var. lacerata *
  V. tobacco ring spot
    Wingard, S.A., 1928
N. tabacum var. latissima, (Mill.) Voss
  V. tobacco ring spot
    Wingard, S.A., 1928
N. tabacum var. macrophylla, Schrank
  V. chilli (pepper) mosaic
    Dale, W.T., 1954
    Ferguson, I.A.C., 1951
  V. tobacco mosaic
    Ainsworth, G.C., 1933
    Kunkel, L.O., 1932
  V. tobacco ring spot
    Wingard, S.A., 1928
  V. turnip mosaic
    Dale, W.T., 1948
N. tabacum var. microphylla *
  V. tobacco ring spot
    Wingard, S.A., 1928
N. tabacum var. purpurea *
  V. tobacco mosaic
    Kunkel, L.O., 1932
  V. tobacco ring spot
    Wingard, S.A., 1928
N. tabacum var. purpurea x N. glutinosa, L.
  V. tobacco mosaic
    Holmes, F.O., 1934
N. tabacum var. sanguinea *
  V. tobacco ring spot
    Wingard, S.A., 1928
N. tabacum x N. glutinosa, L.
  V. cucumber mosaic
    Bridgmon, G.H. and J.C. Walker, 1952
    Sill, W.H., Jr. and J.C. Walker, 1952
  V. datura distortion mosaic
    Capoor, S.P. and P.M. Varma, 1952
  V. nicotiana glutinosa mosaic *
    Allard, H.A., 1916
  V. tobacco mosaic
    Costa, A.S., 1944
    Fulton, Robert W., 1950
    Holmes, F.O., 1934
    Johnson, James, 1936, 1937

Nicotiana tabacum, L. x N. glutinosa, L. (cont.)
  V. tobacco mosaic
    McKinney, H.H. and Robert W. Fulton, 1949
    Walters, H.J., 1952
  V. tobacco streak
    Johnson, J., 1936
  V. turnip mosaic
    Hoggan, I.A. and J. Johnson, 1935
    LeBeau, Francis J. and J.C. Walker, 1945
N. tabacum x N. longiflora, Cav.
  V. tobacco mosaic
    Weber, Paul V.V., 1951
N. tabacum x N. sylvestris, Speg. & Comes
  V. tobacco mosaic
    Weber, Paul V.V., 1951
N. tomentosa, Ruiz & Pav.
  V. potato stem mottle
    (K.M. Smith, 1957) R.E. Fitzpatrick, et al., 1958
  V. tobacco etch
    Holmes, Francis O., 1946
  V. tobacco mosaic
    Diachun, Stephen and W.D. Valleau, 1954
    Holmes, Francis O., 1946
    Weber, Paul V.V., 1951
  V. tobacco ring spot
    Wingard, S.A., 1928
  V. tobacco streak
    Diachun, Stephen and W.D. Valleau, 1954
N. tomentosiformis, Goodspeed
  V. chilli (pepper) mosaic
    Adsuar, J. and L. Lopez Matos, 1955
  V. potato stem mottle
    (K.M. Smith, 1957) R.E. Fitzpatrick, et al., 1958
  V. tobacco mosaic
    Adsuar, J. and L. Lopez Matos, 1955
    Diachun, Stephen and W.D. Valleau, 1954
    Holmes, Francis O., 1946
    Weber, Paul V.V., 1951
  V. tobacco streak
    Diachun, Stephen and W.D. Valleau, 1954
N. trigonophylla, Dun.
  V. tobacco etch
    Holmes, Francis O., 1946
  V. tobacco mosaic
    Diachun, Stephen and W.D. Valleau, 1954
    Holmes, F.O., 1934, 1946
  V. tobacco ring spot
    Wingard, S.A., 1928
  V. tobacco streak
    Diachun, Stephen and W.D. Valleau, 1954
  V. turnip mosaic
    Walker, J.C., Francis J. LeBeau and Glenn S.
    Pound, 1945
  V. vaccinium false blossom
    (K.M. Smith, 1957) R.E. Fitzpatrick, et al., 1958
N. undulata, Ruiz & Pav.
  V. chilli (pepper) mosaic
    Adsuar, J. and L. Lopez Matos, 1955
  V. potato yellow dwarf
    Black, L.M., 1938
  V. tobacco etch
    Holmes, Francis O., 1946
  V. tobacco mosaic
    Adsuar, J. and L. Lopez Matos, 1955
    Diachun, Stephen and W.D. Valleau, 1954
    Holmes, Francis O., 1946
  V. tobacco streak
    Diachun, Stephen and W.D. Valleau, 1954
N. velutina, Wheeler
  V. chilli (pepper) mosaic
    Adsuar, J. and L. Lopez Matos, 1955
  V. tobacco mosaic
    Adsuar, J. and L. Lopez Matos, 1955
    Diachun, Stephen and W.D. Valleau, 1954
  V. tobacco streak
    Diachun, Stephen and W.D. Valleau, 1954
N. wigandioides, Koch & Fint
  V. tobacco mosaic
    Holmes, Francis O., 1946

NIEREMBERGIA Ruiz & Pav. 1794 (Solanaceae)
N. frutescens, Dur.
  V. clover big vein
    Black, L.M., 1945

N. frutescens, Dur. (cont.)
  V. vaccinium false blossom
    Kunkel, L.O., 1945
N. hippomanica, Miers
  V. prunus B *
    Fulton, Robert W., 1957
  V. tobacco etch
    Holmes, Francis O., 1946
  V. tobacco mosaic
    Holmes, Francis O., 1946

NIGELLA ((Tourn.)) L. 1735 (Ranunculaceae)
N. damascena, L.
  V. aster yellows
    Severin, Henry H.P. and Julius H. Freitag, 1945
  V. beet curly top
    Freitag, Julius H. and Henry H.P. Severin, 1936

NITROPHILA S. Wats. 1871 (Chenopodiaceae)
N. occidentalis, S. Wats.
  V. beet curly top
    Severin, Henry H.P. and Charles F. Henderson,
    1928

NOLANA L. 1762 (Nolanaceae)
N. atriplicifolia, Hort. ex D. Don
  V. clover big vein
    Black, L.M., 1945
N. lanceolata, Miers
  V. potato leaf roll
    (K.M. Smith, 1957) R.E. Fitzpatrick, et al., 1958
  V. tobacco etch
    Holmes, Francis O., 1946
  V. tobacco mosaic
    Holmes, Francis O., 1946

NOTHOPANAX Miq., Seem. 1866 (Araliaceae)
N. guilfoylei, Merr.
  V. panax ring spot
    Aragaki, M. and H. Murakishi, and J.W. Hendrix,
    1953

NOTHOSCORDUM Kunth 1843 (Liliaceae)
N. fragrans, (Vent.) Kunth
  V. nothoscordum mosaic
    McKinney, H.H., 1950

ODONTOGLOSSUM H. B. & K. 1815 (Orchidaceae)
O. grande, Lindl.
  V. orchid (odontoglossum) ring spot
    Jensen, D.D. and A. Herbert Gold, 1951, 1952

OENANTHE ((Tourn.)) L. 1735 (Umbelliferae)
O. sarmentosa, Presl ex DC.
  V. lucerne dwarf
    Freitag, J.H., 1951

OENOTHERA L. 1735 (Onagraceae)
O. biennis, L.
  V. tobacco streak
    Fulton, Robert W., 1948
O. hookeri, Torr. & Gray
  V. lucerne dwarf
    Freitag, J.H., 1951
O. spp.
  V. tobacco ring spot no. 2
    Wilkinson, R.E., 1952

ONCIDIUM Sw. 1800 (Orchidaceae)
O. rogers, Hort. *
  V. orchid (oncidium rogers) *
    Jensen, D.D. and A. Herbert Gold, 1952
O. spp.
  V. orchid (cymbidium) mosaic
    Jensen, D.D. and A.H. Gold, 1955

ORNITHOGALUM ((Tourn.)) L. 1735 (Liliaceae)
O. thyrsoides, Jacq.
  V. ornithogalum mosaic
    Smith, Floyd F. and Philip Brierley, 1944

ORYZA L. 1735 (Gramineae)
O. minuta, J. & C. Presl
   V. rice and corn leaf-gall *
      Agati, Julian A. and Carlos A. Calica, 1950
O. sativa, L.
   V. barley stripe mosaic
      Kahn, Robert P. and Ottie J. Dickerson, 1957
      McKinney, H.H., 1951
   V. brome mosaic
      Kahn, Robert P. and Ottie J. Dickerson, 1957
   V. oat pseudo-rosette
      (K.M. Smith, 1957) R.E. Fitzpatrick, et al., 1958
   V. rice and corn leaf-gall *
      Agati, Julian A. and Carlos Calica, 1949
   V. rice dwarf
      Agati, Julian A., Pedro L. Sison and Roman
      Abalos, 1941
   V. rice stunt
      Katsura, S., 1936.

ORYZOPSIS Michx. 1803 (Gramineae)
O. hymenoides, (Roem. & Schult.) Ricker
   V. wheat streak mosaic
      McKinney, H.H. and Hurley Fellows, 1951
      Slykhuis, John T., 1954, 1955

OXALIS L. 1737 (Oxalidaceae)
O. corniculata, L.
   V. beet curly top
      Severin, Henry H.P., 1934
O. corniculata var. atropurpurea, Planch.
   V. beet curly top
      Severin, Henry H.P., 1934
O. spp.
   V. beet curly top
      Bennett, C.W. and A.S. Costa, 1949
   V. euphorbia mosaic
      Costa, A.S. and C.W. Bennett, 1950
O. stricta, L.
   V. beet curly top
      Starrett, Ruth C., 1929

PAEONIA ((Tourn.)) L. 1735 (Ranunculaceae)
P. officinalis, L.
   V. peony leaf curl *
      Brierley, Philip and Paul Lorentz, 1957
P. spp.
   V. peony ring spot
      (K.M. Smith, 1957) R.E. Fitzpatrick, et al., 1958
   V. tomato spotted wilt
      (K.M. Smith, 1957) R.E. Fitzpatrick, et al., 1958

PAMBURUS Swingle 1916 (Rutaceae)
P. missionis, Swingle
   V. citrus tristeza
      Knorr, L.C., 1956

PANICUM L. 1735 (Gramineae)
P. capillare, L.
   V. barley stripe mosaic
      Slykhuis, J.T., 1952
   V. barley yellow dwarf
      Oswald, John W. and Byron R. Houston, 1953
   V. panicum mosaic *
      Sill, W.H., Jr. and R.C. Pickett, 1957
   V. wheat streak mosaic
      Slykhuis, J.T., 1952, 1955
   V. wheat striate mosaic
      Slykhuis, J.T., 1952, 1953
P. dichotomiflorum, Michx.
   V. sugarcane mosaic
      Brandes, E.W., 1920
      Brandes, E.W. and Peter J. Klaphaak, 1923
P. hallii, Vasey
   V. panicum mosaic *
      Sill, W.H., Jr. and R.C. Pickett, 1957
P. miliaceum, L.
   V. barley stripe mosaic
      Slykhuis, J.T., 1952
   V. oat pseudo-rosette
      (K.M. Smith, 1957) R.E. Fitzpatrick, et al., 1958
   V. panicum mosaic *
      Sill, W.H., Jr. and R.C. Pickett, 1957

P. miliaceum, L. (cont.)
   V. rice dwarf
      (K.M. Smith, 1957) R.E. Fitzpatrick, et al., 1958
   V. wheat streak mosaic
      Sill, W.H., Jr. and Patrick C. Agusiobo, 1955
      Slykhuis, John T., 1955
P. ramosum, L.
   V. wheat streak mosaic
      Sill, W.H., Jr. and Patrick C. Agusiobo, 1955
P. scribnerianum, Nash
   V. panicum mosaic *
      Sill, W.H., Jr. and R.C. Pickett, 1957
P. virgatum, L.
   V. panicum mosaic *
      Sill, W.H., Jr., 1957
      Sill, W.H., Jr. and R.C. Pickett, 1957

PAPAVER Tourn. ex L. 1735 (Papaveraceae)
P. dubium, L.
   V. beet yellows
      Roland, G. and J. Tahon, 1961
P. nudicaule, L.
   V. beet curly top
      Freitag, Julius H. and Henry H.P. Severin, 1936
   V. cabbage black ring spot
      Hamlyn, Brenda M.G., 1953
      Tompkins, C.M., M.W. Gardner and H. Rex
      Thomas, 1938
   V. tobacco mosaic
      Holmes, Francis O., 1946
P. orientale, L.
   V. beet curly top
      Freitag, Julius H. and Henry H.P. Severin, 1936
   V. tobacco necrosis
      Price, W.C., 1940
   V. tomato spotted wilt
      Gardner, M.W., C.M. Tompkins and O.C.
      Whipple, 1935
P. rhoeas, L.
   V. anemone mosaic *
      Hollings, M., 1957
   V. beet yellows
      (K.M. Smith, 1957) R.E. Fitzpatrick, et al., 1958
      Roland, G. and J. Tahon, 1961
   V. cabbage black ring spot
      Hamlyn, Brenda M.G., 1953
P. somniferum, L.
   V. anemone mosaic *
      Hollings, M., 1957
   V. cabbage black ring spot
      Hamlyn, Brenda M.G., 1953
      Hollings, M., 1957
   V. chrysanthemum latent *
      Hollings, M., 1957
P. spp.
   V. tomato spotted wilt
      (K.M. Smith, 1957) R.E. Fitzpatrick, et al., 1958

PARTHENIUM L. 1735 (Compositae)
P. argentatum, A. Gray
   V. tobacco mosaic
      Severin, Henry H.P., 1945
   V. tobacco ring spot
      Severin, Henry H.P., 1945

PARTHENOCISSUS Planch. in DC. 1887 (Vitaceae)
P. tricuspidata, (Sieb. & Zucc.) Planch.
   V. lucerne dwarf
      Freitag, J.H., 1951

PASPALUM L. 1759 (Gramineae)
P. boscianum, Flugge
   V. sugarcane mosaic
      Brandes, E.W. and Peter J. Klaphaak, 1923
P. conjugatum, Bergius
   V. sugarcane mosaic
      Lawas, Orencio M. and William L. Fernandez,
      1949
P. dilatatum, Poir.
   V. lucerne dwarf
      Freitag, J.H., 1951

PASSIFLORA L. 1735 (Passifloraceae)
P. alba, Link & Otto
  V. cucumber mosaic
    McKnight, T., 1953
P. caerulea, L.
  V. anemone mosaic *
    Hollings, M., 1957
  V. cabbage black ring spot
    Hollings, M., 1957
  V. chrysanthemum B (mild mosaic) *
    Hollings, M., 1957
  V. cucumber mosaic
    Nattrass, R.M., 1944
P. edulis, Sims
  V. cucumber mosaic
    McKnight, T., 1953
    Nattrass, R.M., 1944
P. edulis f. flavicarpa *
  V. cucumber mosaic
    McKnight, T., 1953
P. foetida, L.
  V. cucumber mosaic
    McKnight, T., 1953
  V. passiflora foetida mosaic *
    Jensen, D.D., 1949
P. ligularis, Juss.
  V. cucumber mosaic
    Nattrass, R.M., 1944
P. pfordtii, X Hort. ex Degener
  V. passiflora pfordti mosaic *
    Jensen, D.D., 1949
P. suberosa, L.
  V. cucumber mosaic
    McKnight, T., 1953
P. subpeltata, Ort.
  V. cucumber mosaic
    Nattrass, R.M., 1944

PASTINACA L. 1737 (Umbelliferae)
P. sativa, L.
  V. aster yellows
    Severin, Henry H.P., 1932, 1934
    Severin, Henry H.P. and Julius H. Freitag, 1945
  V. celery mosaic
    Freitag, Julius H. and Henry H.P. Severin, 1945
  V. celery yellow spot
    Freitag, Julius H. and Henry H.P. Severin, 1945
  V. cucumber mosaic
    Wellman, F.L., 1935
  V. datura rugose leaf curl
    (K.M. Smith, 1957) R.E. Fitzpatrick, et al., 1958
  V. poison hemlock ring spot
    Freitag, Julius H. and Henry H.P. Severin, 1945
  V. tobacco ring spot no. 2
    Wilkinson, R.E., 1952
  V. vaccinium false blossom
    Kunkel, L.O., 1945

PECTOCARYA DC. ex Meissn. 1840 (Boraginaceae)
P. pusilla, A. Gray
  V. beet yellows
    Roland, G. and J. Tahon, 1961

PELARGONIUM L'Herit. 1787 (Geraniaceae)
P. domesticum, Bailey
  V. filaree red leaf
    Anderson, Chris W., 1952
P. hederaceum *
  V. pelargonium leaf curl
    (K.M. Smith, 1957) R.E. Fitzpatrick, et al., 1958
P. hortorum, Bafley (X P. zonale, Willd.)
  V. beet curly top
    Freitag, Julius H. and Henry H.P. Severin, 1936
    Severin, Henry H.P., 1939
    Severin, Henry H.P. and Julius H. Freitag, 1934
  V. cucumber mosaic
    Wellman, F.L., 1935
  V. lucerne dwarf
    Freitag, J.H., 1951
  V. pelargonium leaf curl
    (K.M. Smith, 1957) R.E. Fitzpatrick, et al., 1958
    Jones, L.K., 1938, 1940
  V. pelargonium mosaic
    Jones, L.K., 1938, 1940

P. hortorum, Bailey (X P. zonale, Willd.) (cont.)
  V. pelargonium ring spot *
    Hollings, M., 1957
  V. tobacco necrosis
    (K.M. Smith, 1957) R.E. Fitzpatrick, et al., 1958
  V. tobacco ring spot no. 2
    Hildebrand, E.M., 1942
    Price, W.C., 1940
P. peltatum, Ait.
  V. pelargonium ring spot *
    Hollings, M., 1957
P. spp.
  V. pelargonium leaf curl
    McWhorter, Frank P., 1957

PENNISETUM Rich. 1805 (Gramineae)
P. clandestimum, Hochst. ex Chiov.
  V. lucerne dwarf
    Freitag, J.H., 1951
P. glaucum, (L.) R. Br.
  V. sugarcane mosaic
    Brandes, E.W. and Peter J. Klaphaak, 1923
P. purpureum, Schumach.
  V. sugarcane chlorotic streak *
    Bruehl, G.W., 1953

PENSTEMON
(PENTSTEMON) Mitch. 1748 (Scrophulariaceae)
P. barbatus, Roth
  V. tobacco mosaic
    Grant, T.J., 1934
P. grandiflorus, Nutt.
  V. tobacco etch
    Holmes, Francis O., 1946
  V. tobacco mosaic
    Holmes, Francis O., 1946
P. hirsutus, (L.) Willd.
  V. tomato spotted wilt
    Gardner, M.W., C.M. Tompkins and O.C.
    Whipple, 1935
P. spp.
  V. cucumber mosaic
    (K.M. Smith, 1957) R.E. Fitzpatrick, et al., 1958
  V. lucerne mosaic
    Price, W.C., 1940
  V. tobacco necrosis
    Price, W.C., 1940
  V. tobacco ring spot
    Price, W.C., 1940
  V. tobacco ring spot no. 2
    Price, W.C., 1940

PERSEA Plum. ex L. 1737 (Lauraceae)
P. americana, Mill.
  V. avocado pear sun blotch
    Horne, W.T. and E.R. Parker, 1931
    Stevens, H.E., 1939

PETROSELINUM Hoffm. 1814 (Umbelliferae)
P. crispum, (Mill.) Nym.
  V. aster yellows
    Severin, H.H.P., 1930
    Severin, Henry H.P. and Julius H. Freitag, 1945
  V. peach western X disease
    Weathers, Lewis G. and George W. Cochran, 1950
  V. peach X disease
    Kunkel, L.O., 1944
    Slack, Derald A., 1952
  V. poison hemlock ring spot
    Freitag, Julius H. and Henry H.P. Severin, 1939,
    1945
P. crispum var. latifolium, (Mill.) Nym.
  V. celery mosaic
    Freitag, Julius H. and Henry H.P. Severin, 1945
  V. poison hemlock ring spot
    Freitag, Julius H. and Henry H.P. Severin, 1945
P. hortense, Hoffm.
  V. aster yellows
    Severin, Henry H.P., 1932, 1934
  V. beet curly top
    Severin, Henry H.P., 1929
  V. celery mosaic
    Severin, Henry H.P. and Julius H. Freitag, 1938

Petroselinum hortense, Hoffm. (cont.)
  V. cucumber mosaic
    Wellman, F.L., 1935
  V. tobacco mosaic
    Holmes, Francis O., 1946
  V. vaccinium false blossom
    Kunkel, L.O., 1945
P. hortense var. crispum *
  V. aster yellows
    Severin, Henry H.P., 1932
P. hortense var. radicosum, Bailey *
  V. aster yellows
    Severin, Henry H.P., 1932, 1934
    Severin, Henry H.P. and Julius H. Freitag, 1945
  V. poison hemlock ring spot
    Freitag, Julius H. and Henry H.P. Severin, 1945

PETUNIA Juss. 1803 (Solanaceae)
P. axillaris, (Lam.) BSP.
  V. tomato ring spot
    Samson, R.W. and E.P. Imle, 1942
P. hybrida, Vilm.
  V. anemone mosaic *
    Hollings, M., 1957
  V. aster yellows
    Severin, Henry H.P. and Julius H. Freitag, 1945
  V. beet curly top
    Bennett, C.W., Eubanks Carsner, F.H. Coons
    and E.W. Brandes, 1946
    Bennett, C.W. and Aziz Tanrisever, 1957
    Costa, A.S., 1952
    Freitag, Julius H. and Henry H.P. Severin, 1936
    Fulton, Robert W., 1955
    Severin, Henry H.P. and Julius H. Freitag, 1934
  V. beet ring spot *
    Harrison, B.D., 1957
  V. cabbage black ring spot
    Hamlyn, Brenda M.G., 1953
    Hollings, M., 1957
    Tompkins, C.M., M.W. Gardner and H. Rex
    Thomas, 1938
  V. cabbage ring necrosis
    Larson, R.H. and J.C. Walker, 1940, 1941
  V. chilli (pepper) mosaic
    Dale, W.T., 1954
    Jha, Ashrafi and S.P. Raychaudhuri, 1956
  V. chrysanthemum B (mild mosaic) *
    Hollings, M., 1957
  V. chrysanthemum Q
    Brierley, Philip, 1955
    Brierley, Philip and Floyd F. Smith, 1953
  V. chrysanthemum vein mottle *
    Hollings, M., 1957
  V. cucumber mosaic
    Berkeley, G.H., 1953
    Berkeley, G.H. and J.H. Tremaine, 1954
    Burnett, G., 1934
    Dale, W.T., 1954
    Doolittle, S.P. and W.J. Zaumeyer, 1953
    Govier, D.A., 1957
    Harrison, B.D., 1958
    Harter, L.L., 1938
    Nariani, T.K. and Nirmaljit Singh, 1952
    Nienow, Inez, 1948
    Pound, Glenn S. and J.C. Walker, 1948
    Wellman, F.L., 1935
  V. datura distortion mosaic
    Capoor, S.P. and P.M. Varma, 1952
  V. delphinium ring spot
    Severin, Henry H.P. and R.C. Dickson, 1942
  V. eggplant mosaic
    Dale, W.T., 1954
  V. lucerne mosaic
    Berkeley, G.H., 1947
    Kreitlow, K.W. and W.C. Price, 1948, 1949
    Pierce, W.H., 1934
    Richardson, D.E. and T.W. Tinsley, 1956
    Severin, Henry H.P., 1942
    Snyder, William C. and Saul Rich, 1942
    Zaumeyer, W.J., 1938
  V. pea die back *
    Zaumeyer, W.J., 1939
  V. pea stem streak *
    Zaumeyer, W.J., 1939

P. hybrida, Vilm. (cont.)
  V. (physalis) mosaic *
    Melhus, I.E., 1922
  V. potato A
    MacLachlan, D.S., R.H. Larson and J.C. Walker,
    1953
  V. potato leaf roll
    Webb, R.E., R.H. Larson and J.C. Walker, 1952
  V. potato X
    Dykstra, T.P., 1933
  V. potato Y
    Dykstra, T.P., 1933, 1939
    Sakimura, K., 1953
    Vasudeva, R. Sahai and T.B. Lal, 1945
  V. prunus A *
    Fulton, Robert W., 1957
  V. prunus B *
    Fulton, Robert W., 1957
  V. prunus E *
    Fulton, Robert W., 1957
  V. prunus G *
    Fulton, Robert W., 1957
  V. raspberry Scottish leaf curl
    Harrison, B.D., 1958
    Lister, R.M., 1958
  V. raspberry yellow dwarf *
    Harrison, B.D., 1958
    Lister, R.M., 1958
  V. red currant ring spot
    Klesser, P.J., 1951
  V. rose mosaic
    Fulton, Robert W., 1952
  V. sweet clover new *
    Henderson, R.G., 1934
  V. sweet potato mosaic
    Elmer, O.H., 1957
  V. tobacco etch
    Holmes, Francis O., 1946
  V. tobacco mosaic
    Allard, H.A., 1916
    Holmes, Francis O., 1946
  V. tobacco ring spot
    Berkeley, G.H., 1953
    Cheo, Pen Ching and W.J. Zaumeyer, 1952
    Cooper, W.E., 1949
    Dunleavy, John M., 1957
    Grogan, R.G., Roy Bardin and W.C. Schnathorst,
    1954
    Grogan, R.G. and W.C. Schnathorst, 1955
    Pound, Glenn S., 1949
    Priode, C.N., 1928
    Shepherd, Robert J. and F. Ben Struble, 1956
    Smith, Kenneth M., 1929
    Starr, Chester K. and W.E. Cooper, 1944
    Steere, Russell L., 1956
  V. tobacco ring spot no. 2
    Brierley, Philip, 1954
  V. tobacco streak
    Fulton, Robert W., 1948
  V. tomato aspermy
    Brierley, Philip and Floyd F. Smith, 1953
    Brierley, Philip, Floyd F. Smith and S.P.
    Doolittle, 1953, 1955
  V. tomato black ring
    Harrison, B.D., 1958
  V. tomato spotted wilt
    Gardner, M.W. and O.C. Whipple, 1934
    Milbrath, J.A., 1939
    Sakimura, K., 1940
  V. turnip mosaic
    Berkeley, G.H. and J.H. Tremaine, 1954
    Berkeley, G.H. and M. Weintraub, 1952
    LeBeau, Francis J. and J.C. Walker, 1945
    Tompkins, C.M., 1938, 1939
  V. vaccinium false blossom
    Kunkel, L.O., 1945
P. hybrida var. erecta *
  V. tomato aspermy
    Hollings, M., 1955
P. hybrida var. grandiflora *
  V. tomato ring spot
    Samson, R.W. and E.P. Imle, 1942

Petunia hybrida, Vilm., var. nana compacta *
   V. bayberry yellows
      Raychaudhuri, S.P., 1953
   V. tomato aspermy
      Hollings, M., 1955
P. nyctaginiflora, Juss.
   V. potato X
      Dennis, R.W.G., 1939
   V. potato Y
      Smith, Kenneth M. and R.W.G. Dennis, 1940
P. spp.
   V. carrot motley dwarf
      (K.M. Smith, 1957) R.E. Fitzpatrick, et al., 1958
   V. henbane mosaic
      Hamilton, Marion A., 1932
   V. lucerne mosaic
      Porter, D.R., 1935
   V. lucerne witches' broom
      Helms, Katie, 1957
   V. potato aucuba mosaic
      (K.M. Smith, 1957) R.E. Fitzpatrick, et al., 1958
   V. raspberry Scottish leaf curl
      Cadman, C.H., 1956
   V. tobacco leaf curl
      Pal, B.P. and R.K. Tandon, 1937
   V. tobacco mosaic
      Ainsworth, G.C., 1933
      Das, C.R. and S.P. Raychaudhuri, 1953
   V. tomato big bud
      Helms, Katie, 1957
   V. tomato spotted wilt
      Berkeley, G.H., 1935
      Norris, D.O., 1951
      Smith, Kenneth M., 1932
   V. tropaeolum ring spot
      (K.M. Smith, 1957) R.E. Fitzpatrick, et al., 1958
   V. tulip white streak
      (K.M. Smith, 1957) R.E. Fitzpatrick, et al., 1958
P. violacea, Lindl.
   V. cucumber mosaic
      Hoggan, Isme A., 1927
      Johnson, J., 1926, 1927
   V. petunia mosaic
      Johnson, J., 1926, 1927
   V. potato X
      Hoggan, Isme A., 1927
      Johnson, James, 1925, 1927
      Smith, J. Henderson, 1928
   V. potato Y
      Hoggan, Isme A., 1927
      Johnson, James, 1927
   V. tobacco broad ring spot
      Johnson, James and Robert W. Fulton, 1942
   V. tobacco etch
      Fulton, Robert W., 1941
   V. tobacco mosaic
      Fulton, Robert W., 1941
      Hoggan, Isme A., 1927
      Jarrett, Phyllis H., 1930
      Johnson, J., 1926, 1927
   V. tobacco ring spot
      Fulton, Robert W., 1941
      Henderson, R.G., 1931
      Henderson, R.G. and S.A. Wingard, 1931
      Wingard, S.A., 1928

PHACELIA Juss. 1789 (Hydrophyllaceae)
P. campanularia, Gray
   V. beet mosaic
      Bennett, C.W., 1949
   V. clover big vein
      Black, L.M., 1945
   V. lucerne mosaic
      Price, W.C., 1940
   V. squash mosaic
      Freitag, J.H., 1956
   V. tobacco etch
      Holmes, Francis O., 1946
      Grant, T.J., 1934
   V. tobacco mosaic
      Holmes, Francis O., 1946
   V. tobacco necrosis
      Price, W.C., 1940

P. campanularia, Gray (cont.)
   V. tobacco ring spot
      Price, W.C., 1940
P. ciliata, Benth.
   V. tobacco etch
      Holmes, Francis O., 1946
   V. tobacco mosaic
      Holmes, Francis O., 1946
P. parryi, Torr.
   V. tobacco mosaic
      Grant, T.J., 1934
P. ramosissima, Dougl. ex Lehm.
   V. beet curly top
      Severin, Henry H.P., 1934, 1939
P. tanacetifolia, Benth.
   V. cucumber mosaic
      Wellman, F.L., 1935
   V. tobacco mosaic
      Grant, T.J., 1934
P. viscida, (Benth.) Torr.
   V. tobacco etch
      Holmes, Francis O., 1946
   V. tobacco mosaic
      Holmes, Francis O., 1946
P. whitlavia, A. Gray (Whitlavia grandiflora, Harv.)
   V. cucumber mosaic
      Wellman, F.L., 1934, 1935
   V. tobacco etch
      Holmes, Francis O., 1946
   V. tobacco mosaic
      Grant, T.J., 1934
      Holmes, Francis O., 1946

PHALARIS L. 1735 (Gramineae)
P. arundinacea, L.
   V. barley yellow dwarf
      Bruehl, G.W. and H.V. Toko, 1957
P. minor, Retz.
   V. lucerne dwarf
      Freitag, J.H., 1951
P. paradoxa, L.
   V. barley yellow dwarf
      Oswald, John W. and Byron R. Houston, 1953
   V. lucerne dwarf
      Freitag, J.H., 1951
   V. wheat streak mosaic
      McKinney, H.H. and Hurley Fellows, 1951
P. spp.
   V. barley yellow dwarf
      Oswald, John W. and Byron R. Houston, 1952
P. tuberosa, L.
   V. barley yellow dwarf
      Oswald, John W. and Byron R. Houston, 1953
P. tuberosa var. stenoptera, (Hack.) Hitchc.
   V. maize leaf fleck
      Stoner, Warren N., 1952

PHARBITIS Choisy 1833 (Convolvulaceae)
P. diversifolia *
   V. sweet potato internal cork
      Hildebrand, E.M. and H.A. Borthwick, 1956
      Hildebrand, E.M. and F.F. Smith, 1956
P. hederacea, Choisy
   V. sweet potato internal cork
      Hildebrand, E.M. and H.A. Borthwick, 1956

PHASEOLUS ((Tourn.)) L. 1735 (Leguminosae)
P. aconitifolius, Jacq.
   V. bean common mosaic
      Nelson, Ray, 1932
      Thomas, H. Rex and W.J. Zaumeyer, 1953
   V. lucerne mosaic
      Thomas, H. Rex, 1951
   V. rose mosaic
      Fulton, Robert W., 1952
   V. tobacco ring spot
      Cheo, Pen Ching and W.J. Zaumeyer, 1952
   V. tobacco streak
      Fulton, Robert W., 1948
      Thomas, H. Rex and W.J. Zaumeyer, 1950
P. acutifolius, A. Gray
   V. lucerne mosaic
      Thomas, H. Rex, 1951

Phaseolus acutifolius, A. Gray, var. latifolius, Freeman
 V. bean common mosaic
  Nelson, Ray, 1932
  Pierce, W.H., 1934
  Reddick, D. and V.B. Stewart, 1919
 V. bean yellow mosaic
  Pierce, W.H., 1934
  Thomas, H. Rex and W.J. Zaumeyer, 1953
  Zaumeyer, W.J. and H.H. Fisher, 1953
 V. bean yellow stipple
  Zaumeyer, W.J. and H. Rex Thomas, 1950
 V. cucumber mosaic
  Doolittle, S.P. and W.J. Zaumeyer, 1953
 V. lucerne mosaic
  Thomas, H.R., 1953
  Zaumeyer, W.J., 1953
 V. pea mosaic
  Murphy, D.M. and W.H. Pierce, 1937
 V. tobacco ring spot
  Cheo, Pen Ching and W.J. Zaumeyer, 1952
P. angularis, (Willd.) W.F. Wright
 V. bean common mosaic
  Nelson, Ray, 1932
 V. bean yellow mosaic
  Zaumeyer, W.J. and B.L. Wade, 1935
 V. cowpea mosaic
  Yu, T.F., 1946
 V. lucerne mosaic
  Pierce, W.H., 1934
  Thomas, H. Rex, 1951
  Zaumeyer, W.J., 1938
  Zaumeyer, W.J. and B.L. Wade, 1935
 V. tobacco ring spot
  Cheo, Pen Ching and W.J. Zaumeyer, 1952
  Pierce, W.H., 1934
P. aureus, Roxb.
 V. bean common mosaic
  Pierce, W.H., 1934
 V. bean double yellow mosaic
  (K.M. Smith, 1957) R.E. Fitzpatrick, et al., 1958
 V. bean yellow mosaic
  Osborn, H.T., 1938
  Pierce, W.H., 1934
  Zaumeyer, W.J. and H.H. Fisher, 1953
  Zaumeyer, W.J. and B.L. Wade, 1935
 V. cowpea mosaic
  Dale, W.T., 1949
 V. cucumber mosaic
  Price, W.C., 1940
 V. lucerne mosaic
  Pierce, W.H., 1934
  Thomas, H. Rex, 1951
  Zaumeyer, W.J., 1938
  Zaumeyer, W.J. and B.L. Wade, 1935
 V. pea mottle
  Johnson, Folke, 1942
 V. pea wilt
  Johnson, Folke, 1942
 V. red clover mosaic *
  Zaumeyer, W.J. and B.L. Wade, 1935
 V. rose mosaic
  Fulton, Robert W., 1952
 V. tobacco necrosis
  Price, W.C., 1940
 V. tobacco ring spot
  Cheo, Pen Ching and W.J. Zaumeyer, 1952
  Cooper, W.E., 1949
  Pierce, W.H., 1934
  Starr, Chester K. and W.E. Cooper, 1944
 V. tobacco streak
  Fulton, Robert W., 1948
  Thomas, H. Rex and W.J. Zaumeyer, 1950
P. calcaratus, Roxb.
 V. bean common mosaic
  Nelson, Ray, 1932
  Pierce, W.H., 1934
 V. bean yellow stipple
  Zaumeyer, W.J. and H. Rex Thomas, 1950
 V. cucumber mosaic
  Doolittle, S.P. and W.J. Zaumeyer, 1953
 V. lucerne mosaic
  Pierce, W.H., 1934
  Thomas, H. Rex, 1951
  Zaumeyer, W.J. and B.L. Wade, 1935

P. calcaratus, Roxb. (cont.)
 V. tobacco ring spot
  Pierce, W.H., 1934
P. coccineus, L.
 V. bean common mosaic
  Nelson, Ray, 1932
 V. bean yellow stipple
  Zaumeyer, W.J. and H. Rex Thomas, 1950
 V. lucerne mosaic
  Thomas, H. Rex, 1951
 V. tobacco ring spot
  Cheo, Pen Ching and W.J. Zaumeyer, 1952
 V. tobacco streak
  Thomas, H. Rex and W.J. Zaumeyer, 1950
P. lathyroides, L.
 V. tobacco ring spot
  Cheo, Pen Ching and W.J. Zaumeyer, 1952
P. limensis, MacF.
 V. bean common mosaic
  Nelson, Ray, 1932
 V. bean double yellow mosaic
  (K.M. Smith, 1957) R.E. Fitzpatrick, et al., 1958
 V. bean yellow mosaic
  (K.M. Smith, 1957) R.E. Fitzpatrick, et al., 1958
 V. cowpea mosaic
  Anderson, C.W., 1955
 V. cucumber mosaic
  Anderson, C.W., 1955
  Harter, L.L., 1936
  Thomas, H. Rex, W.J. Zaumeyer and Hans
   Jorgensen, 1951
 V. tobacco ring spot
  Pierce, W.H., 1934
P. lunatus, L.
 V. bean common mosaic
  Nelson, Ray, 1932
  Pierce, W.H., 1934
 V. bean double yellow mosaic
  (K.M. Smith, 1957) R.E. Fitzpatrick, et al., 1958
 V. bean pod mottle
  Zaumeyer, W.J. and H. Rex Thomas, 1948
 V. bean southern mosaic
  Zaumeyer, W.J. and L.L. Harter, 1943
 V. bean yellow mosaic
  Zaumeyer, W.J. and H.H. Fisher, 1953
 V. beet curly top
  Severin, Henry H.P. and Charles F. Henderson,
   1928
 V. cowpea mosaic
  Dale, W.T., 1949
 V. cucumber mosaic
  Doolittle, S.P. and W.J. Zaumeyer, 1953
  Whipple, O.C. and J.C. Walker, 1941
 V. kaimi clover disease *
  Murakishi, Harry H., 1952
 V. lucerne mosaic
  Kreitlow, K.W. and W.C. Price, 1948, 1949
  Thomas, H. Rex, 1951
  Zaumeyer, W.J., 1938, 1953
 V. pea die back *
  Zaumeyer, W.J., 1939
 V. pea stem streak *
  Zaumeyer, W.J., 1939
 V. tobacco ring spot
  Cooper, W.E., 1949
  LeBeau, F.J., 1947
  Pierce, W.H., 1934
  Wingard, S.A., 1928
P. lunatus f. macrocarpus, (Benth.) Van Ess.
 V. bean common mosaic
  Pierce, W.H., 1934
  Reddick, D. and V.B. Stewart, 1919
 V. cowpea mosaic
  Capoor, S.P. and P.M. Varma, 1956
  Dale, W.T., 1949
  McLean, D.M., 1941
  Yu, T.F., 1946
 V. cucumber mosaic
  Harter, L.L., 1938
  Pryor, Dean E. and Robert E. Wester, 1946
 V. subterranean clover mosaic
  Aitken, Y. and B.J. Grieve, 1943

Phaseolus lunatus, L. x P. lunatus f. macrocarpus,
(Benth.) Van Ess.
   V. bean pod mottle
      Zaumeyer, W.J. and H. Rex Thomas, 1948
   V. bean southern mosaic
      Zaumeyer, W.J. and L.L. Harter, 1943
P. multiflora, Willd.
   V. tobacco ring spot
      LeBeau, F.J., 1947
P. mungo, L.
   V. bean common mosaic
      Nelson, Ray, 1932
   V. bean yellow stipple
      Zaumeyer, W.J. and H. Rex Thomas, 1950
   V. cowpea mosaic
      Dale, W.T., 1949
   V. lucerne mosaic
      Thomas, H. Rex, 1951
      Zaumeyer, W.J., 1938
      Zaumeyer, W.J. and B.L. Wade, 1935
   V. tobacco ring spot
      Cheo, Pen Ching and W.J. Zaumeyer, 1952
   V. tobacco streak
      Thomas, H. Rex and W.J. Zaumeyer, 1950
P. radiatus, L. var. aurea *
   V. bean common mosaic
      Matsumoto, T., 1922
P. trinervius, Heyne ex Wall.
   V. cowpea mosaic
      Dale, W.T., 1949
P. vulgaris, L.
   V. alsike clover mosaic
      Harrison, Arthur L., 1935
      Zaumeyer, W.J., 1933, 1940
      Zaumeyer, W.J. and B.L. Wade, 1935, 1936
   V. apple mosaic
      Yarwood, C.E., 1955
      Yarwood, C.E. and H.E. Thomas, 1954
   V. apricot ring pox
      Yarwood, C.E., 1957
   V. arabis mosaic
      Smith, Kenneth M. and Roy Markham, 1944
   V. aster ring spot
      (K.M. Smith, 1957) R.E. Fitzpatrick, et al., 1958
   V. atropa belladonna mosaic
      (K.M. Smith, 1957) R.E. Fitzpatrick, et al., 1958
   V. bean common mosaic
      Ainsworth, G.C., 1940
      Bridgmon, G.H. and J.C. Walker, 1951
      Dean, Leslie L. and C.W. Hungerford, 1946, 1954
      Fajardo, T.G., 1928, 1930
      Fernow, Karl Hermann, 1925
      (K.M. Smith, 1957) R.E. Fitzpatrick, et al., 1958
      Fulton, Robert W., 1941
      Grogan, Raymond G. and J.C. Walker, 1948
      Harrison, Arthur L., 1935
      Jenkins, Wilbert A., 1940
      Mackie, W.W. and Katherine Esau, 1932
      Murphy, Donald M., 1940
      Murphy, Donald M. and W.H. Pierce, 1938
      Nelson, Ray, 1932
      Parker, M.C., 1936
      Pierce, W.H., 1934, 1935, 1937
      Pierce, W.H. and C.W. Hungerford, 1929
      Reddick, D. and V.B. Stewart, 1918, 1919
      Richards, B. Lorin and Walter H. Burkholder, 1943
      Smith, Francis L. and Wm. B. Hewitt, 1938
      Snyder, W.C., 1942
      Stewart, V.B. and Donald Reddick, 1917
      Thomas, H. Rex and W.J. Zaumeyer, 1953
      Wade, B.L. and C.F. Andrus, 1941
      Walker, J.C. and J.P. Jolivette, 1943
      Yerkes, William D., Jr. and Alfonso Crispin Medina, 1957
      Zaumeyer, W.J. and H.H. Fisher, 1951
      Zaumeyer, W.J. and H. Rex Thomas, 1947, 1948
      Zaumeyer, W.J. and B.L. Wade, 1933, 1935
   V. bean double yellow mosaic
      (K.M. Smith, 1957) R.E. Fitzpatrick, et al., 1958
   V. bean leaf wilt
      Johnson, James, 1942
   V. bean Montana *
      Afanasiev, M.M. and H.E. Morris, 1946

P. vulgaris, L. (cont.)
   V. bean mosaic 3 *
      Zaumeyer, W.J. and B.L. Wade, 1933, 1935
   V. bean pod mottle
      Thomas, H. Rex and W.J. Zaumeyer, 1950
      Zaumeyer, W.J. and H. Rex Thomas, 1948, 1950
   V. bean southern mosaic
      Bain, Douglas C., 1950
      Bridgmon, G.H., 1951
      Bridgmon, G.H. and J.C. Walker, 1951
      Mitchell, J.W., W.H. Preston, Jr. and J.M. Beal, 1956
      Price, W.C. and Betty R. Holt, 1948
      Zaumeyer, W.J. and H.H. Fisher, 1951
      Zaumeyer, W.J. and L.L. Harter, 1942, 1943, 1944
      Zaumeyer, W.J. and H. Rex Thomas, 1948, 1950
   V. bean yellow mosaic
      Afanasiev, M.M. and H.E. Morris, 1952
      Ainsworth, G.C., 1940
      Baggett, James R., 1956, 1957
      Berkeley, G.H., 1953
      Bridgmon, G.H. and J.C. Walker, 1952
      Brierley, Philip, 1952
      Conover, Robert A., 1948
      Grogan, Ray G., 1948
      Grogan, Raymond G. and J.C. Walker, 1948
      Hagedorn, D.J. and J.C. Walker, 1949, 1950, 1954
      Harrison, Arthur L., 1935
      Houston, Byron R. and John W. Oswald, 1953
      Hungerford, C.W. and Irvin G. Hillyer, 1954
      Johnson, James, 1942
      McWhorter, Frank P., 1949
      Murphy, Donald M., 1940
      Osborn, H.T., 1938
      Pierce, W.H., 1934, 1935, 1937
      Thomas, H.R., 1953
      Thomas, H. Rex and W.J. Zaumeyer, 1953
      Yerkes, William D., Jr. and Alfonso Crispin Medina, 1957
      Zaumeyer, W.J., 1933, 1940, 1952
      Zaumeyer, W.J. and H.H. Fisher, 1953
      Zaumeyer, W.J. and B.L. Wade, 1933, 1935, 1936
   V. bean yellow stipple
      Zaumeyer, W.J. and H. Rex Thomas, 1950
   V. beet curly top
      Bennett, C.W., 1934
      Carsner, E., 1925, 1926
      Dana, B.F., 1940
      Dean, Leslie L. and C.W. Hungerford, 1954
      Giddings, N.J., 1938, 1944
      Lackey, C.F., 1942
      Mackie, W.W. and Katherine Esau, 1932
      Murphy, Donald M., 1940
      Pierce, W.H., 1937
      Severin, Henry H.P. and Charles F. Henderson, 1928
   V. beet leaf curl
      (K.M. Smith, 1957) R.E. Fitzpatrick, et al., 1958
   V. beet ring spot *
      Harrison, B.D., 1957
   V. broad bean mottle
      Bawden, F.C., R.P. Chaudhuri and B. Kassanis, 1951
   V. brome mosaic
      McKinney, H.H., 1944, 1953
   V. canna mosaic
      Castillo, B.S., C.E. Yarwood and A.H. Gold, 1956
   V. carnation ring spot
      Brierley, Philip and Floyd F. Smith, 1955, 1957
      Kassanis, B., 1955
   V. cucumber mosaic
      Anderson, C.W., 1955
      Berkeley, G.H., 1951
      Bhargava, K.S., 1951
      Doolittle, S.P. and W.J. Zaumeyer, 1952, 1953
      Fulton, Joseph P., 1950
      Hagedorn, D.J., 1950
      Hagedorn, D.J. and J.C. Walker, 1954
      Harrison, B.D., 1958
      Hollings, M., 1955

Phaseolus vulgaris, L. (cont.)
V. cucumber mosaic
Silberschmidt, K., 1955
Thomas, H. Rex and W.J. Zaumeyer, 1953
Whipple, O.C. and J.C. Walker, 1938, 1941
V. elm mosaic
Varney, E.H. and J. Duain Moore, 1952
V. gladiolus *
Snow, Gordon F., 1955
V. iris ring spot *
Travis, R.V., 1957
V. kaimi clover disease *
Murakishi, Harry H., 1952
V. laburnum vein mosaic *
Brierley, Philip and Floyd F. Smith, 1954
V. lovage mosaic
Smith, Kenneth M. and Roy Markham, 1944
V. lucerne mosaic
Berkeley, G.H., 1947
Black, L.M. and W.C. Price, 1940
Houston, Byron R. and John W. Oswald, 1951, 1953
Johnson, E.M., 1946
Kreitlow, K.W. and W.C. Price, 1948, 1949
McWhorter, Frank P., 1949
Milbrath, J.A., 1952
Oswald, John W., 1950
Pierce, W.H., 1934, 1937
Richardson, D.E. and T.W. Tinsley, 1956
Thomas, H. Rex, 1951, 1953
Zaumeyer, W.J., 1938, 1952, 1953
Zaumeyer, W.J. and B.L. Wade, 1933, 1935
V. pea enation mosaic
Johnson, Folke and Leon K. Jones, 1937
V. pea mosaic
Hagedorn, D.J., 1948
Johnson, F. and L.K. Jones, 1936
Osborn, H.T., 1937
Zaumeyer, W.J., 1933
Zaumeyer, W.J. and B.L. Wade, 1933
V. pea mottle
Johnson, Folke, 1942
Johnson, F. and L.K. Jones, 1936, 1937
V. pea streak
Kim, Woon S. and D.J. Hagedorn, 1957
V. pea wilt
Johnson, Folke, 1942
V. peach ring spot
Yarwood, C.E., 1957
V. peach yellow bud mosaic
Karle, Harry P., 1957
Yarwood, C.E., 1956
Yarwood, C.E. and H.E. Thomas, 1954
V. ranunculus mosaic
Raabe, Robert D. and A. Herbert Gold, 1957
V. raspberry Scottish leaf curl
Cadman, C.H., 1956
Harrison, B.D., 1958
Lister, R.M., 1958
V. raspberry yellow dwarf *
Harrison, B.D., 1958
Lister, R.M., 1958
V. red clover mosaic *
Harrison, Arthur L., 1935
V. red clover vein mosaic
Graves, Clinton H., Jr. and D.J. Hagedorn, 1956
V. rhubarb ring spot *
Vaughan, Edward K. and John W. Yale, Jr., 1953
Yale, John W., Jr. and Edward K. Vaughan, 1954
V. rose mosaic
Fulton, Robert W., 1952
V. strawberry green petal
Dana, B.F., 1947
V. subterranean clover mosaic
Aitken, Y. and B.J. Grieve, 1943
V. sweet pea mosaic *
Zaumeyer, W.J., 1933
Zaumeyer, W.J. and B.L. Wade, 1933, 1935
V. tobacco bergerac ring spot
(K.M. Smith, 1957) R.E. Fitzpatrick, et al., 1958
V. tobacco broad ring spot
Johnson, James and Robert W. Fulton, 1942
V. tobacco broken ring spot
Smith, Kenneth M. and Roy Markham, 1944

P. vulgaris, L. (cont.)
V. tobacco mosaic
Berkeley, G.H., 1951
Costa, A.S., 1944
Doolittle, S.P. and F.S. Beecher, 1942
(K.M. Smith, 1957) R.E. Fitzpatrick, et al., 1958
Grant, T.J., 1934
Holmes, F.O., 1934, 1941, 1946
McKinney, H.H., 1943
McKinney, H.H. and Robert W. Fulton, 1949
Nagaich, B.B. and H.H. Thornberry, 1957
Peterson, Paul D. and H.H. McKinney, 1938
Pierce, W.H., 1934
Price, W.C., 1930
Silberschmidt, K. and M. Kramer, 1941
Spencer, E.L., 1935
Zaumeyer, W.J. and B.L. Wade, 1935
V. tobacco necrosis
Bawden, F.C. and B. Kassanis, 1947
Bawden, F.C. and F.M. Roberts, 1948
Frazier, Norman W., 1955
Fulton, J.P., 1952
Fulton, Robert W., 1950
Kassanis, B., 1949, 1955
Price, W.C., 1938
Price, W.C., Frank P. McWhorter and Betty H. Steranka, 1950
Price, W.C. and Ralph W.G. Wyckoff, 1939
V. tobacco ring spot
Allington, William B., 1946
Anderson, C.W., 1954
Berkeley, G.H., 1951, 1953
Bridgmon, G.H. and J.C. Walker, 1952
Brierley, Philip, 1952
Cheo, Pen Ching and W.J. Zaumeyer, 1952
Cooper, W.E., 1949
Grogan, R.G., Roy Bardin and W.C. Schnathorst, 1954
Grogan, R.G. and W.C. Schnathorst, 1955
Kahn, Robert P. and Frances M. Latterell, 1955
LeBeau, F.J., 1947
McKinney, H.H. and E.E. Clayton, 1944
Pierce, W.H., 1934
Pound, Glenn S., 1949
Roberts, Daniel A., 1952
Rosberg, David W., 1953
Shepherd, Robert J. and F. Ben Struble, 1956
Stubbs, M.W., 1937
Tall, M.G., W.C. Price and Kenneth Wertman, 1949
Thomas, H. Rex and W.J. Zaumeyer, 1950
Travis, R.V. and Philip Brierley, 1957
Wingard, S.A., 1928
Zaumeyer, W.J. and B.L. Wade, 1935
V. tobacco ring spot no. 2
Hildebrand, E.M., 1942
Price, W.C., 1936
Tall, M.G., W.C. Price and Kenneth Wertman, 1949
Thomas, H. Rex and W.J. Zaumeyer, 1950
V. tobacco streak
Fulton, Robert W., 1948
Thomas, H. Rex and W.J. Zaumeyer, 1950
Thomas, W.D., Jr., 1949
Thomas, W.D., Jr. and R.W. Graham, 1951
V. tomato aspermy
Hollings, M., 1955
V. tomato black ring
Harrison, B.D., 1958
V. tomato bushy stunt
(K.M. Smith, 1957) R.E. Fitzpatrick, et al., 1958
V. tomato ring spot
Kahn, Robert P. and Frances M. Latterell, 1955
V. tomato spotted wilt
(K.M. Smith, 1957) R.E. Fitzpatrick, et al., 1958
V. tomato V-52-1
Miller, Patrick M., 1953
V. tulip white streak
(K.M. Smith, 1957) R.E. Fitzpatrick, et al., 1958
V. watermelon mosaic
Pound, Glenn S., 1949
P. vulgaris var. humulis, Alef. *
V. bean common mosaic
Nelson, Ray, 1932

Phaseolus vulgaris, L. x P. coccineus, L.
  V. bean yellow mosaic
    Baggett, James R., 1956

PHENAX Wedd. 1854 (Urticaceae)
P. sonneratii, (Poir.) Wedd.
  V. abutilon infectious variegation
    Silberschmidt, Karl M., 1948

PHLEUM L. 1735 (Gramineae)
P. pratense, L.
  V. barley yellow dwarf
    Bruehl, G.W. and H.V. Toko, 1957
    Watson, Marion A. and T. Mulligan, 1957
  V. lucerne dwarf
    Freitag, J.H., 1951

PHLOX L. 1737 (Polemoniaceae)
P. drummondii, Hook.
  V. aster yellows
    Kunkel, L.O., 1926
    Severin, Henry H.P., 1943
    Severin, Henry H.P. and Julius H. Freitag, 1945
  V. beet curly top
    Freitag, Julius H. and Henry H.P. Severin, 1936
  V. cucumber mosaic
    Faan, Hwei Chung and James Johnson, 1951
    Govier, D.A., 1957
    Pound, Glenn S. and J.C. Walker, 1948
    Wellman, F.L., 1935
  V. cucumber western mosaic *
    Severin, Henry H.P., 1943
  V. lucerne mosaic
    Price, W.C., 1940
  V. prunus B *
    Fulton, Robert W., 1957
  V. tobacco mosaic
    Grant, T.J., 1934
    Holmes, Francis O., 1946
  V. tobacco necrosis
    Price, W.C., 1940
  V. tobacco ring spot no. 2
    Brierley, Philip, 1954
    Hildebrand, E.M., 1942
    Price, W.C., 1940
  V. tomato aspermy
    Brierley, Philip, Floyd F. Smith and S.P.
      Doolittle, 1955
    Hollings, M., 1955
  V. vaccinium false blossom
    Kunkel, L.O., 1945
P. paniculata, L.
  V. aster yellows
    Kunkel, L.O., 1926
  V. cucumber mosaic
    Faan, Hwei-Chung and James Johnson, 1951

PHORMIUM Forst. 1776 (Liliaceae)
P. tenax, Forst.
  V. phormium yellow leaf
    Boyce, W.R., 1958

PHOTINIA Lindl. 1821 (Rosaceae)
P. arbutifolia, (Ait.) Lindl.
  V. lucerne dwarf
    Freitag, J.H., 1951
P. spp.
  V. apple mosaic
    (K.M. Smith, 1957) R.E. Fitzpatrick, et al., 1958

PHYLLANTHUS L. 1737 (Euphorbiaceae)
P. corcovadensis, Muell.
  V. beet curly top
    Bennett, C.W. and A.S. Costa, 1949
  V. euphorbia mosaic
    Costa, A.S. and C.W. Bennett, 1950

PHYSALIS L. 1735 (Solanaceae)
P. aequata, Jacq. f. ex Nees
  V. prunus B *
    Fulton, Robert W., 1957
P. alkekengi, L.
  V. cucumber mosaic
    Wellman, F.L., 1935

P. alkekengi, L. (cont.)
  V. tobacco etch
    Holmes, Francis O., 1946
  V. tobacco mosaic
    Doolittle, S.P. and F.S. Beecher, 1942
    Hoggan, Isme A., 1927
    Holmes, Francis O., 1946
  V. tomato ring spot
    Samson, R.W. and E.P. Imle, 1942
P. angulata, L.
  V. cucumber mosaic
    Adsuar, Jose and A. Cruz Miret, 1950
    Wellman, F.L., 1935
  V. iris ring spot *
    Travis, R.V., 1957
  V. physalis floridana yellow net
    Webb, R.E., 1955
  V. potato leaf roll
    Hovey, Charles and Reiner Bonde, 1948
    Kirkpatrick, Hugh C. and A. Frank Ross, 1952
    Klostermeyer, E.C., 1953
    MacCarthy, H.R., 1954
    Webb, R.E., R.H. Larson and J.C. Walker, 1952
    Williams, W. Llewelyn and A. Frank Ross, 1957
  V. red currant ring spot
    Klesser, P.J., 1951
  V. tobacco etch
    Holmes, Francis O., 1946
  V. tobacco leaf curl
    Bird, Julio, 1957
  V. tobacco mosaic
    Doolittle, S.P. and F.S. Beecher, 1942
    Holmes, F.O., 1934, 1941, 1946
    Jensen, J.H., 1933
  V. tobacco ring spot
    Wingard, S.A., 1928
  V. tomato aspermy
    Brierley, Philip and Floyd F. Smith, 1953
    Brierley, Philip, Floyd F. Smith and S.P.
      Doolittle, 1953, 1955
  V. tomato bunchy top
    (K.M. Smith, 1957) R.E. Fitzpatrick, et al., 1958
P. elliottii, Kunze
  V. tobacco mosaic
    Anderson, C.W. and M.K. Corbett, 1957
P. floridana, Rydb.
  V. chilli (pepper) mosaic
    Dale, W.T., 1954
  V. cucumber mosaic
    Ross, A. Frank, 1950, 1953
  V. datura rugose leaf curl
    (K.M. Smith, 1957) R.E. Fitzpatrick, et al., 1958
  V. eggplant mosaic
    Dale, W.T., 1954
  V. nicotiana glutinosa root necrosis *
    Cetas, Robert C. and A. Frank Ross, 1952
  V. physalis floridana yellow net
    Webb, R.E., 1955
  V. potato leaf roll
    Kirkpatrick, Hugh C. and A. Frank Ross, 1952
    Klostermeyer, E.C., 1953
    MacCarthy, H.R., 1954
    Webb, R.E. and R.H. Larson, 1952
    Webb, R.E., R.H. Larson and J.C. Walker, 1952
    Webb, R.E. and E.S. Schultz, 1954
    Williams, W. Llewelyn and A. Frank Ross, 1957
  V. potato stunt
    (K.M. Smith, 1957) R.E. Fitzpatrick, et al., 1958
  V. potato X
    Ross, A. Frank, 1950, 1953
  V. potato Y
    Darby, J.F., R.H. Larson and J.C. Walker, 1951
    Easton, G.D., R.H. Larson and R.W. Hougas,
      1958
    Hutton, E.M. and J.W. Peak, 1952
    Richardson, D.E., 1958
    Ross, A. Frank, 1948, 1949, 1950, 1953
  V. tobacco etch
    Greenleaf, W.H., 1953
  V. tobacco mosaic
    Ross, A. Frank, 1953
  V. tomato aspermy
    Brierley, Philip, Floyd F. Smith and S.P.
      Doolittle, 1955

Physalis franchetti, Mast.
  V. cucumber mosaic
    Hoggan, Isme A., 1927
  V. potato X
    Hoggan, Isme A., 1927
  V. potato Y
    Hoggan, Isme A., 1927
  V. tobacco mosaic
    Hoggan, Isme A., 1927
P. heterophylla, Nees
  V. cucumber mosaic
    Walker, M.N., 1925
  V. cucurbit mosaic *
    Walker, M.N., 1924
  V. elm mosaic
    Varney, E.H. and J. Duain Moore, 1952
  V. physalis heterophylla mosaic *
    Walker, M.N., 1925
  V. potato X
    Goss, R.W., 1931
  V. potato Y
    Darby, J.F., R.H. Larson and J.C. Walker, 1951
    Larson, R.H., 1947
  V. potato yellow dwarf
    Black, L.M., 1937
    Larson, R.H., 1947
  V. tobacco mosaic
    Doolittle, S.P. and F.S. Beecher, 1942
    Fernow, Karl Hermann, 1925
    Gardner, Max W. and James B. Kendrick, 1922
P. heterophylla var. nyctaginea, (Dun.) Rydb.
  V. cucumber mosaic
    Johnson, E.M., 1930
  V. potato X
    Johnson, E.M., 1930
  V. potato Y
    Johnson, E.M., 1930
  V. tobacco coarse etch
    Johnson, E.M., 1930
  V. tobacco etch
    Johnson, E.M., 1930
  V. tobacco mosaic
    Johnson, E.M., 1930
  V. tobacco ring spot
    Johnson, E.M., 1930
P. ixocarpa, Brot.
  V. tobacco etch
    Greenleaf, W.H., 1953
P. lagascae, Roem. & Schult.
  V. celery mosaic
    Doolittle, S.P. and F.L. Wellman, 1934
  V. cucumber mosaic
    Wellman, F.L., 1934, 1935
P. longifolia, Nutt.
  V. (physalis longifolia) mosaic *
    Melhus, I.E., 1922
  V. tobacco mosaic
    Crawford, R.F., 1921
P. peruviana, L.
  V. anemone mosaic *
    Hollings, M., 1957
  V. cabbage black ring spot
    Hollings, M., 1957
  V. chilli veinbanding
    Simons, John N., 1956
  V. cucumber mosaic
    Govier, D.A., 1957
    Holmes, Francis O., 1942
    Simons, John N., 1957
    Wellman, F.L., 1935
  V. lucerne mosaic
    Price, W.C., 1940
  V. nicotiana glutinosa root necrosis *
    Cetas, Robert C. and A. Frank Ross, 1952
  V. potato aucuba mosaic
    Holmes, Francis O., 1942
  V. potato Y
    Larson, R.H. and J.F. Darby, 1951
    Sakimura, K., 1953
    Simons, J.N., Robert A. Conover and James M. Walter, 1956
  V. tobacco etch
    Anderson, C.W., 1954
    Costa, A.S., 1944

P. peruviana, L. (cont.)
  V. tobacco etch
    Holmes, Francis O., 1941, 1942, 1946
  V. tobacco leaf curl
    Nariani, T.K. and P.S. Pathanian, 1953
  V. tobacco mosaic
    Holmes, Francis O., 1942, 1946
  V. tobacco ring spot
    Price, W.C., 1940
  V. tomato bunchy top
    (K.M. Smith, 1957) R.E. Fitzpatrick, et al., 1958
P. philadelphica, Lam.
  V. potato leaf roll
    MacCarthy, H.R., 1954
  V. potato M *
    Bagnall, R.H. and R.H. Larson, 1957
  V. potato paracrinkle
    Bagnall, R.H. and R.H. Larson, 1957
    Bagnall, R.H., R.H. Larson and J.C. Walker, 1956
P. pruinosa, L.
  V. tobacco etch
    Anderson, C.W., 1954
P. pubescens, L.
  V. celery mosaic
    Doolittle, S.P., 1931
    Doolittle, S.P. and F.L. Wellman, 1934
  V. cucumber mosaic
    Hoggan, Isme A., 1927
    Johnson, E.M., 1930
    Johnson, J., 1926, 1927
    Pound, Glenn S. and J.C. Walker, 1948
    Walker, M.N., 1925, 1926
    Wellman, F.L., 1934, 1935
  V. cucurbit mosaic *
    Walker, M.N., 1924
  V. petunia mosaic
    Johnson, J., 1926, 1927
  V. physalis heterophylla mosaic *
    Walker, M.N., 1925
  V. (physalis) mosaic *
    Walker, M.N., 1926
  V. physalis subglabrata mosaic *
    Walker, M.N., 1925
  V. pokeweed mosaic *
    Walker, M.N., 1924, 1925
  V. potato M *
    Bagnall, R.H., R.H. Larson and J.C. Walker, 1956
  V. potato paracrinkle
    Bagnall, R.H., R.H. Larson and J.C. Walker, 1956
  V. potato X
    Fernow, K.H., 1923
    Folsom, Donald and Reiner Bonde, 1937
    Hoggan, Isme A., 1927
    Johnson, E.M., 1930
    Johnson, James, 1925, 1927
  V. potato Y
    Hoggan, Isme A., 1927
    Johnson, James, 1927
    Koch, K.L., 1933
  V. potato yellow dwarf
    Black, L.M., 1938
  V. tobacco coarse etch
    Johnson, E.M., 1930
  V. tobacco etch
    Johnson, E.M., 1930
  V. tobacco mosaic
    Ainsworth, G.C., 1933
    Doolittle, S.P. and F.S. Beecher, 1942
    Hoggan, Isme A., 1927
    Johnson, E.M., 1930
    Johnson, J., 1926, 1927
    Walker, M.N., 1924, 1925, 1926
  V. tobacco ring spot
    Cooper, W.E., 1949
  V. tobacco streak
    Fulton, Robert W., 1948
    Johnson, J., 1936
  V. tomato spotted wilt
    Gardner, M.W. and O.C. Whipple, 1934
    Tompkins, C.M. and M.W. Gardner, 1934

Physalis pubescens, L. (cont.)
   V. turnip mosaic
      Walker, J.C., Francis J. LeBeau and Glenn S.
      Pound, 1945
P. spp.
   V. beet curly top
      Bennett, C.W., Eubanks Carsner, F.H. Coons
      and E.W. Brandes, 1946
   V. cucumber mosaic
      Wellman, F.L., 1935
   V. cucurbit mosaic *
      Doolittle, S.P. and M.N. Walker, 1924
   V. potato X
      Dykstra, T.P., 1933
   V. potato Y
      Dykstra, T.P., 1933
   V. tobacco broad ring spot
      Johnson, James and Robert W. Fulton, 1942
P. subglabrata, Mackenzie & Bush
   V. cucumber mosaic
      Walker, M.N., 1925
   V. cucurbit mosaic *
      Walker, M.N., 1924
   V. physalis subglabrata mosaic *
      Walker, M.N., 1925
   V. tobacco etch
      Holmes, Francis O., 1943, 1946
   V. tobacco mosaic
      Fernow, Karl Hermann, 1925
      Gardner, Max W. and James B. Kendrick, 1922
      Holmes, Francis O., 1946
P. turbinata, Medic.
   V. potato Y
      Darby, J.F., R.H. Larson and J.C. Walker, 1951
P. virginiana, Mill.
   V. potato Y
      Darby, J.F., R.H. Larson and J.C. Walker, 1951
      Larson, R.H., 1947
   V. potato yellow dwarf
      Larson, R.H., 1947
   V. tobacco mosaic
      Gardner, M.W. and J.B. Kendrick, 1922
P. viscosa, L.
   V. tomato bunchy top
      (K.M. Smith, 1957) R.E. Fitzpatrick, et al., 1958
P. wrightii, A. Gray
   V. beet curly top
      Severin, Henry H.P., 1929, 1934

PHYSOSTEGIA Benth. 1829 (Labiatae)
P. virginiana, (L.) Benth.
   V. tobacco ring spot
      Price, W.C., 1940

PHYTOLACCA Tourn. ex L. 1735 (Phytolaccaceae)
P. americana, L.
   V. apple mosaic
      Yarwood, C.E., 1955
   V. cucumber mosaic
      Harter, L.L., 1938
      Wellman, F.L., 1935
   V. cucurbit mosaic *
      Doolittle, S.P. and M.N. Walker, 1922
   V. dodder latent mosaic
      Bennett, C.W., 1944, 1949
   V. lucerne mosaic
      Johnson, E.M., 1946
P. decandra, L.
   V. cucumber mosaic
      Diachun, Stephen, 1952
      Hoggan, Isme A., 1935
      Johnson, E.M., 1930
      Johnson, J., 1926, 1927
   V. cucurbit mosaic *
      Doolittle, S.P. and M.N. Walker, 1924, 1925
   V. lucerne mosaic
      Price, W.C., 1940
   V. petunia mosaic
      Johnson, J., 1926, 1927
   V. pokeweed mosaic *
      Allard, H.A., 1918
      Fernow, Karl Hermann, 1925
   V. potato X
      Johnson, E.M., 1930

P. decandra, L. (cont.)
   V. tobacco coarse etch
      Johnson, E.M., 1930
   V. tobacco mosaic
      Holmes, Francis O., 1938, 1946
   V. tobacco necrosis
      Price, W.C., 1940
   V. tobacco ring spot
      Johnson, E.M., 1930
      Priode, C.N., 1928
      Wingard, S.A., 1928
   V. tobacco ring spot no. 2
      Hildebrand, E.M., 1942
      Price, W.C., 1940
P. esculenta, Van Houtte
   V. cucumber mosaic
      Bhargava, K.S., 1951
P. rigida, Small
   V. cucumber mosaic
      Wellman, F.L., 1935

PICRIS L. 1735 (Compositae)
P. echioides, L.
   V. aster yellows
      Frazier, Norman W. and Henry H.P. Severin,
      1945

PIMPINELLA ((Riv.)) L. 1735 (Umbelliferae)
P. anisum, L.
   V. aster yellows
      Kunkel, L.O., 1926
   V. celery mosaic
      Freitag, Julius H. and Henry H.P. Severin, 1945

PISUM ((Tourn.)) L. 1735 (Leguminosae)
P. sativum, L.
   V. alsike clover mosaic
      Wade, B.L. and W.J. Zaumeyer, 1938
      Zaumeyer, W.J., 1940
      Zaumeyer, W.J. and B.L. Wade, 1936
   V. bean yellow mosaic
      Ainsworth, G.C., 1940
      Baggett, James R., 1957
      Berkeley, G.H., 1953
      Conover, Robert A., 1948
      Corbett, M.K., 1957
      Grogan, Raymond G. and J.C. Walker, 1948
      Hagedorn, D.J., 1951, 1952
      Hagedorn, D.J. and J.C. Walker, 1949, 1950,
      1954
      Hanson, E.W. and D.J. Hagedorn, 1954
      Hungerford, C.W. and Irvin G. Hillyer, 1954
      Johnson, James, 1942
      McWhorter, Frank P., 1949
      Osborn, H.T., 1935
      Oshima, Nagayoshi and M.F. Kernkamp, 1957
      Pierce, W.H., 1935, 1937
      Thomas, H. Rex and W.J. Zaumeyer, 1953
      Zaumeyer, W.J., 1940
      Zaumeyer, W.J. and B.L. Wade, 1933, 1935, 1936
   V. bean yellow stipple
      Zaumeyer, W.J. and H. Rex Thomas, 1950
   V. beet mosaic
      Bennett, C.W., 1949
   V. broad bean mottle
      Bawden, F.C., R.P. Chaudhuri and B. Kassanis,
      1951
   V. cucumber mosaic
      Ainsworth, G.C., 1940
      Anderson, C.W., 1955
      Berkeley, G.H., 1951
      Bhargava, K.S., 1951
      Doolittle, S.P. and W.J. Zaumeyer, 1953
      Fulton, Joseph P., 1950
      Hagedorn, D.J., 1950, 1952
      Hagedorn, D.J. and J.C. Walker, 1954
      Pound, Glenn S. and J.C. Walker, 1948
      Whipple, O.C. and J.C. Walker, 1938, 1941
   V. elm mosaic
      Varney, E.H. and J. Duain Moore, 1952
   V. (legume) western ring spot *
      McWhorter, Frank P., 1954
   V. lettuce mosaic
      Ainsworth, G.C., 1940

Pisum sativum, L. (cont.)
  V. lettuce mosaic
    Ainsworth, G.C. and L. Ogilvie, 1939
  V. lovage mosaic
    Smith, Kenneth M. and Roy Markham, 1944
  V. lucerne mosaic
    Berkeley, G.H., 1947
    Hanson, E.W. and D.J. Hagedorn, 1954
    Johnson, E.M., 1946
    Kreitlow, K.W. and W.C. Price, 1948, 1949
    McWhorter, Frank P., 1949, 1954
    Oswald, John W., 1950
    Pierce, W.H., 1934
    Richardson, D.E. and T.W. Tinsley, 1956
    Thomas, H. Rex, 1951, 1953
    Zaumeyer, W.J., 1937, 1938, 1953
    Zaumeyer, W.J. and B.L. Wade, 1936
  V. pea die back *
    Zaumeyer, W.J., 1939
  V. pea enation mosaic
    Ainsworth, G.C., 1940
    Chaudhuri, R.P., 1950
    Hagedorn, D.J., 1952
    Hagedorn, D.J. and J.C. Walker, 1954
    Johnson, Folke and Leon K. Jones, 1937
    McEwen, F.L. and W.T. Schroeder, 1956
    McWhorter, Frank P., 1954
    Osborn, H.T., 1938
    Pierce, W.H., 1935, 1937
    Simons, John N., 1954
    Stubbs, M.W., 1936, 1937
  V. pea leaf roll
    (K.M. Smith, 1957) R.E. Fitzpatrick, et al., 1958
  V. pea mosaic
    Ainsworth, G.C., 1940
    Chaudhuri, R.P., 1950
    Doolittle, S.P. and F.R. Jones, 1925
    Hagedorn, D.J., 1948
    Hagedorn, D.J. and J.C. Walker, 1954
    Johnson, F. and L.K. Jones, 1936
    Murphy, D.M. and W.H. Pierce, 1937
    Osborn, H.T., 1934, 1935
    Oshima, Nagayoshi and M.F. Kernkamp, 1957
    Pierce, W.H., 1935, 1937
    Snyder, W.C., 1934
    Stubbs, M.W., 1936, 1937
    Yen, D.E. and P.R. Fry, 1956
    Zaumeyer, W.J. and B.L. Wade, 1936
  V. pea mottle
    Johnson, Folke, 1942
    Johnson, F. and L.K. Jones, 1936, 1937
  V. pea stem streak *
    Zaumeyer, W.J., 1939
  V. pea streak
    Kim, Woon S. and D.J. Hagedorn, 1957
    Linford, M.B., 1931
    Oshima, Nagayoshi and M.F. Kernkamp, 1957
    Zaumeyer, W.J., 1937, 1938
    Zaumeyer, W.J. and B.L. Wade, 1937
  V. pea wilt
    Johnson, Folke, 1942
    Pierce, W.H., 1935
  V. pea yellow mosaic *
    Ainsworth, G.C., 1940
  V. prunus A *
    Fulton, Robert W., 1957
  V. prunus G *
    Fulton, Robert W., 1957
  V. red clover mosaic *
    Doolittle, S.P. and F.R. Jones, 1925
    Zaumeyer, W.J. and B.L. Wade, 1933, 1935, 1936
  V. red clover vein mosaic
    Graves, Clinton H., Jr. and D.J. Hagedorn, 1956
    Hagedorn, D.J., 1952, 1954
    Hagedorn, D.J. and E.W. Hanson, 1951
    Hagedorn, D.J. and J.C. Walker, 1949, 1954
    Hanson, E.W. and D.J. Hagedorn, 1954
    Osborn, H.T., 1937
    Roberts, D.A., 1957
  V. squash mosaic
    Freitag, J.H., 1956
  V. subterranean clover mosaic
    Aitken, Y. and B.J. Grieve, 1943

P. sativum, L. (cont.)
  V. sweet pea mosaic *
    Doolittle, S.P. and F.R. Jones, 1925
  V. tobacco broad ring spot
    Johnson, James and Robert W. Fulton, 1942
  V. tobacco mosaic
    Berkeley, G.H., 1951
  V. tobacco necrosis
    Price, W.C., 1940
  V. tobacco ring spot
    Berkeley, G.H., 1951, 1953
    Bridgmon, G.H. and J.C. Walker, 1952
    Cheo, Pen Ching and W.J. Zaumeyer, 1952
    Cooper, W.E., 1949
    Grogan, R.G. and W.C. Schnathorst, 1955
    LeBeau, F.J., 1947
    Pound, Glenn S., 1949
    Rosberg, David W., 1953
    Stubbs, M.W., 1937
  V. tobacco ring spot no. 2
    Wilkinson, R.E., 1952
  V. tobacco streak
    Fulton, Robert W., 1948
    Thomas, H. Rex and W.J. Zaumeyer, 1950
  V. tomato spotted wilt
    Ainsworth, G.C., 1940
    Jones, Leon K., 1944
    Milbrath, J.A., 1939
    Snyder, W.C. and H. Rex Thomas, 1936
    Whipple, O.C., 1936
  V. watermelon mosaic
    Pound, Glenn S., 1949
  V. Wisconsin pea streak
    Hagedorn, D.J., 1952
    Hagedorn, D.J. and J.C. Walker, 1949, 1954
    Skotland, C.B., 1953
    Skotland, C.B. and D.J. Hagedorn, 1954, 1955
P. sativum var. arvense, (L.) Poir.
  V. bean yellow mosaic
    Grogan, Raymond G. and J.C. Walker, 1948
    Hagedorn, D.J. and J.C. Walker, 1950, 1954
  V. broad bean mottle
    Yu, T.F., 1939
  V. pea enation mosaic
    Osborn, H.T., 1938
  V. pea mosaic
    Hagedorn, D.J., 1948
    Murphy, D.M. and W.H. Pierce, 1937
    Osborn, H.T., 1934, 1935
  V. red clover vein mosaic
    Hagedorn, D.J. and J.C. Walker, 1949, 1954
    Osborn, H.T., 1937
  V. tobacco ring spot
    LeBeau, F.J., 1947
  V. Wisconsin pea streak
    Hagedorn, D.J. and J.C. Walker, 1949, 1954
P. sativum var. saccharatum, Hort.
  V. bean yellow mosaic
    Pierce, W.H., 1935
  V. pea enation mosaic
    Pierce, W.H., 1935
  V. pea mosaic
    Pierce, W.H., 1935
  V. pea wilt
    Pierce, W.H., 1935

PITTOSPORUM Banks, ex Gaertn. 1788 (Pittosporaceae)
P. crassifolium, Cunn.
  V. lucerne dwarf
    Freitag, J.H., 1951

PLANTAGO Tourn. L. 1735 (Plantaginaceae)
P. erecta, Morris
  V. beet curly top
    Giddings, N.J., 1938, 1944
    Severin, Henry H.P., 1934
  V. beet yellows
    Roland, T. and J. Tahon, 1961
P. insularis, Eastw.
  V. beet yellows
    Roland, G. and J. Tahon, 1961
P. lanceolata, L.
  V. beet yellows
    Roland, G. and J. Tahon, 1961

Plantago lanceolata, L.
  V. beet yellows
    Roland, G. and J. Tahon, 1961
  V. tobacco mosaic
    Boyle, John S. and David C. Wharton, 1957
    Harrison, B.C., 1955
    Holmes, Francis O., 1938, 1941, 1946, 1950
    McKinney, H.H., 1952
  V. tobacco ring spot
    Price, W.C., 1940
P. major, L.
  V. aster yellows
    Frazier, Norman W. and Harold E. Thomas, 1953
    Freitag, J.H., 1956
    Kunkel, L.O., 1926, 1928
    Severin, Henry H.P., 1929, 1934
  V. beet curly top
    Giddings, N.J., 1944
    Severin, Henry H.P., 1934
  V. beet yellows
    Roland, G. and J. Tahon, 1961
  V. clover witches' broom *
    Frazier, N.W. and A.F. Posnette, 1957
  V. dodder latent mosaic
    Bennett, C.W., 1944
  V. stone fruit *
    Boyle, J.S., J. Duain Moore and G.W. Keitt, 1954
  V. tobacco mosaic
    Boyle, John S. and David C. Wharton, 1956
    Harrison, B.D., 1955
    Holmes, Francis O., 1938, 1941, 1946, 1950
    Valleau, W.D. and E.M. Johnson, 1943
  V. tobacco streak
    Fulton, Robert W., 1948
  V. tomato spotted wilt
    Smith, Kenneth M., 1932
P. rugelii, Dcne.
  V. tobacco mosaic
    Boyle, John S. and David C. Wharton, 1957
    Holmes, Francis O., 1938, 1946, 1950
    McKinney, H.H., 1952
P. rumosa, L. *
  V. beet yellows
    Roland, G. and J. Tahon, 1961
P. spp.
  V. raspberry yellow dwarf *
    Harrison, B.D., 1958
P. virginica, L.
  V. prunus B *
    Fulton, Robert W., 1957

PLATYCODON A. DC. 1830 (Campanulaceae)
P. grandiflorum, DC.
  V. tobacco ring spot
    Price, W.C., 1940
  V. tobacco ring spot no. 2
    Brierley, Philip, 1954

POA L. 1737 (Gramineae)
P. ampla, Merr.
  V. barley yellow dwarf
    Bruehl, G.W. and H.V. Toko, 1957
P. annua, L.
  V. barley yellow dwarf
    Oswald, John W. and Byron R. Houston, 1953
  V. lucerne dwarf
    Freitag, J.H., 1951
P. bulbosa, L.
  V. wheat streak mosaic
    McKinney, H.H. and Hurley Fellows, 1951
P. canbyi, (Scribn.) Piper
  V. barley yellow dwarf
    Bruehl, G.W. and H.V. Toko, 1957
P. compressa, L.
  V. wheat streak mosaic
    McKinney, H.H. and Hurley Fellows, 1951
    Slykhuis, John T., 1954, 1955
P. pratensis, L.
  V. barley yellow dwarf
    Bruehl, G.W. and H.V. Toko, 1957
    Oswald, John W. and Byron R. Houston, 1953
  V. rice dwarf
    (K.M. Smith, 1957) R.E. Fitzpatrick, et al., 1958

P. stenantha, Turcz. ex Steud.
  V. wheat streak mosaic
    McKinney, H.H. and Hurley Fellows, 1951

POLANISIA Rafin. 1818 (Capparidaceae)
P. trachysperma, Torr. & Gray
  V. cucumber mosaic
    Price, W.C., 1940
  V. tobacco mosaic
    Holmes, Francis O., 1946
  V. tobacco necrosis
    Price, W.C., 1940
  V. tobacco ring spot
    Price, W.C., 1940

POLEMONIUM ((Tourn.)) L. 1735 (Polemoniaceae)
P. caeruleum, L.
  V. cucumber mosaic
    Faan, Hwei Chung and James Johnson, 1951

POLYANTHUS Auct. ex Benth. & Hook. 1883
P. spp.   (Amaryllidaceae)
  V. tobacco necrosis
    (K.M. Smith, 1957) R.E. Fitzpatrick, et al., 1958

POLYGONUM ((Tourn.)) L. 1735 (Polygonaceae)
P. amphibium, L., var. hartwrightii, Bissel
  V. beet curly top
    Severin, Henry H.P., 1929, 1934
P. aviculare, L.
  V. aster yellows
    Frazier, Norman W. and Henry H.P. Severin, 1945
  V. beet curly top
    Carsner, E., 1919
    Severin, Henry H.P., 1929, 1934
  V. beet ring spot *
    Harrison, B.D., 1957
  V. datura rugose leaf curl
    (K.M. Smith, 1957) R.E. Fitzpatrick, et al., 1958
  V. tobacco mosaic
    Holmes, Francis O., 1938
P. convolvulus, L.
  V. aster yellows
    Frazier, Norman W. and Henry H.P. Severin, 1945
  V. beet ring spot *
    Harrison, B.D., 1957
  V. beet yellows
    (K.M. Smith, 1957) R.E. Fitzpatrick, et al., 1958
    Roland, G. and J. Tahon, 1961
  V. lucerne dwarf
    Freitag, J.H., 1951
  V. raspberry Scottish leaf curl
    Harrison, B.D., 1958
  V. tobacco mosaic
    Holmes, Francis O., 1938
  V. tomato spotted wilt
    (K.M. Smith, 1957) R.E. Fitzpatrick, et al., 1958
P. erectum, L.
  V. tobacco mosaic
    Holmes, Francis O., 1938
P. hydropiper, L.
  V. tobacco mosaic
    Holmes, Francis O., 1938, 1946
  V. tobacco ring spot
    Wingard, S.A., 1928
P. lapathifolium, L.
  V. beet curly top
    Severin, Henry H.P., 1929, 1934
P. muhlenbergii, (Meissn.) S. Wats.
  V. beet curly top
    Severin, Henry H.P., 1929, 1934
P. pensylvanicum, L.
  V. dodder latent mosaic
    Bennett, C.W., 1944
P. persicarae, L. *
  V. tobacco streak
    Fulton, Robert W., 1948
P. persicaria, L.
  V. beet curly top
    Severin, Henry H.P., 1929, 1934
  V. beet ring spot *
    Harrison, B.D., 1957

Polygonum persicaria, L. (cont.)
    V. beet yellows
        Roland, G. and J. Tahon, 1961
    V. lucerne dwarf
        Freitag, J.H., 1951
    V. tobacco mosaic
        Holmes, Francis O., 1938
P. spp.
    V. tomato spotted wilt
        (K.M. Smith, 1957) R.E. Fitzpatrick, et al., 1958

PORTULACA L. 1735 (Portulacaceae)
P. grandiflora, Hook.
    V. aster yellows
        Kunkel, L.O., 1926
    V. beet curly top
        Freitag, Julius H. and Henry H.P. Severin, 1936
    V. clover big vein
        Black, L.M., 1945
    V. cucumber mosaic
        Price, W.C., 1940
    V. tobacco necrosis
        Price, W.C., 1940
    V. tobacco ring spot
        Price, W.C., 1940
P. oleracea, L.
    V. anemone brown ring *
        Hollings, M., 1958
    V. aster yellows
        Frazier, Norman W. and Henry H.P. Severin,
        1945
    V. beet curly top
        Severin, Henry H.P., 1934
    V. chilli veinbanding
        Simons, John N., 1956
    V. clover big vein
        Black, L.M., 1945
    V. tobacco broad ring spot
        Johnson, James and Robert W. Fulton, 1942
    V. tobacco etch
        Holmes, Francis O., 1946
    V. tobacco mosaic
        Holmes, Francis O., 1946
    V. tobacco streak
        Fulton, Robert W., 1948

POTENTILLA L. 1735 (Rosaceae)
P. monspeliensis, L.
    V. rose mosaic
        Fulton, Robert W., 1952
    V. tobacco streak
        Fulton, Robert W., 1948
P. palustris, (L.) Scop.
    V. prunus G *
        Fulton, Robert W., 1957
P. recta, L.
    V. rose mosaic
        (K.M. Smith, 1957) R.E. Fitzpatrick, et al., 1958
        Fulton, Robert W., 1952
P. simplex, Michx.
    V. strawberry mottle
        Demaree, J.B. and C.P. Marcus, 1951
    V. strawberry, type 2 *
        Demaree, J.B. and C.P. Marcus, 1951

PRIMULA L. 1735 (Primulaceae)
P. elatior, Hill
    V. aster yellows
        Kunkel, L.O., 1926
    V. beet curly top
        Freitag, Julius H. and Henry H.P. Severin, 1936
P. malacoides, Franch.
    V. primula mosaic
        Tompkins, C.M. and John T. Middleton, 1941
    V. tobacco etch
        Holmes, Francis O., 1946
    V. tobacco mosaic
        Holmes, Francis O., 1946
    V. tobacco necrosis
        Bawden, F.C. and B. Kassanis, 1947
        Price, W.C., Frank P. McWhorter and Betty H.
        Steranka, 1950
    V. tomato spotted wilt
        (K.M. Smith, 1957) R.E. Fitzpatrick, et al., 1958

P. obconica, Hance
    V. aster yellows
        Severin, Henry H.P. and C.M. Tompkins, 1950
    V. beet curly top
        Freitag, Julius H. and Henry H.P. Severin, 1936
    V. cucumber mosaic
        (K.M. Smith, 1957) R.E. Fitzpatrick, et al., 1958
        Govier, D.A., 1957
        Severin, Henry H.P. and C.M. Tompkins, 1950
        Smith, Kenneth M., 1935
    V. cucumber western mosaic *
        Severin, Henry H.P. and C.M. Tompkins, 1950
    V. lucerne mosaic
        Price, W.C., 1940
        Severin, Henry H.P. and C.M. Tompkins, 1950
    V. primula mosaic
        Severin, Henry H.P. and C.M. Tompkins, 1950
        Tompkins, C.M. and John T. Middleton, 1941
    V. tobacco mosaic
        Holmes, Francis O., 1946
        Severin, Henry H.P. and C.M. Tompkins, 1950
    V. tobacco necrosis
        Bawden, F.C. and B. Kassanis, 1947
        Price, W.C., Frank P. McWhorter and Betty H.
        Steranka, 1950
        Severin, Henry H.P. and C.M. Tompkins, 1950
    V. tobacco ring spot
        Price, W.C., 1940
    V. tomato spotted wilt
        Gardner, M.W., C.M. Tompkins and O.C.
        Whipple, 1935
        Severin, Henry H.P. and C.M. Tompkins, 1950
P. polyantha, Mill.
    V. aster yellows
        Severin, Henry H.P. and Julius H. Freitag, 1945
P. saxatalis, Komar
    V. beet curly top
        Freitag, Julius H. and Henry H.P. Severin, 1936
P. sinensis, Lindl.
    V. anemone mosaic *
        Hollings, M., 1957
    V. cucumber mosaic
        Govier, D.A., 1957
        Smith, Kenneth M., 1935
    V. primula mosaic
        Tompkins, C.M. and John T. Middleton, 1941
    V. tomato aspermy
        Hollings, M., 1955
    V. tomato spotted wilt
        (K.M. Smith, 1957) R.E. Fitzpatrick, et al., 1958
P. sinensis var. stellata, Hort.
    V. tomato aspermy
        (K.M. Smith, 1957) R.E. Fitzpatrick, et al., 1958
P. veris, L.
    V. beet curly top
        Freitag, Julius H. and Henry H.P. Severin, 1936
P. vulgaris, Huds.
    V. tobacco necrosis
        Bawden, F.C. and B. Kassanis, 1947

PROBOSCIDEA Schmid. 1747 (Martyniaceae)
P. louisiana, (Mill.) Thell.
    V. tobacco etch
        Holmes, Francis O., 1946
    V. tobacco mosaic
        Holmes, Francis O., 1946
    V. tobacco necrosis
        Price, W.C., 1940
    V. tobacco ring spot
        Price, W.C., 1940
    V. tobacco ring spot no. 2
        Price, W.C., 1940

PRUNELLA L. 1753 (Labiatae)
P. vulgaris, L.
    V. tobacco mosaic
        Holmes, Francis O., 1938, 1946

PRUNUS ((Tourn.)) L. 1735 (Rosaceae)
(AMYGDALUS) ((Tourn.)) L. 1735
P. alabamensis, Mohr
    V. peach ring spot
        Gilmer, R.M., 1955

Prunus alleghaniensis, Porter
  V. peach ring spot
    Gilmer, R.M., 1955
P. americana, Marsh.
  V. peach mosaic
    Richards, B.L. and L.C. Cochran, 1956
  V. peach ring spot
    Gilmer, R.M., 1954, 1955
    Moore, J. Duain and G.W. Keitt, 1946
  V. peach X disease
    Gilmer, R.M., J. Duain Moore and G.W. Keitt, 1954
    Hildebrand, E.M., 1953
  V. stone fruit *
    Boyle, J.S., J. Duain Moore and G.W. Keitt, 1954
P. americana var. mollis, Torr. & Gray
  V. peach western X disease
    Schneider, Henry, 1945
P. americana x P. salicina, Lindl.
  V. apple mosaic
    Gilmer, R.M., 1956
    Posnette, A.F. and Christina E. Ellenberger, 1957
  V. plum white spot
    Valleau, W.D., 1932
  V. prunus A *
    Ehlers, Clifford G. and J. Duain Moore, 1957
  V. prunus B *
    Ehlers, Clifford G. and J. Duain Moore, 1957
  V. prunus E *
    Ehlers, Clifford G. and J. Duain Moore, 1957
  V. prunus G *
    Ehlers, Clifford G. and J. Duain Moore, 1957
P. amygdalus, Batsch
  V. almond bud failure
    (K.M. Smith, 1957) R.E. Fitzpatrick, et al., 1958
  V. almond calico
    (K.M. Smith, 1957) R.E. Fitzpatrick, et al., 1958
  V. cherry rugose mosaic
    Nyland, George, 1954
  V. peach asteroid spot
    Richards, B.L. and L.C. Cochran, 1956
  V. peach mosaic
    Cochran, L.C. and L.M. Hutchins, 1937, 1938
  V. peach ring spot
    Cochran, L.C. and Lee M. Hutchins, 1941
  V. peach rosette
    McClintock, J.A., 1923
  V. peach X disease
    Palmiter, D.H. and E.M. Hildebrand, 1943
  V. peach yellow bud mosaic
    Thomas, H. Earl, 1940
    Thomas, H. Earl, C. Emlen Scott, E.E. Wilson and J.H. Freitag, 1944
  V. phony peach
    (K.M. Smith, 1957) R.E. Fitzpatrick, et al., 1958
P. andersoni, A. Gray
  V. peach ring spot
    Gilmer, R.M., 1955
  V. peach yellow bud mosaic
    Thomas, H. Earl, 1940
    Thomas, H. Earl and T.E. Rawlins, 1939
P. angustifolia, Marsh.
  V. peach mosaic
    (K.M. Smith, 1957) R.E. Fitzpatrick, et al., 1958
  V. peach ring spot
    Gilmer, R.M., 1955
  V. peach rosette
    McClintock, J.A., 1923
  V. phony peach
    Bruer, H.L. and C.E. Shepard, 1952
    Bruer, H.L., C.E. Shepard and T.D. Persons, 1951
    Cochran, L.C., J.H. Weinberger and W.F. Turner, 1951
    Hutchins, Lee M., L.C. Cochran, W.F. Turner and J.H. Weinberger, 1953
    Hutchins, Lee M. and John L. Rue, 1949
    KenKnight, Glenn, H.L. Bruer and C.E. Shepard, 1951
P. apetala, Franch. & Sav.
  V. peach ring spot
    Gilmer, R.M., 1954, 1955

P. armeniaca, L.
  V. apricot moorpark mottle
    (K.M. Smith, 1957) R.E. Fitzpatrick, et al., 1958
  V. apricot ring pox
    Reeves, E.L. and Philip W. Cheney, 1956
    Simonds, Austin O., 1951
  V. cherry bark splitting *
    Cameron, H. Ronald, 1954
  V. cherry rasp leaf
    Posnette, A.F., 1954
  V. cherry rusty mottle
    Posnette, A.F., 1954
  V. peach asteroid spot
    Richards, B.L. and L.C. Cochran, 1956
  V. peach little peach
    Manns, T.F., 1942
  V. peach mosaic
    Bodine, E.W. and L.W. Durrell, 1941
    Cochran, L.C. and L.M. Hutchins, 1937, 1938
    Thomas, H. Earl and T.E. Rawlins, 1939
  V. peach ring spot
    Gilmer, R.M., 1954, 1955
    Posnette, A.F., 1954
    Yarwood, C.E., 1957
  V. peach rosette
    McClintock, J.A., 1923
  V. peach western X disease
    Rawlins, T.E. and H. Earl Thomas, 1941
  V. peach X disease
    Palmiter, D.H. and E.M. Hildebrand, 1943
  V. peach yellow bud mosaic
    Schlocker, Archie, H. Keith Wagnon and James R. Breece, 1957
    Thomas, H. Earl and T.E. Rawlins, 1939
    Thomas, H. Earl, C. Emlen Scott, E.E. Wilson and J.H. Freitag, 1944
  V. peach yellows
    Manns, T.F., 1942
  V. phony peach
    Hutchins, Lee M. and John L. Rue, 1949
  V. plum line pattern
    Bodine, E.W. and L.W. Durrell, 1941
    Willison, R.S., 1945
  V. prune dwarf
    Moore, J. Duain and H.R. Cameron, 1956
    Willison, R.S., 1944
  V. (sour) cherry yellows
    Moore, J. Duain and H.R. Cameron, 1956
  V. stone fruit necrotic ring spot *
    Moore, J. Duain and H.R. Cameron, 1956
  V. stone fruit ring spot *
    Richards, B.L. and L.C. Cochran, 1956
P. armeniaca var. mandshurica, Maxim.
  V. peach ring spot
    Gilmer, R.M., 1955
  V. peach X disease
    Hildebrand, E.M., 1953
P. avium, L.
  V. almond calico
    Thomas, H. Earl and T.E. Rawlins, 1939
  V. apple mosaic
    Posnette, A.F. and Christina E. Ellenberger, 1957
  V. cherry albino
    Zeller, S.M., J.A. Milbrath and C.B. Cordy, 1944
  V. cherry black canker
    (K.M. Smith, 1957) R.E. Fitzpatrick, et al., 1958
  V. cherry bud abortion disasee *
    Milbrath, J.A. and H.E. Williams, 1956
  V. cherry dusty yellows
    Posnette, A.F., 1954
  V. cherry freckle fruit disease *
    Williams, H.E. and J.A. Milbrath, 1955
  V. cherry (frogmore) canker *
    Posnette, A.F. and R. Cropley, 1957
  V. cherry little cherry
    Blodgett, E.C., E.L. Reeves, C.M. Wright and H.E. Williams, 1948
    Foster, W.R. and T.B. Lott, 1947
    Milbrath, J.A. and H.E. Williams, 1956
    Reeves, E.L. and Philip W. Cheney, 1956
    Welsh, Maurice F., 1952

Prunus avium, L. (cont.)
  V. cherry little cherry
    Wilks, J.M. and M.F. Welsh, 1955
    Wilks, Jack M. and J.A. Milbrath, 1956
  V. cherry midleaf necrosis *
    Milbrath, J.A., 1957
  V. cherry mora
    Milbrath, J.A., 1952
  V. cherry mottle *
    Hildebrand, E.M., 1944
  V. cherry mottle leaf
    Lott, T.B., 1945
    Reeves, E.L., 1941
    Richards, B.L. and L.C. Cochran, 1956
    Zeller, S.M. and A.W. Evans, 1941
  V. cherry necrotic etch *
    Posnette, A.F., 1954
  V. cherry necrotic line pattern
    Posnette, A.F. and R. Cropley, 1956
  V. cherry necrotic rusty mottle
    Afanasiev, M.M. and H.E. Morris, 1954
    (K.M. Smith, 1957) R.E. Fitzpatrick, et al., 1958
    Lott, T.B., 1945
    Reeves, E.L. and B.L. Richards, 1946
    Richards, B.L. and L.C. Cochran, 1956
    Richards, B.L. and Bryce N. Wadley, 1950
  V. cherry pinto leaf
    Kienholz, J.R., 1947
  V. cherry rasp leaf
    Blodgett, Earle C., 1943
    Bodine, E.W. and J.H. Newton, 1942
    Milbrath, J.A., 1954
    Posnette, A.F., 1954
    Posnette, A.F. and R. Cropley, 1956
    Richards, B.L. and L.C. Cochran, 1956
  V. cherry rugose mosaic
    Berkeley, G.H., 1950
    Nyland, George, 1954
    Posnette, A.F., 1954
    Posnette, A.F. and R. Cropley, 1956
    Richards, B.L. and L.C. Cochran, 1956
    Thomas, H. Earl and T.E. Rawlins, 1939
  V. cherry rusty mottle
    Posnette, A.F., 1954
    Posnette, A.F. and R. Cropley, 1956
    Reeves, E.L., 1940
    Zeller, S.M. and J.A. Milbrath, 1947
  V. cherry sunken mottle *
    Posnette, A.F., 1954
  V. cherry twisted leaf
    Lott, T.B., 1943
    Reeves, E.L. and Philip W. Cheney, 1956
  V. cherry vein clearing *
    Zeller, S.M. and A.W. Evans, 1941
  V. clover enation *
    (K.M. Smith, 1957) R.E. Fitzpatrick, et al., 1958
  V. elm mosaic
    Callahan, Kemper L. and J. Duain Moore, 1957
  V. (flowering) cherry rough bark
    Nichols, Carl W. and R.L. McClain, 1957
  V. peach asteroid spot
    Richards, B.L. and L.C. Cochran, 1956
  V. peach mottle
    Blodgett, Earle C., 1941
  V. peach necrotic leaf spot
    Cation, Donald, 1942
    Richards, B.L. and L.C. Cochran, 1956
  V. peach ring spot
    Cation, Donald, 1952
    Cochran, L.C. and Lee M. Hutchins, 1941
    Gilmer, R.M., 1954, 1955
    Gilmer, R.M., K.D. Brase and K.G. Parker, 1957
    Hildebrand, E.M., 1944
    Milbrath, J.A., 1950
    Millikan, D.F., 1953, 1955
    Posnette, A.F., 1954
    Posnette, A.F. and R. Cropley, 1956
    Tomlinson, N., 1955
    Willison, R.S. and G.H. Berkeley, 1946
  V. peach rosette
    McClintock, J.A., 1923
  V. peach wart
    Zeller, S.M. and J.A. Milbrath, 1945

P. avium, L. (cont.)
  V. peach western X disease
    Jensen, D.D. and H. Earl Thomas, 1954, 1955
    Kaloostian, George H., 1951
    Kaloostian, George H., Mervin W. Nielson and
      L.S. Jones, 1951
    Lott, T.B., 1950
    Rawlins, T.E., 1939
    Rawlins, T.E. and W.T. Horne, 1931
    Rawlins, T.E. and K.G. Parker, 1934
    Rawlins, T.E. and H. Earl Thomas, 1941
    Richards, B.L., L.M. Hutchins and E.L. Reeves, 1949
    Richards, B.L., E.L. Reeves and L.M. Hutchins, 1946
    Schneider, Henry, 1945
    Thomas, H. Earl, 1940
    Thomas, H. Earl and T.E. Rawlins, 1941
    Wadley, Bryce N., 1952
    Wilks, Jack M. and J.A. Milbrath, 1956
    Zeller, S.M. and J.A. Milbrath, 1948, 1950
  V. peach X disease
    (K.M. Smith, 1957) R.E. Fitzpatrick, et al., 1958
    Gilmer, R.M., J. Duain Moore and G.W. Keitt, 1954
  V. peach yellow bud mosaic
    Thomas, H. Earl, 1940
    Thomas, H. Earl and T.E. Rawlins, 1939
  V. plum line pattern
    Gilmer, R.M., K.D. Brase and K.G. Parker, 1957
    Richards, B.L. and L.C. Cochran, 1956
    Willison, R.S., 1945
    Zeller, S.M. and J.A. Milbrath, 1942
  V. prune dwarf
    Gilmer, R.M., K.D. Brase and K.G. Parker, 1957
    Willison, R.S., 1944
  V. (sour) cherry yellows
    Cation, Donald, 1952
    Richards, B.L. and L.C. Cochran, 1956
  V. stone fruit *
    Boyle, J.S., J. Duain Moore and G.W. Keitt, 1954
  V. stone fruit ring spot *
    Heinis, Julius L., 1956
    Heinis, J.L. and J.A. Milbrath, 1954
    Richards, B.L. and L.C. Cochran, 1956
  V. tobacco ring spot
    Wilkinson, R.E., 1952
P. avium on P. avium, L.
  V. peach western X disease
    Richards, B.L. and L.C. Cochran, 1956
P. avium x P. cerasus, L.
  V. cherry mottle leaf
    Reeves, E.L., 1941
  V. cherry necrotic rusty mottle
    Richards, B.L. and L.C. Cochran, 1956
  V. peach mosaic
    Bodine, E.W. and L.W. Durrell, 1941
P. avium on P. mahaleb, L.
  V. peach western X disease
    Richards, B.L. and L.C. Cochran, 1956
P. besseyi, Bailey
  V. elm mosaic
    Callahan, Kemper L. and J. Duain Moore, 1957
  V. peach mosaic
    (K.M. Smith, 1957) R.E. Fitzpatrick, et al., 1958
  V. peach necrotic leaf spot
    Fridlund, Paul R., 1954
  V. peach ring spot
    Gilmer, R.M., 1954, 1955
    Moore, J. Duain and G.W. Keitt, 1946
  V. peach western X disease
    Richards, B.L. and L.C. Cochran, 1956
  V. peach X disease
    Fridlund, Paul R., 1954
    Gilmer, R.M., J. Duain Moore and G.W. Keitt, 1954
    Hildebrand, E.M., 1943, 1953
  V. stone fruit *
    Boyle, J.S., J. Duain Moore and G.W. Keitt, 1954

Prunus besseyi, Bailey x P. hortulana, Bailey
    V. peach necrotic leaf spot
        Fridlund, Paul R., 1954
P. besseyi x P. salicina, Lindl.
    V. peach necrotic leaf spot
        Fridlund, Paul R., 1954
P. blirieana, Carr.
    V. peach ring spot
        Gilmer, R.M., 1954, 1955
P. bokhariensis, Royle
    V. peach ring spot
        Gilmer, R.M., 1955
P. bucharica, B. Fedtsch.
    V. peach ring spot
        Gilmer, R.M., 1955
P. campanulata, Maxim.
    V. peach ring spot
        Gilmer, R.M., 1955
P. canescens, Vilm. & Bois.
    V. peach ring spot
        Gilmer, R.M., 1954, 1955
P. caroliniana, (Mill.) Ait.
    V. peach ring spot
        Gilmer, R.M., 1954, 1955
P. cerasifera, Ehrh.
    V. apple mosaic
        Posnette, A.F. and Christina E. Ellenberger,
        1957
    V. apricot moorpark mottle
        (K.M. Smith, 1957) R.E. Fitzpatrick, et al., 1958
    V. cherry rasp leaf
        Posnette, A.F., 1954
    V. cherry rugose mosaic
        Posnette, A.F., 1954
    V. peach little peach
        Manns, T.F., 1942
    V. peach mosaic
        (K.M. Smith, 1957) R.E. Fitzpatrick, et al., 1958
    V. peach ring spot
        Cochran, L.C. and Lee M. Hutchins, 1941
        Gilmer, R.M., 1954, 1955
        Posnette, A.F., 1954
        Willison, R.S. and G.H. Berkeley, 1946
    V. peach yellows
        Manns, T.F., 1942
    V. plum bark split
        Posnette, A.F. and Christina E. Ellenberger,
        1957
    V. plum line pattern
        Cochran, L.C. and L.M. Hutchins, 1937
        Gilmer, R.M., K.D. Brase and K.G. Parker,
        1957
        Richards, B.L. and L.C. Cochran, 1956
        Thomas, H. Earl and T.E. Rawlins, 1939
        Willison, R.S., 1945
    V. prune dwarf
        Willison, R.S., 1944
P. cerasifera var. pissardii, Koehne
    V. peach little peach
        Manns, T.F., 1942
    V. peach ring spot
        Gilmer, R.M., 1954
    V. peach yellows
        Manns, T.F., 1942
P. cerasoides, D. Don
    V. peach ring spot
        Gilmer, R.M., 1955
P. cerasus, L.
    V. cherry bark splitting *
        Cameron, H. Ronald, 1954
        Milbrath, J.A., 1957
    V. cherry bud abortion disease *
        Milbrath, J.A. and H.E. Williams, 1956
    V. cherry dusty yellows
        Posnette, A.F., 1954
    V. cherry green ring mottle *
        Fink, Harry C., 1955
        Gilmer, R.M., K.D. Brase and K.G. Parker,
        1957
        Parker, K.G. and E.J. Klos, 1953
    V. cherry little cherry
        Milbrath, J.A. and H.E. Williams, 1956
        Wilks, Jack M. and J.A. Milbrath, 1956

P. cerasus, L. (cont.)
    V. cherry midleaf necrosis *
        Milbrath, J.A., 1957
    V. cherry mottle leaf
        Reeves, E.L., 1941
        Richards, B.L. and L.C. Cochran, 1956
    V. cherry necrotic rusty mottle
        Richards, B.L. and L.C. Cochran, 1956
        Richards, B.L. and Bryce N. Wadley, 1950
    V. cherry rasp leaf
        Blodgett, Earle C., 1943
        Posnette, A.F., 1954
        Richards, B.L. and L.C. Cochran, 1956
    V. cherry rugose mosaic
        Berkeley, G.H., 1950
        Hildebrand, E.M., 1944
        Posnette, A.F., 1954
        Richards, B.L. and L.C. Cochran, 1956
    V. cherry rusty mottle
        Posnette, A.F., 1954
        Zeller, S.M. and J.A. Milbrath, 1947
    V. elm mosaic
        Callahan, Kemper L. and J. Duain Moore, 1957
    V. peach mottle
        Blodgett, Earle C., 1941
    V. peach necrotic leaf spot
        Richards, B.L. and L.C. Cochran, 1956
    V. peach ring spot
        Berkeley, G.H. and R.S. Willison, 1948
        Cation, Donald, 1949, 1952
        Fink, Harry C., 1950, 1955
        Fulton, Robert W., 1956
        Gilmer, R.M., 1954, 1955
        Gilmer, R.M., K.D. Brase and K.G. Parker,
        1957
        Hildebrand, E.M., 1944
        Milbrath, J.A., 1950, 1952, 1957
        Millikan, D.F. and A.D. Hibbard, 1952
        Moore, J. Duain and G.W. Keitt, 1944, 1946
        Moore, J. Duain and D.A. Slack, 1952
        Nyland, George, 1952
        Parker, K.G. and L.C. Cochran, 1951
        Posnette, A.F., 1954
        Willison, R.S. and G.H. Berkeley, 1946
    V. peach rosette mosaic
        Fink, Harry C., 1955
    V. peach stunt *
        Milbrath, J.A., 1957
    V. peach western X disease
        Kaloostian, George H., 1951
        Nielson, Mervin W. and Laurence S. Jones, 1954
        Rawlins, T.E. and K.G. Parker, 1934
        Rawlins, T.E. and H. Earl Thomas, 1941
        Richards, B.L., L.M. Hutchins and E.L. Reeves,
        1949
        Richards, B.L., E.L. Reeves and Lee M.
        Hutchins, 1946
        Schneider, Henry, 1945
        Wilks, Jack M. and J.A. Milbrath, 1956
        Zeller, S.M. and J.A. Milbrath, 1948, 1950
    V. peach X disease
        Fridlund, Paul R., 1954
        Gilmer, R.M., J. Duain Moore and G.W. Keitt,
        1954
        Hildebrand, E.M., 1953
        Palmiter, D.H. and K.G. Parker, 1948
        Parker, K.G. and D.H. Palmiter, 1948
    V. plum line pattern
        Gilmer, R.M., K.D. Brase and K.G. Parker,
        1957
        Richards, B.L. and L.C. Cochran, 1956
        Willison, R.S., 1945
    V. prune dwarf
        Fink, Harry C., 1955
        Gilmer, R.M., K.D. Brase and K.G. Parker,
        1957
        Milbrath, J.A., 1957
        Moore, J. Duain and H.R. Cameron, 1956
        Willison, R.S., 1944
    V. prunus A *
        Ehlers, Clifford G. and J. Duain Moore, 1957
        Fulton, Robert W., 1957
    V. prunus B *
        Ehlers, Clifford G. and J. Duain Moore, 1957

Prunus cerasus, L. (cont.)
    V. prunus B *
    Fulton, Robert W., 1957
    V. prunus E *
    Ehlers, Clifford G. and J. Duain Moore, 1957
    Fulton, Robert W., 1957
    V. prunus G *
    Ehlers, Clifford G. and J. Duain Moore, 1957
    Fulton, Robert W., 1957
    V. (sour) cherry yellows
    Berkeley, G.H. and R.S. Willison, 1948
    Cation, Donald, 1952
    Fink, Harry C., 1955
    Fulton, Robert W., 1956
    Gilmer, R.M., K.D. Brase and K.G. Parker, 1957
    Hildebrand, E.M., 1942, 1943, 1944
    Hildebrand, E.M. and W.D. Mills, 1941
    Keitt, G.W. and C.N. Clayton, 1939, 1940, 1941, 1943
    Milbrath, J.A., 1957
    Moore, J. Duain and H.R. Cameron, 1956
    Moore, J. Duain and G.W. Keitt, 1944, 1946
    Moore, J. Duain and D.A. Slack, 1952
    Nyland, George, 1952
    Rasmussen, E.J. and Donald Cation, 1942
    Richards, B.L. and L.C. Cochran, 1956
    V. stone fruit *
    Boyle, J.S., J. Duain Moore and G.W. Keitt, 1954
    V. stone fruit necrotic ring spot *
    Moore, J. Duain and H.R. Cameron, 1956
    V. stone fruit ring spot *
    Heinis, J.L. and J.A. Milbrath, 1954
    Millikan, D.F., 1955
    Richards, B.L. and L.C. Cochran, 1956
P. cerasus var. umbraculifera *
    V. cherry rasp leaf
    Milbrath, J.A., 1954
P. cerasus on P. avium, L.
    V. peach western X disease
    Richards, B.L. and L.C. Cochran, 1956
P. cerasus on P. mahaleb, L.
    V. peach western X disease
    Richards, B.L. and L.C. Cochran, 1956
P. cistena *
    V. peach ring spot
    Gilmer, R.M., 1954, 1955
    Young, H.C., Jr., 1951
P. communis, Fritsch
    V. almond calico
    Thomas, H. Earl and T.E. Rawlins, 1939
    V. peach little peach
    Manns, T.F., 1942
    V. peach mosaic
    Bodine, E.W. and L.W. Durrell, 1941
    V. peach ring spot
    Gilmer, R.M., 1954, 1955
    V. peach western X disease
    Rawlins, T.E. and H. Earl Thomas, 1941
    V. peach X disease
    Hildebrand, E.M., 1953
    V. peach yellow bud mosaic
    Thomas, H. Earl and T.E. Rawlins, 1939
    V. peach yellows
    Manns, T.F., 1942
P. communis x P. fenzliana, Fritsch
    V. peach western X disease
    Rawlins, T.E. and H. Earl Thomas, 1941
P. conradinae, Koehne
    V. peach ring spot
    Gilmer, R.M., 1955
P. cyclamina, Koehne
    V. peach ring spot
    Gilmer, R.M., 1955
P. dasycarpa, Ehrh.
    V. peach ring spot
    Gilmer, R.M., 1955
P. davidiana, (Carr.) Franch. (Amygdalus davidiana, (Carr.) Zabel)
    V. peach mosaic
    (K.M. Smith, 1957) R.E. Fitzpatrick, et al., 1958
    V. peach ring spot
    Gilmer, R.M., 1955

P. davidiana, (Carr.) Franch. (Amygdalus davidiana, (Carr.) Zabel) (cont.)
    V. peach western X disease
    Rawlins, T.E. and H. Earl Thomas, 1941
    V. phony peach
    (K.M. Smith, 1957) R.E. Fitzpatrick, et al., 1958
P. davidiana x P. communis, Fritsch
    V. peach western X disease
    Rawlins, T.E. and H. Earl Thomas, 1941
P. demissa, (Nutt.) Walp.
    V. peach ring spot
    Gilmer, R.M., 1955
    V. peach western X disease
    Richards, B.L. and Lee M. Hutchins, 1941
    Richards, B.L., L.M. Hutchins and E.L. Reeves, 1949
    Wilks, Jack M. and J.A. Milbrath, 1956
    Zeller, S.M. and J.A. Milbrath, 1950
P. demissa var. melanocarpa, (A. Nels.) Sarg.
    V. peach X disease
    Hildebrand, E.M., 1953
P. dielsiana *
    V. peach ring spot
    Gilmer, R.M., 1955
P. domestica, L.
    V. apple mosaic
    Posnette, A.F. and Christina E. Ellenberger, 1957
    V. apricot ring pox
    Simonds, Austin O., 1951
    V. cherry mottle *
    Hildebrand, E.M., 1944
    V. cherry rugose mosaic
    Nyland, George, 1954
    V. cherry rusty mottle
    Zeller, S.M. and J.A. Milbrath, 1947
    V. elm mosaic
    Callahan, Kemper L. and J. Duain Moore, 1957
    V. peach asteroid spot
    Richards, B.L. and L.C. Cochran, 1956
    V. peach little peach
    Manns, T.F., 1942
    V. peach mosaic
    Bodine, E.W., 1937
    Bodine, E.W. and L.W. Durrell, 1941
    Cochran, L.C. and L.M. Hutchins, 1937, 1938
    V. peach ring spot
    Berkeley, G.H., 1947
    Berkeley, G.H. and R.S. Willison, 1948
    Gilmer, R.M., 1954, 1955
    Gilmer, R.M., K.D. Brase and K.G. Parker, 1957
    Moore, J. Duain, 1951
    Willison, R.S. and G.H. Berkeley, 1946
    V. peach rosette
    McClintock, J.A., 1923, 1931
    V. peach rosette mosaic
    Cation, Donald, 1942
    V. peach X disease
    (K.M. Smith, 1957) R.E. Fitzpatrick, et al., 1958
    Gilmer, R.M., 1951
    Gilmer, R.M., J. Duain Moore and G.W. Keitt, 1954
    V. peach yellows
    Manns, T.F., 1942
    V. plum bark split
    Posnette, A.F. and Christina E. Ellenberger, 1957
    V. plum line pattern
    Bodine, E.W. and L.W. Durrell, 1941
    Cochran, L.C. and L.M. Hutchins, 1937, 1938
    Gilmer, R.M., K.D. Brase and K.G. Parker, 1957
    Moore, J. Duain and H.R. Cameron, 1956
    Willison, R.S., 1945
    V. plum white spot
    Valleau, W.D., 1932
    V. prune diamond canker
    Smith, Ralph E., 1941
    Yarwood, C.E. and H.E. Thomas, 1954
    V. prune dwarf
    Cochran, L.C., 1956
    Gilmer, R.M., K.D. Brase and K.G. Parker, 1957

Prunus domestica, L. (cont.)
  V. prune dwarf
    Hildebrand, E.M., 1942
    Moore, J. Duain and H.R. Cameron, 1956
    Richards, B.L. and L.C. Cochran, 1956
    Thomas, H.E. and E.M. Hildebrand, 1936
    Willison, R.S., 1944
  V. (sour) cherry yellows
    Berkeley, G.H., 1947
    Berkeley, G.H. and R.S. Willison, 1948
    Hildebrand, E.M., 1944
    Moore, J. Duain, 1951
    Moore, J. Duain and H.R. Cameron, 1956
    Richards, B.L. and L.C. Cochran, 1956
  V. (standard) prune constricting mosaic
    (K.M. Smith, 1957) R.E. Fitzpatrick, et al., 1958
    Thomas, H. Earl and T.E. Rawlins, 1939
  V. stone fruit *
    Boyle, J.S., J. Duain Moore and G.W. Keitt, 1954
  V. stone fruit necrotic ring spot *
    Fridlund, Paul R., 1954
    Moore, J. Duain and H.R. Cameron, 1956
  V. stone fruit ring spot *
    Richards, B.L. and L.C. Cochran, 1956
P. dropmoreana *
  V. peach ring spot
    Gilmer, R.M., 1954, 1955
P. dunbarii, Rehder
  V. peach ring spot
    Gilmer, R.M., 1954, 1955
  V. peach X disease
    (K.M. Smith, 1957) R.E. Fitzpatrick, et al., 1958
    Gilmer, R.M., 1951
    Gilmer, R.M., J. Duain Moore and G.W. Keitt, 1954
  V. stone fruit *
    Boyle, J.S., J. Duain Moore and G.W. Keitt, 1954
P. effusa *
  V. peach ring spot
    Gilmer, R.M., 1955
P. emarginata, (Dougl.) Walp.
  V. cherry mottle leaf
    Reeves, E.L., 1941
    Richards, B.L. and L.C. Cochran, 1956
  V. peach ring spot
    Gilmer, R.M., 1955
P. fasciculata, A. Gray
  V. peach ring spot
    Gilmer, R.M., 1955
P. fenzliana, Fritsch
  V. peach ring spot
    Gilmer, R.M., 1955
  V. peach western X disease
    Rawlins, T.E. and H. Earl Thomas, 1941
P. fontanesiana, Schneid.
  V. peach ring spot
    Gilmer, R.M., 1955
P. fremonti, S. Wats.
  V. peach ring spot
    Gilmer, R.M., 1955
P. fruticosa, Pall.
  V. peach ring spot
    Gilmer, R.M., 1954, 1955
P. gigantea *
  V. apple mosaic
    Posnette, A.F. and Christina E. Ellenberger, 1957
  V. peach ring spot
    Gilmer, R.M., 1955
P. glandulifolia, Rupr. ex Maxim.
  V. peach ring spot
    Gilmer, R.M., 1955
P. glandulosa, Thunb.
  V. peach ring spot
    Gilmer, R.M., 1954, 1955
  V. peach X disease
    (K.M. Smith, 1957) R.E. Fitzpatrick, et al., 1958
    Gilmer, R.M., 1951
    Gilmer, R.M., J. Duain Moore and G.W. Keitt, 1954
  V. stone fruit *
    Boyle, J.S., J. Duain Moore and G.W. Keitt, 1954
P. gracilis, Engelm. & Gray
  V. peach ring spot
    Gilmer, R.M., 1955

P. gravesii, Small
  V. peach ring spot
    Gilmer, R.M., 1955
P. grayana, Maxim.
  V. peach ring spot
    Gilmer, R.M., 1955
P. hillieri *
  V. peach ring spot
    Gilmer, R.M., 1955
P. hortulana, Bailey
  V. peach ring spot
    Gilmer, R.M., 1955
  V. peach X disease
    Hildebrand, E.M., 1953
  V. phony peach
    Hutchins, Lee M., L.C. Cochran, W.F. Turner
    and J.H. Weinberger, 1953
    Hutchins, Lee M. and John L. Rue, 1949
P. hybrid
  V. plum line pattern
    Richards, B.L. and L.C. Cochran, 1956
P. ilicifolia, (Nutt.) Walp.
  V. peach ring spot
    Gilmer, R.M., 1954, 1955
P. incana, Stev.
  V. peach ring spot
    Gilmer, R.M., 1955
P. incisa, Thunb.
  V. peach ring spot
    Gilmer, R.M., 1955
P. insititia, L.
  V. apple mosaic
    Posnette, A.F. and Christina E. Ellenberger, 1957
  V. peach little peach
    Manns, T.F., 1942
  V. peach mosaic
    Bodine, E.W. and L.W. Durrell, 1941
  V. peach ring spot
    Gilmer, R.M., 1955
  V. peach rosette
    (K.M. Smith, 1957) R.E. Fitzpatrick, et al., 1958
  V. peach yellows
    Manns, T.F., 1942
  V. prune dwarf
    Hildebrand, E.M., 1942
P. jacquemontii, Hook. f.
  V. peach ring spot
    Gilmer, R.M., 1955
P. japonica, Thunb.
  V. peach ring spot
    Gilmer, R.M., 1954, 1955
  V. peach X disease
    Fridlund, Paul R., 1954
    Gilmer, R.M., J. Duain Moore and G.W. Keitt, 1954
    Hildebrand, E.M., 1953
  V. stone fruit *
    Boyle, J.S., J. Duain Moore and G.W. Keitt, 1954
P. juddii, X E. Anders.
  V. peach ring spot
    Gilmer, R.M., 1955
P. kansuensis, Rehder
  V. peach ring spot
    Gilmer, R.M., 1955
P. lanata, Mack. & Bush.
  V. peach ring spot
    Gilmer, R.M., 1955
P. lannesiana, Wils.
  V. peach ring spot
    Gilmer, R.M., 1955
  V. peach X disease
    Gilmer, R.M., J. Duain Moore and G.W. Keitt, 1954
P. laucheana, Bolle
  V. peach ring spot
    Gilmer, R.M., 1955
P. laurocerasus, L.
  V. peach ring spot
    Gilmer, R.M., 1954, 1955
P. lobulata, Koehne
  V. peach ring spot
    Gilmer, R.M., 1955

Prunus lusitanica, L.
  V. peach ring spot
    Gilmer, R.M., 1955
  V. peach yellow bud mosaic
    Thomas, H. Earl, 1940
P. lycioides, C.K. Schneid.
  V. peach ring spot
    Gilmer, R.M., 1955
P. lyoni, (Eastw.) Sarg.
  V. peach ring spot
    Gilmer, R.M., 1954, 1955
P. maackii, Rupr.
  V. peach ring spot
    Gilmer, R.M., 1954, 1955
  V. peach X disease
    Gilmer, R.M., 1951
    Gilmer, R.M., J. Duain Moore and G.W. Keitt,
    1954
  V. stone fruit *
    Boyle, J.S., J. Duain Moore and G.W. Keitt, 1954
P. mahaleb, L.
  V. cherry chlorosis *
    Keitt, G.W. and C.N. Clayton, 1941
  V. cherry mottle leaf
    Reeves, E.L., 1941
  V. cherry rasp leaf
    Posnette, A.F., 1954
  V. cherry rugose mosaic
    Berkeley, G.H., 1950
    Thomas, H. Earl and T.E. Rawlins, 1939
  V. cherry rusty mottle
    Zeller, S.M. and J.A. Milbrath, 1947
  V. elm mosaic
    Callahan, Kemper L. and J. Duain Moore, 1957
  V. peach ring spot
    Berkeley, G.H. and R.S. Willison, 1948
    Cation, Donald, 1949, 1952
    Cochran, L.C. and Lee M. Hutchins, 1941
    Fink, Harry C., 1950, 1955
    Gilmer, R.M., 1954, 1955
    Milbrath, J.A., 1957
    Posnette, A.F., 1954
    Willison, R.S. and G.H. Berkeley, 1946
  V. peach western X disease
    Rawlins, T.E. and H. Earl Thomas, 1941
    Schneider, Henry, 1945
  V. peach X disease
    Gilmer, R.M., J. Duain Moore and G.W. Keitt,
    1954
  V. plum line pattern
    Cation, Donald, 1941
    Willison, R.S., 1945
  V. prune dwarf
    Willison, R.S., 1944
  V. prunus A *
    Fulton, Robert W., 1957
  V. prunus B *
    Fulton, Robert W., 1957
  V. prunus E *
    Fulton, Robert W., 1957
  V. prunus G *
    Fulton, Robert W., 1957
  V. (sour) cherry yellows
    Berkeley, G.H. and R.S. Willison, 1948
    Cation, Donald, 1949, 1952
    Keitt, G.W. and C.N. Clayton, 1943
    Rasmussen, E.J. and Donald Cation, 1942
    Richards, B.L. and L.C. Cochran, 1956
  V. stone fruit *
    Boyle, J.S., J. Duain Moore and G.W. Keitt, 1954
  V. stone fruit ring spot *
    Heinis, J.L. and J.A. Milbrath, 1954
P. makii *
  V. peach X disease
    (K.M. Smith, 1957) R.E. Fitzpatrick, et al., 1958
P. maritima, Marsh.
  V. peach ring spot
    Gilmer, R.M., 1954, 1955
  V. peach X disease
    Gilmer, R.M., 1951
    Gilmer, R.M., J. Duain Moore and G.W. Keitt,
    1954

P. maximowiczi, Rupr.
  V. peach ring spot
    Gilmer, R.M., 1955
P. mexicana, S. Wats.
  V. peach mosaic
    (K.M. Smith, 1957) R.E. Fitzpatrick, et al., 1958
  V. peach ring spot
    Gilmer, R.M., 1955
  V. phony peach
    Hutchins, Lee M., L.C. Cochran, W.F. Turner
    and J.H. Weinberger, 1953
    Hutchins, Lee M. and John L. Rue, 1949
P. meyeri, Boeckel
  V. peach ring spot
    Gilmer, R.M., 1955
P. mira, Koehne
  V. peach ring spot
    Gilmer, R.M., 1955
  V. peach western X disease
    Rawlins, T.E. and H. Earl Thomas, 1941
P. mira x P. persica, (L.) Batsch
  V. peach western X disease
    Rawlins, T.E. and H. Earl Thomas, 1941
P. mollis, Walp.
  V. cherry little cherry
    Wilks, J.M. and M.F. Welsh, 1955
P. monticola, C. Koch
  V. peach ring spot
    Gilmer, R.M., 1955
P. mugus, Hand. -Mazz.
  V. peach ring spot
    Gilmer, R.M., 1955
P. mume, Sieb. & Zucc.
  V. peach asteroid spot
    Richards, B.L. and L.C. Cochran, 1956
  V. peach mosaic
    (K.M. Smith, 1957) R.E. Fitzpatrick, et al., 1958
  V. peach ring spot
    Gilmer, R.M., 1955
  V. peach yellow bud mosaic
    Thomas, H. Earl and T.E. Rawlins, 1939
  V. phony peach
    Hutchins, Lee M. and John L. Rue, 1949
P. munsoniana, Wight & Hedr.
  V. peach little peach
    Manns, T.F., 1942
  V. peach mosaic
    Richards, B.L. and L.C. Cochran, 1956
  V. peach ring spot
    Gilmer, R.M., 1955
  V. peach X disease
    (K.M. Smith, 1957) R.E. Fitzpatrick, et al., 1958
  V. peach yellows
    Manns, T.F., 1942
  V. phony peach
    Bruer, H.L. and C.E. Shepard, 1952
P. munsoniana x P. salicina, Lindl.
  V. peach little peach
    Manns, T.F., 1942
  V. peach yellows
    Manns, T.F., 1942
P. nana, Stokes
  V. peach ring spot
    Gilmer, R.M., 1954, 1955
P. newporti, Hort.
  V. peach ring spot
    Gilmer, R.M., 1954, 1955
  V. peach X disease
    Gilmer, R.M., J. Duain Moore and G.W. Keitt,
    1954
P. nigra, Ait.
  V. peach ring spot
    Gilmer, R.M., 1955
P. nipponica, Matsum.
  V. peach ring spot
    Gilmer, R.M., 1955
P. nipponica var. kurilensis, (Miyabe) Wilson
  V. peach ring spot
    Gilmer, R.M., 1955
P. padus, L.
  V. peach ring spot
    Gilmer, R.M., 1954, 1955

Prunus padus, L. (cont.)
  V. peach X disease
    (K.M. Smith, 1957) R.E. Fitzpatrick, et al., 1958
    Gilmer, R.M., 1951
    Gilmer, R.M., J. Duain Moore and G.W. Keitt,
    1954
  V. stone fruit *
    Boyle, J.S., J. Duain Moore and G.W. Keitt, 1954
P. padus var. cornuta, Henry
  V. peach ring spot
    Gilmer, R.M., 1955
P. pensylvanica, L. f.
  V. elm mosaic
    Callahan, Kemper L. and J. Duain Moore, 1957
  V. peach ring spot
    Gilmer, R.M., 1954, 1955
  V. peach X disease
    (K.M. Smith, 1957) R.E. Fitzpatrick, et al., 1958
    Gilmer, R.M., 1951
    Gilmer, R.M., J. Duain Moore and G.W. Keitt,
    1954
  V. prunus A *
    Fulton, Robert W., 1957
  V. prunus B *
    Fulton, Robert W., 1957
  V. prunus E *
    Fulton, Robert W., 1957
  V. prunus G *
    Fulton, Robert W., 1957
  V. (sour) cherry yellows
    Keitt, G.W. and C.N. Clayton, 1943
  V. stone fruit *
    Boyle, J.S., J. Duain Moore and G.W. Keitt, 1954
P. persica, (L.) Batsch (Amygdalus persica, L.)
  V. almond calico
    Thomas, H. Earl and T.E. Rawlins, 1939
  V. apple mosaic
    Kirkpatrick, Hugh C., 1955
    Posnette, A.F. and Christina E. Ellenberger, 1957
  V. apricot moorpark mottle
    (K.M. Smith, 1957) R.E. Fitzpatrick, et al., 1958
  V. apricot ring pox
    Simonds, Austin O., 1951
    Yarwood, C.E., 1957
  V. cherry dusty yellows
    Posnette, A.F., 1954
  V. cherry mottle leaf
    Richards, B.L. and L.C. Cochran, 1956
  V. cherry necrotic etch *
    Posnette, A.F., 1954
  V. cherry necrotic rusty mottle
    Richards, B.L. and L.C. Cochran, 1956
    Richards, B.L. and Bryce N. Wadley, 1950
  V. cherry rasp leaf
    Posnette, A.F., 1954
  V. cherry rugose mosaic
    Berkeley, G.H., 1950
    Nyland, George, 1954
    Posnette, A.F., 1954
    Thomas, H. Earl and T.E. Rawlins, 1939
  V. cherry rusty mottle
    Posnette, A.F., 1954
    Zeller, S.M. and J.A. Milbrath, 1947
  V. cherry sunken mottle *
    Posnette, A.F., 1954
  V. cherry twisted leaf
    (K.M. Smith, 1957) R.E. Fitzpatrick, et al., 1958
  V. elm mosaic
    Moore, J. Duain and E.H. Varney, 1954
  V. (flowering) cherry rough bark
    Nichols, Carl W. and R.L. McClain, 1957
  V. peach asteroid spot
    Clayton, C.N., 1949
    Cochran, L.C. and Clayton O. Smith, 1938
    Richards, B.L. and L.C. Cochran, 1956
  V. peach blotch
    Willison, R.S., 1946
  V. peach calico
    Blodgett, Earle C., 1944
  V. peach little peach
    Cook, M.T., 1922
    Kunkel, L.O., 1936, 1938
    Manns, T.F., 1936, 1942

P. persica, (L.) Batsch (Amygdalus persica, L.) (cont.)
  V. peach mosaic
    Bennett, C.W., 1944
    Bodine, E.W., 1937, 1942
    Bodine, E.W. and L.W. Durrell, 1941
    Cation, D., 1934
    Cochran, L.C. and L.M. Hutchins, 1937
    Cochran, L.C. and John L. Rue, 1944, 1946
    Hutchins, L.M., 1933
    Hutchins, Lee M. and L.C. Cochran, 1940
    Kunkel, L.O., 1938
    Richards, B.L. and L.C. Cochran, 1956
    Stout, Gilbert L., 1939
    Wilson, Norton S., Laurence S. Jones and L.C.
    Cochran, 1955
  V. peach mottle
    Blodgett, Earle C., 1941
  V. peach necrotic leaf spot
    Cation, Donald, 1942
    Richards, B.L. and L.C. Cochran, 1956
  V. peach red suture
    (K.M. Smith, 1957) R.E. Fitzpatrick, et al., 1958
  V. peach ring spot
    Berkeley, G.H., 1947
    Berkeley, G.H. and R.S. Willison, 1948
    Cation, Donald, 1949
    Cochran, L.C., 1950, 1952
    Cochran, L.C. and Lee M. Hutchins, 1941
    Cochran, L.C. and R.L. McClain, 1951
    Fink, Harry C., 1950, 1955
    Gilmer, R.M., 1954, 1955, 1956
    Gilmer, R.M., K.D. Brase and K.G. Parker,
    1957
    Hildebrand, E.M., 1944
    Moore, J. Duain and G.W. Keitt, 1944
    Posnette, A.F., 1954
    Willison, R.S. and G.H. Berkeley, 1946
    Yarwood, C.E., 1957
    Young, H.C., Jr., 1951
  V. peach rosette
    KenKnight, Glenn, 1957
    Kunkel, L.O., 1936, 1938
    McClintock, J.A., 1923, 1931
  V. peach rosette mosaic
    Cation, Donald, 1942
    Hildebrand, E.M., 1941
  V. peach wart
    Blodgett, Earle C., 1941, 1943, 1946
    Zeller, S.M. and J.A. Milbrath, 1945
  V. peach western X disease
    Jensen, D.D., 1953, 1955, 1957
    Jensen, D.D. and H. Earl Thomas, 1954, 1955
    Kaloostian, George H., 1951
    Keener, Paul D., 1953
    Nielson, Mervin W. and Laurence S. Jones, 1954
    Nyland, George, 1955
    Nyland, George and Archie Schlocker, 1951
    Rawlins, T.E. and H. Earl Thomas, 1941
    Richards, B.L. and L.C. Cochran, 1956
    Richards, B.L. and Lee M. Hutchins, 1941
    Richards, B.L., L.M. Hutchins and E.L. Reeves,
    1949
    Schneider, Henry, 1945
    Thomas, H. Earl, 1940
    Thomas, H. Earl and T.E. Rawlins, 1941
    Thomas, H. Earl, T.E. Rawlins and K.G. Parker,
    1940
    Wadley, Bryce N., 1952
    Weathers, Lewis G. and George W. Cochran, 1950
    Wilks, Jack M. and J.A. Milbrath, 1956
    Wolfe, H.R., 1955
    Wolfe, H.R., E.W. Anthon and L.S. Jones, 1950
    Zeller, S.M. and J.A. Milbrath, 1948, 1950
  V. peach X disease
    Fridlund, Paul R., 1954
    Gilmer, R.M., J. Duain Moore and G.W. Keitt,
    1954
    Hildebrand, E.M., 1943, 1953
    Hildebrand, E.M. and D.H. Palmiter, 1940
    Kunkel, L.O., 1944
    Palmiter, D.H. and E.M. Hildebrand, 1943
    Palmiter, D.H. and K.G. Parker, 1948
    Parker, K.G. and D.H. Palmiter, 1948

Prunus persica, (L.) Batsch (Amygdalus persica, L.)
V. peach X disease (cont.)
Slack, Derald A., 1952
Stoddard, E.M., 1938, 1947
Thornberry, H.H., 1954
V. peach yellow bud mosaic
Alcorn, Stanley M., Stephen Wilhelm and H. Earl
Thomas, 1955
Schlocker, Archie, H. Keith Wagnon and James R.
Breece, 1957
Thomas, H. Earl, 1940
Thomas, H. Earl and T.E. Rawlins, 1939
Thomas, H. Earl, C. Emlen Scott, E.E. Wilson
and J.H. Freitag, 1944
Wagnon, H. Keith and James R. Breece, 1955
Yarwood, C.E., 1956, 1957
Yarwood, C.E. and H.E. Thomas, 1954
V. peach yellows
Blake, M.A., Mel. T. Cook and C.H. Connors,
1921
Cook, M.T., 1922
Kunkel, L.O., 1936, 1938
Manns, T.F., 1936, 1942
V. phony peach
Hutchins, L.M., 1929, 1939
Hutchins, Lee M., L.C. Cochran, W.F. Turner
and J.H. Weinberger, 1953
Hutchins, Lee M. and John L. Rue, 1949
KenKnight, Glenn, 1957
V. plum line pattern
Cation, Donald, 1941
Cochran, L.C. and L.M. Hutchins, 1937, 1938
Richards, B.L. and L.C. Cochran, 1956
Willison, R.S., 1945
V. plum white spot
Thomas, H. Earl and T.E. Rawlins, 1939
Valleau, W.D., 1932
V. prune dwarf
Hildebrand, E.M., 1942
Richards, B.L. and L.C. Cochran, 1956
Willison, R.S., 1944
V. (sour) cherry yellows
Berkeley, G.H., 1947
Berkeley, G.H. and R.S. Willison, 1948
Cation, Donald, 1949
Gilmer, R.M., K.D. Brase and K.G. Parker,
1957
Hildebrand, E.M., 1942, 1943, 1944
Rasmussen, E.J. and Donald Cation, 1942
Richards, B.L. and L.C. Cochran, 1956
Young, H.C., Jr., 1951
V. (standard) prune constricting mosaic
(K.M. Smith, 1957) R.E. Fitzpatrick, et al., 1958
Thomas, H. Earl and T.E. Rawlins, 1939
V. stone fruit ring spot *
Heinis, Julius L., 1956
Heinis, J.L. and J.A. Milbrath, 1954
Richards, B.L. and L.C. Cochran, 1956
P. persica var. nectarina, (Ait.) Maxim. (Amygdalus
persica var. nectarina, Ait.)
V. peach asteroid spot
(K.M. Smith, 1957) R.E. Fitzpatrick, et al., 1958
V. peach mosaic
(K.M. Smith, 1957) R.E. Fitzpatrick, et al., 1958
V. peach necrotic leaf spot
Richards, B.L. and L.C. Cochran, 1956
V. peach western X disease
Richards, B.L. and L.C. Cochran, 1956
V. peach X disease
Palmiter, D.H. and E.M. Hildebrand, 1943
V. peach yellows
(K.M. Smith, 1957) R.E. Fitzpatrick, et al., 1958
V. phony peach
(K.M. Smith, 1957) R.E. Fitzpatrick, et al., 1958
P. persica var. nucipersica, Schneid.
V. peach X disease
Hildebrand, E.M., 1953
P. petunnikowi, Rehder
V. peach ring spot
Gilmer, R.M., 1955
P. pilosiuscula, Koehne
V. peach ring spot
Gilmer, R.M., 1955

P. pleiocerasus, Koehne
V. peach ring spot
Gilmer, R.M., 1955
P. potanini *
V. peach ring spot
Gilmer, R.M., 1955
P. pumila, L.
V. peach ring spot
Gilmer, R.M., 1955
Moore, J. Duain and G.W. Keitt, 1946
V. peach rosette
McClintock, J.A., 1931
V. peach X disease
Gilmer, R.M., 1951
Gilmer, R.M., J. Duain Moore and G.W. Keitt,
1954
Slack, Derald A., 1952
V. stone fruit *
Boyle, J.S., J. Duain Moore and G.W. Keitt,
1954
P. reverchonii, Sarg.
V. peach ring spot
Gilmer, R.M., 1955
P. rufa, Steud.
V. peach ring spot
Gilmer, R.M., 1955
P. salicina, Lindl.
V. peach asteroid spot
Richards, B.L. and L.C. Cochran, 1956
V. peach little peach
Manns, T.F., 1936, 1942
V. peach mosaic
Bodine, E.W. and L.W. Durrell, 1941
Richards, B.L. and L.C. Cochran, 1956
V. peach ring spot
Gilmer, R.M., 1953, 1954, 1955
Willison, R.S. and G.H. Berkeley, 1946
V. peach rosette mosaic
(K.M. Smith, 1957) R.E. Fitzpatrick, et al., 1958
V. peach X disease
Gilmer, R.M., J. Duain Moore and G.W. Keitt,
1954
V. peach yellows
Manns, T.F., 1936, 1942
V. plum line pattern
Bodine, E.W. and L.W. Durrell, 1941
Cation, Donald, 1941
Gilmer, R.M., K.D. Brase and K.G. Parker,
1957
Willison, R.S., 1945
V. plum white spot
Thomas, H. Earl and T.E. Rawlins, 1939
Valleau, W.D., 1932
V. prune dwarf
Hildebrand, E.M., 1942
Willison, R.S., 1944
P. salicina x P. simonii, Carr.
V. peach mosaic
Bodine, E.W. and L.W. Durrell, 1941
V. peach yellow bud mosaic
Schlocker, Archie, H. Keith Wagnon and James
R. Breece, 1957
P. sargenti, Rehd.
V. peach ring spot
Gilmer, R.M., 1955
P. scopulorum, Koehne
V. peach ring spot
Gilmer, R.M., 1955
P. serotina, Ehrh.
V. elm mosaic
Callahan, Kemper L. and J. Duain Moore, 1957
V. peach ring spot
Fink, Harry C., 1950, 1955
Gilmer, R.M., 1954, 1955
V. peach X disease
Hildebrand, E.M., 1953
V. prunus A *
Fulton, Robert W., 1957
V. prunus B *
Fulton, Robert W., 1957
V. prunus E *
Fulton, Robert W., 1957
V. prunus G *
Fulton, Robert W., 1957

Prunus serotina, Ehrh. (cont.)
   V. (sour) cherry yellows
      Keitt, G.W. and C.N. Clayton, 1943
      Richards, B.L. and L.C. Cochran, 1956
   V. stone fruit *
      Boyle, J.S., J. Duain Moore and G.W. Keitt, 1954
P. serrula, Franch.
   V. peach ring spot
      Gilmer, R.M., 1955
P. serrulata, Lindl.
   V. cherry little cherry
      Milbrath, J.A. and H.E. Williams, 1956
   V. cherry midleaf necrosis *
      Milbrath, J.A., 1957
   V. cherry rusty mottle
      Zeller, S.M. and J.A. Milbrath, 1947
   V. cherry vein clearing *
      Zeller, S.M. and A.W. Evans, 1941
   V. (flowering) cherry rough bark
      Milbrath, J.A. and S.M. Zeller, 1942
      Nichols, Carl W. and R.L. McClain, 1957
   V. peach ring spot
      Gilmer, R.M., 1954, 1955
      Gilmer, R.M., K.D. Brase and K.G. Parker, 1957
      Milbrath, J.A., 1952
      Tomlinson, N., 1955
   V. peach X disease
      Gilmer, R.M., J. Duain Moore and G.W. Keitt, 1954
   V. plum line pattern
      Richards, B.L. and L.C. Cochran, 1956
      Zeller, S.M. and J.A. Milbrath, 1942
   V. stone fruit ring spot *
      Heinis, Julius L., 1956
      Heinis, J.L. and J.A. Milbrath, 1954
      Richards, B.L. and L.C. Cochran, 1956
P. setulosa, Batalin
   V. peach ring spot
      Gilmer, R.M., 1955
P. sibirica, L.
   V. peach ring spot
      Gilmer, R.M., 1955
P. sieboldi, (Carr.) Wittm.
   V. peach ring spot
      Gilmer, R.M., 1954, 1955
   V. peach X disease
      Gilmer, R.M., J. Duain Moore and G.W. Keitt, 1954
P. simonii, Carr.
   V. peach little peach
      Manns, T.F., 1942
   V. peach ring spot
      Gilmer, R.M., 1955
   V. peach yellows
      Manns, T.F., 1942
P. skinneri, X Rehder
   V. peach ring spot
      Gilmer, R.M., 1955
P. slavinii, X Palmer
   V. peach ring spot
      Gilmer, R.M., 1955
P. spinosa, L.
   V. peach ring spot
      Gilmer, R.M., 1955
   V. peach X disease
      Gilmer, R.M., J. Duain Moore and G.W. Keitt, 1954
P. spp.
   V. plum fruit crinkle *
      Chamberlain, E.E., J.D. Atkinson and J.A. Hunter, 1959
P. ssiori, Schmidt
   V. peach ring spot
      Gilmer, R.M., 1955
P. subcordata, Benth.
   V. peach ring spot
      Gilmer, R.M., 1955
P. subhirtella, Miq.
   V. peach ring spot
      Gilmer, R.M., 1955
P. sultana *
   V. peach ring spot
      Gilmer, R.M., 1955

P. tangutica, Koehne
   V. peach mosaic
      (K.M. Smith, 1957) R.E. Fitzpatrick, et al., 1958
P. tenella, Batsch (Amygdalus nana, L.)
   V. peach ring spot
      Gilmer, R.M., 1954, 1955
P. tomentosa, Thunb.
   V. cherry green ring mottle *
      Fink, Harry C., 1955
   V. peach mosaic
      (K.M. Smith, 1957) R.E. Fitzpatrick, et al., 1958
   V. peach ring spot
      Fink, Harry C., 1950, 1955
      Gilmer, R.M., 1954, 1955, 1956
      Gilmer, R.M., K.D. Brase and K.G. Parker, 1957
      Young, H.C., Jr., 1951
   V. peach rosette mosaic
      Fink, Harry C., 1955
   V. peach western X disease
      Richards, B.L. and L.C. Cochran, 1956
   V. peach X disease
      (K.M. Smith, 1957) R.E. Fitzpatrick, et al., 1958
      Gilmer, R.M., 1951
      Gilmer, R.M., J. Duain Moore and G.W. Keitt, 1954
   V. peach yellow bud mosaic
      Schlocker, Archie, H. Keith Wagnon and James R. Breece, 1957
   V. prune dwarf
      Fink, Harry C., 1955
   V. (sour) cherry yellows
      Fink, Harry C., 1955
      Young, H.C., Jr., 1951
   V. stone fruit necrotic ring spot *
      Fridlund, Paul R., 1954
P. triloba, Lindl.
   V. peach ring spot
      Gilmer, R.M., 1954, 1955
P. umbellata, Ell.
   V. peach ring spot
      Gilmer, R.M., 1955
   V. phony peach
      Bruer, H.L. and C.E. Shepard, 1952
      Bruer, H.L., C.E. Shepard and T.D. Persons, 1951
P. umbellata var. injucunda, Sarg.
   V. phony peach
      Bruer, H.L. and C.E. Shepard, 1952
      Bruer, H.L., C.E. Shepard and T.D. Persons, 1951
P. ursina, Kotschy ex Boiss.
   V. peach ring spot
      Gilmer, R.M., 1955
P. ussuriensis, Kovalev & Kostina
   V. peach ring spot
      Gilmer, R.M., 1955
P. venulosa, Sarg.
   V. peach ring spot
      Gilmer, R.M., 1955
P. virginiana, L.
   V. cherry chlorosis *
      Keitt, G.W. and C.N. Clayton, 1941
   V. peach ring spot
      Gilmer, R.M., 1955
      Moore, J. Duain and G.W. Keitt, 1946
   V. peach western X disease
      Rawlins, T.E. and H. Earl Thomas, 1941
      Richards, B.L. and L.C. Cochran, 1956
      Richards, B.L., L.M. Hutchins and E.L. Reeves, 1949
      Richards, B.L., E.L. Reeves and Lee M. Hutchins, 1946
      Zeller, S.M. and J.A. Milbrath, 1948
   V. peach X disease
      Fridlund, Paul R., 1954
      Gilmer, R.M., 1951, 1954
      Gilmer, R.M., J. Duain Moore and G.W. Keitt, 1954
      Hildebrand, E.M., 1953
      Hildebrand, E.M. and D.H. Palmiter, 1940
      Palmiter, D.H. and E.M. Hildebrand, 1943
      Palmiter, D.H. and K.G. Parker, 1948

Prunus virginiana, L. (cont.)
    V. peach X disease
        Parker, K.G. and D.H. Palmiter, 1948
        Stoddard, E.M., 1947
        Thornberry, H.H., 1946, 1954
    V. prunus A *
        Fulton, Robert W., 1957
    V. prunus B *
        Fulton, Robert W., 1957
    V. prunus E *
        Fulton, Robert W., 1957
    V. prunus G *
        Fulton, Robert W., 1957
    V. (sour) cherry yellows
        Keitt, G.W. and C.N. Clayton, 1943
        Richards, B.L. and L.C. Cochran, 1956
    V. stone fruit *
        Boyle, J.S., J. Duain Moore and G.W. Keitt, 1954
    V. stone fruit necrotic ring spot *
        Fridlund, Paul R., 1954
P. virginiana var. demissa, (Torr. & Gray) Torr.
    V. cherry necrotic rusty mottle
        Richards, B.L. and L.C. Cochran, 1956
    V. peach ring spot
        Gilmer, R.M., 1954
    V. peach western X disease
        Kaloostian, George H., 1951
        Richards, B.L. and L.C. Cochran, 1956
P. yedoensis, Matsum.
    V. peach ring spot
        Gilmer, R.M., 1955

PSOPHOCARPUS Neck. 1790 (Leguminosae)
P. tetragonolobus, DC.
    V. cowpea mosaic
        Dale, W.T., 1949

PSORALEA L. 1742 (Leguminosae)
P. bituminosa, L.
    V. psoralea bituminosa mosaic *
        McKinney, H.H., 1928
    V. tobacco streak
        Fulton, Robert W., 1948

PTERYGOTA Schott & Endl. 1832 (Sterculiaceae)
P. macrocarpa, K. Schum.
    V. cacao swollen shoot
        Tinsley, T.W. and A.L. Wharton, 1958

PYRETHRUM Hall. 1742 (Compositae)
P. spp.
    V. aster yellows
        Kunkel, L.O., 1926

PYRUS ((Tourn.)) L. 1735 (Rosaceae)
P. aucuparia, Ehrh.
    V. ash infectious variegation
        (K.M. Smith, 1957) R.E. Fitzpatrick, et al., 1958
P. communis, L.
    V. pear mosaic
        Posnette, A.F., 1957
    V. pear red mottle *
        Posnette, A.F., 1957
    V. pear stony pit
        Kienholz, J.R., 1939
    V. pear vein yellows *
        Posnette, A.F., 1957
    V. quince sooty ring spot *
        Posnette, A.F., 1957
    V. quince stunt *
        Posnette, A.F., 1957

QUAMOCLIT Tourn. ex Moench 1794 (Convolvulaceae)
Q. lobata, House
    V. beet curly top
        Freitag, Julius H. and Henry H.P. Severin, 1936
    V. sweet potato feathery mottle
        Webb, Raymon E., 1954
Q. pennata, Bojer
    V. tobacco mosaic
        Grant, T.J., 1934

RADICULA Dill. ex Moench 1794 (Cruciferae)
R. nasturtium-aquaticum, (L.) Brit. & Rend.
    V. cabbage black ring spot
        Tompkins, C.M., M.W. Gardner and H. Rex
        Thomas, 1938
R. palustris, (L.) Moench
    V. tobacco mosaic
        Holmes, Francis O., 1938

RANUNCULUS ((Tourn.)) L. 1735 (Ranunculaceae)
R. asiaticus, L.
    V. aster yellows
        Severin, Henry H.P. and Julius H. Freitag, 1934,
        1945
    V. delphinium ring spot
        Severin, Henry H.P. and R.C. Dickson, 1942
    V. ranunculus mosaic
        Raabe, Robert D. and A. Herbert Gold, 1957
R. spp.
    V. anemone mosaic *
        Hollings, M., 1957
    V. tomato spotted wilt
        (K.M. Smith, 1957) R.E. Fitzpatrick, et al., 1958

RAPHANUS ((Tourn.)) L. 1735 (Cruciferae)
R. raphanistrum, L.
    V. cabbage black ring spot
        (K.M. Smith, 1957) R.E. Fitzpatrick, et al., 1958
    V. cauliflower mosaic
        Tompkins, C.M., 1937
    V. turnip crinkle
        Broadbent, L. and G.D. Heathcote, 1958
    V. turnip rosette *
        Broadbent, L. and G.D. Heathcote, 1958
    V. turnip yellow mosaic
        Broadbent, L. and G.D. Heathcote, 1958
R. sativus, L.
    V. aster yellows
        Frazier, Norman W. and Henry H.P. Severin,
        1945
        Severin, Henry H.P. and Julius H. Freitag, 1945
    V. beet curly top
        Severin, Henry H.P., 1929, 1934
    V. cabbage ring necrosis
        Larson, R.H. and J.C. Walker, 1941
    V. cauliflower mosaic
        Alvarez-Garcia, L.A., 1951
        Berkeley, G.H. and J.H. Tremaine, 1954
        Caldwell, John and Ian W. Prentice, 1942
        Tompkins, C.M., 1937
        Tompkins, C.M. and H. Rex Thomas, 1938
        Walker, J.C., Francis J. LeBeau and Glenn S.
        Pound, 1945
    V. cucumber mosaic
        Berkeley, G.H. and J.H. Tremaine, 1954
    V. radish mosaic
        Raychaudhuri, S.P. and P.S. Pathanian, 1955
        Severin, Henry H.P. and C.M. Tompkins, 1950
        Takahashi, William N., 1952
        Tompkins, C.M., 1939
    V. tobacco ring spot no. 2
        Price, W.C., 1940
    V. turnip crinkle
        Broadbent, L. and G.D. Heathcote, 1958
    V. turnip mosaic
        Tompkins, C.M., 1939
        Walker, J.C., Francis J. LeBeau and Glenn S.
        Pound, 1945
    V. turnip rosette *
        Broadbent, L. and G.D. Heathcote, 1958
    V. turnip yellow mosaic
        Broadbent, L. and G.D. Heathcote, 1958
R. sativus var. hortensis, Backer *
    V. turnip mosaic
        Dale, W.T., 1948
R. sativus var. longipinnatus, Bailey *
    V. cabbage black ring spot
        Tompkins, C.M., M.W. Gardner and H.R.
        Thomas, 1937, 1938
    V. radish mosaic
        Tompkins, C.M., 1939

Raphanus sativus, L., var. longipinnatus, Bailey *
   V. rape savoy   (cont.)
      Ling, Lee and Juhwa Y. Yang, 1940
   V. turnip mosaic
      Tompkins, C.M., 1938, 1939

RESEDA Tourn. ex L. 1735 (Resedaceae)
R. odorata, L.
   V. aster yellows
      Kunkel, L.O., 1926
   V. beet curly top
      Freitag, Julius H. and Henry H.P. Severin, 1936
   V. beet yellows
      Roland, G. and J. Tahon, 1961
   V. cabbage black ring spot
      Tompkins, C.M., M.W. Gardner and H. Rex
      Thomas, 1938
   V. clover big vein
      Black, L.M., 1945
   V. cucumber mosaic
      Pound, Glenn S. and J.C. Walker, 1948
   V. lucerne dwarf
      Freitag, J.H., 1951
   V. tobacco ring spot no. 2
      Hildebrand, E.M., 1942
      Price, W.C., 1940
   V. turnip crinkle
      Broadbent, L. and G.D. Heathcote, 1958
   V. turnip mosaic
      Tompkins, C.M., 1938, 1939
      Walker, J.C., Francis J. LeBeau and Glenn S.
      Pound, 1945
   V. turnip rosette *
      Broadbent, L. and G.D. Heathcote, 1958
   V. turnip yellow mosaic
      Broadbent, L. and G.D. Heathcote, 1958

RHAGODIA R. Br. 1810 (Chenopodiaceae)
R. nutans, R. Br.
   V. beet yellows
      Roland, G. and J. Tahon, 1961

RHEUM L. 1735 (Polygonaceae)
R. officinale, Baill.
   V. rhubarb mosaic *
      (K.M. Smith, 1957) R.E. Fitzpatrick, et al., 1958
R. rhaponticum, L.
   V. beet curly top
      Severin, Henry H.P., 1929
   V. cabbage black ring spot
      Tompkins, C.M., M.W. Gardner and H.R.
      Thomas, 1937, 1938
   V. clover big vein
      Black, L.M., 1945
   V. cucumber mosaic
      Price, W.C., 1940
   V. lucerne dwarf
      Freitag, J.H., 1951
   V. lucerne mosaic
      Price, W.C., 1940
   V. prunus G *
      Fulton, Robert W., 1957
   V. rhubarb ring spot *
      Vaughan, Edward K. and John W. Yale, Jr., 1953
      Yale, John W., Jr. and Edward K. Vaughan, 1954
   V. tobacco necrosis
      Price, W.C., 1940
   V. tobacco ring spot
      Price, W.C., 1940
   V. tobacco ring spot no. 2
      Price, W.C., 1940
   V. tomato aspermy
      (K.M. Smith, 1957) R.E. Fitzpatrick, et al., 1958

RHUS ((Tourn.)) L. 1737 (Anacardiaceae)
R. diversiloba, Torr. & Gray
   V. lucerne dwarf
      Freitag, J.H., 1951

RHYNCHOSIA Lour. 1790 (Leguminosae)
(RYNCHOSIA) MacFad. 1837
R. hagenbeckii, Harms
   V. (legume) little leaf disease *
      Hutton, E.M. and N.E. Grylls, 1956
R. minima, DC.
   V. (legume) little leaf disease *
      Hutton, E.M. and N.E. Gryllis, 1956
R. resinosa, Hochst. ex Baker
   V. groundnut rosette
      Evans, A.C., 1954

RIBES L. 1737 (Saxifragaceae)
R. grossularia, L.
   V. gooseberry veinbanding
      (K.M. Smith, 1957) R.E. Fitzpatrick, et al., 1958
R. nigrum, L.
   V. black currant reversion
      Lees, A.H., 1925
   V. black currant vein pattern
      (K.M. Smith, 1957) R.E. Fitzpatrick, et al., 1958
R. rubrum, L.
   V. red currant mosaic
      Hildebrand, E.M., 1939
   V. red currant ring spot
      Klesser, P.J., 1951
R. sativum, (Reichb.) Syme
   V. tobacco ring spot no. 2
      Hildebrand, E.M., 1941, 1942

RICINUS ((Tourn.)) L. 1735 (Euphorbiaceae)
R. communis, L.
   V. tobacco necrosis
      Price, W.C., 1940
   V. tobacco ring spot
      Cook, A.A., 1956
      Wingard, S.A., 1928
   V. tobacco ring spot no. 2
      Hildebrand, E.M., 1942
      Price, W.C., 1940

ROBINIA L. 1737 (Leguminosae)
R. pseudoacacia, L.
   V. robinia brooming
      Grant, Theodore J., 1939
      Hartley, C. and L.W.R. Jackson, 1933
      Jackson, L.W.R. and C. Hartley, 1933
   V. tobacco streak
      Fulton, Robert W., 1948

RORIPPA Scop. 1760 (Cruciferae)
(RORIPA) Scop. 1760
R. curvisiliqua, Bessey
   V. aster yellows
      Frazier, Norman W. and Henry H.P. Severin,
      1945
R. sylvestris, (L.) Bess.
   V. aster yellows
      (K.M. Smith, 1957) R.E. Fitzpatrick, et al., 1958

ROSA Tourn. ex L. 1735 (Rosaceae)
R. californica, Cham. & Schlecht.
   V. lucerne dwarf
      Freitag, J.H., 1951
   V. rose rosette
      Thomas, H. Earl and C. Emlen Scott, 1953
R. canina, L.
   V. rose mosaic
      Brierley, Philip and Floyd F. Smith, 1940
   V. rose streak
      Brierley, Philip and Floyd F. Smith, 1940
   V. rose yellow mosaic
      Brierley, Philip and Floyd F. Smith, 1940
R. chinensis, Jacq., var. manetti, Dipp.
   V. rose mosaic
      Brierley, Philip and Floyd F. Smith, 1940
      Nelson, R., 1930
      Thomas, H. Earl and L.M. Massey, 1939
      White, R.P., 1930, 1932

Rosa chinensis, Jacq., var. manetti, Dipp. (cont.)
  V. rose rosette
    Thomas, H. Earl and C. Emlen Scott, 1953
  V. rose yellow mosaic
    Brierley, Philip and Floyd F. Smith, 1940
    Thomas, H. Earl and L.M. Massey, 1939
(R. chinensis, Jacq. x R. moschata, Herrm.) x R.
foetida, Herrm.
  V. rose mosaic
    Nelson, R., 1930
R. hugonis, Hemsl.
  V. rose mosaic
    Brierley, Philip and Floyd F. Smith, 1940
  V. rose yellow mosaic
    Brierley, Philip and Floyd F. Smith, 1940
R. hybrid
  V. apple mosaic
    Thomas, H. Earl and L.M. Massey, 1939
  V. rose mosaic
    Thomas, H. Earl and L.M. Massey, 1939
  V. rose streak
    Brierley, P., 1935
  V. rose yellow mosaic
    Thomas, H. Earl and L.M. Massey, 1939
R. multiflora, Thunb.
  V. peach ring spot
    Gilmer, R.M., 1956
  V. rose mosaic
    Brierley, Philip and Floyd F. Smith, 1940
    Fulton, Robert W., 1952
    Thomas, H. Earl and L.M. Massey, 1939
    White, R.P., 1930, 1932
  V. rose rosette
    Thomas, H. Earl and C. Emlen Scott, 1953
  V. rose streak
    Brierley, Philip and Floyd F. Smith, 1940
  V. rose yellow mosaic
    Brierley, Philip and Floyd F. Smith, 1940
    Thomas, H. Earl and L.M. Massey, 1939
R. multiflora x R. chinensis, Jacq.
  V. rose mosaic
    Brierley, Philip and Floyd F. Smith, 1940
  V. rose streak
    Brierley, Philip and Floyd F. Smith, 1940
  V. rose yellow mosaic
    Brierley, Philip and Floyd F. Smith, 1940
R. noisettiana, Thory
  V. rose mosaic
    Brierley, Philip and Floyd F. Smith, 1940
  V. rose streak
    Brierley, Philip and Floyd F. Smith, 1940
  V. rose yellow mosaic
    Brierley, Philip and Floyd F. Smith, 1940
R. nutkana, Presl
  V. rose mosaic
    Brierley, Philip and Floyd F. Smith, 1940
  V. rose rosette
    Thomas, H. Earl and C. Emlen Scott, 1953
  V. rose streak
    Brierley, Philip and Floyd F. Smith, 1940
  V. rose yellow mosaic
    Brierley, Philip and Floyd F. Smith, 1940
R. odorata, Sweet
  V. peach yellow bud mosaic
    Thomas, H. Earl and L.M. Massey, 1939
  V. rose mosaic
    Brierley, Philip and Floyd F. Smith, 1940
    Nelson, R., 1930
    Thomas, H. Earl and L.M. Massey, 1939
    White, R.P., 1930, 1932, 1934
  V. rose rosette
    Thomas, H. Earl and C. Emlen Scott, 1953
  V. rose streak
    Brierley, Philip and Floyd F. Smith, 1940
  V. rose yellow mosaic
    Brierley, Philip and Floyd F. Smith, 1940
    Thomas, H. Earl and L.M. Massey, 1939
R. odorata var. gigantea, Rehd. & Wilson
  V. rose rosette
    Thomas, H. Earl and C. Emlen Scott, 1953
R. pisocarpa, Gray
  V. rose rosette
    Thomas, H. Earl and C. Emlen Scott, 1953

R. rubrifolia, Vill.
  V. rose rosette
    Thomas, H. Earl and C. Emlen Scott, 1953
R. setigera, Michx.
  V. rose mosaic
    Fulton, Robert W., 1952
R. spinosissima, L.
  V. rose rosette
    Thomas, H. Earl and C. Emlen Scott, 1953
R. spp.
  V. peach necrotic leaf spot
    (K.M. Smith, 1957) R.E. Fitzpatrick, et al., 1958
  V. peach ring spot
    Cochran, L.C., 1950
  V. peach yellow bud mosaic
    Thomas, H. Earl and L.M. Massey, 1939
    Thomas, H. Earl and T.E. Rawlins, 1939
  V. rose cowl forming
    (K.M. Smith, 1957) R.E. Fitzpatrick, et al., 1958
  V. rose mosaic
    Brierley, Philip and Floyd F. Smith, 1940
    Thomas, H. Earl and L.M. Massey, 1939
    White, R.P., 1932
  V. rose streak
    Brierley, Philip and Floyd F. Smith, 1940
  V. rose wilt
    (K.M. Smith, 1957) R.E. Fitzpatrick, et al., 1958
  V. rose yellow mosaic
    Brierley, Philip and Floyd F. Smith, 1940
    Thomas, H. Earl and L.M. Massey, 1939
R. wichuraiana, Crep.
  V. rose mosaic
    Brierley, Philip and Floyd F. Smith, 1940
  V. rose streak
    Brierley, Philip and Floyd F. Smith, 1940
  V. rose yellow mosaic
    Brierley, Philip and Floyd F. Smith, 1940

ROSMARINUS ((Tourn.)) L. 1735 (Labiatae)
R. officinalis, L.
  V. lucerne dwarf
    Freitag, J.H., 1951

ROTTBOELLIA L. f. 1779 (Gramineae)
R. exaltata, L. f.
  V. rice and corn leaf-gall *
    Agati, Julian A. and Carlos A. Calica, 1950

RUBUS ((Tourn.)) L. 1735 (Rosaceae)
R. albescens, Roxb.
  V. black raspberry necrosis
    (K.M. Smith, 1957) R.E. Fitzpatrick, et al., 1958
  V. rubus yellow net
    (K.M. Smith, 1957) R.E. Fitzpatrick, et al., 1958
R. allegheniensis, Porter
  V. blackberry dwarfing
    Wilhelm, Stephen, H.E. Thomas and D.D. Jensen,
    1948
  V. blackberry variegation
    Horn, Norman L., 1948
  V. raspberry alpha leaf curl
    Bennett, C.W., 1927
R. fruticosus, L.
  V. blackberry dwarf
    (K.M. Smith, 1957) R.E. Fitzpatrick, et al., 1958
  V. rubus stunt
    Prentice, I.W., 1951
R. henryi, Hemsl. & Kuntze
  V. black raspberry necrosis
    Cadman, C.H., 1951
R. idaeus, L.
  V. black raspberry necrosis
    Cadman, C.H., 1951, 1954
  V. blackberry variegation
    (K.M. Smith, 1957) R.E. Fitzpatrick, et al., 1958
  V. cucumber mosaic
    Harrison, B.D., 1958
  V. peach yellow bud mosaic
    Alcorn, Stanley M., Stephen Wilhelm and H. Earl
    Thomas, 1955
  V. raspberry curly dwarf
    (K.M. Smith, 1957) R.E. Fitzpatrick, et al., 1958
  V. raspberry leaf spot
    Cadman, C.H., 1952

Rubus idaeus, L.
   V. raspberry (mild) yellows
      Cadman, C.H., 1952
   V. raspberry (moderate) vein chlorosis
      Cadman, C.H., 1952
   V. raspberry mosaic 2 *
      Cadman, C.H., 1952
      Harris, R.V., 1940
      Prentice, I.W. and R.V. Harris, 1950
   V. raspberry necrotic fern leaf mosaic
      Chamberlain, G.C., 1941
   V. raspberry Scottish leaf curl
      Cadman, C.H., 1956
      Cadman, C.H. and R.V. Harris, 1952
      Harrison, B.D., 1958
   V. raspberry veinbanding
      Cadman, C.H., 1952
      Harris, R.V., 1940
      Prentice, I.W. and R.V. Harris, 1950
   V. raspberry yellow blotch curl
      Cadman, C.H. and R.V. Harris, 1952
      (K.M. Smith, 1957) R.E. Fitzpatrick, et al., 1958
   V. raspberry yellow dwarf *
      Harrison, B.D., 1958
   V. red raspberry mottle mosaic *
      Vaughan, Edward K. and Harold W. Wiedman, 1955
   V. rubus stunt
      Prentice, I.W., 1951
   V. tomato black ring
      Harrison, B.D., 1958
R. idaeus var. strigosus, (Michx.) Maxim.
   V. black raspberry necrosis
      Bennett, C.W., 1927, 1932
      Schwartze, C.D. and Glenn A. Huber, 1939
      Wilcox, R.B. and F.F. Smith, 1924
   V. raspberry alpha leaf curl
      Bennett, C.W., 1927, 1930
      Rankin, W.H., J.F. Hockey and J.B. McCurry, 1922
   V. raspberry beta leaf curl
      Bennett, C.W., 1930
   V. raspberry veinbanding
      Cadman, C.H., 1952
   V. raspberry yellow blotch curl
      Zeller, S.M. and A.J. Braun, 1943
   V. raspberry yellow mosaic
      Bennett, C.W., 1932
   V. red raspberry mottle mosaic *
      Vaughan, Edward K. and Harold W. Wiedman, 1955
R. laciniatus, Willd.
   V. black raspberry necrosis
      Bennett, C.W., 1932
   V. rubus stunt
      Prentice, I.W., 1951
R. loganobaccus, Bailey
   V. blackberry dwarf
      Zeller, S.M., 1925
   V. rubus stunt
      Prentice, I.W., 1951
R. macropetalus, Dougl.
   V. black raspberry necrosis
      Bennett, C.W., 1932
   V. raspberry alpha leaf curl
      Bennett, C.W., 1927
R. neglectus, Peck
   V. black raspberry necrosis
      Bennett, C.W., 1927, 1932
      Cooley, L.M., 1936
   V. raspberry beta leaf curl
      Bennett, C.W., 1927
R. occidentalis, L.
   V. black raspberry necrosis
      Bennett, C.W., 1927, 1932
      Cadman, C.H., 1951, 1954
      Cooley, L.M., 1936
      Rankin, W.H., 1930, 1931
      Wilcox, R.B. and F.F. Smith, 1924
   V. blackberry variegation
      Horn, Norman L., 1948
   V. raspberry alpha leaf curl
      Rankin, W.H. and J.F. Hockey, 1922

R. occidentalis, L.
   V. raspberry beta leaf curl
      Bennett, C.W., 1927, 1930
      Rankin, W. Howard, 1931
   V. raspberry necrotic fern leaf mosaic
      Chamberlain, G.C., 1941
   V. raspberry streak
      Bennett, C.W., 1927
      Horn, Norman L., 1948
      Horn, N.L. and M.W. Woods, 1949
      Rankin, W. Howard, 1931
   V. raspberry veinbanding
      Cadman, C.H., 1952
   V. raspberry yellow mosaic
      Bennett, C.W., 1927, 1932
      Rankin, W. Howard, 1931
   V. red raspberry mottle mosaic *
      Vaughan, Edward K. and Harold W. Wiedman, 1955
   V. rubus yellow net
      (K.M. Smith, 1957) R.E. Fitzpatrick, et al., 1958
R. occidentalis x R. idaeus, L.
   V. raspberry veinbanding
      Cadman, C.H., 1952
R. parviflorus, Nutt.
   V. rose mosaic
      (K.M. Smith, 1957) R.E. Fitzpatrick, et al., 1958
R. phoenicolasius, Maxim.
   V. raspberry alpha leaf curl
      Rankin, W.H. and J.F. Hockey, 1922
R. procerus, P.J. Muell.
   V. black raspberry necrosis
      (K.M. Smith, 1957) R.E. Fitzpatrick, et al., 1958
   V. peach yellow bud mosaic
      Alcorn, Stanley M., Stephen Wilhelm and H. Earl Thomas, 1955
   V. rubus yellow net
      (K.M. Smith, 1957) R.E. Fitzpatrick, et al., 1958
R. saxatilis, L.
   V. black raspberry necrosis
      Cadman, C.H., 1951
   V. raspberry veinbanding
      Cadman, C.H., 1952
R. spp.
   V. blackberry dwarf
      Zeller, S.M., 1927
   V. peach yellow bud mosaic
      Alcorn, Stanley M., Stephen Wilhelm and H. Earl Thomas, 1955
R. strigosus, Michx.
   V. black raspberry necrosis
      Huber, Glenn A. and C.D. Schwartze, 1938
   V. raspberry alpha leaf curl
      Bennett, C.W., 1927
      Rankin, W.H. and J.F. Hockey, 1922
   V. rubus yellow net
      (K.M. Smith, 1957) R.E. Fitzpatrick, et al., 1958
R. ursinus, Cham. & Schlecht.
   V. blackberry dwarfing
      Wilhelm, Stephen, H.E. Thomas and D.D. Jensen, 1948
   V. peach yellow bud mosaic
      Alcorn, Stanley M., Stephen Wilhelm and H. Earl Thomas, 1955
R. ursinus var. vitifolius, (Cham. & Schlecht.) Focke
   V. lucerne dwarf
      Freitag, J.H., 1951

RUDBECKIA L. 1735 (Compositae)
R. bicolor, Nutt.
   V. clover big vein
      Black, L.M., 1945
R. hirta, L.
   V. aster yellows
      Severin, Henry H.P. and Julius H. Freitag, 1945
   V. clover big vein
      Black, L.M., 1945
   V. tobacco mosaic
      Holmes, Francis O., 1946
R. spp.
   V. cucumber mosaic
      Faan, Hwei Chung and James Johnson, 1951

RUELLIA Plum. ex L. 1735 (Acanthaceae)
R. tuberosa, L.
V. cucumber mosaic
Adsuar, Jose and A. Cruz Miret, 1950

RUMEX L. 1735 (Polygonaceae)
R. acetosa, L.
V. clover big vein
Black, L.M., 1945
R. acetosella, L.
V. aster yellows
Frazier, Norman W. and Henry H.P. Severin,
1945
V. clover big vein
Black, L.M., 1945
V. tobacco mosaic
Holmes, Francis O., 1938
R. britannica, L.
V. lettuce mosaic
Newhall, A.G., 1923
V. tobacco streak
Fulton, Robert W., 1948
R. crispus, L.
V. beet curly top
Carsner, E., 1925
Severin, Henry H.P., 1929, 1934
V. clover big vein
Black, L.M., 1945
V. cucumber mosaic
Price, W.C., 1940
V. lucerne dwarf
Freitag, J.H., 1951
V. lucerne mosaic
Price, W.C., 1940
V. rhubarb ring spot *
Vaughan, Edward K. and John W. Yale, Jr., 1953
Yale, John W., Jr. and Edward K. Vaughan, 1954
V. tobacco broad ring spot
Johnson, James and Robert W. Fulton, 1942
V. tobacco mosaic
Holmes, Francis O., 1938, 1946
V. tobacco necrosis
Price, W.C., 1940
V. tobacco ring spot
Price, W.C., 1940
V. tobacco ring spot no. 2
Price, W.C., 1940
V. tobacco streak
Fulton, Robert W., 1948
R. lanceolatus, Thunb.
V. dock mosaic
(K.M. Smith, 1957) R.E. Fitzpatrick, et al., 1958
R. obtusifolius, L.
V. clover big vein
Black, L.M., 1945
V. dock mosaic
Fernow, Karl Hermann, 1925
V. rhubarb mosaic *
(K.M. Smith, 1957) R.E. Fitzpatrick, et al., 1958
V. tobacco mosaic
Holmes, Francis O., 1946
R. sanguineus, L.
V. dock mosaic
(K.M. Smith, 1957) R.E. Fitzpatrick, et al., 1958
R. scutatus, L.
V. beet curly top
Severin, Henry H.P., 1929

SACCHARUM L. 1737 (Gramineae)
S. narenga, Wall.
V. sugarcane mosaic
Brandes, E.W. and Peter J. Klaphaak, 1923
S. officinarum, L.
V. grass natal mosaic *
Storey, H.H., 1929
V. maize mosaic
Brandes, E.W., 1920
V. maize streak
(K.M. Smith, 1957) R.E. Fitzpatrick, et al., 1958
V. rice and corn leaf-gall *
Agati, Julian A. and Carlos A. Calica, 1950
V. sugarcane chlorotic streak
Abbott, E.V., 1945, 1947
Abbott, E.V. and J.W. Ingram, 1942

S. officinarum, L. (cont.)
V. sugarcane chlorotic streak
Adsuar, Jose, 1946
V. sugarcane dwarf
(K.M. Smith, 1957) R.E. Fitzpatrick, et al., 1958
V. sugarcane fiji disease
Ocfemia, Gerardo Offimaria, 1934
Ocfemia, Gerardo Offimaria and Martin S. Celino,
1939
Ocfemia, G.O., Evaristo A. Hurtado and
Crispiniano C. Hernandez, 1933
V. sugarcane green mosaic *
Forbes, I.L. and P.J. Mills, 1942
V. sugarcane mosaic
Abbott, E.V., 1929, 1931, 1949, 1952
Adsuar, Jose, 1950, 1954
Brandes, E.W., 1920
Brandes, E.W. and Peter J. Klaphaak, 1923
Bruehl, George W., 1953, 1954
Chardon, C.E. and R.A. Veve, 1923
Chona, B.L. and S.A. Rafay, 1950
Costa, A.S. and M.P. Penteado, 1951
Edgerton, C.W., I.L. Forbes and P.J. Mills,
1937
Edgerton, C.W. and W.G. Taggart, 1924
Forbes, I.L. and Jean Dufrenoy, 1943
Forbes, I.L. and P.J. Mills, 1943, 1945
Gonzales-Rios, P. and J. Adsuar, 1953
Ingram, J.W., 1936
Ingram, J.W. and E.M. Summers, 1938
Kunkel, L.O., 1927
Luthra, Jai Chand and Abdus Sattar, 1935
Matz, Julius, 1933, 1934
McKinney, H.H., 1929
Ocfemia, G.O., 1932
Ocfemia, G.O., Evaristo A. Hurtado and
Crispiniano C. Hernandez, 1933
Sein, Francisco, Jr., 1930
Storey, H.H., 1929
Summers, E.M., 1934
Tate, H.D. and S.R. Vandenberg, 1939
Tims, E.C., 1935
Tims, E.C. and C.W. Edgerton, 1931, 1932
Tims, E.C., P.J. Mills and C.W. Edgerton, 1935
V. sugarcane ratoon stunting
Bruehl, G.W., 1955
Steib, R.J., I.L. Forbes and S.J.P. Chilton, 1957
V. sugarcane sereh disease
(K.M. Smith, 1957) R.E. Fitzpatrick, et al., 1958
V. sugarcane streak
(K.M. Smith, 1957) R.E. Fitzpatrick, et al., 1958
V. sugarcane yellow mosaic *
Forbes, I.L. and P.J. Mills, 1942
V. wheat streak mosaic
McKinney, H.H., 1949
S. spp.
V. maize streak
Storey, H.H. and A.P.D. McClean, 1930
V. sugarcane streak
Storey, H.H. and A.P.D. McClean, 1930

SAINTPAULIA H. Wendl. 1893 (Gesneriaceae)
S. ionantha, Wendl.
V. anemone mosaic *
Hollings, M., 1957

SALIX ((Tourn.)) L. 1735 (Salicaceae)
S. spp.
V. lucerne dwarf
Freitag, J.H., 1951

SALPIGLOSSIS Ruiz & Pav. 1794 (Solanaceae)
S. sinuata, Ruiz & Pav.
V. anemone mosaic *
Hollings, M., 1957
V. aster yellows
Kunkel, L.O., 1926
Severin, Henry H.P. and Julius H. Freitag, 1945
V. beet curly top
Freitag, Julius H. and Henry H.P. Severin, 1936
V. cabbage black ring spot
Hollings, M., 1957
V. cucumber mosaic
Price, W.C., 1940

Salpiglossis sinuata, Ruiz & Pav.
  V. lucerne mosaic
    Price, W.C., 1940
  V. potato X
    Smith, J. Henderson, 1928
  V. prunus B *
    Fulton, Robert W., 1957
  V. tobacco etch
    Holmes, Francis O., 1946
  V. tobacco mosaic
    Holmes, Francis O., 1946
  V. tobacco necrosis
    Price, W.C., 1940
    Price, W.C., Frank P. McWhorter and Betty H.
      Steranka, 1950
  V. tobacco ring spot
    Price, W.C., 1940
  V. tomato aspermy
    Hollings, M., 1955
  V. tomato spotted wilt
    Gardner, M.W. and O.C. Whipple, 1934
    Tompkins, C.M. and M.W. Gardner, 1934
  V. turnip mosaic
    Walker, J.C., Francis J. LeBeau and Glenn S.
      Pound, 1945
S. spp.
  V. vaccinium false blossom
    Kunkel, L.O., 1945
S. variabilis, Hort. ex Vilm.
  V. potato X
    Dennis, R.W.G., 1939
  V. potato Y
    Smith, Kenneth M. and R.W.G. Dennis, 1940

SALSOLA L. 1735 (Chenopodiaceae)
S. kali, L.
  V. beet yellows
    Roland, G. and J. Tahon, 1961
S. kali var. tenuifolia, Tausch
  V. beet curly top
    Carsner, E., 1919
    Severin, Henry H.P., 1934
    Severin, Henry H.P. and Charles F. Henderson,
      1928
    Severin, Henry H.P. and Byron R. Houston, 1945
  V. beet mosaic
    Severin, Henry H.P. and Roger M. Drake, 1947

SALVIA ((Tourn.)) L. 1735 (Labiatae)
S. azurea, Lam.
  V. tobacco mosaic
    Holmes, Francis O., 1946
S. azurea var. pitcheri, Sheldon
  V. aster yellows
    Severin, Henry H.P. and Julius H. Freitag, 1945
S. coccinea, Juss.
  V. salvia chlorosis *
    Verma, G.S. and A.K. Bose, 1955
S. farinacea, Benth.
  V. tobacco mosaic
    Holmes, Francis O., 1946
S. patens, Cav.
  V. cucumber mosaic
    Faan, Hwei Chung and James Johnson, 1951
  V. tobacco mosaic
    Holmes, Francis O., 1946
S. splendens, Ker-Gawl.
  V. beet curly top
    Freitag, Julius H. and Henry H.P. Severin, 1936
  V. cucumber mosaic
    Price, W.C., 1940
  V. tobacco mosaic
    Holmes, Francis O., 1946
  V. tobacco ring spot
    Fulton, Robert W., 1941
    Wingard, S.A., 1928
  V. tomato spotted wilt
    Gardner, M.W., C.M. Tompkins and O.C.
      Whipple, 1935

SAMBUCUS Tourn. ex L. 1735 (Caprifoliaceae)
S. caerulea, Raf.
  V. lucerne dwarf
    Freitag, J.H., 1951

S. canadensis, L.
  V. tobacco ring spot
    Wilkinson, R.E., 1952

SAMOLUS ((Tourn.)) L. 1735 (Primulaceae)
S. floribundus, H. B. & K.
  V. beet curly top
    Costa, A.S., 1952
  V. dodder latent mosaic
    Bennett, C.W., 1944
S. parviflorus, Raf.
  V. beet curly top
    Bennett, C.W., 1952, 1955
    Giddings, N.J., 1944
  V. beet mosaic
    Bennett, C.W., 1949

SANGUISORBA Rupp. ex L. 1735 (Rosaceae)
S. minor, Scop.
  V. datura rugose leaf curl
    (K.M. Smith, 1957) R.E. Fitzpatrick, et al., 1958

SANTALUM   1742 (Santalaceae)
S. album, L.
  V. sandal leaf curl mosaic
    (K.M. Smith, 1957) R.E. Fitzpatrick, et al., 1958
  V. sandal spike
    Iyengar, A.V. Varadaraja, 1938
    Narasimhan, M.J., 1928

SANVITALIA Gualt. in Lam. 1792 (Compositae)
S. procumbens, Lam.
  V. chrysanthemum stunt
    Brierley, Philip, 1953
  V. dahlia mosaic
    Brierley, Philip and Floyd F. Smith, 1950
  V. tobacco mosaic
    Holmes, Francis O., 1946

SAPONARIA L. 1735 (Caryophyllaceae)
S. ocymoides, L.
  V. carnation ring spot
    Brierley, Philip and Floyd F. Smith, 1957

SARACHA Ruiz & Pav. 1794 (Solanaceae)
S. umbellata, Don. *
  V. potato M *
    Bagnall, R.H., R.H. Larson and J.C. Walker,
      1956
  V. potato paracrinkle
    Bagnall, R.H. and R.H. Larson, 1957
    Bagnall, R.H., R.H. Larson and J.C. Walker,
      1956

SATUREIA L. 1737 (Labiatae)
S. hortensis, L.
  V. aster yellows
    Kunkel, L.O., 1926

SCABIOSA ((Tourn.)) L. 1735 (Dipsaceae)
S. atropurpurea, L.
  V. aster yellows
    Kunkel, L.O., 1926
    Severin, Henry H.P. and Julius H. Freitag, 1945
  V. beet curly top
    Severin, Henry H.P. and Julius H. Freitag, 1934
  V. cabbage black ring spot
    Tompkins, C.M., M.W. Gardner and H. Rex
      Thomas, 1938
  V. clover big vein
    Black, L.M., 1945
  V. cucumber mosaic
    Wellman, F.L., 1935
  V. teasel mosaic
    Stoner, Warren N., 1951
  V. tobacco ring spot
    Wingard, S.A., 1928
  V. turnip mosaic
    Walker, J.C., Francis J. LeBeau and Glenn S.
      Pound, 1945
  V. vaccinium false blossom
    Kunkel, L.O., 1945

Scabiosa japonica, Miq.
  V. cucumber mosaic
    Price, W.C., 1940
S. spp.
  V. tomato spotted wilt
    (K.M. Smith, 1957) R.E. Fitzpatrick, et al., 1958

SCAEVOLA L. 1771 (Goodeniaceae)
S. frutescens, K. Krause
  V. scaevola frutescens ring spot *
    Jensen, D.D., 1949

SCHIZANTHUS Ruiz & Pav. 1794 (Solanaceae)
S. pinnatus, Ruiz & Pav.
  V. anemone mosaic *
    Hollings, M., 1957
  V. aster yellows
    Kunkel, L.O., 1926
  V. cabbage black ring spot
    Hollings, M., 1957
  V. tobacco etch
    Holmes, Francis O., 1946
  V. tobacco mosaic
    Holmes, Francis O., 1946
  V. tomato spotted wilt
    Gardner, M.W. and O.C. Whipple, 1934
    Tompkins, C.M. and M.W. Gardner, 1934
S. retusus, Hook
  V. potato X
    Larson, R.H., 1947
  V. potato Y
    Smith, Kenneth M. and R.W.G. Dennis, 1940
S. spp.
  V. tomato black ring
    (K.M. Smith, 1957) R.E. Fitzpatrick, et al., 1958
  V. vaccinium false blossom
    Kunkel, L.O., 1945
S. wisetonensis, Hort.
  V. beet curly top
    Freitag, Julius H. and Henry H.P. Severin, 1936
  V. clover big vein
    Black, L.M., 1945
  V. cucumber mosaic
    Price, W.C., 1940
  V. tobacco streak
    Fulton, Robert W., 1948

SCOPARIA L. 1748 (Scrophulariaceae)
S. dulcis, L.
  V. tobacco leaf curl
    Pruthi, Hem Singh and C.K. Samuel, 1941

SCORZONERA ((Tourn.)) L. 1735 (Compositae)
S. hispanica, L.
  V. aster yellows
    Severin, Henry H.P. and Julius H. Freitag, 1945

SCROPHULARIA Tourn. ex L. 1735 (Scrophulariaceae)
S. californica, Cham. & Schlect.
  V. aster yellows
    Frazier, Norman W. and Henry H.P. Severin,
    1945
S. marilandica, L.
  V. tobacco mosaic
    Grant, T.J., 1934

SECALE ((Tourn.)) L. 1735 (Gramineae)
S. cereale, L.
  V. agropyron mosaic
    Slykhuis, J.T., 1952
  V. barley stripe mosaic
    Sill, W.H., Jr. and E.D. Hansing, 1955
    Slykhuis, J.T., 1952
  V. barley yellow dwarf
    Allen, Thomas C., Jr., 1957
    Allen, Thomas C., Jr. and Byron R. Houston,
    1956
    Takeshita, R.M., 1956
  V. brome mosaic
    McKinney, H.H., 1944
  V. cucumber mosaic
    Wellman, F.L., 1934, 1935
  V. maize streak
    (K.M. Smith, 1957) R.E. Fitzpatrick, et al., 1958

S. cereale, L. (cont.)
  V. oat pseudo-rosette
    (K.M. Smith, 1957) R.E. Fitzpatrick, et al., 1958
  V. rice dwarf
    (K.M. Smith, 1957) R.E. Fitzpatrick, et al., 1958
  V. soil-borne wheat mosaic
    McKinney, H.H., 1925, 1930
    Sill, W.J., Jr., 1955
  V. tobacco necrosis
    Price, W.C., 1940
  V. wheat streak mosaic
    McKinney, H.H. and W.J. Sando, 1951
    Slykhuis, John T., 1954, 1955
  V. wheat striate mosaic
    Slykhuis, John T. and Marion A. Watson, 1958
S. cereale subsp. ancestrale, Zhuk. *
  V. wheat streak mosaic
    McKinney, H.H. and W.J. Sando, 1951
S. montanum, Guss.
  V. wheat streak mosaic
    McKinney, H.H. and W.J. Sando, 1951
S. spp.
  V. wheat streak mosaic
    Sill, W.H., Jr. and Patrick C. Agusiobo, 1955

SEDUM Tourn. ex L. 1735 (Crassulaceae)
S. acre, L.
  V. tobacco ring spot no. 2
    Hildebrand, E.M., 1942
    Price, W.C., 1940

SENECIO ((Tourn.)) L. 1735 (Compositae)
S. cruentus, (Mass.) DC.
  V. cabbage black ring spot
    Tompkins, C.M., M.W. Gardner and H. Rex
    Thomas, 1938
  V. chrysanthemum B (mild mosaic) *
    Hollings, M., 1957
  V. chrysanthemum ring spot
    Brierley, Philip and Floyd F. Smith, 1955
  V. chrysanthemum stunt
    Brierley, Philip, 1950, 1953
    Keller, John R., 1953
  V. tobacco ring spot no. 2
    Brierley, Philip, 1954
  V. tomato aspermy
    Brierley, Philip, Floyd F. Smith and S.P.
    Doolittle, 1955
    Hollings, M., 1955
  V. tomato spotted wilt
    Gardner, M.W. and O.C. Whipple, 1934
  V. turnip mosaic
    Walker, J.C., Francis J. LeBeau and Glenn S.
    Pound, 1945
S. glastifolius, Hook. f.
  V. chrysanthemum stunt
    Brierley, Philip, 1953
S. hybridus, Hort. ex Regel
  V. aster yellows
    (K.M. Smith, 1957) R.E. Fitzpatrick, et al., 1958
S. mikanioides, Otto
  V. chrysanthemum stunt
    Brierley, Philip, 1953
S. vulgaris, L.
  V. anemone mosaic *
    Hollings, M., 1957
  V. aster yellows
    Frazier, Norman W. and Henry H.P. Severin,
    1945
  V. beet curly top
    Severin, Henry H.P., 1934
  V. beet ring spot *
    Harrison, B.D., 1957
  V. beet yellows
    (K.M. Smith, 1957) R.E. Fitzpatrick, et al., 1958
    Roland, G. and J. Tahon, 1961
  V. lettuce mosaic
    Ainsworth, G.C. and L. Ogilvie, 1939

SESAMUM L. 1737 (Pedaliaceae)
S. indicum, L.
  V. sesamum phyllody *
    Pal, B.P. and Pushkar Nath, 1935

Sesamum occidentale, Heer & Regel *
  V. sesamum phyllody *
    Vasudeva, R.S. and H.S. Sahambi, 1955
S. orientale, L.
  V. sesamum phyllody *
    Vasudeva, R.S. and H.S. Sahambi, 1955
  V. tobacco ring spot
    Cooper, W.D., 1949

SESBANIA Scop. 1777 (Leguminosae)
S. bispinosa, Steud.
  V. prunus A *
    Fulton, Robert W., 1957
  V. prunus B *
    Fulton, Robert W., 1957
  V. prunus E *
    Fulton, Robert W., 1957
  V. prunus G *
    Fulton, Robert W., 1957
S. cannabina, Poir.
  V. prunus A *
    Fulton, Robert W., 1957
  V. prunus B *
    Fulton, Robert W., 1957
  V. prunus E *
    Fulton, Robert W., 1957
  V. prunus G *
    Fulton, Robert W., 1957
S. cinerascens, Welw. ex Baker
  V. prunus A *
    Fulton, Robert W., 1957
  V. prunus B *
    Fulton, Robert W., 1957
  V. prunus E *
    Fulton, Robert W., 1957
  V. prunus G *
    Fulton, Robert W., 1957
S. exaltata, (Raf.) Cory
  V. prunus A *
    Ehlers, Clifford G. and J. Duain Moore, 1957
    Fulton, Robert W., 1957
  V. prunus B *
    Ehlers, Clifford G. and J. Duain Moore, 1957
    Fulton, Robert W., 1957
  V. prunus E *
    Ehlers, Clifford G. and J. Duain Moore, 1957
    Fulton, Robert W., 1957
  V. prunus G *
    Fulton, Robert W., 1957
  V. (sour) cherry yellows
    Fulton, Robert W., 1956
S. macrocarpa, Muhl. ex Raf.
  V. bean yellow mosaic
    Johnson, James, 1942
S. paulensis, Barb. & Rodr.
  V. prunus A *
    Fulton, Robert W., 1957
  V. prunus B *
    Fulton, Robert W., 1957
  V. prunus E *
    Fulton, Robert W., 1957
  V. prunus G *
    Fulton, Robert W., 1957
S. sesban, Merr.
  V. prunus A *
    Fulton, Robert W., 1957
  V. prunus B *
    Fulton, Robert W., 1957
S. speciosa, Taub. ex Engl.
  V. cowpea mosaic
    Dale, W.T., 1949
  V. prunus A *
    Fulton, Robert W., 1957
  V. prunus B *
    Fulton, Robert W., 1957
  V. prunus E *
    Fulton, Robert W., 1957
  V. prunus G *
    Fulton, Robert W., 1957
S. spp.
  V. lucerne mosaic
    Thomas, H. Rex, 1951

SETAROA Beauv. 1807 (Gramineae)
(CHAETOCHLOA) Scribn. 1897
S. italica, (L.) Beauv.
  V. barley stripe mosaic
    Slykhuis, J.T., 1952
  V. panicum mosaic *
    Sill, W.H., Jr., 1957
    Sill, W.H., Jr. and R.C. Pickett, 1957
  V. wheat spot mosaic *
    Slykhuis, John T., 1956
  V. wheat streak mosaic
    Sill, W.H., Jr. and Patrick C. Agusiobo, 1955
    Slykhuis, John T., 1955
S. lutescens, (Weigel) F.T. Hubb
  V. barley yellow dwarf
    Bruehl, G.W. and H.V. Toko, 1957
  V. lucerne dwarf
    Freitag, J.H., 1951
  V. sugarcane mosaic
    Brandes, E.W., 1920
    Brandes, E.W. and Peter J. Klaphaak, 1923
S. sulcata, Raddi
  V. grass natal mosaic *
    Storey, H.H., 1929
  V. sugarcane mosaic
    (K.M. Smith, 1957) R.E. Fitzpatrick, et al., 1958
S. verticillata, (L.) Beauv.
  V. barley stripe mosaic
    Slykhuis, J.T., 1952
  V. wheat spot mosaic *
    Slykhuis, John T., 1956
  V. wheat streak mosaic
    Slykhuis, J.T., 1952, 1955
S. virdis, (L.) Beauv.
  V. barley stripe mosaic
    Slykhuis, J.T., 1952
  V. corn new mosaic *
    Finley, A.M., 1954
  V. oat pseudo-rosette
    (K.M. Smith, 1957) R.E. Fitzpatrick, et al., 1958
  V. soybean new disease *
    Dunleavy, John, 1957
  V. wheat spot mosaic *
    Slykhuis, John T., 1956
  V. wheat streak mosaic
    Finley, A.M., 1957
    McKinney, H.H. and Hurley Fellows, 1951
    Slykhuis, John T., 1951, 1952, 1955
(C. magna), (Griseb.) Scribn.
  V. sugarcane mosaic
    Brandes, E.W. and Peter J. Klaphaak, 1923

SICANA Naud. 1862 (Cucurbitaceae)
S. odorifera, Naud.
  V. cucumber mosaic
    Adsuar, Jose and A. Cruz Miret, 1950
  V. prunus A *
    Fulton, Robert W., 1957
  V. prunus B *
    Fulton, Robert W., 1957
  V. prunus E *
    Fulton, Robert W., 1957
  V. prunus G *
    Fulton, Robert W., 1957

SICYOS L. 1735 (Cucurbitaceae)
S. angulatus, L.
  V. cucurbit mosaic *
    Doolittle, S.P. and M.N. Walker, 1925
  V. tobacco streak
    Fulton, Robert W., 1948
  V. wild cucumber mosaic *
    Freitag, J.H., 1952

SIDA L. 1735 (Malvaceae)
S. carpinifolia, L. f.
  V. abutilon infectious variegation
    Bird, Julio, 1958
S. rhombifolia, L.
  V. abutilon infectious variegation
    Bird, Julio, 1958
    Costa, A.S. and C.W. Bennett, 1950
    Kunkel, L.O., 1930
    Silberschmidt, K. and L.R. Tommasi, 1956

Sida rhombifolia, L. (cont.)
　V. tobacco leaf curl
　　Pruthi, Hem Singh and C.K. Samuel, 1941
S. spp.
　V. cotton leaf curl
　　(K.M. Smith, 1957) R.E. Fitzparrick, et al., 1958

SILENE L. 1735 (Caryophyllaceae)
S. anglica, L.
　V. tobacco etch
　　Holmes, Francis O., 1946
　V. tobacco mosaic
　　Holmes, Francis O., 1946
S. armeria, L.
　V. beet yellows
　　Roland, G. and J. Tahon, 1961
S. compacta, Fisch.
　V. carnation mosaic
　　Brierley, Philip and Floyd F. Smith, 1957
　V. carnation mottle
　　Brierley, Philip and Floyd F. Smith, 1957
　V. carnation ring spot
　　Brierley, Philip and Floyd F. Smith, 1957
　V. tobacco ring spot no. 2
　　Brierley, Philip, 1954
S. gallica, L.
　V. beet yellows
　　Roland, G. and J. Tahon, 1961
S. latifolia, Brit. & Rendle
　V. clover big vein
　　Black, L.M., 1945
S. noctiflora, L.
　V. tobacco streak
　　Fulton, Robert W., 1948
S. pendula, L.
　V. aster yellows
　　Kunkel, L.O., 1926
　V. beet curly top
　　Freitag, Julius H. and Henry H.P. Severin, 1936
　V. tobacco mosaic
　　Holmes, Francis O., 1946

SILYBUM Baill. ex Adans. 1763 (Compositae)
S. marianum, Gaertn.
　V. cynarus curly dwarf
　　Leach, L.D. and J.W. Oswald, 1950
　V. tobacco yellow dwarf
　　Helson, G.A.H., 1950

SINNINGIA Nees 1825 (Gesneriaceae)
S. speciosa, Benth. & Hook.
　V. aster yellows
　　Kunkel, L.O., 1926
　V. lucerne mosaic
　　Price, W.C., 1940
　V. tobacco mosaic
　　Holmes, Francis O., 1946
　V. tobacco necrosis
　　Price, W.C., 1940
　　Price, W.C., Frank P. McWhorter and Betty H. Steranka, 1950
　V. tobacco ring spot no. 2
　　Brierley, Philip, 1954
　　Hildebrand, E.M., 1942
　　Price, W.C., 1940
　V. tomato spotted wilt
　　Gardner, M.W., C.M. Tompkins and O.C. Whipple, 1935

SISYMBRIUM ((Tourn.)) L. 1735 (Cruciferae)
S. altissimum, L.
　V. cabbage ring necrosis
　　Larson, R.H. and J.C. Walker, 1941
　V. cauliflower mosaic
　　Walker, J.C., Francis J. LeBeau and Glenn S. Pound, 1945
　V. turnip mosaic
　　Walker, J.C., Francis J. LeBeau and Glenn S. Pound, 1945
S. officinale, (L.) Scop.
　V. anemone mosaic *
　　Hollings, M., 1957
　V. cabbage black ring spot
　　Hollings, M., 1957

S. officinale, (L.) Scop. (cont.)
　V. cabbage ring necrosis
　　Larson, R.H. and J.C. Walker, 1941
　V. cauliflower mosaic
　　(K.M. Smith, 1957) R.E. Fitzpatrick, et al., 1958
　V. cucumber mosaic
　　Pound, Glenn S. and J.C. Walker, 1948
　V. tobacco mosaic
　　Holmes, Francis O., 1938
　V. tobacco streak
　　Fulton, Robert W., 1948
　V. turnip crinkle
　　Broadbent, L. and G.D. Heathcote, 1958
　V. turnip mosaic
　　Pound, Glenn S., 1948
　V. turnip rosette *
　　Broadbent, L. and G.D. Heathcote, 1958
　V. turnip yellow mosaic
　　Broadbent, L. and G.D. Heathcote, 1958
S. thalianum, J. Gay
　V. tobacco mosaic
　　Holmes, Francis O., 1938

SITANION Raf. 1819 (Gramineae)
S. hystrix, (Nutt.) J.G. Sm.
　V. barley yellow dwarf
　　Bruehl, G.W. and H.V. Toko, 1957
　　Oswald, John W. and Byron R. Houston, 1953
S. jubatum, J.G. Sm.
　V. barley yellow dwarf
　　Bruehl, G.W. and H.V. Toko, 1957

SOLANUM ((Tourn.)) L. 1735 (Solanaceae)
S. acaule, Bitt.
　V. potato Y
　　Easton, G.D., R.H. Larson and R.W. Hougas, 1958
S. acaule var. subexinterruptum, Bitt.
　V. potato yellow dwarf
　　Black, L.M., 1937
S. aculeastrum, Dun.
　V. tomato bunchy top
　　(K.M. Smith, 1957) R.E. Fitzpatrick, et al., 1958
S. aculeatissimum, Jacq.
　V. potato X
　　Fernow, Karl Hermann, 1925
　　Larson, R.H., 1947
　V. tobacco mosaic
　　Fernow, Karl Hermann, 1925
　V. tobacco streak
　　Fulton, Robert W., 1948
　V. tomato bunchy top
　　(K.M. Smith, 1957) R.E. Fitzpatrick, et al., 1958
　V. tomato spotted wilt
　　Smith, Kenneth M., 1932
S. ajuscoense, Buk.
　V. potato Y
　　Easton, G.D., R.H. Larson and R.W. Hougas, 1958
　V. potato yellow dwarf
　　Black, L.M., 1937
S. andigenum, Juz. & Buk. * or S. tuberosum, L.
　V. beet curly top
　　Watson, R.D. and T.E. Randall, 1951
S. antipoviczii, Buk.
　V. beet curly top
　　Watson, R.D. and T.E. Randall, 1951
　V. potato yellow dwarf
　　Black, L.M., 1937
S. antipoviczii or S. neo-antipoviczii, Buk.
　V. beet curly top
　　Watson, R.D. and T.E. Randall, 1951
S. atropurpureum, Schrank *
　V. cucumber mosaic
　　Hoggan, Isme A., 1927
　V. potato X
　　Fernow, Karl Hermann, 1925
　　Hoggan, Isme A., 1927
　V. potato Y
　　Hoggan, Isme A., 1927
　V. tobacco mosaic
　　Fernow, Karl Hermann, 1925
　　Hoggan, Isme A., 1927

Solanum aviculare, Forst.
  V. cucumber mosaic
    Wellman, F.L., 1935
S. cabiliense var. argenteum *
  V. tobacco mosaic
    Hoggan, Isme A., 1927
S. capsicastrum, Link
  V. tobacco etch
    Holmes, Francis O., 1946
  V. tobacco mosaic
    Holmes, Francis O., 1946
  V. tomato spotted wilt
    Milbrath, J.A., 1939
    Smith, Kenneth M., 1931, 1932
S. cardiophyllum, Lindl.
  V. potato Y
    Easton, G.D., R.H. Larson and R.W. Hougas,
    1958
S. cardiophyllum subsp. ehrenbergii, Bitt.
  V. potato Y
    Easton, G.D., R.H. Larson and R.W. Hougas,
    1958
S. cardiophyllum f. coyoacanum, Buk. *
  V. potato yellow dwarf
    Black, L.M., 1937
S. caribaeum, Dun.
  V. cucumber mosaic
    Adsuar, Jose and A. Cruz Miret, 1950
  V. tobacco leaf curl
    Bird, Julio, 1957
S. carolinense, L.
  V. cucumber mosaic
    Johnson, E.M., 1930
  V. potato X
    Fernow, Karl Hermann, 1925
    Johnson, E.M., 1930
  V. tobacco etch
    Greenleaf, W.H., 1953
    Johnson, E.M., 1930
  V. tobacco mosaic
    Boyle, John S. and David C. Wharton, 1956, 1957
    Fernow, Karl Hermann, 1925
    Gardner, Max W. and James B. Kendrick, 1922
    Johnson, E.M., 1930
  V. tobacco ring spot
    Wingard, S.A., 1928
  V. tobacco ring spot no. 2
    Wilkinson, R.E., 1952
  V. tomato ring spot
    Samson, R.W. and E.P. Imle, 1942
S. chacoense, Bitt.
  V. potato Y
    Easton, G.D., R.H. Larson and R.W. Hougas,
    1958
S. ciliatum, Lam.
  V. tobacco mosaic
    Ainsworth, G.C., 1933
S. demissum, Lindl.
  V. beet curly top
    Watson, R.D. and T.E. Randall, 1951
  V. potato A
    MacLachlan, D.S., R.H. Larson and J.C. Walker,
    1953
  V. potato stunt
    (K.M. Smith, 1957) R.E. Fitzpatrick, et al., 1958
(S. demissum x S. gibberulosum, Juz. & Buk.) x (S.
stoloniferum, Schlecht. & Bouche)
  V. potato Y
    Easton, G.D., R.H. Larson and R.W. Hougas,
    1958
(S. demissum x S. saltense, Hawkes) x (S. stoloniferum,
Schlecht. & Bouche)
  V. potato Y
    Easton, G.D., R.H. Larson and R.W. Hougas,
    1958
(S. demissum x S. schickii, Juz. & Buk.) x (S.
stoloniferum, Schlecht. & Bouche)
  V. potato Y
    Easton, G.D., R.H. Larson and R.W. Hougas,
    1958
(S. demissum x S. simplicifolium, Bitt) x (S. stoloniferum,
Schlecht. & Bouche)
  V. potato Y
    Easton, G.D., R.H. Larson and R.W. Hougas, 1958

S. demissum x S. tuberosum, L., var. aquila *
  V. potato A
    Raymer, W.B. and J.A. Milbrath, 1957
  V. potato X
    Raymer, W.B. and J.A. Milbrath, 1957
S. douglasii, Dun.
  V. beet curly top
    Severin, Henry H.P., 1934
S. dulcamara, L.
  V. potato leaf roll
    Dykstra, T.P., 1930, 1933
  V. potato X
    Smith, J. Henderson, 1928
    Thompson, A.D., 1956
  V. potato Y
    (K.M. Smith, 1957) R.E. Fitzpatrick, et al., 1958
  V. tobacco mosaic
    Crawford, R.F., 1921
    Gardner, Max W. and James B. Kendrick, 1922
    Holmes, Francis O., 1946
    Jarrett, Phyllis H., 1930
  V. tobacco streak
    Fulton, Robert W., 1948
  V. tomato spotted wilt
    Smith, Kenneth M., 1932
S. elaeagnifolium, Cav.
  V. chilli veinbanding
    Simons, John N., 1956
S. gibberulosum, Juz. & Buk.
  V. potato Y
    Easton, G.D., R.H. Larson and R.W. Hougas,
    1958
S. giganteum, Jacq.
  V. tomato bunchy top
    (K.M. Smith, 1957) R.E. Fitzpatrick, et al., 1958
S. gigantophyllum, Bitt.
  V. potato Y
    Easton, G.D., R.H. Larson and R.W. Hougas,
    1958
S. gracile, Link *
  V. cucumber mosaic
    Anderson, C.W., 1955
    Simons, John N., 1957
  V. chilli veinbanding
    Simons, John N., 1956, 1957
  V. potato Y
    Simons, J.N., Robert A. Conover and James M.
    Walter, 1956
S. incanum, L.
  V. tomato bunchy top
    (K.M. Smith, 1957) R.E. Fitzpatrick, et al., 1958
S. indicum, L.
  V. tomato bunchy top
    (K.M. Smith, 1957) R.E. Fitzpatrick, et al., 1958
S. integrifolium, Poir.
  V. cucumber mosaic
    Pound, Glenn S. and J.C. Walker, 1948
  V. tobacco etch
    Greenleaf, W.H., 1953
    Holmes, Francis O., 1946
  V. tobacco mosaic
    Gardner, Max W. and James B. Kendrick, 1922
    Holmes, Francis O., 1946
  V. tobacco streak
    Fulton, Robert W., 1948
  V. turnip mosaic
    Pound, Glenn S., 1948
    Walker, J.C., Francis J. LeBeau and Glenn S.
    Pound, 1945
S. kesselbrenneri, Juz. & Buk.
  V. potato Y
    Easton, G.D., R.H. Larson and R.W. Hougas,
    1958
S. laciniatum, Ait.
  V. cucumber mosaic
    Hoggan, Isme A., 1927
  V. potato X
    Hoggan, Isme A., 1927
    Thompson, A.D., 1956
  V. potato Y
    Hoggan, Isme A., 1927
  V. tobacco mosaic
    Hoggan, Isme A., 1927

Solanum laciniatum, Ait. (cont.)
  V. tobacco yellow dwarf
    Hill, A.V., 1950
  V. tomato spotted wilt
    Smith, Kenneth M., 1931, 1932
S. marginatum, L. f.
  V. tobacco mosaic
    Hoggan, Isme A., 1927
  V. tomato spotted wilt
    Smith, Kenneth M., 1932
S. melongena, L.
  V. chilli veinbanding
    Simons, John N., 1956
  V. cucumber mosaic
    Adsuar, Jose and A. Cruz Miret, 1950
    Doolittle, S.P. and W.J. Zaumeyer, 1953
    Fulton, Robert W., 1941
    Harter, L.L., 1938
    Hoggan, Isme A., 1935
    Nariani, T.K. and Nirmaljit Singh, 1952
    Simons, John N., 1957
    Wellman, F.L., 1935
  V. eggplant mosaic
    Dale, W.T., 1954
    Ferguson, I.A.C., 1951
  V. lucerne mosaic
    Berkeley, G.H., 1947
    Porter, D.R., 1935
  V. (physalis) mosaic *
    Melhus, I.E., 1922
  V. potato calico
    Berkeley, G.H., 1947
  V. potato M *
    Bagnall, R.H. and R.H. Larson, 1957
    Bagnall, R.H., R.H. Larson and J.C. Walker, 1956
  V. potato X
    Fulton, Robert W., 1941
    Johnson, James, 1925
  V. potato Y
    Roque, Arturo and Jose Adsuar, 1941
    Sakimura, K., 1953
  V. potato yellow dwarf
    Black, L.M., 1938
  V. sweet potato mosaic
    Elmer, O.H., 1957
  V. tobacco broad ring spot
    Johnson, James and Robert W. Fulton, 1942
  V. tobacco etch
    Holmes, Francis O., 1946
  V. tobacco mosaic
    Ainsworth, G.C., 1933
    Das, C.R. and S.P. Raychaudhuri, 1953
    Holmes, F.O., 1934, 1946
    Jensen, J.H., 1933
    Johnson, J., 1926
  V. tobacco ring spot
    Fulton, Robert W., 1941
    Ivanoff, S.S., 1942
    Jones, S.E., 1942
    Valleau, W.D., 1951
  V. tobacco streak
    Fulton, Robert W., 1948
  V. tomato aspermy
    Brierley, Philip, Floyd F. Smith and S.P. Doolittle, 1955
  V. tomato big bud
    Hill, A.V. and M. Mandryk, 1954
  V. tomato ring spot
    (K.M. Smith, 1957) R.E. Fitzpatrick, et al., 1958
    Samson, R.W. and E.P. Imle, 1942
  V. tomato spotted wilt
    Ferguson, I.A.C., 1951
    Gardner, M.W. and O.C. Whipple, 1934
    Sakimura, K., 1940
    Smith, Kenneth M., 1932
    Tompkins, C.M. and M.W. Gardner, 1934
  V. tomato V-52-1
    Miller, Patrick M., 1953
S. melongena var. esculentum, Nees
  V. cucumber mosaic
    Johnson, E.M., 1930
  V. potato X
    Johnson, E.M., 1930

S. melongena var. esculentum, Nees (cont.)
  V. potato Y
    Johnson, E.M., 1930
  V. tobacco coarse etch
    Johnson, E.M., 1930
  V. tobacco mosaic
    Johnson, E.M., 1930
  V. tobacco ring spot
    Wingard, S.A., 1928
S. melongena var. Hangchow Long x var. Black Beauty
  V. tobacco mosaic
    Holmes, F.O., 1934
S. melongena var. Peking Green x var. Black Beauty
  V. tobacco mosaic
    Holmes, F.O., 1934
S. muricatum, Ait.
  V. red currant ring spot
    Klesser, P.J., 1951
S. miniatum, Bernh. ex Willd.
  V. cucumber mosaic
    Hoggan, Isme A., 1927
  V. potato X
    Hoggan, Isme A., 1927
  V. potato Y
    Hoggan, Isme A., 1927
    Koch, K.L., 1933
  V. tobacco mosaic
    Hoggan, Isme A., 1927
  V. tomato spotted wilt
    (K.M. Smith, 1957) R.E. Fitzpatrick, et al., 1958
S. neo-antipoviczii, Buk.
  V. potato yellow dwarf
    Black, L.M., 1937
S. nigrum, L.
  V. aster yellows
    Frazier, Norman W. and Henry H.P. Severin, 1945
  V. atropa belladonna mosaic
    (K.M. Smith, 1957) R.E. Fitzpatrick, et al., 1958
  V. beet curly top
    Costa, A.S., 1952
  V. chilli (pepper) mosaic
    Jha, Ashrafi and S.P. Raychaudhuri, 1956
  V. cucumber green mottle mosaic
    Vasudeva, R.S. and T.K. Nariani, 1952
  V. cucumber mosaic
    Burnett, G., 1934
    Fulton, Robert W., 1941
    Govier, D.A., 1957
    Hoggan, Isme A., 1935
    Johnson, J., 1926
    Nariani, T.K. and Nirmaljit Singh, 1952
    Wellman, F.L., 1935
  V. petunia mosaic
    Johnson, J., 1926
  V. potato A
    Schultz, E.S. and Donald Folsom, 1923
  V. potato leaf roll
    Dykstra, T.P., 1930
    Webb, R.E., R.H. Larson and J.C. Walker, 1952
  V. potato X
    Dennis, R.W.G., 1939
    Folsom, Donald and Reiner Bonde, 1937
    Fulton, Robert W., 1941
    Johnson, James, 1925
    Smith, J. Henderson, 1928
    Thompson, A.D., 1956
  V. potato Y
    Koch, K.L., 1933
    Smith, Kenneth M. and R.W.G. Dennis, 1940
  V. red currant ring spot
    Klesser, P.J., 1951
  V. tobacco broad ring spot
    Johnson, James and Robert W. Fulton, 1942
  V. tobacco etch
    Anderson, C.W. and M.K. Corbett, 1957
    Fulton, Robert W., 1941
    Holmes, Francis O., 1946
  V. tobacco leaf curl
    Pal, B.P. and R.K. Tandon, 1937
    Pruthi, Hem Singh and C.K. Samuel, 1941
  V. tobacco mosaic
    Caldwell, John, 1932
    Crawford, R.F., 1921

Solanum nigrum, L. (cont.)
    V. tobacco mosaic
        Das, C.R. and S.P. Raychaudhuri, 1953
        Fernow, Karl Hermann, 1925
        Fulton, Robert W., 1941
        Hoggan, Isme A., 1927
        Holmes, Francis O., 1946
        Jarrett, Phyllis H., 1930
        Johnson, J., 1926
        Sheffield, F.M.L., 1931
        Stover, W.G., 1928
        Stover, W.G. and M.T. Vermillion, 1933
    V. tobacco ring spot
        Wingard, S.A., 1928
    V. tobacco streak
        Fulton, Robert W., 1948
    V. tobacco yellow dwarf
        Hill, A.V., 1950
    V. tomato bunchy top
        (K.M. Smith, 1957) R.E. Fitzpatrick, et al., 1958
    V. tomato spotted wilt
        Milbrath, J.A., 1939
        Smith, Kenneth M., 1931, 1932
    V. vaccinium false blossom
        (K.M. Smith, 1957) R.E. Fitzpatrick, et al., 1958
S. nigrum var. douglassi, Dun. *
    V. beet curly top
        Severin, Henry H.P., 1929
S. nigrum var. nodiflorum *
    V. tobacco mosaic
        Holmes, F.O., 1934
S. nigrum var. villosum, Mill.
    V. potato leaf roll
        Dykstra, T.P., 1933
    V. potato M *
        Bagnall, R.H. and R.H. Larson, 1957
        Bagnall, R.H., R.H. Larson and J.C. Walker,
        1956
    V. potato paracrinkle
        Bagnall, R.H. and R.H. Larson, 1957
        Bagnall, R.H., R.H. Larson and J.C. Walker,
        1956
    V. potato X
        Dykstra, T.P., 1933
        Smith, J. Henderson, 1928
    V. potato Y
        Dykstra, T.P., 1933
    V. tobacco mosaic
        Jarrett, Phyllis H., 1930
S. nodiflorum, Jacq.
    V. arabis mosaic
        Smith, Kenneth M. and Roy Markham, 1944
    V. cucumber green mottle mosaic
        Vasudeva, R.S. and T.K. Nariani, 1952
    V. cucumber mosaic
        Govier, D.A., 1957
        Nariani, T.K. and Nirmaljit Singh, 1952
        Price, W.C., 1940
    V. lucerne mosaic
        Price, W.C., 1940
    V. potato aucuba mosaic
        (K.M. Smith, 1957) R.E. Fitzpatrick, et al., 1958
    V. potato stunt
        (K.M. Smith, 1957) R.E. Fitzpatrick, et al., 1958
    V. potato X
        Cockerham, George, 1943
        Dennis, R.W.G., 1939
        Smith, J. Henderson, 1928
        Thompson, A.D., 1956
        Vasudeva, R. Sahai and T.B. Lal, 1944
    V. potato Y
        Cockerham, George, 1943
        Sakimura, K., 1953
        Smith, Kenneth M. and R.W.G. Dennis, 1940
        Vasudeva, R. Sahai and T.B. Lal, 1945
    V. red currant ring spot
        Klesser, P.J., 1951
    V. tobacco mosaic
        Caldwell, John, 1932
        Jarrett, Phyllis H., 1930
        Sheffield, F.M.L., 1931, 1936
        Smith, J. Henderson, 1930
    V. tobacco necrosis
        Price, W.C., 1940

S. nodiflorum, Jacq. (cont.)
    V. tobacco ring spot
        Price, W.C., 1940
    V. tobacco ring spot no. 2
        Hildebrand, E.M., 1942
    V. tomato spotted wilt
        Smith, Kenneth M., 1931, 1932
S. opacum, A. Br. & Bouche
    V. tobacco yellow dwarf
        Hill, A.V. and M. Mandryk, 1954
    V. tomato big bud
        Hill, A.V. and M. Mandryk, 1954
S. polyadenium, Greenm.
    V. beet curly top
        Watson, R.D. and T.E. Randall, 1951
    V. potato Y
        Easton, G.D., R.H. Larson and R.W. Hougas,
        1958
S. pseudocapsicum, L.
    V. tobacco etch
        Greenleaf, W.H., 1953
    V. tobacco mosaic
        Greenleaf, W.H., 1953
        Holmes, F.O., 1934
    V. tobacco ring spot
        Wingard, S.A., 1928
    V. tomato ring spot
        Samson, R.W. and E.P. Imle, 1942
S. pyracanthum, Jacq.
    V. tobacco mosaic
        Hoggan, Isme A., 1927
S. rostratum, Dun.
    V. potato M *
        Bagnall, R.H. and R.H. Larson, 1957
        Bagnall, R.H., R.H. Larson and J.C. Walker,
        1956
    V. potato paracrinkle
        Bagnall, R.H. and R.H. Larson, 1957
        Bagnall, R.H., R.H. Larson and J.C. Walker,
        1956
    V. potato X
        Johnson, James, 1925
    V. turnip mosaic
        Walker, J.C., Francis J. LeBeau and Glenn S.
        Pound, 1945
S. rybinii, Juz. & Buk.
    V. potato Y
        Easton, G.D., R.H. Larson and R.W. Hougas,
        1958
S. saltense, Hawkes
    V. potato Y
        Easton, G.D., R.H. Larson and R.W. Hougas,
        1958
S. sanitwongsei, Craib
    V. tobacco mosaic
        Holmes, Francis O., 1946
    V. tomato spotted wilt
        (K.M. Smith, 1957) R.E. Fitzpatrick, et al., 1958
S. seaforthianum, Andr.
    V. tomato spotted wilt
        (K.M. Smith, 1957) R.E. Fitzpatrick, et al., 1958
    V. vaccinium false blossom
        (K.M. Smith, 1957) R.E. Fitzpatrick, et al., 1958
S. simplicifolium, Bitt.
    V. beet curly top
        Watson, R.D. and T.E. Randall, 1951
S. simplicifolium x S. rybinii, Juz. & Buk.
    V. potato Y
        Easton, G.D., R.H. Larson and R.W. Hougas,
        1958
S. simplicifolium x S. toralapanum, Card. & Hawkes
    V. potato Y
        Easton, G.D., R.H. Larson and R.W. Hougas,
        1958
S. sisymbrifolium, Lam.
    V. potato M *
        Bagnall, R.H., R.H. Larson and J.C. Walker,
        1956
    V. potato paracrinkle
        Bagnall, R.H., R.H. Larson and J.C. Walker,
        1956
    V. tomato bunchy top
        (K.M. Smith, 1957) R.E. Fitzpatrick, et al., 1958

Solanum sodomaeum, Hort. ex Dun.
  V. tomato bunchy top
    (K.M. Smith, 1957) R.E. Fitzpatrick, et al., 1958
  V. tomato spotted wilt
    (K.M. Smith, 1957) R.E. Fitzpatrick, et al., 1958
S. spp.
  V. beet curly top
    Watson, R.D. and T.E. Randall, 1951
S. stoloniferum, Schlecht. & Bouche
  V. potato Y
    Easton, G.D., R.H. Larson and R.W. Hougas,
    1958
S. torvum, Sw.
  V. cucumber mosaic
    Adsuar, Jose and A. Cruz Miret, 1950
S. triflorum, Nutt.
  V. cucumber mosaic
    Pound, Glenn S. and J.C. Walker, 1948
  V. tobacco ring spot
    Pound, Glenn S., 1949
  V. tobacco streak
    Fulton, Robert W., 1948
  V. turnip mosaic
    Pound, Glenn S., 1948
S. trilobatum, L.
  V. vaccinium false blossom
    (K.M. Smith, 1957) R.E. Fitzpatrick, et al., 1958
S. tuberosum, L.
  V. abutilon infectious variegation
    (K.M. Smith, 1957) R.E. Fitzpatrick, et al., 1958
  V. aster yellows
    Bonde, Reiner and E.S. Schultz, 1947
    Burke, O.D., 1941
    Jensen, James H. and H. Douglas Tate, 1947
    Leach, J.G. and C. Franklin Bishop, 1944
    Milbrath, J.A. and W.H. English, 1948, 1949
    Raymer, W.B., 1956
    Raymer, W.B. and Clark R. Amen, 1954
    Self, R.L. and H.M. Darling, 1949
    Severin, Henry H.P., 1940
    Severin, Henry H.P. and Julius H. Freitag, 1945
    Severin, Henry H.P. and Frank A. Haasis, 1934
    Younkin, S.G., 1943
  V. beet curly top
    Giddings, N.J., 1944, 1947, 1952, 1953, 1954
    Jones, Leon K., C.L. Vincent and Earl F. Burk,
    1940
    Menzies, J.D. and N.J. Giddings, 1952, 1953
    Milbrath, J.A., 1946
    Severin, Henry H.P., 1929
  V. beet ring spot *
    Harrison, B.D., 1957
  V. chilli (pepper) mosaic
    Jha, Ashrafi and S.P. Raychaudhuri, 1956
  V. clover witches' broom *
    Frazier, N.W. and A.F. Posnette, 1957
  V. cucumber mosaic
    Johnson, James, 1927
  V. cucurbit mosaic *
    Doolittle, S.P. and M.N. Walker, 1922
  V. dodder latent mosaic
    Bennett, C.W., 1944, 1949
  V. eggplant mosaic
    Dale, W.T., 1954
    Ferguson, I.A.C., 1951
  V. lucerne mosaic
    Black, L.M. and W.C. Price, 1940
    Dykstra, T.P., 1939
    Folsom, Donald, 1953
    Hoggan, Isme A., 1927
    Houston, Byron R. and John W. Oswald, 1951,
    1953
    McKay, M.B. and T.P. Dykstra, 1932
    Milbrath, J.A., 1952
    Oswald, John W., 1950
    Porter, D.R., 1931, 1935
    Richardson, D.E. and T.W. Tinsley, 1956
  V. lucerne witches' broom
    Helms, Katie, 1957
    Kunkel, L.O., 1952
  V. (physalis) mosaic *
    Melhus, I.E., 1922
  V. potato A
    Abbott, E.V., 1929

S. tuberosum, L. (cont.)
  V. potato A
    Bawden, F.C., 1936
    Cockerham, George, 1943
    Dykstra, T.P., 1935, 1936, 1939
    Dykstra, T.P. and W.C. Whitaker, 1938
    Goss, R.W., 1929
    Hoggan, Isme A., 1927
    Johnson, James, 1929
    Koch, Karl and James Johnson, 1935
    MacLachlan, D.S. and R.H. Larson, 1953
    MacLachlan, D.S., R.H. Larson and J.C. Walker,
    1953
    McKay, M.B. and T.P. Dykstra, 1932
    Peterson, Paul D. and H.H. McKinney, 1938
    Porter, D.R., 1935
    Schultz, E.S., C.F. Clark, R. Bonde, W.P.
    Raleigh and F.J. Stevenson, 1934
    Schultz, E.S., C.F. Clark, W.P. Raleigh, F.J.
    Stevenson, R. Bonde and J.H. Beaumont, 1937
    Schultz, E.S., C.F. Clark and F.J. Stevenson,
    1940
    Schultz, E.S. and Donald Folsom, 1923, 1925
    Schultz, E.S. and W.P. Raleigh, 1936
    Valleau, W.D. and E.M. Johnson, 1930
    Vasudeva, R. Sahai and C.S. Ramamoorthy, 1946
    Young, P.A., 1930
    Young, P.A. and H.E. Morris, 1930
  V. potato anecrotic mosaic *
    Quanjer, H.M., 1931
  V. potato aucuba mosaic
    Atanasoff, D., 1926
    Dennis, R.W.G., 1939
    Dykstra, T.P., 1939
    Quanjer, H.M., 1931
  V. (potato) giant hill *
    Porter, D.R., 1935
  V. potato leaf roll
    Abbott, E.V., 1929
    Artschwager, Ernest F., 1918
    Atanasoff, D., 1924
    Bald, J.G. and E.M. Hutton, 1950
    Barton-Wright, Eustace and Alan McBain, 1933
    Bawden, F.C. and B. Kassanis, 1946
    Broadbent, L., 1946
    Broadbent, L., R.P. Chaudhuri and L. Kapica,
    1950
    Broadbent, L. and T.W. Tinsley, 1951
    Davidson, T.R., 1955
    Davidson, T.R. and G.B. Sanford, 1955
    Dennis, R.W.G., 1939
    Dykstra, T.P., 1933
    Dykstra, T.P. and W.C. Whitaker, 1938
    Elze, D.L., 1931
    Folsom, Donald, 1921
    Gardner, Max W. and James B. Kendrick, 1924
    Gilbert, Alfred H., 1923, 1928
    Gilbert, G.H., 1929
    Goss, R.W., 1929
    Hoggan, Isme A., 1927
    Jones, Leon K., 1944
    Kassanis, B., 1952
    Kendrick, James B., Sr., 1952
    Kirkpatrick, Hugh C. and A. Frank Ross, 1952
    Klostermeyer, E.C., 1953
    Koch, Karl and James Johnson, 1935
    Link, G.K.K., 1923
    Locke, Seth Barton, 1947
    MacCarthy, H.R., 1954
    McKay, M.B. and T.P. Dykstra, 1932
    Porter, D.R., 1935
    Quanjer, H.M., 1920, 1931
    Quanjer, H.M. and D.L. Elze, 1930
    Rich, Avery E., 1949, 1951
    Schultz, E.S. and R. Bonde, 1929
    Schultz, E.S., C.F. Clark, R. Bonde, W.P.
    Raleigh and F.J. Stevenson, 1934
    Schultz, E.S., C.F. Clark, W.P. Raleigh, F.J.
    Stevenson, R. Bonde and J.H. Beaumont, 1937
    Schultz, E.S. and Donald Folsom, 1921, 1923,
    1925
    Sheffield, F.M.L., 1943
    Smith, Kenneth M., 1929, 1931
    Stewart, F.C. and Hugh Glasgow, 1930, 1931

Solanum tuberosum, L. (cont.)

V. potato leaf roll
Webb, R.E., 1956
Webb, R.E., R.H. Larson and J.C. Walker, 1952
Webb, R.E. and E.S. Schultz, 1954
Whitehead, T., 1924, 1931
Whitehead, T. and J.F. Currie, 1931
Whitehead, T., J.F. Currie and W. Maldwyn Davies, 1932
Young, P.A., 1930
Young, P.A. and H.E. Morris, 1930

V. potato leaf rolling mosaic
Dykstra, T.P., 1935, 1936
Dykstra, T.P. and W.C. Whitaker, 1938
Hoggan, Isme A., 1927
Johnson, James, 1929
McKay, M.B. and T.P. Dykstra, 1932
Porter, D.R., 1935
Schultz, E.S. and Donald Folsom, 1923, 1925
Young, P.A., 1930
Young, P.A. and H.E. Morris, 1930

V. potato M *
Bagnall, R.H. and R.H. Larson, 1957

V. potato necrotic *
Schultz, E.S. and W.P. Raleigh, 1933

V. potato paracrinkle
Alfieri, S.A. and R.F. Stouffer, 1957
Bagnall, R.H. and R.H. Larson, 1957
Bagnall, R.H., R.H. Larson and J.C. Walker, 1956
Barton-Wright, Eustace and Alan McBain, 1933
Dykstra, T.P., 1936, 1939
(K.M. Smith, 1957) R.E. Fitzpatrick, et al., 1958
Kassanis, B., 1955
Whitehead, T., 1937

V. potato rosette
Hutton, E.M. and C.E.W. Oldaker, 1949

V. potato spindle tuber
Abbott, E.V., 1929
Bald, J.G., D.O. Norris and B.T. Dickson, 1941
Fernow, K.H., 1923
Folsom, Donald, 1923
Folsom, Donald and E.S. Schultz, 1924
Goss, R.W., 1926, 1928, 1929, 1930, 1931
McKay, M.B. and T.P. Dykstra, 1932
Porter, D.R., 1935
Schultz, E.S., C.F. Clark, R. Bonde, W.P. Raleigh and F.J. Stevenson, 1934
Schultz, E.S., C.F. Clark, W.P. Raleigh, F.J. Stevenson, R. Bonde and J.H. Beaumont, 1937
Schultz, E.S. and D. Folsom, 1922, 1923, 1925
Werner, H.O., 1926
Young, P.A., 1930
Young, P.A. and H.E. Morris, 1930

V. potato stem mottle
(K.M. Smith, 1957) R.E. Fitzpatrick, et al., 1958

V. (potato) stem-end browning *
Ross, A. Frank, 1946

V. potato stunt
(K.M. Smith, 1957) R.E. Fitzpatrick, et al., 1958

V. potato witches' broom
Kunkel, L.O., 1952
McKay, M.B. and T.P. Dykstra, 1932
Porter, D.R., 1935
Young, P.A., 1930
Young, P.A. and H.E. Morris, 1928, 1930

V. potato X
Ainsworth, G.C., G.H. Berkeley and J. Caldwell, 1934
Atanasoff, D., 1924
Bagnall, R.H., R.H. Larson and J.C. Walker, 1956
Bald, J.G., 1945
Bawden, F.C., 1936
Bawden, F.C. and F.M.L. Sheffield, 1944
Blodgett, F.M., 1927
Burnett, Grover and Leon K. Jones, 1931
Cockerham, George, 1943
Dennis, R.W.G., 1939
Dykstra, T.P., 1933, 1935, 1936, 1939
Fernow, Karl Hermann, 1925
Folsom, Donald, 1920
Folsom, Donald and Reiner Bonde, 1937
Folsom, Donald and E.S. Schultz, 1924

S. tuberosum, L. (cont.)

V. potato X
Gilbert, Alfred H., 1923
Goss, R.W., 1931
Gussow, H.T., 1918
Hoyman, Wm. G., 1951
Jones, Leon K. and C.L. Vincent, 1937
Jones, Leon K., C.L. Vincent and Earl F. Burk, 1940
Koch, K.L., 1933
Koch, Karl and James Johnson, 1935
Krantz, F.A. and G.R. Bisby, 1921
Ladeburg, R.C. and R.H. Larson, 1949
Larson, R.H., 1943, 1944, 1947
Larson, R.H. and R.C. Ladeburg, 1949
Link, G.K.K., 1923
Matthews, R.E.F., 1949
McKay, M.B. and T.P. Dykstra, 1932
McKinney, H.H., 1928
Norris, D.O., 1953, 1954
Quanjer, H.M., 1931
Roberts, F.M., 1948
Ross, A. Frank, 1950
Schultz, E.S., 1951
Schultz, E.S., C.F. Clark, R. Bonde, W.P. Raleigh and F.J. Stevenson, 1934
Schultz, E.S., C.F. Clark, W.P. Raleigh, F.J. Stevenson, R. Bonde and J.H. Beaumont, 1937
Schultz, E.S., C.F. Clark and F.J. Stevenson, 1940
Schultz, E.S. and Donald Folsom, 1920
Schultz, E.S., Donald Folsom, F. Merrill Hildebrandt and Lon A. Hawkins, 1919
Schultz, E.S. and W.P. Raleigh, 1933, 1936
Smith, J. Henderson, 1928
Smith, Kenneth M., 1927, 1929, 1930
Thompson, A.D., 1956
Timian, Roland G., W.J. Hooker and C.E. Peterson, 1955
Tompkins, C.M., 1926
Valleau, W.D. and E.M. Johnson, 1930
Vasudeva, R. Sahai and T.B. Lal, 1944
Whitehead, T., 1937
Whitehead, T. and J.F. Currie, 1931
Whitehead, T., J.F. Currie and W. Maldwyn Davies, 1932

V. potato Y
Atanasoff, D., 1924, 1925
Bald, J.G., 1945
Bald, J.G. and D.O. Norris, 1945
Bawden, F.C., 1936
Bawden, F.C. and B. Kassanis, 1946, 1947, 1951
Bawden, F.C. and F.M.L. Sheffield, 1944
Broadbent, L., 1946
Broadbent, L., R.P. Chaudhuri and L. Kapica, 1950
Broadbent, L. and T.W. Tinsley, 1951
Cockerham, George, 1943
Corbett, M.K., 1955
Darby, J.F., R.H. Larson and J.C. Walker, 1951
Dennis, R.W.G., 1939
Dykstra, T.P., 1933, 1936, 1939
Easton, G.D., R.H. Larson and R.W. Hougas, 1958
Hoggan, Isme A., 1927
Hutton, E.M. and J.W. Peak, 1952
Johnson, James, 1927
Jones, Leon K. and C.L. Vincent, 1937
Jones, Leon K., C.L. Vincent and Earl F. Burk, 1940
Kassanis, B., 1942
Koch, K.L., 1933
Koch, Karl and James Johnson, 1935
Larson, R.H., 1947
Larson, R.H. and J.F. Darby, 1951
Oswald, John W., 1948
Quanjer, H.M., 1931
Richardson, D.E., 1958
Ross, A. Frank, 1948, 1950
Samson, R.W., 1930
Schultz, E.S., C.F. Clark, R. Bonde, W.P. Raleigh and F.J. Stevenson, 1934
Schultz, E.S., C.F. Clark, W.P. Raleigh, F.J. Stevenson, R. Bonde and J.H. Beaumont, 1937

Solanum tuberosum, L. (cont.)
    V. potato Y
        Schultz, E.S. and D. Folsom, 1922, 1923, 1925
        Smith, Kenneth M. and R.W.G. Dennis, 1940
        Valleau, W.D. and E.M. Johnson, 1930
        Vasudeva, R. Sahai and T.B. Lal, 1945
        Vincent, C.L. and L.K. Jones, 1936
        Watson, Marion A., 1956
        Whitehead, T., 1937
    V. potato yellow dwarf
        Black, L.M., 1937, 1938, 1940, 1943
        Hansing, E.D., 1942, 1943
        Hougas, R.W., 1951
        Koch, K., 1934
        Larson, R.H., 1945, 1947
        Muncie, J.H., 1935
        Walker, J.C. and R.H. Larson, 1939
    V. potato yellow spot
        Bonde, Reiner and Donald Merriam, 1954
    V. potato yellow vein
        (K.M. Smith, 1957) R.E. Fitzpatrick, et al., 1958
    V. strawberry green petal
        Frazier, N.W. and A.F. Posnette, 1957
    V. tobacco broad ring spot
        Johnson, James and Robert W. Fulton, 1942
    V. tobacco etch
        Holmes, Francis O., 1946
    V. tobacco leaf curl
        Vasudeva, R.S. and J. Sam Raj, 1948
    V. tobacco leaf roll *
        Goenaga, Alvaro, 1945
    V. tobacco mosaic
        Berkeley, G.H., 1927
        Blodgett, F.M., 1927
        Fernow, Karl Hermann, 1925
        Hoggan, Isme A., 1927
        Holmes, Francis O., 1946
        Johnson, James, 1927, 1929
        Jones, Leon K., C.L. Vincent and Earl F. Burk, 1940
        Quanjer, H.M., 1920
    V. tobacco ring spot
        Cheo, Pen Ching and W.J Zaumeyer, 1952
        Grogan, R.G. and W.C. Schnathorst, 1955
        Henderson, R.G. and S.A. Wingard, 1931
        Valleau, W.D., 1932
    V. tobacco streak
        Fulton, Robert W., 1948
    V. tomato big bud
        Helms, Katie, 1957
        Hill, A.V. and M. Mandryk, 1954
        Norris, D.O., 1954
    V. tomato bushy stunt
        Smith, Kenneth M., 1935
    V. tomato ring spot
        Samson, R.W. and E.P. Imle, 1942
    V. tomato spotted wilt
        Gardner, M.W. and O.C. Whipple, 1934
        Hutton, E.M., 1947
        Hutton, E.M. and A.R. Peak, 1952
        Milbrath, J.A., 1939
        Norris, D.O., 1951
        Norris, D. and J.G. Bald, 1943
        Parris, G.K., 1940
        Sakimura, K., 1940
        Smith, Kenneth M., 1931, 1932
    V. vaccinium false blossom
        Kunkel, L.O., 1945
S. verrucosum, Schlecht.
    V. potato yellow dwarf
        Black, L.M., 1937
S. xanthocarpum, Schrad. & Wendl.
    V. vaccinium false blossom
        (K.M. Smith, 1957) R.E. Fitzpatrick, et al., 1958

SOLIDAGO ((Vaill.)) L. 1735 (Compositae)
S. spp.
    V. prunus B *
        Fulton, Robert W., 1957

SONCHUS ((Tourn.)) L. 1735 (Compositae)
S. arvensis, L.
    V. aster yellows
        Kunkel, L.O., 1926

S. arvensis, L. (cont.)
    V. beet mosaic
        (K.M. Smith, 1957) R.E. Fitzpatrick, et al., 1958
S. asper, (L.) Hill
    V. aster yellows
        Frazier, Norman W. and Henry H.P. Severin, 1945
    V. beet curly top
        Severin, Henry H.P., 1934
    V. beet ring spot *
        Harrison, B.D., 1957
    V. lettuce mosaic
        Ainsworth, G.C. and L. Ogilvie, 1939
    V. lucerne dwarf
        Freitag, J.H., 1951
S. oleraceus, L.
    V. aster yellows
        Frazier, Norman W. and Henry H.P. Severin, 1945
        Kunkel, L.O., 1926
    V. beet curly top
        Severin, Henry H.P., 1934
    V. datura rugose leaf curl
        (K.M. Smith, 1957) R.E. Fitzpatrick, et al., 1958
    V. tobacco streak
        Fulton, Robert W., 1948
    V. tobacco yellow dwarf
        Helson, G.A.H., 1950

SORBUS ((Tourn.)) L. 1735 (Rosaceae)
S. aucuparia, L.
    V. mountain ash infectious variegation
        (K.M. Smith, 1957) R.E. Fitzpatrick, et al., 1958
S. sitchensis, Roem.
    V. apple mosaic
        Thomas, H. Earl and L.M. Massey, 1939

SORGHUM L. 1735 (Gramineae)
S. arundinaceum, Roem. & Schult.
    V. grass natal mosaic *
        Storey, H.H., 1929
    V. sugarcane mosaic
        Storey, H.H., 1929
S. halepense, (L.) Pers.
    V. brome mosaic
        McKinney, H.H., 1944
S. spp.
    V. sugarcane mosaic
        Storey, H.H., 1929
S. vulgare, Pers.
    V. barley yellow dwarf
        Oswald, John W. and Byron R. Houston, 1953
    V. brome mosaic
        McKinney, H.H., 1944
    V. rice and corn leaf-gall *
        Agati, Julian A. and Carlos A. Calica, 1950
    V. sugarcane mosaic
        Costa, A.S. and M.P. Penteado, 1951
        Chona, B.L. and S.A. Rafay, 1950
S. vulgare var. saccharatum, (L.) Boerl.
    V. sugarcane mosaic
        Brandes, E.W., 1920
        Matz, Julius, 1933
S. vulgare var. sudanense, (Piper) Hichtc.
    V. barley yellow dwarf
        Oswald, John W. and Byron R. Houston, 1953
    V. brome mosaic
        McKinney, H.H., 1944

SPARAXIS Ker-Gawl. 1804 (Iridaceae)
S. spp.
    V. cucumber mosaic
        Smith, Floyd F. and Philip Brierley, 1944
    V. sparaxis mosaic
        Smith, Floyd F. and Philip Brierley, 1944

SPATHOGLOTTIS Blume 1825 (Orchidaceae)
S. spp.
    V. orchid *
        Murakishi, H. and M. Ishii, 1954

SPERGULA L. 1735 (Caryophyllaceae)
S. arvensis, L.
    V. aster yellows
        Frazier, Norman W. and Henry H.P. Severin,
        1945
    V. beet yellows
        Roland, G. and J. Tahon, 1961
    V. raspberry Scottish leaf curl
        Harrison, B.D., 1957, 1958
    V. tobacco streak
        Fulton, Robert W., 1948

SPINACIA ((Tourn.)) L. 1735 (Chenopodiaceae)
S. oleracea, L.
    V. aster yellows
        Kunkel, L.O., 1926
        Severin, Henry H.P. and Julius H. Freitag, 1945
    V. beet curly top
        Carsner, E., 1919
        Costa, A.S., 1952
        Giddings, N.J., 1944
        Lackey, C.F., 1929
        Severin, H.H.P., 1928
        Severin, Henry H.P. and Charles F. Henderson,
        1928
    V. beet leaf curl
        (K.M. Smith, 1957) R.E. Fitzpatrick, et al., 1958
    V. beet mosaic
        Hoggan, I.A., 1933
        McLean, D.M., 1952
        Pound, Glenn S., 1947
        Severin, Henry H.P., 1948
        Severin, Henry H.P. and Roger M. Drake, 1948
    V. beet yellows
        Bennett, C.W. and A.S. Costa, 1949
        McLean, D.M., 1953
        Roland, G. and J. Tahon, 1961
    V. cabbage black ring spot
        Tompkins, C.M., M.W. Gardner and H. Rex
        Thomas, 1937, 1938
    V. cabbage ring necrosis
        Larson, R.H. and J.C. Walker, 1940, 1941
    V. carnation ring spot
        Brierley, Philip and Floyd F. Smith, 1957
    V. cucumber green mottle mosaic
        Storey, I.F., 1939
    V. cucumber mosaic
        Berkeley, G.H. and J.H. Tremaine, 1954
        Bridgmon, G.H. and J.C. Walker, 1952
        Cheo, Pen-Ching and Glenn S. Pound, 1952
        Doolittle, S.P. and W.J. Zaumeyer, 1952, 1953
        Fulton, Joseph P., 1950
        Fulton, Robert W., 1941
        Govier, D.A., 1957
        Hoggan, I.A., 1930, 1933, 1935
        Larsh, Howard W. and J.R. Shay, 1945
        McClintock, J.A. and Loren B. Smith, 1918
        Nienow, Inez, 1948
        Pound, Glenn S. and Pen-Ching Cheo, 1952
        Price, W.C., 1934
        Wellman, F.L., 1935
        Whipple, O.C. and J.C. Walker, 1941
    V. cucumber western mosaic *
        Severin, Henry H.P., 1948
        Severin, Henry H.P. and Julius H. Freitag, 1948
    V. lucerne mosaic
        Price, W.C., 1940
        Severin, Henry H.P., 1948
    V. pea mottle
        Johnson, Folke, 1942
    V. radish mosaic
        Tompkins, C.M., 1939
    V. red currant ring spot
        Klesser, P.J., 1951
    V. rhubarb ring spot *
        Vaughan, Edward K. and John W. Yale, Jr., 1953
        Yale, John W., Jr. and Edward K. Vaughan, 1954
    V. spinach yellow dwarf
        Severin, Henry H.P. and Donald H. Little, 1947
    V. tobacco broad ring spot
        Johnson, James and Robert W. Fulton, 1942
    V. tobacco mosaic
        Fulton, Robert W., 1941
        Grant, T.J., 1934

S. oleracea, L. (cont.)
    V. tobacco mosaic
        Holmes, Francis O., 1946
        Jones, L.K., 1934
    V. tobacco ring spot
        Bridgmon, G.H. and J.C. Walker, 1952
        Cheo, Pen Ching and W.J. Zaumeyer, 1952
        (K.M. Smith, 1957) R.E. Fitzpatrick, et al., 1958
        Fulton, Robert W., 1941
        Grogan, R.G. and W.C. Schnathorst, 1955
        Hoggan, I.A., 1933
    V. tobacco ring spot no. 2
        Brierley, Philip, 1954
    V. tobacco streak
        Fulton, Robert W., 1948
    V. tomato aspermy
        Brierley, Philip, Floyd F. Smith and S.P.
        Doolittle, 1953, 1955
        Hollings, M., 1955
    V. tomato black ring
        (K.M. Smith, 1957) R.E. Fitzpatrick, et al., 1958
    V. tomato spotted wilt
        Sakimura, K., 1940
    V. turnip mosaic
        Berkeley, G.H. and J.H. Tremaine, 1954
        Hoggan, I.A. and J. Johnson, 1935
        LeBeau, Francis J. and J.C. Walker, 1945
        Tompkins, C.M., 1939
        Walker, J.C., Francis J. LeBeau and Glenn S.
        Pound, 1945
S. tetranda, Stev. ex Bieb.
    V. beet yellows
        Roland, G. and J. Tahon, 1961

STACHYTARPHETA Vahl 1805 (Verbenaceae)
S. cayennensis, Schau.
    V. stachytarpheta cayennensis mosaic *
        Jensen, D.D., 1949
S. indica, Vahl
    V. sandal spike
        (K.M. Smith, 1957) R.E. Fitzpatrick, et al., 1958

STATICE Tourn. ex L. 1735 (Plumbaginaceae)
S. armeria, L.
    V. tobacco necrosis
        Price, W.C., 1940

STELLARIA L. 1753 (Caryophyllaceae)
S. media, (L.) Cyr.
    V. aster yellows
        Frazier, Norman W. and Henry H.P. Severin,
        1945
    V. beet curly top
        Bennett, C.W., Eubanks Carsner, F.H. Coons and
        E.W. Brandes, 1946
        Bennett, C.W. and A.S. Costa, 1949
        Bennett, C.W. and Aziz Tanrisever, 1957
        Carsner, E., 1919
        Carsner, Eubanks and C.F. Stahl, 1924
        Costa, A.S., 1952
        Lackey, C.F., 1932, 1937
        Severin, Henry H.P., 1934
    V. beet mosaic
        Pound, Glenn S., 1947
    V. beet ring spot *
        Harrison, B.D., 1957
    V. beet yellows
        (K.M. Smith, 1957) R.E. Fitzpatrick, et al., 1958
        Roland, G. and J. Tahon, 1961
    V. cabbage black ring spot
        Tompkins, C.M., M.W. Gardner and H. Rex
        Thomas, 1937, 1938
    V. cucumber mosaic
        Burnett, G., 1934
    V. pea mottle
        Johnson, Folke, 1942
    V. peach yellow bud mosaic
        Karle, Harry P., 1957
    V. raspberry Scottish leaf curl
        Harrison, B.D., 1958
    V. tobacco mosaic
        Holmes, Francis O., 1938, 1946
    V. tomato spotted wilt
        Holmes, Francis O., 1948

Stellaria media, (L.) Cyr. (cont.)
   V. turnip mosaic
      Walker, J.C., Francis J. LeBeau and Glenn S.
      Pound, 1945

STERCULIA L. 1747 (Sterculiaceae)
S. laevis, Wall.
   V. cacao swollen shoot
      Tinsley, T.W. and A.L. Wharton, 1958
S. rhinopetala, K. Schum.
   V. cacao swollen shoot
      Posnette, A.F., N.F. Robertson and J. McA.
      Todd, 1950
      Tinsley, T.W. and A.L. Wharton, 1958
S. setigera, Del.
   V. cacao swollen shoot
      Tinsley, T.W. and A.L. Wharton, 1958
S. tragacantha, Lindl.
   V. cacao swollen shoot
      Posnette, A.F., N.F. Robertson and J. McA.
      Todd, 1950
      Tinsley, T.W. and A.L. Wharton, 1958

STIPA L. 1753 (Gramineae)
S. comata, Trin. & Rupr.
   V. barley yellow dwarf
      Bruehl, G.W. and H.V. Toko, 1957
S. robusta, Scribn.
   V. wheat streak mosaic
      McKinney, H.H. and Hurley Fellows, 1951

STREPTANTHERA Sweet 1827 (Iridaceae)
S. cuprea, Sweet
   V. streptanthera mosaic
      Smith, Floyd F. and Philip Brierley, 1944

STREPTOSOLEN Miers 1850 (Solanaceae)
S. jamesonii, Miers
   V. tomato spotted wilt
      (K.M. Smith, 1957) R.E. Fitzpatrick, et al., 1958

STRYCHNOS L. 1735 (Loganiaceae)
S. subifera, Gilg. & Busse
   V. groundnut rosette
      Evans, A.C., 1954

STYLOSANTHES Sw. 1788 (Leguminosae)
S. bojeri, Vog.
   V. (legume) little leaf disease *
      Hutton, E.M. and N.E. Grylls, 1956
S. erecta, Beauv.
   V. (legume) little leaf disease *
      Hutton, E.M. and N.E. Grylls, 1956
S. gracilis, H. B. & K.
   V. (legume) little leaf disease *
      Hutton, E.M. and N.E. Grylls, 1956
S. guianensis, Sw.
   V. (legume) little leaf disease *
      Hutton, E.M. and N.E. Grylls, 1956
S. leiocarpa, Vog.
   V. (legume) little leaf disease *
      Hutton, E.M. and N.E. Grylls, 1956
S. montevidensis, Vog.
   V. (legume) little leaf disease *
      Hutton, E.M. and N.E. Grylls, 1956
S. spp.
   V. (legume) little leaf disease *
      Hutton, E.M. and N.E. Grylls, 1956
S. sundaica, Taub.
   V. (legume) little leaf disease *
      Hutton, E.M. and N.E. Grylls, 1956

SUAEDA Forsk. 1775 (Chenopodiaceae)
S. fruticosa, Forsk.
   V. beet yellows
      Roland, G. and J. Tahon, 1961
S. moquini, Greene
   V. beet curly top
      Carsner, E., 1925
      Severin, Henry H.P., 1939
   V. beet yellows
      Roland, G. and J. Tahon, 1961
S. splendens, Gren. & Godr.
   V. beet yellows
      Roland, G. and J. Tahon, 1961

SYMPHORICARPOS Dill. ex Juss. 1789 (Caprifoliaceae)
S. albus, (L.) Blake
   V. lucerne dwarf
      Freitag, J.H., 1951

SYNEDRELLA Gaert. 1791 (Compositae)
S. nodiflora, Gaertn.
   V. tobacco leaf curl
      (K.M. Smith, 1957) R.E. Fitzpatrick, et al., 1958

SYNTHERISMA Walt. 1788 (Gramineae)
S. sanguinale, Dulac.
   V. sugarcane mosaic
      Brandes, E.W., 1920
      Brandes, E.W. and Peter J. Klaphaak, 1923
      Chardon, C.E. and R.A. Veve, 1923

SYRINGA L. 1735 (Oleaceae)
S. japonica, Decne.
   V. lilac witches' broom
      Brierley, Philip, 1955
      Lorentz, Paul and Philip Brierley, 1953
S. vulgaris, L.
   V. lilac ring mosaic
      Beale, J.H. and Helen Purdy Beale, 1952
   V. lilac witches' broom
      Brierley, Philip, 1955
      Lorentz, Paul and Philip Brierley, 1953
   V. lucerne dwarf
      Freitag, J.H., 1951

TABEBUIA Gomez 1803 (Bignoniaceae)
T. pallida, Miers
   V. tabebuia witches' broom
      Cook, M.T., 1937, 1938

TACSONIA Juss. 1789 (Passifloraceae)
T. spp.
   V. cucumber mosaic
      Nattrass, R.M., 1944

TAGETES L. 1737 (Compositae)
T. erecta, L.
   V. anemone mosaic *
      Hollings, M., 1957
   V. aster yellows
      Kunkel, L.O., 1926
      Severin, Henry H.P., 1929
      Severin, Henry H.P. and Julius H. Freitag, 1934,
      1945
   V. beet curly top
      Freitag, Julius H. and Henry H.P. Severin, 1936
   V. cucumber mosaic
      Wellman, F.L., 1935
   V. lettuce mosaic
      (K.M. Smith, 1957) R.E. Fitzpatrick, et al., 1958
   V. tobacco mosaic
      Holmes, Francis O., 1946
   V. tobacco ring spot
      Grogan, R.G. and W.C. Schnathorst, 1955
      Wingard, S.A., 1928
   V. vaccinium false blossom
      Kunkel, L.O., 1945
T. patula, L.
   V. aster yellows
      Severin, Henry H.P. and Julius H. Freitag, 1934,
      1945
   V. beet curly top
      Freitag, Julius H. and Henry H.P. Severin, 1936
   V. carnation ring spot
      Brierley, Philip and Floyd F. Smith, 1957
   V. cucumber mosaic
      Nienow, Inez, 1948
      Wellman, F.L., 1934, 1935
   V. tobacco mosaic
      Grant, T.J., 1934
      Holmes, Francis O., 1946
T. signata, Bartl.
   V. tobacco mosaic
      Holmes, Francis O., 1946
T. singata var. pumila, Hort.
   V. bayberry yellows
      (K.M. Smith, 1957) R.E. Fitzpatrick, et al., 1958

TALINUM Adans. 1763 (Portulacaceae)
T. caffrum, Eckl. & Zeyh.
  V. groundnut rosette
    Evans, A.C., 1954

TANACETUM Tourn. ex L. 1735 (Compositae)
T. boreale, Fisch. ex Link
  V. chrysanthemum stunt
    Brierley, Philip, 1953
T. camphoratum, Less.
  V. chrysanthemum stunt
    Brierley, Philip, 1953
T. vulgare, L.
  V. chrysanthemum stunt
    Brierley, Philip, 1953

TARAXACUM L. 1735 (Compositae)
T. officinale, Weber
  V. aster yellows
    Kunkel, L.O., 1926
  V. beet ring spot *
    Harrison, B.D., 1957
  V. chrysanthemum latent *
    Hollings, M., 1957
  V. dandelion yellow mosaic
    Kassanis, B., 1947
  V. raspberry yellow dwarf *
    Harrison, B.D., 1958
  V. tobacco streak
    Fulton, Robert W., 1948

TEPHROSIA Pers. 1807 (Leguminosae)
T. spp.
  V. (legume) little leaf disease *
    Hutton, E.M. and N.E. Grylls, 1956

TETRAGONIA L. 1735 (Aizoaceae)
T. echinata, Ait.
  V. beet yellows
    Roland, G. and J. Tahon, 1961
T. expansa, Thunb.
  V. anemone brown ring *
    Hollings, M., 1958
  V. anemone mosaic *
    Hollings, M., 1957
  V. beet mosaic
    Pound, Glenn S., 1947
    Severin, Henry H.P. and Roger M. Drake, 1948
  V. beet yellows
    Roland, G. and J. Tahon, 1961
  V. chrysanthemum B (mild mosaic) *
    Hollings, M., 1957
  V. chrysanthemum latent *
    Hollings, M., 1957
  V. cabbage black ring spot
    Hollings, M., 1957
  V. clover big vein
    Black, L.M., 1945
  V. cucumber mosaic
    Hollings, M., 1955
    Wellman, F.L., 1935
  V. cucumber western mosaic *
    Severin, Henry H.P., 1948
  V. datura distortion mosaic
    Capoor, S.P. and P.M. Varma, 1952
  V. lucerne mosaic
    Price, W.C., 1940
  V. ranunculus mosaic
    (K.M. Smith, 1957) R.E. Fitzpatrick, et al., 1958
  V. red currant ring spot
    Klesser, P.J., 1951
  V. tobacco etch
    Holmes, Francis O., 1946
  V. tobacco mosaic
    Grant, T.J., 1934
    Holmes, Francis O., 1946
  V. tobacco necrosis
    Price, W.C., 1940
  V. tobacco ring spot
    Cheo, Pen Ching and W.J. Zaumeyer, 1952
    Priode, C.N., 1928
    Wingard, S.A., 1928
  V. tobacco ring spot no. 2
    Brierley, Philip, 1954

T. expansa, Thunb. (cont.)
  V. tobacco ring spot no. 2
    Price, W.C., 1940
  V. tomato aspermy
    Brierley, Philip, Floyd F. Smith and S.P.
    Doolittle, 1955
  V. tomato black ring
    (K.M. Smith, 1957) R.E. Fitzpatrick, et al., 1958
  V. turnip crinkle
    Broadbent, L. and G.D. Heathcote, 1958

THEA L. 1735 (Theaceae)
T. sinensis, L. (Camellia sinensis, (L.) Kuntze)
  V. tea phloem necrosis
    Bond, T.E.T., 1947

THELYPODIUM Endl. 1839 (Cruciferae)
T. lasiophyllum, Greene
  V. beet curly top
    Severin, Henry H.P., 1934

THEOBROMA L. 1737 (Sterculiaceae)
T. angustifolia, ((Moc. & Sesse)) ex DC.
  V. cacao swollen shoot
    Tinsley, T.W. and A.L. Wharton, 1958
T. bicolor, Humb. & Bonpl.
  V. cacao swollen shoot
    Posnette, A.F. and J. McA. Todd, 1951
    Posnette, A.F., N.F. Robertson and J. McA.
    Todd, 1950
    Tinsley, T.W. and A.L. Wharton, 1958
T. cacao, L.
  V. cacao swollen shoot
    Attafuah, A. and T.W. Tinsley, 1958
    Baker, R.E.D. and W.T. Dale, 1947
    Crowdy, S.H. and A.F. Posnette, 1947
    Goodall, D.W., 1949
    Hanna, A.D. and W. Heatherington, 1957
    Posnette, A.F., 1947, 1950
    Posnette, A.F. and N.F. Robertson, 1950
    Posnette, A.F., N.F. Robertson and J. McA.
    Todd, 1950
    Posnette, A.F. and A.H. Strickland, 1948
    Posnette, A.F. and J. McA. Todd, 1951, 1955
    Tinsley, T.W. and A.L. Wharton, 1958
T. grandiflorum, K. Schum.
  V. cacao swollen shoot
    Tinsley, T.W. and A.L. Wharton, 1958
T. microcarpa, Mart.
  V. cacao swollen shoot
    Tinsley, T.W. and A.L. Wharton, 1958
T. obovata, Klotzsch, ex Bern.
  V. cacao swollen shoot
    Tinsley, T.W. and A.L. Wharton, 1958
T. speciosa, Willd. ex Spreng.
  V. cacao swollen shoot
    Tinsley, T.W. and A.L. Wharton, 1958

THLASPI ((Tourn.)) L. 1737 (Cruciferae)
T. arvense, L.
  V. anemone mosaic *
    Hollings, M., 1957
  V. beet yellows
    (K.M. Smith, 1957) R.E. Fitzpatrick, et al., 1958
    Roland, G. and J. Tahon, 1961
  V. cabbage black ring spot
    Hollings, M., 1957
  V. cabbage ring necrosis
    Larson, R.H. and J.C. Walker, 1941
  V. cauliflower mosaic
    Walker, J.C., Francis J. LeBeau and Glenn S.
    Pound, 1945
  V. chrysanthemum latent *
    Hollings, M., 1957
  V. cucumber mosaic
    Pound, Glenn S. and J.C. Walker, 1948
  V. tobacco ring spot
    Pound, Glenn S., 1949
  V. turnip crinkle
    Broadbent, L. and G.D. Heathcote, 1958
  V. turnip mosaic
    Pound, Glenn S., 1948
    Walker, J.C., Francis J. LeBeau and Glenn S.
    Pound, 1945

Thlaspi arvense, L. (cont.)
  V. turnip rosette *
    Broadbent, L. and G.D. Heathcote, 1958
  V. turnip yellow mosaic
    Broadbent, L. and G.D. Heathcote, 1958

THUNBERGIA Retz. 1776 (Acanthaceae)
T. alata, Bojer
  V. beet curly top
    Freitag, Julius H. and Henry H.P. Severin, 1936
  V. lucerne mosaic
    Price, W.C., 1940
  V. prunus B *
    Fulton, Robert W., 1957

TIGRIDIA Juss. 1789 (Iridaceae)
T. pavonia, Ker-Gawl.
  V. tigridia mosaic
    Smith, Floyd F. and Philip Brierley, 1944

TILIA ((Tourn.)) L. 1735 (Tiliaceae)
T. platyphyllos, Scop.
  V. rose cowl forming
    (K.M. Smith, 1957) R.E. Fitzpatrick, et al., 1958
T. spp.
  V. rose cowl forming
    (K.M. Smith, 1957) R.E. Fitzpatrick, et al., 1958

TITHONIA Desf. ex Juss. 1789 (Compositae)
T. rotundifolia, (Mill.) Blake
  V. chrysanthemum stunt
    Brierley, Philip, 1953
    Keller, John R., 1953
  V. tithonia rotundifolia mosaic *
    Cook, M.T., 1936
T. speciosa, Hook.
  V. prunus B *
    Fulton, Robert W., 1957

TORENIA L. 1751 (Scrophulariaceae)
T. fournieri, Lind.
  V. clover big vein
    Black, L.M., 1945
  V. tobacco etch
    Holmes, Francis O., 1946
  V. tobacco mosaic
    Holmes, Francis O., 1946

TRACHELIUM Tourn. ex L. 1735 (Campanulaceae)
T. caeruleum, L.
  V. tomato spotted wilt
    (K.M. Smith, 1957) R.E. Fitzpatrick, et al., 1958
T. spp.
  V. tomato spotted wilt
    (K.M. Smith, 1957) R.E. Fitzpatrick, et al., 1958

TRACHYMENE Rudge 1811 (Umbelliferae)
T. caerulea, R. Graham
  V. aster yellows
    Severin, Henry H.P. and Julius H. Freitag, 1945
  V. beet curly top
    Freitag, Julius H. and Henry H.P. Severin, 1936
  V. tobacco necrosis
    Price, W.C., 1940
  V. tobacco ring spot
    Price, W.C., 1940

TRADESCANTIA Rupp. ex L. 1735 (Commelinaceae)
T. spp.
  V. cucumber mosaic
    Wellman, F.L., 1935

TRAGOPOGON ((Tourn.)) L. 1735 (Compositae)
T. porrifolius, L.
  V. aster yellows
    Kunkel, L.O., 1926
    Severin, Henry H.P., 1934
  V. vaccinium false blossom
    Kunkel, L.O., 1945

TRIANTHEMA L. 1753 (Aizoaceae)
T. portulacastrum, L.
  V. beet yellows
    Roland, G. and J. Tahon, 1961

TRICHOSANTHES L. 1737 (Cucurbitaceae)
T. anguina, L.
  V. beet curly top
    Freitag, Julius H. and Henry H.P. Severin, 1936
  V. cucumber green mottle mosaic
    Azad, R.N., 1956
  V. cucumber mosaic
    Jagger, I.C., 1918
    Nariani, T.K. and Nirmaljit Singh, 1952
  V. cucurbit mosaic *
    Doolittle, S.P. and M.N. Walker, 1925
  V. prunus A *
    Fulton, Robert W., 1957
  V. prunus B *
    Fulton, Robert W., 1957
  V. prunus E *
    Fulton, Robert W., 1957
  V. prunus G *
    Fulton, Robert W., 1957
  V. squash mosaic
    Freitag, J.H., 1956

TRIFOLIUM ((Tourn.)) L. 1735 (Leguminosae)
T. agrarium, L.
  V. pea mosaic
    Murphy, D.M. and W.H. Pierce, 1937
  V. potato yellow dwarf
    Black, L.M., 1937
T. alexandrinum, L.
  V. lucerne mosaic
    Kreitlow, K.W. and W.C. Price, 1949
T. angustifolium, L.
  V. subterranean clover mosaic
    Aitken, Y. and B.J. Grieve, 1943
T. carolinianum, Michx.
  V. pea mosaic
    Murphy, D.M. and W.H. Pierce, 1937
T. dubium, Sibth.
  V. lucerne mosaic
    Kreitlow, K.W. and W.C. Price, 1949
  V. pea mosaic
    Murphy, D.M. and W.H. Pierce, 1937
T. fragiferum, L.
  V. lucerne dwarf
    Freitag, J.H., 1951
  V. lucerne mosaic
    Kreitlow, K.W. and W.C. Price, 1949
T. giganteum *
  V. lucerne mosaic
    (K.M. Smith, 1957) R.E. Fitzpatrick, et al., 1958
T. glomeratum, L.
  V. lucerne mosaic
    Kreitlow, K.W. and W.C. Price, 1949
  V. pea enation mosaic
    Hagedorn, D.J., 1957
  V. pea mosaic
    Murphy, D.M. and W.H. Pierce, 1937
  V. subterranean clover mosaic
    Aitken, Y. and B.J. Grieve, 1943
  V. tobacco streak
    Fulton, Robert W., 1948
T. hirtum, All.
  V. lucerne mosaic
    Kreitlow, K.W. and W.C. Price, 1949
T. hybridum, L.
  V. alsike clover mosaic
    Wade, B.L. and W.J. Zaumeyer, 1938
    Zaumeyer, W.J. and B.L. Wade, 1935
  V. aster yellows
    Raymer, W.B., 1956
  V. bean yellow mosaic
    Baggett, James R., 1957
    Grogan, Raymond G. and J.C. Walker, 1948
    Hagedorn, D.J. and E.W. Hanson, 1953, 1957
    Hagedorn, D.J. and J.C. Walker, 1950, 1954
    Hanson, E.W. and D.J. Hagedorn, 1954, 1956
    Hungerford, C.W. and Irvin G. Hillyer, 1954
  V. beet curly top
    Giddings, N.J., 1944
    Severin, Henry H.P. and Charles F. Henderson, 1928
  V. cucumber mosaic
    Hagedorn, D.J., 1950
    Hagedorn, D.J. and J.C. Walker, 1954

Trifolium hybridum, L. (cont.)
  V. gladiolus *
    Snow, Gordon F., 1955
  V. lucerne dwarf
    Freitag, J.H., 1951
  V. lucerne mosaic
    Hagedorn, D.J. and E.W. Hanson, 1953, 1957
    Hanson, E.W. and D.J. Hagedorn, 1954, 1956
    Kreitlow, K.W. and W.C. Price, 1949
  V. pea enation mosaic
    Johnson, Folke and Leon K. Jones, 1937
  V. pea mosaic
    Johnson, F. and L.K. Jones, 1936
    Murphy, D.M. and W.H. Pierce, 1937
    Pierce, W.H., 1937
  V. pea mottle
    Johnson, Folke, 1942
    Johnson, F. and L.K. Jones, 1936, 1937
  V. pea streak
    Hagedorn, D.J., 1948
  V. pea wilt
    Johnson, Folke, 1942
  V. potato yellow dwarf
    Black, L.M., 1937
  V. red clover mosaic *
    Dickson, B.T., 1922
  V. red clover vein mosaic
    Graves, Clinton H., Jr. and D.J. Hagedorn, 1956
    Hagedorn, D.J. and E.W. Hanson, 1951, 1953,
    1957
    Hagedorn, D.J. and J.C. Walker, 1949, 1954
    Hanson, E.W. and D.J. Hagedorn, 1954, 1956
    Osborn, H.T., 1937
  V. subterranean clover mosaic
    Aitken, Y. and B.J. Grieve, 1943
  V. tobacco ring spot
    Rich, Saul, 1940
  V. Wisconsin pea streak
    Hagedorn, D.J. and J.C. Walker, 1949, 1954
    Skotland, C.B., 1953
T. incarnatum, L.
  V. alsike clover mosaic
    Zaumeyer, W.J., 1940
  V. aster yellows
    Raymer, W.B., 1956
  V. bean yellow mosaic
    Baggett, James R., 1957
    Conover, Robert A., 1948
    Diachun, Stephen and Lawrence Henson, 1956
    Grogan, Raymond G. and J.C. Walker, 1948
    Hagedorn, D.J., 1948, 1952
    Hagedorn, D.J. and E.W. Hanson, 1953, 1957
    Hagedorn, D.J. and J.C. Walker, 1950, 1954
    Hanson, E.W. and D.J. Hagedorn, 1954, 1956
    Pierce, W.H., 1934
    Thomas, H. Rex and W.J. Zaumeyer, 1953
    Zaumeyer, W.J., 1940
  V. beet curly top
    Giddings, N.J., 1944
    Severin, Henry H.P. and Charles F. Henderson,
    1928
  V. beet mosaic
    Bennett, C.W., 1949
  V. broad bean mottle
    Bawden, F.C., R.P. Chaudhuri and B. Kassanis,
    1951
  V. clover big vein
    Black, L.M., 1945, 1953
    Black, L.M. and M.K. Brakke, 1952
    Maramorosch, Karl, 1950
  V. clover club leaf
    Black, L.M., 1948, 1949
  V. clover disease, European leafhopper-borne *
    Maramorosch, Karl, 1953, 1954
  V. clover enation *
    (K.M. Smith, 1957) R.E. Fitzpatrick, et al., 1958
  V. clover witches' broom *
    Frazier, N.W. and A.F. Posnette, 1957
  V. cucumber mosaic
    Brierley, Philipand Floyd F. Smith, 1944
    Doolittle, S.P. and W.J. Zaumeyer, 1952, 1953
    Hagedorn, D.J., 1950, 1952
    Hagedorn, D.J. and J.C. Walker, 1954
    Price, W.C., 1940

T. incarnatum, L. (cont.)
  V. filaree red leaf
    Anderson, Chris W., 1952
  V. lucerne dwarf
    Freitag, J.H., 1951
  V. lucerne mosaic
    Black, L.M. and W.C. Price, 1940
    Hagedorn, D.J. and E.W. Hanson, 1953, 1957
    Hanson, E.W. and D.J. Hagedorn, 1954, 1956
    Kreitlow, K.W. and W.C. Price, 1949
    Pierce, W.H., 1934
    Thomas, H. Rex, 1951
    Zaumeyer, W.J., 1938, 1953
  V. pea enation mosaic
    Chaudhuri, R.P., 1950
    Hagedorn, D.J., 1952
    Hagedorn, D.J. and J.C. Walker, 1954
    McEwen, F.L. and W.T. Schroeder, 1956
    Osborn, H.T., 1938
    Simons, John N., 1954
    Stubbs, M.W., 1937
  V. pea mosaic
    Chaudhuri, R.P., 1950
    Hagedorn, D.J., 1948
    Hagedorn, D.J. and J.C. Walker, 1954
    Murphy, D.M. and W.H. Pierce, 1937
    Osborn, H.T., 1935, 1937
    Stubbs, M.W., 1936, 1937
  V. pea mottle
    Johnson, Folke, 1942
  V. pea streak
    Hagedorn, D. ., 1948
    Zaumeyer, W.J., 1938
  V. pea wilt
    Johnson, Folke, 1942
  V. potato yellow dwarf
    Black, L.M., 1938, 1943, 1953
    Hougas, R.W., 1951
  V. red clover mosaic *
    Dickson, B.T., 1922
  V. red clover vein mosaic
    Hagedorn, D.J., 1952
    Hagedorn, D.J. and E.W. Hanson, 1951, 1953,
    1957
    Hagedorn, D.J. and J.C. Walker, 1949, 1954
    Hanson, E.W. and D.J. Hagedorn, 1954, 1956
    Osborn, H.T., 1937
  V. strawberry green petal
    Frazier, N.W. and A.F. Posnette, 1957
  V. subterranean clover mosaic
    Aitken, Y. and B.J. Grieve, 1943
  V. tobacco broad ring spot
    Johnson, James and Robert W. Fulton, 1942
  V. tobacco necrosis
    Price, W.C., 1940
  V. tobacco ring spot
    Cheo, Pen Ching and W.J. Zaumeyer, 1952
    Pierce, W.H., 1934
    Stubbs, M.W., 1937
  V. tobacco streak
    Fulton, Robert W., 1948
    Thomas, H. Rex and W.J. Zaumeyer, 1950
  V. Wisconsin pea streak
    Hagedorn, D.J., 1952
    Hagedorn, D.J. and J.C. Walker, 1949, 1954
T. minus, Relhan
  V. subterranean clover mosaic
    Aitken, Y. and B.J. Grieve, 1943
T. pratense, L.
  V. alsike clover mosaic
    Hanson, E.W. and D.J. Hagedorn, 1952
  V. aster yellows
    Raymer, W.B., 1956
  V. bean yellow mosaic
    Diachun, Stephen and Lawrence Henson, 1953,
    1956, 1957
    Elliott, J.A., 1921
    Hagedorn, D.J., 1948, 1952
    Hagedorn, D.J. and E.W. Hanson, 1953, 1957
    Hagedorn, D.J. and J.C. Walker, 1950, 1954
    Hanson, E.W. and D.J. Hagedorn, 1952, 1954,
    1956
    McWhorter, Frank P., 1949
    Oshima, Nagayoshi and M.F. Kernkamp, 1957

Trifolium pratense, L.
  V. bean yellow mosaic
    Pierce, W.H., 1935, 1937
    Zaumeyer, W.J., 1940
    Zaumeyer, W.J. and B.L. Wade, 1935
  V. beet curly top
    Severin, Henry H.P. and Charles F. Henderson, 1928
  V. broad bean mottle
    Bawden, F.C., R.P. Chaudhuri and B. Kassanis, 1951
    Yu, T.F., 1939
  V. clover big vein
    Black, L.M., 1945
  V. clover witches' broom *
    Frazier, N.W. and A.F. Posnette, 1957
  V. cucumber mosaic
    Hagedorn, D.J., 1950, 1952
    Hagedorn, D.J. and J.C. Walker, 1954
  V. datura rugose leaf curl
    Grylls, N.E., 1955
  V. (legume) little leaf disease *
    Hutton, E.M. and N.E. Grylls, 1956
  V. lucerne dwarf
    Freitag, J.H., 1951
  V. lucerne mosaic
    Berkeley, G.H., 1947
    Black, L.M. and W.C. Price, 1940
    Hagedorn, D.J. and E.W. Hanson, 1953, 1957
    Hanson, E.W. and D.J. Hagedorn, 1952, 1954, 1956
    Johnson, E.M., 1946
    Kreitlow, K.W. and W.C. Price, 1949
    Pierce, W.H., 1934, 1937
    Thomas, H. Rex, 1951
    Zaumeyer, W.J., 1938
    Zaumeyer, W.J. and B.L. Wade, 1935
  V. lucerne witches' broom
    Klostermeyer, E.C. and J.D. Menzies, 1951
    Menzies, J.D., 1946
  V. pea enation mosaic
    Hagedorn, D.J., 1952
  V. pea mosaic
    Doolittle, S.P. and F.R. Jones, 1925
    Hagedorn, D.J., 1948
    Hanson, E.W. and D.J. Hagedorn, 1952
    Murphy, D.M. and W.H. Pierce, 1937
    Osborn, H.T., 1937
    Oshima, Nagayoshi and M.F. Kernkamp, 1957
    Pierce, W.H., 1935, 1937
  V. pea mottle
    Johnson, Folke, 1942
    Johnson, F. and L.K. Jones, 1936, 1937
  V. pea streak
    Hagedorn, D.J., 1948
    Oshima, Nagayoshi and M.F. Kernkamp, 1957
    Zaumeyer, W.J., 1938
  V. pea wilt
    Johnson, Folke, 1942
  V. pea yellow mosaic *
    Ainsworth, G.C., 1940
  V. potato yellow dwarf
    Black, L.M., 1936, 1937
    Hansing, E.D., 1942
  V. red clover mosaic *
    Dickson, B.T., 1922
    Dickson, B.T. and G.P. McRostie, 1922
    Elliott, J.A., 1921
    Zaumeyer, W.J. and B.L. Wade, 1935
  V. red clover vein mosaic
    Graves, Clinton H., Jr. and D.J. Hagedorn, 1956
    Hagedorn, D.J., 1952
    Hagedorn, D.J. and E.W. Hanson, 1951, 1953, 1957
    Hagedorn, D.J. and J.C. Walker, 1949, 1954
    Hanson, E.W. and D.J. Hagedorn, 1952, 1954, 1956
    Osborn, H.T., 1937, 1938
  V. strawberry green petal
    Frazier, N.W. and A.F. Posnette, 1957
  V. subterranean clover mosaic
    Aitken, Y. and B.J. Grieve, 1943
  V. sweet pea mosaic *
    Doolittle, S.P. and F.R. Jones, 1925

T. pratense, L. (cont.)
  V. tobacco necrosis
    Fulton, Robert W., 1950
  V. tobacco ring spot
    Benedict, W.G., 1955
    Cheo, Pen Ching and W.J. Zaumeyer, 1952
    Pound, Glenn S., 1949
  V. tobacco streak
    Fulton, Robert W., 1948
    Thomas, H. Rex and W.J. Zaumeyer, 1950
  V. Wisconsin pea streak
    Hagedorn, D.J., 1952
    Hagedorn, D.J. and J.C. Walker, 1949, 1954
    Hanson, E.W. and D.J. Hagedorn, 1952
    Skotland, C.B., 1953
    Skotland, C.B. and D.J. Hagedorn, 1954
T. pratense var. perenne, Host
  V. beet curly top
    Severin, Henry H.P. and Charles F. Henderson, 1928
T. procumbens, L.
  V. pea mosaic
    Murphy, D.M. and W.H. Pierce, 1937
T. reflexum, L.
  V. pea mosaic
    Murphy, D.M. and W.H. Pierce, 1937
T. repens, L.
  V. aster yellows
    Raymer, W.B., 1956
    Raymer, W.B. and Clark R. Amen, 1954
    Webb, R.E. and E.S. Schultz, 1955
  V. bean yellow mosaic
    Ainsworth, G.C., 1940
    Houston, Byron R. and John W. Oswald, 1953
    Kreitlow, K.W., O.J. Hunt and H.L. Wilkins, 1957
  V. beet curly top
    Giddings, N.J., 1944
    Severin, Henry H.P. and Charles F. Henderson, 1928
  V. broad bean mottle
    Yu, T.F., 1939
  V. clover witches' broom *
    Frazier, N.W. and A.F. Posnette, 1957
  V. cucumber mosaic
    Hagedorn, D.J., 1950
    Hagedorn, D.J. and J.C. Walker, 1954
  V. datura rugose leaf curl
    Grylls, N.E., 1955
  V. (legume) little leaf disease *
    Hutton, E.M. and N.E. Grylls, 1956
  V. lucerne dwarf
    Freitag, J.H., 1951
  V. lucerne mosaic
    Black, L.M. and W.C. Price, 1940
    Houston, Byron R. and John W. Oswald, 1953
    Johnson, E.M., 1946
    Kreitlow, K.W., O.J. Hunt and H.L. Wilkins, 1957
    Kreitlow, K.W. and W.C. Price, 1949
    Pierce, W.H., 1934
    Roberts, D.A., 1956
    Snyder, William C. and Saul Rich, 1942
    Zaumeyer, W.J., 1938, 1953
  V. lucerne witches' broom
    Klostermeyer, E.C. and J.D. Menzies, 1951
    Menzies, J.D., 1946
  V. pea enation mosaic
    McEwen, F.L. and W.T. Schroeder, 1956
  V. pea mottle
    Johnson, Folke, 1942
    Johnson, F. and L.K. Jones, 1936, 1937
    Zaumeyer, W.J. and B.L. Wade, 1935
  V. pea streak
    Zaumeyer, W.J., 1938
  V. pea wilt
    Johnson, Folke, 1942
  V. potato yellow dwarf
    Black, L.M., 1937
    Hansing, E.D., 1942
  V. prunus A *
    Fulton, Robert W., 1957
  V. prunus B *
    Fulton, Robert W., 1957

Trifolium repens, L. (cont.)
  V. red clover mosaic *
    Dickson, B.T., 1922
  V. red clover vein mosaic
    Hagedorn, D.J. and E.W. Hanson, 1951
    Hagedorn, D.J. and J.C. Walker, 1954
    Osborn, H.T., 1937
    Roberts, D.A., 1957
  V. strawberry green petal
    Frazier, N.W. and A.F. Posnette, 1957
  V. tobacco necrosis
    Fulton, Robert W., 1950
  V. tobacco ring spot
    (K.M. Smith, 1957) R.E. Fitzpatrick, et al., 1958
  V. tobacco streak
    Fulton, Robert W., 1948
  V. tobacco yellow dwarf
    Helson, G.A.H., 1950
  V. Wisconsin pea streak
    Hagedorn, D.J. and J.C. Walker, 1949, 1954
T. repens var. giganteum *
  V. lucerne mosaic
    Kreitlow, K.W. and W.C. Price, 1948
T. repens var. latum, McCarthy *
  V. lucerne dwarf
    Freitag, J.H., 1951
  V. lucerne mosaic
    Houston, Byron R. and John W. Oswald, 1951
  V. red clover vein mosaic
    Graves, Clinton H., Jr. and D.J. Hagedorn, 1956
T. repens f. giganteum, Lagr.-Foss. *
  V. bean yellow mosaic
    Thomas, H. Rex and W.J. Zaumeyer, 1953
  V. lucerne mosaic
    Thomas, H. Rex, 1951
T. resupinatum, L.
  V. lucerne mosaic
    Kreitlow, K.W. and W.C. Price, 1949
  V. pea enation mosaic
    Hagedorn, D.J., 1957
T. spp.
  V. lucerne mosaic
    Kreitlow, K.W. and W.C. Price, 1948
  V. potato yellow dwarf
    Black, L.M., 1938
  V. raspberry yellow dwarf *
    Harrison, B.D., 1958
T. striatum, L.
  V. subterranean clover mosaic
    Aitken, Y. and B.J. Grieve, 1943
T. suaveolens, Willd.
  V. pea mosaic
    Murphy, D.M. and W.H. Pierce, 1937
T. subterraneum, L.
  V. bean yellow mosaic
    Hutton, E.M. and J.W. Peak, 1954
    McWhorter, Frank P. and John R. Hardison, 1949
  V. broad bean mottle
    Bawden, F.C., R.P. Chaudhuri and B. Kassanis, 1951
  V. gladiolus *
    Snow, Gordon F., 1955
  V. kaimi clover disease *
    Murakishi, Harry H., 1952
  V. (legume) little leaf disease *
    Hutton, E.M. and N.E. Grylls, 1956
  V. lucerne mosaic
    Kreitlow, K.W. and W.C. Price, 1949
  V. lucerne witches' broom
    Klostermeyer, E.C. and J.D. Menzies, 1951
  V. pea enation mosaic
    Hagedorn, D.J., 1957
  V. pea mosaic
    Chaudhuri, R.P., 1950
  V. subterranean clover, aphid-transmitted *
    Grylls, N.E. and F.C. Butler, 1956

TRIGONELLA L. 1737 (Leguminosae)
T. caerulea, Ser. in DC.
  V. clover big vein
    Black, L.M., 1951
T. foenum-graecum, L.
  V. bean yellow mosaic
    Grogan, Raymond G. and J.C. Walker, 1948

T. foenum-graecum, L. (cont.)
  V. bean yellow mosaic
    Hagedorn, D.J., 1948, 1952
    Hagedorn, D.J. and J.C. Walker, 1950, 1954
  V. cucumber mosaic
    Hagedorn, D.J., 1952
  V. pea enation mosaic
    Hagedorn, D.J., 1952
  V. pea mosaic
    Hagedorn, D.J., 1948
  V. red clover vein mosaic
    Hagedorn, D.J., 1952
    Hagedorn, D.J. and J.C. Walker, 1949, 1954
  V. subterranean clover mosaic
    Aitken, Y. and B.J. Grieve, 1943
  V. tobacco ring spot
    Grogan, R.G. and W.C. Schnathorst, 1955
  V. Wisconsin pea streak
    Hagedorn, D.J., 1952
    Hagedorn, D.J. and J.C. Walker, 1949, 1954
T. ornithopodioides, DC.
  V. subterranean clover mosaic
    Aitken, Y. and B.J. Grieve, 1943
T. spp.
  V. tobacco streak
    Fulton, Robert W., 1948

TRIPSACUM L. 1759 (Gramineae)
T. laxum, Nash
  V. sugarcane mosaic
    (K.M. Smith, 1957) R.E. Fitzpatrick, et al., 1958

TRITICUM L. 1735 (Gramineae)
T. aegilopoides, (Link) Bal. *
  V. wheat streak mosaic
    McKinney, H.H. and W.J. Sando, 1951
T. aestivum, L.
  V. barley stripe mosaic
    Fitzgerald, Paul J., Harland Stevens and R.G. Timian, 1957
    Lal, S.B. and W.H. Sill, Jr., 1957
    McKinney, H.H., 1951, 1953, 1956
    McNeal, F.H. and M.M. Afanasiev, 1955, 1956
    Sill, W.H., Jr. and E.D. Hansing, 1955
  V. barley yellow dwarf
    Allen, Thomas C., Jr., 1957
    Allen, Thomas C., Jr. and Byron R. Houston, 1956
    Bruehl, G.W. and H. Toko, 1955, 1957
    Oswald, John W. and Byron R. Houston, 1951, 1952, 1953
    Takeshita, R.M., 1956
    Toko, H.V. and G.W. Bruehl, 1957
  V. beet ring spot *
    Harrison, B.D., 1957
  V. brome mosaic
    Lal, S.B. and W.H. Sill, Jr., 1957
    McKinney, H.H., 1944, 1953, 1956
    McKinney, H.H., H. Fellows and C.O. Johnston, 1942
  V. (cereal) California mosaic disease *
    Houston, Byron R. and John W. Oswald, 1952
  V. (cereal) enanismo disease *
    Gibler, John W., 1957
  V. corn new mosaic *
    Finley, A.M., 1954
  V. cucumber mosaic
    Wellman, F.L., 1934, 1935
  V. maize streak
    (K.M. Smith, 1957) R.E. Fitzpatrick, et al., 1958
  V. oat pseudo-rosette
    (K.M. Smith, 1957) R.E. Fitzpatrick, et al., 1958
  V. rice dwarf
    (K.M. Smith, 1957) R.E. Fitzpatrick, et al., 1958
  V. ryegrass mosaic *
    Bruehl, G.W., H. Toko and H.H. McKinney, 1957
  V. soil-borne oat mosaic
    McKinney, H.H., 1946
  V. soil-borne wheat mosaic
    Bever, Wayne M. and J.W. Pendleton, 1954
    Koehler, Benjamin, W.M. Bever and O.T. Bonnett, 1952
    McKinney, H.H., 1925, 1947, 1948

Triticum aestivum, L. (cont.)
    V. soil-borne wheat mosaic
        Moseman, J.G., H.H. McKinney and C.W. Roane, 1954
        Roane, C.W., T.M. Starling and H.H. McKinney, 1954
        Wadsworth, D.F. and H.C. Young, Jr., 1953
    V. tobacco necrosis
        Price, W.C., 1940
    V. wheat spot mosaic *
        Slykhuis, John T., 1956
    V. wheat streak mosaic
        Andrews, J.E. and J.T. Slykhuis, 1956
        Atkinson, R.E., 1949
        Bellingham, Roscoe C., Hurley Fellows and Webster H. Sill, Jr., 1957
        Fellows, Hurley and John W. Schmidt, 1953
        Fellows, H., W.H. Sill, Jr. and H.H. McKinney, 1952
        Finley, A.M., 1957
        Lal, S.B. and W.H. Sill, Jr., 1957
        Lal, S.B., W.H. Sill, Jr., Maria S. Del Rosario and J.M. Kainski, 1957
        McKinney, H.H., 1949, 1956
        McKinney, H.H. and W.J. Sando, 1951
        Meiners, Jack P. and H.H. McKinney, 1954
        Sill, W.H., Jr., 1952, 1953
        Sill, W.H., Jr. and H. Fellows, 1953
        Slykhuis, J.T., 1953, 1954, 1955
    V. wheat striate mosaic
        Slykhuis, John T. and Marion A. Watson, 1958
    V. winter wheat mosaic
        Webb, Robert W., 1927, 1928
T. compactum, Host
    V. soil-borne wheat mosaic
        McKinney, H.H., 1930
T. dicoccoides, Koern.
    V. wheat streak mosaic
        McKinney, H.H. and W.J. Sando, 1951
T. dicoccoides var. strausianum, Schulz *
    V. wheat streak mosaic
        McKinney, H.H. and W.J. Sando, 1951
T. dicoccum, Schrank
    V. soil-borne wheat mosaic
        McKinney, H.H., 1930
    V. wheat spot mosaic *
        Slykhuis, John T., 1956
    V. wheat streak mosaic
        McKinney, H.H., 1949
        McKinney, H.H. and W.J. Sando, 1951
        Slykhuis, John T., 1955,
    V. wheat striate mosaic
        Slykhuis, J.T., 1953
T. durum, Desf.
    V. agropyron mosaic
        Slykhuis, J.T., 1952
    V. barley stripe mosaic
        Slykhuis, J.T., 1952
    V. soil-borne wheat mosaic
        McKinney, H.H., 1930
    V. wheat spot mosaic *
        Slykhuis, John T., 1956
    V. wheat streak mosaic
        McKinney, H.H. and W.J. Sando, 1951
        Slykhuis, John T., 1955
    V. wheat striate mosaic
        Slykhuis, J.T., 1953
T. monococcum, L.
    V. soil-borne wheat mosaic
        McKinney, H.H., 1930
    V. wheat streak mosaic
        McKinney, H.H. and W.J. Sando, 1951
T. monococcum var. flavescens, Koern. *
    V. wheat streak mosaic
        McKinney, H.H. and W.J. Sando, 1951
T. monococcum var. laetissimum, Koern. *
    V. wheat streak mosaic
        McKinney, H.H. and W.J. Sando, 1951
T. orientale, Bieb.
    V. wheat streak mosaic
        McKinney, H.H. and W.J. Sando, 1951
T. persicum var. stramineum, Zhukov. *
    V. wheat streak mosaic
        McKinney, H.H. and W.J. Sando, 1951

T. polonicum, L.
    V. soil-borne wheat mosaic
        McKinney, H.H., 1930
    V. wheat streak mosaic
        McKinney, H.H., 1949
        McKinney, H.H. and W.J. Sando, 1951
T. spelta, L.
    V. soil-borne wheat mosaic
        McKinney, H.H., 1930, 1953
        Wadsworth, D.F. and H.C. Young, Jr., 1953
    V. wheat streak mosaic
        McKinney, H.H., 1949
        McKinney, H.H. and W.J. Sando, 1951
T. sphaerococcum, Perciv.
    V. wheat streak mosaic
        McKinney, H.H. and W.J. Sando, 1951
T. timopheevi, Zhuk.
    V. wheat spot mosaic *
        Slykhuis, John T., 1956
    V. wheat streak mosaic
        McKinney, H.H. and W.J. Sando, 1951
        Slykhuis, John T., 1955
T. turgidum, L.
    V. soil-borne wheat mosaic
        McKinney, H.H., 1930
    V. wheat streak mosaic
        McKinney, H.H., 1949
        McKinney, H.H. and W.J. Sando, 1951
T. vulgare, Vill.
    V. agropyron mosaic
        Slykhuis, J.T., 1952
    V. barley stripe mosaic
        Slykhuis, J.T., 1952
    V. soil-borne wheat mosaic
        McKinney, H.H., 1930
    V. wheat streak mosaic
        Slykhuis, J.T., 1952
    V. wheat striate mosaic
        Slykhuis, J.T., 1952, 1953

TRITONIA Ker-Gawl. 1802 (Iridaceae)
T. crocata, Ker-Gawl.
    V. babiana mosaic
        Smith, Floyd F. and Philip Brierley, 1944
    V. ixia mosaic
        Smith, Floyd F. and Philip Brierley, 1944
    V. sparaxis mosaic
        Smith, Floyd F. and Philip Brierley, 1944
    V. streptanthera mosaic
        Smith, Floyd F. and Philip Brierley, 1944
    V. tigridia mosaic
        Smith, Floyd F. and Philip Brierley, 1944
    V. watsonia mosaic *
        Smith, Floyd F. and Philip Brierley, 1944

TROPAEOLUM L. 1737 (Tropaeolaceae)
T. majus, L.
    V. aster yellows
        Severin, Henry H.P. and Julius H. Freitag, 1945
    V. beet curly top
        Severin, Henry H.P. and Julius H. Freitag, 1934
    V. cabbage black ring spot
        (K.M. Smith, 1957) R.E. Fitzpatrick, et al., 1958
    V. cucumber mosaic
        Govier, D.A., 1957
        Wellman, F.L., 1935
    V. tobacco broad ring spot
        Johnson, James and Robert W. Fulton, 1942
    V. tobacco mosaic
        Holmes, Francis O., 1946
    V. tobacco ring spot
        Anderson, C.W., 1954
        Price, W.C., 1940
    V. tobacco ring spot no. 2
        Brierley, Philip, 1954
    V. tobacco streak
        Fulton, Robert W., 1948
    V. tomato aspermy
        Hollings, M., 1955
    V. tomato black ring
        (K.M. Smith, 1957) R.E. Fitzpatrick, et al., 1958
    V. tomato spotted wilt
        Black, L.M., M.K. Brakke and A.E. Vatter, 1952
        Gardner, M.W. and O.C. Whipple, 1934

Tropaeolum majus, L. (cont.)
  V. tomato spotted wilt
    Milbrath, J.A., 1939
    Whipple, O.C., 1936
  V. tropaeolum mosaic
    Jensen, D.D., 1950
    Silberschmidt, Karl, 1953
  V. tropaeolum ring spot
    (K.M. Smith, 1957) R.E. Fitzpatrick, et al., 1958
T. peregrinum, L.
  V. beet curly top
    Freitag, Julius H. and Henry H.P. Severin, 1936
  V. tobacco ring spot
    Price, W.C., 1940

TULIPA L. 1735 (Liliaceae)
T. clusiana, DC.
  V. tulip breaking
    Cayley, Dorothy M., 1932
T. eichleri, Regel
  V. tulip breaking
    Cayley, Dorothy M., 1932
T. gesneriana, L.
  V. cucumber mosaic
    Ainsworth, G.C., 1938
    Brierley, Philip, 1941
    Brierley, Philip and S.P. Doolittle, 1940
    Brierley, Philip and Floyd F. Smith, 1944
    Porter, Clark A., 1954
    Smith, Floyd F. and Philip Brierley, 1944
  V. lily symptomless
    Brierley, Philip, 1940, 1941
  V. tobacco necrosis
    Fulton, Robert W., 1950
    Kassanis, B., 1949, 1954
  V. tulip breaking
    Brierley, Philip, 1939, 1941
    Brierley, Philip and S.P. Doolittle, 1940
    Brierley, Philip and M.B. McKay, 1938
    Brierley, Philip and Floyd F. Smith, 1944
    Cayley, D.M., 1928, 1932
    Hughes, A.W. McKenny, 1930, 1931, 1934
    McWhorter, F.P., 1935, 1938
T. gesneriana var. spathulata, Hort.
  V. tulip breaking
    Cayley, Dorothy M., 1932
T. greigii, Regel
  V. tulip breaking
    Cayley, Dorothy M., 1932
T. linifolia, Regel
  V. tulip breaking
    Cayley, Dorothy M., 1932
T. spp.
  V. tobacco mosaic
    (K.M. Smith, 1957) R.E. Fitzpatrick, et al., 1958
  V. tulip white streak
    (K.M. Smith, 1957) R.E. Fitzpatrick, et al., 1958

TUNICA Hall. 1742 (Caryophyllaceae)
T. saxifraga, Scop.
  V. carnation mosaic
    Brierley, Philip and Floyd F. Smith, 1957
  V. carnation ring spot
    Brierley, Philip and Floyd F. Smith, 1957

TUSSILAGO ((Tourn.)) L. 1735 (Compositae)
T. farfara, L.
  V. beet ring spot *
    Harrison, B.D., 1957

ULMUS ((Tourn.)) L. 1735 (Ulmaceae)
U. americana, L.
  V. carnation ring spot
    Brierley, Philip and Floyd F. Smith, 1957
  V. elm mosaic
    Bretz, T.W., 1950
    Callahan, Kemper L., 1957
    Moore, J. Duain and E.H. Varney, 1954
    Swingle, R.U., P.E. Tilford and Charles F. Irish,
      1941, 1943
    Varney, E.H. and J. Duain Moore, 1952
  V. elm phloem necrosis
    McLean, D.M., 1944
    Swingle, Roger U., 1938, 1940

U. americana, L. (cont.)
  V. elm phloem necrosis
    Swingle, Roger U., B.S. Meyer and Curtis May,
      1945
  V. elm zonate canker
    Swingle, Roger U. and T.W. Bretz, 1950
  V. tobacco ring spot
    Wilkinson, R.E., 1952
  V. tomato ring spot
    Varney, E.H. and J. Duain Moore, 1952
U. fulva, Michx. x U. pumila, L.
  V. elm phloem necrosis
    Swingle, Roger U., B.S. Meyer and Curtis May,
      1945

URENA Dill. ex L. 1735 (Malvaceae)
U. lobata, L.
  V. cotton leaf curl
    (K.M. Smith, 1957) R.E. Fitzpatrick, et al., 1958

UROCHLOA Beauv. 1812 (Gramineae)
U. panicoides, Beauv.
  V. maize streak
    (K.M. Smith, 1957) R.E. Fitzpatrick, et al., 1958

URTICA ((Tourn.)) L. 1735 (Urticaceae)
U. californica, Greene
  V. aster yellows
    Frazier, Norman W. and Henry H.P. Severin, 1945
U. dioica, L.
  V. tomato spotted wilt
    Gardner, M.W. and O.C. Whipple, 1934
U. gracilis, Ait., var. holosericea, Jepson
  V. lucerne dwarf
    Freitag, J.H., 1951
U. urens, L.
  V. beet curly top
    Carsner, E., 1919
    Severin, Henry H.P., 1934
  V. beet ring spot *
    Harrison, B.D., 1957
  V. datura rugose leaf curl
    (K.M. Smith, 1957) R.E. Fitzpatrick, et al., 1958

VACCINIUM L. 1735 (Ericaceae)
V. angustifolium, Ait.
  V. vaccinium mosaic *
    Varney, E.H., 1957
  V. vaccinium ring spot
    Hilborn, M.T. and Reiner Bonde, 1956
  V. vaccinium shoestring *
    Varney, E.H., 1957
  V. vaccinium stunt
    Demaree, J.B., 1946
V. atrococcum, Heller
  V. vaccinium stunt
    Hutchinson, M.T., A.C. Goheen and E.H. Varney,
      1955
V. australe, Small
  V. vaccinium stunt
    (K.M. Smith, 1957) R.E. Fitzpatrick, et al., 1958
V. corymbosum, L.
  V. vaccinium ring spot
    Hutchinson, M.T. and E.H. Varney, 1954
  V. vaccinium stunt
    Hutchinson, M.T., A.C. Goheen and E.H. Varney,
      1955
V. macrocarpon, Ait. (Oxycoccus macrocarpon, (Ait.)
  V. vaccinium false blossom   Pers.)
    Bergman, H.F. and W.E. Truran, 1933
    Kunkel, L.O., 1943, 1945
    Stevens, Neil E., 1944
    Wilcox, R.B., 1951
    Wilcox, R.B. and C.S. Beckwith, 1933
V. stamineum, L.
  V. vaccinium stunt
    Hutchinson, M.T., A.C. Goheen and E.H. Varney,
      1955
V. vacillans, Torr.
  V. vaccinium stunt
    Hutchinson, M.T., A.C. Goheen and E.H. Varney,
      1955

VALERIANA Tourn. ex L. 1735 (Valerianaceae)
V. officinalis, L.
   V. cucumber mosaic
      Faan, Hwei Chung and James Johnson, 1951

VALERIANELLA Tourn. ex Hall. 1742 (Valerianaceae)
V. olitoria, (L.) Poll
   V. beet curly top
      Severin, Henry H.P., 1929

VANDA Jones 1795 (Orchidaceae)
V. boschii *
   V. orchid (vanda) mosaic
      Murakishi, Harry H., 1952
V. cooperii *
   V. orchid (vanda) mosaic
      Murahishi, Harry H., 1952
V. spp.
   V. orchid (vanda) mosaic
      Murakishi, Harry H., 1952
      Murakishi, H. and M. Ishii, 1954

VENIDIUM Less. 1831 (Compositae)
V. fastuosum, Stapf
   V. chrysanthemum stunt
      Brierley, Philip, 1953
   V. clover big vein
      Black, L.M., 1945
   V. tobacco streak
      Fulton, Robert W., 1948

VERBASCUM Tourn. ex L. 1737 (Scrophulariaceae)
V. phoeniceum, L.
   V. cucumber mosaic
      Price, W.C., 1940
   V. lucerne mosaic
      Price, W.C., 1940
   V. tobacco mosaic
      Holmes, Francis O., 1946
   V. tobacco necrosis
      Price, W.C., 1940
   V. tobacco ring spot
      Price, W.C., 1940
   V. tobacco ring spot no. 2
      Price, W.C., 1940
V. thapsus, L.
   V. prunus B *
      Fulton, Robert W., 1957
   V. prunus G *
      Fulton, Robert W., 1957
   V. tobacco mosaic
      Grant, T.J., 1934
   V. tobacco streak
      Fulton, Robert W., 1948

VERBENA L. 1737 (Verbenaceae)
V. canadensis, (L.) Britton
   V. tobacco mosaic
      Holmes, Francis O., 1946
V. hybrida, Voss
   V. anemone mosaic *
      Hollings, M., 1957
   V. beet mosaic
      Pound, Glenn S., 1947
   V. cabbage black ring spot
      Hamlyn, Brenda M.G., 1953
      Hollings, M., 1957
      Tompkins, C.M., M.W. Gardner and H. Rex
      Thomas, 1938
   V. clover big vein
      Black, L.M., 1945
   V. tobacco etch
      Holmes, Francis O., 1946
   V. tobacco mosaic
      Holmes, Francis O., 1946
   V. tomato spotted wilt
      Gardner, M.W., C.M. Tompkins and O.C.
      Whipple, 1935
   V. turnip mosaic
      Tompkins, C.M., 1938
      Walker, J.C., Francis J. LeBeau and Glenn S.
      Pound, 1945

V. urticifolia, L.
   V. tobacco mosaic
      Holmes, Francis O., 1938
V. venosa, Gill. & Hook.
   V. tobacco ring spot
      Price, W.C., 1940
   V. tobacco ring spot no. 2
      Price, W.C., 1940

VERBESINA L. 1735 (Compositae)
V. alternifolia, Britton ex Kearney
   V. tobacco ring spot
      Fenne, S.B., 1931
      Henderson, R.G. and S.A. Wingard, 1931
V. encelioides, (Cav.) Benth. & Hook.
   V. chrysanthemum stunt
      Brierley, Philip, 1953
   V. cucumber mosaic
      Brierley, Philip, 1951
   V. dahlia mosaic
      Brierley, Philip, 1951
      Brierley, Philip and Floyd F. Smith, 1950
   V. tobacco ring spot no. 2
      Brierley, Philip, 1954
   V. tomato aspermy
      Brierley, Philip, Floyd F. Smith and S.P.
      Doolittle, 1955

VERNONIA Schreb. 1791 (Compositae)
V. cinerea, Less.
   V. tobacco leaf curl
      Pruthi, Hem Singh and C.K. Samuel, 1941

VERONICA ((Tourn.)) L. 1735 (Scrophulariaceae)
V. agrestis, L.
   V. potato X
      (K.M. Smith, 1957) R.E. Fitzpatrick, et al., 1958
V. americana, (Raf.) Schwein.
   V. aster yellows
      Frazier, Norman W. and Henry H.P. Severin, 1945
V. buxbaumii, Ten.
   V. aster yellows
      Frazier, Norman W. and Henry H.P. Severin, 1945
V. longifolia, L.
   V. cucumber mosaic
      Price, W.C., 1940
   V. lucerne mosaic
      Price, W.C., 1940
   V. tobacco mosaic
      Holmes, Francis O., 1946
   V. tobacco necrosis
      Price, W.C., 1940
   V. tobacco ring spot
      Price, W.C., 1940
   V. tobacco ring spot no. 2
      Price, W.C., 1940
V. officinalis, L.
   V. tobacco mosaic
      Holmes, Francis O., 1938, 1946
V. peregrina, L.
   V. aster yellows
      (K.M. Smith, 1957) R.E. Fitzpatrick, et al., 1958
   V. tobacco mosaic
      Holmes, Francis O., 1938, 1946
   V. vaccinium false blossom
      Kunkel, L.O., 1945
V. persica, Poir.
   V. beet ring spot *
      Harrison, B.D., 1957
   V. raspberry Scottish leaf curl
      Harrison, B.D., 1958
V. spp.
   V. lucerne dwarf
      Freitag, J.H., 1951

VICIA Tourn. ex L. 1735 (Leguminosae)
V. americana, Muhl.
   V. bean yellow mosaic
      Zaumeyer, W.J. and B.L. Wade, 1935
   V. lucerne mosaic
      Zaumeyer, W.J. and B.L. Wade, 1935
   V. red clover mosaic *
      Zaumeyer, W.J. and B.L. Wade, 1935

Vicia atropurpurea, Desf.
  V. bean yellow mosaic
    Grogan, Raymond G. and J.C. Walker, 1948
    Hagedorn, D.J. and J.C. Walker, 1950, 1954
  V. beet curly top
    Severin, Henry H.P. and Charles F. Henderson,
    1928
  V. red clover vein mosaic
    Hagedorn, D.J. and J.C. Walker, 1949, 1954
  V. Wisconsin pea streak
    Hagedorn, D.J. and J.C. Walker, 1949, 1954
V. dasycarpa, Ten.
  V. pea enation mosaic
    Hagedorn, D.J., 1957
V. faba, L.
  V. alsike clover mosaic
    Wade, B.L. and W.J. Zaumeyer, 1938
    Zaumeyer, W.J., 1940
    Zaumeyer, W.J. and B.L. Wade, 1936
  V. anemone mosaic *
    Hollings, M., 1957
  V. apple mosaic
    Yarwood, C.E., 1955
    Yarwood, C.E. and H.E. Thomas, 1954
  V. bean common mosaic
    Nelson, Ray, 1932
    Reddick, D. and V.B. Stewart, 1919
  V. bean yellow mosaic
    Afanasiev, M.M. and H.E. Morris, 1952
    Ainsworth, G.C., 1940
    Baggett, James R., 1957
    Brierley, Philip and Floyd F. Smith, 1948
    Conover, Robert A., 1948
    Elliott, J.A., 1921
    Grogan, Raymond G. and J.C. Walker, 1948
    Houston, Byron R. and John W. Oswald, 1953
    McWhorter, Frank P., 1949
    McWhorter, Frank P. and John R. Hardison, 1949
    Osborn, H.T., 1938
    Thomas, H. Rex and W.J. Zaumeyer, 1953
    Zaumeyer, W.J., 1940, 1952
    Zaumeyer, W.J. and H.H. Fisher, 1953
    Zaumeyer, W.J. and B.L. Wade, 1935, 1936
  V. beet curly top
    Severin, Henry H.P. and Charles F. Henderson,
    1928
  V. broad bean mottle
    Bawden, F.C., R.P. Chaudhuri and B. Kassanis,
    1951
    Yu, T.F., 1939
  V. cabbage black ring spot
    Hollings, M., 1957
  V. chrysanthemum B (mild mosaic) *
    Hollings, M., 1957
  V. cowpea mosaic
    Anderson, C.W., 1955
  V. crotalaria mosaic
    Johnson, H.W. and C.L. Lefebvre, 1938
  V. cucumber mosaic
    Anderson, C.W., 1955
    Costa, A.S., 1944
    Doolittle, S.P. and W.J. Zaumeyer, 1953
    Hagedorn, D.J., 1950
    Harter, L.L., 1938
    Milbrath, J.A. and Roy A. Young, 1956
    Porter, Clark A., 1954
    Wellman, F.L., 1934, 1935
    Whipple, O.C. and J.C. Walker, 1941
  V. gladiolus *
    Snow, Gordon F., 1955
  V. lucerne mosaic
    Berkeley, G.H., 1947
    Black, L.M. and W.C. Price, 1940
    Houston, Byron R. and John W. Oswald, 1953
    Richardson, D.E. and T.W. Tinsley, 1956
    Snyder, William C. and Saul Rich, 1942
    Swenson, K.G., 1952
    Thomas, H. Rex, 1951
    Zaumeyer, W.J., 1938, 1953
    Zaumeyer, W.J. and B.L. Wade, 1935
  V. pea die back *
    Zaumeyer, W.J., 1939
  V. pea enation mosaic
    Ainsworth, G.C., 1940

V. faba, L. (cont.)
  V. pea enation mosaic
    McEwen, F.L. and W.T. Schroeder, 1956
    Osborn, H.T., 1934, 1935, 1938
    Stubbs, M.W., 1936
  V. pea leaf roll
    (K.M. Smith, 1957) R.E. Fitzpatrick, et al., 1958
  V. pea mosaic
    Ainsworth, G.C., 1940
    Chaudhuri, R.P., 1950
    Hagedorn, D.J., 1948
    Johnson, F. and L.K. Jones, 1936
    Osborn, H.T., 1937
    Stubbs, M.W., 1936
  V. pea mottle
    Johnson, Folke, 1942
    Johnson, F. and L.K. Jones, 1936, 1937
  V. pea stem streak *
    Zaumeyer, W.J., 1939
  V. pea streak
    Zaumeyer, W.J., 1938
  V. pea wilt
    Johnson, Folke, 1942
  V. pea yellow mosaic *
    Ainsworth, G.C., 1940
  V. potato yellow dwarf
    Black, L.M., 1938
    Hougas, R.W., 1951
  V. red clover mosaic *
    Elliott, J.A., 1921
    Zaumeyer, W.J. and B.L. Wade, 1935, 1936
  V. red clover vein mosaic
    Hagedorn, D.J. and E.W. Hanson, 1951
    Osborn, H.T., 1937
    Roberts, D.A., 1957
  V. rhubarb ring spot *
    Vaughan, Edward K. and John W. Yale, Jr., 1953
    Yale, John W., Jr. and Edward K. Vaughan, 1954
  V. tobacco ring spot
    Cheo, Pen Ching and W.J. Zaumeyer, 1952
    (K.M. Smith, 1957) R.E. Fitzpatrick, et al., 1958
    Pound, Glenn S., 1949
  V. tobacco streak
    Fulton, Robert W., 1948
    Thomas, H. Rex and W.J. Zaumeyer, 1950
  V. tomato spotted wilt
    Gardner, M.W. and O.C. Whipple, 1934
    Sakimura, K., 1940
    Yu, T.F., 1947
  V. tropaeolum ring spot
    (K.M. Smith, 1957) R.E. Fitzpatrick, et al., 1958
V. faba var. major *
  V. bean yellow mosaic
    Hagedorn, D.J. and J.C. Walker, 1950, 1954
  V. pea mosaic
    Murphy, D.M. and W.H. Pierce, 1937
  V. subterranean clover mosaic
    Aitken, Y. and B.J. Grieve, 1943
  V. Wisconsin pea streak
    Hagedorn, D.J. and J.C. Walker, 1954
V. faba var. minor *
  V. bean common mosaic
    Pierce, W.H., 1934
  V. bean yellow mosaic
    Hagedorn, D.J. and J.C. Walker, 1950, 1954
    Pierce, W.H., 1934, 1935
  V. cucumber mosaic
    Hagedorn, D.J. and J.C. Walker, 1954
  V. lucerne mosaic
    Pierce, W.H., 1934
    Zaumeyer, W.J., 1938
  V. pea enation mosaic
    Hagedorn, D.J. and J.C. Walker, 1954
    Pierce, W.H., 1935
    Stubbs, M.W., 1937
  V. pea mosaic
    Hagedorn, D.J. and J.C. Walker, 1954
    Murphy, D.M. and W.H. Pierce, 1937
    Pierce, W.H., 1935
    Stubbs, M.W., 1937
  V. pea streak
    Zaumeyer, W.J., 1938
  V. pea wilt
    Pierce, W.H., 1935

Vicia faba var. minor * (cont.)
V. red clover vein mosaic
Hagedorn, D.J. and J.C. Walker, 1954
V. subterranean clover mosaic
Aitkey, Y. and B.J. Grieve, 1943
V. tobacco ring spot
Pierce, W.H., 1934
Stubbs, M.W., 1937
V. Wisconsin pea streak
Hagedorn, D.J. and J.C. Walker, 1954
Skotland, C.B. and D.J. Hagedorn, 1954
V. grandiflora, Scop.
V. bean yellow mosaic
Hagedorn, D.J. and J.C. Walker, 1950, 1954
V. red clover vein mosaic
Hagedorn, D.J. and J.C. Walker, 1949, 1954
V. Wisconsin pea streak
Hagedorn, D.J. and J.C. Walker, 1949, 1954
V. lathyroides, L.
V. bean common mosaic
(K.M. Smith, 1957) R.E. Fitzpatrick, et al., 1958
V. bean yellow mosaic
(K.M. Smith, 1957) R.E. Fitzpatrick, et al., 1958
V. monantha, Retz.
V. bean yellow mosaic
Grogan, Raymond G. and J.C. Walker, 1948
Hagedorn, D.J. and J.C. Walker, 1950, 1954
V. lucerne dwarf
Freitag, J.H., 1951
V. red clover vein mosaic
Hagedorn, D.J. and J.C. Walker, 1949, 1954
V. Wisconsin pea streak
Hagedorn, D.J. and J.C. Walker, 1949, 1954
V. pannonica, Crantz
V. pea enation mosaic
Hagedorn, D.J., 1957
V. sativa, L.
V. bean common mosaic
Pierce, W.H., 1934
V. bean yellow mosaic
Grogan, Raymond G. and J.C. Walker, 1948
Hagedorn, D.J. and J.C. Walker, 1950, 1954
Pierce, W.H., 1934
V. beet curly top
Severin, Henry H.P. and Charles F. Henderson, 1928
V. broad bean mottle
Yu, T.F., 1939
V. lucerne mosaic
Pierce, W.H., 1934
Zaumeyer, W.J., 1938
V. pea enation mosaic
McEwen, F.L. and W.T. Schroeder, 1956
V. pea mosaic
Chaudhuri, R.P., 1950
Murphy, D.M. and W.H. Pierce, 1937
V. pea mottle
Johnson, Folke, 1942
Johnson, F. and L.K. Jones, 1936, 1937
V. pea streak
Zaumeyer, W.J., 1938
V. pea wilt
Johnson, Folke, 1942
V. red clover vein mosaic
Hagedorn, D.J. and J.C. Walker, 1949, 1954
V. tobacco ring spot
Cheo, Pen Ching and W.J. Zaumeyer, 1952
LeBeau, F.J., 1947
Pierce, W.H., 1934
V. tobacco streak
Thomas, H. Rex and W.J. Zaumeyer, 1950
V. tetrasperma, Moench
V. broad bean mottle
Yu, T.F., 1939
V. villosa, Roth
V. bean yellow mosaic
Grogan, Raymond G. and J.C. Walker, 1948
Hagedorn, D.J. and J.C. Walker, 1950, 1954
Hungerford, C.W. and Irvin G. Hillyer, 1954
V. beet curly top
Severin, Henry H.P. and Charles F. Henderson, 1928
V. broad bean mottle
Yu, T.F., 1939

V. villosa, Roth
V. lucerne mosaic
Zaumeyer, W.J., 1938
V. pea enation mosaic
McEwen, F.L. and W.T. Schroeder, 1956
V. Wisconsin pea streak
Hagedorn, D.J. and J.C. Walker, 1949, 1954

VIGNA Savi 1826? (Leguminosae)
V. cylindrica, (L.) Skeels (V. catjang, Walp.)
V. cowpea mosaic
Capoor, S.P. and P.M. Varma, 1956
Vasudeva, R. Sahai, 1942
V. tobacco ring spot
Cooper, W.E., 1949
V. chinensis, Endl. *
V. potato Y
Darby, J.F., R.H. Larson and J.C. Walker, 1951
V. reticulata, Hook. f.
V. groundnut rosette
Evans, A.C., 1954
V. sesquipedalis, (L.) Fruwirth
V. bean common mosaic
Nelson, Ray, 1932
Snyder, W.C., 1942
V. bean yellow mosaic
Thomas, H. Rex and W.J. Zaumeyer, 1953
Zaumeyer, W.J. and H.H. Fisher, 1953
V. cowpea mosaic
Capoor, S.P. and P.M. Varma, 1956
V. cucumber mosaic
Doolittle, S.P. and W.J. Zaumeyer, 1953
V. lucerne mosaic
Pierce, W.H., 1934
Snyder, William C. and Saul Rich, 1942
Zaumeyer, W.J., 1938
V. tobacco ring spot
Cooper, W.E., 1949
Pierce, W.H., 1934
V. tobacco streak
Thomas, H. Rex and W.J. Zaumeyer, 1950
V. sinensis, (Torner) Savi
V. apple mosaic
Yarwood, C.E., 1955
Yarwood, C.E. and H.E. Thomas, 1954
V. bean common mosaic
Snyder, W.C., 1942
V. bean yellow mosaic
Osborn, H.T., 1938
Zaumeyer, W.J. and H.H. Fisher, 1953
V. bean yellow stipple
Zaumeyer, W.J. and H. Rex Thomas, 1950
V. beet curly top
Severin, Henry H.P. and Charles F. Henderson, 1928
V. celery mosaic
Price, W.C., 1935
V. cowpea mosaic
Anderson, C.W., 1955, 1957
Capoor, S.P. and P.M. Varma, 1956
Dale, W.T., 1953
McLean, D.M., 1941
Yu, T.F., 1946
V. cucumber mosaic
Anderson, C.W., 1955, 1957
Anderson, C.W. and M.K. Corbett, 1957
Bhargava, K.S., 1951
Bridgmon, G.H. and J.C. Walker, 1952
Costa, A.S., 1944
Diachun, Stephen, 1952
Doolittle, S.P. and W.J. Zaumeyer, 1952, 1953
Fulton, Joseph P., 1950
Hagedorn, D.J., 1950
Hagedorn, D.J. and J.C. Walker, 1954
Harter, L.L., 1938
Hollings, M., 1955
Lindberg, G.D., D.H. Hall and J.C. Walker, 1956
Milbrath, J.A. and Roy A. Young, 1956
Nienow, Inez, 1948
Price, W.C., 1934, 1935
Silberschmidt, K., 1955
Sill, Webster H., Jr., 1951
Sill, W.H., Jr. and J.C. Walker, 1952
Sinclair, J.B. and J.C. Walker, 1954, 1955, 1956

Vigna sinensis, (Torner) Savi (cont.)
V. cucumber mosaic
Smith, Kenneth M., 1935
Whipple, O.C. and J.C. Walker, 1941
V. elm mosaic
Varney, E.H. and J. Duain Moore, 1952
V. kaimi clover disease *
Murakishi, Harry H., 1952
V. lucerne mosaic
Black, L.M. and W.C. Price, 1940
Kreitlow, K.W. and W.C. Price, 1949
Milbrath, J.A. and F.P. McWhorter, 1954
Oswald, John W., 1950
Snyder, William C. and Saul Rich, 1942
Thomas, H. Rex, 1951, 1953
Zaumeyer, W.J., 1938, 1953
V. pea streak
Kim, Woon S. and D.J. Hagedorn, 1957
V. pea wilt
Johnson, Folke, 1942
V. peach ring spot
Milbrath, J.A., 1953
Thornberry, H.H., 1957
V. peach yellow bud mosaic
Karle, Harry P., 1957
Yarwood, C.E., 1956, 1957
Yarwood, C.E. and H.E. Thomas, 1954
V. potato M *
Bagnall, R.H. and R.H. Larson, 1957
Bagnall, R.H., R.H. Larson and J.C. Walker, 1956
V. potato paracrinkle
Bagnall, R.H., R.H. Larson and J.C. Walker, 1956
V. potato Y
Dykstra, T.P., 1939
Ross, A. Frank, 1948
V. rose mosaic
Fulton, Robert W., 1952
V. tobacco broad ring spot
Johnson, James and Robert W. Fulton, 1942
V. tobacco green ring spot *
Price, W.C., 1936
V. tobacco mosaic
Nagaich, B.B. and H.H. Thornberry, 1957
V. tobacco necrosis
Fulton, J.P., 1952
Fulton, Robert W., 1950, 1952
Price, W.C., 1938
Price, W.C. and Ralph W.G. Wyckoff, 1939
V. tobacco ring spot
Anderson, C.W., 1954
Benedict, W.G., 1955
Berkeley, G.H., 1953
Bridgmon, G.H. and J.C. Walker, 1952
Cheo, Pen Ching and W.J. Zaumeyer, 1952
Cooper, W.E., 1949
Desjardins, P.R., R.L. Latterell and J.E. Mitchell, 1954
Dunleavy, John M., 1957
Grogan, R.G., Roy Bardin and W.C. Schnathorst, 1954
Grogan, R.G. and W.C. Schnathorst, 1955
Kahn, Robert P., 1956
Kahn, Robert P. and Frances M. Latterell, 1955
LeBeau, F.J., 1947
Pierce, W.H., 1934
Pound, Glenn S., 1949
Price, W.C., 1936
Rosberg, David W., 1953
Shepherd, Robert J. and F. Ben Struble, 1956
Starr, Chester K. and W.E. Cooper, 1944
Steere, Russell L., 1956
Walters, H.J., 1952
Wingard, S.A., 1928
V. tobacco ring spot no. 2
Hildebrand, E.M., 1942
Price, W.C., 1936
V. tobacco streak
Thomas, H. Rex and W.J. Zaumeyer, 1950
V. tomato aspermy
Hollings, M., 1955
V. tomato bushy stunt
(K.M. Smith, 1957) R.E. Fitzpatrick, et al., 1958

V. sinensis, (Torner) Savi (cont.)
V. tomato bushy stunt
Smith, Kenneth M., 1935
V. tomato ring spot
Kahn, Robert P., 1956
Kahn, Robert P. and Frances M. Latterell, 1955
Varney, E.H. and J. Duain Moore, 1952
V. tomato spotted wilt
Yu, T.F., 1947
V. tomato V-52-1
Miller, Patrick M., 1953
V. vigna 1 *
Warid, W.A. and A.G. Plakidas, 1950, 1952
V. vigna 2 *
Warid, W.A. and A.G. Plakidas, 1950, 1952
V. vigna 3 *
Warid, W.A. and A.G. Plakidas, 1950, 1952
V. vigna 3a *
Warid, W.A. and A.G. Plakidas, 1950, 1952
V. triloba, Walp.
V. groundnut rosette
Evans, A.C., 1954
V. unguiculata, Walp.
V. cowpea mosaic
Dale, W.T., 1949
V. cucumber mosaic
Adsuar, Jose and A. Cruz Miret, 1950
V. eggplant mosaic
Dale, W.T., 1954
V. groundnut rosette
Evans, A.C., 1954
V. vexillata, A. Rich.
V. cowpea mosaic
Dale, W.T., 1949

VINCA L. 1735 (Apocynaceae)
V. major, L.
V. lucerne dwarf
Freitag, J.H., 1951
V. minor, L.
V. bayberry yellows
Raychaudhuri, S.P., 1952
V. peach western X disease
Weathers, Lewis G. and George W. Cochran, 1950
V. peach X disease
Kunkel, L.O., 1944
Slack, Derald A., 1952
V. sweet potato mosaic
Elmer, O.H., 1957
V. turnip mosaic
Walker, J.C., Francis J. LeBeau and Glenn S. Pound, 1945
V. rosea, L.
V. asclepias yellows *
Kunkel, L.O., 1950
V. aster yellows
Brierley, Philip and Floyd F. Smith, 1957
Fulton, J.P., 1957
Maramorosch, Karl, 1957
V. bayberry yellows
Raychaudhuri, S.P., 1953
V. beet curly top
Freitag, Julius H. and Henry H.P. Severin, 1936
V. cabbage black ring spot
(K.M. Smith, 1957) R.E. Fitzpatrick, et al., 1958
V. clover big vein
Black, L.M., 1945
V. cucumber mosaic
Anderson, C.W. and M.K. Corbett, 1957
Fulton, Robert W., 1953
Wellman, F.L., 1935
V. lilac witches' broom
Brierley, Philip, 1955
V. lucerne mosaic
Kreitlow, K.W. and W.C. Price, 1948, 1949
Price, W.C., 1940
V. lucerne witches' broom
Kunkel, L.O., 1952
V. peach X disease
(K.M. Smith, 1957) R.E. Fitzpatrick, et al., 1958
V. prunus A *
Fulton, Robert W., 1957
V. prunus B *
Fulton, Robert W., 1957

Vinca rosea, L. (cont.)
  V. prunus G *
    Fulton, Robert W., 1957
  V. rose mosaic
    Fulton, Robert W., 1952
  V. sandal spike
    (K.M. Smith, 1957) R.E. Fitzpatrick, et al., 1958
  V. tobacco necrosis
    Price, W.C., 1940
    Price, W.C., Frank P. McWhorter and Betty H.
    Steranka, 1950
  V. tobacco ring spot
    Price, W.C., 1940
  V. tobacco ring spot no. 2
    Hildebrand, E.M., 1942
    Price, W.C., 1940
  V. tobacco streak
    Fulton, Robert W., 1948
  V. tomato big bud
    Hill, A.V. and M. Mandryk, 1954
  V. vaccinium false blossom
    Kunkel, L.O., 1945
  V. vaccinium stunt
    Hutchinson, M.T., A.C. Goheen and E.H. Varney,
    1955
  V. vinca yellows *
    Maramorosch, Karl, 1956
V. rosea var. alba, Sweet
  V. lucerne witches' broom
    Helms, Katie, 1957
  V. tomato big bud
    Helms, Katie, 1957
V. rosea var. oculata *
  V. lucerne witches' broom
    Helms, Katie, 1957
  V. tomato big bud
    Helms, Katie, 1957

VIOLA Tourn. ex L. 1735 (Violaceae)
V. cornuta, L.
  V. beet curly top
    Freitag, Julius H. and Henry H.P. Severin, 1936
    Severin, Henry H.P. and Julius H. Freitag, 1934
  V. cucumber mosaic
    Severin, Henry H.P., 1947
  V. cucumber western mosaic *
    Severin, Henry H.P., 1947
  V. lucerne mosaic
    Severin, Henry H.P., 1947
  V. tobacco necrosis
    Price, W.C., 1940
    Price, W.C., Frank P. McWhorter and Betty H.
    Steranka, 1950
  V. tobacco ring spot
    Price, W.C., 1940
  V. tobacco ring spot no. 2
    Price, W.C., 1940
V. spp.
  V. tomato black ring
    (K.M. Smith, 1957) R.E. Fitzpatrick, et al., 1958
V. papilionacea, Pursh
  V. tobacco ring spot
    Wingard, S.A., 1928
V. tricolor, L.
  V. aster yellows
    Brierley, Philip and Floyd F. Smith, 1954
  V. beet curly top
    Dana, B.F. and F.P. McWhorter, 1935
  V. tobacco ring spot
    (K.M. Smith, 1957) R.E. Fitzpatrick, et al., 1958
    McKinney, H.H. and E.E. Clayton, 1944
    Wingard, S.A., 1928
V. tricolor var. hortensis, (Murr.) DC.
  V. beet curly top
    Severin, Henry H.P. and Julius H. Freitag, 1934
  V. beet mosaic
    Pound, Glenn S., 1947
  V. cucumber mosaic
    Severin, Henry H.P., 1947
  V. cucumber western mosaic *
    Severin, Henry H.P., 1947
  V. lucerne mosaic
    Severin, Henry H.P., 1947

VITIS ((Tourn.)) L. 1735 (Vitaceae)
V. californica, Benth.
  V. lucerne dwarf
    Freitag, J.H., 1951
    Severin, Henry H.P., 1949
V. rupestris, Scheele
  V. vine infectious degeneration
    Hewitt, Wm. B., 1956
V. vinifera, L.
  V. lucerne dwarf
    Crall, J.M. and L.H. Stover, 1957
    Frazier, Norman W. and J.H. Freitag, 1946
    Freitag, J.H., 1951
    Freitag, J.H. and Norman W. Frazier, 1954
    Freitag, J.H., N.W. Frazier and R.A. Flock,
    1952
    Hewitt, Wm. B., 1939
    Hewitt, Wm. B., N.W. Frazier and Byron R.
    Houston, 1942
    Hewitt, Wm. B., Byron R. Houston, Norman W.
    Frazier and J.H. Freitag, 1946
    Houston, Byron R., Katherine Esau and Wm. B.
    Hewitt, 1946
    Severin, Henry H.P., 1949
    Stoner, Warren N., 1953
  V. vine infectious degeneration
    (K.M. Smith, 1957) R.E. Fitzpatrick, et al., 1958
    Hewitt, Wm. B., 1945, 1956
  V. vine leaf roll
    Harmon, F.N. and J.H. Weinberger, 1956
  V. vine yellow mosaic
    Hewitt, Wm. B. and Charles J. Delp, 1953
  V. (vine) yellow vein *
    Hewitt, Wm. B., 1956

WATSONIA Mill. 1759 (Iridaceae)
W. marginata, Ker-Gawl.
  V. watsonia mosaic *
    Smith, Floyd F. and Philip Brierley, 1944

WISTARIA Nutt. 1818 (Leguminosae)
(WISTERIA) Nutt. 1818
W. floribunda, (hort. var. Koshigaya) (Willd.) DC.
  V. wisteria mosaic *
    Brierley, Philip and Paul Lorentz, 1957
W. sinensis, (Sims) Sweet
  V. wisteria mosaic *
    Brierley, Philip and Paul Lorentz, 1957
W. spp.
  V. wisteria mosaic *
    Brierley, Philip and Paul Lorentz, 1957

WITHANIA Pauq. 1824 (Solanaceae)
W. somnifera, Dun.
  V. vaccinium false blossom
    (K.M. Smith, 1957) R.E. Fitzpatrick, et al., 1958

XANTHIUM ((Tourn.)) L. 1735 (Compositae)
X. canadense, Mill.
  V. lucerne dwarf
    Freitag, J.H., 1951
X. spinosum, L.
  V. beet curly top
    Severin, Henry H.P., 1934

ZALUZIANSKYA F.W. Schmidt 1793 (Scrophulariaceae)
Z. villosa, F.W. Schmidt
  V. cucumber mosaic
    Price, W.C., 1940
  V. lucerne mosaic
    Price, W.C., 1940
  V. tobacco etch
    Holmes, Francis O., 1946
  V. tobacco mosaic
    Holmes, Francis O., 1946
  V. tobacco necrosis
    Price, W.C., 1940
  V. tobacco ring spot
    Price, W.C., 1940
  V. tobacco ring spot no. 2
    Price, W.C., 1940

ZANTEDESCHIA Spreng. 1826 (Araceae)
Z. aethiopica, Spreng.
    V. tomato spotted wilt
        Gardner, M.W., C.M. Tompkins and O.C.
            Whipple, 1935
        Tompkins, C.M. and Henry H.P. Severin, 1950
        Whipple, O.C., 1936
Z. albo-maculata, Baill.
    V. tomato spotted wilt
        Tompkins, C.M. and Henry H.P. Severin, 1950
Z. elliottiana, Engler
    V. tomato spotted wilt
        Tompkins, C.M. and Henry H.P. Severin, 1950
Z. melanoleuca, Engler
    V. tomato spotted wilt
        Tompkins, C.M. and Henry H.P. Severin, 1950
Z. rehmannii, Engler
    V. tomato spotted wilt
        Tompkins, C.M. and Henry H.P. Severin, 1950

ZEA L. 1737 (Gramineae)
Z. mays, L.
    V. barley stripe mosaic
        McKinney, H.H., 1951
        Sill, W.H., Jr., 1956
        Sill, W.H., Jr. and E.D. Hansing, 1955
        Slykhuis, J.T., 1952
    V. barley yellow dwarf
        Allen, Thomas C., Jr., 1957
    V. brome mosaic
        McKinney, H.H., 1944
        Sill, W.H., Jr., 1956
    V. canna mosaic
        Castillo, B.S., C.E. Yarwood and A.H. Gold,
            1956
    V. celery mosaic
        Price, W.C., 1935
    V. cucumber mosaic
        Bhargava, K.S., 1951
        Bridgmon, G.H., 1951
        Bridgmon, G.H. and J.C. Walker, 1952
        Celino, M.S. and Aureo L. Martinez, 1955, 1956
        Celino, M.S. and G.O. Ocfemia, 1941
        Doolittle, S.P. and W.J. Zaumeyer, 1953
        Lawas, Orencio M. and William L. Fernandez,
            1949
        McWhorter, F.P. and H.H. Millsap, 1954
        Price, W.C., 1935
        Wellman, F.L., 1934, 1935
    V. filaree red leaf
        Anderson, Chris W., 1952
    V. grass natal mosaic *
        Storey, H.H., 1929
    V. maize leaf fleck
        Stoner, Warren N., 1952
    V. maize mosaic
        Brandes, E.W., 1920
        Kunkel, L.O., 1927
    V. maize streak
        Finley, A.M., 1954
        McKinney, H.H., 1929
        Storey, H.H., 1925, 1928, 1932, 1937
        Storey, H.H. and A.P.D. McClean, 1930
    V. maize stunt
        Hildebrand, E.M., 1949
        Maramorosch, Karl, 1951, 1955, 1956, 1957
        Niederhauser, John S. and Javier Cervantes, 1950
    V. maize wallaby ear
        (K.M. Smith, 1957) R.E. Fitzpatrick, et al., 1958
    V. oat pseudo-rosette
        (K.M. Smith, 1957) R.E. Fitzpatrick, et al., 1958
    V. rice and corn leaf-gall *
        Agati, Julian A. and Carlos Calica, 1949
    V. sugarcane mosaic
        Brandes, E.W., 1920
        Brandes, E.W. and Peter J. Klaphaak, 1923
        Chona, B.L. and S.A. Rafay, 1950
        Costa, A.S. and M.P. Penteado, 1951
        Lawas, Orencio M. and William L. Fernandez, 1949
        Storey, H.H., 1929
        Tims, E.C., P.J. Mills and C.W. Edgerton, 1935
    V. sugarcane streak
        Storey, H.H. and A.P.D. McClean, 1930

Z. mays, L. (cont.)
    V. sunflower mosaic
        (K.M. Smith, 1957) R.E. Fitzpatrick, et al., 1958
    V. tobacco necrosis
        Fulton, J.P., 1952
        Fulton, Robert W., 1950
    V. tobacco ring spot
        Bridgmon, G.H., 1951
        Bridgmon, G.H. and J.C. Walker, 1952
    V. wheat spot mosaic *
        Slykhuis, John T., 1956
    V. wheat streak mosaic
        Finley, A.M., 1957
        McKinney, H.H., 1949
        Meiners, Jack P. and H.H. McKinney, 1954
        Sill, W.H., Jr., 1956
        Sill, W.H., Jr. and Patrick C. Agusiobo, 1955
        Slykhuis, John T., 1955
Z. mays var. everta, (Sturtev.) Bailey
    V. cucumber mosaic
        Harter, L.L., 1938
Z. mays var. rugosa, Bonaf. *
    V. cucumber mosaic
        Fulton, Joseph P., 1950
        Pound, Glenn S. and J.C. Walker, 1948
Z. mays var. saccharata, (Sturtev.) Bailey
    V. barley stripe mosaic
        McKinney, H.H., 1951, 1953
    V. brome mosaic
        McKinney, H.H., 1953
    V. wheat streak mosaic
        McKinney, H.H., 1949

ZEBRINA Schnizl. 1849 (Commelinaceae)
Z. pendula, Schnizl.
    V. cucumber mosaic
        Wellman, F.L., 1935

ZINNIA L. 1759 (Compositae)
Z. elegans, Jacq.
    V. anemone mosaic *
        Hollings, M., 1957
    V. aster yellows
        George, J.A. and J.K. Richardson, 1957
        Magie, R.O., Floyd F. Smith and Philip Brierley,
            1952
        Severin, Henry H.P., 1929, 1934
        Severin, Henry H.P. and Julius H. Freitag, 1934,
            1945
        Smith, Floyd F. and Philip Brierley, 1953
    V. beet curly top
        Bennett, C.W., Eubanks Carsner, F.H. Coons and
            E.W. Brandes, 1946
        Bennett, C.W. and A.S. Costa, 1949
        Bennett, C.W. and Aziz Tanrisever, 1957
        Freitag, Julius H. and Henry H.P. Severin, 1936
        Severin, Henry H.P., 1934
        Severin, Henry H.P. and Julius H. Freitag, 1934
    V. beet mosaic
        McLean, D.M., 1952
        Pound, Glenn S., 1947
    V. cabbage black ring spot
        Hamlyn, Brenda M.G., 1953
        Hollings, M., 1957
        Tompkins, C.M., M.W. Gardner and H. Rex
            Thomas, 1938
    V. cabbage ring necrosis
        Larson, R.H. and J.C. Walker, 1940, 1941
    V. celery mosaic
        Price, W.C., 1935
    V. chilli veinbanding
        Simons, John N., 1956
    V. chrysanthemum stunt
        Brierley, Philip, 1953
    V. cotton leaf curl
        Mathur, R.N., 1933
    V. cowpea mosaic
        Anderson, C.W., 1955
    V. cucumber mosaic
        Ainsworth, G.C., 1938
        Anderson, C.W., 1951, 1955
        Berkeley, G.H. and J.H. Tremaine, 1954
        Bridgmon, G.H. and J.C. Walker, 1952
        Brierley, Philip, 1951, 1952

Zinnia elegans, Jacq. (cont.)
 V. cucumber mosaic
  Burnett, G., 1934
  Doolittle, S.P. and W.J. Zaumeyer, 1952, 1953
  Fulton, Joseph P., 1950
  Fulton, Robert W., 1941
  Harter, L.L., 1938
  Lindberg, G.D., D.H. Hall and J.C. Walker, 1956
  Nienow, Inez, 1948
  Pound, Glenn S. and J.C. Walker, 1948
  Price, W.C., 1935, 1937, 1939, 1941
  Simons, John N., 1957
  Sinclair, J.B. and J.C. Walker, 1956
  Smith, Floyd F. and Philip Brierley, 1944
  Wellman, F.L., 1934, 1935
  Whipple, O.C. and J.C. Walker, 1941
 V. cynarus curly dwarf
  Leach, L.D. and J.W. Oswald, 1950
  Morton, Donald J., 1957
 V. dahlia mosaic
  Brierley, Philip, 1951
  Brierley, Philip and Floyd F. Smith, 1950
 V. hydrangea ring spot
  Brierley, Philip and Floyd F. Smith, 1952
 V. lettuce mosaic
  Grogan, R.G., J.E. Welch and Roy Bardin, 1952
 V. lucerne mosaic
  Berkeley, G.H., 1947
  (K.M. Smith, 1957) R.E. Fitzpatrick, et al., 1958
  Johnson, E.M., 1946
  Kreitlow, K.W. and W.C. Price, 1948, 1949
  Richardson, D.E. and T.W. Tinsley, 1956
  Swenson, K.G., 1952
  Thomas, H. Rex, 1951, 1953
  Zaumeyer, W.J., 1938, 1953
 V. orchid (odontoglossum) ring spot
  Jensen, D.D. and A. Herbert Gold, 1952
 V. pea streak
  Kim, Woon S. and D.J. Hagedorn, 1957
 V. potato Y
  Simons, J.N., Robert A. Conover and James M. Walter, 1956
 V. prunus *
  Varney, E.H. and J. Duain Moore, 1954
 V. prunus B *
  Fulton, Robert W., 1957
 V. prunus G *
  Fulton, Robert W., 1957
 V. red currant ring spot
  Klesser, P.J., 1951
 V. rhubarb ring spot *
  Vaughan, Edward K. and John W. Yale, Jr., 1953
  Yale, John W., Jr. and Edward K. Vaughan, 1954
 V. sweet potato mosaic
  Elmer, O.H., 1957
 V. tobacco broad ring spot
  Johnson, James and Robert W. Fulton, 1942
 V. tobacco etch
  Holmes, Francis O., 1946
  Price, W.C., 1935
 V. tobacco leaf curl
  Kerling, L.C.P., 1933
  Pruthi, Hem Singh and C.K. Samuel, 1941
 V. tobacco mosaic
  Grant, T.J., 1934
  Holmes, Francis O., 1946
  Price, W.C., 1935
 V. tobacco necrosis
  Price, W.C., 1940
 V. tobacco ring spot
  Anderson, C.W., 1954
  Bridgmon, G.H. and J.C. Walker, 1952
  Cheo, Pen Ching and W.J. Zaumeyer, 1952
  Fulton, Robert W., 1941
  Grogan, R.G. and W.C. Schnathorst, 1955
  Pound, Glenn S., 1949
  Price, W.C., 1935
  Wingard, S.A., 1928
 V. tobacco ring spot no. 2
  Brierley, Philip, 1954
  Hildebrand, E.M., 1942
  Price, W.C., 1940
 V. tobacco streak
  Fulton, Robert W., 1948

Z. elegans, Jacq. (cont.)
 V. tomato aspermy
  Brierley, Philip, Floyd F. Smith and S.P. Doolittle, 1955
  Hollings, M., 1955
 V. tomato bunchy top
  (K.M. Smith, 1957) R.E. Fitzpatrick, et al., 1958
 V. tomato bushy stunt
  (K.M. Smith, 1957) R.E. Fitzpatrick, et al., 1958
  Smith, Kenneth M., 1935
 V. tomato spotted wilt
  Gardner, M.W. and O.C. Whipple, 1934
  Milbrath, J.A., 1939
  Smith, Kenneth M., 1932
  Yu, T.F., 1947
 V. tropaeolum mosaic
  (K.M. Smith, 1957) R.E. Fitzpatrick, et al., 1958
  Silberschmidt, Karl, 1953
 V. turnip mosaic
  Berkeley, G.H. and J.H. Tremaine, 1954
  Dale, W.T., 1948
  LeBeau, Francis J. and J.C. Walker, 1945
Z. elegans var. dahliiflora *
 V. cucumber mosaic
  Govier, D.A., 1957
Z. haageana, Regel
 V. aster yellows
  Severin, Henry H.P., 1934
 V. beet curly top
  Freitag, Julius H. and Henry H.P. Severin, 1936
  Severin, Henry H.P., 1934
 V. tobacco mosaic
  Holmes, Francis O., 1946

ZIZYPHUS Tourn. ex L. 1735 (Rhamnaceae)
Z. oenoplia, Mill.
 V. sandal spike
  (K.M. Smith, 1957) R.E. Fitzpatrick, et al., 1958

ZYGADENUS Michx. 1803 (Liliaceae)
Z. fremontii, Torr.
 V. tulip breaking
  Brierley, Philip and Floyd F. Smith, 1944

ZYGOPETALUM Hook. 1827 (Orchidaceae)
Z. spp.
 V. orchid (cymbidium) mosaic
  Jensen, D.D. and A.H. Gold, 1955

ABELMOSCHUS Medic. 1787 (Malvaceae)
A. esculentus, Moench
    V. abutilon infectious variegation
        Bird, Julio, 1958
    V. cucumber mosaic
        Adsuar, Jose and A. Cruz Miret, 1950
    V. papaw mosaic
        Adsuar, Jose, 1950
    V. tobacco mosaic
        Das, C.R. and S.P. Raychaudhuri, 1953

ABUTILON Tourn. ex Adans. 1763 (Malvaceae)
A. asiaticum, G. Don
    V. cacao swollen shoot
        Tinsley, T.W. and A.L. Wharton, 1958
A. indicum, Sweet
    V. hibiscus yellow vein mosaic
        Capoor, S.P. and P.M. Varma, 1950
A. theophrasti, Medic.
    V. cauliflower mosaic
        Walker, J.C., Francis J. LeBeau and Glenn S.
        Pound, 1945
    V. stone fruit *
        Boyle, J.S., J. Duain Moore and G.W. Keitt, 1954
    V. tomato ring spot
        Samson, R.W. and E.P. Imle, 1942

ACALYPHA L. 1737 (Euphorbiaceae)
A. virginica, L.
    V. tobacco etch
        Holmes, Francis O., 1946
    V. tobacco mosaic
        Holmes, Francis O., 1938, 1946

ACANTHOSPERMUM Schrank 1819 (Compositae)
A. hispidum, DC.
    V. citrus tristeza
        Bennett, C.W. and A.S. Costa, 1949
    V. euphorbia mosaic
        Costa, A.S. and C.W. Bennett, 1950

ACHILLEA L. 1735 (Compositae)
A. filipendulina, Lam.
    V. chrysanthemum stunt
        Brierley, Philip, 1953
A. millefolium, L.
    V. beet yellows
        Roland, G. and J. Tahon, 1961
    V. cucumber mosaic
        Wellman, F.L., 1935

ADENOROPIUM Pohl. 1827 (Euphorbiaceae)
A. gossypifolium, Pohl.
    V. cucumber mosaic
        Adsuar, Jose and A. Cruz Miret, 1950
    V. papaw mosaic
        Adsuar, Jose, 1950

ADIANTUM ((Tourn.)) L. 1753 (Polypodiaceae)
A. capillus-veneris, L.
    V. cucumber mosaic
        Wellman, F.L., 1935

ADLUMIA Raf. 1808 (Papaveraceae)
A. fungosa, Greene
    V. tobacco etch
        Holmes, Francis O., 1946

AEGLOPSIS Swingle 1911 (Rutaceae)
A. chevalieri, Swingle
    V. citrus tristeza
        Knorr, L.C., 1956

AEGLE Correa 1800 (Rutaceae)
A. marmelos, Correa
    V. citrus tristeza
        Knorr, L.C., 1956

AEGOPODIUM Knaut. ex L. 1735 (Umbelliferae)
A. podagraria, L.
    V. beet yellows
        Roland, G. and J. Tahon, 1961

AESCULUS L. 1740 (Hippocastanaceae)
A. californica, (Spach) Nutt.
    V. lucerne dwarf
        Freitag, J.H., 1951

AGAPANTHUS L'Herit. 1788 (Liliaceae)
A. africanus, Hoffmgg.
    V. cucumber mosaic
        Brierley, Philip and Floyd F. Smith, 1944
    V. lily symptomless
        Brierley, Philip and Floyd F. Smith, 1944
    V. ornithogalum mosaic
        Smith, Floyd F. and Philip Brierley, 1944
    V. tulip breaking
        Brierley, Philip and Floyd F. Smith, 1944

AGERATUM L. 1737 (Compositae)
A. conyzoides, L.
    V. anemone brown ring *
        Hollings, M., 1958
    V. chrysanthemum B (mild mosaic) *
        Hollings, M., 1957
    V. hibiscus yellow vein mosaic
        Capoor, S.P. and P.M. Varma, 1950
    V. tobacco etch
        Holmes, Francis O., 1946
    V. tobacco mosaic
        Holmes, Francis O., 1946
A. houstonianum, Mill.
    V. chrysanthemum stunt
        Brierley, Philip, 1953
    V. cucumber mosaic
        Wellman, F.L., 1935
A. officinalis *
    V. henbane mosaic
        Hamilton, Marion A., 1932

AGROPYRON J. Gaertn. 1770 (Gramineae)
A. amurense, Drobov. *
    V. barley yellow dwarf
        Bruehl, G.W. and H.V. Toko, 1957
    V. wheat streak mosaic
        McKinney, H.H. and W.J. Sando, 1951
A. ciliare, (Trin.) Franch. *
    V. agropyron mosaic
        Slykhuis, J.T., 1952
    V. barley stripe mosaic
        Slykhuis, J.T., 1952
    V. wheat streak mosaic
        Slykhuis, J.T., 1952
A. cristatum, (L.) Gaertn.
    V. agropyron mosaic
        Slykhuis, J.T., 1952
    V. barley stripe mosaic
        Slykhuis, J.T., 1952
    V. barley yellow dwarf
        Bruehl, G.W. and H.V. Toko, 1957
        Oswald, John W. and Byron R. Houston, 1953
    V. wheat streak mosaic
        McKinney, H.H. and W.J. Sando, 1951
        Slykhuis, J.T., 1952, 1955
A. dasystachyum, (Hook.) Scribn.
    V. agropyron mosaic
        Slykhuis, J.T., 1952
    V. barley stripe mosaic
        Slykhuis, J.T., 1952
    V. wheat streak mosaic
        McKinney, H.H. and W.J. Sando, 1951
        Slykhuis, J.T., 1952
A. desertorum, (Fisch.) Schult.
    V. agropyron mosaic
        Slykhuis, J.T., 1952
    V. barley stripe mosaic
        Slykhuis, J.T., 1952
    V. wheat streak mosaic
        Slykhuis, J.T., 1952
A. divaricatum, Boiss. & Bal.
    V. wheat streak mosaic
        McKinney, H.H. and W.J. Sando, 1951
A. elongatum, (Host) Beauv.
    V. barley stripe mosaic
        Slykhuis, J.T., 1952
    V. barley yellow dwarf
        Bruehl, G.W. and H.V. Toko, 1957

Agropyron elongatum, (Host) Beauv. (cont.)
  V. panicum mosaic *
    Sill, W.H., Jr. and R.C. Pickett, 1957
  V. wheat streak mosaic
    Fellows, Hurley and John W. Schmidt, 1953
    Slykhuis, J.T., 1952, 1955
A. inerme, (Scribn. & Sm.) Rydb.
  V. barley stripe mosaic
    Slykhuis, J.T., 1952
  V. barley yellow dwarf
    Bruehl, G.W. and H.V. Toko, 1957
  V. wheat streak mosaic
    Slykhuis, J.T., 1952
A. intermedium, (Host) Beauv.
  V. barley stripe mosaic
    Slykhuis, J.T., 1952
  V. barley yellow dwarf
    Bruehl, G.W. and H.V. Toko, 1957
  V. wheat streak mosaic
    Fellows, Hurley and John W. Schmidt, 1953
    Slykhuis, J.T., 1952, 1955
A. junceum, (L.) Beauv.
  V. barley stripe mosaic
    Slykhuis, J.T., 1952
  V. wheat streak mosaic
    Slykhuis, J.T., 1952
A. pertenue, (Mey.) Nevski
  V. barley stripe mosaic
    Slykhuis, J.T., 1952
  V. wheat streak mosaic
    Slykhuis, J.T., 1952
A. repens, L.
  V. barley stripe mosaic
    Slykhuis, J.T., 1952
  V. barley yellow dwarf
    Bruehl, G.W. and H.V. Toko, 1957
  V. beet ring spot *
    Harrison, B.D., 1957
  V. beet yellows
    Roland, G. and J. Tahon, 1961
  V. panicum mosaic *
    Sill, W.H., Jr. and R.C. Pickett, 1957
  V. wheat streak mosaic
    McKinney, H.H. and W.J. Sando, 1951
    Slykhuis, J.T., 1952, 1955
A. rigidum, Beauv.
  V. barley stripe mosaic
    Slykhuis, J.T., 1952
  V. wheat streak mosaic
    Slykhuis, J.T., 1952
A. semicostatum, Nees, ex Steud.
  V. wheat streak mosaic
    McKinney, H.H. and W.J. Sando, 1951
A. sibiricum, (Willd.) Beauv.
  V. barley yellow dwarf
    Bruehl, G.W. and H.V. Toko, 1957
  V. wheat streak mosaic
    McKinney, H.H. and W.J. Sando, 1951
A. smithii, Rydb.
  V. barley yellow dwarf
    Bruehl, G.W. and H.V. Toko, 1957
  V. wheat streak mosaic
    Sill, W.H., Jr. and Patrick C. Agusiobo, 1955
    Slykhuis, John T., 1955
A. spicatum, (Pursh) Scribn. & Sm.
  V. wheat streak mosaic
    McKinney, H.H. and W.J. Sando, 1951
A. trachycaulum, (Link) Malte
  V. agropyron mosaic
    Slykhuis, J.T., 1952
  V. barley stripe mosaic
    Slykhuis, J.T., 1952
  V. barley yellow dwarf
    Bruehl, G.W. and H.V. Toko, 1957
  V. wheat streak mosaic
    Slykhuis, J.T., 1952, 1955
A. trichophorum, C. Richt.
  V. agropyron mosaic
    Slykhuis, J.T., 1952
  V. barley stripe mosaic
    Slykhuis, J.T., 1952
  V. barley yellow dwarf
    Bruehl, G.W. and H.V. Toko, 1957

A. trichophorum, C. Richt. (cont.)
  V. wheat streak mosaic
    Slykhuis, J.T., 1952

AGROSTIS L. 1735 (Gramineae)
A. alba, L.
  V. barley yellow dwarf
    Bruehl, G.W. and H.V. Toko, 1957
    Oswald, John W. and Byron R. Houston, 1953
  V. wheat streak mosaic
    Slykhuis, John T., 1955
A. exarata, Trin.
  V. barley yellow dwarf
    Oswald, John W. and Byron R. Houston, 1953
A. palustris, Huds.
  V. barley yellow dwarf
    Bruehl, G.W. and H.V. Toko, 1957
  V. sugarcane mosaic
    Brandes, E.W. and Peter J. Klaphaak, 1923

AJUGA L. 1737 (Labiatae)
A. reptans, L.,var. rubra, Hort.
  V. cabbage black ring spot
    Tompkins, C.M., M.W. Gardner and H. Rex
    Thomas, 1938

ALLIUM ((Tourn.)) L. 1735 (Liliaceae)
A. canadense, L.
  V. onion yellow dwarf
    Henderson, W.J., 1935
A. cepa, L.
  V. beet yellows
    Roland, G. and J. Tahon, 1961
  V. cucumber mosaic
    Brierley, Philip and Floyd F. Smith, 1944
  V. lily symptomless
    Brierley, Philip and Floyd F. Smith, 1944
  V. maize leaf fleck
    Stoner, Warren N., 1952
  V. muskmelon mosaic
    Rader, Wm. E., Hugh F. Fitzpatrick and E.M.
    Hildebrand, 1947
  V. narcissus mosaic
    Haasis, Frank A., 1939
  V. nothoscordum mosaic
    McKinney, H.H., 1950
  V. ornithogalum mosaic
    Smith, Floyd F. and Philip Brierley, 1944
  V. pea mosaic
    Murphy, D.M. and W.H. Pierce, 1937
  V. tobacco etch
    Holmes, Francis O., 1946
  V. tobacco mosaic
    Holmes, Francis O., 1946
  V. tulip breaking
    Brierley, Philip and Floyd F. Smith, 1944
    McWhorter, F.P., 1935
  V. wheat streak mosaic
    Sill, W.H., Jr. and Patrick C. Agusiobo, 1955
A. cernuum, Roth
  V. cucumber mosaic
    Brierley, Philip and Floyd F. Smith, 1944
  V. lily symptomless
    Brierley, Philip and Floyd F. Smith, 1944
  V. ornithogalum mosaic
    Smith, Floyd F. and Philip Brierley, 1944
  V. tulip breaking
    Brierley, Philip and Floyd F. Smith, 1944
A. fistulosum, L.
  V. onion yellow dwarf
    Brierley, Philip and Floyd F. Smith, 1946
  V. ornithogalum mosaic
    Smith, Floyd F. and Philip Brierley, 1944
A. fistulosum x A. cepa, L.
  V. onion yellow dwarf
    Brierley, Philip and Floyd F. Smith, 1946
A. odorum, L.
  V. cucumber mosaic
    Brierley, Philip and Floyd F. Smith, 1944
  V. lily symptomless
    Brierley, Philip and Floyd F. Smith, 1944
  V. tulip breaking
    Brierley, Philip and Floyd F. Smith, 1944

Allium porrum, L.
  V. onion yellow dwarf
    Henderson, W.J., 1935
  V. ornithogalum mosaic
    Smith, Floyd F. and Philip Brierley, 1944
A. sativum, L.
  V. onion yellow dwarf
    Henderson, W.J., 1935
A. schoenoprasum, L.
  V. onion yellow dwarf
    Henderson, W.J., 1935
A. speciosum, Cyr.
  V. cucumber mosaic
    Brierley, Philip and Floyd F. Smith, 1944
  V. lily symptomless
    Brierley, Philip and Floyd F. Smith, 1944
  V. tulip breaking
    Brierley, Philip and Floyd F. Smith, 1944
A. tuberosum, Roxb.
  V. orchid (vanda) mosaic
    Murakishi, Harry H., 1952
A. vineale, L.
  V. nothoscordum mosaic
    McKinney, H.H., 1950

ALOE Tourn. ex L. 1735 (Liliaceae)
A. spp.
  V. cucumber mosaic
    Brierley, Philip and Floyd F. Smith, 1944
  V. lily symptomless
    Brierley, Philip and Floyd F. Smith, 1944
  V. tulip breaking
    Brierley, Philip and Floyd F. Smith, 1944

ALONSOA Ruiz & Pav. 1798 (Scrophulariaceae)
A. warscewiczii, Regel
  V. anemone brown ring *
    Hollings, M., 1958
  V. chrysanthemum B (mild mosaic) *
    Hollings, M., 1957
  V. pelargonium ring spot *
    Hollings, M., 1957

ALOPECURUS L. 1735 (Gramineae)
A. arundinaceus, Poir.
  V. barley yellow dwarf
    Bruehl, G.W. and H.V. Toko, 1957
A. pratensis, L.
  V. barley yellow dwarf
    Bruehl, G.W. and H.V. Toko, 1957
    Oswald, John W. and Byron R. Houston, 1953
  V. wheat streak mosaic
    Sill, W.H., Jr. and Patrick C. Agusiobo, 1955

ALSINE Scop. 1772 (Caryophyllaceae)
A. media, L.
  V. cucumber mosaic
    Wellman, F.L., 1935

ALSTONIA R. Br. 1809 (Apocynaceae)
A. congensis, Engl.
  V. cacao swollen shoot
    Posnette, A.F., N.F. Robertson and J. McA.
    Todd, 1950

ALTHAEA ((Tourn.)) L. 1735 (Malvaceae)
A. rosea, (L.) Cav.
  V. cabbage black ring spot
    Tompkins, C.M., M.W. Gardner and H. Rex
    Thomas, 1938
  V. cucumber mosaic
    Burnett, G., 1934
  V. malva yellow vein mosaic *
    Costa, A.S. and James E. Duffus, 1957
  V. tobacco etch
    Holmes, Francis O., 1946
  V. tobacco mosaic
    Holmes, Francis O., 1946
  V. tobacco ring spot
    Wingard, S.A., 1928

ALYSSUM Tourn. ex L. 1735 (Cruciferae)
A. maritimum, Lam.
  V. cauliflower mosaic
    Caldwell, John and Ian W. Prentice, 1942
    Tompkins, C.M., 1937
  V. turnip mosaic
    Tompkins, C.M., 1938, 1939
    Walker, J.C., Francis J. LeBeau and Glenn S.
    Pound, 1945
A. saxatile, L.
  V. cabbage black ring spot
    Tompkins, C.M., M.W. Gardner and H. Rex
    Thomas, 1938
  V. cauliflower mosaic
    Tompkins, C.M., 1937
  V. squash mosaic
    Freitag, J.H., 1956
  V. turnip mosaic
    Tompkins, C.M., 1939
A. saxatile var. compactum, Hort.
  V. cauliflower mosaic
    Caldwell, John and Ian W. Prentice, 1942

AMARANTHUS L. 1735 (Amaranthaceae)
A. caudatus, L.
  V. beet curly top
    Bennett, C.W. and A.S. Costa, 1949
  V. chrysanthemum B (mild mosaic) *
    Hollings, M., 1957
  V. citrus tristeza
    Bennett, C.W. and A.S. Costa, 1949
  V. euphorbia mosaic
    Costa, A.S. and C.W. Bennett, 1950
  V. pelargonium ring spot *
    Hollings, M., 1957
  V. turnip crinkle
    Broadbent, L. and G.D. Heathcote, 1958
  V. turnip rosette *
    Broadbent, L. and G.D. Heathcote, 1958
A. cruentus, L.
  V. cucumber mosaic
    Adsuar, Jose and A. Cruz Miret, 1950
  V. papaw mosaic
    Adsuar, Jose, 1950
A. dubius, Mart.
  V. cucumber mosaic
    Adsuar, Jose and A. Cruz Miret, 1950
  V. papaw mosaic
    Adsuar, Jose, 1950
A. graecizans, L.
  V. dodder latent mosaic
    Bennett, C.W., 1944
  V. lucerne mosaic
    Porter, D.R., 1935
  V. stone fruit *
    Boyle, J.S., J. Duain Moore and G.W. Keitt, 1954
A. hybridus, L.
  V. cucumber mosaic
    Wellman, F.L., 1935
A. retroflexus, L.
  V. beet curly top
    Bennett, C.W. and A.S. Costa, 1949
  V. cucumber mosaic
    Burnett, G., 1934
  V. dodder latent mosaic
    Bennett, C.W., 1944
  V. onion yellow dwarf
    Henderson, W.J., 1935
  V. squash mosaic
    Freitag, J.H., 1956
  V. tobacco ring spot
    Henderson, R.G. and S.A. Wingard, 1931
A. spinosus, L.
  V. chilli veinbanding
    Simons, John N., 1956
  V. cucumber mosaic
    Wellman, F.L., 1935
A. spp.
  V. beet curly top
    Bennett, C.W., Eubanks Carsner, F.H. Coons and
    E.W. Brandes, 1946

Amaranthus tricolor, L.
V. cauliflower mosaic
Walker, J.C., Francis J. LeBeau and Glenn S.
Pound, 1945
V. tobacco etch
Holmes, Francis O., 1946

AMARYLLIS L. 1735 (Amaryllidaceae)
(HIPPEASTRUM) Herb. 1821
A. spp.
V. narcissus mosaic
Haasis, Frank A., 1939
V. sweet potato mosaic
Borders, H.I. and T.J. Ratcliff, 1954
V. tulip breaking
Brierley, Philip and Floyd F. Smith, 1944
V. wheat streak mosaic
Sill, W.H., Jr. and Patrick C. Agusiobo, 1955
(H. puniceum), Urb.
V. tobacco etch
Holmes, Francis O., 1946
V. tobacco mosaic
Holmes, Francis O., 1946
(H. vittatum), Herb.
V. cucumber mosaic
Wellman, F.L., 1935

AMBROSIA L. 1737 (Compositae)
A. artemisiifolia, L.
V. chrysanthemum stunt
Brierley, Philip, 1953
V. cowpea mosaic
Anderson, C.W., 1955
V. cucumber mosaic
Anderson, C.W., 1955
V. tomato aspermy
Brierley, Philip, Floyd F. Smith and S.P.
Doolittle, 1955
V. tomato ring spot
Samson, R.W. and E.P. Imle, 1942
A. psilostachya, DC.
V. beet yellows
Roland, G. and J. Tahon, 1961
V. lucerne mosaic
Porter, D.R., 1935
A. trifida, L.
V. beet yellows
Roland, G. and J. Tahon, 1961
V. tobacco etch
Holmes, Francis O., 1946

AMMANNIA ((Houst.)) L. 1737 (Lythraceae)
A. coccinea, Rothb.
V. beet yellows
Roland, G. and J. Tahon, 1961

ANAGALLIS ((Tourn.)) L. 1735 (Primulaceae)
A. arvensis, L.
V. beet yellows
Roland, G. and J. Tahon, 1961
V. primula mosaic
Tompkins, C.M. and John T. Middleton, 1941
V. tobacco etch
Holmes, Francis O., 1946

ANANAS Tourn. ex L. 1735 (Bromeliaceae)
A. comosus, (L.) Merr.
V. potato Y
Sakimura, K., 1953
A. sativus, Schult. f.
V. cacao swollen shoot
Tinsley, T.W. and A.L. Wharton, 1958
V. cucumber mosaic
Wellman, F.L., 1935

ANCHUSA L. 1735 (Boraginaceae)
A. azurea, Mill.
V. anemone mosaic *
Hollings, M., 1957
V. chrysanthemum B (mild mosaic) *
Hollings, M., 1957
V. tobacco etch
Holmes, Francis O., 1946

A. capensis, Thunb.
V. tobacco etch
Holmes, Francis O., 1946
A. officinalis, L.
V. cabbage black ring spot
Tompkins, C.M., M.W. Gardner and H. Rex
Thomas, 1938
V. cucumber mosaic
Wellman, F.L., 1935

ANDROPOGON L. 1753 (Gramineae)
A. elliottii, Chapm.
V. sugarcane mosaic
Brandes, E.W. and Peter J. Klaphaak, 1923
A. hallii, Hack.
V. wheat streak mosaic
Sill, W.H., Jr. and Patrick C. Agusiobo, 1955
A. ischaemum, Thunb.
V. wheat streak mosaic
Sill, W.H., Jr. and Patrick C. Agusiobo, 1955
A. scoparius, Michx.
V. sugarcane mosaic
Brandes, E.W. and Peter J. Klaphaak, 1923
A. sibiricus, Steud.
V. wheat streak mosaic
Sill, W.H., Jr. and Patrick C. Agusiobo, 1955
A. virginicus, L.
V. sugarcane mosaic
Brandes, E.W. and Peter J. Klaphaak, 1923

ANEMONE L. 1735 (Ranunculaceae)
A. coronaria, L.
V. cabbage black ring spot
Hollings, M., 1957
V. primula mosaic
Tompkins, C.M. and John T. Middleton, 1941

ANEMOPSIS Hook. & Arn. * (Saururaceae)
A. californica, Hook.
V. beet yellows
Roland, G. and J. Tahon, 1961

ANTHEMIS Mich. ex L. 1735 (Compositae)
A. cotula, L.
V. muskmelon mosaic
Rader, Wm. E., Hugh F. Fitzpatrick and E.M.
Hildebrand, 1947
V. stone fruit *
Boyle, J.S., J. Duain Moore and G.W. Keitt, 1954

ANTHURIUM Schott. 1829 (Araceae)
A. andraeanum, Lind.
V. orchid (vanda) mosaic
Murakishi, Harry H., 1952

ANTIRRHINUM Tourn. ex L. 1735 (Scrophulariaceae)
A. majus, L.
V. anemone brown ring *
Hollings, M., 1958
V. anemone mosaic *
Hollings, M., 1957
V. bean yellow mosaic
Thomas, H. Rex and W.J. Zaumeyer, 1953
V. cabbage black ring spot
Tompkins, C.M., M.W. Gardner and H. Rex
Thomas, 1938
V. cabbage ring necrosis
Larson, R.H. and J.C. Walker, 1941
V. chrysanthemum B (mild mosaic) *
Hollings, M., 1957
V. chrysanthemum ring spot
Brierley, Philip and Floyd F. Smith, 1955
V. cucumber mosaic
Govier, D.A., 1957
V. euphorbia mosaic
Costa, A.S. and C.W. Bennett, 1950
V. gladiolus *
Snow, Gordon F., 1955
V. hydrangea ring spot
Brierley, Philip and Floyd F. Smith, 1952
V. pea wilt
Johnson, Folke, 1942
V. pelargonium ring spot *
Hollings, M., 1957

tirrhinum majus, L. (cont.)
V. peony leaf curl *
    Brierley, Philip and Paul Lorentz, 1957
V. primula mosaic
    Tompkins, C.M. and John T. Middleton, 1941
V. radish mosaic
    Tompkins, C.M., 1939
V. squash mosaic
    Freitag, J.H., 1956
V. tobacco etch
    Holmes, Francis O., 1946
V. tomato ring spot
    Samson, R.W. and E.P. Imle, 1942
V. turnip mosaic
    Tompkins, C.M., 1938, 1939
    Tompkins, C.M. and H. Rex Thomas, 1938
spp.
V. tomato spotted wilt
    Smith, Kenneth M., 1931, 1932

EIBA Aubl. 1775 (Tiliaceae)
tibourbou, Aubl., var. membranacea, Lockh. *
V. cacao swollen shoot
    Tinsley, T.W. and A.L. Wharton, 1958

IOS Moench 1794 (Leguminosae)
americana, Medic. (A. tuberosa, Moench)
V. pea mosaic
    Murphy, D.M. and W.H. Pierce, 1937

IUM ((Tourn.)) L. 1735 (Umbelliferae)
graveolens, L.
V. anemone brown ring *
    Hollings, M., 1958
V. bean yellow stipple
    Zaumeyer, W.J. and H. Rex Thomas, 1950
V. beet yellows
    Roland, G. and J. Tahon, 1961
V. cabbage black ring spot
    Tompkins, C.M., M.W. Gardner and H. Rex
    Thomas, 1938
V. cabbage ring necrosis
    Larson, R.H. and J.C. Walker, 1941
V. cauliflower mosaic
    Alvarez-Garcia, L.A., 1951
    Tompkins, C.M., 1937
V. chilli (pepper) mosaic
    Dale, W.T., 1954
V. chrysanthemum B (mild mosaic) *
    Hollings, M., 1957
V. cowpea mosaic
    Anderson, C.W., 1955
V. cucumber mosaic
    Bhargava, K.S., 1951
V. dandelion yellow mosaic
    Kassanis, B., 1947
V. eggplant mosaic
    Dale, W.T., 1954
V. lovage mosaic
    Smith, Kenneth M. and Roy Markham, 1944
V. maize leaf fleck
    Stoner, Warren N., 1952
V. muskmelon mosaic
    Rader, Wm. E., Hugh F. Fitzpatrick and E.M.
    Hildebrand, 1947
V. orchid (cymbidium) mosaic
    Jensen, D.D., 1951
V. orchid (odontoglossum) ring spot
    Jensen, D.D. and A. Herbert Gold, 1951
V. primula mosaic
    Tompkins, C.M. and John T. Middleton, 1941
V. radish mosaic
    Tompkins, C.M., 1939
V. teasel mosaic
    Stoner, Warren N., 1951
V. tobacco etch
    Anderson, C.W., 1954
    Holmes, Francis O., 1946
V. tobacco mosaic
    Doolittle, S.P. and F.S. Beecher, 1942
V. tobacco streak
    Thomas, H. Rex and W.J. Zaumeyer, 1950

A. graveolens, L. (cont.)
V. tomato aspermy
    Brierley, Philip, Floyd F. Smith and S.P.
    Doolittle, 1955
    Hollings, M., 1955
V. turnip mosaic
    Tompkins, C.M., 1938, 1939
    Tompkins, C.M. and H. Rex Thomas, 1938
A. graveolens var. dulce, DC.
V. anemone mosaic *
    Hollings, M., 1957
V. aster yellows
    Severin, Henry H.P., 1934
V. beet curly top
    Carsner, E., 1919
V. beet mosaic
    Severin, Henry H.P. and Roger M. Drake, 1948
V. chilli veinbanding
    Simons, John N., 1956
V. cucumber mosaic
    Simons, John N., 1957
V. filaree red leaf
    Frazier, Norman W., 1951
V. pea enation mosaic
    Simons, John N., 1954
V. primula mosaic
    Severin, Henry H.P. and C.M. Tompkins, 1950
V. spinach yellow dwarf
    Severin, Henry H.P. and Donald H. Little, 1947
V. squash mosaic
    Freitag, J.H., 1956
V. squash mosaic (southern)
    Anderson, C.W., 1951
A. graveolus, L.
V. cowpea mosaic
    Yu, T.F., 1946

AQUILEGIA ((Tourn.)) L. 1735 (Ranunculaceae)
A. caerulea, James
V. chrysanthemum B (mild mosaic) *
    Hollings, M., 1957
V. tobacco etch
    Holmes, Francis O., 1946
V. tobacco mosaic
    Holmes, Francis O., 1946
A. canadensis, L.
V. tobacco streak
    Thomas, H. Rex and W.J. Zaumeyer, 1950
A. spp.
V. squash mosaic
    Freitag, J.H., 1956

ARABIS L. 1737 (Cruciferae)
A. albida, Stev.
V. cabbage black ring spot
    Tompkins, C.M., M.W. Gardner and H. Rex
    Thomas, 1938
V. cauliflower mosaic
    Tompkins, C.M., 1937
V. turnip mosaic
    LeBeau, Francis J. and J.C. Walker, 1945
    Tompkins, C.M., 1939

ARACHIS L. 1735 (Leguminosae)
A. hypogaea, L.
V. bean yellow mosaic
    Grogan, Raymond G. and J.C. Walker, 1948
V. beet curly top
    Bennett, C.W., Eubanks Carsner, F.H. Coons and
    E.W. Brandes, 1946
V. beet yellows
    Roland, G. and J. Tahon, 1961
V. cacao swollen shoot
    Tinsley, T.W. and A.L. Wharton, 1958
V. cowpea mosaic
    Yu, T.F., 1946
V. cucumber mosaic
    Wellman, F.L., 1935
V. pea enation mosaic
    Osborn, H.T., 1938
V. squash mosaic
    Freitag, J.H., 1956
V. tobacco mosaic
    Das, C.R. and S.P. Raychaudhuri, 1953

Arachis hypogaea, L. (cont.)
　V. tobacco ring spot
　　Cooper, W.E., 1949

ARCTIUM L. 1735 (Compositae)
A. lappa, L.
　V. tobacco etch
　　Holmes, Francis O., 1946
　V. tobacco ring spot
　　Fenne, S.B., 1931
A. minus, Bernh.
　V. stone fruit *
　　Boyle, J.S., J. Duain Moore and G.W. Keitt, 1954
　V. tobacco mosaic
　　Stover, W.G. and M.T. Vermillion, 1933
A. tomentosum, Mill.
　V. beet yellows
　　Roland, G. and J. Tahon, 1961

ARCTOTIS L. 1737 (Compositae)
A. stoechadifolia, Berg., var. grandis, (Thunb.) Less.
　V. chrysanthemum stunt
　　Brierley, Philip, 1953

ARMERIA L. 1735 (Plumbaginaceae)
A. formosa, Hort.
　V. pea mosaic
　　Murphy, D.M. and W.H. Pierce, 1937

ARRHENATHERUM Beauv. 1812 (Gramineae)
A. elatius, (L.) Presl.
　V. barley yellow dwarf
　　Bruehl, G.W. and H.V. Toko, 1957
　　Oswald, John W. and Byron R. Houston, 1953
　V. wheat streak mosaic
　　Sill, W.H., Jr. and Patrick C. Agusiobo, 1955

ARTEMISIA L. 1735 (Compositae)
A. californica, Less.
　V. beet curly top
　　Severin, Henry H.P., 1939
A. vulgaris, L.
　V. beet yellows
　　Roland, G. and J. Tahon, 1961
　V. chrysanthemum stunt
　　Brierley, Philip, 1953

ARTOCARPUS Forst. 1776 (Moraceae)
A. incisa, L. f.
　V. cacao swollen shoot
　　Posnette, A.F., N.F. Robertson and J. McA. Todd, 1950

ASCLEPIAS L. 1737 (Asclepiadaceae)
A. curassavica, L.
　V. tobacco etch
　　Holmes, Francis O., 1946
A. mexicana, Cav.
　V. beet curly top
　　Carsner, E., 1919
A. spp.
　V. tobacco ring spot
　　Fenne, S.P., 1931
A. syriaca, L.
　V. onion yellow dwarf
　　Henderson, W.J., 1935
　V. prunus B *
　　Fulton, Robert W., 1957
　V. prunus E *
　　Fulton, Robert W., 1957
　V. stone fruit *
　　Boyle, J.S., J. Duain Moore and G.W. Keitt, 1954
　V. tobacco etch
　　Holmes, Francis O., 1946
　V. tobacco mosaic
　　Holmes, Francis O., 1946
A. tuberosa, L.
　V. squash mosaic
　　Freitag, J.H., 1956
　V. tomato ring spot
　　Samson, R.W. and E.P. Imle, 1942

ASPARAGUS Tourn. ex L. 1735 (Liliaceae)
A. asparagoides, (L.) Wight
　V. cucumber mosaic
　　Brierley, Philip and Floyd F. Smith, 1944
　V. lily symptomless
　　Brierley, Philip and Floyd F. Smith, 1944
　V. tulip breaking
　　Brierley, Philip and Floyd F. Smith, 1944
A. officinalis, L.
　V. cucumber mosaic
　　Wellman, F.L., 1935
A. plumosus, Baker
　V. cucumber mosaic
　　Wellman, F.L., 1935
A. sprengeri, Regel
　V. cucumber mosaic
　　Brierley, Philip and Floyd F. Smith, 1944
　V. lily symptomless
　　Brierley, Philip and Floyd F. Smith, 1944
　V. tulip breaking
　　Brierley, Philip and Floyd F. Smith, 1944

ASPHODELINE Reichb. 1830 (Liliaceae)
A. lutea, Reichb.
　V. cucumber mosaic
　　Brierley, Philip and Floyd F. Smith, 1944
　V. lily symptomless
　　Brierley, Philip and Floyd F. Smith, 1944
　V. tulip breaking
　　Brierley, Philip and Floyd F. Smith, 1944

ASTER Tourn. ex L. 1735 (Compositae)
A. ericoides, L.
　V. tobacco mosaic
　　Holmes, Francis O., 1938
A. lateriflorus, (L.) Britt.
　V. tobacco mosaic
　　Holmes, Francis O., 1938
A. multiflorus, Ait.
　V. tobacco mosaic
　　Holmes, Francis O., 1938
A. novae-angliae, L.
　V. cucumber mosaic
　　Wellman, F.L., 1935
A. spp.
　V. cucumber mosaic
　　Burnett, G., 1934
　V. muskmelon mosaic
　　Rader, Wm. E., Hugh F. Fitzpatrick and E.M. Hildebrand, 1947
　V. panicum mosaic *
　　Sill, W.H., Jr. and R.C. Pickett, 1957
　V. pea mosaic
　　Murphy, D.M. and W.H. Pierce, 1937

ASTRAGALUS Tourn. ex L. 1737 (Leguminosae)
A. canadensis, L.
　V. lucerne witches' broom
　　Klostermeyer, E.C. and J.D. Menzies, 1951
A. cicer, L.
　V. lucerne witches' broom
　　Klostermeyer, E.C. and J.D. Menzies, 1951
A. rubyi, Greene & Morris
　V. prunus E *
　　Fulton, Robert W., 1957
　V. prunus G *
　　Fulton, Robert W., 1957
A. spp.
　V. muskmelon mosaic
　　Rader, Wm. E., Hugh F. Fitzpatrick and E.M. Hildebrand, 1947

ATALANTIA Correa 1805 (Rutaceae)
A. ceylanica, Oliver
　V. citrus tristeza
　　Knorr, L.C., 1956
A. citroides, Pierre
　V. citrus tristeza
　　Knorr, L.C., 1956

ATLYSANUS Greene 1885 (Cruciferae)
A. pusillus, Greene
　V. cauliflower mosaic
　　Tompkins, C.M., 1937

ATRIPLEX ((Tourn.)) L. 1735 (Chenopodiaceae)
A. bracteosa, S. Wats.
  V. squash mosaic
    Freitag, J.H., 1956
A. expansa, (D. & H.) S. Wats.
  V. squash mosaic
    Freitag, J.H., 1956
A. lentiformis, (Torr.) S. Wats.
  V. beet yellows
    Roland, G. and J. Tahon, 1961
A. patula, L.
  V. beet yellow net
    Sylvester, Edward S., 1948
A. polycarpa, (Torr.) S. Wats.
  V. beet curly top
    Carsner, E., 1919
    Severin, Henry H.P. and Charles F. Henderson,
    1928
  V. beet yellows
    Roland, G. and J. Tahon, 1961
A. rosea, L.
  V. beet yellow net
    Sylvester, Edward S., 1948
A. semibaccata, R. Br.
  V. beet curly top
    Bennett, C.W. and A.S. Costa, 1949
A. spinifera, Macbride
  V. beet curly top
    Severin, Henry H.P. and Charles F. Henderson,
    1928

ATROPA L. 1737 (Solanaceae)
A. belladonna, L.
  V. beet mosaic
    Pound, Glenn S., 1947
  V. cauliflower mosaic
    Walker, J.C., Francis J. LeBeau and Glenn S.
    Pound, 1945
  V. dodder latent mosaic
    Bennett, C.W., 1944
  V. henbane mosaic
    Hamilton, Marion A., 1932
  V. nicotiana glutinosa mosaic *
    Allard, H.A., 1916
  V. potato X
    Cockerham, George, 1943
    Dennis, R.W.G., 1939
  V. potato Y
    Cockerham, Goerge, 1943
  V. tobacco mosaic
    Allard, H.A., 1916
  V. turnip mosaic
    Walker, J.C., Francis J. LeBeau and Glenn S.
    Pound, 1945

AVENA L. 1735 (Gramineae)
A. fatua, L.
  V. agropyron mosaic
    Slykhuis, J.T., 1952
  V. barley stripe mosaic
    Slykhuis, J.T., 1952
  V. wheat spot mosaic *
    Slykhuis, John T., 1956
  V. wheat streak mosaic
    Slykhuis, J.T., 1952
A. sativa, L.
  V. agropyron mosaic
    Slykhuis, J.T., 1952
  V. barley stripe mosaic
    Sill, W.H., Jr. and E.D. Hansing, 1955
    Slykhuis, J.T., 1952
  V. beet yellows
    Roland, G. and J. Tahon, 1961
  V. cabbage black ring spot
    Tompkins, C.M., M.W. Gardner and H. Rex
    Thomas, 1938
  V. corn new mosaic *
    Finley, A.M., 1954
  V. cucumber mosaic
    McWhorter, F.P. and H.H. Millsap, 1954
    Wellman, F.L., 1935
  V. maize leaf fleck
    Stoner, Warren N., 1952

A. sativa, L. (cont.)
  V. nothoscordum mosaic
    McKinney, H.H., 1950
  V. panicum mosaic *
    Sill, W.H., Jr. and R.C. Pickett, 1957
  V. soil-borne wheat mosaic
    McKinney, H.H., 1930
  V. sugarcane mosaic
    Brandes, E.W. and Peter J. Klaphaak, 1923
  V. tobacco etch
    Holmes, Francis O., 1946
  V. tobacco mosaic
    Holmes, Francis O., 1946
  V. tulip breaking
    Brierley, Philip and Floyd F. Smith, 1944
  V. turnip mosaic
    Tompkins, C.M. and H. Rex Thomas, 1938
  V. wheat spot mosaic *
    Slykhuis, John T., 1956

BAPHIA Afzel. ex Lodd. 1825 (Leguminosae)
B. nitida, Lodd.
  V. cacao swollen shoot
    Tinsley, T.W. and A.L. Wharton, 1958

BAPTISIA Vent. 1808 (Leguminosae)
B. australis, R. Br.
  V. pea mosaic
    Murphy, D.M. and W.H. Pierce, 1937
B. spp.
  V. muskmelon mosaic
    Rader, Wm. E., Hugh F. Fitzpatrick and E.M.
    Hildebrand, 1947

BARBAREA R. Br. 1812 (Cruciferae)
B. vulgaris, R. Br.
  V. cauliflower mosaic
    Walker, J.C., Francis J. LeBeau and Glenn S.
    Pound, 1945
  V. muskmelon mosaic
    Rader, Wm. E., Hugh F. Fitzpatrick and E.M.
    Hildebrand, 1947
  V. pea mottle
    Johnson, Folke, 1942
  V. pea wilt
    Johnson, Folke, 1942
  V. tobacco etch
    Holmes, Francis O., 1946
  V. tobacco mosaic
    Holmes, Francis O., 1946
  V. turnip mosaic
    Pound, Glenn S., 1948
    Walker, J.C., Francis J. LeBeau and Glenn S.
    Pound, 1945

BECKMANNIA Host 1805 (Gramineae)
B. syzigachne, (Steud.) Fern.
  V. barley yellow dwarf
    Bruehl, G.W. and H.V. Toko, 1957

BEGONIA ((Tourn.)) L. 1742 (Begoniaceae)
B. semperflorens, Link & Otto
  V. primula mosaic
    Tompkins, C.M. and John T. Middleton, 1941
  V. radish mosaic
    Tompkins, C.M., 1939
  V. tobacco etch
    Holmes, Francis O., 1946
  V. tobacco mosaic
    Holmes, Francis O., 1946
  V. tobacco necrosis
    Price, W.C., Frank P. McWhorter and Betty H.
    Steranka, 1950
  V. tomato ring spot
    Samson, R.W. and E.P. Imle, 1942
  V. turnip mosaic
    Tompkins, C.M., 1939
    Tompkins, C.M. and H. Rex Thomas, 1938
B. spp.
  V. vaccinium false blossom
    Kunkel, L.O., 1945

BELAMCANDA Adans. 1763 (Iridaceae)
B. chinensis, (L.) DC.
   V. bean yellow mosaic
      Brierley, Philip and Floyd F. Smith, 1948
   V. cucumber mosaic
      Brierley, Philip and Floyd F. Smith, 1944
   V. iris mosaic
      Brierley, Philip and Floyd F. Smith, 1948
      Travis, R.V., 1957
   V. iris ring spot *
      Travis, R.V., 1957
   V. lily symptomless
      Brierley, Philip and Floyd F. Smith, 1944
   V. tomato aspermy
      Brierley, Philip, Floyd F. Smith and S.P.
      Doolittle, 1955
   V. tulip breaking
      Brierley, Philip and Floyd F. Smith, 1944
   V. wheat streak mosaic
      Sill, W.H., Jr. and Patrick C. Agusiobo, 1955

BELLIS ((Tourn.)) L. 1737 (Compositae)
B. perennis, L.
   V. cabbage black ring spot
      Tompkins, C.M., M.W. Gardner and H. Rex
      Thomas, 1938
   V. primula mosaic
      Tompkins, C.M. and John T. Middleton, 1941
   V. radish mosaic
      Tompkins, C.M., 1939
   V. tobacco etch
      Holmes, Francis O., 1946
   V. tomato aspermy
      Hollings, M., 1955
   V. turnip mosaic
      Tompkins, C.M., 1938, 1939
      Tompkins, C.M. and H. Rex Thomas, 1938

BENINCASA Savi 1818 (Cucurbitaceae)
B. hispida, Cogn.
   V. prunus A *
      Fulton, Robert W., 1957
   V. prunus E *
      Fulton, Robert W., 1957

BERBERIS ((Tourn.)) L. 1737 (Berberidaceae)
B. vulgaris, L.
   V. tobacco ring spot
      Wingard, S.A., 1928

BERRYA DC. 1824 (Tiliaceae)
B. ammonilla, Roxbg.
   V. cacao swollen shoot
      Tinsley, T.W. and A.L. Wharton, 1958

BERTEROA DC. 1821 (Cruciferae)
B. incana, (L.) DC.
   V. cauliflower mosaic
      Walker, J.C., Francis J. LeBeau and Glenn S.
      Pound, 1945

BETA ((Tourn.)) L. 1735 (Chenopodiaceae)
B. macrocarpa, Guss.
   V. beet curly top
      Costa, A.S., 1952
B. patellaris, Moq.
   V. beet curly top
      Bennett, C.W. and A.S. Costa, 1949
      Costa, A.S., 1952
B. patula, ((Soland. in)) Ait. Hort. Kew.
   V. beet curly top
      Costa, A.S., 1952
B. vulgaris, L.
   V. anemone brown ring *
      Hollings, M., 1958
   V. anemone mosaic *
      Hollings, M., 1957
   V. aster yellows
      Severin, Henry H.P., 1929
   V. barley stripe mosaic
      Sill, W.H., Jr. and E.D. Hansing, 1955
   V. bean pod mottle
      Zaumeyer, W.J. and H. Rex Thomas, 1948

B. vulgaris, L. (cont.)
   V. bean southern mosaic
      Zaumeyer, W.J. and L.L. Harter, 1943
   V. bean yellow mosaic
      Conover, Robert A., 1948
   V. bean yellow stipple
      Zaumeyer, W.J. and H. Rex Thomas, 1950
   V. beet curly top
      Costa, A.S., 1952
   V. cabbage black ring spot
      Tompkins, C.M., M.W. Gardner and H. Rex
      Thomas, 1938
   V. carnation mottle
      Brierley, Philip and Floyd F. Smith, 1957
   V. cauliflower mosaic
      Alvarez-Garcia, L.A., 1951
      Berkeley, G.H. and J.H. Tremaine, 1954
      Walker, J.C., Francis J. LeBeau and Glenn S.
      Pound, 1945
   V. celery mosaic
      Freitag, Julius H. and Henry H.P. Severin, 1945
   V. chilli (pepper) mosaic
      Jha, Ashrafi and S.P. Raychaudhuri, 1956
   V. chrysanthemum B (mild mosaic) *
      Hollings, M., 1957
   V. chrysanthemum latent *
      Hollings, M., 1957
   V. citrus tristeza
      Knorr, L.C., 1956
   V. cowpea mosaic
      Yu, T.F., 1946
   V. cucumber mosaic
      Adsuar, Jose and A. Cruz Miret, 1950
      Govier, D.A., 1957
      Nienow, Inez, 1948
   V. (cucumber) O.S.C. isolate 606 *
      Porter, Clark A. and Frank P. McWhorter, 1951
   V. datura distortion mosaic
      Capoor, S.P. and P.M. Varma, 1952
   V. filaree red leaf
      Frazier, Norman W., 1951
   V. lucerne dwarf
      Freitag, J.H., 1951
   V. lucerne mosaic
      Kreitlow, K.W. and W.C. Price, 1949
      Thomas, H. Rex, 1951
   V. maize leaf fleck
      Stoner, Warren N., 1952
   V. malva yellow vein mosaic *
      Costa, A.S. and James E. Duffus, 1957
   V. muskmelon mosaic
      Rader, Wm. E., Hugh F. Fitzpatrick and E.M.
      Hildebrand, 1947
   V. nothoscordum mosaic
      McKinney, H.H., 1950
   V. onion yellow dwarf
      Henderson, W.J., 1935
   V. orchid (cymbidium) mosaic
      Jensen, D.D., 1951
   V. orchid (odontoglossum) ring spot
      Jensen, D.D. and A. Herbert Gold, 1951
   V. orchid (vanda) mosaic
      Murakishi, Harry H., 1952
   V. papaw mosaic
      Adsuar, Jose, 1950
   V. papaw ring spot
      Jensen, D.D., 1949
   V. pea enation mosaic
      Simons, John N., 1954
   V. pea mottle
      Johnson, Folke, 1942
   V. pea wilt
      Johnson, Folke, 1942
   V. physalis floridana yellow net
      Webb, R.E., 1955
   V. primula mosaic
      Severin, Henry H.P. and C.M. Tompkins, 1950
   V. potato Y
      Johnson, E.M., 1930
   V. red currant ring spot
      Klesser, P.J., 1951
   V. soybean mosaic
      Conover, Robert A., 1948

Beta vulgaris, L. (cont.)
  V. spinach yellow dwarf
    Severin, Henry H.P. and Donald H. Little, 1947
  V. squash mosaic
    Freitag, J.H., 1956
  V. squash mosaic (southern)
    Anderson, C.W., 1951
  V. teasel mosaic
    Stoner, Warren N., 1951
  V. tobacco broad ring spot
    Johnson, James and Robert W. Fulton, 1942
  V. tobacco coarse etch
    Johnson, E.M., 1930
  V. tobacco etch
    Bennett, C.W., 1944
    Holmes, Francis O., 1946
    Johnson, E.M., 1930
  V. tobacco mosaic
    Doolittle, S.P. and F.S. Beecher, 1942
    Johnson, E.M., 1930
  V. tobacco ring spot
    Johnson, E.M., 1930
  V. tobacco streak
    Thomas, H. Rex and W.J. Zaumeyer, 1950
  V. tomato ring spot
    Samson, R.W. and E.P. Imle, 1942
  V. tomato spotted wilt
    Sakimura, K., 1940
    Smith, Kenneth M., 1931
  V. tomato yellow net
    Sylvester, Edward S., 1954
  V. turnip crinkle
    Broadbent, L. and G.D. Heathcote, 1958
  V. turnip mosaic
    Berkeley, G.H. and J.H. Tremaine, 1954
    Dale, W.T., 1948
  V. turnip rosette *
    Broadbent, L. and G.D. Heathcote, 1958
B. vulgaris var. cicla, (L.) Moq.
  V. barley stripe mosaic
    Sill, W.H., Jr. and E.D. Hansing, 1955
  V. beet curly top
    Costa, A.S., 1952
  V. cabbage black ring spot
    Tompkins, C.M., M.W. Gardner and H. Rex
    Thomas, 1938
  V. cauliflower mosaic
    Alvarez-Garcia, L.A., 1951
    Berkeley, G.H. and J.H. Tremaine, 1954
    Walker, J.C., Francis J. LeBeau and Glenn S.
    Pound, 1945
  V. chilli veinbanding
    Simons, John N., 1956
  V. cucumber mosaic
    Govier, D.A., 1957
  V. spinach yellow dwarf
    Severin, Henry H.P. and Donald H. Little, 1947
  V. tomato ring spot
    Samson, R.W. and E.P. Imle, 1942
  V. tomato spotted wilt
    Sakimura, K., 1940
  V. turnip mosaic
    Berkeley, G.H. and J.H. Tremaine, 1954
    Dale, W.T., 1948

BIDENS ((Tourn.)) L. 1737 (Compositae)
B. bipinnata, L.
  V. tomato ring spot
    Samson, R.W. and E.P. Imle, 1942
B. cynapiifolia, H. B. & K.
  V. cucumber mosaic
    Adsuar, Jose and A. Cruz Miret, 1950
  V. papaw mosaic
    Adsuar, Jose, 1950
B. discoidea, (Torr. & Gray) Brit.
  V. tomato ring spot
    Samson, R.W. E.P. Imle, 1942
B. frondosa, L.
  V. tobacco etch
    Holmes, Francis O., 1946
B. leucantha, L. *
  V. celery mosaic
    Doolittle, S.P. and F.L. Wellman, 1934

B. leucantha, L. * (cont.)
  V. cucumber mosaic
    Wellman, F.L., 1935
B. pilosa, L.
  V. cowpea mosaic
    Anderson, C.W., 1955
  V. cucumber mosaic
    Anderson, C.W., 1955
  V. lucerne dwarf
    Freitag, J.H., 1951

BIXA L. 1737 (Bixaceae)
B. orellana, L.
  V. cacao swollen shoot
    Tinsley, T.W. and A.L. Wharton, 1958

BOEHMERIA Jacq. 1760 (Urticaceae)
B. nivea, Gaud.
  V. abutilon infectious variegation
    Silberschmidt, Karl M., 1948

BOLTONIA L'Herit. 1788 (Compositae)
B. latisquama, A. Gray
  V. chrysanthemum stunt
    Brierley, Philip, 1953
  V. prunus A *
    Fulton, Robert W., 1957
  V. prunus E *
    Fulton, Robert W., 1957
  V. prunus G *
    Fulton, Robert W., 1957

BOMBAX L. 1753 (Bombacaceae)
B. buonopozense, Beauv.
  V. cacao swollen shoot
    Posnette, A.F., N.F. Robertson and J. McA.
    Todd, 1950
    Tinsley, T.W. and A.L. Wharton, 1958

BORAGO L. 1753 (Boraginaceae)
B. officinalis, L.
  V. beet yellows
    Roland, G. and J. Tahon, 1961

BOUTELOUA Lag. 1805 (Gramineae)
B. gracilis, (H. B. & K.) Lag.
  V. barley yellow dwarf
    Oswald, John W. and Byron R. Houston, 1953

BRASSICA ((Tourn.)) L. 1735 (Cruciferae)
(SINAPIS) L. 1735
B. adpressa, Boiss.
  V. beet curly top
    Giddings, N.J., 1944
  V. turnip mosaic
    Tompkins, C.M., 1939
B. campestris, L.
  V. beet mosaic
    Severin, Henry H.P. and Roger M. Drake, 1947
  V. beet yellow net
    Sylvester, Edward S., 1948
  V. beet yellows
    Roland, G. and J. Tahon, 1961
  V. lucerne dwarf
    Freitag, J.H., 1951
  V. potato leaf roll
    MacCarthy, H.R., 1954
  V. spinach yellow dwarf
    Severin, Henry H.P. and Donald H. Little, 1947
B. campestris var. napobrassica, (L.) DC.
  V. cucumber mosaic
    Wellman, F.L., 1935
  V. physalis floridana yellow net
    Webb, R.E., 1955
  V. potato leaf roll
    MacCarthy, H.R., 1954
  V. radish mosaic
    Tompkins, C.M., 1939
  V. tobacco etch
    Holmes, Francis O., 1946
  V. tobacco ring spot
    Wingard, S.A., 1928
  V. turnip mosaic
    Tompkins, C.M., 1939

Brassica campestris, L., var. toria *
  V. chilli (pepper) mosaic
    Jha, Ashrafi and S.P. Raychaudhuri, 1956
B. chinensis, L.
  V. beet yellow net
    Sylvester, Edward S., 1948
  V. cucumber green mottle mosaic
    Vasudeva, R.S., S.P. Raychaudhuri and Jagannath
    Singh, 1949
  V. orchid (cymbidium) mosaic
    Jensen, D.D., 1951
  V. orchid (odontoglossum) ring spot
    Jensen, D.D. and A. Herbert Gold, 1951
  V. papaw ring spot
    Jensen, D.D., 1949
  V. tomato aspermy
    Hollings, M., 1955
B. hirta, Moench (B. alba, (L.) Rabh.)
  V. cucumber mosaic
    Johnson, E.M., 1930
    Wellman, F.L., 1935
  V. potato X
    Johnson, E.M., 1930
  V. potato Y
    Johnson, E.M., 1930
  V. tobacco coarse etch
    Johnson, E.M., 1930
  V. tobacco etch
    Johnson, E.M., 1930
  V. tobacco mosaic
    Johnson, E.M., 1930
  V. tobacco ring spot
    Johnson, E.M., 1930
    Wingard, S.A., 1928
  V. tomato ring spot
    Samson, R.W. and E.P. Imle, 1942
  V. turnip mosaic
    Tompkins, C.M., 1938
    Tompkins, C.M. and H. Rex Thomas, 1938
  V. turnip rosette *
    Broadbent, L. and G.D. Heathcote, 1958
B. integrifolia, O.E. Schulz, var. chevalieri,
  V. cabbage black ring spot   R. Porteres *
    Tompkins, C.M., M.W. Gardner and H. Rex
    Thomas, 1938
  V. radish mosaic
    Tompkins, C.M., 1939
  V. turnip mosaic
    Tompkins, C.M., 1938
    Tompkins, C.M. and H. Rex Thomas, 1938
B. juncea, (L.) Coss (B. japonica, Hort.)
  V. beet mosaic
    Pound, Glenn S., 1947
  V. cauliflower mosaic
    Tompkins, C.M., 1937
  V. pea enation mosaic
    Simons, John N., 1954
  V. potato leaf roll
    MacCarthy, H.R., 1954
  V. turnip mosaic
    Tompkins, C.M., 1939
    Tompkins, C.M. and H. Rex Thomas, 1938
B. kaber, (DC.) L.C. Wheeler (B. arvensis, (L.) Rabh.)
  V. beet yellows
    Roland, G. and J. Tahon, 1961
  V. muskmelon mosaic
    Rader, Wm. E., Hugh F. Fitzpatrick and E.M.
    Hildebrand, 1947
  V. stone fruit *
    Boyle, J.S., J. Duain Moore and G.W. Keitt, 1954
  V. turnip mosaic
    Tompkins, C.M., 1938
B. napus, L.
  V. beet yellows
    Roland, G. and J. Tahon, 1961
  V. cucumber mosaic
    Wellman, F.L., 1935
  V. potato leaf roll
    MacCarthy, H.R., 1954
  V. radish mosaic
    Tompkins, C.M., 1939
  V. tobacco ring spot
    Pound, Glenn S., 1949

B. napus, L. (cont.)
  V. turnip mosaic
    Tompkins, C.M., 1938, 1939
B. napus var. chinensis, (L.) O.E. Schulz *
  V. orchid (vanda) mosaic
    Murakishi, Harry H., 1952
B. nigra, (L.) Koch
  V. beet mosaic
    Bennett, C.W., 1949
  V. beet yellows
    Roland, G. and J. Tahon, 1961
  V. cucumber mosaic
    Wellman, F.L., 1935
  V. potato leaf roll
    MacCarthy, H.R., 1954
  V. turnip mosaic
    Tompkins, C.M., 1938
  V. turnip rosette *
    Broadbent, L. and G.D. Heathcote, 1958
B. oleracea, L.
  V. bean yellow stipple
    Zaumeyer, W.J. and H. Rex Thomas, 1950
  V. beet curly top
    Carsner, E., 1919
  V. beet yellows
    Roland, G. and J. Tahon, 1961
  V. chilli veinbanding
    Simons, John N., 1956
  V. citrus tristeza
    Knorr, L.C., 1956
  V. cucumber green mottle mosaic
    Vasudeva, R.S., S.P. Raychaudhuri and Jagannath
    Singh, 1949
  V. cucumber mosaic
    Doolittle, S.P. and W.J. Zaumeyer, 1953
    Johnson, E.M., 1930
    Simons, John N., 1957
  V. dodder latent mosaic
    Bennett, C.W., 1944
  V. henbane mosaic
    Hamilton, Marion A., 1932
  V. potato X
    Johnson, E.M., 1930
  V. potato Y
    Johnson, E.M., 1930
  V. sweet potato mosaic
    Borders, H.I. and T.J. Ratcliff, 1954
  V. tobacco coarse etch
    Johnson, E.M., 1930
  V. tobacco etch
    Holmes, Francis O., 1946
    Johnson, E.M., 1930
  V. tobacco mosaic
    Holmes, Francis O., 1946
    Johnson, E.M., 1930
  V. tobacco ring spot
    Johnson, E.M., 1930
  V. tomato ring spot
    Samson, R.W. and E.P. Imle, 1942
B. oleracea var. acephala, DC.
  V. anemone mosaic *
    Hollings, M., 1957
  V. cucumber mosaic
    Wellman, F.L., 1935
  V. physalis floridana yellow net
    Webb, R.E., 1955
  V. tobacco ring spot
    Wingard, S.A., 1928
  V. turnip mosaic
    Sylvester, Edward S., 1953
    Takahashi, William N., 1949
    Tompkins, C.M., 1938, 1939
B. oleracea var. botrytis, L.
  V. anemone mosaic *
    Hollings, M., 1957
  V. bean pod mottle
    Zaumeyer, W.J. and H. Rex Thomas, 1948
  V. beet mosaic
    Severin, Henry H.P. and Roger M. Drake, 1948
  V. cauliflower mosaic
    Berkeley, G.H. and J.H. Tremaine, 1954
  V. celery mosaic
    Freitag, Julius H. and Henry H.P. Severin, 1945

Brassica oleracea, L., var. botrytis, L. (cont.)
  V. chilli (pepper) mosaic
    Jha, Ashrafi and S.P. Raychaudhuri, 1956
  V. chrysanthemum B (mild mosaic) *
    Hollings, M., 1957
  V. cucumber mosaic
    Berkeley, G.H. and J.H. Tramaine, 1954
    Wellman, F.L., 1935
  V. filaree red leaf
    Frazier, Norman W., 1951
  V. orchid (cymbidium) mosaic
    Jensen, D.D., 1951
  V. physalis floridana yellow net
    Webb, R.E., 1955
  V. potato leaf roll
    MacCarthy, H.R., 1954
  V. primula mosaic
    Tompkins, C.M. and John T. Middleton, 1941
  V. rape savoy
    Ling, Lee and Juhwa Y. Yang, 1940
  V. squash mosaic
    Freitag, J.H., 1956
  V. tobacco ring spot
    Pound, Glenn S., 1949
  V. tobacco streak
    Thomas, H. Rex and W.J. Zaumeyer, 1950
  V. tomato aspermy
    Brierley, Philip, Floyd F. Smith and S.P.
    Doolittle, 1955
    Hollings, M., 1955
  V. tomato spotted wilt
    Sakimura, K., 1940
  V. turnip mosaic
    Dale, W.T., 1948
    LeBeau, Francis J. and J.C. Walker, 1945
    Pound, Glenn S., 1948
    Severin, Henry H.P. and C.M. Tompkins, 1950
    Sylvester, Edward S., 1953
    Takahashi, William N., 1949
    Tompkins, C.M., 1938, 1939
B. oleracea var. botrytis cymosa *
  V. lettuce mosaic
    Ainsworth, G.C. and L. Ogilvie, 1939
B. oleracea var. capitata, L.
  V. bean yellow mosaic
    Thomas, H. Rex and W.J. Zaumeyer, 1953
  V. beet mosaic
    Pound, Glenn S., 1947
    Severin, Henry H.P. and Roger M. Drake, 1948
  V. chilli (pepper) mosaic
    Jha, Ashrafi and S.P. Raychaudhuri, 1956
  V. chrysanthemum B (mild mosaic) *
    Hollings, M., 1957
  V. cucumber mosaic
    Berkeley, G.H. and J.H. Tremaine, 1954
    Bridgmon, G.H. and J.C. Walker, 1952
    Wellman, F.L., 1935
  V. lucerne mosaic
    Thomas, H. Rex, 1951
  V. pea mosaic
    Murphy, D.M. and W.H. Pierce, 1937
  V. pea mottle
    Johnson, Folke, 1942
  V. pea wilt
    Johnson, Folke, 1942
  V. potato leaf roll
    MacCarthy, H.R., 1954
  V. potato Y
    Bawden, F.C. and F.M.L. Sheffield, 1944
  V. primula mosaic
    Tompkins, C.M. and John T. Middleton, 1941
  V. rape savoy
    Ling, Lee and Juhwa Y. Yang, 1940
  V. red currant ring spot
    Klesser, P.J., 1951
  V. spinach yellow dwarf
    Severin, Henry H.P. and Donald H. Little, 1947
  V. squash mosaic
    Freitag, J.H., 1956
  V. tobacco ring spot
    Bridgmon, G.H. and J.C. Walker, 1952
    Smith, Kenneth M., 1929
    Wingard, S.A., 1928

B. oleracea var. capitata, L. (cont.)
  V. tomato aspermy
    Brierley, Philip, Floyd F. Smith and S.P.
    Doolittle, 1955
    Hollings, M., 1955
  V. tomato spotted wilt
    Sakimura, K., 1940
  V. turnip mosaic
    Clayton, E.E., 1930
    Dale, W.T., 1948
    LeBeau, Francis J. and J.C. Walker, 1945
    Sylvester, Edward S., 1953
    Takahashi, William N., 1949
    Tompkins, C.M., 1939
B. oleracea var. caulorapa, DC.
  V. anemone mosaic *
    Hollings, M., 1957
  V. chilli (pepper) mosaic
    Jha, Ashrafi and S.P. Raychaudhuri, 1956
  V. cucumber mosaic
    Nienow, Inez, 1948
    Wellman, F.L., 1935
  V. rape savoy
    Ling, Lee and Juhwa Y. Yang, 1940
  V. turnip mosaic
    Dale, W.T., 1948
    Sylvester, Edward S., 1953
    Takahashi, William N., 1949
    Tompkins, C.M., 1938, 1939
B. oleracea var. gemmifera, DC.
  V. anemone mosaic *
    Hollings, M., 1957
  V. beet mosaic
    Pound, Glenn S., 1947
  V. chrysanthemum B (mild mosaic) *
    Hollings, M., 1957
  V. cucumber mosaic
    Berkeley, G.H. and J.H. Tremaine, 1954
    Wellman, F.L., 1935
  V. potato Y
    Bawden, F.C. and F.M.L. Sheffield, 1944
  V. tobacco etch
    Bennett, C.W., 1944
  V. tobacco ring spot
    Pound, Glenn S., 1949
  V. turnip mosaic
    LeBeau, Francis J. and J.C. Walker, 1945
    Sylvester, Edward S., 1953
    Takahashi, William N., 1949
    Tompkins, C.M., 1938, 1939
B. oleracea var. gongylodes, L.
  V. beet mosaic
    Pound, Glenn S., 1947
  V. cucumber green mottle mosaic
    Vasudeva, R.S., S.P. Raychaudhuri and Jagannath
    Singh, 1949
  V. cucumber mosaic
    Berkeley, G.H. and J.H. Tremaine, 1954
  V. turnip mosaic
    LeBeau, Francis J. and J.C. Walker, 1945
B. oleracea var. italica, Plenck. *
  V. chrysanthemum B (mild mosaic) *
    Hollings, M., 1957
B. oleracea var. viridis, L.
  V. cucumber mosaic
    Berkeley, G.H. and J.H. Tremaine, 1954
  V. turnip mosaic
    LeBeau, Francis J. and J.C. Walker, 1945
B. pekinensis, (Lour.) Rupr.
  V. anemone brown ring *
    Hollings, M., 1958
  V. beet curly top
    Costa, A.S., 1952
    Severin, Henry H.P., 1929
  V. beet mosaic
    Pound, Glenn S., 1947
  V. chrysanthemum B (mild mosaic) *
    Hollings, M., 1957
  V. chrysanthemum latent *
    Hollings, M., 1957
  V. citrus tristeza
    Bennett, C.W. and A.S. Costa, 1949
  V. cucumber mosaic
    Berkeley, G.H. and J.H. Tremaine, 1954

Brassica pekinensis, (Lour.) Rupr. (cont.)
V. cucumber mosaic
Wellman, F.L., 1935
V. euphorbia mosaic
Costa, A.S. and C.W. Bennett, 1950
V. pelargonium ring spot *
Hollings, M., 1957
V. potato leaf roll
MacCarthy, H.R., 1954
V. primula mosaic
Tompkins, C.M. and John T. Middleton, 1941
V. tobacco etch
Holmes, Francis O., 1946
V. tobacco mosaic
Holmes, Francis O., 1946
B. rapa, L.
V. anemone brown ring *
Hollings, M., 1958
V. bean southern mosaic
Zaumeyer, W.J. and L.L. Harter, 1943
V. beet yellows
Roland, G. and J. Tahon, 1961
V. cauliflower mosaic
Caldwell, John and Ian W. Prentice, 1942
V. chilli (pepper) mosaic
Jha, Ashrafi and S.P. Raychaudhuri, 1956
V. chrysanthemum B (mild mosaic) *
Hollings, M., 1957
V. cucumber mosaic
Brierley, Philip and Floyd F. Smith, 1944
Nienow, Inez, 1948
Wellman, F.L., 1935
V. henbane mosaic
Hamilton, Marion A., 1932
V. lily symptomless
Brierley, Philip and Floyd F. Smith, 1944
V. muskmelon mosaic
Rader, Wm. E., Hugh F. Fitzpatrick and E.M.
Hildebrand, 1947
V. physalis floridana yellow net
Webb, R.E., 1955
V. primula mosaic
Tompkins, C.M. and John T. Middleton, 1941
V. squash mosaic
Freitag, J.H., 1956
V. tobacco ring spot
Wingard, S.A., 1928
V. tomato ring spot
Samson, R.W. and E.P. Imle, 1942
V. tulip breaking
Brierley, Philip and Floyd F. Smith, 1944
B. rapa var. depressa *
V. cucumber mosaic
Johnson, E.M., 1930
V. potato X
Johnson, E.M., 1930
V. potato Y
Johnson, E.M., 1930
V. tobacco coarse etch
Johnson, E.M., 1930
V. tobacco etch
Johnson, E.M., 1930
V. tobacco mosaic
Johnson, E.M., 1930
V. tobacco ring spot
Johnson, E.M., 1930
B. sinensis, L. *
V. red currant ring spot
Klesser, P.J., 1951

BRICKELLIA Ell. 1824 (Compositae)
B. laciniata, A. Gray
V. chrysanthemum stunt
Brierley, Philip, 1953

BRODIAEA Sm. 1811 (Liliaceae)
B. capitata, Benth.
V. tulip breaking
McWhorter, F.P., 1935
B. uniflora, Engl.
V. cucumber mosaic
Brierley, Philip and Floyd F. Smith, 1944
V. lily symptomless
Brierley, Philip and Floyd F. Smith, 1944

B. uniflora, Engl. (cont.)
V. tulip breaking
Brierley, Philip and Floyd F. Smith, 1944

BROMUS Dill. ex L. 1735 (Gramineae)
B. brizaeformis, Fisch. & Mey.
V. pea mosaic
Murphy, D.M. and W.H. Pierce, 1937
B. carinatus, Hook. & Arn.
V. wheat streak mosaic
McKinney, H.H., 1949
B. inermis, Leyss
V. agropyron mosaic
Slykhuis, J.T., 1952
V. barley stripe mosaic
Slykhuis, J.T., 1952
V. barley yellow dwarf
Bruehl, G.W. and H.V. Toko, 1957
V. panicum mosaic *
Sill, W.H., Jr. and R.C. Pickett, 1957
V. wheat streak mosaic
Sill, W.H., Jr. and Patrick C. Agusiobo, 1955
Slykhuis, J.T., 1952, 1955
B. japonicus, Thunb.
V. agropyron mosaic
Slykhuis, J.T., 1952
V. wheat spot mosaic *
Slykhuis, John T., 1956
B. secalinus, L.
V. agropyron mosaic
Slykhuis, J.T., 1952
V. wheat spot mosaic *
Slykhuis, John T., 1956
B. tectorum, L.
V. agropyron mosaic
Slykhuis, J.T., 1952
V. wheat spot mosaic *
Slykhuis, John T., 1956

BROWALLIA L. 1737 (Solanaceae)
B. americana, L. (B. demissa, L.)
V. tobacco etch
Holmes, Francis O., 1946
B. elata, L.
V. muskmelon mosaic
Rader, Wm. E., Hugh F. Fitzpatrick and E.M.
Hildebrand, 1947
V. prunus A *
Fulton, Robert W., 1957

BRYONIA L. 1735 (Cucurbitaceae)
B. dioica, Jacq.
V. cucumber green mottle mosaic
Ainsworth, G.C., 1935

BUCHLOE Engelm. 1859 (Gramineae)
B. dactyloides, (Nutt.) Engelm.
V. wheat streak mosaic
Sill, W.H., Jr. and Patrick C. Agusiobo, 1955

BUETTNERIA Loefl. 1758 (Sterculiaceae)
(BYTTNERIA) Loefl. 1758
B. catalpifolia, Wall.
V. cacao swollen shoot
Tinsley, T.W. and A.L. Wharton, 1958

CAESALPINIA L. 1753 (Leguminosae)
C. pulcherrima, (L.) Sw.
V. cacao swollen shoot
Tinsley, T.W. and A.L. Wharton, 1958

CAJANUS DC. 1813 (Leguminosae)
C. cajan, (L.) Millsp.
V. chilli (pepper) mosaic
Jha, Ashrafi and S.P. Raychaudhuri, 1956
V. cowpea mosaic
Capoor, S.P. and P.M. Varma, 1956
V. cucumber green mottle mosaic
Vasudeva, R.S., S.P. Raychaudhuri and Jagannath
Singh, 1949
C. indicus, Spreng.
V. bean common mosaic
Zaumeyer, W.J. and B.L. Wade, 1935

Cajanus indicus, Spreng. (cont.)
    V. bean yellow mosaic
        Zaumeyer, W.J. and B.L. Wade, 1935
    V. lucerne mosaic
        Zaumeyer, W.J., 1938
        Zaumeyer, W.J. and B.L. Wade, 1935
    V. pea streak
        Zaumeyer, W.J., 1938
    V. red clover mosaic *
        Zaumeyer, W.J. and B.L. Wade, 1935

CALENDULA L. 1735 (Compositae)
C. chrysantha, L. *
    V. chrysanthemum B (mild mosaic) *
        Hollings, M., 1957
C. officinalis, L.
    V. bayberry yellows
        Raychaudhuri, S.P., 1953
    V. beet mosaic
        Pound, Glenn S., 1947
    V. beet yellow net
        Sylvester, Edward S., 1948
    V. beet yellows
        Roland, G. and J. Tahon, 1961
    V. cauliflower mosaic
        Walker, J.C., Francis J. LeBeau and Glenn S.
        Pound, 1945
    V. celery mosaic
        Freitag, Julius H. and Henry H.P. Severin, 1945
    V. chilli (pepper) mosaic
        Jha, Ashrafi and S.P. Raychaudhuri, 1956
    V. chrysanthemum stunt
        Brierley, Philip, 1953
    V. cucumber mosaic
        Wellman, F.L., 1935
    V. dandelion yellow mosaic
        Kassanis, B., 1947
    V. euphorbia mosaic
        Costa, A.S. and C.W. Bennett, 1950
    V. muskmelon mosaic
        Rader, Wm. E., Hugh F. Fitzpatrick and E.M.
        Hildebrand, 1947
    V. pea mosaic
        Murphy, D.M. and W.H. Pierce, 1937
    V. red currant ring spot
        Klesser, P.J., 1951
    V. squash mosaic
        Freitag, J.H., 1956
    V. tobacco etch
        Holmes, Francis O., 1946
    V. tomato ring spot
        Samson, R.W. and E.P. Imle, 1942
C. spp.
    V. citrus tristeza
        Knorr, L.C., 1956
    V. tomato spotted wilt
        Smith, Kenneth M., 1932

CALLISTEPHUS Cass. 1825 (Compositae)
C. chinensis, (L.) Nees
    V. anemone brown ring *
        Hollings, M., 1958
    V. anemone mosaic *
        Hollings, M., 1957
    V. aster yellows
        Brierley, Philip and Floyd F. Smith, 1957
    V. bayberry yellows
        Raychaudhuri, S.P., 1953
    V. bean pod mottle
        Zaumeyer, W.J. and H. Rex Thomas, 1948
    V. beet curly top
        Bennett, C.W. and A.S. Costa, 1949
        Costa, A.S., 1952
        Severin, Henry H.P., 1929
    V. beet yellow net
        Sylvester, Edward S., 1948
    V. cabbage black ring spot
        Tompkins, C.M., M.W. Gardner and H. Rex
        Thomas, 1938
    V. cabbage ring necrosis
        Larson, R.H. and J.C. Walker, 1941
    V. carnation mosaic
        Brierley, Philip and Floyd F. Smith, 1955, 1957

C. chinensis, (L.) Nees
    V. carnation mottle
        Brierley, Philip and Floyd F. Smith, 1957
    V. chilli (pepper) mosaic
        Jha, Ashrafi and S.P. Raychaudhuri, 1956
    V. chrysanthemum B (mild mosaic) *
        Hollings, M., 1957
    V. chrysanthemum ring spot
        Brierley, Philip and Floyd F. Smith, 1955
    V. chrysanthemum stunt
        Brierley, Philip, 1953
    V. citrus tristeza
        Bennett, C.W. and A.S. Costa, 1949
    V. cucumber mosaic
        Doolittle, S.P. and W.J. Zaumeyer, 1953
        Simons, John N., 1957
        Wellman, F.L., 1935
    V. euphorbia mosaic
        Costa, A.S. and C.W. Bennett, 1950
    V. filaree red leaf
        Frazier, Norman W., 1951
    V. hydrangea ring spot
        Brierley, Philip and Paul Lorentz, 1956
    V. lilac witches' broom
        Brierley, Philip, 1955
    V. lucerne mosaic
        Kreitlow, K.W. and W.C. Price, 1949
    V. orchid (cymbidium) mosaic
        Jensen, D.D., 1951
    V. orchid (odontoglossum) ring spot
        Jensen, D.D. and A. Herbert Gold, 1951
    V. orchid (vanda) mosaic
        Murakishi, Harry H., 1952
    V. pea mottle
        Johnson, Folke, 1942
    V. pea wilt
        Johnson, Folke, 1942
    V. potato A
        MacLachlan, D.S., R.H. Larson and J.C. Walker,
        1953
    V. primula mosaic
        Tompkins, C.M. and John T. Middleton, 1941
    V. prunus A *
        Fulton, Robert W., 1957
    V. prunus E *
        Fulton, Robert W., 1957
    V. radish mosaic
        Tompkins, C.M., 1939
    V. spinach yellow dwarf
        Severin, Henry H.P. and Donald H. Little, 1947
    V. squash mosaic
        Freitag, J.H., 1956
    V. tobacco mosaic
        Stover, W.G. and M.T. Vermillion, 1933
    V. tomato ring spot
        Samson, R.W. and E.P. Imle, 1942
    V. tomato spotted wilt
        Smith, Kenneth M., 1931
    V. turnip mosaic
        Tompkins, C.M., 1939
        Tompkins, C.M. and H. Rex Thomas, 1938
    V. vaccinium false blossom
        Kunkel, L.O., 1945

CALONYCTION Choisy 1833 (Convolvulaceae)
C. aculeatum, (L.) House
    V. pea mosaic
        Murphy, D.M. and W.H. Pierce, 1937
    V. tobacco etch
        Holmes, Francis O., 1946

CALYCANTHUS L. 1759 (Calycanthaceae)
C. occidentalis, Hook. & Arn.
    V. lucerne dwarf
        Freitag, J.H., 1951

CALYSTEGIA R. Br. 1810 (Convolvulaceae)
C. sepium, L.
    V. chrysanthemum B (mild mosaic) *
        Hollings, M., 1957

CAMASSIA Lindl. 1832 (Liliaceae)
C. leichtlinii, (Baker) S. Wats.
    V. cucumber mosaic
        Brierley, Philip and Floyd F. Smith, 1944
    V. lily symptomless
        Brierley, Philip and Floyd F. Smith, 1944
    V. ornithogalum mosaic
        Smith, Floyd F. and Philip Brierley, 1944
    V. tulip breaking
        Brierley, Philip and Floyd F. Smith, 1944
C. quamash, (Pursh) Greene
    V. tulip breaking
        McWhorter, F.P., 1935

CAMPANULA ((Tourn.)) L. 1735 (Campanulaceae)
C. carpatica, Jacq.
    V. squash mosaic
        Freitag, J.H., 1956
    V. tobacco etch
        Holmes, Francis O., 1946
    V. tobacco mosaic
        Holmes, Francis O., 1946
C. lactiflora, Bieb.
    V. tobacco etch
        Holmes, Francis O., 1946
    V. tobacco mosaic
        Holmes, Francis O., 1946
C. medium, L.
    V. beet mosaic
        Pound, Glenn S., 1947
    V. cabbage black ring spot
        Tompkins, C.M., M.W. Gardner and H. Rex
        Thomas, 1938
    V. cucumber mosaic
        Wellman, F.L., 1935
    V. pea mosaic
        Murphy, D.M. and W.H. Pierce, 1937
    V. primula mosaic
        Tompkins, C.M. and John T. Middleton, 1941
    V. radish mosaic
        Tompkins, C.M., 1939
    V. spinach yellow dwarf
        Severin, Henry H.P. and Donald H. Little, 1947
    V. squash mosaic
        Freitag, J.H., 1956
    V. tobacco etch
        Holmes, Francis O., 1946
    V. tobacco mosaic
        Holmes, Francis O., 1946
    V. turnip mosaic
        Tompkins, C.M., 1938, 1939
        Tompkins, C.M. and H. Rex Thomas, 1938
C. petiolata, DC. (C. rotundifolia of Amer. auths.)
    V. tobacco etch
        Holmes, Francis O., 1946
    V. tobacco mosaic
        Holmes, Francis O., 1946
C. pyramidalis, L.
    V. pea mosaic
        Murphy, D.M. and W.H. Pierce, 1937
    V. tobacco etch
        Holmes, Francis O., 1946
    V. tobacco mosaic
        Holmes, Francis O., 1946

CANAVALIA DC. 1825 (Leguminosae)
C. ensiformis, (L.) DC.
    V. bean common mosaic
        Reddick, D. and V.B. Stewart, 1919
    V. bean yellow stipple
        Zaumeyer, W.J. and H. Rex Thomas, 1950
    V. citrus tristeza
        Bennett, C.W. and A.S. Costa, 1949
    V. cowpea mosaic
        Yu, T.F., 1946
    V. cucumber mosaic
        Anderson, C.W., 1955
    V. euphorbia mosaic
        Costa, A.S. and C.W. Bennett, 1950
    V. tobacco streak
        Thomas, H. Rex and W.J. Zaumeyer, 1950
C. gladiata, (Jacq.) DC.
    V. bean common mosaic
        Nelson, Ray, 1932

C. gladiata, (Jacq.) DC. (cont.)
    V. bean common mosaic
        Zaumeyer, W.J. and B.L. Wade, 1935
    V. bean yellow mosaic
        Zaumeyer, W.J. and B.L. Wade, 1935
    V. cucumber mosaic
        Anderson, C.W., 1955
    V. lucerne mosaic
        Zaumeyer, W.J. and B.L. Wade, 1935
    V. red clover mosaic *
        Zaumeyer, W.J. and B.L. Wade, 1935

CANNA L. 1735 (Cannaceae)
C. edulis, Ker-Gawl.
    V. cucumber mosaic
        Celino, Martin S., 1940
C. generalis, Bailey
    V. onion yellow dwarf
        Henderson, W.J., 1935
    V. tulip breaking
        Brierley, Philip and Floyd F. Smith, 1944
C. glauca, L.
    V. cucumber mosaic
        Wellman, F.L., 1935
C. indica, L.
    V. anemone mosaic *
        Hollings, M., 1957
C. spp.
    V. wheat streak mosaic
        Sill, W.H., Jr. and Patrick C. Agusiobo, 1955

CANTHIUM Lam. 1783 (Rubiaceae)
C. glabriflorum, Hiern
    V. cacao swollen shoot
        Posnette, A.F., N.F. Robertson and J. McA.
        Todd, 1950

CAPSELLA Medic. 1792 (Cruciferae)
(BURSA) Weber 1780
C. bursa-pastoris, (L.) Medik.
    V. beet yellow net
        Sylvester, Edward S., 1948
    V. cauliflower mosaic
        Caldwell, John and Ian W. Prentice, 1942
    V. stone fruit *
        Boyle, J.S., J. Duain Moore and G.W. Keitt, 1954
    V. tobacco etch
        Holmes, Francis O., 1946
    V. turnip rosette *
        Broadbent, L. and G.D. Heathcote, 1958

CAPSICUM ((Tourn.)) L. 1735 (Solanaceae)
C. cerasiforme, Mill.
    V. nicotiana glutinosa mosaic *
        Allard, H.A., 1916
C. frutescens, L. (C. annuum, L.)
    V. anemone mosaic *
        Hollings, M., 1957
    V. bean pod mottle
        Zaumeyer, W.J. and H. Rex Thomas, 1948
    V. bean southern mosaic
        Zaumeyer, W.J. and L.L. Harter, 1943
    V. beet curly top
        Bennett, C.W., Eubanks Carsner, F.H. Coons
        and E.W. Brandes, 1946
        Costa, A.S., 1952
    V. beet yellows
        Roland, G. and J. Tahon, 1961
    V. cacao swollen shoot
        Tinsley, T.W. and A.L. Wharton, 1958
    V. cauliflower mosaic
        Alvarez-Garcia, L.A., 1951
    V. chrysanthemum B (mild mosaic) *
        Hollings, M., 1957
    V. cowpea mosaic
        Anderson, C.W., 1955
        Capoor, S.P. and P.M. Varma, 1956
        McLean, D.M., 1941
        Yu, T.F., 1946
    V. cucumber green mottle mosaic
        Vasudeva, R.S. and T.K. Nariani, 1952
    V. cucumber mosaic
        Adsuar, Jose and A. Cruz Miret, 1950
        Anderson, C.W. and M.K. Corbett, 1957

Capsicum frutescens, L. (C. annuum, L.) (cont.)
  V. cucumber mosaic
    Burnett, G., 1934
    Govier, D.A., 1957
    Vasudeva, R. Sahai and T.B. Lal, 1943
  V. (cucumber) O.S.C. isolate 606 *
    Porter, Clark A. and Frank P. McWhorter, 1951
  V. hibiscus yellow vein mosaic
    Capoor, S.P. and P.M. Varma, 1950
  V. hydrangea ring spot
    Brierley, Philip and Paul Lorentz, 1957
  V. lucerne mosaic
    Johnson, E.M., 1946
    Thomas, H. Rex, 1951
    Zaumeyer, W.J., 1953
  V. muskmelon mosaic
    Anderson, C.W., 1954
    Rader, Wm. E., Hugh F. Fitzpatrick and E.M.
    Hildebrand, 1947
  V. nicotiana glutinosa root necrosis *
    Cetas, Robert C. and A. Frank Ross, 1952
  V. orchid (vanda) mosaic
    Murakishi, Harry H., 1952
  V. papaw mosaic
    Adsuar, Jose, 1950
  V. papaw ring spot
    Jensen, D.D., 1949
  V. pea streak
    Zaumeyer, W.J., 1938
  V. petunia mosaic
    Johnson, J., 1926, 1927
  V. potato A
    MacLachlan, D.S., R.H. Larson and J.C. Walker,
    1953
  V. potato leaf roll
    Dykstra, T.P., 1933
  V. potato M *
    Bagnall, R.H. and R.H. Larson, 1957
    Bagnall, R.H., R.H. Larson and J.C. Walker, 1956
  V. potato paracrinkle
    Bagnall, R.H. and R.H. Larson, 1957
    Bagnall, R.H., R.H. Larson and J.C. Walker, 1956
  V. potato X
    Dykstra, T.P., 1933
  V. potato Y
    Cockerham, George, 1943
    Dykstra, T.P., 1933
  V. spinach yellow dwarf
    Severin, Henry H.P. and Donald H. Little, 1947
  V. squash mosaic (southern)
    Anderson, C.W., 1951
  V. sweet potato mosaic
    Borders, H.I. and T.J. Ratcliff, 1954
  V. tobacco coarse etch
    Johnson, E.M., 1930
  V. tobacco etch
    McKinney, H.H., 1952
  V. tobacco leaf curl
    Bird, Julio, 1957
  V. tobacco mosaic
    Das, C.R. and S.P. Raychaudhuri, 1953
    Johnson, J., 1926, 1927
  V. tobacco ring spot
    Berkeley, G.H., 1953
    Cheo, Pen Ching and W.J. Zaumeyer, 1952
    Cooper, W.E., 1949
    Johnson, E.M., 1930
    Johnson, J., 1936
  V. tomato spotted wilt
    Parris, G.K., 1940
  V. tropaeolum mosaic
    Silberschmidt, Karl, 1953
  V. watermelon mosaic
    Anderson, C.W., 1954
C. frutescens var. cerasiforme, Bailey
  V. beet mosaic
    Pound, Glenn S., 1947
  V. cauliflower mosaic
    Walker, J.C., Francis J. LeBeau and Glenn S.
    Pound, 1945
  V. cucumber mosaic
    Pound, Glenn S. and J.C. Walker, 1948
  V. turnip mosaic
    Walker, J.C., Francis J. LeBeau and Glenn S.
    Pound, 1945

C. frutescens var. grossum, Bailey
  V. beet curly top
    Costa, A.S., 1952
  V. beet mosaic
    Severin, Henry H.P. and Roger M. Drake, 1948
  V. cauliflower mosaic
    Tompkins, C.M., 1937
  V. celery mosaic
    Freitag, Julius H. and Henry H.P. Severin, 1945
  V. primula mosaic
    Tompkins, C.M. and John T. Middleton, 1941
  V. squash mosaic
    Freitag, J.H., 1956
  V. tobacco ring spot
    Pound, Glenn S., 1949
    Wingard, S.A., 1928
C. spp.
  V. beet curly top
    Carsner, E., 1919
  V. citrus tristeza
    Knorr, L.C., 1956

CARDAMINE ((Tourn.)) L. 1735 (Cruciferae)
C. hirsuta, L.
  V. cauliflower mosaic
    Caldwell, John and Ian W. Prentice, 1942
C. pratensis, L.
  V. cauliflower mosaic
    Caldwell, John and Ian W. Prentice, 1942

CARDUUS ((Tourn.)) L. 1735 (Compositae)
C. arvensis, Robs.
  V. lettuce mosaic
    Ainsworth, G.C. and L. Ogilvie, 1939

CARICA L. 1737 (Caricaceae)
C. papaya, L.
  V. cacao swollen shoot
    Posnette, A.F., N.F. Robertson and J. McA.
    Todd, 1950
  V. crotalaria mosaic
    Jensen, D.D., 1949
  V. cucumber mosaic
    Adsuar, Jose and A. Cruz Miret, 1950
    Wellman, F.L., 1935
  V. orchid (vanda) mosaic
    Murakishi, Harry H., 1952
  V. tobacco etch
    Holmes, Francis O., 1946

CARTHAMUS ((Tourn.)) L. 1735 (Compositae)
C. tinctorius, L.
  V. beet yellows
    Roland, G. and J. Tahon, 1961

CARUM Rupp. ex L. 1735 (Umbelliferae)
C. carvi, L.
  V. squash mosaic
    Freitag, J.H., 1956

CASIMIROA La Llave 1825 (Rutaceae)
C. edulis, La Lave & Lex.
  V. citrus tristeza
    Knorr, L.C., 1956

CASSIA Tourn. ex L. 1735 (Leguminosae)
C. marilandica, L.
  V. prunus A *
    Fulton, Robert W., 1957
  V. prunus B *
    Fulton, Robert W., 1957
  V. prunus G *
    Fulton, Robert W., 1957
C. medsgeri, Shafer
  V. pea mosaic
    Murphy, D.M. and W.H. Pierce, 1937
C. occidentalis, L.
  V. cacao swollen shoot
    Tinsley, T.W. and A.L. Wharton, 1958
C. sophera, L.
  V. datura distortion mosaic
    Capoor, S.P. and P.M. Varma, 1952
C. tora, L.
  V. cucumber mosaic
    Anderson, C.W., 1954, 1955

Cassia tora, L. (cont.)
   V. hibiscus yellow vein mosaic
      Capoor, S.P. and P.M. Varma, 1950
   V. lucerne mosaic
      Anderson, C.W., 1954
   V. potato Y
      Anderson, C.W., 1954
   V. prunus B *
      Fulton, Robert W., 1957
   V. tobacco mosaic
      Anderson, C.W., 1954

CATANANCHE L. 1735 (Compositae)
C. caerulea, L.
   V. chrysanthemum stunt
      Brierley, Philip, 1953

CATHARANTHUS G. Don 1836 (Apocynaceae)
C. roseus, (L.) Don
   V. cucumber mosaic
      Adsuar, Jose and A. Cruz Miret, 1950
   V. papaw mosaic
      Adsuar, Jose, 1950

CATTLEYA Lindl. 1824 (Orchidaceae)
C. gaskelliana, Reichb. f.
   V. orchid (vanda) mosaic
      Murakishi, Harry H., 1952
C. spp.
   V. orchid (vanda) mosaic
      Murakishi, Harry H., 1952
C. trianaei, Lind. & Reichb. f.
   V. orchid (cymbidium) mosaic
      Jensen, D.D., 1951
   V. orchid (vanda) mosaic
      Murakishi, Harry H., 1952

CEANOTHUS L. 1741 (Rhamnaceae)
C. cuneatus, Nutt.
   V. beet curly top
      Severin, Henry H.P., 1939

CEIBA Gaertn. (Bombacaceae)
C. pentandra, Gaertn.
   V. cacao swollen shoot
      Tinsley, T.W. and A.L. Wharton, 1958

CELERI Adans. 1763 (Umbelliferae)
C. graveolens, Britton
   V. cucumber mosaic
      Adsuar, Jose and A. Cruz Miret, 1950

CELOSIA L. 1737 (Amaranthaceae)
C. argentea, L.
   V. anemone brown ring *
      Hollings, M., 1958
   V. chrysanthemum B (mild mosaic) *
      Hollings, M., 1957
   V. cucumber mosaic
      Wellman, F.L., 1935
   V. euphorbia mosaic
      Costa, A.S. and C.W. Bennett, 1950
   V. squash mosaic
      Freitag, J.H., 1956
C. argentea var. cristata, Kuntze
   V. cauliflower mosaic
      Walker, J.C., Francis J. LeBeau and Glenn S.
      Pound, 1945
C. argentea var. plumosa *
   V. turnip rosette *
      Broadbent, L. and G.D. Heathcote, 1958
C. spp.
   V. citrus tristeza
      Knorr, L.C., 1956

CENTAUREA L. 1737 (Compositae)
C. americana, Nutt.
   V. tobacco etch
      Holmes, Francis O., 1946
C. cyanus, L.
   V. aster yellows
      Kunkel, L.O., 1928
   V. beet yellows
      Roland, G. and J. Tahon, 1961

C. cyanus, L. (cont.)
   V. cucumber mosaic
      Wellman, F.L., 1935
   V. euphorbia mosaic
      Costa, A.S. and C.W. Bennett, 1950
C. imperialis, Hort.
   V. chrysanthemum stunt
      Brierley, Philip, 1953
C. montana, L.
   V. tobacco etch
      Holmes, Francis O., 1946
C. moschata, L.
   V. cauliflower mosaic
      Walker, J.C., Francis J. LeBeau and Glenn S.
      Pound, 1945
   V. tobacco etch
      Holmes, Francis O., 1946
   V. tobacco mosaic
      Holmes, Francis O., 1946
C. nigra, L.
   V. beet mosaic
      Pound, Glenn S., 1947
   V. cauliflower mosaic
      Walker, J.C., Francis J. LeBeau and Glenn S.
      Pound, 1945
   V. turnip mosaic
      Walker, J.C., Francis J. LeBeau and Glenn S.
      Pound, 1945
C. repens, L.
   V. beet mosaic
      Pound, Glenn S., 1947
C. spp.
   V. stone fruit *
      Boyle, J.S., J. Duain Moore and G.W. Keitt, 1954

CENTRANTHUS DC. 1805 (Valerianaceae)
C. ruber, (L.) DC.
   V. tobacco ring spot
      Wingard, S.A., 1928

CERASTIUM ((Dill.)) L. 1735 (Caryophyllaceae)
C. caespitosum, Gilib.
   V. beet yellows
      Roland, G. and J. Tahon, 1961
C. vulgatum, L.
   V. stone fruit *
      Boyle, J.S., J. Duain Moore and G.W. Keitt, 1954

CHAEREFOLIUM Haller 1768 (Umbelliferae)
C. silvestre, Schinz
   V. beet yellows
      Roland, G. and J. Tahon, 1961

CHAMAESYCE S.F. Gary 1821 (Euphorbiaceae)
C. hypericifolia, Millsp.
   V. abutilon infectious variegation
      Bird, Julio, 1958

CHAPMANNIA Torr. & Gray 1839 (Leguminosae)
C. floridana, Torr. & Gray
   V. cucumber mosaic
      Wellman, F.L., 1935

CHEIRANTHUS L. 1737 (Cruciferae)
C. allionii, Hort.
   V. cauliflower mosaic
      Caldwell, John and Ian W. Prentice, 1942
   V. tobacco etch
      Holmes, Francis O., 1946
   V. turnip mosaic
      LeBeau, Francis J. and J.C. Walker, 1945
C. cheiri, L.
   V. anemone mosaic *
      Hollings, M., 1957
   V. beet mosaic
      Pound, Glenn S., 1947
   V. beet yellows
      Roland, G. and J. Tahon, 1961
   V. cauliflower mosaic
      Caldwell, John and Ian W. Prentice, 1942
      Tompkins, C.M., 1937
   V. chrysanthemum B (mild mosaic) *
      Hollings, M., 1957

Cheiranthus cheiri, L. (cont.)
  V. cucumber mosaic
    Govier, D.A., 1957
  V. squash mosaic
    Freitag, J.H., 1956
  V. tobacco etch
    Holmes, Francis O., 1946
  V. tobacco ring spot no. 2
    Brierley, Philip, 1954
  V. tomato aspermy
    Brierley, Philip, Floyd F. Smith and S.P. Doolittle,
    1955
    Hollings, M., 1955
  V. turnip mosaic
    Tompkins, C.M., 1938, 1939

CHELIDONIUM Tourn. ex L. 1735 (Papaveraceae)
C. majus, L.
  V. tobacco etch
    Holmes, Francis O., 1946

CHELONE L. 1735 (Scrophulariaceae)
C. glabra, L.
  V. stone fruit *
    Boyle, J.S., J. Duain Moore and G.W. Keitt, 1954

CHENOPODIUM ((Tourn.)) L. 1735 (Chenopodiaceae)
C. album, L.
  V. beet curly top
    Bennett, C.W. and A.S. Costa, 1949
  V. beet rosette *
    Bennett, C.W. and James E. Duffus, 1957
  V. cabbage ring necrosis
    Larson, R.H. and J.C. Walker, 1941
  V. cauliflower mosaic
    Walker, J.C., Francis J. LeBeau and Glenn S.
    Pound, 1945
  V. chrysanthemum B (mild mosaic) *
    Hollings, M., 1957
  V. cucumber mosaic
    Burnett, G., 1934
  V. onion yellow dwarf
    Henderson, W.J., 1935
  V. prunus A *
    Fulton, Robert W., 1957
  V. prunus B *
    Fulton, Robert W., 1957
  V. prunus E *
    Fulton, Robert W., 1957
  V. prunus G *
    Fulton, Robert W., 1957
  V. stone fruit *
    Boyle, J.S., J. Duain Moore and G.W. Keitt, 1954
  V. tobacco etch
    Holmes, Francis O., 1946
  V. tobacco ring spot
    Fenne, S.B., 1931
    Henderson, R.G. and S.A. Wingard, 1931
  V. tomato ring spot
    Samson, R.W. and E.P. Imle, 1942
  V. turnip mosaic
    Tompkins, C.M., 1939
    Tompkins, C.M. and H. Rex Thomas, 1938
  V. turnip rosette *
    Broadbent, L. and G.D. Heathcote, 1958
  V. turnip yellow mosaic
    Broadbent, L. and G.D. Heathcote, 1958
  V. wheat streak mosaic
    Meiners, Jack P. and H.H. McKinney, 1954
C. amaranticolor, Coste & Reyn.
  V. beet rosette *
    Bennett, C.W. and James E. Duffus, 1957
  V. chrysanthemum B (mild mosaic) *
    Hollings, M., 1957
  V. pelargonium ring spot *
    Hollings, M., 1957
  V. turnip rosette *
    Broadbent, L. and G.D. Heathcote, 1958
  V. turnip yellow mosaic
    Broadbent, L. and G.D. Heathcote, 1958
C. ambrosioides, L.
  V. tobacco etch
    Holmes, Francis O., 1946

C. botrys, L.
  V. cucumber mosaic
    Wellman, F.L., 1935
C. capitatum, (L.) Asch.
  V. beet rosette *
    Bennett, C.W. and James E. Duffus, 1957
C. glaucum, L.
  V. tobacco etch
    Holmes, Francis O., 1946
C. hybridum, L.
  V. chilli (pepper) mosaic
    Dale, W.T., 1954
C. leptophyllum, Nutt. ex S. Wats.
  V. beet curly top
    Carsner, E., 1919
C. murale, L.
  V. beet curly top
    Carsner, E., 1919
  V. beet yellow net
    Sylvester, Edward S., 1948
  V. turnip mosaic
    Tompkins, C.M., 1938, 1939
    Tompkins, C.M. and H. Rex Thomas, 1938
C. rubrum, L.
  V. tobacco etch
    Holmes, Francis O., 1946

CHLORIS Sw. 1788 (Gramineae)
C. barbata, Nash
  V. rice and corn leaf-gall *
    Agati, Julian A. and Carlos A. Calica, 1950

CHORISIA H. B. & K. 1821 (Bombacaceae)
C. spp.
  V. beet yellows
    Roland, G. and J. Tahon, 1961

CHRISTIANA DC. 1824 (Tiliaceae)
C. africana, DC.
  V. cacao swollen shoot
    Tinsley, T.W. and A.L. Wharton, 1958

CHRYSANTHEMUM ((Tourn.)) L. 1735 (Compositae)
C. carinatum, L.
  V. cucumber mosaic
    Wellman, F.L., 1935
  V. muskmelon mosaic
    Rader, Wm. E., Hugh F. Fitzpatrick and E.M.
    Hildebrand, 1947
  V. tobacco ring spot
    Wingard, S.A., 1928
C. cinerariifolium, (Trev.) Vis.
  V. euphorbia mosaic
    Costa, A.S. and C.W. Bennett, 1950
C. coccineum, Willd.
  V. cucumber mosaic
    Govier, D.A., 1957
C. coronarium, L.
  V. radish mosaic
    Tompkins, C.M., 1939
  V. tomato spotted wilt
    Sakimura, K., 1940
  V. turnip mosaic
    Tompkins, C.M., 1938, 1939
    Tompkins, C.M. and H. Rex Thomas, 1938
C. leucanthemum, L.
  V. cucumber mosaic
    Wellman, F.L., 1935
  V. tobacco etch
    Holmes, Francis O., 1946
  V. tobacco mosaic
    Holmes, Francis O., 1946
C. maximum, Ramond
  V. cabbage black ring spot
    Tompkins, C.M., M.W. Gardner and H. Rex
    Thomas, 1938
  V. radish mosaic
    Tompkins, C.M., 1939
  V. turnip mosaic
    Tompkins, C.M., 1939
C. morifolium, (Ramat.) Hemsl.
  V. anemone brown ring *
    Hollings, M., 1958

Chrysanthemum morifolium, (Ramal.) Hemsl. (cont.)
  V. anemone mosaic *
    Hollings, M., 1957
  V. beet mosaic
    Pound, Glenn S., 1947
  V. chilli (pepper) mosaic
    Jha, Ashrafi and S.P. Raychaudhuri, 1956
  V. cucumber mosaic
    Wellman, F.L., 1935
  V. hydrangea ring spot
    Brierley, Philip and Paul Lorentz, 1957
C. parthenium, (L.) Bernh.
  V. cucumber mosaic
    Govier, D.A., 1957
    Wellman, F.L., 1935
  V. squash mosaic
    Freitag, J.H., 1956
C. segetum, L.
  V. muskmelon mosaic
    Rader, Wm. E., Hugh F. Fitzpatrick and E.M.
    Hildebrand, 1947

CHRYSOPSIS Ell. 1824 (Compositae)
C. spp.
  V. tobacco ring spot
    Henderson, R.G. and S.A. Wingard, 1931
C. villosa, Nutt.
  V. beet curly top
    Severin, Henry H.P., 1939

CICER ((Tourn.)) L. 1735 (Leguminosae)
C. arietinum, L.
  V. bean common mosaic
    Reddick, D. and V.B. Stewart, 1919
    Snyder, W.C., 1942
    Zaumeyer, W.J. and B.L. Wade, 1935
  V. bean southern mosaic
    Zaumeyer, W.J. and L.L. Harter, 1943
  V. chilli (pepper) mosaic
    Jha, Ashrafi and S.P. Raychaudhuri, 1956
  V. cucumber green mottle mosaic
    Vasudeva, R.S., S.P. Raychaudhuri and Jagannath
    Singh, 1949
  V. cucumber mosaic
    Wellman, F.L., 1935
  V. filaree red leaf
    Frazier, Norman W., 1951
  V. lucerne mosaic
    Zaumeyer, W.J. and B.L. Wade, 1935
  V. pea enation mosaic
    Johnson, Folke and Leon K. Jones, 1937
  V. pea mottle
    Johnson, F. and L.K. Jones, 1936, 1937

CICHORIUM ((Tourn.)) L. 1735 (Compositae)
C. endivia, L.
  V. cucumber mosaic
    Wellman, F.L., 1935
  V. dahlia mosaic
    Brierley, Philip and Floyd F. Smith, 1950
  V. tobacco etch
    Holmes, Francis O., 1946
C. intybus, L.
  V. beet yellows
    Roland, G. and J. Tahon, 1961
  V. celery mosaic
    Freitag, Julius H. and Henry H.P. Severin, 1945
  V. chrysanthemum stunt
    Brierley, Philip, 1953
  V. cucumber mosaic
    Pound, Glenn S. and J.C. Walker, 1948
    Wellman, F.L., 1935
  V. dandelion yellow mosaic
    Kassanis, B., 1947
  V. stone fruit *
    Boyle, J.S., J. Duain Moore and G.W. Keitt, 1954

CINERARIA L. p.p. 1763 (Compositae)
C. cruenta, Mass.
  V. lettuce mosaic
    Jones, Leon K., 1944

CIRCAEA Tourn. ex L. 1735 (Onagraceae)
C. lutetiana, L.
  V. tobacco mosaic
    Holmes, Francis O., 1938

CIRSIUM ((Tourn.)) Adans. 1763 (Compositae)
C. arvense, (L.) Scop.
  V. beet mosaic
    Pound, Glenn S., 1947
  V. beet yellows
    Roland, G. and J. Tahon, 1961
  V. stone fruit *
    Boyle, J.S., J. Duain Moore and G.W. Keitt, 1954
  V. tobacco mosaic
    Holmes, Francis O., 1938
  V. tobacco ring spot
    Wingard, S.A., 1928
C. vulgare, (Savi) Tenore
  V. beet yellows
    Roland, G. and J. Tahon, 1961

CISTANTHERA C.K. Schum. 1897 (Tiliaceae)
C. papaverifera, A. Chev.
  V. cacao swollen shoot
    Posnette, A.F., N.F. Robertson and J. McA.
    Todd, 1950

CITRULLUS Forsk. 1775 (Cucurbitaceae)
C. citrullus, Small
  V. cucumber mosaic
    Adsuar, Jose and A. Cruz Miret, 1950
  V. papaw mosaic
    Adsuar, Jose, 1950
C. colocynthis, Schrad.
  V. prunus E *
    Fulton, Robert W., 1957
  V. prunus G *
    Fulton, Robert W., 1957
C. vulgaris, Schrad.
  V. beet yellows
    Roland, G. and J. Tahon, 1961
  V. cabbage ring necrosis
    Larson, R.H. and J.C. Walker, 1941
  V. chilli (pepper) mosaic
    Jha, Ashrafi and S.P. Raychaudhuri, 1956
  V. cucumber green mottle mosaic
    Ainsworth, G.C., 1935
  V. cucumber mosaic
    Nariani, T.K. and Nirmaljit Singh, 1952
  V. (cucumber) O.S.C. isolate 606 *
    Porter, Clark A. and Frank P. McWhorter, 1951
  V. cucurbit mosaic *
    Doolittle, S.P. and M.N. Walker, 1925
  V. muskmelon mosaic
    Rader, Wm. E., Hugh F. Fitzpatrick and E.M.
    Hildebrand, 1947
  V. peach ring spot
    Hobbs, Gordon A., 1951
  V. prunus E *
    Fulton, Robert W., 1957
  V. prunus G *
    Fulton, Robert W., 1957
  V. spinach yellow dwarf
    Severin, Henry H.P. and Donald H. Little, 1947
  V. squash mosaic
    Freitag, J.H., 1956
    Lindberg, G.D., D.H. Hall and J.C. Walker, 1956
  V. stone fruit *
    Boyle, J.S., J. Duain Moore and G.W. Keitt, 1954
  V. tobacco broad ring spot
    Johnson, James and Robert W. Fulton, 1942
  V. tobacco etch
    Holmes, Francis O., 1946
  V. tobacco mosaic
    Doolittle, S.P. and F.S. Beecher, 1942
    Holmes, Francis O., 1946
  V. tomato ring spot
    Samson, R.W. and E.P. Imle, 1942
C. vulgaris var. citroides, Bailey *
  V. prunus E *
    Fulton, Robert W., 1957
  V. prunus G *
    Fulton, Robert W., 1957

Citrullus vulgaris, Schrad. var. fistulosus *
   V. chilli (pepper) mosaic
      Jha, Ashrafi and S.P. Raychaudhuri, 1956
   V. cucumber mosaic
      Nariáni, T.K. and Nirmaljit Singh, 1952

CITRUS L. 1735 (Rutaceae)
C. aurantifolia, (Christm.) Swingle
   V. cacao swollen shoot
      Tinsley, T.W. and A.L. Wharton, 1958
   V. citrus exocortis
      Olson, E.O. and A.V. Shull, 1956
   V. citurs xyloporosis
      Olson, E.O. and A.V. Shull, 1956
C. aurantium, L.
   V. cucumber mosaic
      Wellman, F.L., 1935
C. grandis, (L.) Osbeck
   V. citrus tristeza
      Knorr, L.C., 1956
   V. cucumber mosaic
      Wellman, F.L., 1935
C. limon, (L.) Burm. f.
   V. chilli (pepper) mosaic
      Jha, Ashrafi and S.P. Raychaudhuri, 1956
   V. citrus tristeza
      Knorr, L.C., 1956
   V. lucerne dwarf
      Freitag, J.H., 1951
C. nobilis, Lour.
   V. cucumber mosaic
      Wellman, F.L., 1935
C. nobilis var. unshiu, Swingle on C. sinensis, (L.)
Osbeck x Poncirus trifoliata, (L.) Raf.
   V. citrus tristeza
      Olson, Edward O. and James R. McDonald, 1954
C. nobilis var. unshiu, Swingle on Poncirus trifoliata,
   V. citrus tristeza   (L.) Raf.
      Olson, Edward O. and James R. McDonald, 1954
C. paradisi, Macf. on C. paradisi x Poncirus trifoliata,
   V. citrus tristeza   (L.) Raf.
      Olson, Edward O. and James R. McDonald, 1954
C. paradisi x C. reticulata, Blanco
   V. citrus xyloporosis
      Olson, E.O. and A.V. Shull, 1956
C. paradisi x C. reticulata, Blanco on C. sinensis, (L.)
Osbeck x Poncirus trifoliata, (L.) Raf.
   V. citrus tristeza
      Olson, Edward O. and James R. McDonald, 1954
C. paradisi on (C. sinensis, (L.) Osbeck x Poncirus
trifoliata, (L.) Raf.)
   V. citrus tristeza
      Olson, Edward O. and James R. McDonald, 1954
C. reticulata, Blanco
   V. citrus tristeza
      Knorr, L.C., 1956
   V. lucerne dwarf
      Freitag, J.H., 1951
C. sinensis, (L.) Osbeck
   V. beet yellows
      Roland, G. and J. Tahon, 1961
   V. cacao swollen shoot
      Tinsley, T.W. and A.L. Wharton, 1958
   V. citrus tristeza
      Olson, Edward O. and James R. McDonald, 1954
   V. cucumber mosaic
      Wellman, F.L., 1935
C. sinensis on C. paradisi, Macf. x Poncirus trifoliata,
   V. citrus tristeza   (L.) Raf.
      Olson, Edward O. and James R. McDonald, 1954
C. sinensis on Poncirus trifoliata, (L.) Raf.
   V. citrus tristeza
      Olson, Edward O. and James R. McDonald, 1954
C. spp.
   V. cucumber mosaic
      Bennett, C.W., 1944

CLAPPERTONIA Meissn. 1837 (Tiliaceae)
C. ficifolia, Decne.
   V. cacao swollen shoot
      Tinsley, T.W. and A.L. Wharton, 1958

CLARKIA Pursh 1814 (Onagraceae)
C. elegans, Dougl.
   V. cabbage black ring spot
      Tompkins, C.M., M.W. Gardner and H. Rex
      Thomas, 1938
   V. cucumber mosaic
      Wellman, F.L., 1935
   V. radish mosaic
      Tompkins, C.M., 1939
   V. tobacco etch
      Holmes, Francis O., 1946
   V. tobacco mosaic
      Holmes, Francis O., 1946
   V. turnip mosaic
      Tompkins, C.M., 1938, 1939
      Tompkins, C.M. and H. Rex Thomas, 1938

CLEOME L. 1735 (Capparidaceae)
C. spinosa, L.
   V. cucumber mosaic
      Adsuar, Jose and A. Cruz Miret, 1950
   V. papaw mosaic
      Adsuar, Jose, 1950
   V. tobacco etch
      Holmes, Francis O., 1946

CLERODENDRON L. 1737 (Verbenaceae)
C. fragans, Vent.
   V. cucumber mosaic
      Adsuar, Jose and A. Cruz Miret, 1950

CLITORIA L. 1737 (Leguminosae)
C. ternatea, L.
   V. cucumber mosaic
      Wellman, F.L., 1935

COBAEA Cav. 1791 (Polemoniaceae)
C. scandens, Cav.
   V. tobacco etch
      Holmes, Francis O., 1946
   V. tobacco mosaic
      Holmes, Francis O., 1946

COCHLEARIA Tourn. ex L. 1735 (Cruciferae)
C. armoracia, L.
   V. beet yellows
      Roland, G. and J. Tahon, 1961

COCHLOSPERMUM Kunth 1822 (Cochlospermaceae)
C. vitifolia, Spreng.
   V. cacao swollen shoot
      Tinsley, T.W. and A.L. Wharton, 1958

CODIAEUM Rumph. ex A. Juss. 1824 (Euphorbiaceae)
C. variegatum, Blume
   V. cucumber mosaic
      Wellman, F.L., 1935
   V. wheat streak mosaic
      Sill, W.H., Jr. and Patrick C. Agusiobo, 1955

COFFEA L. 1735 (Rubiaceae)
C. arabica, L.
   V. beet curly top
      Bennett, C.W. and A.S. Costa, 1949

COIX L. 1737 (Gramineae)
C. lachyrma-jobi, L.
   V. sugarcane mosaic
      Brandes, E.W. and Peter J. Klaphaak, 1923
   V. wheat streak mosaic
      Sill, W.H., Jr. and Patrick C. Agusiobo, 1955

COLA Schott & Endl. 1832 (Sterculiaceae)
C. caricaefolia, (G. Don) K. Schum. *
   V. cacao swollen shoot
      Tinsley, T.W. and A.L. Wharton, 1958
C. chlamydantha, K. Schum.
   V. cacao swollen shoot
      Posnette, A.F., N.F. Robertson and J. McA.
      Todd, 1950
      Tinsley, T.W. and A.L. Wharton, 1958

Cola gigantea, A. Chev., var. glabrescens, Brenan &
   V. cacao swollen shoot   Keay
     Tinsley, T.W. and A.L. Wharton, 1958
C. heterophylla, Schott & Endl.
   V. cacao swollen shoot
     Tinsley, T.W. and A.L. Wharton, 1958
C. lateritia, K. Schum., var. maclaudi, (A. Chev.)
   V. cacao swollen shoot   Brenan & Keay
     Tinsley, T.W. and A.L. Wharton, 1958
C. millenii, K. Schum. (Cola togoensis, Endl. & Krause)
   V. cacao swollen shoot
     Tinsley, T.W. and A.L. Wharton, 1958
C. nitida, Schott & Endl.
   V. cacao swollen shoot
     Posnette, A.F., N.F. Robertson and J. McA.
     Todd, 1950
     Tinsley, T.W. and A.L. Wharton, 1958
C. togoensis, Engl. & Krause
   V. cacao swollen shoot
     Posnette, A.F., N.F. Robertson and J. McA.
     Todd, 1950
C. umbratilis, Brenan & Keay *
   V. cacao swollen shoot
     Tinsley, T.W. and A.L. Wharton, 1958
C. verticillata, Stafp ex A. Chev.
   V. cacao swollen shoot
     Posnette, A.F., N.F. Robertson and J. McA.
     Todd, 1950
     Tinsley, T.W. and A.L. Wharton, 1958

COLEUS Lour. 1790 (Labiatae)
C. blumei, Benth.
   V. muskmelon mosaic
     Rader, Wm. E., Hugh F. Fitzpatrick and E.M.
     Hildebrand, 1947
   V. prunus A *
     Fulton, Robert W., 1957
   V. prunus G *
     Fulton, Robert W., 1957
   V. tobacco etch
     Holmes, Francis O., 1946
   V. tomato aspermy
     Brierley, Philip, Floyd F. Smith and S.P.
     Doolittle, 1955
C. blumei var. verschaffeltii, Lem.
   V. tobacco ring spot
     Wingard, S.A., 1928
C. lanuginosus, Hochst. ex Benth.
   V. cucumber mosaic
     Adsuar, Jose and A. Cruz Miret, 1950
   V. papaw mosaic
     Adsuar, Jose, 1950

COMMELINA Plum. ex L. 1735 (Commelinaceae)
C. coelestis, Willd.
   V. cucumber mosaic
     Brierley, Philip and Floyd F. Smith, 1944
   V. lily symptomless
     Brierley, Philip and Floyd F. Smith, 1944
   V. tulip breaking
     Brierley, Philip and Floyd F. Smith, 1944
C. communis, L.
   V. tulip breaking
     Brierley, Philip and Floyd F. Smith, 1944
C. diffusa, Burm. f.
   V. papaw ring spot
     Jensen, D.D., 1949
C. nudiflora, L.
   V. cowpea mosaic
     Anderson, C.W., 1955
   V. cucumber mosaic
     Anderson, C.W., 1955
     Brierley, Philip and Floyd F. Smith, 1944
   V. lily symptomless
     Brierley, Philip and Floyd F. Smith, 1944
   V. tomato spotted wilt
     Sakimura, K., 1940
   V. tulip breaking
     Brierley, Philip and Floyd F. Smith, 1944
C. spp.
   V. chilli veinbanding
     Simons, John N., 1956
   V. cucumber mosaic
     Simons, John N., 1957

C. venghalensis, L. *
   V. tomato spotted wilt
     Sakimura, K., 1940

CONIUM L. 1735 (Umbelliferae)
C. maculatum, L.
   V. beet yellows
     Roland, G. and J. Tahon, 1961
   V. celery mosaic
     Freitag, Julius H. and Henry H.P. Severin, 1945

CONVALLARIA L. 1735 (Liliaceae)
C. majalis, L.
   V. cucumber mosaic
     Brierley, Philip and Floyd F. Smith, 1944
   V. lily symptomless
     Brierley, Philip and Floyd F. Smith, 1944
   V. tulip breaking
     Brierley, Philip and Floyd F. Smith, 1944
   V. wheat streak mosaic
     Sill, W.H., Jr. and Patrick C. Agusiobo, 1955

CONVOLVULUS ((Tourn.)) L. 1735 (Convolvulaceae)
C. arvensis, L.
   V. beet yellows
     Roland, G. and J. Tahon, 1961
C. sepium, L.
   V. anemone mosaic *
     Hollings, M., 1957
   V. tomato aspermy
     Brierley, Philip, Floyd F. Smith and S.P.
     Doolittle, 1955
C. tricolor, L.
   V. anemone brown ring *
     Hollings, M., 1958
   V. chrysanthemum B (mild mosaic) *
     Hollings, M., 1957

COOPERIA Herb. 1836 (Amaryllidaceae)
C. spp.
   V. narcissus mosaic
     Haasis, Frank A., 1939

CORCHORUS ((Tourn.)) L. 1735 (Tiliaceae)
C. trilocularis, L.
   V. hibiscus yellow vein mosaic
     Capoor, S.P. and P.M. Varma, 1950

COREOPSIS L. 1737 (Compositae)
C. douglasii, Hall
   V. chrysanthemum stunt
     Brierley, Philip, 1953
   V. tomato aspermy
     Brierley, Philip, Floyd F. Smith and S.P.
     Doolittle, 1955
C. drummondii, Torr. & Gray
   V. chrysanthemum stunt
     Brierley, Philip, 1953
   V. cucumber mosaic
     Wellman, F.L., 1935
C. grandiflora, Nutt.
   V. tobacco etch
     Holmes, Francis O., 1946
C. lanceolata, L.
   V. chrysanthemum stunt
     Brierley, Philip, 1953
   V. dahlia mosaic
     Brierley, Philip and Floyd F. Smith, 1950
C. tinctoria, Nutt.
   V. cucumber mosaic
     Wellman, F.L., 1935

CORTADERIA Stapf 1897 (Gramineae)
C. selloana, (Schult.) Aschers. & Graebn.
   V. wheat streak mosaic
     Sill, W.H., Jr. and Patrick C. Agusiobo, 1955

CORYDALIS Vent. Choix, 19 1803, in nota;
C. lutea, DC.   (Fumariaceae)
   V. turnip crinkle
     Broadbent, L. and G.D. Heathcote, 1958

COSMOS Cav. 1791 (Compositae)
C. bipinnatus, Cav.
    V. chrysanthemum stunt
        Brierley, Philip, 1953
    V. cucumber mosaic
        Wellman, F.L., 1935
    V. dahlia mosaic
        Brierley, Philip and Floyd F. Smith, 1950
    V. squash mosaic
        Freitag, J.H., 1956
C. diversifolius, Otto
    V. tobacco ring spot
        Wingard, S.A., 1928
C. sulphureus, Cav.
    V. tomato aspermy
        Brierley, Philip, Floyd F. Smith and S.P. Doolittle, 1955

COTONEASTER Rupp. 1745 (Rosaceae)
C. franchetii, Bois
    V. lucerne dwarf
        Freitag, J.H., 1951

CRASSINA Scepin 1758 (Compositae)
C. elegans, Kuntze
    V. cucumber mosaic
        Adsuar, Jose and A. Cruz Miret, 1950
    V. papaw mosaic
        Adsuar, Jose, 1950

CROCUS ((Tourn.)) L. 1735 (Iridaceae)
C. spp.
    V. wheat streak mosaic
        Sill, W.H., Jr. and Patrick C. Agusiobo, 1955

CROTALARIA Dill. ex L. 1737 (Leguminosae)
C. capensis, Jacq.
    V. prunus A *
        Fulton, Robert W., 1957
    V. prunus E *
        Fulton, Robert W., 1957
C. incana, L.
    V. papaw ring spot
        Jensen, D.D., 1949
C. intermedia, Kotschy
    V. prunus B *
        Fulton, Robert W., 1957
    V. tobacco ring spot
        Cooper, W.E., 1949
C. juncea, L.
    V. chilli (pepper) mosaic
        Jha, Ashrafi and S.P. Raychaudhuri, 1956
    V. datura distortion mosaic
        Capoor, S.P. and P.M. Varma, 1952
C. mucronata, Desv.
    V. chilli (pepper) mosaic
        Jha, Ashrafi and S.P. Raychaudhuri, 1956
    V. prunus A *
        Fulton, Robert W., 1957
    V. prunus B *
        Fulton, Robert W., 1957
    V. tobacco mosaic
        Das, C.R. and S.P. Raychaudhuri, 1953
C. retusa, L.
    V. alsike clover mosaic
        Zaumeyer, W.J., 1940
    V. bean yellow mosaic
        Zaumeyer, W.J., 1940
    V. cowpea mosaic
        Capoor, S.P. and P.M. Varma, 1956
    V. pea mosaic
        Murphy, D.M. and W.H. Pierce, 1937
C. spectabilis, Roth
    V. alsike clover mosaic
        Zaumeyer, W.J., 1940
    V. bean southern mosaic
        Zaumeyer, W.J. and L.L. Harter, 1943
    V. bean yellow mosaic
        Conover, Robert A., 1948
    V. cucumber mosaic
        Anderson, C.W., 1955
        Wellman, F.L., 1935
    V. prunus A *
        Fulton, Robert W., 1957

C. spectabilis, Roth (cont.)
    V. prunus E *
        Fulton, Robert W., 1957
    V. prunus G *
        Fulton, Robert W., 1957
    V. soybean mosaic
        Conover, Robert A., 1948
C. spp.
    V. cucumber mosaic
        Wellman, F.L., 1935
C. striata, DC.
    V. abutilon infectious variegation
        Bird, Julio, 1958

CUCUMIS ((Tourn.)) L. 1735 (Cucurbitaceae)
C. anguria, L.
    V. tomato ring spot
        Samson, R.W. and E.P. Imle, 1942
C. melo, L.
    V. beet curly top
        Carsner, E., 1919
    V. cabbage ring necrosis
        Larson, R.H. and J.C. Walker, 1941
    V. canna mosaic
        Castillo, B.S., C.E. Yarwood and A.H. Gold, 1956
    V. chilli (pepper) mosaic
        Jha, Ashrafi and S.P. Raychaudhuri, 1956
    V. cucumber mosaic
        Govier, D.A., 1957
    V. (cucumber) O.S.C. isolate 606 *
        Porter, Clark A. and Frank P. McWhorter, 1951
    V. stone fruit *
        Boyle, J.S., J. Duain Moore and G.W. Keitt, 1954
    V. tobacco etch
        Holmes, Francis O., 1946
    V. tobacco mosaic
        Doolittle, S.P. and F.S. Beecher, 1942
        Holmes, Francis O., 1946
    V. tomato ring spot
        Samson, R.W. and E.P. Imle, 1942
C. prophetarum, L.
    V. prunus B *
        Fulton, Robert W., 1957
C. sativus, L.
    V. anemone brown ring *
        Hollings, M., 1958
    V. anemone mosaic *
        Hollings, M., 1957
    V. barley stripe mosaic
        McKinney, H.H., 1953
        Sill, W.H., Jr. and E.D. Hansing, 1955
    V. bean common mosaic
        Ainsworth, G.C., 1940
        Doolittle, S.P. and W.W. Gilbert, 1918
    V. bean pod mottle
        Zaumeyer, W.J. and H. Rex Thomas, 1948
    V. bean southern mosaic
        Zaumeyer, W.J. and L.L. Harter, 1943
    V. bean yellow mosaic
        Ainsworth, G.C., 1940
        Grogan, Raymond G. and J.C. Walker, 1948
        Hagedorn, D.J. and J.C. Walker, 1950, 1954
        Thomas, H. Rex and W.J. Zaumeyer, 1953
        Zaumeyer, W.J. and H.H. Fisher, 1953
    V. bean yellow stipple
        Zaumeyer, W.J. and H. Rex Thomas, 1950
    V. beet curly top
        Carsner, E., 1919
    V. beet mosaic
        Bennett, C.W., 1949
        Pound, Glenn S., 1947
        Severin, Henry H.P. and Roger M. Drake, 1948
    V. beet yellow net
        Sylvester, Edward S., 1948
    V. beet yellow wilt
        Bennett, C.W. and Carlos Munck, 1946
    V. beet yellows
        Roland, G. and J. Tahon, 1961
    V. broad bean mottle
        Yu, T.F., 1939
    V. cabbage black ring spot
        Tompkins, C.M., M.W. Gardner and H. Rex Thomas, 1938

Cucumis sativus, L. (cont.)
  V. cacao swollen shoot
    Tinsley, T.W. and A.L. Wharton, 1958
  V. canna mosaic
    Brierley, Philip and Floyd F. Smith, 1948
    Castillo, B.S., C.E. Yarwood and A.H. Gold, 1956
    Celino, M.S. and G.O. Ocfemia, 1941
  V. carnation mosaic
    Brierley, Philip and Floyd F. Smith, 1955, 1957
  V. cauliflower mosaic
    Alvarez-Garcia, L.A., 1951
  V. celery mosaic
    Freitag, Julius H. and Henry H.P. Severin, 1945
    Severin, Henry H.P. and Julius H. Freitag, 1938
  V. chilli (pepper) mosaic
    Dale, W.T., 1954
  V. chilli veinbanding
    Simons, John N., 1956
  V. chrysanthemum B (mild mosaic) *
    Hollings, M., 1957
  V. chrysanthemum latent *
    Hollings, M., 1957
  V. chrysanthemum stunt
    Keller, John R., 1953
  V. cineraria mosaic
    Jones, Leon K., 1944
  V. citrus tristeza
    Knorr, L.C., 1956
  V. cowpea mosaic
    Anderson, C.W., 1955
    Capoor, S.P. and P.M. Varma, 1956
    Dale, W.T., 1949
    McLean, D.M., 1941
    Yu, T.F., 1946
  V. cucumber mosaic
    McWhorter, F.P. and H.H. Millsap, 1954
    Peterson, Paul D. and H.H. McKinney, 1938
  V. dahlia mosaic
    Brierley, Philip and Floyd F. Smith, 1950
  V. datura distortion mosaic
    Capoor, S.P. and P.M. Varma, 1952
  V. eggplant mosaic
    Ferguson, I.A.C., 1951
  V. filaree red leaf
    Frazier, Norman W., 1951
  V. gladiolus *
    Snow, Gordon F., 1955
  V. lettuce mosaic
    Ainsworth, G.C., 1940
    Ainsworth, G.C. and L. Ogilvie, 1939
  V. lucerne mosaic
    Berkeley, G.H., 1947
    Johnson, E.M., 1946
    Kreitlow, K.W. and W.C. Price, 1949
    Zaumeyer, W.J., 1938, 1953
  V. nicotiana glutinosa root necrosis *
    Cetas, Robert C. and A. Frank Ross, 1952
  V. nothoscordum mosaic
    McKinney, H.H., 1950
  V. onion yellow dwarf
    Henderson, D.M., 1953
    Henderson, W.J., 1935
  V. orchid (odontoglossum) ring spot
    Jensen, D.D. and A. Herbert Gold, 1951
  V. orchid (vanda) mosaic
    Murakishi, Harry H., 1952
  V. papaw mosaic
    Adsuar, Jose, 1950
  V. papaw ring spot
    Jensen, D.D., 1949
  V. pea enation mosaic
    Ainsworth, G.C., 1940
    Simons, John N., 1954
  V. pea mosaic
    Ainsworth, G.C., 1940
    Murphy, D.M. and W.H. Pierce, 1937
  V. pea streak
    Zaumeyer, W.J., 1938
  V. pea wilt
    Johnson, Folke, 1942
  V. pea yellow mosaic *
    Ainsworth, G.C., 1940
  V. pelargonium ring spot *
    Hollings, M., 1957

C. sativus, L. (cont.)
  V. pokeweed mosaic *
    Doolittle, S.P. and W.W. Gilbert, 1918
  V. potato A
    MacLachlan, D.S., R.H. Larson and J.C. Walker, 1953
  V. potato Y
    Alvarez-Garcia, L.A. and Jose Adsuar, 1943
    Bald, J.G. and D.O. Norris, 1945
    Johnson, E.M., 1930
    Roque, Arturo and Jose Adsuar, 1941
  V. potato yellow dwarf
    Hougas, R.W., 1951
  V. primula mosaic
    Severin, Henry H.P. and C.M. Tompkins, 1950
    Tompkins, C.M. and John T. Middleton, 1941
  V. radish mosaic
    Tompkins, C.M., 1939
  V. red clover vein mosaic
    Hagedorn, D.J. and E.W. Hanson, 1951
    Hagedorn, D.J. and J.C. Walker, 1949, 1954
    Roberts, D.A., 1957
  V. spinach yellow dwarf
    Severin, Henry H.P. and Donald H. Little, 1947
  V. sweet potato feathery mottle
    Doolittle, S.P. and L.L. Harter, 1945
    Webb, Raymon E., 1954
  V. sweet potato mosaic
    Borders, H.I. and T.J. Ratcliff, 1954
  V. teasel mosaic
    Stoner, Warren N., 1951
  V. tobacco coarse etch
    Johnson, E.M., 1930
  V. tobacco etch
    Anderson, C.W., 1954
    Bennett, C.W., 1944
    Holmes, Francis O., 1946
    Johnson, E.M., 1930
  V. tobacco green mosaic
    Peterson, Paul D. and H.H. McKinney, 1938
  V. tobacco mosaic
    Ainsworth, G.C., 1933, 1937
    Doolittle, S.P. and F.S. Beecher, 1942
    Doolittle, S.P. and W.W. Gilbert, 1918
    Holmes, Francis O., 1941, 1946
    Jarrett, Phyllis H., 1930
    Johnson, E.M., 1930
    Peterson, Paul D. and H.H. McKinney, 1938
    Stover, W.G. and M.T. Vermillion, 1933
  V. tomato aspermy
    Blencowe, J.W. and John Caldwell, 1949
  V. tomato ring spot
    Samson, R.W. and E.P. Imle, 1942
  V. tomato spotted wilt
    Ainsworth, G.C., 1940
  V. turnip mosaic
    Tompkins, C.M., 1938, 1939
    Tompkins, C.M. and H. Rex Thomas, 1938
  V. turnip rosette *
    Broadbent, L. and G.D. Heathcote, 1958
  V. turnip yellow mosaic
    Broadbent, L. and G.D. Heathcote, 1958
  V. Wisconsin pea streak
    Hagedorn, D.J. and J.C. Walker, 1949, 1954

CUCURBITA ((Tourn.)) L. 1735 (Cucurbitaceae)
(PEPO) ((Tourn.)) L. 1735
C. lagenaria, L.
  V. cucumber mosaic
    Adsuar, Jose and A. Cruz Miret, 1950
  V. papaw mosaic
    Adsuar, Jose, 1950
C. maxima, Dcne.
  V. dodder latent mosaic
    Bennett, C.W., 1944
  V. orchid (cymbidium) mosaic
    Jensen, D.D., 1951
  V. orchid (odontoglossum) ring spot
    Jensen, D.D. and A. Herbert Gold, 1951
  V. pea mosaic
    Murphy, D.M. and W.H. Pierce, 1937
  V. peach ring spot
    Hobbs, Gordon A., 1951

Cucurbita maxima, Dcne. (cont.)
  V. stone fruit *
    Boyle, J.S., J. Duain Moore and G.W. Keitt, 1954
  V. tobacco etch
    Holmes, Francis O., 1946
  V. tobacco mosaic
    Holmes, Francis O., 1946
  V. tomato ring spot
    Samson, R.W. and E.P. Imle, 1942
C. moschata, Dcne.
  V. (cucumber) O.S.C. isolate 606 *
    Porter, Clark A. and Frank P. McWhorter, 1951
  V. onion yellow dwarf
    Henderson, W.J., 1935
  V. papaw mosaic
    Adsuar, Jose, 1950
  V. tomato ring spot
    Samson, R.W. and E.P. Imle, 1942
C. pepo, L.
  V. beet mosaic
    Pound, Glenn S., 1947
  V. celery mosaic
    Freitag, Julius H. and Henry H.P. Severin, 1945
  V. chilli (pepper) mosaic
    Dale, W.T., 1954
  V. chrysanthemum B (mild mosaic) *
    Hollings, M., 1957
  V. cowpea mosaic
    Capoor, S.P. and P.M. Varma, 1956
  V. cucumber green mottle mosaic
    Ainsworth, G.C., 1935
  V. dodder latent mosaic
    Bennett, C.W., 1944
  V. eggplant mosaic
    Dale, W.T., 1954
    Ferguson, I.A.C., 1951
  V. filaree red leaf
    Frazier, Norman W., 1951
  V. maize leaf fleck
    Stoner, Warren N., 1952
  V. orchid (vanda) mosaic
    Murakishi, Harry H., 1952
  V. papaw mosaic
    Adsuar, Jose, 1950
  V. primula mosaic
    Severin, Henry H.P. and C.M. Tompkins, 1950
  V. prunus G *
    Fulton, Robert W., 1957
  V. red currant ring spot
    Klesser, P.J., 1951
  V. spinach yellow dwarf
    Severin, Henry H.P. and Donald H. Little, 1947
  V. stone fruit *
    Boyle, J.S., J. Duain Moore and G.W. Keitt, 1954
  V. sweet potato mosaic
    Borders, H.I. and T.J. Ratcliff, 1954
  V. teasel mosaic
    Stoner, Warren N., 1951
  V. tobacco etch
    Holmes, Francis O., 1946
  V. tobacco mosaic
    Holmes, Francis O., 1946
  V. tomato aspermy
    Hollings, M., 1955
  V. tomato ring spot
    Samson, R.W. and E.P. Imle, 1942
C. pepo var. melopepo, (L.) Alef. (condensa, Bailey)
  V. chilli veinbanding
    Simons, Jons N., 1956
  V. primula mosaic
    Tompkins, C.M. and John T. Middleton, 1941

CUSCUTA ((Tourn.)) L. 1735 (Convolvulaceae)
C. americana, L.
  V. beet yellows
    Roland, G. and J. Tahon, 1961
  V. citrus tristeza
    Bennett, C.W. and A.S. Costa, 1949
C. californica, Choisy
  V. beet curly top
    Bennett, C.W., 1944, 1951, 1955
    Lackey, C.F., 1941
    Lackey, C.F. and C.W. Bennett, 1949

C. californica, Choisy (cont.)
  V. beet mosaic
    Bennett, C.W., 1944
  V. beet rosette *
    Bennett, C.W. and James E. Duffus, 1957
  V. beet yellow vein disease *
    Bennett, C.W., 1944, 1956
  V. citrus psorosis
    Bennett, C.W., 1944
  V. cucumber mosaic
    Bennett, C.W., 1940, 1944
  V. dodder latent mosaic
    Bennett, C.W., 1944
  V. peach mosaic
    Bennett, C.W., 1944
  V. tobacco etch
    Bennett, C.W., 1944
  V. tobacco mosaic
    Bennett, C.W., 1944
  V. tomato ring spot
    Bennett, C.W., 1944
  V. tomato spotted wilt
    Bennett, C.W., 1944
  V. turnip mosaic
    Bennett, C.W., 1944
C. campestris, Yuncker
  V. apple mosaic
    Yarwood, C.E., 1955
  V. asclepias yellows *
    Kunkel, L.O., 1950
  V. aster yellows
    Brierley, Philip and Floyd F. Smith, 1957
    Fulton, J.P., 1957
    Johnson, Folke, 1941
  V. bayberry yellows
    Raychaudhuri, S.P., 1952, 1953
  V. beet curly top
    Bennett, C.W., 1944
    Johnson, Folke, 1941
  V. beet mosaic
    Bennett, C.W., 1944
  V. beet rosette *
    Bennett, C.W. and James E. Duffus, 1957
  V. beet yellow vein disease *
    Bennett, C.W., 1944, 1956
  V. beet yellow wilt
    Bennett, C.W. and Carlos Munck, 1946
  V. citrus psorosis
    Bennett, C.W., 1944
  V. citrus tristeza
    Bennett, C.W. and A.S. Costa, 1949
  V. clover witches' broom *
    Frazier, N.W. and A.F. Posnette, 1957
  V. cucumber green mottle mosaic
    Johnson, Folke, 1941
  V. cucumber mosaic
    Bennett, C.W., 1944
    Costa, A.S., 1944
  V. cucurbit mosaic *
    Johnson, Folke, 1941
  V. dodder latent mosaic
    Bennett, C.W., 1944
  V. lilac witches' broom
    Brierley, Philip, 1955
  V. lucerne mosaic
    Kreitlow, K.W. and W.C. Price, 1949
  V. lucerne witches' broom
    Helms, Katie, 1957
    Kunkel, L.O., 1952
  V. pea mottle
    Johnson, Folke, 1942
  V. pea wilt
    Johnson, Folke, 1942
  V. peach mosaic
    Bennett, C.W., 1944
  V. peach western X disease
    Weathers, Lewis G. and George W. Cochran, 1950
  V. peach X disease
    Hildebrand, E.M., 1953
    Kunkel, L.O., 1944
  V. potato stem mottle
    Van der Want, J.P.H., 1955
  V. rose mosaic
    Fulton, Robert W., 1952

Cuscuta campestris, Yuncker (cont.)
   V. stone fruit *
      Boyle, J.S., J. Duain Moore and G.W. Keitt, 1954
   V. strawberry green petal
      Frazier, N.W. and A.F. Posnette, 1957
   V. strawberry mottle
      Demaree, J.B. and C.P. Marcus, 1951
   V. tobacco etch
      Bennett, C.W., 1944
   V. tobacco mosaic
      Bennett, C.W., 1944
      Cochran, G.W., 1946
      Costa, A.S., 1944
      Johnson, Folke, 1941
   V. tobacco ring spot
      Johnson, Folke, 1941
   V. tomato aspermy
      Brierley, Philip and Floyd F. Smith, 1957
   V. tomato big bud
      Helms, Katie, 1957
      Hill, A.V. and M. Mandryk, 1954
      Kunkel, L.O., 1951
   V. tomato bushy stunt
      Johnson, Folke, 1941
   V. tomato ring spot
      Bennett, C.W., 1944
   V. tomato spotted wilt
      Bennett, C.W., 1944
   V. turnip mosaic
      Bennett, C.W., 1944
   V. vaccinium false blossom
      Costa, A.S., 1944
      Kunkel, L.O., 1943, 1945
C. epithymum, Murr.
   V. beet yellows
      Roland, G. and J. Tahon, 1961
C. europaea, L.
   V. clover witches' broom *
      Frazier, N.W. and A.F. Posnette, 1957
   V. strawberry green petal
      Frazier, N.W. and A.F. Posnette, 1957
C. gronovii, Willd.
   V. chrysanthemum stunt
      Keller, John R., 1953
   V. rose mosaic
      Fulton, Robert W., 1952
   V. strawberry mottle
      Smith, Harlan E. and J. Duain Moore, 1952
C. indecora, Choisy
   V. citrus tristeza
      Bennett, C.W. and A.S. Costa, 1949
C. reflexa, Roxb.
   V. hibiscus yellow vein mosaic
      Capoor, S.P. and P.M. Varma, 1950
C. sandwichiana, Choisy
   V. cucumber mosaic
      Sakimura, K., 1947
C. spp.
   V. aster yellows
      Self, R.L. and H.M. Darling, 1949
   V. raspberry streak
      Horn, Norman L., 1948
   V. vaccinium ring spot
      Hilborn, M.T. and Reiner Bonde, 1956
   V. vinca yellows *
      Maramorosch, Karl, 1957
C. subinclusa, Dur. & Hilg.
   V. apple mosaic
      Yarwood, C.E., 1955
      Yarwood, C.E. and H.E. Thomas, 1954
   V. bayberry yellows
      Raychaudhuri, S.P., 1953
   V. beet curly top
      Bennett, C.W., 1940, 1944
      Fulton, Robert W., 1955
      Giddings, N.J., 1947
      Lackey, C.F. and C.W. Bennett, 1949
   V. beet mosaic
      Bennett, C.W., 1940, 1944
   V. beet rosette *
      Bennett, C.W. and James E. Duffus, 1957
   V. beet yellow vein disease *
      Bennett, C.W., 1944, 1956

C. subinclusa, Dur. & Hilg. (cont.)
   V. beet yellow wilt
      Bennett, C.W. and Carlos Munck, 1946
   V. citrus psorosis
      Bennett, C.W., 1944
   V. citrus tristeza
      Bennett, C.W. and A.S. Costa, 1949
   V. clover witches' broom *
      Frazier, N.W. and A.F. Posnette, 1957
   V. cucumber mosaic
      Bennett, C.W., 1940, 1944
   V. dodder latent mosaic
      Bennett, C.W., 1944
   V. lilac witches' broom
      Brierley, Philip, 1955
   V. peach mosaic
      Bennett, C.W., 1944
   V. peach western X disease
      Weathers, Lewis G. and George W. Cochran, 1950
   V. peach X disease
      Slack, Derald A., 1952
   V. potato stem mottle
      Van der Want, J.P.H., 1955
   V. raspberry streak
      Horn, N.L. and M.W. Woods, 1949
   V. rose mosaic
      Fulton, Robert W., 1952
   V. strawberry crinkle
      Smith, Harlan E. and J. Duain Moore, 1952
   V. strawberry green petal
      Frazier, N.W. and A.F. Posnette, 1957
   V. strawberry mottle
      Smith, Harlan E. and J. Duain Moore, 1952
   V. strawberry, type 2 *
      Smith, Harlan E. and J. Duain Moore, 1952
   V. tobacco etch
      Bennett, C.W., 1944
   V. tobacco mosaic
      Bennett, C.W., 1940, 1944
   V. tomato ring spot
      Bennett, C.W., 1944
   V. tomato spotted wilt
      Bennett, C.W., 1944
   V. turnip mosaic
      Bennett, C.W., 1944
   V. vaccinium stunt
      Hutchinson, M.T., A.C. Goheen and E.H. Varney, 1955
   V. vinca yellows *
      Maramorosch, Karl, 1956

CYAMOPSIS DC. 1825 (Leguminosae)
C. psoraloides, DC.
   V. pigeon pea sterility mosaic
      Capoor, S.P., 1952
C. tetragonoloba, (L.) Taub.
   V. beet yellows
      Roland, G. and J. Tahon, 1961
   V. chilli (pepper) mosaic
      Jha, Ashrafi and S.P. Raychaudhuri, 1956
   V. hydrangea ring spot
      Brierley, Philip and Paul Lorentz, 1956, 1957
   V. prunus B *
      Fulton, Robert W., 1957

CYCLAMEN ((Tourn.)) L. 1735 (Primulaceae)
C. persicum, Mill. (C. indicum, Auct.)
   V. beet yellows
      Roland, G. and J. Tahon, 1961
   V. orchid (cymbidium) mosaic
      Jensen, D.D., 1951
   V. primula mosaic
      Tompkins, C.M. and John T. Middleton, 1941

CYMBIDIUM Sw. 1799 (Orchidaceae)
C. spp.
   V. orchid (odontoglossum) ring spot
      Jensen, D.D. and A. Herbert Gold, 1951

CYNARA Vaill. ex L. 1737 (Compositae)
C. cardunculus, L.
   V. chrysanthemum stunt
      Brierley, Philip, 1953

Cynara cardunculus, L. (cont.)
  V. dahlia mosaic
    Brierley, Philip and Floyd F. Smith, 1950
C. scolymus, L.
  V. orchid (odontoglossum) ring spot
    Jensen, D.D. and A. Herbert Gold, 1951

CYNODON Rich. 1805 (Gramineae)
C. dactylon, (L.) Pers.
  V. cucumber mosaic
    Wellman, F.L., 1935

CYNOGLOSSUM ((Tourn.)) L. 1735 (Boraginaceae)
C. amabile, Stapf & Drum.
  V. prunus E *
    Fulton, Robert W., 1957
  V. prunus G *
    Fulton, Robert W., 1957
  V. squash mosaic
    Freitag, J.H., 1956
  V. tobacco etch
    Holmes, Francis O., 1946

CYPERUS ((Mich.)) L. 1735 (Cyperaceae)
C. alternifolius, L.
  V. wheat streak mosaic
    Sill, W.H., Jr. and Patrick C. Agusiobo, 1955
C. compressus, L.
  V. cucumber mosaic
    Wellman, F.L., 1935
C. esculentus, L.
  V. cucumber mosaic
    Wellman, F.L., 1935
  V. panicum mosaic *
    Sill, W.H., Jr. and R.C. Pickett, 1957
  V. wheat streak mosaic
    Sill, W.H., Jr. and Patrick C. Agusiobo, 1955

CYPHOMANDRA Mart. ex Sendtn. 1845 (Solanaceae)
C. betacea, (Cav.) Sendt.
  V. tobacco etch
    Holmes, Francis O., 1946
  V. tobacco mosaic
    Holmes, Francis O., 1946

CYPRIPEDIUM L. 1735 (Orchidaceae)
C. spp.
  V. wheat streak mosaic
    Sill, W.H., Jr. and Patrick C. Agusiobo, 1955

DACTYLIS L. 1742 (Gramineae)
D. glomerata, L.
  V. maize streak
    Finley, A.M., 1954
  V. panicum mosaic *
    Sill, W.H., Jr. and R.C. Pickett, 1957
  V. tobacco ring spot
    Wingard, S.A., 1928
  V. wheat streak mosaic
    Finley, A.M., 1957
    Sill, W.H., Jr. and Patrick C. Agusiobo, 1955

DAHLIA Cav. 1791 (Compositae)
D. merckii, Lehm.
  V. tobacco ring spot
    Wingard, S.A., 1928
D. pinnata, Cav.
  V. anemone mosaic *
    Hollings, M., 1957
  V. beet mosaic
    Pound, Glenn S., 1947
  V. beet yellow net
    McLean, D.M., 1952
  V. chrysanthemum B (mild mosaic) *
    Hollings, M., 1957
  V. cucumber mosaic
    Wellman, F.L., 1935
  V. datura distortion mosaic
    Capoor, S.P. and P.M. Varma, 1952
  V. tobacco etch
    Holmes, Francis O., 1946
  V. tobacco mosaic
    Holmes, Francis O., 1946

D. pinnata, Cav. (cont.)
  V. tomato aspermy
    Brierley, Philip, Floyd F. Smith and S.P.
    Doolittle, 1955
    Hollings, M., 1955
D. spp.
  V. beet yellows
    Roland, G. and J. Tahon, 1961
D. variabilis, (Willd.) Desf.
  V. cucumber mosaic
    Brierley, Philip and Floyd F. Smith, 1950
  V. red currant ring spot
    Klesser, P.J., 1951

DAPHNE Tourn. ex L. 1735 (Thymeleaceae)
D. cneorum, L.
  V. cucumber mosaic
    Milbrath, J.A. and Roy A. Young, 1956

DATURA L. 1735 (Solanaceae)
D. aegyptiaca, Vesl.
  V. potato A
    MacLachlan, D.S., R.H. Larson and J.C. Walker,
    1953
  V. potato Y
    Darby, J.F., R.H. Larson and J.C. Walker, 1951
D. alba, Nees
  V. hibiscus yellow vein mosaic
    Capoor, S.P. and P.M. Varma, 1950
D. bernhardii, Lund.
  V. potato A
    MacLachlan, D.S., R.H. Larson and J.C. Walker,
    1953
D. chlorantha, Hook.
  V. potato A
    MacLachlan, D.S., R.H. Larson and J.C. Walker,
    1953
D. fastuosa, L.
  V. potato A
    MacLachlan, D.S., R.H. Larson and J.C. Walker,
    1953
  V. potato Y
    Darby, J.F., R.H. Larson and J.C. Walker, 1951
  V. tobacco mosaic
    Allard, H.A., 1916
D. ferox, L.
  V. potato A
    MacLachlan, D.S., R.H. Larson and J.C. Walker,
    1953
D. inoxia, Mill.
  V. cowpea mosaic
    Capoor, S.P. and P.M. Varma, 1956
  V. pigeon pea sterility mosaic
    Capoor, S.P., 1952
D. metel, L.
  V. beet mosaic
    Pound, Glenn S., 1947
  V. cauliflower mosaic
    Walker, J.C., Francis J. LeBeau and Glenn S.
    Pound, 1945
  V. potato A
    MacLachlan, D.S., R.H. Larson and J.C. Walker,
    1953
D. meteloides, DC.
  V. beet curly top
    Bennett, C.W., Eubanks Carsner, F.H. Coons and
    E.W. Brandes, 1946
    Giddings, N.J., C.W. Bennett and A.L. Harrison,
    1951
  V. beet mosaic
    Bennett, C.W., 1949
  V. beet yellows
    Roland, G. and J. Tahon, 1961
  V. cauliflower mosaic
    Walker, J.C., Francis J. LeBeau and Glenn S.
    Pound, 1945
  V. dodder latent mosaic
    Bennett, C.W., 1944
  V. orchid (cymbidium) mosaic
    Jensen, D.D. and A.H. Gold, 1955
  V. potato A
    MacLachlan, D.S., R.H. Larson and J.C. Walker,
    1953

Datura meteloides, DC. (cont.)
  V. potato Y
      Darby, J.F., R.H. Larson and J.C. Walker, 1951
  V. tobacco ring spot
      Cooper, W.E., 1949
D. spp.
  V. beet curly top
      Bennett, C.W. and A.S. Costa, 1949
  V. citrus tristeza
      Bennett, C.W. and A.S. Costa, 1949
      Knorr, L.C., 1956
  V. cucumber mosaic
      Adsuar, Jose and A. Cruz Miret, 1950
D. stramonium, L.
  V. abutilon infectious variegation
      Bird, Julio, 1958
  V. alsike clover mosaic
      Zaumeyer, W.J., 1940
  V. anemone brown ring *
      Hollings, M., 1958
  V. anemone mosaic *
      Hollings, M., 1957
  V. bayberry yellows
      Raychaudhuri, S.P., 1953
  V. bean pod mottle
      Zaumeyer, W.J. and H. Rex Thomas, 1948
  V. bean southern mosaic
      Zaumeyer, W.J. and L.L. Harter, 1943
  V. bean yellow mosaic
      Hagedorn, D.J. and J.C. Walker, 1950, 1954
      Thomas, H. Rex and W.J. Zaumeyer, 1953
      Zaumeyer, W.J., 1940
  V. bean yellow stipple
      Zaumeyer, W.J. and H. Rex Thomas, 1950
  V. beet curly top
      Bennett, C.W., Eubanks Carsner, F.H. Coons and
      E.W. Brandes, 1946
  V. beet mosaic
      Bennett, C.W., 1949
      Severin, Henry H.P. and Roger M. Drake, 1947
  V. beet yellow net
      Sylvester, Edward S., 1948
  V. beet yellows
      Roland, G. and J. Tahon, 1961
  V. broad bean mottle
      Bawden, F.C., R.P. Chaudhuri and B. Kassanis,
      1951
  V. cabbage black ring spot
      Tompkins, C.M., M.W. Gardner and H. Rex
      Thomas, 1938
  V. cabbage ring necrosis
      Larson, R.H. and J.C. Walker, 1941
  V. cacao swollen shoot
      Tinsley, T.W. and A.L. Wharton, 1958
  V. cauliflower mosaic
      Alvarez-Garcia, L.A., 1951
      Walker, J.C., Francis J. LeBeau and Glenn S.
      Pound, 1945
  V. celery mosaic
      Freitag, Julius H. and Henry H.P. Severin, 1945
  V. chilli veinbanding
      Simons, John N., 1956
  V. chrysanthemum B (mild mosaic) *
      Hollings, M., 1957
  V. chrysanthemum ring spot
      Brierley, Philip and Floyd F. Smith, 1955
  V. citrus tristeza
      Bennett, C.W. and A.S. Costa, 1949
  V. cowpea mosaic
      McLean, D.M., 1941
      Yu, T.F., 1946
  V. cucumber green mottle mosaic
      Ainsworth, G.C., 1935
  V. cucumber mosaic
      Burnett, G., 1934
      Harter, L.L., 1938
      Lindberg, G.D., D.H. Hall and J.C. Walker, 1956
      McKnight, T., 1953
      Vasudeva, R. Sahai and T.B. Lal, 1943
  V. dodder latent mosaic
      Bennett, C.W., 1944
  V. hydrangea ring spot
      Brierley, Philip and Paul Lorentz, 1957

D. stramonium, L. (cont.)
  V. lettuce mosaic
      Ainsworth, G.C. and L. Ogilvie, 1939
  V. muskmelon mosaic
      Lindberg, G.D., D.H. Hall and J.C. Walker, 1956
  V. nicotiana glutinosa root necrosis *
      Cetas, Robert C. and A. Frank Ross, 1952
  V. nothoscordum mosaic
      McKinney, H.H., 1950
  V. onion yellow dwarf
      Henderson, D.M., 1953
  V. orchid (odontoglossum) ring spot
      Jensen, D.D. and A. Herbert Gold, 1951
  V. papaw mosaic
      Adsuar, Jose, 1950
  V. pea mottle
      Johnson, Folke, 1942
  V. pea streak
      Zaumeyer, W.J., 1938
  V. pea wilt
      Johnson, Folke, 1942
  V. pokeweed mosaic *
      Allard, H.A., 1918
  V. potato spindle tuber
      Goss, R.W., 1931
  V. potato Y
      Anderson, C.W. and M.K. Corbett, 1957
      Bagnall, R.H., R.H. Larson and J.C. Walker, 1956
      Bald, J.G. and D.O. Norris, 1945
      Bawden, F.C. and B. Kassanis, 1951
      Bawden, F.C. and F.M.L. Sheffield, 1944
      Cockerham, George, 1943
      Conover, Robert A. and Robert W. Fulton, 1953
      Dennis, R.W.G., 1939
      Dykstra, T.P., 1933
      Johnson, E.M., 1930
      Jones, Leon K. and C.L. Vincent, 1937
      Koch, K.L., 1933
      Roque, Arturo and Jose Adsuar, 1941
      Smith, Kenneth M. and R.W.G. Dennis, 1940
      Vasudeva, R. Sahai and T.B. Lal, 1945
  V. primula mosaic
      Tompkins, C.M. and John T. Middleton, 1941
  V. prunus A *
      Fulton, Robert W., 1957
  V. prunus G *
      Fulton, Robert W., 1957
  V. radish mosaic
      Tompkins, C.M., 1939
  V. red clover vein mosaic
      Hagedorn, D.J. and J.C. Walker, 1949, 1954
  V. spinach yellow dwarf
      Severin, Henry H.P. and Donald H. Little, 1947
  V. squash mosaic
      Freitag, J.H., 1956
      Lindberg, G.D., D.H. Hall and J.C. Walker, 1956
  V. stone fruit *
      Boyle, J.S., J. Duain Moore and G.W. Keitt, 1954
  V. sweet potato feathery mottle
      Doolittle, S.P. and L.L. Harter, 1945
  V. tobacco leaf curl
      Bird, Julio, 1957
  V. tobacco ring spot
      Fenne, S.B., 1931
  V. tomato aspermy
      Blencowe, J.W. and John Caldwell, 1949
  V. turnip mosaic
      Tompkins, C.M., 1938, 1939
      Tompkins, C.M. and H. Rex Thomas, 1938
      Walker, J.C., Francis J. LeBeau and Glenn S.
      Pound, 1945
  V. turnip yellow mosaic
      Broadbent, L. and G.D. Heathcote, 1958
  V. watermelon mosaic
      Lindberg, G.D., D.H. Hall and J.C. Walker, 1956
  V. Wisconsin pea streak
      Hagedorn, D.J. and J.C. Walker, 1949, 1954
D. stramonium var. chalybea, Koch *
  V. potato Y
      Sakimura, K., 1953
D. stramonium var. tatula, (L.) Torr.
  V. beet yellows
      Roland, G. and J. Tahon, 1961

Datura stramonium, L., var. tatula, (L.) Torr. (cont.)
  V. potato Y
    Darby, J.F., R.H. Larson and J.C. Walker, 1951
    Dykstra, T.P., 1933
  V. sweet potato feathery mottle
    Webb, Raymon E., 1954

DAUCUS ((Tourn.)) L. 1735 (Umbelliferae)
D. carota, L.
  V. beet mosaic
    Pound, Glenn S., 1947
  V. beet yellows
    Roland, G. and J. Tahon, 1961
  V. chilli (pepper) mosaic
    Jha, Ashrafi and S.P. Raychaudhuri, 1956
  V. dodder latent mosaic
    Bennett, C.W., 1944
  V. lovage mosaic
    Smith, Kenneth M. and Roy Markham, 1944
  V. tobacco etch
    Holmes, Francis O., 1946
  V. tobacco mosaic
    Holmes, Francis O., 1938
  V. tomato ring spot
    Samson, R.W. and E.P. Imle, 1942
D. carota var. sativa, DC.
  V. squash mosaic
    Freitag, J.H., 1956
  V. tobacco ring spot
    Wingard, S.A., 1928

DELPHINIUM Tourn. ex L. 1735 (Ranunculaceae)
D. ajacis, L.
  V. beet mosaic
    Pound, Glenn S., 1947
  V. cabbage black ring spot
    Tompkins, C.M., M.W. Gardner and H. Rex
    Thomas, 1938
  V. cauliflower mosaic
    Walker, J.C., Francis J. LeBeau and Glenn S.
    Pound, 1945
  V. tomato ring spot
    Samson, R.W. and E.P. Imle, 1942
  V. turnip mosaic
    Tompkins, C.M., 1928, 1939
    Tompkins, C.M. and H. Rex Thomas, 1938
D. cultorum, Voss
  V. cabbage black ring spot
    Tompkins, C.M., M.W. Gardner and H. Rex
    Thomas, 1938
  V. primula mosaic
    Tompkins, C.M. and John T. Middleton, 1941
  V. tobacco etch
    Holmes, Francis O., 1946
  V. tobacco mosaic
    Holmes, Francis O., 1946
  V. turnip mosaic
    Tompkins, C.M., 1939
    Tompkins, C.M. and H. Rex Thomas, 1938
D. grandiflorum, L.
  V. chrysanthemum B (mild mosaic) *
    Hollings, M., 1957
  V. pea mosaic
    Murphy, D.M. and W.H. Pierce, 1937
D. hybrid
  V. beet curly top
    Severin, Henry H.P., 1942
D. hybridum, Steph.
  V. tomato aspermy
    Brierley, Philip, Floyd F. Smith and S.P.
    Doolittle, 1955
D. spp.
  V. euphorbia mosaic
    Costa, A.S. and C.W. Bennett, 1950
  V. squash mosaic
    Freitag, J.H., 1956

DENDROPOGON Raf. 1825 (Bromeliaceae)
D. usneoides, (L.) Raf.
  V. cucumber mosaic
    Wellman, F.L., 1935

DESCHAMPSIA Beauv. 1812 (Gramineae)
D. caespitosa, (L.) Beauv.
  V. barley yellow dwarf
    Bruehl, G.W. and H.V. Toko, 1957
D. danthonioides, (Trin.) Munro
  V. barley yellow dwarf
    Oswald, John W. and Byron R. Houston, 1953

DESMODIUM Desv. 1813 (Leguminosae)
D. incanum, DC.
  V. cucumber mosaic
    Anderson, C.W., 1955

DESPLATZIA Bocquill. 1866-67 (Tiliaceae)
D. dewevrei, (DeWild. & Th. Dur.) Burret *
  V. cacao swollen shoot
    Tinsley, T.W. and A.L. Wharton, 1958
D. lutea, A. Chev.
  V. cacao swollen shoot
    Posnette, A.F., N.F. Robertson and J. McA.
    Todd, 1950

DIANTHUS L. 1735 (Caryophyllaceae)
D. barbatus, L.
  V. anemone brown ring *
    Hollings, M., 1958
  V. anemone mosaic *
    Hollings, M., 1957
  V. beet mosaic
    Pound, Glenn S., 1947
  V. beet yellows
    Roland, G. and J. Tahon, 1961
  V. cabbage black ring spot
    Tompkins, C.M., M.W. Gardner and H. Rex
    Thomas, 1938
  V. chrysanthemum B (mild mosaic) *
    Hollings, M., 1957
  V. chrysanthemum latent *
    Hollings, M., 1957
  V. pea mosaic
    Murphy, D.M. and W.H. Pierce, 1937
  V. peony leaf curl *
    Brierley, Philip and Paul Lorentz, 1957
  V. primula mosaic
    Tompkins, C.M. and John T. Middleton, 1941
  V. radish mosaic
    Tompkins, C.M., 1939
  V. tobacco etch
    Holmes, Francis O., 1946
  V. tobacco mosaic
    Holmes, Francis O., 1946
  V. tobacco necrosis
    Kassanis, B., 1955
  V. tobacco ring spot
    Wingard, S.A., 1928
  V. tomato aspermy
    Hollings, M., 1955
  V. turnip mosaic
    Tompkins, C.M., 1938, 1939
    Tompkins, C.M. and H. Rex Thomas, 1938
D. caryophyllus, L.
  V. aster yellows
    Smith, Floyd F. and Philip Brierley, 1953
  V. beet yellows
    Roland, G. and J. Tahon, 1961
  V. citrus tristeza
    Knorr, L.C., 1956
  V. cucumber mosaic
    Wellman, F.L., 1935
  V. orchid (vanda) mosaic
    Murakishi, Harry H., 1952
  V. squash mosaic
    Freitag, J.H., 1956
  V. tobacco necrosis
    Kassanis, B., 1955
  V. tomato aspermy
    Brierley, Philip, Floyd F. Smith and S.P.
    Doolittle, 1955
    Hollings, M., 1955
  V. turnip mosaic
    Tompkins, C.M., 1939

Dianthus chinensis, L.
  V. beet yellows
    Roland, G. and J. Tahon, 1961
  V. tobacco etch
    Holmes, Francis O., 1946
  V. tobacco mosaic
    Holmes, Francis O., 1946
  V. tomato aspermy
    Brierley, Philip, Floyd F. Smith and S.P.
    Doolittle, 1955
D. deltoides, L.
  V. pea mosaic
    Murphy, D.M. and W.H. Pierce, 1937
D. plumarius, L.
  V. cucumber mosaic
    Wellman, F.L., 1935
  V. tobacco ring spot no. 2
    Brierley, Philip, 1954
D. superbus, L.
  V. bean pod mottle
    Zaumeyer, W.J. and H. Rex Thomas, 1948

DIGITALIS ((Tourn.)) L. 1735 (Scrophulariaceae)
D. purpurea, L.
  V. beet mosaic
    Pound, Glenn S., 1947
  V. cauliflower mosaic
    Walker, J.C., Francis J. LeBeau and Glenn S.
    Pound, 1945
  V. cucumber mosaic
    Wellman, F.L., 1935
  V. pea mosaic
    Murphy, D.M. and W.H. Pierce, 1937
  V. squash mosaic
    Freitag, J.H., 1956
  V. tobacco etch
    Holmes, Francis O., 1946

DIGITARIA Heist. ex Adans. 1763 (Gramineae)
D. horizontalis, Willd.
  V. sugarcane streak
    Storey, H.H. and A.P.D. McClean, 1930
D. macrobachne, (Presl) Henr. *
  V. rice and corn leaf-gall *
    Agati, Julian A. and Carlos A. Calica, 1950
D. sanguinalis, (L.) Scop.
  V. agropyron mosaic
    Slykhuis, J.T., 1952
  V. barley yellow dwarf
    Oswald, John W. and Byron R. Houston, 1953
  V. rice and corn leaf-gall *
    Agati, Julian A. and Carlos A. Calica, 1950
  V. wheat spot mosaic *
    Slykhuis, John T., 1956

DIMORPHOTHECA Vaill. ex L. 1735 (Compositae)
D. aurantiaca, DC.
  V. cauliflower mosaic
    Walker, J.C., Francis J. LeBeau and Glenn S.
    Pound, 1945
  V. celery mosaic
    Freitag, Julius H. and Henry H.P. Severin, 1945
  V. radish mosaic
    Tompkins, C.M., 1939
  V. turnip mosaic
    Tompkins, C.M., 1938, 1939
    Tompkins, C.M. and H. Rex Thomas, 1938
D. sinuata, DC.
  V. squash mosaic
    Freitag, J.H., 1956

DIOSCOREA Plum. ex L. 1737 (Dioscoreaceae)
D. alata, L.
  V. cucumber mosaic
    Brierley, Philip and Floyd F. Smith, 1944
  V. lily symptomless
    Brierley, Philip and Floyd F. Smith, 1944
  V. tulip breaking
    Brierley, Philip and Floyd F. Smith, 1944
D. bulbifera, L.
  V. cucumber mosaic
    Wellman, F.L., 1935

DIPLACUS Nutt. 1838 (Scrophulariaceae)
D. aurantiacus, Hort. ex Vilmorin's Blumeng
  V. lucerne dwarf
    Freitag, J.H., 1951

DISTICHLIS Raf. 1819 (Gramineae)
D. spicata, (L.) Greene
  V. lucerne dwarf
    Freitag, J.H., 1951

DITHYREA Harv. 1845 (Cruciferae)
D. wislizenii, Engelm.
  V. beet yellows
    Roland, G. and J. Tahon, 1961

DOLICHOS L. 1737 (Leguminosae)
D. biflorus, L.
  V. cowpea mosaic
    Capoor, S.P. and P.M. Varma, 1956
D. lablab, L.
  V. bean common mosaic
    Nelson, Ray, 1932
    Reddick, D. and V.B. Stewart, 1919
    Zaumeyer, W.J. and B.L. Wade, 1935
  V. bean yellow mosaic
    Zaumeyer, W.J. and H.H. Fisher, 1953
    Zaumeyer, W.J. and B.L. Wade, 1935
  V. broad bean mottle
    Yu, T.F., 1939
  V. cauliflower mosaic
    Walker, J.C., Francis J. LeBeau and Glenn S.
    Pound, 1945
  V. chilli (pepper) mosaic
    Jha, Ashrafi and S.P. Raychaudhuri, 1956
  V. cowpea mosaic
    Capoor, S.P. and P.M. Varma, 1956
    Yu, T.F., 1946
  V. cucumber mosaic
    Wellman, F.L., 1935
  V. datura distortion mosaic
    Capoor, S.P. and P.M. Varma, 1952
  V. hibiscus yellow vein mosaic
    Capoor, S.P. and P.M. Varma, 1950
  V. lucerne mosaic
    Zaumeyer, W.J. and B.L. Wade, 1935
  V. pea mosaic
    Murphy, D.M. and W.H. Pierce, 1937
  V. red clover mosaic *
    Zaumeyer, W.J. and B.L. Wade, 1935
  V. tobacco etch
    Holmes, Francis O., 1946
  V. tobacco mosaic
    Holmes, Francis O., 1946
  V. turnip mosaic
    Walker, J.C., Francis J. LeBeau and Glenn S.
    Pound, 1945
D. lignosus, L.
  V. pea mosaic
    Murphy, D.M. and W.H. Pierce, 1937

DOMBEYA Cav. 1787 (Sterculiaceae)
D. buettneri, K. Schum.
  V. cacao swollen shoot
    Tinsley, T.W. and A.L. Wharton, 1958

DORONICUM Tourn. ex L. 1735 (Compositae)
D. caucasicum, Bieb.
  V. dahlia mosaic
    Brierley, Philip and Floyd F. Smith, 1950
D. cordatum, Sch. Bip.
  V. chrysanthemum stunt
    Brierley, Philip, 1953

DRACAENA Vand. 1762 (Liliaceae)
D. fragans, Ker-Gawl.
  V. tulip breaking
    Brierley, Philip and Floyd F. Smith, 1944
D. sanderiana, Hort.
  V. cucumber mosaic
    Brierley, Philip and Floyd F. Smith, 1944
  V. lily symptomless
    Brierley, Philip and Floyd F. Smith, 1944
  V. tulip breaking
    Brierley, Philip and Floyd F. Smith, 1944

ECBALLIUM A. Rich. 1824 (Cucurbitaceae)
E. elaterium, A. Rich
  V. cucumber mosaic
    Jagger, I.C., 1918

ECHINOCHLOA Beauv. 1812 (Gramineae)
E. crus-galli, (L.) Beauv.
  V. agropyron mosaic
    Slykhuis, J.T., 1952
  V. barley yellow dwarf
    Bruehl, G.W. and H.V. Toko, 1957
    Oswald, John W. and Byron R. Houston, 1953
  V. wheat spot mosaic *
    Slykhuis, John T., 1956
  V. wheat streak mosaic
    Sill, W.H., Jr. and Patrick C. Agusiobo, 1955
E. spp.
  V. rice and corn leaf-gall *
    Agati, Julian A. and Carlos A. Calica, 1950

ECHINOCYSTIS Torr. & Gray 1840 (Cucurbitaceae)
(MICRAMPELIS) Raf. 1808
E. lobata, (Michx.) Torr. & Gray (Micrampelis
lobata, Greene)
  V. stone fruit *
    Boyle, J.S., J. Duain Moore and G.W. Keitt, 1954

ECHINOPS L. 1737 (Compositae)
E. ritro, L.
  V. chrysanthemum stunt
    Brierley, Philip, 1953

ECHIUM Tourn. ex L. 1737 (Boraginaceae)
E. vulgare, L.
  V. anemone mosaic *
    Hollings, M., 1957
  V. tobacco etch
    Holmes, Francis O., 1946

ECLIPTA L. 1771 (Compositae)
E. alba, Hassk.
  V. beet yellows
    Roland, G. and J. Tahon, 1961
  V. hibiscus yellow vein mosaic
    Capoor, S.P. and P.M. Varma, 1950

ELAEIS Jacq. 1763 (Palmaceae)
E. guineensis, Jacq.
  V. cacao swollen shoot
    Tinsley, T.W. and A.L. Wharton, 1958

ELAEOPHORBIA Stapf 1906 (Euphorbiaceae)
E. drupifera, Stapf
  V. cacao swollen shoot
    Tinsley, T.W. and A.L. Wharton, 1958

ELEUSINE Gaertn. 1788 (Gramineae)
E. coracana, (L.) Gaertn.
  V. sugarcane mosaic
    Brandes, E.W. and Peter J. Klaphaak, 1923
E. indica, (L.) Gaertn.
  V. maize streak
    Storey, H.H. and A.P.D. McClean, 1930
  V. panicum mosaic *
    Sill, W.H., Jr. and R.C. Pickett, 1957
  V. sugarcane streak
    Storey, H.H. and A.P.D. McClean, 1930

ELYMUS L. 1748 (Gramineae)
E. canadensis, L.
  V. barley yellow dwarf
    Bruehl, G.W. and H.V. Toko, 1957
E. condensatus, Presl
  V. barley yellow dwarf
    Bruehl, G.W. and H.V. Toko, 1957
E. giganteus, Vahl
  V. barley yellow dwarf
    Bruehl, G.W. and H.V. Toko, 1957
E. glaucus, Buckl.
  V. barley yellow dwarf
    Bruehl, G.W. and H.V. Toko, 1957
    Oswald, John W. and Byron R. Houston, 1953

E. junceus, Fisch.
  V. barley yellow dwarf
    Bruehl, G.W. and H.V. Toko, 1957
E. triticoides, Buckl.
  V. barley yellow dwarf
    Bruehl, G.W. and H.V. Toko, 1957

EMILIA Cass. 1817 (Compositae)
E. flammea, Cass.
  V. tobacco etch
    Holmes, Francis O., 1946
E. sonchifolia, Hort.
  V. cucumber mosaic
    Adsuar, Jose and A. Cruz Miret, 1950
  V. papaw mosaic
    Adsuar, Jose, 1950
  V. potato Y
    Sakimura, K., 1953
  V. tomato ring spot
    Samson, R.W. and E.P. Imle, 1942

EPILOBIUM Dill. ex L. 1735 (Onagraceae)
E. angustifolium, L.
  V. beet yellows
    Roland, G. and J. Tahon, 1961
E. montanum, L.
  V. anemone mosaic *
    Hollings, M., 1957
  V. chrysanthemum B (mild mosaic) *
    Hollings, M., 1957
E. paniculatum, Nutt.
  V. beet yellows
    Roland, G. and J. Tahon, 1961

EQUISETUM ((Tourn.)) L. 1753 (Equisetaceae)
E. arvense, L.
  V. beet ring spot *
    Harrison, B.D., 1957
  V. beet yellows
    Roland, G. and J. Tahon, 1961

ERAGROSTIS Host 1809 (Gramineae)
E. amabilis, (L.) Wight & Arn.
  V. rice and corn leaf-gall *
    Agati, Julian A. and Carlos A. Calica, 1950
E. cilianensis, (All.) Link (E. major, Host)
  V. agropyron mosaic
    Slykhuis, J.T., 1952

EREMOCARPUS Benth. 1844 (Euphorbiaceae)
E. setigerus, Benth.
  V. beet curly top
    Carsner, E., 1919
  V. beet yellows
    Roland, G. and J. Tahon, 1961

ERIGERON L. 1737 (Compositae)
E. annuus, (L.) Pers.
  V. tobacco etch
    Holmes, Francis O., 1946
  V. tomato aspermy
    Brierley, Philip, Floyd F. Smith and S.P.
    Doolittle, 1955
E. bonariensis, L.
  V. beet curly top
    Bennett, C.W. and A.S. Costa, 1949
  V. citrus tristeza
    Bennett, C.W. and A.S. Costa, 1949
  V. euphorbia mosaic
    Costa, A.S. and C.W. Bennett, 1950
E. canadensis, L.
  V. beet eyllows
    Roland, G. and J. Tahon, 1961
  V. peach rosette
    McClintock, J.A., 1931
  V. tobacco mosaic
    Holmes, Francis O., 1938
  V. tomato aspermy
    Brierley, Philip, Floyd F. Smith and S.P.
    Doolittle, 1955
E. speciosus, DC.
  V. tobacco etch
    Holmes, Francis O., 1946

Erigeron speciosus, DC. (cont.)
   V. tobacco mosaic
      Holmes, Francis O., 1946
   V. tomato ring spot
      Samson, R.W. and E.P. Imle, 1942
E. spp.
   V. cucumber mosaic
      Wellman, F.L., 1935

ERIOCHLOA H. B. & K. 1815 (Gramineae)
E. subglabra, Hitchcock
   V. sugarcane mosaic
      Chardon, C.E. and R.A. Veve, 1923

ERIOGONUM Michx. 1803 (Polygonaceae)
E. fasciculatum, Benth.
   V. beet yellows
      Roland, G. and J. Tahon, 1961
   V. cucumber mosaic
      Bennett, C.W., 1944
   V. dodder latent mosaic
      Bennett, C.W., 1944

ERODIUM L'Herit. 1787 (Geraniaceae)
E. cicutarium, (L.) L'Herit.
   V. beet yellows
      Roland, G. and J. Tahon, 1961
E. moschatum, L'Herit.
   V. beet yellow net
      Sylvester, Edward S., 1948
   V. orchid (cymbidium) mosaic
      Jensen, D.D., 1951

ERYSIMUM ((Tourn.)) L. 1735 (Cruciferae)
E. cheiranthoides, L.
   V. muskmelon mosaic
      Rader, Wm. E., Hugh F. Fitzpatrick and E.M.
      Hildebrand, 1947
   V. stone fruit *
      Boyle, J.S., J. Duain Moore and G.W. Keitt, 1954
E. perofskianum, Fisch. & Mey.
   V. cauliflower mosaic
      Tompkins, C.M., 1937
E. spp.
   V. cauliflower mosaic
      Caldwell, John and Ian W. Prentice, 1942

ERYTHRONIUM L. 1735 (Liliaceae)
E. spp.
   V. cucumber mosaic
      Brierley, Philip and Floyd F. Smith, 1944
   V. lily symptomless
      Brierley, Philip and Floyd F. Smith, 1944
   V. tulip breaking
      Brierley, Philip and Floyd F. Smith, 1944

ERYTHROPSIS Endl. * (Sterculiaceae)
E. barteri, (Mast.) Ridley
   V. cacao swollen shoot
      Posnette, A.F., N.F. Robertson and J. McA.
      Todd, 1950

ESCHSCHOLTZIA Cham. 1820 (Papaveraceae)
(ESCHSCHOLZIA) Cham. 1820
E. californica, Cham.
   V. beet curly top
      Carsner, E., 1919
   V. beet yellows
      Roland, G. and J. Tahon, 1961
   V. muskmelon mosaic
      Rader, Wm. E., Hugh F. Fitzpatrick and E.M.
      Hildebrand, 1947
   V. squash mosaic
      Freitag, J.H., 1956

EUCHLAENA Schrad. 1832 (Gramineae)
E. mexicana, Schrad.
   V. sugarcane mosaic
      Brandes, E.W. and Peter J. Klaphaak, 1923

EUPHORBIA L. 1737 (Euphorbiaceae)
E. esula, L.
   V. stone fruit *
      Boyle, J.S., J. Duain Moore and G.W. Keitt, 1954
E. geniculata, Ort.
   V. hibiscus yellow vein mosaic
      Capoor, S.P. and P.M. Varma, 1950
E. helioscopia, L.
   V. beet yellows
      Roland, G. and J. Tahon, 1961
E. heterophylla, L.
   V. tobacco etch
      Holmes, Francis O., 1946
   V. tobacco mosaic
      Holmes, Francis O., 1946
   V. tomato ring spot
      Samson, R.W. and E.P. Imle, 1942
E. maculata, L.
   V. beet yellows
      Roland, G. and J. Tahon, 1961
   V. tobacco mosaic
      Holmes, Francis O., 1938
E. marginata, Pursh
   V. cucumber mosaic
      Wellman, F.L., 1935
   V. squash mosaic
      Freitag, J.H., 1956
   V. tobacco etch
      Holmes, Francis O., 1946
   V. tobacco mosaic
      Holmes, Francis O., 1946
E. peplus, L.
   V. anemone mosaic *
      Hollings, M., 1957
   V. beet yellows
      Roland, G. and J. Tahon, 1961
E. pilulifera, L.
   V. citrus tristeza
      Bennett, C.W. and A.S. Costa, 1949
   V. euphorbia mosaic
      Costa, A.S. and C.W. Bennett, 1950
E. preslii, Guss.
   V. tobacco etch
      Holmes, Francis O., 1946 ·
   V. tobacco mosaic
      Holmes, Francis O., 1946
E. prunifolia, Jacq.
   V. abutilon infectious variegation
      Bird, Julio, 1958
      Costa, A.S. and C.W. Bennett, 1950
   V. beet curly top
      Costa, A.S., 1952
   V. citrus tristeza
      Bennett, C.W. and A.S. Costa, 1949
E. pulcherrima, Willd.
   V. cucumber mosaic
      Wellman, F.L., 1935
   V. sweet potato mosaic
      Borders, H.I. and T.J. Ratcliff, 1954
E. serphyllifolia, Pers.
   V. beet yellows
      Roland, G. and J. Tahon, 1961

EVODIA Forst. 1776 (Rutaceae)
E. spp.
   V. citrus tristeza
      Knorr, L.C., 1956

FAGOPYRUM Tourn. ex Hall. 1742 (Polygonaceae)
F. esculentum, Moench
   V. anemone brown ring *
      Hollings, M., 1958
   V. beet curly top
      Costa, A.S., 1952
   V. chrysanthemum B (mild mosaic) *
      Hollings, M., 1957
   V. muskmelon mosaic
      Rader, Wm. E., Hugh F. Fitzpatrick and E.M.
      Hildebrand, 1947
   V. stone fruit *
      Boyld, J.S., J. Duain Moore and G.W. Keitt, 1954
   V. tobacco etch
      Holmes, Francis O., 1946

FEIJOA Berg 1858 (Myrtaceae)
F. sellowiana, Berg
  V. beet curly top
    Giddings, N.J., 1944

FERULA Tourn. ex L. 1737 (Umbelliferae)
F. communis, L.
  V. cucumber mosaic
    Wellman, F.L., 1935

FESTUCA ((Tourn.)) L. 1735 (Gramineae)
F. elatior, L.
  V. wheat streak mosaic
    Slykhuis, John T., 1955
F. rubra, L.
  V. barley stripe mosaic
    Slykhuis, J.T., 1952
  V. wheat streak mosaic
    Slykhuis, J.T., 1952, 1955

FICUS Tourn. ex L. 1735 (Moraceae)
F. elastica, Roxb.
  V. wheat streak mosaic
    Sill, W.H., Jr. and Patrick C. Agusiobo, 1955
F. exasperata, Vahl
  V. cacao swollen shoot
    Posnette, A.F., N.F. Robertson and J. McA.
    Todd, 1950
F. palmata, Forsk.
  V. fig mosaic
    Condit, I.J. and W.T. Horne, 1933

FOENICULUM Tourn. ex L. 1735 (Umbelliferae)
F. vulgare, Mill., var. dulce, (Mill.) Fiori
  V. spinach yellow dwarf
    Severin, Henry H.P. and Donald H. Little, 1947

FORSYTHIA Vahl 1805 (Oleaceae)
F. suspensa, (Thunb.) Vahl
  V. lilac witches' broom
    Brierley, Philip, 1955

FORTUNELLA Swingle 1915 (Rutaceae)
F. margarita, (Lour.) Swingle on Poncirus trifoliata, Raf.
  V. citrus tristeza
    Olson, Edward O. and James R. McDonald, 1954

FRAGARIA ((Tourn.)) L. 1735 (Rosaceae)
F. bracteata, Heller
  V. orchid (cymbidium) mosaic
    Jensen, D.D., 1951
F. chiloensis, Dcne., var. ananassa, Bailey
  V. filaree red leaf
    Frazier, Norman W., 1951
F. vesca, L.
  V. beet yellow net
    McLean, D.M., 1952

FRANKENIA L. 1737 (Frankeniaceae)
F. grandifolia, Cham. & Schlecht.
  V. beet curly top
    Severin, Henry H.P., 1939

FRAXINUS Tourn. ex L. 1735 (Oleaceae)
F. pennsylvanica, Marsh.
  V. lilac witches' broom
    Brierley, Philip, 1955

FREESIA Klatt 1865-66 (Iridaceae)
F. hybrida, Hort.
  V. cucumber mosaic
    Brierley, Philip and Floyd F. Smith, 1944
  V. lily symptomless
    Brierley, Philip and Floyd F. Smith, 1944
  V. tulip breaking
    Brierley, Philip and Floyd F. Smith, 1944
F. refracta, Klatt.
  V. maize leaf fleck
    Stoner, Warren N., 1952
  V. orchid (cymbidium) mosaic
    Jensen, D.D., 1951

FUCHSIA ((Plum.)) L. 1735 (Onagraceae)
F. magellanica, Lam.
  V. tomato aspermy
    Brierley, Philip, Floyd F. Smith and S.P.
    Doolittle, 1955

FUMARIA Tourn. ex L. 1735 (Papaveraceae)
F. officinalis, L.
  V. anemone brown ring *
    Hollings, M., 1958

FUNTUMIA Stapf 1901 (Apocynaceae)
F. elastica, Stapf
  V. cacao swollen shoot
    Posnette, A.F., N.F. Robertson and J. McA.
    Todd, 1950

GAILLARDIA Fouger. 1788 (Compositae)
G. aristata, Pursh
  V. tobacco etch
    Holmes, Francis O., 1946
  V. tobacco mosaic
    Holmes, Francis O., 1946
G. pulchella, Foug.
  V. cucumber mosaic
    Wellman, F.L., 1935
G. pulchella var. picta, Gray
  V. cabbage black ring spot
    Tompkins, C.M., M.W. Gardner and H. Rex
    Thomas, 1938
  V. chrysanthemum stunt
    Brierley, Philip, 1953
  V. radish mosaic
    Tompkins, C.M., 1939
  V. turnip mosaic
    Tompkins, C.M., 1938, 1939
    Tompkins, C.M. and H. Rex Thomas, 1938

GALEOPSIS L. 1735 (Labiatae)
G. speciosa, Mill.
  V. beet yellows
    Roland, G. and J. Tahon, 1961
G. tetrahit, L.
  V. beet yellows
    Roland, G. and J. Tahon, 1961

GALINSOGA Ruiz & Pav. 1794 (Compositae)
G. parviflora, Cav.
  V. beet curly top
    Costa, A.S., 1952
  V. beet yellows
    Roland, G. and J. Tahon, 1961
  V. chrysanthemum stunt
    Brierley, Philip, 1953
  V. tobacco etch
    Holmes, Francis O., 1946

GALIUM L. 1737 (Rubiaceae)
G. triflorum, Michx.
  V. tobacco mosaic
    Holmes, Francis O., 1938

GALTONIA Decne. 1880 (Liliaceae)
G. candicans, (Baker) Decne.
  V. cucumber mosaic
    Brierley, Philip and Floyd F. Smith, 1944
  V. lily symptomless
    Brierley, Philip and Floyd F. Smith, 1944
  V. tulip breaking
    Brierley, Philip and Floyd F. Smith, 1944

GAZANIA Gaertn. 1791 (Compositae)
G. spp.
  V. chrysanthemum stunt
    Brierley, Philip, 1953

GERANIUM ((Tourn.)) L. 1735 (Geraniaceae)
G. carolinianum, L.
  V. tobacco etch
    Holmes, Francis O., 1946
G. dissectum, L.
  V. beet yellows
    Roland, G. and J. Tahon, 1961

Geranium maculatum, L.
   V. beet yellows
      Roland, G. and J. Tahon, 1961
G. sanguineum, L.
   V. pea mosaic
      Murphy, D.M. and W.H. Pierce, 1937

GERARDIA L. 1737 (Scrophulariaceae)
G. divaricata, Chapm.
   V. cucumber mosaic
      Wellman, F.L., 1935

GERBERA Gronov. 1737 (Compositae)
G. jamesonii, Bolus
   V. chrysanthemum stunt
      Brierley, Philip, 1953
   V. primula mosaic
      Tompkins, C.M. and John T. Middleton, 1941
G. jamesonii var. transvaalensis, Hort.
   V. cabbage black ring spot
      Tompkins, C.M., M.W. Gardner and H. Rex
      Thomas, 1938
   V. turnip mosaic
      Tompkins, C.M., 1939

GEUM L. 1735 (Rosaceae)
G. canadense, Jacq.
   V. tobacco etch
      Holmes, Francis O., 1946
   V. tobacco mosaic
      Holmes, Francis O., 1938, 1946
G. chiloense, Balb.
   V. cabbage black ring spot
      Tompkins, C.M., M.W. Gardner and H. Rex
      Thomas, 1938
   V. chrysanthemum B (mild mosaic) *
      Hollings, M., 1957
   V. primula mosaic
      Tompkins, C.M. and John T. Middleton, 1941
   V. radish mosaic
      Tompkins, C.M., 1939
   V. tobacco etch
      Holmes, Francis O., 1946
   V. tobacco mosaic
      Holmes, Francis O., 1946
   V. tomato yellow net
      Sylvester, Edward S., 1954
   V. turnip mosaic
      Tompkins, C.M., 1938, 1939
      Tompkins, C.M. and H. Rex Thomas, 1938

GILIA Ruiz & Pav. 1794 (Polemoniaceae)
G. capitata, Dougl.
   V. tobacco etch
      Holmes, Francis O., 1946
G. liniflora, Benth.
   V. tobacco etch
      Holmes, Francis O., 1946

GLADIOLUS ((Tourn.)) L. 1735 (Iridaceae)
G. hortulanus, Bailey
   V. iris spuria mosaic *
      Brierley, Philip and Floyd F. Smith, 1948
G. lemoinei, Hort.
   V. cucumber mosaic
      Wellman, F.L., 1935
G. spp.
   V. beet yellow net
      McLean, D.M., 1952
   V. onion yellow dwarf
      Henderson, W.J., 1935
   V. tomato aspermy
      Brierley, Philip, Floyd F. Smith and S.P.
      Doolittle, 1955
   V. wheat streak mosaic
      Sill, W.H., Jr. and Patrick C. Agusiobo, 1955

GLEDITSIA L. 1742 (Leguminosae)
G. triacanthos, L.
   V. prunus A *
      Fulton, Robert W., 1957
   V. prunus E *
      Fulton, Robert W., 1957

G. triacanthos, L. (cont.)
   V. prunus G *
      Fulton, Robert W., 1957

GLORIOSA L. 1735 (Liliaceae)
G. rothschildiana, O'Brien
   V. ornithogalum mosaic
      Smith, Floyd F. and Philip Brierley, 1944
   V. tulip breaking
      Brierley, Philip and Floyd F. Smith, 1944
G. superba, L.
   V. tulip breaking
      Brierley, Philip and Floyd F. Smith, 1944

GLYCINE L. 1737 (Leguminosae)
(SOJA) Moench 1794
(SOYA) Benth. 1838
G. hispida, Maxim.
   V. cucumber mosaic
      Vasudeva, R. Sahai and T.B. Lal, 1943
   V. tobacco ring spot
      Wingard, S.A., 1928
G. max, (L.) Merr.
   V. alsike clover mosaic
      Zaumeyer, W.J., 1940
   V. barley stripe mosaic
      Sill, W.H., Jr. and E.D. Hansing, 1955
   V. bean common mosaic
      Snyder, W.C., 1942
      Zaumeyer, W.J. and B.L. Wade, 1935
   V. bean southern mosaic
      Zaumeyer, W.J. and L.L. Harter, 1943
   V. bean yellow mosaic
      Baggett, James R., 1957
      Grogan, Raymond G. and J.C. Walker, 1948
      Johnson, James, 1942
      Zaumeyer, W.J., 1940, 1952
      Zaumeyer, W.J. and B.L. Wade, 1935
   V. broad bean mottle
      Yu, T.F., 1939
   V. cauliflower mosaic
      Walker, J.C., Francis J. LeBeau and Glenn S.
      Pound, 1945
   V. cowpea mosaic
      Yu, T.F., 1946
   V. cucumber mosaic
      Anderson, C.W., 1955
      Bridgmon, G.H. and J.C. Walker, 1952
      Costa, A.S., 1944
      Harter, L.L., 1938
      Johnson, E.M., 1930
      Wellman, F.L., 1935
      Whipple, O.C. and J.C. Walker, 1941
   V. datura distortion mosaic
      Capoor, S.P. and P.M. Varma, 1952
   V. filaree red leaf
      Frazier, Norman W., 1951
   V. lucerne mosaic
      Zaumeyer, W.J. and B.L. Wade, 1935
   V. lupine disease *
      Weimer, J.L., 1950
   V. muskmelon mosaic
      Rader, Wm. E., Hugh F. Fitzpatrick and E.M.
      Hildebrand, 1947
   V. orchid (cymbidium) mosaic
      Jensen, D.D., 1951
   V. orchid (vanda) mosaic
      Murakishi, Harry H., 1952
   V. pea mosaic
      Chaudhuri, R.P., 1950
      Hagedorn, D.J. and J.C. Walker, 1954
      Murphy, D.M. and W.H. Pierce, 1937
      Pierce, W.H., 1935
      Stubbs, M.W., 1937
   V. pea mottle
      Johnson, Folke, 1942
   V. pea wilt
      Johnson, Folke, 1942
   V. potato X
      Johnson, E.M., 1930
   V. potato Y
      Johnson, E.M., 1930
   V. red clover mosaic *
      Zaumeyer, W.J. and B.L. Wade, 1935

Glycine max, (L.) Merr. (cont.)
   V. red clover vein mosaic
      Hagedorn, D.J. and E.W. Hanson, 1951
      Hagedorn, D.J. and J.C. Walker, 1949, 1954
   V. squash mosaic
      Freitag, J.H., 1956
   V. tobacco coarse etch
      Johnson, E.M., 1930
   V. tobacco etch
      Holmes, Francis O., 1946
      Johnson, E.M., 1930
   V. tobacco mosaic
      Holmes, Francis O., 1946
      Johnson, E.M., 1930
   V. tobacco ring spot
      Johnson, E.M., 1930
   V. tomato ring spot
      Samson, R.W. and E.P. Imle, 1942
   V. turnip mosaic
      Walker, J.C., Francis J. LeBeau and Glenn S. Pound, 1945
G. soya, Sieb. & Zucc.
   V. cacao swollen shoot
    . Tinsley, T.W. and A.L. Wharton, 1958

GLYPHAEA Hook. f. 1848 (Tiliaceae)
G. brevis, (Spreng.) Monachino
   V. cacao swollen shoot
      Tinsley, T.W. and A.L. Wharton, 1958

GNAPHALIUM L. 1737 (Compositae)
G. beneolens, Davidson
   V. beet yellows
      Roland, G. and J. Tahon, 1961

GODETIA Spach 1835 (Onagraceae)
G. amoena, G. Don
   V. cauliflower mosaic
      Walker, J.C., Francis J. LeBeau and Glenn S. Pound, 1945
G. grandiflora, Lindl.
   V. cabbage black ring spot
      Tompkins, C.M., M.W. Gardner and H. Rex Thomas, 1938
   V. radish mosaic
      Tompkins, C.M., 1939
   V. turnip mosaic
      Tompkins, C.M., 1938, 1939
      Tompkins, C.M. and H. Rex Thomas, 1938

GOMPHRENA L. 1737 (Amaranthaceae)
G. globosa, L.
   V. bayberry yellows
      Raychaudhuri, S.P., 1953
   V. carnation mosaic
      Brierley, Philip and Floyd F. Smith, 1955
   V. carnation vein mottle
      Kassanis, B., 1955
   V. cauliflower mosaic
      Alvarez-Garcia, L.A., 1951
      Berkeley, G.H. and J.H. Tremaine, 1954
   V. chrysanthemum B (mild mosaic) *
      Hollings, M., 1957
   V. chrysanthemum ring spot
      Brierley, Philip and Floyd F. Smith, 1955
   V. cucumber mosaic
      Wellman, F.L., 1935
   V. nicotiana glutinosa root necrosis *
      Cetas, Robert C. and A. Frank Ross, 1952
   V. panicum mosaic *
      Sill, W.H., Jr. and R.C. Pickett, 1957
   V. pelargonium ring spot *
      Hollings, M., 1957
   V. potato Y
      Ross, A. Frank, 1950
   V. prunus B *
      Fulton, Robert W., 1957
   V. prunus E *
      Fulton, Robert W., 1957
   V. tobacco ring spot
      Cooper, W.E., 1949
   V. turnip rosette *
      Broadbent, L. and G.D. Heathcote, 1958

G. globosa, L. (cont.)
   V. turnip yellow mosaic
      Broadbent, L. and G.D. Heathcote, 1958
G. haageana, Klotzsch
   V. tobacco etch
      Holmes, Francis O., 1946
   V. tobacco mosaic
      Holmes, Francis O., 1946
G. spp.
   V. peony leaf curl *
      Brierley, Philip and Paul Lorentz, 1957

GOSSYPIUM L. 1735 (Malvaceae)
G. arboreum, L.
   V. chilli (pepper) mosaic
      Jha, Ashrafi and S.P. Raychaudhuri, 1956
G. barbadense, L.
   V. hibiscus yellows *
      Hendrix, J. Walter, 1950
G. hirsutum, L.
   V. abutilon infectious variegation
      Bird, Julio, 1958
   V. beet curly top
      Bennett, C.W. and A.S. Costa, 1949, 1952
      Giddings, N.J., 1944
      Severin, Henry H.P., 1929
   V. beet yellows
      Roland, G. and J. Tahon, 1961
   V. cacao swollen shoot
      Posnette, A.F., N.F. Robertson and J. McA. Todd, 1950
   V. canna mosaic
      Castillo, B.S., C.E. Yarwood and A.H. Gold, 1956
   V. citrus tristeza
      Bennett, C.W. and A.S. Costa, 1949
   V. cucumber mosaic
      Wellman, F.L., 1935
   V. euphorbia mosaic
      Costa, A.S. and C.W. Bennett, 1950
   V. hibiscus yellows *
      Hendrix, J. Walter, 1950
   V. malva yellow vein mosaic *
      Costa, A.S. and James E. Duffus, 1957
   V. prunus G *
      Fulton, Robert W., 1957
   V. spinach yellow dwarf
      Severin, Henry H.P. and Donald H. Little, 1947
   V. squash mosaic
      Freitag, J.H., 1956
   V. stone fruit *
      Boyle, J.S., J. Duain Moore and G.W. Keitt, 1954
   V. tobacco etch
      Holmes, Francis O., 1946
   V. tobacco leaf curl
      Nariani, T.K., 1956
   V. tobacco mosaic
      Das, C.R. and S.P. Raychaudhuri, 1953
      Holmes, Francis O., 1946
   V. tomato aspermy
      Brierley, Philip, Floyd F. Smith and S.P. Doolittle, 1955
   V. tomato spotted wilt
      Smith, Kenneth M., 1931
G. peruvianum, Cav. x G. barbadense, L.
   V. hibiscus yellow vein mosaic
      Capoor, S.P. and P.M. Varma, 1950
G. spp.
   V. beet curly top
      Carsner, E., 1919
   V. canna mosaic
      Celino, M.S. and G.O. Ocfemia, 1941
   V. cucumber mosaic
      Celino, Martin S., 1940

GREWIA L. 1735 (Tiliaceae)
G. similis, K. Schum.
   V. cacao swollen shoot
      Tinsley, T.W. and A.L. Wharton, 1958

GRINDELIA Willd. 1807 (Compositae)
G. camporum, Greene
   V. beet curly top
      Severin, Henry H.P., 1939

GUAZUMA Plum. ex Adans. 1763 (Sterculiaceae)
G. ulmifolia, Lam.
 V. cacao swollen shoot
  Tinsley, T.W. and A.L. Wharton, 1958

GUTIERREZIA Lag. 1816 (Compositae)
G. californica, Torr. & Gray
 V. beet curly top
  Severin, Henry H.P., 1939

GYCOSMIS Correa 1805 (Rutaceae)
G. citrifolia, (Willd.) Lindley *
 V. citrus tristeza
  Knorr, L.C., 1956

GYPSOPHILA L. 1751 (Caryophyllaceae)
G. paniculata, L.
 V. cabbage black ring spot
  Tompkins, C.M., M.W. Gardner and H. Rex
  Thomas, 1938
 V. cucumber mosaic
  Wellman, F.L., 1935
 V. radish mosaic
  Tompkins, C.M., 1939
 V. turnip mosaic
  Tompkins, C.M., 1938, 1939
  Tompkins, C.M. and H. Rex Thomas, 1938

HAPLOPAPPUS Endl. 1838 (Compositae)
H. venetus subsp. verononioides *
 V. beet curly top
  Severin, Henry H.P., 1939

HARPULLIA Roxb. 1814 (Sapindaceae)
H. pendula, Planch. ex F. Muell.
 V. cacao swollen shoot
  Tinsley, T.W. and A.L. Wharton, 1958

HAWORTHIA Duval 1809 (Liliaceae)
H. altilinea, Haw.
 V. cucumber mosaic
  Brierley, Philip and Floyd F. Smith, 1944
 V. lily symptomless
  Brierley, Philip and Floyd F. Smith, 1944
 V. tulip breaking
  Brierley, Philip and Floyd F. Smith, 1944

HEDYCHIUM Koen. 1783 (Zingiberaceae)
H. coronarium, Koen.
 V. canna mosaic
  Brierley, Philip and Floyd F. Smith, 1948
 V. cucumber mosaic
  Brierley, Philip and Floyd F. Smith, 1944
  Celino, Martin S., 1940
 V. lily symptomless
  Brierley, Philip and Floyd F. Smith, 1944
 V. tulip breaking
  Brierley, Philip and Floyd F. Smith, 1944

HEDYSARUM ((Tourn.)) L. 1735 (Leguminosae)
H. coronarium, L.
 V. prunus B *
  Fulton, Robert W., 1957
 V. prunus E *
  Fulton, Robert W., 1957

HELENIUM L. 1753 (Compositae)
H. autumnale, L.
 V. tomato aspermy
  Hollings, M., 1955

HELIANTHUS L. 1735 (Compositae)
H. annuus, L.
 V. beet yellows
  Roland, G. and J. Tahon, 1961
H. cucumerifolius, Torr. & Gray
 V. chrysanthemum stunt
  Brierley, Philip, 1953
H. spp.
 V. lucerne dwarf
  Freitag, J.H., 1951
H. tuberosus, L.
 V. beet yellows
  Roland, G. and J. Tahon, 1961

H. tuberosus, L. (cont.)
 V. tobacco etch
  Holmes, Francis O., 1946
 V. tobacco mosaic
  Holmes, Francis O., 1938, 1946

HELICHRYSUM Vaill. ex L. 1737 (Compositae)
H. brackatum, Andr. *
 V. beet yellows
  Roland, G. and J. Tahon, 1961
H. bracteatum, Andr.
 V. anemone mosaic *
  Hollings, M., 1957
 V. chrysanthemum B (mild mosaic) *
  Hollings, M., 1957
 V. chrysanthemum stunt
  Brierley, Philip, 1953
 V. cucumber mosaic
  Wellman, F.L., 1935
 V. tobacco etch
  Holmes, Francis O., 1946

HELIOPSIS Pers. 1807 (Compositae)
H. scabra, Dun.
 V. tobacco etch
  Holmes, Francis O., 1946
 V. tobacco mosaic
  Holmes, Francis O., 1946

HELIOTROPIUM ((Tourn.)) L. 1735 (Boraginaceae)
H. corymbosum, Ruiz & Pav.
 V. tobacco etch
  Holmes, Francis O., 1946
H. curassavicum, L.
 V. beet yellows
  Roland, G. and J. Tahon, 1961
H. peruvianum, L.
 V. cabbage black ring spot
  Tompkins, C.M., M.W. Gardner and H. Rex
  Thomas, 1938
 V. cucumber mosaic
  Wellman, F.L., 1935
 V. radish mosaic
  Tompkins, C.M., 1939
 V. turnip mosaic
  Tompkins, C.M., 1938, 1939
  Tompkins, C.M. and H. Rex Thomas, 1938

HEMEROCALLIS L. 1735 (Liliaceae)
H. flava, L.
 V. cucumber mosaic
  Wellman, F.L., 1935
 V. orchid (vanda) mosaic
  Murakishi, Harry H., 1952
H. fulva, L.
 V. tomato aspermy
  Brierley, Philip, Floyd F. Smith and S.P.
  Doolittle, 1955

HEMIZONIA DC. 1836 (Compositae)
H. virgata, A. Gray
 V. beet curly top
  Severin, Henry H.P., 1939

HERACLEUM L. 1735 (Umbelliferae)
H. maximum, Bartr. (H. lanatum, Michx.)
 V. celery mosaic
  Freitag, Julius H. and Henry H.P. Severin, 1945

HERMANNIA L. 1735 (Sterculiaceae)
H. candicans, Ait., var. discolor *
 V. cacao swollen shoot
  Tinsley, T.W. and A.L. Wharton, 1958

HERRANIA Goudot 1844 (Sterculiaceae)
H. balaensis, Preuss
 V. cacao swollen shoot
  Tinsley, T.W. and A.L. Wharton, 1958
H. spp.
 V. cacao swollen shoot
  Tinsley, T.W. and A.L. Wharton, 1958

HESPERIS L. 1735 (Cruciferae)
H. matronalis, L.
  V. beet mosaic
    Pound, Glenn S., 1947
  V. cauliflower mosaic
    Berkeley, G.H. and J.H. Tremaine, 1954
    Tompkins, C.M., 1937
    Walker, J.C., Francis J. LeBeau and Glenn S.
    Pound, 1945
  V. radish mosaic
    Tompkins, C.M., 1939
  V. squash mosaic
    Freitag, J.H., 1956
  V. stone fruit *
    Boyle, J.S., J. Duain Moore and G.W. Keitt, 1954
  V. turnip mosaic
    LeBeau, Francis J. and J.C. Walker, 1945
H. spp.
  V. cauliflower mosaic
    Caldwell, John and Ian W. Prentice, 1942

HEVEA Aubl. 1775 (Euphorbiaceae)
H. brasiliensis, Muell.-Arg. (Siphonia ridleyana, O.F.
  V. cacao swollen shoot   Cook)
    Tinsley, T.W. and A.L. Wharton, 1958

HIBISCUS L. 1737 (Malvaceae)
H. esculentus, L.
  V. beet curly top
    Giddings, N.J., 1944
  V. beet yellows
    Roland, G. and J. Tahon, 1961
  V. cacao swollen shoot
    Tinsley, T.W. and A.L. Wharton, 1958
  V. cauliflower mosaic
    Walker, J.C., Francis J. LeBeau and Glenn S.
    Pound, 1945
  V. cucumber green mottle mosaic
    Vasudeva, R.S., S.P. Raychaudhuri and Jagannath
    Singh, 1949
  V. cucumber mosaic
    Wellman, F.L., 1935
  V. datura distortion mosaic
    Capoor, S.P. and P.M. Varma, 1952
  V. hibiscus yellows *
    Hendrix, J. Walter, 1950
  V. malva yellow vein mosaic *
    Costa, A.S. and James E. Duffus, 1957
  V. squash mosaic
    Freitag, J.H., 1956
  V. tobacco etch
    Holmes, Francis O., 1946
  V. tobacco leaf curl
    Nariani, T.K., 1956
  V. tobacco mosaic
    Holmes, Francis O., 1946
  V. tomato ring spot
    Samson, R.W. and E.P. Imle, 1942
  V. turnip mosaic
    Walker, J.C., Francis J. LeBeau and Glenn S.
    Pound, 1945
H. furcatus, Willd.
  V. hibiscus yellow vein mosaic
    Capoor, S.P. and P.M. Varma, 1950
H. manihot, L.
  V. hibiscus yellow vein mosaic
    Capoor, S.P. and P.M. Varma, 1950
  V. tobacco etch
    Holmes, Francis O., 1946
  V. tobacco mosaic
    Holmes, Francis O., 1946
H. rosa-sinensis, L.
  V. beet yellows
    Roland, G. and J. Tahon, 1961
  V. chilli (pepper) mosaic
    Jha, Ashrafi and S.P. Raychaudhuri, 1956
  V. cucumber mosaic
    Wellman, F.L., 1935
  V. orchid (vanda) mosaic
    Murakishi, Harry H., 1952
  V. tobacco leaf curl
    Nariani, T.K., 1956

H. sabdariffa, L.
  V. hibiscus yellows *
    Hendrix, J. Walter, 1950
H. tiliaceus, L. (Pariti tiliaceum, (L.) St. Hil.)
  V. hibiscus yellows *
    Hendrix, J. Walter, 1950
H. youngianus, Gaudich.
  V. hibiscus yellows *
    Hendrix, J. Walter, 1950

HIERACIUM ((Tourn.)) L. 1735 (Compositae)
H. argutum, Nutt.
  V. dodder latent mosaic
    Bennett, C.W., 1944
H. scabrum, Michx.
  V. tobacco mosaic
    Holmes, Francis O., 1938

HOLCUS L. 1735 (Gramineae)
H. halepensis, L.
  V. sugarcane mosaic
    Brandes, E.W. and Peter J. Klaphaak, 1923
H. lanatus, L.
  V. barley yellow dwarf
    Bruehl, G.W. and H.V. Toko, 1957
    Oswald, John W. and Byron R. Houston, 1953
H. sorghum, L.
  V. cucumber mosaic
    Adsuar, Jose and A. Cruz Miret, 1950
H. sudanensis, Bailey
  V. tobacco etch
    Holmes, Francis O., 1946
  V. tobacco mosaic
    Holmes, Francis O., 1946

HORDEUM ((Tourn.)) L. 1735 (Gramineae)
H. jubatum, L.
  V. agropyron mosaic
    Slykhuis, J.T., 1952
  V. wheat streak mosaic
    Slykhuis, J.T., 1952, 1955
H. vulgare, L.
  V. agropyron mosaic
    Slykhuis, J.T., 1952
  V. beet curly top
    Carsner, E., 1919
  V. beet yellows
    Roland, G. and J. Tahon, 1961
  V. cucumber mosaic
    McWhorter, F.P. and H.H. Millsap, 1954
    Wellman, F.L., 1935
  V. maize leaf fleck
    Stoner, Warren N., 1952
  V. panicum mosaic *
    Sill, W.H., Jr. and R.C. Pickett, 1957
  V. soil-borne wheat mosaic
    McKinney, H.H., 1947
  V. sugarcane mosaic
    Brandes, E.W. and Peter J. Klaphaak, 1923
  V. tobacco etch
    Holmes, Francis O., 1946
  V. tobacco mosaic
    Holmes, Francis O., 1946

HOSTA Tratt. 1812 (Liliaceae)
H. plantaginea, Aschers.
  V. cucumber mosaic
    Brierley, Philip and Floyd F. Smith, 1944
  V. lily symptomless
    Brierley, Philip and Floyd F. Smith, 1944
  V. tulip breaking
    Brierley, Philip and Floyd F. Smith, 1944

HUNNEMANNIA Sweet 1828 (Papaveraceae)
H. fumariaefolia, Sweet
  V. tobacco etch
    Holmes, Francis O., 1946
  V. tobacco mosaic
    Holmes, Francis O., 1946

HYACINTHUS ((Tourn.)) L. 1735 (Liliaceae)
H. azureus, Baker
    V. ornithogalum mosaic
        Smith, Floyd F. and Philip Brierley, 1944
H. orientalis, L.
    V. onion yellow dwarf
        Henderson, W.J., 1935
    V. tulip breaking
        Brierley, Philip and Floyd F. Smith, 1944

HYMENOCALLIS Salisb. 1812 (Amaryllidaceae)
H. spp.
    V. cucumber mosaic
        Wellman, F.L., 1935

HYOSCYAMUS ((Tourn.)) L. 1735 (Solanaceae)
H. albus, L.
    V. muskmelon mosaic
        Rader, Wm. E., Hugh F. Fitzpatrick and E.M.
        Hildebrand, 1947
H. niger, L.
    V. anemone brown ring *
        Hollings, M., 1958
    V. beet yellows
        Roland, G. and J. Tahon, 1961
    V. muskmelon mosaic
        Rader, Wm. E., Hugh F. Fitzpatrick and E.M.
        Hildebrand, 1947
    V. red currant ring spot
        Klesser, P.J., 1951
    V. tomato aspermy
        Blencowe, J.W. and John Caldwell, 1949

HYPERICUM Tourn. ex L. 1737 (Hypericaceae)
H. boreale, (Britt.) Bickn.
    V. tobacco etch
        Holmes, Francis O., 1946
    V. tobacco mosaic
        Holmes, Francis O., 1938, 1946
H. perforatum, L.
    V. stone fruit *
        Boyle, J.S., J. Duain Moore and G.W. Keitt, 1954

HYPOCHOERIS L. 1737 (Compositae)
H. radicata, L.
    V. beet yellows
        Roland, G. and J. Tahon, 1961

HYPOXIS L. 1759 (Amaryllidaceae)
H. spp.
    V. narcissus mosaic
        Haasis, Frank A., 1939

IBERIS Dill. ex L. 1735 (Cruciferae)
I. amara, L.
    V. cauliflower mosaic
        Caldwell, John and Ian W. Prentice, 1942
I. gibraltarica, L.
    V. tobacco etch
        Holmes, Francis O., 1946
I. sempervirens, L.
    V. tobacco etch
        Holmes, Francis O., 1946
    V. tobacco mosaic
        Holmes, Francis O., 1946
I. spp.
    V. citrus tristeza
        Knorr, L.C., 1956
I. umbellata, L.
    V. cucumber mosaic
        Wellman, F.L., 1935
    V. squash mosaic
        Freitag, J.H., 1956
    V. tobacco etch
        Holmes, Francis O., 1946

IMPATIENS Riv. ex L. 1735 (Balsaminaceae)
I. balsamina, L.
    V. cucumber mosaic
        Doolittle, S.P. and W.J. Zaumeyer, 1953
        Wellman, F.L., 1935
    V. euphorbia mosaic
        Costa, A.S. and C.W. Bennett, 1950

I. balsamina, L. (cont.)
    V. pea mosaic
        Murphy, D.M. and W.H. Pierce, 1937
    V. tobacco etch
        Holmes, Francis O., 1946
    V. tobacco mosaic
        Holmes, Francis O., 1946
    V. tobacco necrosis
        Price, W.C., Frank P. McWhorter and Betty H.
        Steranka, 1950
I. biflora, Walt.
    V. tobacco mosaic
        Holmes, Francis O., 1938
I. spp.
    V. beet yellows
        Roland, G. and J. Tahon, 1961
I. sultanii, Hook. f. (or sometimes I. holstii, Engler &
    V. orchid (vanda) mosaic   Warb.)
        Murakishi, Harry H., 1952
    V. tobacco etch
        Holmes, Francis O., 1946

INCARVILLEA Juss. 1789 (Bignoniaceae)
I. variabilis, Batalin
    V. tobacco etch
        Holmes, Francis O., 1946

INDIGOFERA L. 1737 (Leguminosae)
I. hirsuta, L.
    V. prunus B *
        Fulton, Robert W., 1957

IODANTHUS Torr. & Gray 1838 (Cruciferae)
I. pinnatifidus, (Michx.) Steud.
    V. stone fruit *
        Boyle, J.S., J. Duain Moore and G.W. Keitt, 1954

IONOXALIS Small 1903 (Oxalidaceae)
I. violacea, Small
    V. cucumber mosaic
        Wellman, F.L., 1935

IPOMOEA L. 1735 (Convolvulaceae)
I. batata, (L.) Lam.
    . V. abutilon infectious variegation
        Bird, Julio, 1958
    V. cucumber mosaic
        Doolittle, S.P. and L.L. Harter, 1945
    V. sweet potato feathery mottle
        Doolittle, S.P. and L.L. Harter, 1945
    V. tobacco etch
        Holmes, Francis O., 1946
    V. tobacco mosaic
        Doolittle, S.P. and L.L. Harter, 1945
        Holmes, Francis O., 1946
    V. tobacco ring spot
        Cheo, Pen Ching and W.J. Zaumeyer, 1952
    V. tomato ring spot
        Samson, R.W. and E.P. Imle, 1942
I. cairica, Sweet
    V. sweet potato feathery mottle
        Webb, Raymon E., 1954
I. crassicaulis, B.L. Robinson
    V. papaw mosaic
        Adsuar, Jose, 1950
I. nil, (L.) Roth
    V. squash mosaic
        Freitag, J.H., 1956
    V. sweet potato feathery mottle
        Webb, Raymon E., 1954
    V. tobacco etch
        Holmes, Francis O., 1946
I. pes-caprae, (L.) Roth
    V. papaw mosaic
        Adsuar, Jose, 1950
I. purpurea, (L.) Lam.
    V. beet yellow net
        Sylvester, Edward S., 1948
    V. beet yellows
        Roland, G. and J. Tahon, 1961
    V. cabbage black ring spot
        Tompkins, C.M., M.W. Gardner and H. Rex
        Thomas, 1938

Ipomoea purpurea, (L.) Lam. (cont.)
V. cauliflower mosaic
Walker, J.C., Francis J. LeBeau and Glenn S. Pound, 1945
V. sweet potato feathery mottle
Doolittle, S.P. and L.L. Harter, 1945
V. sweet potato mosaic
Borders, H.I. and T.J. Ratcliff, 1954
V. tomato ring spot
Samson, R.W. and E.P. Imle, 1942
V. turnip mosaic
Tompkins, C.M., 1939
Walker, J.C., Francis J. LeBeau and Glenn S. Pound, 1945
I. quinquefolia, L
V. abutilon infectious variegation
Bird, Julio, 1958
V. cucumber mosaic
Adsuar, Jose and A. Cruz Miret, 1950
V. papaw mosaic
Adsuar, Jose, 1950
I. rubra, Murr.
V. papaw mosaic
Adsuar, Jose, 1950
V. sweet potato feathery mottle
Webb, Raymon E., 1954
I. setosa, Ker.
V. tobacco etch
Holmes, Francis O., 1946
V. tobacco mosaic
Holmes, Francis O., 1946
I. sinuata, Ort.
V. sweet potato feathery mottle
Webb, Raymon E., 1954
I. spp.
V. euphorbia mosaic
Costa, A.S. and C.W. Bennett, 1950
V. sweet potato feathery mottle
Webb, Raymon E., 1954
V. sweet potato mosaic
Borders, H.I. and T.J. Ratcliff, 1954
I. tricolor, Cav.
V. anemone mosaic *
Hollings, M., 1957
V. sweet potato feathery mottle
Webb, Raymon E., 1954
V. sweet potato mosaic
Borders, H.I. and T.J. Ratcliff, 1954
V. tobacco etch
Holmes, Francis O., 1946

IRIS Tourn. ex L. 1735 (Iridaceae)
I. filifolia, Boiss.
V. cucumber mosaic
Brierley, Philip and Floyd F. Smith, 1944
V. lily symptomless
Brierley, Philip and Floyd F. Smith, 1944
V. tulip breaking
Brierley, Philip and Floyd F. Smith, 1944
I. germanica, L.
V. cucumber mosaic
Brierley, Philip and Frank P. McWhorter, 1936
V. tulip breaking
Brierley, Philip and Frank P. McWhorter, 1936
McWhorter, F.P., 1935
I. pallida, Lam.
V. cucumber mosaic
Brierley, Philip and Floyd F. Smith, 1944
V. lily symptomless
Brierley, Philip and Floyd F. Smith, 1944
V. tulip breaking
Brierley, Philip and Floyd F. Smith, 1944
I. persica, L.
V. onion yellow dwarf
Henderson, W.J., 1935
I. spp.
V. wheat streak mosaic
Sill, W.H., Jr. and Patrick C. Agusiobo, 1955
I. versicolor, L.
V. cucumber mosaic
Brierley, Philip and Floyd F. Smith, 1944
V. lily symptomless
Brierley, Philip and Floyd F. Smith, 1944
V. tulip breaking
Brierley, Philip and Floyd F. Smith, 1944

ISATIS Tourn. ex L. 1735 (Cruciferae)
I. glauca, Auch.
V. cauliflower mosaic
Caldwell, John and Ian W. Prentice, 1942

ISOMERIS Nutt. ex Torr. & Gray 1838 (Capparidaceae)
I. arborea, Nutt. ex Torr. & Gray
V. beet curly top
Severin, Henry H.P., 1939

ISOTOMA Lindl. 1826 (Campanulaceae)
I. longiflora, Presl
V. cucumber mosaic
Adsuar, Jose and A. Cruz Miret, 1950
V. papaw mosaic
Adsuar, Jose, 1950

JATROPHA L. 1735 (Euphorbiaceae)
J. gossypifolia, L.
V. abutilon infectious variegation
Bird, Julio, 1958

JUSSIAEA L. 1747 (Onagraceae)
J. angustifolia, Lam.
V. cucumber mosaic
Adsuar, Jose and A. Cruz Miret, 1950
V. papaw mosaic
Adsuar, Jose, 1950

KALANCHOE Adans. 1763 (Crassulaceae)
(BRYOPHYLLUM) Salisb. 1805
K. daigremontiana, Hamet. & Perrier
V. tobacco etch
Holmes, Francis O., 1946
K. spp.
V. wheat streak mosaic
Sill, W.H., Jr. and Patrick C. Agusiobo, 1955
(B. calycinum), Salisb.
V. papaw ring spot
Jensen, D.D., 1949
(B. pinnatum), Kurz.
V. tobacco ring spot
Wingard, S.A., 1928

KLEINHOVIA L. 1763 (Sterculiaceae)
K. hospita, L.
V. cacao swollen shoot
Tinsley, T.W. and A.L. Wharton, 1958

KNIPHOFIA Moench 1794 (Liliaceae)
K. tucki, Baker
V. cucumber mosaic
Brierley, Philip and Floyd F. Smith, 1944
V. lily symptomless
Brierley, Philip and Floyd F. Smith, 1944
V. tulip breaking
Brierley, Philip and Floyd F. Smith, 1944

KOCHIA Roth 1801 (Chenopodiaceae)
K. scoparia, (L.) Schrad.
V. cucumber mosaic
Wellman, F.L., 1935
V. squash mosaic
Freitag, J.H., 1956
V. tobacco etch
Holmes, Francis O., 1946

LACTUCA ((Tourn.)) L. 1735 (Compositae)
L. bourgaei, Irish & Taylor
V. aster yellows
Tompson, Ross C., 1944
L. marschallii, Stebbins *
V. aster yellows
Tompson, Ross C., 1944
L. muralis, (L.) Gaertn.
V. chrysanthemum B (mild mosaic) *
Hollings, M., 1957
L. sativa, L.
V. anemone brown ring *
Hollings M., 1958
V. anemone mosaic *
Hollings, M., 1957
V. bean pod mottle
Zaumeyer, W.J. and H. Rex Thomas, 1948

Lactuca sativa, L. (cont.)
  V. beet curly top
    Bennett, C.W. and A.S. Costa, 1949
    Carsner, E., 1919
    Severin, Henry H.P., 1929
  V. beet mosaic
    Bennett, C.W., 1949
    Pound, Glenn S., 1947
    Roland, G. and J. Tahon, 1961
  V. cauliflower mosaic
    Alvarez-Garcia, L.A., 1951
  V. chrysanthemum B (mild mosaic) *
    Hollings, M., 1957
  V. chrysanthemum stunt
    Brierley, Philip, 1953
  V. cineraria mosaic
    Jones, Leon K., 1944
  V. citrus tristeza
    Knorr, L.C., 1956
  V. cucumber mosaic
    Burnett, G., 1934
    Govier, D.A., 1957
    Nienow, Inez, 1948
  V. dahlia mosaic
    Brierley, Philip and Floyd F. Smith, 1950
  V. dock mosaic
    Newhall, A.G., 1923
  V. dodder latent mosaic
    Bennett, C.W., 1944
  V. lucerne mosaic
    Kreitlow, K.W. and W.C. Price, 1949
  V. milkweed mosaic *
    Newhall, A.G., 1923
  V. muskmelon mosaic
    Rader, Wm. E., Hugh F. Fitzpatrick and E.M.
    Hildebrand, 1947
  V. orchid (odontoglossum) ring spot
    Jensen, D.D. and A. Herbert Gold, 1951
  V. papaw ring spot
    Jensen, D.D., 1949
  V. pea mottle
    Johnson, Folke, 1942
  V. pea wilt
    Johnson, Folke, 1942
  V. pelargonium ring spot *
    Hollings, M., 1957
  V. prunus E *
    Fulton, Robert W., 1957
  V. prunus G *
    Fulton, Robert W., 1957
  V. spinach yellow dwarf
    Severin, Henry H.P. and Donald H. Little, 1947
  V. squash mosaic
    Freitag, J.H., 1956
  V. tobacco mosaic
    Doolittle, S.P. and F.S. Beecher, 1942
  V. tomato aspermy
    Hollings, M., 1955
  V. tomato spotted wilt
    Parris, G.K., 1940
  V. tropaeolum mosaic
    Silberschmidt, Karl, 1953
L. sativa var. capitata, L.
  V. bean common mosaic
    Ainsworth, G.C., 1940
  V. bean yellow mosaic
    Ainsworth, G.C., 1940
  V. cabbage black ring spot
    Tompkins, C.M., M.W. Gardner and H. Rex
    Thomas, 1938
  V. cauliflower mosaic
    Tompkins, C.M., 1937
  V. celery mosaic
    Freitag, Julius H. and Henry H.P. Severin, 1945
  V. cucumber mosaic
    Ainsworth, G.C., 1940
    Wellman, F.L., 1935
  V. pea enation mosaic
    Ainsworth, G.C., 1940
  V. pea mosaic
    Ainsworth, G.C., 1940
  V. pea yellow mosaic *
    Ainsworth, G.C., 1940

L. sativa var. capitata, L. (cont.)
  V. radish mosaic
    Tompkins, C.M., 1939
  V. turnip mosaic
    Tompkins, C.M., 1938, 1939
    Tompkins, C.M. and H. Rex Thomas, 1938
L. sativa var. crispa, L.
  V. cucumber mosaic
    Wellman, F.L., 1935
L. sativa var. longifolia, Lam.
  V. cucumber mosaic
    Wellman, F.L., 1935
  V. primula mosaic
    Tompkins, C.M. and John T. Middleton, 1941
  V. squash mosaic
    Freitag, J.H., 1956
L. sativa var. romana, Hort.
  V. beet yellow net
    Sylvester, Edward S., 1948
  V. cauliflower mosaic
    Tompkins, C.M., 1937
L. serriola, L.
  V. beet yellows
    Roland, G. and J. Tahon, 1961
L. tatarica, C.A. Mey.
  V. aster yellows
    Tompson, Ross C., 1944
L. virosa, Rydb.
  V. tobacco ring spot
    Fenne, S.B., 1931

LAELIOCATTLEYA X, Rolfe 1887 (Orchidaceae)
L. spp.
  V. orchid (vanda) mosaic
    Murakishi, Harry H., 1952

LAGENARIA Ser. 1825 (Cucurbitaceae)
L. siceraria, (Mol.) Standl. (L. leucantha, Rusby)
  V. chilli (pepper) mosaic
    Jha, Ashrafi and S.P. Raychaudhuri, 1956
  V. cowpea mosaic
    Capoor, S.P. and P.M. Varma, 1956
  V. cucumber mosaic
    Nariani, T.K. and Nirmaljit Singh, 1952
  V. prunus A *
    Fulton, Robert W., 1957
  V. prunus E *
    Fulton, Robert W., 1957
  V. prunus G *
    Fulton, Robert W., 1957
  V. tobacco mosaic
    Das, C.R. and S.P. Raychaudhuri, 1953
  V. tomato ring spot
    Samson, R.W. and E.P. Imle, 1942
L. vulgaris, Ser.
  V. datura distortion mosaic
    Capoor, S.P. and P.M. Varma, 1952
  V. potato X
    Vasudeva, R. Sahai and T.B. Lal, 1944

LAMIUM ((Tourn.)) L. 1735 (Labiatae)
L. album, L.
  V. beet yellows
    Roland, G. and J. Tahon, 1961
L. amplexicaule, L.
  V. cucumber mosaic
    Burnett, G., 1934
L. purpureum, L.
  V. beet yellows
    Roland, G. and J. Tahon, 1961

LANTANA L. 1737 (Verbenaceae)
L. camara, L.
  V. tobacco etch
    Holmes, Francis O., 1946
  V. tobacco mosaic
    Holmes, Francis O., 1946
L. sellowiana, Link & Otto
  V. cucumber mosaic
    Wellman, F.L., 1935

LATHYRUS ((Tourn.)) L. 1735 (Leguminosae)
L. latifolius, L.
   V. pea mosaic
      Murphy, D.M. and W.H. Pierce, 1937
L. odoratus, L.
   V. bean common mosaic
      Ainsworth, G.C., 1940
      Doolittle, S.P. and F.R. Jones, 1925
      Snyder, W.C., 1942
      Zaumeyer, W.J. and B.L. Wade, 1933, 1935
   V. bean mosaic 3 *
      Zaumeyer, W.J. and B.L. Wade, 1935
   V. bean yellow mosaic
      Doolittle, S.P. and F.R. Jones, 1925
   V. beet mosaic
      Pound, Glenn S., 1947
   V. beet yellows
      Roland, G. and J. Tahon, 1961
   V. cowpea mosaic
      McLean, D.M., 1941
      Yu, T.F., 1946
   V. cucumber mosaic
      Bhargava, K.S., 1951
      Harter, L.L., 1938
      Wellman, F.L., 1935
   V. filaree red leaf
      Frazier, Norman W., 1951
   V. kaimi clover disease *
      Murakishi, Harry H., 1952
   V. lucerne mosaic
      Zaumeyer, W.J., 1938
      Zaumeyer, W.J. and B.L. Wade, 1933
   V. nicotiana glutinosa mosaic *
      Allard, H.A., 1916
   V. pea streak
      Zaumeyer, W.J., 1938
   V. red clover mosaic *
      Zaumeyer, W.J. and B.L. Wade, 1933
   V. tobacco mosaic
      Allard, H.A., 1916
L. pratensis, L.
   V. lucerne witches' broom
      Klostermeyer, E.C. and J.D. Menzies, 1951
L. sativus, L.
   V. cowpea mosaic
      Capoor, S.P. and P.M. Varma, 1956
L. tuberosus, L.
   V. pea mosaic
      Murphy, D.M. and W.H. Pierce, 1937

LAVATERA L. 1737 (Malvaceae)
L. assurgentiflora, Kellogg
   V. beet curly top
      Carsner, E., 1919
L. trimestris, L.
   V. chrysanthemum B (mild mosaic) *
      Hollings, M., 1957
   V. pea mosaic
      Murphy, D.M. and W.H. Pierce, 1937
   V. pelargonium ring spot *
      Hollings, M., 1957
   V. tobacco etch
      Holmes, Francis O., 1946
   V. tobacco mosaic
      Holmes, Francis O., 1946

LENS ((Tourn.)) L. 1735 (Leguminosae)
L. esculenta, Moench
   V. bean common mosaic
      Zaumeyer, W.J. and B.L. Wade, 1935
   V. cowpea mosaic
      Yu, T.F., 1946
   V. cucumber mosaic
      Harter, L.L., 1938
   V. pea enation mosaic
      Johnson, Folke and Leon K. Jones, 1937
   V. tobacco etch
      Holmes, Francis O., 1946
   V. tobacco mosaic
      Holmes, Francis O., 1946

LEONOTIS R. Br. in Ait. 1811 (Labiatae)
L. nepetaefolia, (L.) R. Br.
   V. cucumber mosaic
      Adsuar, Jose and A. Cruz Miret, 1950
   V. papaw mosaic
      Adsuar, Jose, 1950

LEONURUS L. 1735 (Labiatae)
L. cardiaca, L.
   V. stone fruit *
      Boyle, J.S., J. Duain Moore and G.W. Keitt, 1954

LEPIDIUM L. 1735 (Cruciferae)
L. lasiocarpum, Nutt. ex Torr. & Gray
   V. beet yellows
      Roland, G. and J. Tahon, 1961
   V. beet curly top
      Giddings, N.J., 1938
L. virginicum, L.
   V. beet mosaic
      Pound, Glenn S., 1947
   V. cucumber mosaic
      Wellman, F.L., 1935

LEPIDOSPARTUM A. Gray 1883 (Compositae)
L. squamatum, A. Gray
   V. beet curly top
      Severin, Henry H.P., 1939

LEPTOCHLOA Beauv. 1812 (Gramineae)
L. filiformis, (Lam.) Beauv.
   V. sugarcane mosaic
      Brandes, E.W. and Peter J. Klaphaak, 1923

LEPTONYCHIA Turcz. 1858 (Sterculiaceae)
L. pubescens, Keay
   V. cacao swollen shoot
      Tinsley, T.W. and A.L. Wharton, 1958

LEPTOSYNE DC. 1836 (Compositae)
L. maritima, (Hook. f.) A. Gray
   V. tobacco etch
      Holmes, Francis O., 1946

LESPEDEZA Michx. 1803 (Leguminosae)
L. bicolor, Turcz.
   V. cowpea mosaic
      Yu, T.F., 1946
L. striata, (Thunb.) Hook. & Arn.
   V. bean yellow mosaic
      Conover, Robert A., 1948
   V. lucerne mosaic
      Zaumeyer, W.J., 1938
   V. pea streak
      Zaumeyer, W.J., 1938
   V. soybean mosaic
      Conover, Robert A., 1948

LESSINGIA Cham. 1829 (Compositae)
L. glandulifera, A. Gray
   V. beet curly top
      Severin, Henry H.P., 1939

LIGULARIA Cass. 1816 (Compositae)
L. clivorum, Maxim.
   V. chrysanthemum stunt
      Brierley, Philip, 1953

LIGUSTRUM ((Tourn.)) L. 1735 (Oleaceae)
L. lucidum, Ait.
   V. lilac witches' broom
      Brierley, Philip, 1955
      Lorentz, Paul and Philip Brierley, 1953
L. obtusifolium, Sieb. & Zucc., var. regelianum,
(Koehne) Rehd.
   V. lilac witches' broom
      Brierley, Philip, 1955
L. ovalifolium, Hassk.
   V. lilac witches' broom
      Lorentz, Paul and Philip Brierley, 1953

LILIUM Tourn. ex L. 1737 (Liliaceae)
L. auratum, Lindl.
  V. onion yellow dwarf
    Henderson, W.J., 1935
L. candidum, L.
  V. onion yellow dwarf
    Henderson, W.J., 1935
  V. wheat streak mosaic
    Sill, W.H., Jr. and Patrick C. Agusiobo, 1955
L. davidi, Duch.
  V. cucumber mosaic
    Brierley, Philip, 1940
  V. tulip breaking
    Brierley, Philip, 1940
L. formosanum, (Baker) Wallace or Stapf *
  V. nothoscordum mosaic
    McKinney, H.H., 1950
  V. ornithogalum mosaic
    Smith, Floyd F. and Philip Brierley, 1944
  V. pea mottle
    Johnson, Folke, 1942
  V. pea wilt
    Johnson, Folke, 1942
  V. tomato aspermy
    Brierley, Philip, Floyd F. Smith and S.P.
    Doolittle, 1955
L. hansonii, Leichtl.
  V. cucumber mosaic
    Brierley, Philip, 1940
    Brierley, Philip and Floyd F. Smith, 1944
  V. lily symptomless
    Brierley, Philip and Floyd F. Smith, 1944
  V. tulip breaking
    Brierley, Philip, 1940
    Brierley, Philip and Floyd F. Smith, 1944
L. henryi, Baker
  V. cucumber mosaic
    Brierley, Philip and Floyd F. Smith, 1944
  V. lily symptomless
    Brierley, Philip and Floyd F. Smith, 1944
  V. tulip breaking
    Brierley, Philip and Floyd F. Smith, 1944
L. humboldtii, Roez. & Leichtl.
  V. cucumber mosaic
    Brierley, Philip and Floyd F. Smith, 1944
  V. lily symptomless
    Brierley, Philip and Floyd F. Smith, 1944
  V. tulip breaking
    Brierley, Philip and Floyd F. Smith, 1944
L. longiflorum, Thunb.
  V. onion yellow dwarf
    Henderson, W.J., 1935
  V. orchid (vanda) mosaic
    Murakishi, Harry H., 1952
  V. ornithogalum mosaic
    Smith, Floyd F. and Philip Brierley, 1944
L. longiflorum var. gigantium, Hort.
  V. narcissus mosaic
    Haasis, Frank A., 1939
L. martagon, L., var. album, Hort. x L. hansonii,
  V. cucumber mosaic   Leichtl.
    Brierley, Philip, 1940
  V. tulip breaking
    Brierley, Philip, 1940
L. nepalense, D. Don
  V. cucumber mosaic
    Brierley, Philip, 1940
  V. tulip breaking
    Brierley, Philip, 1940
L. pardalinum, Kellogg
  V. cucumber mosaic
    Brierley, Philip and Floyd F. Smith, 1944
  V. lily symptomless
    Brierley, Philip and Floyd F. Smith, 1944
  V. tulip breaking
    Brierley, Philip and Floyd F. Smith, 1944
L. pardalinum var. giganteum *
  V. cucumber mosaic
    Brierley, Philip, 1940
  V. tulip breaking
    Brierley, Philip, 1940
L. parryi, Wats.
  V. cucumber mosaic
    Brierley, Philip and Floyd F. Smith, 1944

L. parryi, Wats. (cont.)
  V. lily symptomless
    Brierley, Philip and Floyd F. Smith, 1944
  V. tulip breaking
    Brierley, Philip and Floyd F. Smith, 1944
L. parvum, Kellogg
  V. cucumber mosaic
    Brierley, Philip and Floyd F. Smith, 1944
  V. tulip breaking
    Brierley, Philip and Floyd F. Smith, 1944
L. philippinense, Baker
  V. tobacco etch
    Holmes, Francis O., 1946
  V. tobacco mosaic
    Holmes, Francis O., 1946
L. regale, Wilson
  V. onion yellow dwarf
    Henderson, W.J., 1935
L. sargentiae, Wilson
  V. cucumber mosaic
    Brierley, Philip and Floyd F. Smith, 1944
  V. lily symptomless
    Brierley, Philip and Floyd F. Smith, 1944
  V. tulip breaking
    Brierley, Philip and Floyd F. Smith, 1944
L. speciosum, Thunb.
  V. onion yellow dwarf
    Henderson, W.J., 1935
L. superbum, L.
  V. cucumber mosaic
    Brierley, Philip and Floyd F. Smith, 1944
  V. lily symptomless
    Brierley, Philip and Floyd F. Smith, 1944
  V. tulip breaking
    Brierley, Philip and Floyd F. Smith, 1944
L. tigrinum, Ker-Gawl.
  V. onion eyllow dwarf
    Henderson, W.J., 1935

LIMONIUM Tourn. ex Mill. 1752 (Plumbaginaceae)
L. bonduelli, (Lest.) Kuntze
  V. tobacco etch
    Holmes, Francis O., 1946
L. latifolium, (J.E. Sm.) Kuntze
  V. cabbage black ring spot
    Tompkins, C.M., M.W. Gardner and H. Rex
    Thomas, 1938
  V. cucumber mosaic
    Wellman, F.L., 1935
  V. turnip mosaic
    Tompkins, C.M., 1938
L. sinuatum, (L.) Mill.
  V. squash mosaic
    Freitag, J.H., 1956
  V. tobacco etch
    Holmes, Francis O., 1946

LINARIA Tourn. ex Mill. 1752 (Scrophulariaceae)
L. canadensis, (L.) Dumort.
  V. cucumber mosaic
    Wellman, F.L., 1935
L. floridana, Chapm.
  V. cucumber mosaic
    Wellman, F.L., 1935
L. vulgaris, Mill.
  V. beet yellows
    Roland, G. and J. Tahon, 1961
  V. tobacco etch
    Holmes, Francis O., 1946

LINUM Tourn. ex L. 1735 (Linaceae)
L. flavum, L.
  V. tobacco etch
    Holmes, Francis O., 1946
  V. tobacco mosaic
    Holmes, Francis O., 1946
L. grandiflorum, Desf.
  V. pea mosaic
    Murphy, D.M. and W.H. Pierce, 1937
  V. tobacco etch
    Holmes, Francis O., 1946
  V. tobacco mosaic
    Holmes, Francis O., 1946

Linum lewisii, Pursh
    V. beet yellows
        Roland, G. and J. Tahon, 1961
L. perenne, L.
    V. tobacco etch
        Holmes, Francis O., 1946
    V. tobacco mosaic
        Holmes, Francis O., 1946
L. usitatissimum, L.
    V. beet yellows
        Roland, G. and J. Tahon, 1961

LOBELIA Plum. ex L. 1737 (Lobeliaceae)
L. erinus, L.
    V. cucumber mosaic
        Wellman, F.L., 1935
    V. tobacco etch
        Holmes, Francis O., 1946
L. hybrida, Hort.
    V. cabbage black ring spot
        Tompkins, C.M., M.W. Gardner and H. Rex
        Thomas, 1938
    V. primula mosaic
        Tompkins, C.M. and John T. Middleton, 1941
    V. radish mosaic
        Tompkins, C.M., 1939
    V. turnip mosaic
        Tompkins, C.M., 1938, 1939
        Tompkins, C.M. and H. Rex Thomas, 1938
L. inflata, L.
    V. tobacco mosaic
        Holmes, Francis O., 1938
L. spp.
    V. pea mosaic
        Murphy, D.M. and W.H. Pierce, 1937

LOBULARIA Desv. 1814 (Cruciferae)
L. maritima, (L.) Desv.
    V. anemone mosaic *
        Hollings, M., 1957
    V. beet mosaic
        Pound, Glenn S., 1947
    V. chrysanthemum B (mild mosaic) *
        Hollings, M., 1957
    V. cucumber mosaic
        Wellman, F.L., 1935
    V. tobacco etch
        Holmes, Francis O., 1946

LOLIUM L. 1735 (Gramineae)
L. perenne, L.
    V. barley yellow dwarf
        Bruehl, G.W. and H.V. Toko, 1957
        Oswald, John W. and Byron R. Houston, 1953
L. spp.
    V. panicum mosaic *
        Sill, W.H., Jr. and R.C. Pickett, 1957

LOTUS ((Tourn.)) L. 1735 (Leguminosae)
L. corniculatus, L.
    V. lucerne mosaic
        Kreitlow, K.W. and W.C. Price, 1949
    V. lucerne witches' broom
        Menzies, J.D., 1946
    V. pea enation mosaic
        McEwen, F.L. and W.T. Schroeder, 1956
L. ornithopodioides, L.
    V. pea mosaic
        Murphy, D.M. and W.H. Pierce, 1937
L. uliginosus, Schkuhr
    V. pea enation mosaic
        McEwen, F.L. and W.T. Schroeder, 1956

LUFFA ((Tourn.)) L. 1735 (Cucurbitaceae)
L. acutangula, Roxb.
    V. datura distortion mosaic
        Capoor, S.P. and P.M. Varma, 1952
    V. tobacco etch
        Holmes, Francis O., 1946
    V. tobacco mosaic
        Holmes, Francis O., 1946
L. aegyptiaca, Mill. (L. cylindrica, Roem.)
    V. cucumber mosaic
        Nariani, T.K. and Nirmaljit Singh, 1952

L. aegyptiaca, Mill. (L. cylindrica, Roem.) (cont.)
    V. papaw mosaic
        Adsuar, Jose, 1950
    V. prunus A *
        Fulton, Robert W., 1957
    V. prunus B *
        Fulton, Robert W., 1957
    V. prunus E *
        Fulton, Robert W., 1957
    V. prunus G *
        Fulton, Robert W., 1957
    V. tomato ring spot
        Samson, R.W. and E.P. Imle, 1942
L. spp.
    V. citrus tristeza
        Knorr, L.C., 1956

LUNARIA Tourn. ex L. 1735 (Cruciferae)
L. annua, L.
    V. radish mosaic
        Tompkins, C.M., 1939
    V. tobacco etch
        Holmes, Francis O., 1946
    V. turnip mosaic
        Tompkins, C.M., 1939

LUPINUS ((Tourn.)) L. 1735 (Leguminosae)
L. affinis, Agardh.
    V. beet curly top
        Carsner, E., 1919
L. albus, L.
    V. bean common mosaic
        Zaumeyer, W.J. and B.L. Wade, 1935
    V. bean southern mosaic
        Zaumeyer, W.J. and L.L. Harter, 1943
    V. bean yellow mosaic
        Zaumeyer, W.J. and H.H. Fisher, 1953
        Zaumeyer, W.J. and B.L. Wade, 1935
    V. beet yellows
        Roland, G. and J. Tahon, 1961
    V. cowpea mosaic
        Yu, T.F., 1946
    V. cucumber mosaic
        Harter, L.L., 1938
    V. lucerne mosaic
        Zaumeyer, W.J. and B.L. Wade, 1935
    V. lupine disease *
        Weimer, J.L., 1950
    V. pea enation mosaic
        Hagedorn, D.J. and J.C. Walker, 1954
        Stubbs, M.W., 1937
    V. pea streak
        Zaumeyer, W.J., 1938
    V. red clover mosaic *
        Zaumeyer, W.J. and B.L. Wade, 1935
L. angustifolius, L.
    V. bean yellow mosaic
        Conover, Robert A., 1948
    V. soybean mosaic
        Conover, Robert A., 1948
    V. Wisconsin pea streak
        Hagedorn, D.J. and J.C. Walker, 1949, 1954
L. hartwegii, Lindl.
    V. spinach yellow dwarf
        Severin, Henry H.P. and Donald H. Little, 1947
    V. squash mosaic
        Freitag, J.H., 1956
    V. tobacco etch
        Holmes, Francis O., 1946
    V. tobacco mosaic
        Holmes, Francis O., 1946
    V. tomato ring spot
        Samson, R.W. and E.P. Imle, 1942
L. hirsutus, L.
    V. cucumber mosaic
        Wellman, F.L., 1935
    V. pea wilt
        Johnson, Folke, 1942
L. luteus, L.
    V. bean southern mosaic
        Zaumeyer, W.J. and L.L. Harter, 1943
    V. bean yellow mosaic
        Conover, Robert A., 1948

Lupinus luteus, L. (cont.)
   V. pea streak
      Zaumeyer, W.J., 1938
   V. soybean mosaic
      Conover, Robert A., 1948
L. mutabilis, Sweet
   V. cucumber mosaic
      McKnight, T., 1953
L. polyphyllus, Lindl.
   V. chrysanthemum B (mild mosaic) *
      Hollings, M., 1957
   V. cucumber mosaic
      Govier, D.A., 1957
   V. pea mosaic
      Chaudhuri, R.P., 1950
   V. squash mosaic
      Freitag, J.H., 1956
   V. tomato aspermy
      Hollings, M., 1955
L. pubescens, Benth. (L. hybridus, Voss)
   V. beet mosaic
      Pound, Glenn S., 1947
L. spp.
   V. lucerne mosaic
      Kreitlow, K.W. and W.C. Price, 1949

LYCHNIS ((Tourn.)) L. 1735 (Caryophyllaceae)
L. alba, Mill.
   V. cucumber mosaic
      Faan, Hwei-Chung and James Johnson, 1951
   V. stone fruit *
      Boyle, J.S., J. Duain Moore and G.W. Keitt, 1954
   V. tobacco mosaic
      Holmes, Francis O., 1938
   V. tobacco necrosis
      Fulton, Robert W., 1950
L. coeli-rosa, (L.) Desr.
   V. tobacco etch
      Holmes, Francis O., 1946
L. viscaria, L.
   V. tomato aspermy
      Brierley, Philip, Floyd F. Smith and S.P.
      Doolittle, 1955

LYCIUM L. 1735 (Solanaceae)
L. barbarum, L.
   V. potato X
      Cockerham, George, 1943
   V. red currant ring spot
      Klesser, P.J., 1951
L. halimifolium, Mill.
   V. cauliflower mosaic
      Walker, J.C., Francis J. LeBeau and Glenn S.
      Pound, 1945
   V. stone fruit *
      Boyle, J.S., J. Duain Moore and G.W. Keitt, 1954

LYCOPERSICON Tourn. ex Rupp. 1745 (Solanaceae)
(LYCOPERSICUM) Hill 1765
L. chilense, Dun.
   V. beet curly top
      Virgin, Walter J., 1940
   V. tobacco etch
      Holmes, Francis O., 1946
   V. tobacco mosaic
      Holmes, Francis O., 1943
L. esculentum, Mill. (Solanum lycopersicum, L.)
   V. anemone mosaic *
      Hollings, M., 1957
   V. barley stripe mosaic
      Sill, W.H., Jr. and E.D. Hansing, 1955
   V. bayberry yellows
      Raychaudhuri, S.P., 1953
   V. bean common mosaic
      Ainsworth, G.C., 1940
   V. bean pod mottle
      Zaumeyer, W.J. and H. Rex Thomas, 1948
   V. bean southern mosaic
      Zaumeyer, W.J. and L.L. Harter, 1943
   V. bean yellow mosaic
      Ainsworth, G.C., 1940
      Conover, Robert A., 1948
      Hagedorn, D.J. and J.C. Walker, 1950, 1954
      Thomas, H. Rex and W.J. Zaumeyer, 1953

L. esculentum, Mill. (Solanum lycopersicum, L.) (cont.)
   V. bean yellow stipple
      Zaumeyer, W.J. and H. Rex Thomas, 1950
   V. beet curly top
      Bennett, C.W., Eubanks Carsner, F.H. Coons
      and E.W. Brandes, 1946
      Giddings, N.J., 1938
   V. beet mosaic
      Bennett, C.W., 1949
      Pound, Glenn S., 1947
      Severin, Henry H.P. and Roger M. Drake, 1948
   V. beet yellow net
      Sylvester, Edward S., 1948
   V. beet yellows
      Roland, G. and J. Tahon, 1961
   V. broad bean mottle
      Bawden, F.C., R.P. Chaudhuri and B. Kassanis,
      1951
      Yu, T.F., 1939
   V. cabbage ring necrosis
      Larson, R.H. and J.C. Walker, 1941
   V. canna mosaic
      Castillo, B.S., C.E. Yarwood and A.H. Gold, 1956
   V. cauliflower mosaic
      Alvarez-Garcia, L.A., 1951
      Caldwell, John and Ian W. Prentice, 1942
   V. chilli (pepper) mosaic
      Dale, W.T., 1954
      Ferguson, I.A.C., 1951
      Jha, Ashrafi and S.P. Raychaudhuri, 1956
   V. chrysanthemum B (mild mosaic) *
      Hollings, M., 1957
   V. chrysanthemum latent *
      Hollings, M., 1957
   V. chrysanthemum Q
      Brierley, Philip and Floyd F. Smith, 1953
   V. cineraria mosaic
      Jones, Leon K., 1944
   V. citrus tristeza
      Bennett, C.W. and A.S. Costa, 1949
   V. cowpea mosaic
      Anderson, C.W., 1955
      Capoor, S.P. and P.M. Varma, 1956
      Dale, W.T., 1949
      McLean, D.M., 1941
      Yu, T.F., 1946
   V. cucumber green mottle mosaic
      Ainsworth, G.C., 1935
      Vasudeva, R.S. and T.K. Nariani, 1952
      Vasudeva, R.S., S.P. Raychaudhuri and Jagannath
      Singh, 1949
   V. cucumber mosaic
      Doolittle, S.P. and W.W. Gilbert, 1918
      McKnight, T., 1953
      Vasudeva, R. Sahai and T.B. Lal, 1943
   V. eryngium yellow mosaic *
      Johnson, James and Edith M. Hein, 1948
   V. euphorbia mosaic
      Costa, A.S. and C.W. Bennett, 1950
   V. filaree red leaf
      Frazier, Norman W., 1951
   V. hibiscus yellow vein mosaic
      Capoor, S.P. and P.M. Varma, 1950
   V. hydrangea ring spot
      Brierley, Philip and Paul Lorentz, 1957
   V. iris mosaic
      Brierley, Philip and Frank P. McWhorter, 1936
   V. lettuce mosaic
      Ainsworth, G.C., 1940
      Ainsworth, G.C. and L. Ogilvie, 1939
   V. lucerne mosaic
      Berkeley, G.H., 1947
      Johnson, E.M., 1946
      Kreitlow, K.W. and W.C. Price, 1949
      Oswald, John W., 1950
      Thomas, H. Rex, 1951
      Zaumeyer, W.J., 1938, 1953
   V. lupine disease *
      Weimer, J.L., 1950
   V. malva yellow vein mosaic *
      Costa, A.S. and James E. Duffus, 1957
   V. nicotiana glutinosa mosaic *
      Allard, H.A., 1916

Lycopersicon esculentum, Mill. (Solanum lycopersicon, L. (cont.)
V. nothoscordum mosaic
McKinney, H.H., 1950
V. orchid (cymbidium) mosaic
Jensen, D.D., 1951
V. orchid (odontoglossum) ring spot
Jensen, D.D. and A. Herbert Gold, 1951
V. orchid (vanda) mosaic
Murakishi, Harry H., 1952
V. panax ring spot
Aragaki, M., H. Murakishi and J.W. Hendrix, 1953
V. papaw mosaic
Adsuar, Jose, 1950
V. papaw ring spot
Jensen, D.D., 1949
V. pea enation mosaic
Ainsworth, G.C., 1940
Hagedorn, D.J. and J.C. Walker, 1954
Osborn, H.T., 1938
Simons, John N., 1954
Stubbs, M.W., 1937
V. pea mosaic
Ainsworth, G.C., 1940
Chaudhuri, R.P., 1950
Hagedorn, D.J. and J.C. Walker, 1954
Osborn, H.T., 1937
Stubbs, M.W., 1937
V. pea mottle
Johnson, Folke, 1942
V. pea streak
Zaumeyer, W.J., 1938
V. pea wilt
Johnson, Folke, 1942
V. pea yellow mosaic *
Ainsworth, G.C., 1940
V. pelargonium leaf curl
Jones, Leon K., 1940
V. physalis floridana yellow net
Webb, R.E., 1955
V. pokeweed mosaic *
Allard, H.A., 1918
V. potato A
MacLachlan, D.S., R.H. Larson and J.C. Walker, 1953
V. potato paracrinkle
Bagnall, R.H. and R.H. Larson, 1957
Bagnall, R.H., R.H. Larson and J.C. Walker, 1956
Kassanis, B., 1955
V. potato Y
Hamilton, Marion A., 1932
V. primula mosaic
Severin, Henry H.P. and C.M. Tompkins, 1950
V. red clover vein mosaic
Hagedorn, D.J. and E.W. Hanson, 1951
Hagedorn, D.J. and J.C. Walker, 1949, 1954
Osborn, H.T., 1937
V. soybean mosaic
Conover, Robert A., 1948
V. spinach yellow dwarf
Severin, Henry H.P. and Donald H. Little, 1947
V. squash mosaic
Freitag, J.H., 1956
V. squash mosaic (southern)
Anderson, C.W., 1951
V. stone fruit *
Boyle, J.S., J. Duain Moore and G.W. Keitt, 1954
V. sweet potato mosaic
Borders, H.I. and T.J. Ratcliff, 1954
V. tobacco coarse etch
Johnson, E.M., 1930
V. tobacco green mosaic
McKinney, H.H., 1929
Peterson, Paul D. and H.H. McKinney, 1938
V. tobacco mosaic
McKinney, H.H., 1935
V. tobacco ring spot
Berkeley, G.H., 1953
Bridgmon, G.H. and J.C. Walker, 1952
Cooper, W.E., 1949
Grogan, R.G. and W.C. Schnathorst, 1955
Johnson, E.M., 1930
Pound, Glenn S., 1949
Stubbs, M.W., 1937

L. esculentum, Mill. (Solanum lycopersicon, L.) (cont.)
V. tobacco ring spot
Wingard, S.A., 1928
V. tobacco streak
Johnson, J., 1936
Thomas, H. Rex and W.J. Zaumeyer, 1950
V. tobacco stunt *
Hidaka, Zyun, Tetsuo Uozumi and Chuji Hiruki, 1956
V. tropaeolum mosaic
Silberschmidt, Karl, 1953
V. tulip breaking
McWhorter, F.P., 1935
V. turnip rosette *
Broadbent, L. and G.D. Heathcote, 1958
V. Wisconsin pea streak
Hagedorn, D.J. and J.C. Walker, 1949, 1954
L. esculentum var. commune, Bailey *
V. celery mosaic
Freitag, Julius H. and Henry H.P. Severin, 1945
V. pea mosaic
Murphy, D.M. and W.H. Pierce, 1937
L. esculentum var. vulgare, Bailey
V. cabbage black ring spot
Tompkins, C.M., M.W. Gardner and H. Rex Thomas, 1938
V. cauliflower mosaic
Tompkins, C.M., 1937
V. primula mosaic
Tompkins, C.M. and John T. Middleton, 1941
V. radish mosaic
Tompkins, C.M., 1939
V. turnip mosaic
Tompkins, C.M., 1938, 1939
Tompkins, C.M. and H. Rex Thomas, 1938
L. lycopersicon, (L.) Karst. *
V. cucumber mosaic
Adsuar, Jose and A. Cruz Miret, 1950
L. peruvianum, (L.) Mill.
V. beet curly top
Giddings, N.J., C.W. Bennett and A.L. Harrison, 1951
V. tomato ring spot
Samson, R.W. and E.P. Imle, 1942
V. tomato spotted wilt
Smith, Paul G., 1944
L. pimpinellifolium, (Jusl.) Mill.
V. beet curly top
Giddings, N.J., C.W. Bennett and A.L. Harrison, 1951
V. cabbage black ring spot
Tompkins, C.M., M.W. Gardner and H. Rex Thomas, 1938
V. cabbage ring necrosis
Larson, R.H. and J.C. Walker, 1941
V. cauliflower mosaic
Tompkins, C.M., 1937
V. cowpea mosaic
Yu, T.F., 1946
V. radish mosaic
Tompkins, C.M., 1939
V. turnip mosaic
Tompkins, C.M., 1938, 1939
Tompkins, C.M. and H. Rex Thomas, 1938

LYCOPUS Tourn. ex L. 1735 (Labiatae)
L. rubellus, Moench
V. tobacco etch
Holmes, Francis O., 1946
V. tobacco mosaic
Holmes, Francis O., 1938
L. virginicus, L.
V. tobacco mosaic
Holmes, Francis O., 1938

LYTHRUM L. 1735 (Lythraceae)
L. salicaria, L.
V. anemone brown ring *
Hollings, M., 1958
V. chrysanthemum B (mild mosaic) *
Hollings, M., 1957
V. chrysanthemum latent *
Hollings, M., 1957

MALACHRA L. 1767 (Malvaceae)
M. capitata, L.
V. abutilon infectious variegation
Bird, Julio, 1958

MALCOMIA ((R. Br. in)) Ait. Hort. Kew. 1812
(MALCOLMIA Spreng.) 1818   (Cruciferae)
M. africana, ((R. Br. in)) Ait. Hort. Kew.
V. beet curly top
Giddings, N.J., 1944
M. maritima, R. Br.
V. cauliflower mosaic
Caldwell, John and Ian W. Prentice, 1942
Tompkins, C.M., 1937
Walker, J.C., Francis J. LeBeau and Glenn S.
Pound, 1945
V. tobacco ring spot
Wingard, S.A., 1928
V. turnip mosaic
Tompkins, C.M., 1939

MALOPE L. 1735 (Malvaceae)
M. trifida, Cav.
V. tobacco etch
Holmes, Francis O., 1946
V. tobacco mosaic
Holmes, Francis O., 1946

MALUS Tourn. ex L. 1737 (Rosaceae)
M. spp.
V. beet curly top
Giddings, N.J., 1944
M. sylvestris, Mill.
V. lucerne dwarf
Freitag, J.H., 1951
V. tobacco ring spot
Wingard, S.A., 1928
V. tobacco streak
Fulton, Robert W., 1956

MALVA ((Tourn.)) L. 1735 (Malvaceae)
M. moschata, L.
V. muskmelon mosaic
Rader, Wm. E., Hugh F. Fitzpatrick and E.M.
Hildebrand, 1947
M. parviflora, L.
V. beet yellows
Roland, G. and J. Tahon, 1961
V. cabbage black ring spot
Tompkins, C.M., M.W. Gardner and H. Rex
Thomas, 1938
V. lucerne dwarf
Freitag, J.H., 1951
M. rotundifolia, L.
V. beet mosaic
Severin, Henry H.P. and Roger M. Drake, 1947
V. beet yellows
Roland, G. and J. Tahon, 1961
V. cucumber mosaic
Burnett, G., 1934
V. stone fruit *
Boyle, J.S., J. Duain Moore and G.W. Keitt, 1954
V. tobacco etch
Holmes, Francis O., 1946
V. tobacco mosaic
Holmes, Francis O., 1938, 1946
V. tobacco ring spot
Fenne, S.B., 1931
M. spp.
V. potato leaf roll
MacCarthy, H.R., 1954
M. sylvestris, L.
V. beet yellows
Roland, G. and J. Tahon, 1961

MALVASTRUM A. Gray 1849 (Malvaceae)
M. coromandelianum, Garcke
V. papaw ring spot
Jensen, D.D., 1949

MANIHOT Tourn. ex Adans. 1763 (Euphorbiaceae)
M. esculenta, Crantz (M. utilissima, Pohl)
V. cacao swollen shoot
Tinsley, T.W. and A.L. Wharton, 1958

M. esculenta, Crantz (M. utilissima, Pohl) (cont.)
V. cucumber mosaic
Wellman, F.L., 1935
V. euphorbia mosaic
Costa, A.S. and C.W. Bennett, 1950
M. glaziovii, Muell. Arg.
V. cacao swollen shoot
Tinsley, T.W. and A.L. Wharton, 1958

MANSONIA J.R. Drumm. 1905 (Sterculiaceae)
M. altissima, A. Chev.
V. cacao swollen shoot
Tinsley, T.W. and A.L. Wharton, 1958

MARANTA Plum. ex L. 1737 (Marantaceae)
M. arundinaceae, L.
V. canna mosaic
Castillo, B.S., C.E. Yarwood and A.H. Gold, 1956
M. bicolor, Ker
V. tulip breaking
Brierley, Philip and Floyd F. Smith, 1944
V. wheat streak mosaic
Sill, W.H., Jr. and Patrick C. Agusiobo, 1955

MARRUBIUM Tourn. ex L. 1735 (Labiatae)
M. vulgare, L.
V. beet curly top
Carsner, E., 1919
Severin, Henry H.P., 1939
V. beet yellows
Roland, G. and J. Tahon, 1961
V. tobacco etch
Holmes, Francis O., 1946

MATRICARIA ((Tourn.)) L. 1735 (Compositae)
M. chamomilla, L.
V. beet yellows
Roland, G. and J. Tahon, 1961
M. discoidea, DC.
V. beet yellows
Roland, G. and J. Tahon, 1961
M. inodora, L.
V. beet yellows
Roland, G. and J. Tahon, 1961
M. suaveolens, (Pursh) Buch.
V. lucerne dwarf
Freitag, J.H., 1951

MATTHIOLA R. Br. 1812 (Cruciferae)
M. bicornis, (Sibth. & Sm.) DC.
V. tobacco etch
Holmes, Francis O., 1946
V. turnip mosaic
Tompkins, C.M., 1938
M. incana, (L.) R. Br.
V. beet yellows
Roland, G. and J. Tahon, 1961
V. cucumber mosaic
Govier, D.A., 1957
Wellman, F.L., 1935
V. dodder latent mosaic
Bennett, C.W., 1944
V. filaree red leaf
Frazier, Norman W., 1951
V. orchid (vanda) mosaic
Murakishi, Harry H., 1952
V. pea mosaic
Murphy, D.M. and W.H. Pierce, 1937
V. tobacco etch
Holmes, Francis O., 1946
V. tobacco mosaic
Holmes, Francis O., 1946
V. tomato aspermy
Brierley, Philip, Floyd F. Smith and S.P.
Doolittle, 1955
V. turnip mosaic
Tompkins, C.M., 1939
M. incana var. annua, (L.) Voss
V. beet mosaic
Pound, Glenn S., 1947
Severin, Henry H.P. and Roger M. Drake, 1948
V. cauliflower mosaic
Caldwell, John and Ian W. Prentice, 1942

Matthiola incana, (L.) R. Br., var. annua, (L.) Voss
  V. chrysanthemum B (mild mosaic) *   (cont.)
    Hollings, M., 1957
  V. orchid (odontoglossum) ring spot
    Jensen, D.D. and A. Herbert Gold, 1951
  V. primula mosaic
    Tompkins, C.M. and John T. Middleton, 1941
  V. radish mosaic
    Tompkins, C.M., 1939
  V. spinach yellow dwarf
    Severin, Henry H.P. and Donald H. Little, 1947
  V. squash mosaic
    Freitag, J.H., 1956
  V. turnip mosaic
    LeBeau, Francis J. and J.C. Walker, 1945

MEDEOLA Gronov. ex L. 1735 (Liliaceae)
M. virginica, L.
  V. cucumber mosaic
    Brierley, Philip and Floyd F. Smith, 1944
  V. lily symptomless
    Brierley, Philip and Floyd F. Smith, 1944
  V. tulip breaking
    Brierley, Philip and Floyd F. Smith, 1944

MEDICAGO Tourn. ex L. 1737 (Leguminosae)
M. arabica, (L.) All.
  V. lucerne witches' broom
    Menzies, J.D., 1946
M. hispida, Gaertn.
  V. bean yellow mosaic
    Grogan, Raymond G. and J.C. Walker, 1948
  V. squash mosaic
    Freitag, J.H., 1956
M. lacinata, Mill.
  V. lucerne witches' broom
    Klostermeyer, E.C. and J.D. Menzies, 1951
M. lupulina, L.
  V. beet yellows
    Roland, G. and J. Tahon, 1961
  V. lucerne mosaic
    Kreitlow, K.W. and W.C. Price, 1949
  V. pea enation mosaic
    Johnson, Folke and Leon K. Jones, 1937
    McEwen, F.L. and W.T. Schroeder, 1956
  V. pea mosaic
    Murphy, D.M. and W.H. Pierce, 1937
  V. red currant ring spot
    Klesser, P.J., 1951
M. orbicularis, All.
  V. red clover vein mosaic
    Hagedorn, D.J. and J.C. Walker, 1949, 1954
M. sativa, L.
  V. barley stripe mosaic
    Sill, W.H., Jr. and E.D. Hansing, 1955
  V. bayberry yellows
    Raychaudhuri, S.P., 1953
  V. bean common mosaic
    Snyder, W.C., 1942
    Zaumeyer, W.J. and B.L. Wade, 1935
  V. bean Montana *
    Afanasiev, M.M. and H.E. Morris, 1946
  V. bean southern mosaic
    Zaumeyer, W.J. and L.L. Harter, 1943
  V. bean yellow mosaic
    Afanasiev, M.M. and H.E. Morris, 1952
    Conover, Robert A., 1948
    Elliott, J.A., 1921
    Hagedorn, D.J. and J.C. Walker, 1950, 1954
    Houston, Byron R. and John W. Oswald, 1953
    Pierce, W.H., 1935
    Thomas, H. Rex and W.J. Zaumeyer, 1953
    Zaumeyer, W.J., 1952
    Zaumeyer, W.J. and H.H. Fisher, 1953
    Zaumeyer, W.J. and B.L. Wade, 1935
  V. bean yellow stipple
    Zaumeyer, W.J. and H. Rex Thomas, 1950
  V. beet curly top
    Giddings, N.J., 1944
  V. beet mosaic
    Bennett, C.W., 1949
  V. beet yellows
    Roland, G. and J. Tahon, 1961

M. sativa, L. (cont.)
  V. broad bean mottle
    Bawden, F.C., R.P. Chaudhuri and B. Kassanis,
    1951
  V. cabbage black ring spot
    Tompkins, C.M., M.W. Gardner and H. Rex
    Thomas, 1938
  V. cauliflower mosaic
    Alvarez-Garcia, L.A., 1951
  V. chilli (pepper) mosaic
    Jha, Ashrafi and S.P. Raychaudhuri, 1956
  V. chilli veinbanding
    Simons, John N., 1956
  V. chrysanthemum B (mild mosaic) *
    Hollings, M., 1957
  V. clover big vein
    Black, L.M. and M.K. Brakke, 1952
  V. cowpea mosaic
    Capoor, S.P. and P.M. Varma, 1956
    Yu, T.F., 1946
  V. cucumber mosaic
    Doolittle, S.P. and W.J. Zaumeyer, 1953
    Hagedorn, D.J. and J.C. Walker, 1954
    Simons, John.N., 1957
  V. filaree red leaf
    Frazier, Norman W., 1951
  V. hibiscus yellow vein mosaic
    Capoor, S.P. and P.M. Varma, 1950
  V. kaimi clover disease *
    Murakishi, Harry H., 1952
  V. lucerne mosaic
    Johnson, E.M., 1946
    Kreitlow, K.W. and W.C. Price, 1949
    Porter, D.R., 1935
  V. onion yellow dwarf
    Henderson, W.J., 1935
  V. pea enation mosaic
    Hagedorn, D.J. and J.C. Walker, 1954
    Osborn, H.T., 1938
    Pierce, W.H., 1935
    Simons, John N., 1954
    Stubbs, M.W., 1937
  V. pea mosaic
    Chaudhuri, R.P., 1950
    Hagedorn, D.J. and J.C. Walker, 1954
    Murphy, D.M. and W.H. Pierce, 1937
    Pierce, W.H., 1935
    Stubbs, M.W., 1937
  V. pea wilt
    Johnson, Folke, 1942
  V. potato yellow dwarf
    Black, L.M., 1943
  V. red clover mosaic *
    Elliott, J.A., 1921
    Zaumeyer, W.J. and B.L. Wade, 1935
  V. red clover vein mosaic
    Graves, Clinton H., Jr. and D.J. Hagedorn, 1956
    Hagedorn, D.J. and E.W. Hanson, 1951
    Hagedorn, D.J. and J.C. Walker, 1949, 1954
    Osborn, H.T., 1937
  V. soybean mosaic
    Conover, Robert A., 1948
    Pierce, W.H., 1935
  V. squash mosaic
    Freitag, J.H., 1956
  V. tobacco broad ring spot
    Johnson, James and Robert W. Fulton, 1942
  V. tobacco etch
    Holmes, Francis O., 1946
  V. tobacco mosaic
    Costa, A.S., 1944
    Holmes, Francis O., 1938, 1946
    Johnson, Folke, 1941
  V. tobacco ring spot
    Benedict, W.G., 1955
    Grogan, R.G. and W.C. Schnathorst, 1955
    Stubbs, M.W., 1937
  V. tobacco streak
    Thomas, H. Rex and W.J. Zaumeyer, 1950
  V. vaccinium false blossom
    Costa, A.S., 1944
    Kunkel, L.O., 1945
  V. Wisconsin pea streak
    Hagedorn, D.J. and J.C. Walker, 1949, 1954
    Skotland, C.B. and D.J. Hagedorn, 1954

MELANDRYUM Reichb. 1837 (Caryophyllaceae)
M. album, Garcke
  V. beet yellows
    Roland, G. and J. Tahon, 1961
M. rubrum, Garcke
  V. beet yellows
    Roland, G. and J. Tahon, 1961

MELILOTUS Tourn. ex Hall. 1742 (Leguminosae)
M. alba, Desr.
  V. anemone mosaic *
    Hollings, M., 1957
  V. bean common mosaic
    Snyder, W.C., 1942
    Zaumeyer, W.J. and B.L. Wade, 1935
  V. bean pod mottle
    Zaumeyer, W.J. and H. Rex Thomas, 1948
  V. bean southern mosaic
    Zaumeyer, W.J. and L.L. Harter, 1943
  V. bean yellow mosaic
    Baggett, James R., 1957
    Grogan, Raymond G. and J.C. Walker, 1948
    Zaumeyer, W.J. and B.L. Wade, 1935
  V. bean yellow stipple
    Zaumeyer, W.J. and H. Rex Thomas, 1950
  V. beet mosaic
    Bennett, C.W., 1949
  V. beet yellows
    Roland, G. and J. Tahon, 1961
  V. chrysanthemum B (mild mosaic) *
    Hollings, M., 1957
  V. cowpea mosaic
    Yu, T.F., 1946
  V. cucumber mosaic
    Bridgmon, G.H. and J.C. Walker, 1952
  V. gladiolus *
    Snow, Gordon F., 1955
  V. kaimi clover disease *
    Murakishi, Harry H., 1952
  V. onion yellow dwarf
    Henderson, W.J., 1935
  V. pea enation mosaic
    Hagedorn, D.J. and J.C. Walker, 1954
    Osborn, H.T., 1938
    Stubbs, M.W., 1937
  V. pea mosaic
    Hagedorn, D.J. and J.C. Walker, 1954
    Stubbs, M.W., 1937
  V. prunus E *
    Fulton, Robert W., 1957
  V. red clover mosaic *
    Dickson, B.T., 1922
    Zaumeyer, W.J. and B.L. Wade, 1935
  V. soybean mosaic
    Conover, Robert A., 1948
  V. squash mosaic
    Freitag, J.H., 1956
  V. stone fruit *
    Boyle, J.S., J. Duain Moore and G.W. Keitt, 1954
  V. tobacco broad ring spot
    Johnson, James and Robert W. Fulton, 1942
  V. tobacco ring spot
    Bridgmon, G.H. and J.C. Walker, 1952
    Cheo, Pen Ching and W.J. Zaumeyer, 1952
M. dentata, (Waldst. & Kit.) Pers.
  V. beet yellows
    Roland, G. and J. Tahon, 1961
M. hybridum *
  V. tobacco ring spot
    Benedict, W.G., 1955
M. indica, (L.) All.
  V. bean common mosaic
    Snyder, W.C., 1942
  V. dodder latent mosaic
    Bennett, C.W., 1944
  V. prunus E *
    Fulton, Robert W., 1957
  V. squash mosaic
    Freitag, J.H., 1956
M. officinalis, (L.) Lam.
  V. bean yellow mosaic
    Grogan, Raymond G. and J.C. Walker, 1948
  V. cucumber mosaic
    Whipple, O.C. and J.C. Walker, 1941

M. officinalis, (L.) Lam. (cont.)
  V. kaimi clover disease *
    Murakishi, Harry H., 1952
  V. pea enation mosaic
    Johnson, Folke and Leon K. Jones, 1937
    Pierce, W.H., 1935
  V. pea mosaic
    Osborn, H.T., 1938
  V. prunus A *
    Fulton, Robert W., 1957
  V. prunus E *
    Fulton, Robert W., 1957
  V. prunus G *
    Fulton, Robert W., 1957
  V. red clover mosaic *
    Dickson, B.T., 1922
  V. red currant ring spot
    Klesser, P.J., 1951
  V. soybean mosaic
    Conover, Robert A., 1948
    Pierce, W.H., 1935
  V. squash mosaic
    Freitag, J.H., 1956
  V. stone fruit *
    Boyle, J.S., J. Duain Moore and G.W. Keitt, 1954
  V. tobacco ring spot
    Benedict, W.G., 1955
M. spp.
  V. lucerne witches' broom
    Menzies, J.D., 1944

MELISSA Tourn. ex L. 1737 (Labiatae)
M. officinalis, L.
  V. tobacco etch
    Holmes, Francis O., 1946

MELOCHIA Dill. ex L. 1735 (Sterculiaceae)
M. melissaefolia, Benth.
  V. cacao swollen shoot
    Tinsley, T.W. and A.L. Wharton, 1958
M. pyramidata, L.
  V. cacao swollen shoot
    Tinsley, T.W. and A.L. Wharton, 1958

MELOTHRIA L. 1737 (Cucurbitaceae)
M. guadalupensis, (Spreng.) Cogn.
  V. prunus A *
    Fulton, Robert W., 1957
M. pendula, L.
  V. prunus G *
    Fulton, Robert W., 1957

MENTHA ((Tourn.)) L. 1735 (Labiatae)
M. piperita, L.
  V. tobacco ring spot
    Wingard, S.A., 1928
M. spicata, L.
  V. cucumber mosaic
    Wellman, F.L., 1935
  V. muskmelon mosaic
    Rader, Wm. E., Hugh F. Fitzpatrick and E.M. Hildebrand, 1947
  V. tobacco etch
    Holmes, Francis O., 1946

MENTZELIA Plum. ex L. 1737 (Loascaceae)
M. pumila, Torr. & Gray
  V. beet yellows
    Roland, G. and J. Tahon, 1961

MESEMBRYANTHEMUM Dill. ex L. 1735 (Aizoaceae)
M. aequilaterale, Haw.
  V. beet yellows
    Roland, G. and J. Tahon, 1961
M. crystallinum, L.
  V. pea mosaic
    Murphy, D.M. and W.H. Pierce, 1937
  V. tobacco etch
    Holmes, Francis O., 1946
M. lineare, Thunb.
  V. tobacco etch
    Holmes, Francis O., 1946

MILLETTIA Wight & Arn. 1834 (Leguminosae)
M. thonningii, Baker
    V. cacao swollen shoot
        Tinsley, T.W. and A.L. Wharton, 1958

MIMULUS L. 1741 (Scrophulariaceae)
M. luteus, L.
    V. chrysanthemum B (mild mosaic) *
        Hollings, M., 1957
    V. red currant ring spot
        Klesser, P.J., 1951
    V. tobacco etch
        Holmes, Francis O., 1946
M. moschatus, Dougl.
    V. tobacco etch
        Holmes, Francis O., 1946
M. spp.
    V. beet yellows
        Roland, G. and J. Tahon, 1961

MIRABILIS Riv. ex L. 1735 (Nyctaginaceae)
M. jalapa, L.
    V. beet yellows
        Roland, G. and J. Tahon, 1961
    V. cauliflower mosaic
        Walker, J.C., Francis J. LeBeau and Glenn S.
        Pound, 1945
    V. cucumber mosaic
        Adsuar, Jose and A. Cruz Miret, 1950
        Wellman, F.L., 1935
    V. papaw mosaic
        Adsuar, Jose, 1950
    V. papaw ring spot
        Jensen, D.D., 1949
    V. pea mosaic
        Murphy, D.M. and W.H. Pierce, 1937
    V. spinach yellow dwarf
        Severin, Henry H.P. and Donald H. Little, 1947
    V. squash mosaic
        Freitag, J.H., 1956
    V. tobacco etch
        Holmes, Francis O., 1946
    V. tobacco mosaic
        Holmes, Francis O., 1946
    V. turnip mosaic
        Walker, J.C., Francis J. LeBeau and Glenn S.
        Pound, 1945

MISCANTHUS Anderss. 1855 (Gramineae)
M. sinensis, Anderss., var. variegatus, Beal
    V. sugarcane mosaic
        Brandes, E.W. and Peter J. Klaphaak, 1923
M. sinensis var. zebrinus, Beal
    V. sugarcane mosaic
        Brandes, E.W. and Peter J. Klaphaak, 1923

MOLLUGO L. 1737 (Aizoaceae)
M. verticillata, L.
    V. stone fruit *
        Boyle, J.S., J. Duain Moore and G.W. Keitt, 1954

MOMORDICA ((Tourn.)) L. 1735 (Cucurbitaceae)
M. charantia, L.
    V. chilli (pepper) mosaic
        Jha, Ashrafi and S.P. Raychaudhuri, 1956
    V. cucumber mosaic
        Adsuar, Jose and A. Cruz Miret, 1950
    V. papaw mosaic
        Adsuar, Jose, 1950
    V. prunus A *
        Fulton, Robert W., 1957
    V. prunus E *
        Fulton, Robert W., 1957
    V. prunus G *
        Fulton, Robert W., 1957
    V. tobacco etch
        Holmes, Francis O., 1946
    V. tobacco mosaic
        Holmes, Francis O., 1946
    V. watermelon mosaic
        Anderson, C.W., 1954

MORAEA Mill. ex L. 1762 (Iridaceae)
M. iridioides, L.
    V. cucumber mosaic
        Brierley, Philip and Floyd F. Smith, 1944
    V. lily symptomless
        Brierley, Philip and Floyd F. Smith, 1944
    V. tulip breaking
        Brierley, Philip and Floyd F. Smith, 1944

MUCANA Adans. 1763 (Leguminosae)
(STIZOLOBIUM) P. Br. 1756
M. derringianum, (Bort) Merr.
    V. bean common mosaic
        Zaumeyer, W.J. and B.L. Wade, 1935
    V. bean southern mosaic
        Zaumeyer, W.J. and L.L. Harter, 1943
    V. bean yellow mosaic
        Zaumeyer, W.J. and B.L. Wade, 1935
    V. cowpea mosaic
        Capoor, S.P. and P.M. Varma, 1956
    V. lucerne mosaic
        Zaumeyer, W.J., 1938
        Zaumeyer, W.J. and B.L. Wade, 1935
    V. pea streak
        Zaumeyer, W.J., 1938
    V. red clover mosaic *
        Zaumeyer, W.J. and B.L. Wade, 1935

MUHLENBERGIA Schreb. 1789 (Gramineae)
M. mexicana, (L.) Trin.
    V. onion yellow dwarf
        Henderson, W.J., 1935

MURRAYA Koen. ex L. 1771 (Rutaceae)
M. koenigii, Spreng.
    V. citrus tristeza
        Knorr, L.C., 1956

MUSA L. 1736 (Musaceae)
M. balbisiana, Colla
    V. abaca bunchy top
        Bernardo, Fernando A. and Dioscoro L. Umali,
        1956
    V. cucumber mosaic
        Bernardo, Fernando A. and Dioscoro L. Umali,
        1956
M. banksii, F. Muell.
    V. cucumber mosaic
        Bernardo, Fernando A. and Dioscoro L. Umali,
        1956
M. cavendishii, Lamb.
    V. abaca bunchy top
        Ocfemia, G.O. and Gabino G. Buhay, 1934
    V. canna mosaic
        Brierley, Philip and Floyd F. Smith, 1948
    V. cucumber mosaic
        Brierley, Philip and Floyd F. Smith, 1944
        Celino, M.S. and Aureo L. Martinez, 1956
    V. lily symptomless
        Brierley, Philip and Floyd F. Smith, 1944
    V. tulip breaking
        Brierley, Philip and Floyd F. Smith, 1944
M. ensete, Gmel.
    V. canna mosaic
        Castillo, B.S., C.E. Yarwood and A.H. Gold, 1956
M. ornatus, Roxb.
    V. cucumber mosaic
        Bernardo, Fernando A. and Dioscoro L. Umali,
        1956
M. paradisiaca, L.
    V. cucumber mosaic
        Adsuar, Jose and A. Cruz Miret, 1950
M. paradisiaca subsp. sapientum, (L.) Kuntze
    V. cucumber mosaic
        Adsuar, Jose and A. Cruz Miret, 1950
M. paradisiaca subsp. sapientum var. cinerea, Blanco
    V. abaca bunchy top
        Ocfemia, G.O. and Gabino G. Buhay, 1934
    V. cucumber mosaic
        Celino, Martin S., 1940
M. paradisiaca subsp. sapientum var. lacatan, Blanco
    V. abaca bunchy top
        Ocfemia, G.O. and Gabino G. Buhay, 1934

Musa paradisiaca, L., subsp. sapientum, (L.) Kuntze,
var. lacatan, Blanco (cont.)
    V. cucumber mosaic
      Celino, Martin S., 1940
M. paradisiaca subsp. sapientum var. suaveolens, Blanco
    V. abaca bunchy top
      Ocfemia, G.O. and Gabino G. Buhay, 1934
    V. cucumber mosaic
      Celino, Martin S., 1940
M. sapientum var. compressa, (Blanco) Teodoro *
    V. abaca bunchy top
      Ocfemia, G.O. and Gabino G. Buhay, 1934
    V. cucumber mosaic
      Celino, Martin S., 1940
M. spp.
    V. wheat streak mosaic
      Sill, W.H., Jr. and Patrick C. Agusiobo, 1955
M. textilis, Nee
    V. canna mosaic
      Brierley, Philip and Floyd F. Smith, 1948
    V. cucumber mosaic
      Brierley, Philip and Floyd F. Smith, 1944
    V. lily symptomless
      Brierley, Philip and Floyd F. Smith, 1944
    V. tulip breaking
      Brierley, Philip and Floyd F. Smith, 1944
M. textilis x M. balbisiana, Colla
    V. abaca bunchy top
      Umali, D.L., F.A. Bernardo and G.O. Ocfemia,
      1956
    V. cucumber mosaic
      Umali, D.L., F.A. Bernardo and G.O. Ocfemia,
      1956

MUSCARI Tourn. ex Mill. 1752 (Liliaceae)
M. armeniacum, Leichtl.
    V. wheat streak mosaic
      Sill, W.H., Jr. and Patrick C. Agusiobo, 1955
M. botryoides, (L.) Mill.
    V. ornithogalum mosaic
      Smith, Floyd F. and Philip Brierley, 1944
M. polyanthum, Boiss.
    V. cucumber mosaic
      Brierley, Philip and Floyd F. Smith, 1944
    V. lily symptomless
      Brierley, Philip and Floyd F. Smith, 1944
    V. tulip breaking
      Brierley, Philip and Floyd F. Smith, 1944

MYOSOTIS ((Tourn.)) Dill. ex L. 1735 (Boraginaceae)
M. alpestris, Schmidt
    V. primula mosaic
      Tompkins, C.M. and John T. Middleton, 1941
    V. radish mosaic
      Tompkins, C.M., 1939
    V. turnip mosaic
      Tompkins, C.M., 1938, 1939
      Tompkins, C.M. and H. Rex Thomas, 1938
M. arvensis, Lam.
    V. beet yellows
      Roland, G. and J. Tahon, 1961
M. scorpioides, L.
    V. cucumber mosaic
      Wellman, F.L., 1935
    V. tobacco etch
      Holmes, Francis O., 1946
M. sylvatica, Hoffm.
    V. anemone mosaic *
      Hollings, M., 1957
    V. chrysanthemum B (mild mosaic) *
      Hollings, M., 1957
    V. henbane mosaic
      Hamilton, Marion A., 1932
    V. pea mosaic
      Murphy, D.M. and W.H. Pierce, 1937
    V. tobacco etch
      Holmes, Francis O., 1946

NARCISSUS ((Tourn.)) L. 1735 (Amaryllidaceae)
N. poeticus, L.
    V. onion yellow dwarf
      Henderson, W.J., 1935
    V. tulip breaking
      McWhorter, F.P., 1935

N. pseudo-narcissus, L.
    V. tulip breaking
      Brierley, Philip and Floyd F. Smith, 1944
N. tazetta, L.
    V. cucumber mosaic
      Wellman, F.L., 1935

NASTURTIUM L. 1735 (Cruciferae)
N. officinale, R. Br. (Rorippa nasturtium-aquaticum,
(L.) Schinz & Thell.)
    V. anemone mosaic *
      Hollings, M., 1957
    V. cauliflower mosaic
      Caldwell, John and Ian W. Prentice, 1942
    V. squash mosaic
      Freitag, J.H., 1956
N. palustre, DC.
    V. cauliflower mosaic
      Caldwell, John and Ian W. Prentice, 1942

NEMESIA Vent. 1803 (Scrophulariaceae)
N. spp.
    V. beet yellows
      Roland, G. and J. Tahon, 1961
N. strumosa, Benth.
    V. tobacco etch
      Holmes, Francis O., 1946

NEMOPHILA Nutt. ex Barton 1882 (Hydrophyllaceae)
N. menziessii, Hook. & Arn.
    V. squash mosaic
      Freitag, J.H., 1956

NEOMARICA Sprague 1928 (Iridaceae)
N. caerulea, Sprague
    V. orchid (vanda) mosaic
      Murakishi, Harry H., 1952

NEPETA Riv. ex L. 1737 (Labiatae)
N. cataria, L.
    V. prunus A *
      Fulton, Robert W., 1957
    V. prunus E *
      Fulton, Robert W., 1957
    V. prunus G *
      Fulton, Robert W., 1957
    V. stone fruit *
      Boyle, J.S., J. Duain Moore and G.W. Keitt, 1954
    V. tobacco etch
      Holmes, Francis O., 1946
    V. tobacco mosaic
      Stover, W.G. and M.T. Vermillion, 1933
N. hederacea, (L.) Trev.
    V. tobacco etch
      Holmes, Francis O., 1946
    V. tobacco mosaic
      Holmes, Francis O., 1946
N. mussini, Spreng.
    V. tobacco etch
      Holmes, Francis O., 1946

NESLIA Desv. 1814 (Cruciferae)
N. paniculata, (L.) Desv.
    V. beet mosaic
      Pound, Glenn S., 1947

NESOGORDONIA Baill. 1886 (Theaceae)
N. papaverifera, (A. Chev.) Capuron
    V. cacao swollen shoot
      Tinsley, T.W. and A.L. Wharton, 1958

NICANDRA Adans. 1763 (Solanaceae)
N. physalodes, (L.) Gaertn.
    V. beet curly top
      Costa, A.S., 1952
    V. beet mosaic
      Pound, Glenn S., 1947
    V. beet yellows
      Roland, G. and J. Tahon, 1961
    V. cauliflower mosaic
      Walker, J.C., Francis J. LeBeau and Glenn S.
      Pound, 1945
    V. chrysanthemum B (mild mosaic) *
      Hollings, M., 1957

Nicandra physaloides, (L.) Gaertn. (cont.)
V. pelargonium ring spot *
Hollings, M., 1957
V. potato M *
Bagnall, R.H., R.H. Larson and J.C. Walker, 1956
V. potato paracrinkle
Bagnall, R.H., R.H. Larson and J.C. Walker, 1956
V. potato spindle tuber
Goss, R.W., 1931
V. potato Y
Johnson, E.M., 1930
V. stone fruit *
Boyle, J.S., J. Duain Moore and G.W. Keitt, 1954
V. sweet potato feathery mottle
Webb, Raymon E., 1954
V. tobacco mosaic
Fernow, K.H., 1923

NICOTIANA L. 1735 (Solanaceae)
N. acuminata, Hook.
V. beet curly top
Giddings, N.J., C.W. Bennett and A.L. Harrison, 1951
V. beet mosaic
Bennett, C.W., 1949
V. cauliflower mosaic
Walker, J.C., Francis J. LeBeau and Glenn S. Pound, 1945
N. affinis, T. Moore
V. anemone brown ring *
Hollings, M., 1958
V. cauliflower mosaic
Caldwell, John and Ian W. Prentice, 1942
N. alata, Link & Otto
V. tobacco stunt *
Hidaka, Zyun, Tetsuo Uozumi and Chuji Hiruki, 1956
N. alata var. grandiflora, Comes
V. cauliflower mosaic
Walker, J.C., Francis J. LeBeau and Glenn S. Pound, 1945
V. eggplant mosaic
Ferguson, I.A.C., 1951
V. spinach yellow dwarf
Severin, Henry H.P. and Donald H. Little, 1947
V. squash mosaic
Freitag, J.H., 1956
V. turnip mosaic
Dale, W.T., 1948
N. atropurpureum, Hort. *
V. datura distortion mosaic
Capoor, S.P. and P.M. Varma, 1952
N. benthamiana, Domin
V. prunus G *
Fulton, Robert W., 1957
N. bigelovii, Wats., var. multivalvis, Gray *
V. turnip yellow mosaic
Broadbent, L. and G.D. Heathcote, 1958
N. chinensis, Fisch.
V. eggplant mosaic
Ferguson, I.A.C., 1951
V. turnip mosaic
Dale, W.T., 1948
N. clevelandi, A. Gray
V. anemone brown ring *
Hollings, M., 1958
V. pelargonium ring spot *
Hollings, M., 1957
V. turnip crinkle
Broadbent, L. and G.D. Heathcote, 1958
V. turnip yellow mosaic
Broadbent, L. and G.D. Heathcote, 1958
N. debneyi, Domin
V. tobacco yellow dwarf
Hill, A.V. and M. Mandryk, 1954
N. exigua, Wheeler
V. tobacco yellow dwarf
Hill, A.V. and M. Mandryk, 1954
N. glauca, Graham
V. alsike clover mosaic
Zaumeyer, W.J., 1940
V. bayberry yellows
Raychaudhuri, S.P., 1953

N. glauca, Graham (cont.)
V. bean yellow mosaic
Zaumeyer, W.J., 1940
V. beet curly top
Bennett, C.W. and A.S. Costa, 1949
Costa, A.S., 1952
Giddings, N.J., C.W. Bennett and A.L. Harrison, 1951
V. beet mosaic
Bennett, C.W., 1949
V. beet yellows
Roland, G. and J. Tahon, 1961
V. chilli (pepper) mosaic
Adsuar, J. and L. Lopez Matos, 1955
V. citrus tristeza
Bennett, C.W. and A.S. Costa, 1949
V. cucumber mosaic
Johnson, J., 1926, 1927
V. potato X
Johnson, James, 1927
V. squash mosaic
Freitag, J.H., 1956
V. tobacco etch
Bennett, C.W., 1944
V. tobacco mosaic
Adsuar, J. and L. Lopez Matos, 1955
Johnson, James, 1927
V. tobacco ring spot
Grogan, R.G. and W.C. Schnathorst, 1955
V. tobacco stunt *
Hidaka, Zyun, Tetsuo Uozumi and Chuji Hiruki, 1956
V. tomato spotted wilt
Shapovalov, M., 1934
V. turnip mosaic
Bennett, C.W., 1944
N. glutinosa, L.
V. alsike clover mosaic
Zaumeyer, W.J., 1940
V. anemone brown ring *
Hollings, M., 1958
V. bayberry yellows
Raychaudhuri, S.P., 1953
V. bean common mosaic
Grogan, Raymond G. and J.C. Walker, 1948
Snyder, W.C., 1942
V. bean pod mottle
Zaumeyer, W.J. and H. Rex Thomas, 1948
V. bean southern mosaic
Zaumeyer, W.J. and L.L. Harter, 1943
V. bean yellow mosaic
Thomas, H. Rex and W.J. Zaumeyer, 1953
Zaumeyer, W.J., 1940
Zaumeyer, W.J. and H.H. Fisher, 1953
V. beet curly top
Bennett, C.W., Eubanks Carsner, F.H. Coons and E.W. Brandes, 1946
Costa, A.S., 1952
V. beet mosaic
Bennett, C.W., 1949
Severin, Henry H.P. and Roger M. Drake, 1948
V. beet yellows
Bennett, C.W. and Carlos Munck, 1946
Roland, G. and J. Tahon, 1961
V. broad bean mottle
Bawden, F.C., R.P. Chaudhuri and B. Kassanis, 1951
V. cacao swollen shoot
Tinsley, T.W. and A.L. Wharton, 1958
V. cauliflower mosaic
Alvarez-Garcia, L.A., 1951
Berkeley, G.H. and J.H. Tramaine, 1954
Caldwell, John and Ian W. Prentice, 1942
Smith, Kenneth M., 1935
Tompkins, C.M., 1937
Walker, J.C., Francis J. LeBeau and Glenn S. Pound, 1945
V. celery mosaic
Freitag, Julius H. and Henry H.P. Severin, 1945
V. chilli (pepper) mosaic
Ferguson, I.A.C., 1951
V. chrysanthemum ring spot
Brierley, Philip and Floyd F. Smith, 1955

Nicotiana glutinosa, L. (cont.)
  V. chrysanthemum stunt
    Brierley, Philip, 1953
  V. cowpea mosaic
    Anderson, C.W., 1955
    Capoor, S.P. and P.M. Varma, 1956
    Dale, W.T., 1949
    McLean, D.M., 1941
  V. cucumber green mottle mosaic
    Ainsworth, G.C., 1935
    Vasudeva, R.S., S.P. Raychaudhuri and Jagannath
    Singh, 1949
  V. cucumber mosaic
    Adsuar, Jose and A. Cruz Miret, 1950
    Lindberg, G.D., D.H. Hall and J.C. Walker, 1956
  V. dandelion yellow mosaic
    Kassanis, B., 1947
  V. filaree red leaf
    Frazier, Norman W., 1951
  V. hibiscus yellow vein mosaic
    Capoor, S.P. and P.M. Varma, 1950
  V. hydrangea ring spot
    Brierley, Philip and Paul Lorentz, 1957
  V. lettuce mosaic
    Ainsworth, G.C. and L. Ogilvie, 1939
  V. muskmelon mosaic
    Lindberg, G.D., D.H. Hall and J.C. Walker, 1956
  V. onion yellow dwarf
    Henderson, D.M., 1953
  V. orchid (cymbidium) mosaic
    Jensen, D.D., 1951
  V. orchid (odontoglossum) ring spot
    Jensen, D.D. and A. Herbert Gold, 1951
  V. orchid (vanda) mosaic
    Murakishi, Harry H., 1952
  V. panax ring spot
    Aragaki, M., H. Murakishi and J.W. Hendrix,
    1953
  V. panicum mosaic *
    Sill, W.H., Jr. and R.C. Pickett, 1957
  V. papaw mosaic
    Adsuar, Jose, 1950
  V. pea enation mosaic
    Ainsworth, G.C., 1940
    Chaudhuri, R.P., 1950
    Hagedorn, D.J. and J.C. Walker, 1954
    Osborn, H.T., 1938
    Stubbs, M.W., 1937
  V. pea mosaic
    Chaudhuri, R.P., 1950
    Hagedorn, D.J. and J.C. Walker, 1954
    Osborn, H.T., 1937
    Stubbs, M.W., 1937
  V. pea mottle
    Johnson, Folke, 1942
  V. pea wilt
    Johnson, Folke, 1942
  V. pelargonium ring spot *
    Hollings, M., 1957
  V. physalis floridana yellow net
    Webb, R.E., 1955
  V. potato A
    MacLachlan, D.S., R.H. Larson and J.C. Walker,
    1953
  V. potato M *
    Bagnall, R.H. and R.H. Larson, 1957
  V. potato paracrinkle
    Bagnall, R.H. and R.H. Larson, 1957
    Kassanis, B., 1955
  V. primula mosaic
    Severin, Henry H.P. and C.M. Tompkins, 1950
    Tompkins, C.M. and John T. Middleton, 1941
  V. red clover vein mosaic
    Osborn, H.T., 1937
  V. spinach yellow dwarf
    Severin, Henry H.P. and Donald H. Little, 1947
  V. squash mosaic
    Freitag, J.H., 1956
    Lindberg, G.D., D.H. Hall and J.C. Walker, 1956
  V. squash mosaic (southern)
    Anderson, C.W., 1951
  V. stone fruit *
    Boyle, J.S., J. Duain Moore and G.W. Keitt, 1954

N. glutinosa, L. (cont.)
  V. sweet potato feathery mottle
    Doolittle, S.P. and L.L. Harter, 1945
    Webb, Raymon E., 1954
  V. tobacco mosaic
    Allard, H.A., 1916, 1917
    Johnson, J., 1926, 1927
  V. tobacco ring spot
    Starr, Chester K. and W.E. Cooper, 1944
    Stubbs, M.W., 1937
  V. tobacco streak
    Thomas, H. Rex and W.J. Zaumeyer, 1950
  V. tobacco stunt *
    Hidaka, Zyun, Tetsuo Uozumi and Chuji Hiruki,
    1956
  V. tomato big bud
    Samuel, G., J.G. Bald and C.M. Eardley, 1933
  V. tomato ring spot
    Samson, R.W. and E.P. Imle, 1942
  V. tomato twisted leaf
    Ferguson, I.A.C., 1951
  V. tomato yellow net
    Sylvester, Edward S., 1954
  V. turnip crinkle
    Broadbent, L. and G.D. Heathcote, 1958
  V. turnip mosaic
    Dale, W.T., 1948
    Sylvester, Edward S., 1953
    Takahashi, William N., 1949
    Tompkins, C.M., 1939
  V. turnip rosette *
    Broadbent, L. and G.D. Heathcote, 1958
  V. turnip yellow mosaic
    Broadbent, L. and G.D. Heathcote, 1958
  V. watermelon mosaic
    Lindberg, G.D., D.H. Hall and J.C. Walker, 1956
  V. Wisconsin pea streak
    Hagedorn, D.J. and J.C. Walker, 1949, 1954
N. glutinosa x N. tabacum, L.
  V. tobacco mosaic
    Allard, H.A., 1916
N. gossei, Domin
  V. tobacco stunt *
    Hidaka, Zyun, Tetsuo Uozumi and Chuji Hiruki,
    1956
N. langsdorffii, Weinm.
  V. beet mosaic
    Bennett, C.W., 1949
  V. cauliflower mosaic
    Alvarez-Garcia, L.A., 1951
    Tompkins, C.M., 1937
  V. pea enation mosaic
    Osborn, H.T., 1938
  V. red clover vein mosaic
    Osborn, H.T., 1937
  V. squash mosaic
    Freitag, J.H., 1956
  V. turnip mosaic
    Tompkins, C.M., 1938, 1939
    Tompkins, C.M. and H. Rex Thomas, 1938
N. longiflora, Cav.
  V. beet mosaic
    Bennett, C.W., 1949
  V. cabbage ring necrosis
    Larson, R.H. and J.C. Walker, 1941
  V. cauliflower mosaic
    Walker, J.C., Francis J. LeBeau and Glenn S.
    Pound, 1945
  V. tobacco stunt *
    Hidaka, Zyun, Tetsuo Uozumi and Chuji Hiruki,
    1956
N. multivalvis, Lindl.
  V. cauliflower mosaic
    Walker, J.C., Francis J. LeBeau and Glenn S.
    Pound, 1945
N. nudicaulis, S. Wats.
  V. cabbage ring necrosis
    Larson, R.H. and J.C. Walker, 1941
  V. cauliflower mosaic
    Walker, J.C., Francis J. LeBeau and Glenn S.
    Pound, 1945
N. otophora, Griseb.
  V. tobacco etch
    Holmes, Francis O., 1946

Nicotiana palmeri, A. Gray
  V. beet mosaic
    Bennett, C.W., 1949
  V. tobacco etch
    Holmes, Francis O., 1946
N. paniculata, L.
  V. beet mosaic
    Bennett, C.W., 1949
  V. beet yellows
    Roland, G. and J. Tahon, 1961
  V. cauliflower mosaic
    Walker, J.C., Francis J. LeBeau and Glenn S.
    Pound, 1945
  V. tobacco stunt *
    Hidaka, Zyun, Tetsuo Uozumi and Chuji Hiruki,
    1956
N. plumbaginifolia, Viv.
  V. beet yellows
    Roland, G. and J. Tahon, 1961
N. quadrivalvis, Pursh
  V. cauliflower mosaic
    Walker, J.C., Francis J. LeBeau and Glenn S.
    Pound, 1945
N. raimondii, Macbride
  V. tobacco etch
    Holmes, Francis O., 1946
N. repanda, Willd.
  V. potato Y
    Roque, Arturo and Jose Adsuar, 1941
  V. tobacco stunt *
    Hidaka, Zyun, Tetsuo Uozumi and Chuji Hiruki,
    1956
  V. turnip mosaic
    LeBeau, Francis J. and J.C. Walker, 1945
N. rotundifolia, Lindl.
  V. tobacco yellow dwarf
    Hill, A.V. and M. Mandryk, 1954
N. rustica, L.
  V. anemone brown ring *
    Hollings, M., 1958
  V. bayberry yellows
    Raychaudhuri, S.P., 1953
  V. bean yellow mosaic
    Grogan, Raymond G. and J.C. Walker, 1948
    Hagedorn, D.J. and J.C. Walker, 1950, 1954
  V. beet mosaic
    Bennett, C.W., 1949
    Pound, Glenn S., 1947
  V. beet yellows
    Roland, G. and J. Tahon, 1961
  V. cauliflower mosaic
    Alvarez-Garcia, L.A., 1951
    Walker, J.C., Francis J. LeBeau and Glenn S.
    Pound, 1945
  V. chilli (pepper) mosaic
    Ferguson, I.A.C., 1951
  V. cowpea mosaic
    Capoor, S.P. and P.M. Varma, 1956
  V. cucumber mosaic
    Lindberg, G.D., D.H. Hall and J.C. Walker, 1956
  V. eggplant mosaic
    Ferguson, I.A.C., 1951
  V. lilac witches' broom
    Brierley, Philip, 1955
  V. muskmelon mosaic
    Lindberg, G.D., D.H. Hall and J.C. Walker, 1956
    Rader, Wm. E., Hugh F. Fitzpatrick and E.M.
    Hildebrand, 1947
  V. nicotiana glutinosa mosaic *
    Allard, H.A., 1916
  V. orchid (vanda) mosaic
    Murakishi, Harry H., 1952
  V. pea mottle
    Johnson, Folke, 1942
  V. pea wilt
    Johnson, Folke, 1942
  V. pelargonium ring spot *
    Hollings, M., 1957
  V. physalis floridana yellow net
    Webb, R.E., 1955
  V. potato A
    MacLachlan, D.S., R.H. Larson and J.C. Walker,
    1953
    Vasudeva, R. Sahai and C.S. Ramamoorthy, 1946

N. rustica, L. (cont.)
  V. red clover vein mosaic
    Osborn, H.T., 1937
  V. squash mosaic
    Lindberg, G.D., D.H. Hall and J.C. Walker, 1956
  V. stone fruit *
    Boyle, J.S., J. Duain Moore and G.W. Keitt, 1954
  V. sweet potato feathery mottle
    Webb, Raymon E., 1954
  V. tobacco stunt *
    Hidaka, Zyun, Tetsuo Uozumi and Chuji Hiruki,
    1956
  V. tropaeolum mosaic
    Silberschmidt, Karl, 1953
  V. turnip mosaic
    Dale, W.T., 1948
    LeBeau, Francis J. and J.C. Walker, 1945
  V. watermelon mosaic
    Lindberg, G.D., D.H. Hall and J.C. Walker, 1956
  V. Wisconsin pea streak
    Hagedorn, D.J. and J.C. Walker, 1949, 1954
N. rustica var. humulis, Schrank *
  V. cabbage black ring spot
    Tompkins, C.M., M.W. Gardner and H. Rex
    Thomas, 1938
  V. squash mosaic
    Freitag, J.H., 1956
  V. turnip mosaic
    Tompkins, C.M., 1938, 1939
N. rustica var. jamaicensis *
  V. cauliflower mosaic
    Caldwell, John and Ian W. Prentice, 1942
N. sanderae, W. Wats. (N. alata, Link & Otto x N.
forgetiana, Sander)
  V. cabbage ring necrosis
    Larson, R.H. and J.C. Walker, 1941
  V. cauliflower mosaic
    Walker, J.C., Francis J. LeBeau and Glenn S.
    Pound, 1945
  V. eggplant mosaic
    Ferguson, I.A.C., 1951
  V. tobacco stunt *
    Hidaka, Zyun, Tetsuo Uozumi and Chuji Hiruki,
    1956
  V. turnip mosaic
    Dale, W.T., 1948
N. spp.
  V. prunus A *
    Fulton, Robert W., 1957
  V. prunus E *
    Fulton, Robert W., 1957
  V. prunus G *
    Fulton, Robert W., 1957
N. stocktoni, Brandegee, in Erythea
  V. beet yellows
    Roland, G. and J. Tahon, 1961
N. suaveolens, Lehm.
  V. tobacco stunt *
    Hidaka, Zyun, Tetsuo Uozumi and Chuji Hiruki,
    1956
N. sylvestris, Speg. & Comes
  V. beet mosaic
    Bennett, C.W., 1949
  V. beet yellows
    Roland, G. and J. Tahon, 1961
  V. cauliflower mosaic
    Walker, J.C., Francis J. LeBeau and Glenn S.
    Pound, 1945
  V. chilli (pepper) mosaic
    Ferguson, I.A.C., 1951
  V. dodder latent mosaic
    Bennett, C.W., 1944
  V. eggplant mosaic
    Ferguson, I.A.C., 1951
  V. pea enation mosaic
    Osborn, H.T., 1938
  V. pea mottle
    Johnson, Folke, 1942
  V. pea wilt
    Johnson, Folke, 1942
  V. potato M *
    Bagnall, R.H., R.H. Larson and J.C. Walker, 1956
  V. potato paracrinkle
    Bagnall, R.H., R.H. Larson and J.C. Walker, 1956

Nicotiana sylvestris, Speg. & Comes (cont.)
  V. potato Y
    Roque, Arturo and Jose Adsuar, 1941
  V. red clover vein mosaic
    Osborn, H.T., 1937
  V. sweet potato feathery mottle
    Webb, Raymon E., 1954
  V. tobacco stunt *
    Hidaka, Zyun, Tetsuo Uozumi and Chuji Hiruki, 1956
  V. tomato aspermy
    Blencowe, J.W. and John Caldwell, 1949
  V. tomato ring spot
    Samson, R.W. and E.P. Imle, 1942
  V. turnip mosaic
    Dale, W.T., 1948
    LeBeau, Francis J. and J.C. Walker, 1945
N. tabacum, L.
  V. abutilon infectious variegation
    Silberschmidt, K. and L.R. Tommasi, 1956
  V. alsike clover mosaic
    Zaumeyer, W.J., 1940
  V. anemone brown ring *
    Hollings, M., 1958
  V. bayberry yellows
    Raychaudhuri, S.P., 1953
  V. bean common mosaic
    Snyder, W.C., 1942
  V. bean pod mottle
    Zaumeyer, W.J. and H. Rex Thomas, 1948
  V. bean southern mosaic
    Zaumeyer, W.J. and L.L. Harter, 1943
  V. bean yellow mosaic
    Conover, Robert A., 1948
    Grogan, Raymond G. and J.C. Walker, 1948
    Hagedorn, D.J. and J.C. Walker, 1950, 1954
    Pierce, W.H., 1935
    Zaumeyer, W.J., 1940
  V. bean yellow stipple
    Zaumeyer, W.J. and H. Rex Thomas, 1950
  V. beet curly top
    Bennett, C.W., Eubanks Carsner, F.H. Coons and E.W. Brandes, 1946
    Costa, A.S., 1952
    Giddings, N.J., 1938, 1944
    Giddings, N.J., C.W. Bennett and A.L. Harrison, 1951
  V. beet mosaic
    Bennett, C.W., 1949
    Hoggan, I.A., 1933
    Pound, Glenn S., 1947
  V. beet rosette *
    Bennett, C.W. and James E. Duffus, 1957
  V. beet yellow net
    Sylvester, Edward S., 1948
  V. beet yellow wilt
    Bennett, C.W. and Carlos Munck, 1946
  V. beet yellows
    Roland, G. and J. Tahon, 1961
  V. broad bean mottle
    Bawden, F.C., R.P. Chaudhuri and B. Kassanis, 1951
    Yu, T.F., 1939
  V. cacao swollen shoot
    Tinsley, T.W. and A.L. Wharton, 1958
  V. canna mosaic
    Castillo, B.S., C.E. Yarwood and A.H. Gold, 1956
  V. carnation mosaic
    Brierley, Philip and Floyd F. Smith, 1955, 1957
  V. carnation mottle
    Brierley, Philip and Floyd F. Smith, 1957
    Kassanis, B., 1955
  V. carnation vein mottle
    Kassanis, B., 1955
  V. cauliflower mosaic
    Alvarez-Garcia, L.A., 1951
    Berkeley, G.H. and J.H. Tremaine, 1954
    Caldwell, John and Ian W. Prentice, 1942
    Tompkins, C.M., 1937
    Walker, J.C., Francis J. LeBeau and Glenn S. Pound, 1945
  V. celery mosaic
    Freitag, Julius H. and Henry H.P. Severin, 1945

N. tabacum, L. (cont.)
  V. chrysanthemum B (mild mosaic) *
    Hollings, M., 1957
  V. chrysanthemum Q
    Brierley, Philip and Floyd F. Smith, 1953
  V. chrysanthemum ring spot
    Brierley, Philip and Floyd F. Smith, 1955
  V. chrysanthemum stunt
    Brierley, Philip, 1953
  V. cineraria mosaic
    Jones, Leon K., 1944
  V. citrus tristeza
    Bennett, C.W. and A.S. Costa, 1949
    Knorr, L.C., 1956
  V. cowpea mosaic
    Anderson, C.W., 1955
    Capoor, S.P. and P.M. Varma, 1956
    Dale, W.T., 1949
    McLean, D.M., 1941
    Yu, T.F., 1946
  V. cucumber green mottle mosaic
    Ainsworth, G.C., 1935
    Vasudeva, R.S., S.P. Raychaudhuri and Jagannath Singh, 1949
  V. cucumber mosaic
    Adsuar, Jose and A. Cruz Miret, 1950
    Doolittle, S.P. and W.W. Gilbert, 1918
    Lindberg, G.D., D.H. Hall and J.C. Walker, 1956
    McKnight, T., 1953
    McWhorter, F.P. and H.H. Millsap, 1954
    Vasudeva, R. Sahai and T.B. Lal, 1943
  V. (cucumber) O.S.C. isolate 606 *
    Porter, Clark A. and Frank P. McWhorter, 1951
  V. dandelion yellow mosaic
    Kassanis, B., 1947
  V. eggplant mosaic
    Ferguson, I.A.C., 1951
  V. filaree red leaf
    Frazier, Norman W., 1951
  V. gladiolus *
    Snow, Gordon F., 1955
  V. hibiscus yellow vein mosaic
    Capoor, S.P. and P.M. Varma, 1950
  V. hydrangea *
    Brierley, Philip, 1954
  V. hydrangea ring spot
    Brierley, Philip and Paul Lorentz, 1956, 1957
  V. iris mosaic
    Brierley, Philip and Frank P. McWhorter, 1936
  V. lettuce mosaic
    Ainsworth, G.C. and L. Ogilvie, 1939
  V. lucerne mosaic
    Porter, D.R., 1935
  V. maize leaf fleck
    Stoner, Warren N., 1952
  V. maize streak
    Finley, A.M., 1954
  V. malva yellow vein mosaic *
    Costa, A.S. and James E. Duffus, 1957
  V. muskmelon mosaic
    Anderson, C.W., 1954
    Lindberg, G.D., D.H. Hall and J.C. Walker, 1956
    Rader, Wm. E., Hugh F. Fitzpatrick and E.M. Hildebrand, 1947
  V. nicotiana glutinosa mosaic *
    Allard, H.A., 1916
  V. nothoscordum mosaic
    McKinney, H.H., 1950
  V. onion yellow dwarf
    Henderson, D.M., 1953
  V. orchid (cymbidium) mosaic
    Jensen, D.D., 1951
  V. orchid (odontoglossum) ring spot
    Jensen, D.D. and A. Herbert Gold, 1951
  V. orchid (vanda) mosaic
    Murakishi, Harry H., 1952
  V. ornithogalum mosaic
    Smith, Floyd F. and Philip Brierley, 1944
  V. panicum mosaic *
    Sill, W.H., Jr. and R.C. Pickett, 1957
  V. papaw mosaic
    Adsuar, Jose, 1950
  V. papaw ring spot
    Jensen, D.D., 1949

Nicotiana tabacum, L. (cont.)
V. pea enation mosaic
Ainsworth, G.C., 1940
Chaudhuri, R.P., 1950
Hagedorn, D.J. and J.C. Walker, 1954
Johnson, Folke and Leon K. Jones, 1937
Osborn, H.T., 1938
Pierce, W.H., 1935
Simons, John N., 1954
Stubbs, M.W., 1937
V. pea mosaic
Chaudhuri, R.P., 1950
Hagedorn, D.J. and J.C. Walker, 1954
Murphy, D.M. and W.H. Pierce, 1937
Osborn, H.T., 1937
Pierce, W.H., 1935
Stubbs, M.W., 1937
V. pea mottle
Johnson, Folke, 1942
Johnson, Folke and Leon K. Jones, 1937
V. pea streak
Zaumeyer, W.J., 1938
V. pea wilt
Johnson, Folke, 1942
V. pelargonium ring spot *
Hollings, M., 1957
V. peony leaf curl *
Brierley, Philip and Paul Lorentz, 1957
V. physalis floridana yellow net
Webb, R.E., 1955
V. pigeon pea sterility mosaic
Capoor, S.P., 1952
V. pokeweed mosaic *
Allard, H.A., 1918
V. potato A
Koch, Karl and James Johnson, 1935
Schultz, E.S. and Donald Folsom, 1923
V. potato leaf roll
Koch, Karl and James Fohnson, 1935
Quanjer, H.M., 1920
V. potato leaf rolling
Dykstra, T.P., 1939
V. potato M *
Bagnall, R.H. and R.H. Larson, 1957
Bagnall, R.H., R.H. Larson and J.C. Walker, 1956
V. potato paracrinkle
Bagnall, R.H. and R.H. Larson, 1957
Bagnall, R.H., R.H. Larson and J.C. Walker, 1956
Kassanis, B., 1955
V. potato Y
Dennis, R.W.G., 1939
V. primula mosaic
Severin, Henry H.P. and C.M. Tompkins, 1950
Tompkins, C.M. and John T. Middleton, 1941
V. prunus E *
Fulton, Robert W., 1957
V. raspberry necrotic fern leaf mosaic
Chamberlain, G.C., 1941
V. red clover vein mosaic
Hagedorn, D.J. and E.W. Hanson, 1951
Hagedorn, D.J. and J.C. Walker, 1949, 1954
Osborn, H.T., 1937
Roberts, D.A., 1957
V. soybean mosaic
Conover, Robert A., 1948
Pierce, W.H., 1935
V. spinach yellow dwarf
Severin, Henry H.P. and Donald H. Little, 1947
V. squash mosaic
Freitag, J.H., 1956
Lindberg, G.D., D.H. Hall and J.C. Walker, 1956
V. squash mosaic (southern)
Anderson, C.W., 1951
V. stone fruit *
Boyle, J.S., J. Duain Moore and G.W. Keitt, 1954
V. sweet potato feathery mottle
Doolittle, S.P. and L.L. Harter, 1945
Webb, Raymon E., 1954
V. sweet potato mosaic
Borders, H.I. and T.J. Ratcliff, 1954
V. teasel mosaic
Stoner, Warren N., 1951
V. tithonia rotundifolia mosaic *
Cook, M.T., 1936

N. tabacum, L. (cont.)
V. tobacco mosaic
Valleau, W.D., 1935
V. tomato big bud
Samuel, G., J.G. Bald and C.M. Eardley, 1933
V. tomato twisted leaf
Ferguson, I.A.C., 1951
V. tulip breaking
Brierley, Philip and S.P. Doolittle, 1940
V. turnip mosaic
LeBeau, Francis J. and J.C. Walker, 1945
Sylvester, Edward S., 1953
Takahashi, William N., 1949
Tompkins, C.M., 1938
V. turnip rosette *
Broadbent, L. and G.D. Heathcote, 1958
V. turnip yellow mosaic
Broadbent, L. and G.D. Heathcote, 1958
V. watermelon mosaic
Anderson, C.W., 1954
Lindberg, G.D., D.H. Hall and J.C. Walker, 1956
V. Wisconsin pea streak
Hagedorn, D.J. and J.C. Walker, 1949, 1954
N. tabacum x N. glutinosa, L.
V. cucumber green mottle mosaic
Fulton, Robert W., 1950
V. turnip mosaic
LeBeau, Francis J. and J.C. Walker, 1945
N. tomentosiformis, Goodspeed
V. tobacco etch
Holmes, Francis O., 1946
N. trigonophylla, Dun.
V. cauliflower mosaic
Walker, J.C., Francis J. LeBeau and Glenn S. Pound, 1945
V. tobacco stunt *
Hidaka, Zyun, Tetsuo Uozumi and Chuji Hiruki, 1956
N. velutina, Wheeler
V. tobacco yellow dwarf
Hill, A.V. and M. Mandryk, 1954
N. wigandioides, Koch & Fint
V. tobacco etch
Holmes, Francis O., 1946

NIGELLA ((Tourn.)) L. 1735 (Ranunculaceae)
N. damascena, L.
V. cucumber mosaic
Wellman, F.L., 1935

NOTHOSCORDUM Kunth 1843 (Liliaceae)
N. fragrans, (Vent.) Kunth
V. cucumber mosaic
Brierley, Philip and Floyd F. Smith, 1944
V. lily symptomless
Brierley, Philip and Floyd F. Smith, 1944
V. tulip breaking
Brierley, Philip and Floyd F. Smith, 1944

OCHROMA Sw. 1788 (Bombacaceae)
O. lagopus, Sw.
V. cacao swollen shoot
Tinsley, T.W. and A.L. Wharton, 1958

OCIMUM L. 1737 (Labiatae)
O. basilicum, L.
V. citrus tristeza
Knorr, L.C., 1956

OCTOLOBUS Welw. 1869 (Sterculiaceae)
O. angustatus, Hutchinson
V. cacao swollen shoot
Tinsley, T.W. and A.L. Wharton, 1958

OENOTHERA L. 1735 (Onagraceae)
O. lamarckiana, Hort.
V. tobacco etch
Holmes, Francis O., 1946
V. tobacco mosaic
Holmes, Francis O., 1946
O. missouriensis, Sims
V. pea mosaic
Murphy, D.M. and W.H. Pierce, 1937

OMPHALOCARPUM Beauv. 1805 (Sapotaceae)
O. procerum, Beauv.
     V. cacao swollen shoot
         Tinsley, T.W. and A.L. Wharton, 1958

ONOBRYCHIS L. 1735 (Leguminosae)
O. spp.
     V. lucerne witches' broom
         Menzies, J.D., 1946
O. transcaucasica, Grossheim
     V. lucerne witches' broom
         Klostermeyer, E.C. and J.D. Menzies, 1951
O. viciaefolia, Scop.
     V. lucerne witches' broom
         Klostermeyer, E.C. and J.D. Menzies, 1951

OPHIOPOGON Ker-Gawl. 1807 (Liliaceae)
O. jaburan, Lodd.
     V. cucumber mosaic
         Brierley, Philip and Floyd F. Smith, 1944
     V. lily symptomless
         Brierley, Philip and Floyd F. Smith, 1944
     V. tulip breaking
         Brierley, Philip and Floyd F. Smith, 1944

ORCHIS ((Tourn.)) L. 1735 (Orchidaceae)
O. spp.
     V. wheat streak mosaic
         Sill, W.H., Jr. and Patrick C. Agusiobo, 1955

ORNITHOGALUM ((Tourn.)) L. 1735 (Liliaceae)
O. spp.
     V. wheat streak mosaic
         Sill, W.H., Jr. and Patrick C. Agusiobo, 1955
O. thyrsoides, Jacq.
     V. cucumber mosaic
         Brierley, Philip and Floyd F. Smith, 1944
         Smith, Floyd F. and Philip Brierley, 1944
     V. iris mosaic
         Smith, Floyd F. and Philip Brierley, 1944
     V. lily symptomless
         Brierley, Philip and Floyd F. Smith, 1944
     V. narcissus white streak *
         Smith, Floyd F. and Philip Brierley, 1944
     V. nothoscordum mosaic
         McKinney, H.H., 1950
     V. onion yellow dwarf
         Smith, Floyd F. and Philip Brierley, 1944
     V. tulip breaking
         Brierley, Philip and Floyd F. Smith, 1944
         Smith, Floyd F. and Philip Brierley, 1944

ORYZA L. 1735 (Gramineae)
O. sativa, L.
     V. cucumber mosaic
         Adsuar, Jose and A. Cruz Miret, 1950
         McWhorter, F.P. and H.H. Millsap, 1954
         Wellman, F.L., 1935
     V. sugarcane mosaic
         Brandes, E.W. and Peter J. Klaphaak, 1923
     V. wheat streak mosaic
         Kahn, Robert P. and Ottie J. Dickerson, 1957

ORYZOPSIS Michx. 1803 (Gramineae)
O. hymenoides, (Roem. & Schult.) Ricker
     V. barley yellow dwarf
         Bruehl, G.W. and H.V. Toko, 1957
         Oswald, John W. and Byron R. Houston, 1953

OXALIS L. 1737 (Oxalidaceae)
O. corniculata, L.
     V. beet yellows
         Roland, G. and J. Tahon, 1961
     V. tobacco etch
         Holmes, Francis O., 1946
     V. tobacco mosaic
         Holmes, Francis O., 1938, 1946
O. repens, Thunb.
     V. tobacco ring spot
         Wingard, S.A., 1928
O. spp.
     V. beet curly top
         Bennett, C.W. and A.S. Costa, 1949

O. spp. (cont.)
     V. citrus tristeza
         Bennett, C.W. and A.S. Costa, 1949
     V. tropaeolum mosaic
         Silberschmidt, Karl, 1953
O. stricta, L.
     V. tobacco etch
         Holmes, Francis O., 1946
     V. tobacco mosaic
         Holmes, Francis O., 1938, 1946

PACHIRA Aubl. 1775 (Bombacaceae)
P. oleagina, Decne.
     V. cacao swollen shoot
         Tinsley, T.W. and A.L. Wharton, 1958

PACHYRHIZUS Rich. ex DC. 1825 (Leguminosae)
P. tuberosus, Spreng.
     V. cowpea mosaic
         Yu, T.F., 1946

PANCRATIUM Dill. ex L. 1735 (Amaryllidaceae)
P. maritimum, L.
     V. narcissus mosaic
         Haasis, Frank A., 1939
     V. ornithogalum mosaic
         Smith, Floyd F. and Philip Brierley, 1944

PANICUM L. 1735 (Gramineae)
P. barbinode, Trin.
     V. cucumber mosaic
         Wellman, F.L., 1935
     V. sugarcane mosaic
         Brandes, E.W. and Peter J. Klaphaak, 1923
P. capillare, L.
     V. agropyron mosaic
         Slykhuis, J.T., 1952
     V. wheat spot mosaic *
         Slykhuis, John T., 1956
P. colonum, L.
     V. rice and corn leaf-gall *
         Agati, Julian A. and Carlos A. Calica, 1950
P. depauperatum, Muhl.
     V. panicum mosaic *
         Sill, W.H., Jr. and R.C. Pickett, 1957
P. maximum, Jacq.
     V. panicum mosaic *
         Sill, W.H., Jr. and R.C. Pickett, 1957
     V. wheat streak mosaic
         Sill, W.H., Jr. and Patrick C. Agusiobo, 1955
P. miliaceum, L.
     V. agropyron mosaic
         Slykhuis, J.T., 1952
     V. wheat spot mosaic *
         Slykhuis, John T., 1956
     V. wheat streak mosaic
         Sill, W.H., Jr. and Patrick C. Agusiobo, 1955
         Slykhuis, J.T., 1952
P. virgatum, L.
     V. wheat streak mosaic
         Sill, W.H., Jr. and Patrick C. Agusiobo, 1955

PAPAVER Tourn. ex L. 1735 (Papaveraceae)
P. nudicaule, L.
     V. radish mosaic
         Tompkins, C.M., 1939
     V. tobacco etch
         Holmes, Francis O., 1946
     V. turnip mosaic
         Tompkins, C.M. and H. Rex Thomas, 1938
P. orientale, L.
     V. cabbage black ring spot
         Tompkins, C.M., M.W. Gardner and H. Rex Thomas, 1938
     V. cucumber mosaic
         Wellman, F.L., 1935
     V. primula mosaic
         Tompkins, C.M. and John T. Middleton, 1941
     V. radish mosaic
         Tompkins, C.M., 1939
     V. tobacco etch
         Holmes, Francis O., 1946
     V. tobacco mosaic
         Holmes, Francis O., 1946

Papaver orientale, L. (cont.)
  V. turnip mosaic
    Tompkins, C.M., 1939
    Tompkins, C.M. and H. Rex Thomas, 1938
P. rhoeas, L.
  V. chrysanthemum B (mild mosaic) *
    Hollings, M., 1957
  V. cucumber mosaic
    Wellman, F.L., 1935
  V. turnip crinkle
    Broadbent, L. and G.D. Heathcote, 1958
  V. turnip yellow mosaic
    Broadbent, L. and G.D. Heathcote, 1958
P. somniferum, L.
  V. anemone brown ring *
    Hollings, M., 1958
  V. beet yellows
    Roland, G. and J. Tahon, 1961
  V. chrysanthemum B (mild mosaic) *
    Hollings, M., 1957
  V. cucumber mosaic
    Wellman, F.L., 1935
P. spp.
  V. euphorbia mosaic
    Costa, A.S. and C.W. Bennett, 1950

PARTHENIUM L. 1735 (Compositae)
P. argentatum, A. Gray
  V. aster yellows
    Severin, Henry H.P., 1945
  V. beet curly top
    Severin, Henry H.P., 1945
  V. beet mosaic
    Severin, Henry H.P., 1945
  V. beet yellows
    Roland, G. and J. Tahon, 1961
  V. celery mosaic
    Severin, Henry H.P., 1945
  V. cucumber mosaic
    Severin, Henry H.P., 1945
  V. cucumber western mosaic *
    Severin, Henry H.P., 1945
  V. lucerne mosaic
    Severin, Henry H.P., 1945

PASPALUM L. 1759 (Gramineae)
P. dilatatum, Poir.
  V. barley yellow dwarf
    Oswald, John W. and Byron R. Houston, 1953
P. spp.
  V. panicum mosaic *
    Sill, W.H., Jr. and R.C. Pickett, 1957

PASSIFLORA L. 1735 (Passifloraceae)
P. caerulea, L.
  V. anemone brown ring *
    Hollings, M., 1958
  V. chrysanthemum latent *
    Hollings, M., 1957
P. edulis, Sims
  V. papaw mosaic
    Adsuar, Jose, 1950
P. foetida, L.
  V. papaw mosaic
    Adsuar, Jose, 1950
  V. papaw ring spot
    Jensen, D.D., 1949
P. pfordtii, X Hort. ex Degener
  V. papaw ring spot
    Jensen, D.D., 1949

PASTINACA L. 1737 (Umbelliferae)
P. sativa, L.
  V. dandelion yellow mosaic
    Kassanis, B., 1947
  V. dodder latent mosaic
    Bennett, C.W., 1944
  V. pea mosaic
    Murphy, D.M. and W.H. Pierce, 1937
  V. squash mosaic
    Freitag, J.H., 1956
  V. tobacco etch
    Holmes, Francis O., 1946

P. sativa, L. (cont.)
  V. tobacco mosaic
    Holmes, Francis O., 1946
  V. tobacco ring spot
    Wingard, S.A., 1928

PEDILANTHUS Neck. 1790 (Euphorbiaceae)
P. tithymaloides, Poit.
  V. wheat streak mosaic
    Sill, W.H., Jr. and Patrick C. Agusiobo, 1955

PELARGONIUM L'Herit. 1787 (Geraniaceae)
P. domesticum, Bailey
  V. anemone mosaic *
    Hollings, M., 1957
  V. cacao swollen shoot
    Tinsley, T.W. and A.L. Wharton, 1958
  V. chrysanthemum B (mild mosaic) *
    Hollings, M., 1957
  V. tobacco ring spot
    Wingard, S.A., 1928
P. hortorum, Bailey (X P. zonale, Willd.)
  V. bean pod mottle
    Zaumeyer, W.J. and H. Rex Thomas, 1948
  V. filaree red leaf
    Frazier, Norman W., 1951
  V. tobacco etch
    Holmes, Francis O., 1946
  V. tobacco mosaic
    Holmes, Francis O., 1946
  V. tobacco ring spot no. 2
    Brierley, Philip, 1954
  V. tomato aspermy
    Hollings, M., 1955
  V. tomato ring spot
    Samson, R.W. and E.P. Imle, 1942
  V. tropaeolum mosaic
    Silbberschmidt, Karl, 1953
P. odoratissimum, Ait.
  V. tobacco etch
    Holmes, Francis O., 1946
  V. tobacco mosaic
    Holmes, Francis O., 1946
  V. tomato ring spot
    Samson, R.W. and E.P. Imle, 1942
P. zonale, Willd.
  V. cabbage black ring spot
    Tompkins, C.M., M.W. Gardner and H. Rex
    Thomas, 1938
  V. cucumber mosaic
    Govier, D.A., 1957
  V. radish mosaic
    Tompkins, C.M., 1939
  V. spinach yellow dwarf
    Severin, Henry H.P. and Donald H. Little, 1947
  V. squash mosaic
    Freitag, J.H., 1956
  V. turnip mosaic
    Tompkins, C.M., 1939
    Tompkins, C.M. and H. Rex Thomas, 1938

PENNISETUM Rich. 1805 (Gramineae)
P. glaucum, (L.) R. Br.
  V. panicum mosaic *
    Sill, W.H., Jr. and R.C. Pickett, 1957
  V. wheat streak mosaic
    Sill, W.H., Jr. and Patrick C. Agusiobo, 1955
P. purpureum, Schumach.
  V. sugarcane mosaic
    Brandes, E.W. and Peter J. Klaphaak, 1923

PENSTEMON
(PENTSTEMON) Mitch. 1748 (Scrophulariaceae)
P. barbatus, Roth
  V. cabbage black ring spot
    Tompkins, C.M., M.W. Gardner and H. Rex
    Thomas, 1938
  V. primula mosaic
    Tompkins, C.M. and John T. Middleton, 1941
  V. radish mosaic
    Tompkins, C.M., 1939
  V. turnip mosaic
    Tompkins, C.M., 1938, 1939
    Tompkins, C.M. and H. Rex Thomas, 1938

PEPEROMIA Ruiz & Pav. 1794 (Piperaceae)
P. spp.
    V. wheat streak mosaic
        Sill, W.H., Jr. and Patrick C. Agusiobo, 1955

PERSEA Plum. ex L. 1737 (Lauraceae)
P. americana, Mill.
    V. cacao swollen shoot
        Tinsley, T.W. and A.L. Wharton, 1958

PERSICARIA ((Tourn.)) L. 1735 (Polygonaceae)
P. hydropiperoides, Michx. *
    V. tomato ring spot
        Samson, R.W. and E.P. Imle, 1942

PETROSELINUM Hoffm. 1814 (Umbelliferae)
P. crispum, (Mill.) Nym.
    V. beet yellows
        Roland, G. and J. Tahon, 1961
    V. squash mosaic
        Freitag, J.H., 1956
P. hortense, Hoffm.
    V. tobacco etch
        Holmes, Francis O., 1946
P. sativum, Hoffm.
    V. dandelion yellow mosaic
        Kassanis, B., 1947

PETUNIA Juss. 1803 (Solanaceae)
P. hybrida, Vilm.
    V. alsike clover mosaic
        Zaumeyer, W.J., 1940
    V. anemone brown ring *
        Hollings, M., 1958
    V. bean southern mosaic
        Zaumeyer, W.J. and L.L. Harter, 1943
    V. bean yellow mosaic
        Pierce, W.H., 1935
        Zaumeyer, W.J., 1940
    V. bean yellow stipple
        Zaumeyer, W.J. and H. Rex Thomas, 1950
    V. beet curly top
        Bennett, C.W. and A.S. Costa, 1949
        Costa, A.S., 1952
    V. beet mosaic
        Bennett, C.W., 1949
    V. beet yellow wilt
        Bennett, C.W. and Carlos Munck, 1946
    V. beet yellows
        Roland, G. and J. Tahon, 1961
    V. cauliflower mosaic
        Berkeley, G.H. and J.H. Tremaine, 1954
    V. chrysanthemum ring spot
        Brierley, Philip and Floyd F. Smith, 1955
    V. cowpea mosaic
        Capoor, S.P. and P.M. Varma, 1956
        McLean, D.M., 1941
        Yu, T.F., 1946
    V. cucumber green mottle mosaic
        Vasudeva, R.S., S.P. Raychaudhuri and Jagannath
        Singh, 1949
    V. cucumber mosaic
        Vasudeva, R. Sahai and T.B. Lal, 1943
    V. hibiscus yellow vein mosaic
        Capoor, S.P. and P.M. Varma, 1950
    V. hydrangea ring spot
        Brierley, Philip and Paul Lorentz, 1957
    V. iris mosaic
        Brierley, Philip and Frank P. McWhorter, 1936
    V. lucerne mosaic
        Zaumeyer, W.J., 1953
    V. muskmelon mosaic
        Rader, Wm. E., Hugh F. Fitzpatrick and E.M.
        Hildebrand, 1947
    V. pea enation mosaic
        Pierce, W.H., 1935
    V. pea mosaic
        Murphy, D.M. and W.H. Pierce, 1937
        Pierce, W.H., 1935
    V. pea streak
        Zaumeyer, W.J., 1938
    V. peony leaf curl *
        Brierley, Philip and Paul Lorentz, 1957

P. hybrida, Vilm. (cont.)
    V. pokeweed mosaic *
        Allard, H.A., 1918
    V. potato A
        Vasudeva, R. Sahai and C.S. Ramamoorthy, 1946
    V. potato X
        Vasudeva, R. Sahai and T.B. Lal, 1944
    V. radish mosaic
        Tompkins, C.M., 1939
    V. soybean mosaic
        Pierce, W.H., 1935
    V. spinach yellow dwarf
        Severin, Henry H.P. and Donald H. Little, 1947
    V. squash mosaic
        Freitag, J.H., 1956
    V. tobacco ring spot
        Rosberg, David W., 1953
    V. tobacco streak
        Thomas, H. Rex and W.J. Zaumeyer, 1950
    V. tobacco stunt *
        Hidaka, Zyun, Tetsuo Uozumi and Chuji Hiruki,
        1956
    V. tropaeolum mosaic
        Silberschmidt, Karl, 1953
    V. tulip breaking
        McWhorter, F.P., 1935
        Tompkins, C.M., 1939
    V. turnip mosaic
        Tompkins, C.M. and H. Rex Thomas, 1938
P. violacea, Lindl.
    V. cucumber mosaic
        Johnson, J., 1926

PHACELIA Juss. 1789 (Hydrophyllaceae)
P. campanularia, Gray
    V. beet yellows
        Roland, G. and J. Tahon, 1961
    V. pea mosaic
        Murphy, D.M. and W.H. Pierce, 1937

PHALARIS L. 1735 (Gramineae)
P. arundinacea, L.
    V. agropyron mosaic
        Slykhuis, J.T., 1952
    V. barley stripe mosaic
        Slykhuis, J.T., 1952
    V. panicum mosaic *
        Sill, W.H., Jr. and R.C. Pickett, 1957
    V. wheat streak mosaic
        Sill, W.H., Jr. and Patrick C. Agusiobo, 1955
        Slykhuis, J.T., 1952
P. arundiancea x P. tuberosa, L.
    V. wheat streak mosaic
        Sill, W.H., Jr. and Patrick C. Agusiobo, 1955
P. tuberosa, L.
    V. barley yellow dwarf
        Bruehl, G.W. and H.V. Toko, 1957

PHASEOLUS ((Tourn.)) L. 1735 (Leguminosae)
P. aconitifolius, Jacq.
    V. bean common mosaic
        Reddick, D. and V.B. Stewart, 1919
    V. bean yellow stipple
        Zaumeyer, W.J. and H. Rex Thomas, 1950
    V. cowpea mosaic
        Capoor, S.P. and P.M. Varma, 1956
    V. pea mosaic
        Murphy, D.M. and W.H. Pierce, 1937
P. acutifolius, A. Gray, var. latifolius, Freeman
    V. bean common mosaic
        Zaumeyer, W.J. and B.L. Wade, 1935
    V. bean yellow mosaic
        Zaumeyer, W.J. and B.L. Wade, 1935
    V. lucerne mosaic
        Zaumeyer, W.J., 1938
        Zaumeyer, W.J. and B.L. Wade, 1935
    V. pea streak
        Zaumeyer, W.J., 1938
    V. red clover mosaic *
        Zaumeyer, W.J. and B.L. Wade, 1935
P. angularis, (Willd.) W.F. Wright
    V. bean common mosaic
        Zaumeyer, W.J. and B.L. Wade, 1935

Phaseolus angularis, (Willd.) W.F. Wright
  V. bean pod mottle
    Zaumeyer, W.J. and H. Rex Thomas, 1948
  V. bean southern mosaic
    Zaumeyer, W.J. and L.L. Harter, 1943
  V. bean yellow mosaic
    Zaumeyer, W.J. and H.H. Fisher, 1953
    Zaumeyer, W.J. and B.L. Wade, 1935
  V. bean yellow stipple
    Zaumeyer, W.J. and H. Rex Thomas, 1950
  V. pea streak
    Zaumeyer, W.J., 1938
  V. red clover mosaic *
    Zaumeyer, W.J. and B.L. Wade, 1935
  V. tobacco ring spot
    Cooper, W.E., 1949
  V. tobacco streak
    Thomas, H. Rex and W.J. Zaumeyer, 1950
P. aureus, Roxb.
  V. alsike clover mosaic
    Zaumeyer, W.J., 1940
  V. bean common mosaic
    Nelson, Ray, 1932
    Reddick, D. and V.B. Stewart, 1919
    Zaumeyer, W.J. and B.L. Wade, 1935
  V. bean pod mottle
    Zaumeyer, W.J. and H. Rex Thomas, 1948
  V. bean southern mosaic
    Zaumeyer, W.J. and L.L. Harter, 1943
  V. bean yellow mosaic
    Conover, Robert A., 1948
    Zaumeyer, W.J., 1940
  V. bean yellow stipple
    Zaumeyer, W.J. and H. Rex Thomas, 1950
  V. broad bean mottle
    Yu, T.F., 1939
  V. cowpea mosaic
    Capoor, S.P. and P.M. Varma, 1956
    McLean, D.M., 1941
  V. pea enation mosaic
    Osborn, H.T., 1938
  V. pea mosaic
    Murphy, D.M. and W.H. Pierce, 1937
    Osborn, H.T., 1937
  V. pea streak
    Zaumeyer, W.J., 1938
  V. red clover vein mosaic
    Osborn, H.T., 1937
  V. soybean mosaic
    Conover, Robert A., 1948
  V. tobacco etch
    Holmes, Francis O., 1946
  V. tobacco mosaic
    Holmes, Francis O., 1946
P. calcaratus, Roxb.
  V. bean common mosaic
    Zaumeyer, W.J. and B.L. Wade, 1935
  V. bean yellow mosaic
    Pierce, W.H., 1934
    Zaumeyer, W.J. and H.H. Fisher, 1953
    Zaumeyer, W.J. and B.L. Wade, 1935
  V. cucumber mosaic
    Harter, L.L., 1938
  V. lucerne mosaic
    Zaumeyer, W.J., 1938
  V. pea streak
    Zaumeyer, W.J., 1938
  V. red clover mosaic *
    Zaumeyer, W.J. and B.L. Wade, 1935
  V. tobacco streak
    Thomas, H. Rex and W.J. Zaumeyer, 1950
P. coccineus, L.
  V. anemone brown ring *
    Hollings, M., 1958
  V. bean pod mottle
    Zaumeyer, W.J. and H. Rex Thomas, 1948
  V. bean southern mosaic
    Zaumeyer, W.J. and L.L. Harter, 1943
  V. bean yellow mosaic
    Baggett, James R., 1956
    Conover, Robert A., 1948
    Thomas, H. Rex and W.J. Zaumeyer, 1953
    Zaumeyer, W.J. and H.H. Fisher, 1953

P. coccineus, L. (cont.)
  V. bean yellow stipple
    Zaumeyer, W.J. and H. Rex Thomas, 1950
  V. beet mosaic
    Pound, Glenn S., 1947
  V. cauliflower mosaic
    Walker, J.C., Francis J. LeBeau and Glenn S.
      Pound, 1945
  V. pea mosaic
    Murphy, D.M. and W.H. Pierce, 1937
  V. soybean mosaic
    Conover, Robert A., 1948
  V. tobacco etch
    Holmes, Francis O., 1946
  V. tobacco mosaic
    Holmes, Francis O., 1946
  V. turnip mosaic
    Walker, J.C., Francis J. LeBeau and Glenn S.
      Pound, 1945
P. lathyroides, L.
  V. bean yellow stipple
    Zaumeyer, W.J. and H. Rex Thomas, 1950
  V. tobacco streak
    Thomas, H. Rex and W.J. Zaumeyer, 1950
P. limensis, MacF.
  V. bean yellow mosaic
    Pierce, W.H., 1934
  V. canna mosaic
    Castillo, B.S., C.E. Yarwood and A.H. Gold, 1956
  V. cucumber mosaic
    Simons, John N., 1957
    Wellman, F.L., 1935
  V. datura distortion mosaic
    Capoor, S.P. and P.M. Varma, 1952
  V. pea mosaic
    Murphy, D.M. and W.H. Pierce, 1937
  V. tobacco etch
    Holmes, Francis O., 1946
  V. tobacco mosaic
    Holmes, Francis O., 1946
  V. tomato ring spot
    Samson, R.W. and E.P. Imle, 1942
P. limensis var. limenanus, Bailey *
  V. squash mosaic
    Freitag, J.H., 1956
P. lunatus, L.
  V. alsike clover mosaic
    Zaumeyer, W.J., 1940
  V. bean common mosaic
    Zaumeyer, W.J. and B.L. Wade, 1935
  V. bean yellow mosaic
    Conover, Robert A., 1948
    Grogan, Raymond G. and J.C. Walker, 1948
    Thomas, H. Rex and W.J. Zaumeyer, 1953
    Zaumeyer, W.J., 1940
    Zaumeyer, W.J. and B.L. Wade, 1935
  V. bean yellow stipple
    Zaumeyer, W.J. and H. Rex Thomas, 1950
  V. beet yellows
    Roland, G. and J. Tahon, 1961
  V. cacao swollen shoot
    Tinsley, T.W. and A.L. Wharton, 1958
  V. cowpea mosaic
    McLean, D.M., 1941
  V. cucumber mosaic
    Adsuar, Jose and A. Cruz Miret, 1950
  V. lucerne mosaic
    Zaumeyer, W.J. and B.L. Wade, 1935
  V. muskmelon mosaic
    Rader, Wm. E., Hugh F. Fitzpatrick and E.M.
      Hildebrand, 1947
  V. papaw mosaic
    Adsuar, Jose, 1950
  V. pea streak
    Zaumeyer, W.J., 1938
  V. potato Y
    Roque, Arturo and Jose Adsuar, 1941
  V. potato yellow dwarf
    Hougas, R.W., 1951
  V. red clover mosaic *
    Zaumeyer, W.J. and B.L. Wade, 1935
  V. soybean mosaic
    Conover, Robert A., 1948

Phaseolus lunatus, L., f. macrocarpus, (Benth.) Van Ess.
  V. bean common mosaic
    Zaumeyer, W.J. and B.L. Wade, 1935
  V. bean pod mottle
    Zaumeyer, W.J. and H. Rex Thomas, 1948
  V. bean southern mosaic
    Zaumeyer, W.J. and L.L. Harter, 1943
  V. bean yellow mosaic
    Pierce, W.H., 1934
    Zaumeyer, W.J. and B.L. Wade, 1935
  V. bean yellow stipple
    Zaumeyer, W.J. and H. Rex Thomas, 1950
  V. datura distortion mosaic
    Capoor, S.P. and P.M. Varma, 1952
  V. lucerne mosaic
    Zaumeyer, W.J., 1938
    Zaumeyer, W.J. and B.L. Wade, 1935
  V. pea streak
    Zaumeyer, W.J., 1938
  V. red clover mosaic *
    Zaumeyer, W.J. and B.L. Wade, 1935
P. mungo, L.
  V. bean common mosaic
    Zaumeyer, W.J. and B.L. Wade, 1935
  V. bean pod mottle
    Zaumeyer, W.J. and H. Rex Thomas, 1948
  V. bean southern mosaic
    Zaumeyer, W.J. and L.L. Harter, 1943
  V. bean yellow mosaic
    Conover, Robert A., 1948
    Zaumeyer, W.J. and H.H. Fisher, 1953
    Zaumeyer, W.J. and B.L. Wade, 1935
  V. cowpea mosaic
    Capoor, S.P. and P.M. Varma, 1956
  V. pea streak
    Zaumeyer, W.J., 1938
  V. red clover mosaic *
    Zaumeyer, W.J. and B.L. Wade, 1935
  V. soybean mosaic
    Conover, Robert A., 1948
  V. tobacco streak
    Cooper, W.E., 1949
P. trilobus, Ait.
  V. cowpea mosaic
    Capoor, S.P. and P.M. Varma, 1956
P. vulgaris, L.
  V. abutilon infectious variegation
    Bird, Julio, 1958
  V. anemone brown ring *
    Hollings, M., 1958
  V. anemone mosaic *
    Hollings, M., 1957
  V. barley stripe mosaic
    McKinney, H.H., 1953
    Sill, W.H., Jr. and E.D. Hansing, 1955
  V. bayberry yellows
    Raychaudhuri, S.P., 1953
  V. beet curly top
    Bennett, C.W., Eubanks Carsner, F.H. Coons and
      E.W. Brandes, 1946
    Bennett, C.W. and A.S. Costa, 1949
    Carsner, E., 1919
    Giddings, N.J., 1938
    Murphy, Donald M. and W.H. Pierce, 1938
  V. beet mosaic
    Bennett, C.W., 1949
    Pound, Glenn S., 1947
    Severin, Henry H.P. and Roger M. Drake, 1948
  V. beet yellows
    Roland, G. and J. Tahon, 1961
  V. beet yellow wilt
    Bennett, C.W. and Carlos Munck, 1946
  V. broad bean mottle
    Yu, T.F., 1939
  V. cacao swollen shoot
    Tinsley, T.W. and A.L. Wharton, 1958
  V. carnation mosaic
    Brierley, Philip and Floyd F. Smith, 1955, 1957
  V. carnation mottle
    Brierley, Philip and Floyd F. Smith, 1957
    Kassanis, B., 1955
  V. carnation vein mottle
    Kassanis, B., 1955

P. vulgaris, L. (cont.)
  V. cauliflower mosaic
    Alvarez-Garcia, L.A., 1951
  V. chilli (pepper) mosaic
    Dale, W.T., 1954
  V. chrysanthemum B (mild mosaic) *
    Hollings, M., 1957
  V. chrysanthemum latent *
    Hollings, M., 1957
  V. chrysanthemum ring spot
    Brierley, Philip and Floyd F. Smith, 1955
  V. chrysanthemum stunt
    Brierley, Philip, 1953
  V. citrus tristeza
    Bennett, C.W. and A.S. Costa, 1949
  V. cowpea mosaic
    Anderson, C.W., 1955
    Capoor, S.P. and P.M. Varma, 1956
    Dale, W.T., 1949
    McLean, D.M., 1941
    Yu, T.F., 1946
  V. cucumber mosaic
    Adsuar, Jose and A. Cruz Miret, 1950
    Anderson, C.W., 1951
    Berkeley, G.H., 1953
    Bridgmon, G.H. and J.C. Walker, 1952
    Brierley, Philip, 1952
    Doolittle, S.P. and W.W. Gilbert, 1918
    Govier, D.A., 1957
    Harter, L.L., 1936, 1938
    Johnson, E.M., 1930
    Milbrath, J.A. and Roy A. Young, 1956
    Nienow, Inez, 1948
    Pound, Glenn S. and J.C. Walker, 1948
    Simons, John N., 1957
    Wellman, F.L., 1934, 1935
    Whipple, O.C. and J.C. Walker, 1941
  V. (cucumber) O.S.C. isolate 606 *
    Porter, Clrak A. and Frank P. McWhorter, 1951
  V. datura distortion mosaic
    Capoor, S.P. and P.M. Varma, 1952
  V. dodder latent mosaic
    Bennett, C.W., 1944
  V. filaree red leaf
    Frazier, Norman W., 1951
  V. hibiscus yellow vein mosaic
    Capoor, S.P. and P.M. Varma, 1950
  V. hydrangea ring spot
    Brierley, Philip and Paul Lorentz, 1956, 1957
  V. lettuce mosaic
    Ainsworth, G.C., 1940
  V. lucerne mosaic
    Harrison, Arthur L., 1935
  V. lucerne witches' broom
    Menzies, J.D., 1946
  V. muskmelon mosaic
    Rader, Wm. E., Hugh F. Fitzpatrick and E.M.
      Hildebrand, 1947
  V. nicotiana glutinosa root necrosis *
    Cetas, Robert C. and A. Frank Ross, 1952
  V. nothoscordum mosaic
    McKinney, H.H., 1950
  V. onion yellow dwarf
    Henderson, W.J., 1935
  V. orchid (cymbidium) mosaic
    Jensen, D.D., 1951
  V. orchid (vanda) mosaic
    Murakishi, Harry H., 1952
  V. papaw mosaic
    Adsuar, Jose, 1950
  V. pea die back *
    Zaumeyer, W.J., 1939
  V. pea enation mosaic
    Ainsworth, G.C., 1940
    Chaudhuri, R.P., 1950
    Hagedorn, D.J. and J.C. Walker, 1954
    McEwen, F.L. and W.T. Schroeder, 1956
    Osborn, H.T., 1938
    Pierce, W.H., 1935, 1937
    Simons, John N., 1954
    Stubbs, M.W., 1936, 1937
  V. pea mosaic
    Ainsworth, G.C., 1940
    Chaudhuri, R.P., 1950

Phaseolus vulgaris, L. (cont.)
  V. pea mosaic
    Hagedorn, D.J. and J.C. Walker, 1954
    Harrison, Arthur L., 1935
    Murphy, D.M. and W.H. Pierce, 1937
    Pierce, W.H., 1935, 1937
    Stubbs, M.W., 1936, 1937
    Zaumeyer, W.J. and B.L. Wade, 1936
  V. pea stem streak *
    Zaumeyer, W.J., 1939
  V. pea streak
    Zaumeyer, W.J., 1938
  V. pea wilt
    Pierce, W.H., 1935
  V. pea yellow mosaic *
    Ainsworth, G.C., 1940
  V. pelargonium ring spot *
    Hollings, M., 1957
  V. pigeon pea sterility mosaic
    Capoor, S.P., 1952
  V. potato X
    Folson, Donald and Reiner Bonde, 1937
    Johnson, E.M., 1930
  V. potato Y
    Bald, J.G. and D.O. Norris, 1945
    Johnson, E.M., 1930
    Peterson, Paul D. and H.H. McKinney, 1938
    Roque, Arturo and Jose Adsuar, 1941
  V. red clover mosaic *
    Zaumeyer, W.J., 1933
    Zaumeyer, W.J. and B.L. Wade, 1933, 1935, 1936
  V. red clover vein mosaic
    Hagedorn, D.J. and E.W. Hanson, 1951
    Hagedorn, D.J. and J.C. Walker, 1949, 1954
    Osborn, H.T., 1937
    Roberts, D.A., 1957
  V. red currant ring spot
    Klesser, P.J., 1951
  V. soybean mosaic
    Conover, Robert A., 1948
    Harrison, Arthur L., 1935
    Kendrick, James B. and Max W. Gardner, 1924
    Pierce, W.H., 1935
  V. squash mosaic
    Freitag, J.H., 1956
  V. squash mosaic (southern)
    Anderson, C.W., 1951
  V. stone fruit *
    Boyle, J.S., J. Duain Moore and G.W. Keitt, 1954
  V. sweet potato mosaic
    Borders, H.I. and T.J. Ratcliff, 1954
  V. tobacco coarse etch
    Johnson, E.M., 1930
  V. tobacco etch
    Anderson, C.W., 1954
    Holmes, Francis O., 1946
    Johnson, E.M., 1930
  V. tobacco green mosaic
    Peterson, Paul D. and H.H. McKinney, 1938
  V. tobacco mosaic
    Holmes, Francis O., 1941
    Johnson, E.M., 1930
    McKinney, H.H., 1952
    Price, W.C. and S.B. Fenne, 1951
  V. tobacco ring spot
    Johnson, E.M., 1930
  V. tomato aspermy
    Brierley, Philip, Floyd F. Smith and S.P. Doolittle, 1955
  V. tomato ring spot
    Samson, R.W. and E.P. Imle, 1942
  V. tomato spotted wilt
    Parris, G.K., 1940
    Smith, Kenneth M., 1931, 1932
  V. turnip crinkle
    Broadbent, L. and G.D. Heathcote, 1958
  V. turnip rosette *
    Broadbent, L. and G.D. Heathcote, 1958
  V. turnip yellow mosaic
    Broadbent, L. and G.D. Heathcote, 1958
  V. Wisconsin pea streak
    Hagedorn, D.J. and J.C. Walker, 1949, 1954

PHILADELPHUS ((Riv.)) L. 1735 (Saxifragaceae)
P. coronarius, L.
  V. tobacco ring spot no. 2
    Brierley, Philip, 1954
P. lewisii, Pursh, var. californicus, Gray *
  V. lucerne dwarf
    Freitag, J.H., 1951

PHILODENDRON Schott 1829 (Araceae)
P. spp.
  V. cucumber mosaic
    Brierley, Philip and Floyd F. Smith, 1944
  V. lily symptomless
    Brierley, Philip and Floyd F. Smith, 1944
  V. tulip breaking
    Brierley, Philip and Floyd F. Smith, 1944
  V. wheat streak mosaic
    Sill, W.H., Jr. and Patrick C. Agusiobo, 1955

PHLEUM L. 1735 (Gramineae)
P. boehmeri, Wibel
  V. barley yellow dwarf
    Bruehl, G.W. and H.V. Toko, 1957
P. phleoides, (L.) Karst.
  V. barley yellow dwarf
    Bruehl, G.W. and H.V. Toko, 1957
P. pratense, L.
  V. agropyron mosaic
    Slykhuis, J.T., 1952
  V. barley stripe mosaic
    Slykhuis, J.T., 1952
  V. barley yellow dwarf
    Oswald, John W. and Byron R. Houston, 1953
  V. sugarcane mosaic
    Brandes, E.W. and Peter J. Klaphaak, 1923
  V. tobacco ring spot
    Wingard, S.A., 1928
  V. wheat streak mosaic
    Slykhuis, J.T., 1952, 1955

PHYLLANTHUS L. 1737 (Euphorbiaceae)
P. corcovadensis, Muell.
  V. citrus tristeza
    Bennett, C.W. and A.S. Costa, 1949

PHYLLOSTACHYS Sieb. & Zucc. 1843 (Gramineae)
P. pubescens *
  V. sugarcane mosaic
    Brandes, E.W. and Peter J. Klaphaak, 1923
P. quilioi, A. & C. Riviere *
  V. sugarcane mosaic
    Brandes, E.W. and Peter J. Klaphaak, 1923

PHLOX L. 1737 (Polemoniaceae)
P. drummondii, Hook.
  V. anemone brown ring *
    Hollings, M., 1958
  V. anemone mosaic *
    Hollings, M., 1957
  V. beet mosaic
    Pound, Glenn S., 1947
  V. chrysanthemum B (mild mosaic) *
    Hollings, M., 1957
  V. pea mosaic
    Murphy, D.M. and W.H. Pierce, 1937
  V. prunus A *
    Fulton, Robert W., 1957
  V. prunus E *
    Fulton, Robert W., 1957
  V. prunus G *
    Fulton, Robert W., 1957
  V. red currant ring spot
    Klesser, P.J., 1951
  V. squash mosaic
    Freitag, J.H., 1956
  V. tobacco etch
    Holmes, Francis O., 1946
  V. tomato ring spot
    Samson, R.W. and E.P. Imle, 1942

PHYSALIS L. 1735 (Solanaceae)
P. aequata, Jacq. f. ex Nees
  V. prunus A *
    Fulton, Robert W., 1957
P. alkekengi, L.
  V. datura distortion mosaic
    Capoor, S.P. and P.M. Varma, 1952
P. angulata, L.
  V. abutilon infectious variegation
    Bird, Julio, 1958
  V. chrysanthemum ring spot
    Brierley, Philip and Floyd F. Smith, 1955
  V. cucumber mosaic
    Adsuar, Jose and A. Cruz Miret, 1950
  V. papaw mosaic
    Adsuar, Jose, 1950
  V. potato A
    MacLachlan, D.S., R.H. Larson and J.C. Walker,
    1953
  V. tobacco ring spot no. 2
    Brierley, Philip, 1954
P. floridana, Rydb.
  V. anemone brown ring *
    Hollings, M., 1958
  V. chrysanthemum B (mild mosaic) *
    Hollings, M., 1957
  V. pelargonium ring spot *
    Hollings, M., 1957
  V. potato A
    MacLachlan, D.S., R.H Larson and J.C. Walker,
    1953
  V. potato M *
    Bagnall, R.H. and R.H. Larson, 1957
    Bagnall, R.H., R.H. Larson and J.C. Walker,
    1956
  V. potato paracrinkle
    Bagnall, R.H. and R.H. Larson, 1957
    Bagnall, R.H., R.H. Larson and J.C. Walker,
    1956
  V. sweet potato feathery mottle
    Webb, Raymon E., 1954
P. franchetti, Mast.
  V. potato leaf roll
    MacCarthy, H.R., 1954
  V. potato X
    Smith, J. Henderson, 1928
P. heterophylla, Nees
  V. potato leaf roll
    MacCarthy, H.R., 1954
  V. potato spindle tuber
    Goss, R.W., 1931
P. ixocarpa, Brot.
  V. potato leaf roll
    MacCarthy, H.R., 1954
P. longifolia, Nutt.
  V. potato Y
    Koch, K.L., 1933
P. peruviana, L.
  V. cowpea mosaic
    Capoor, S.P. and P.M. Varma, 1956
  V. datura distortion mosaic
    Capoor, S.P. and P.M. Varma, 1952
  V. pigeon pea sterility mosaic
    Capoor, S.P., 1952
  V. potato A
    MacLachlan, D.S., R.H. Larson and J.C. Walker,
    1953
  V. potato leaf roll
    Webb, R.E., R.H. Larson and J.C. Walker, 1952
  V. tobacco leaf curl
    Bird, Julio, 1957
P. philadelphica, Lam.
  V. potato M *
    Bagnall, R.H., R.H. Larson and J.C. Walker,
    1956
P. pubescens, L.
  V. beet mosaic
    Pound, Glenn S., 1947
  V. cauliflower mosaic
    Walker, J.C., Francis J. LeBeau and Glenn S.
    Pound, 1945
  V. pea mosaic
    Murphy, D.M. and W.H. Pierce, 1937

P. pubescens, L. (cont.)
  V. pokeweed mosaic *
    Allard, H.A., 1918
  V. potato A
    MacLachlan, D.S., R.H. Larson and J.C. Walker,
    1953
  V. potato leaf roll
    MacCarthy, H.R., 1954
    Webb, R.E., R.H. Larson and J.C. Walker, 1952
  V. stone fruit *
    Boyle, J.S., J. Duain Moore and G.W. Keitt, 1954
  V. tobacco ring spot
    Johnson, E.M., 1930
P. spp.
  V. beet curly top
    Costa, A.S., 1952
  V. cauliflower mosaic
    Alvarez-Garcia, L.A., 1951
  V. euphorbia mosaic
    Costa, A.S. and C.W. Bennett, 1950
  V. potato leaf roll
    Dykstra, T.P., 1933
P. virginiana, Mill.
  V. potato A
    MacLachlan, D.S., R.H. Larson and J.C. Walker,
    1953
P. wrightii, A. Gray
  V. beet yellows
    Roland, G. and J. Tahon, 1961

PHYSOSTEGIA Benth. 1829 (Labiatae)
P. virginiana, (L.) Benth.
  V. tobacco ring spot no. 2
    Brierley, Philip, 1954

PHYTOLACCA Tourn. ex L. 1735 (Phytolaccaceae)
P. americana, L.
  V. anemone brown ring *
    Hollings, M., 1958
  V. beet curly top
    Bennett, C.W. and A.S. Costa, 1949
    Giddings, N.J., C.W. Bennett and A.L. Harrison,
    1951
  V. beet mosaic
    Bennett, C.W., 1949
    Pound, Glenn S., 1947
  V. chrysanthemum B (mild mosaic) *
    Hollings, M., 1957
  V. chrysanthemum latent *
    Hollings, M., 1957
  V. lucerne mosaic
    Johnson, E.M., 1946
  V. tobacco ring spot
    Henderson, R.G. and S.A. Wingard, 1931
  V. tobacco streak
    Thomas, H. Rex and W.J. Zaumeyer, 1950
P. decandra, L.
  V. beet yellows
    Roland, G. and J. Tahon, 1961
  V. cucumber mosaic
    Govier, D.A., 1957
    Johnson, J., 1926, 1927
  V. nicotiana glutinosa mosaic *
    Allard, H.A., 1916
  V. potato X
    Johnson, James, 1927
  V. potato Y
    Johnson, E.M., 1930
    Johnson, James, 1927
  V. tobacco etch
    Holmes, Francis O., 1946
    Johnson, E.M., 1930
  V. tobacco mosaic
    Allard, H.A., 1916, 1918
    Doolittle, S.P. and F.S. Beecher, 1942
    Johnson, E.M., 1930
    Johnson, J., 1926, 1927
  V. tobacco ring spot
    Fenne, S.B., 1931
  V. tomato ring spot
    Samson, R.W. and E.P. Imle, 1942
  V. tomato spotted wilt
    Smith, Kenneth M., 1931

Phytolacca rigida, Small
  V. cowpea mosaic
    Anderson, C.W., 1955

PIAROPUS Raf. 1836 (Pontederiaceae)
P. crassipes, Raf.
  V. cucumber mosaic
    Wellman, F.L., 1935

PISUM ((Tourn.)) L. 1735 (Leguminosae)
P. sativum, L.
  V. anemone mosaic *
    Hollings, M., 1957
  V. bean common mosaic
    Ainsworth, G.C., 1940
    Doolittle, S.P. and F.R. Jones, 1925
    Snyder, W.C., 1942
    Zaumeyer, W.J. and B.L. Wade, 1933, 1935
  V. bean mosaic 3 *
    Zaumeyer, W.J. and B.L. Wade, 1935
  V. bean pod mottle
    Zaumeyer, W.J. and H. Rex Thomas, 1948
  V. bean southern mosaic
    Zaumeyer, W.J. and L.L. Harter, 1943
  V. bean yellow mosaic
    Afanasiev, M.M. and H.E. Morris, 1952
    Doolittle, S.P. and F.R. Jones, 1925
    Zaumeyer, W.J., 1952
    Zaumeyer, W.J. and H.H. Fisher, 1953
  V. beet yellows
    Roland, G. and J. Tahon, 1961
  V. cabbage black ring spot
    Tompkins, C.M., M.W. Gardner and H. Rex
    Thomas, 1938
  V. cauliflower mosaic
    Alvarez-Garcia, L.A., 1951
  V. chilli (pepper) mosaic
    Jha, Ashrafi and S.P. Raychaudhuri, 1956
  V. chrysanthemum B (mild mosaic) *
    Hollings, M., 1957
  V. cineraria mosaic
    Jones, Leon K., 1944
  V. cowpea mosaic
    Anderson, C.W., 1955
    McLean, D.M., 1941
    Yu, T.F., 1946
  V. cucumber green mottle mosaic
    Vasudeva, R.S., S.P. Raychaudhuri and Jagannath
    Singh, 1949
  V. cucumber mosaic
    Berkeley, G.H., 1953
    Bridgmon, G.H. and J.C. Walker, 1952
    Burnett, G., 1934
    Govier, D.A., 1957
    Harter, L.L., 1938
    Johnson, E.M., 1930
    Wellman, F.L., 1935
  V. dodder latent mosaic
    Bennett, C.W., 1944
  V. filaree red leaf
    Frazier, Norman W., 1951
  V. kaimi clover disease *
    Murakishi, Harry H., 1952
  V. lucerne mosaic
    Pierce, W.H., 1937
    Zaumeyer, W.J. and B.L. Wade, 1933, 1935
  V. orchid (vanda) mosaic
    Murakishi, Harry H., 1952
  V. potato X
    Johnson, E.M., 1930
  V. potato Y
    Bald, J.G. and D.O. Norris, 1945
    Johnson, E.M., 1930
  V. primula mosaic
    Tompkins, C.M. and John T. Middleton, 1941
  V. prunus B *
    Fulton, Robert W., 1957
  V. prunus E *
    Fulton, Robert W., 1957
  V. radish mosaic
    Tompkins, C.M., 1939
  V. red currant ring spot
    Klesser, P.J., 1951

P. sativum, L. (cont.)
  V. soybean mosaic
    Pierce, W.H., 1935
  V. squash mosaic
    Freitag, J.H., 1956
  V. stone fruit *
    Boyle, J.S., J. Duain Moore and G.W. Keitt, 1954
  V. tobacco coarse etch
    Johnson, E.M., 1930
  V. tobacco etch
    Anderson, C.W., 1954
    Holmes, Francis O., 1946
    Johnson, E.M., 1930
  V. tobacco mosaic
    Das, C.R. and S.P. Raychaudhuri, 1953
    Holmes, Francis O., 1946
    Johnson, E.M., 1930
  V. tobacco ring spot
    Benedict, W.G., 1955
    Johnson, E.M., 1930
    Wingard, S.A., 1928
  V. tomato spotted wilt
    Parris, G.K., 1940
  V. turnip mosaic
    Tompkins, C.M., 1938, 1939
    Tompkins, C.M. and H. Rex Thomas, 1938
P. sativum var. arvense, (L.) Poir.
  V. cowpea mosaic
    McLean, D.M., 1941
    Yu, T.F., 1946
  V. soybean mosaic
    Kendrick, James B. and Max W. Gardner, 1924
P. sativum var. saccharatum, Hort.
  V. bean common mosaic
    Pierce, W.H., 1935
  V. soybean mosaic
    Pierce, W.H., 1935

PLANTAGO Tourn. L. 1735 (Plantaginaceae)
P. coronopus, L.
  V. beet yellows
    Roland, G. and J. Tahon, 1961
P. erecta, Morris
  V. beet curly top
    Giddings, N.J., 1938
P. lanceolata, L.
  V. anemone brown ring *
    Hollings, M., 1958
  V. aster yellows
    Kunkel, L.O., 1928
  V. beet mosaic
    Bennett, C.W., 1949
  V. chrysanthemum B (mild mosaic) *
    Hollings, M., 1957
  V. chrysanthemum latent *
    Hollings, M., 1957
  V. lucerne dwarf
    Freitag, J.H., 1951
  V. pea mottle
    Johnson, Folke, 1942
  V. pea wilt
    Johnson, Folke, 1942
  V. tobacco etch
    Holmes, Francis O., 1946
  V. tomato ring spot
    Samson, R.W. and E.P. Imle, 1942
P. major, L.
  V. beet mosaic
    Severin, Henry H.P. and Roger M. Drake, 1947
  V. beet yellow net
    Sylvester, Edward S., 1948
  V. cucumber mosaic
    Adsuar, Jose and A. Cruz Miret, 1950
  V. filaree red leaf
    Frazier, Norman W., 1951
  V. onion yellow dwarf
    Henderson, W.J., 1935
  V. orchid (cymbidium) mosaic
    Jensen, D.D., 1951
  V. orchid (odontoglossum) ring spot
    Jensen, D.D. and A. Herbert Gold, 1951
  V. papaw mosaic
    Adsuar, Jose, 1950

Plantago major, L. (cont.)
  V. pea mottle
    Johnson, Folke, 1942
  V. pea wilt
    Johnson, Folke, 1942
  V. tobacco etch
    Holmes, Francis O., 1946
  V. tobacco ring spot
    Fenne, S.B., 1931
    Henderson, R.G. and S.A. Wingard, 1931
    Wingard, S.A., 1928
  V. tomato ring spot
    Samson, R.W. and E.P. Imle, 1942
P. media, L.
  V. tomato aspermy
    Hollings, M., 1955
P. rugelii, Dcne.
  V. tobacco etch
    Holmes, Francis O., 1946
P. spp.
  V. cucumber mosaic
    Wellman, F.L., 1935
P. virginica, L.
  V. prunus A *
    Fulton, Robert W., 1957
  V. prunus E *
    Fulton, Robert W., 1957
  V. prunus G *
    Fulton, Robert W., 1957

PLUCHEA Cass. 1817 (Compositae)
P. sericea, Coville
  V. beet curly top
    Severin, Henry H.P., 1939

POA L. 1737 (Gramineae)
P. ampla, Merr.
  V. barley yellow dwarf
    Bruehl, G.W. and H.V. Toko, 1957
P. bulbosa, L.
  V. barley yellow dwarf
    Bruehl, G.W. and H.V. Toko, 1957
P. canbyi, (Scribn.) Piper
  V. barley yellow dwarf
    Bruehl, G.W. and H.V. Toko, 1957
P. compressa, L.
  V. barley yellow dwarf
    Bruehl, G.W. and H.V. Toko, 1957
P. pratensis, L.
  V. agropyron mosaic
    Slykhuis, J.T., 1952
  V. barley stripe mosaic
    Slykhuis, J.T., 1952
  V. barley yellow dwarf
    Bruehl, G.W. and H.V. Toko, 1957
  V. beet yellows
    Roland, G. and J. Tahon, 1961
  V. cucumber mosaic
    Wellman, F.L., 1935
  V. lucerne dwarf
    Freitag, J.H., 1951
  V. sugarcane mosaic
    Brandes, E.W. and Peter J. Klaphaak, 1923
  V. wheat streak mosaic
    Slykhuis, J.T., 1952, 1955

POLANISIA Raf. 1818 (Capparidaceae)
P. trachysperma, Torr. & Gray
  V. tobacco etch
    Holmes, Francis O., 1946

POLYGONATUM ((Tourn.)) Adans. 1763 (Liliaceae)
P. spp.
  V. wheat streak mosaic
    Sill, W.H., Jr. and Patrick C. Agusiobo, 1955

POLYGONUM ((Tourn.)) L. 1735 (Polygonaceae)
P. acre, H. B. & K.
  V. beet yellows
    Roland, G. and J. Tahon, 1961
P. argyrocoleon, Steud. ex Kunze
  V. beet yellows
    Roland, G. and J. Tahon, 1961

P. aviculare, L.
  V. cucumber mosaic
    Harter, L.L., 1938
P. coccineum, Muhl.
  V. beet yellow net
    Sylvester, Edward S., 1948
P. heterophyllum, Soland. ex Meissn.
  V. beet yellows
    Roland, G. and J. Tahon, 1961
P. hydropiper, L.
  V. beet mosaic
    Pound, Glenn S., 1947
  V. tobacco etch
    Holmes, Francis O., 1946
  V. tobacco mosaic
    Holmes, Francis O., 1938
  V. tobacco ring spot
    Henderson, R.G. and S.A. Wingard, 1931
P. lapathifolium, L.
  V. beet yellows
    Roland, G. and J. Tahon, 1961
P. nodosum, Pers.
  V. beet yellows
    Roland, G. and J. Tahon, 1961
P. persicaria, L.
  V. beet yellow net
    Sylvester, Edward S., 1948
  V. tobacco mosaic
    Holmes, Francis O., 1938
P. scandens, L.
  V. beet mosaic
    Pound, Glenn S., 1947
P. spp.
  V. tobacco ring spot
    Fenne, S.B., 1931

POLYPODIUM ((Tourn.)) L. 1753 (Polypodiaceae)
P. vulgare, L.
  V. cucumber mosaic
    Wellman, F.L., 1935

POLYPOGON Desf. 1798 (Gramineae)
P. monspeliensis, (L.) Desf.
  V. lucerne dwarf
    Freitag, J.H., 1951

PONTEDERIA L. 1735 (Pontederiaceae)
P. cordata, L.
  V. cucumber mosaic
    Wellman, F.L., 1935

POPULUS L. 1735 (Salicaceae)
P. spp.
  V. lucerne dwarf
    Freitag, J.H., 1951

PORTULACA L. 1735 (Portulacaceae)
P. grandiflora, Hook.
  V. cucumber mosaic
    Wellman, F.L., 1935
  V. tobacco ring spot no. 2
    Brierley, Philip, 1954
P. marginata, H. B. & K.
  V. beet yellows
    Roland, G. and J. Tahon, 1961
P. oleracea, L.
  V. beet curly top
    Bennett, C.W. and A.S. Costa, 1949
    Carsner, E., 1919
  V. beet yellows
    Roland, G. and J. Tahon, 1961
  V. chrysanthemum B (mild mosaic) *
    Hollings, M., 1957
  V. chrysanthemum latent *
    Hollings, M., 1957
  V. lucerne dwarf
    Freitag, J.H., 1951
  V. muskmelon mosaic
    Rader, Wm. E., Hugh F. Fitzpatrick and E.M. Hildebrand, 1947
  V. papaw ring spot
    Jensen, D.D., 1949
  V. stone fruit *
    Boyle, J.S., J. Duain Moore and G.W. Keitt, 1954

Portulaca oleracea, L. (cont.)
  V. tobacco mosaic
    Holmes, Francis O., 1938
  V. tobacco streak
    Thomas, H. Rex and W.J. Zaumeyer, 1950
P. retusa, Engelm.
  V. beet yellows
    Roland, G. and J. Tahon, 1961
P. spp.
  V. cauliflower mosaic
    Alvarez-Garcia, L.A., 1951

POTENTILLA L. 1735 (Rosaceae)
P. arguta, Pursh.
  V. tobacco etch
    Holmes, Francis O., 1946
  V. tobacco mosaic
    Holmes, Francis O., 1938, 1946
P. monspeliensis, L.
  V. stone fruit *
    Boyle, J.S., J. Duain Moore and G.W. Keitt, 1954
  V. tobacco etch
    Holmes, Francis O., 1946
  V. tobacco mosaic
    Holmes, Francis O., 1938, 1946
P. palustris, (L.) Scop.
  V. prunus B *
    Fulton, Robert W., 1957
  V. prunus E *
    Fulton, Robert W., 1957

PRIMULA L. 1735 (Primulaceae)
P. auricula, L.
  V. primula mosaic
    Tompkins, C.M. and John T. Middleton, 1941
P. kewensis, W. Wats.
  V. beet yellows
    Roland, G. and J. Tahon, 1961
P. malacoides, Franch.
  V. anemone brown ring *
    Hollings, M., 1958
  V. chrysanthemum B (mild mosaic) *
    Hollings, M., 1957
  V. chrysanthemum latent *
    Hollings, M., 1957
P. obconica, Hance
  V. orchid (cymbidium) mosaic
    Jensen, D.D., 1951
  V. tobacco etch
    Holmes, Francis O., 1946
P. polyantha, Mill.
  V. tomato aspermy
    Brierley, Philip, Floyd F. Smith and S.P.
    Doolittle, 1955
P. sinensis, Lindl.
  V. chrysanthemum B (mild mosaic) *
    Hollings, M., 1957
P. veris, L.
  V. primula mosaic
    Tompkins, C.M. and John T. Middleton, 1941
  V. spinach yellow dwarf
    Severin, Henry H.P. and Donald H. Little, 1947
  V. squash mosaic
    Freitag, J.H., 1956
P. vulgaris, Huds.
  V. cucumber mosaic
    Govier, D.A., 1957

PRUNELLA L. 1753 (Labiatae)
P. vulgaris, L.
  V. tobacco etch
    Holmes, Francis O., 1946

PRUNUS ((Tourn.)) L. 1735 (Rosaceae)
(AMYGDALUS) ((Tourn.)) L. 1735
P. andersoni, A. Gray
  V. peach western X disease
    Rawlins, T.E. and H. Earl Thomas, 1941
P. armeniaca, L.
  V. cherry freckle fruit disease *
    Williams, H.E. and J.A. Milbrath, 1955
  V. peach blotch
    Willison, R.S., 1946

P. avium, L.
  V. peach blotch
    Willison, R.S., 1946
  V. peach yellow bud mosaic
    Schlocker, Archie, H. Keith Wagnon and James R.
    Breece, 1957
  V. prune dwarf
    Hildebrand, E.M., 1942
  V. (sour) cherry yellows
    Keitt, G.W. and C.N. Clayton, 1943
P. besseyi, Bailey
  V. peach ring spot
    Fink, Harry C., 1950, 1955
P. cerasifera, Ehrh.
  V. peach blotch
    Willison, R.S., 1946
  V. peach western X disease
    Rawlins, T.E. and H. Earl Thomas, 1941
  V. peach yellow bud mosaic
    Schlocker, Archie, H. Keith Wagnon and James R.
    Breece, 1957
P. cerasus, L.
  V. peach blotch
    Willison, R.S., 1946
  V. peach mosaic
    Richards, B.L. and L.C. Cochran, 1956
  V. peach necrotic leaf spot
    Fridlund, Paul R., 1954
  V. prune dwarf
    Hildebrand, E.M., 1942
    Thomas, H.E. and E.M. Hildebrand, 1936
P. cistena *
  V. (sour) cherry yellows
    Young, H.C., Jr., 1951
P. demissa, (Nutt.) Walp.
  V. cherry little cherry
    Wilks, Jack M. and J.A. Milbrath, 1956
  V. lucerne dwarf
    Freitag, J.H., 1951
P. domestica, L.
  V. cherry rugose mosaic
    Berkeley, G.H., 1950
  V. peach blotch
    Willison, R.S., 1946
  V. peach ring spot
    Moore, J. Duain and G.W. Keitt, 1944
  V. peach western X disease
    Rawlins, T.E. and H. Earl Thomas, 1941
  V. prune dwarf
    Moore, J. Duain and H.R. Cameron, 1956
  V. (sour) cherry yellows
    Moore, J. Duain and H.R. Cameron, 1956
    Moore, J. Duain and G.W. Keitt, 1944
  V. stone fruit necrotic ring spot *
    Moore, J. Duain and H.R. Cameron, 1956
P. emarginata, (Dougl.) Walp.
  V. peach western X disease
    Rawlins, T.E. and H. Earl Thomas, 1941
P. fasciculata, A. Gray
  V. peach mosaic
    Richards, B.L. and L.C. Cochran, 1956
P. fremonti, S. Wats.
  V. peach mosaic
    Richards, B.L. and L.C. Cochran, 1956
  V. peach western X disease
    Rawlins, T.E. and H. Earl Thomas, 1941
P. ilicifolia, (Nutt.) Walp.
  V. peach western X disease
    Rawlins, T.E. and H. Earl Thomas, 1941
P. mahaleb, L.
  V. peach blotch
    Willison, R.S., 1946
  V. peach western X disease
    Rawlins, T.E. and K.G. Parker, 1934
P. marianna *
  V. peach western X disease
    Rawlins, T.E. and H. Earl Thomas, 1941
P. mume, Sieb. & Zucc.
  V. lucerne dwarf
    Freitag, J.H., 1951

Prunus persica, (L.) Batsch (Amygdalus persica, L.)
    V. aster yellows
        McClintock, J.A., 1931
    V. bayberry yellows
        Raychaudhuri, S.P., 1953
    V. beet yellows
        Roland, G. and J. Tahon, 1961
    V. cherry freckle fruit disease *
        Williams, H.E. and J.A. Milbrath, 1955
    V. cherry little cherry
        Milbrath, J.A. and H.E. Williams, 1956
        Wilks, Jack M. and J.A. Milbrath, 1956
    V. peach mosaic
        Bodine, E.W. and L.W. Durrell, 1941
    V. peach necrotic leaf spot
        Fridlund, Paul R., 1954
    V. prune dwarf
        Thomas, H.E. and E.M. Hildebrand, 1936
    V. prunus A *
        Fulton, Robert W., 1957
    V. prunus B *
        Fulton, Robert W., 1957
    V. prunus E *
        Fulton, Robert W., 1957
    V. prunus G *
        Fulton, Robert W., 1957
    V. vaccinium false blossom
        Kunkel, L.O., 1945
P. salicina, Lindl.
    V. peach blotch
        Willison, R.S., 1946
    V. peach yellow bud mosaic
        Schlocker, Archie, H. Keith Wagnon and James R.
        Breece, 1957
    V. prune dwarf
        Cochran, L.C., 1956
P. salicina x P. americana, Marsh.
    V. peach ring spot
        Fink, Harry C., 1950
P. salicina x P. munsoniana, Wight & Hedr.
    V. peach ring spot
        Fink, Harry C., 1955
P. serotina, Ehrh.
    V. peach X disease
        Gilmer, R.M., 1951
        Gilmer, R.M., J. Duain Moore and G.W. Keitt,
        1954
P. serrulata, Lindl.
    V. elm mosaic
        Callahan, Kemper L. and J. Duain Moore, 1957
P. subcordata, Benth.
    V. peach western X disease
        Rawlins, T.E. and H. Earl Thomas, 1941
P. tomentosa, Thunb.
    V. peach necrotic leaf spot
        Fridlund, Paul R., 1954
P. virginiana, L. var. demissa, (Torr. & Gray) Torr.
    V. peach mosaic
        Richards, B.L. and L.C. Cochran, 1956

PSEUDOTSUGA Carr. 1867 (Pinaceae)
P. taxifolia, (Poir.) Britt.
    V. lucerne dwarf
        Freitag, J.H., 1951

PSIDIUM L. 1737 (Myrtaceae)
P. guajava, L.
    V. chilli (pepper) mosaic
        Jha, Ashrafi and S.P. Raychaudhuri, 1956
    V. cucumber mosaic
        Wellman, F.L., 1935

PTELEA L. 1735 (Rutaceae)
P. trifoliata, L.
    V. citrus tristeza
        Knorr, L.C., 1956

PTERIS L. (Pteridium) (Polypodiaceae)
P. aquilina, L. *
    V. beet ring spot *
        Harrison, B.D., 1957

PTERYGOTA Schott & Endl. 1832 (Sterculiaceae)
P. macrocarpa, K. Schum.
    V. cacao swollen shoot
        Posnette, A.F., N.F. Robertson and J. McA.
        Todd, 1950
        Tinsley, T.W. and A.L. Wharton, 1958

PUERARIA DC. 1825 (Leguminosae)
P. hirsuta, Schneid.
    V. pea mosaic
        Murphy, D.M. and W.H. Pierce, 1937
P. lobata, (Willd.) Ohwi
    V. beet yellows
        Roland, G. and J. Tahon, 1961

PUNICA ((Tourn.)) L. 1735 (Punicaceae)
P. granatum, L.
    V. beet curly top
        Giddings, N.J., 1944

PYCNANTHUS Warb. 1895 (Myristicaceae)
P. kombo, Warb. *
    V. cacao swollen shoot
        Posnette, A.F., N.F. Robertson and J. McA.
        Todd, 1950

PYRACANTHA M. Roem. 1847 (Rosaceae)
P. angustifolia, C.K. Schneider
    V. lucerne dwarf
        Freitag, J.H., 1951

QUAMOCLIT Tourn. ex Moench 1794 (Convolvulaceae)
Q. coccinea, (L.) Moench
    V. sweet potato feathery mottle
        Webb, Raymon E., 1954
Q. pennata, Bojer
    V. tomato ring spot
        Samson, R.W. and E.P. Imle, 1942
Q. sloteri, X H.D. House apud L.H. Bailey in Gentes
    V. sweet potato feathery mottle   Herbarum
        Webb, Raymon E., 1954
    V. tomato aspermy
        Brierley, Philip, Floyd F. Smith and S.P.
        Doolittle, 1955

RADICULA Dill. ex Moench 1794 (Cruciferae)
R. palustris, (L.) Moench
    V. tobacco mosaic
        Holmes, Francis O., 1938

RANUNCULUS ((Tourn.)) L. 1735 (Ranunculaceae)
R. acris, L.
    V. anemone mosaic *
        Hollings, M., 1957
R. asiaticus, L.
    V. primula mosaic
        Tompkins, C.M. and John T. Middleton, 1941
    V. tobacco etch
        Holmes, Francis O., 1946
    V. tobacco mosaic
        Holmes, Francis O., 1946
R. ficaria, L.
    V. anemone mosaic *
        Hollings, M., 1957
    V. chrysanthemum B (mild mosaic) *
        Hollings, M., 1957
R. repens, L.
    V. anemone mosaic *
        Hollings, M., 1957
    V. chrysanthemum B (mild mosaic) *
        Hollings, M., 1957

RAPHANUS ((Tourn.)) L. 1735 (Cruciferae)
R. raphanistrum, L.
    V. henbane mosaic
        Hamilton, Marion A., 1932
    V. tobacco etch
        Holmes, Francis O., 1946
    V. tobacco mosaic
        Holmes, Francis O., 1946
R. sativus, L.
    V. anemone mosaic *
        Hollings, M., 1957

Raphanus sativus, L. (cont.)
V. beet curly top
Carsner, E., 1919
V. beet mosaic
Pound, Glenn S., 1947
V. beet yellows
Roland, G. and J. Tahon, 1961
V. cabbage black ring spot
Tompkins, C.M., M.W. Gardner and H. Rex
Thomas, 1938
V. chilli (pepper) mosaic
Jha, Ashrafi and S.P. Raychaudhuri, 1956
V. chrysanthemum B (mild mosaic) *
Hollings, M., 1957
V. cucumber mosaic
Burnett, G., 1934
Johnson, E.M., 1930
Wellman, F.L., 1935
V. euphorbia mosaic
Costa, A.S. and C.W. Bennett, 1950
V. muskmelon mosaic
Rader, Wm. E., Hugh F. Fitzpatrick and E.M.
Hildebrand, 1947
V. orchid (cymbidium) mosaic
Jensen, D.D., 1951
V. pea mosaic
Murphy, D.M. and W.H. Pierce, 1937
V. pea mottle
Johnson, Folke, 1942
V. pea wilt
Johnson, Folke, 1942
V. potato X
Johnson, E.M., 1930
V. potato Y
Johnson, E.M., 1930
V. primula mosaic
Tompkins, C.M. and John T. Middleton, 1941
V. rape savoy
Ling, Lee and Juhwa Y. Yang, 1940
V. squash mosaic
Freitag, J.H., 1956
V. tobacco coarse etch
Johnson, E.M., 1930
V. tobacco etch
Holmes, Francis O., 1946
Johnson, E.M., 1930
V. tobacco mosaic
Holmes, Francis O., 1946
Johnson, E.M., 1930
V. tobacco necrosis
Fulton, Robert W., 1950
V. tobacco ring spot
Johnson, E.M., 1930
Wingard, S.A., 1928
V. turnip mosaic
Berkeley, G.H. and J.H. Tremaine, 1954
Berkeley, G.H. and M. Weintraub, 1952
Gardner, Max W. and James B. Kendrick, 1921
Tompkins, C.M., 1938, 1939
R. sativus var. longipinnatus, Bailey *
V. turnip mosaic
Tompkins, C.M., 1939
R. sativus var. radicula, (Pers.) A. DC. *
V. turnip mosaic
Dale, W.T., 1948

RESEDA Tourn. ex L. 1735 (Resedaceae)
R. odorata, L.
V. anemone brown ring *
Hollings, M., 1958
V. beet mosaic
Pound, Glenn S., 1947
V. cauliflower mosaic
Walker, J.C., Francis J. LeBeau and Glenn S.
Pound, 1945
V. cucumber mosaic
Wellman, F.L., 1935
V. henbane mosaic
Hamilton, Marion A., 1932
V. primula mosaic
Tompkins, C.M. and John T. Middleton, 1941
V. radish mosaic
Tompkins, C.M., 1939

R. odorata, L. (cont.)
V. squash mosaic
Freitag, J.H., 1956
V. tobacco etch
Holmes, Francis O., 1946
V. tobacco mosaic
Holmes, Francis O., 1946
V. tobacco ring spot no. 2
Brierley, Philip, 1954
V. turnip mosaic
Tompkins, C.M. and H. Rex Thomas, 1938

RHEUM L. 1735 (Polygonaceae)
R. rhaponticum, L.
V. prunus A *
Fulton, Robert W., 1957
V. prunus B *
Fulton, Robert W., 1957
V. prunus E *
Fulton, Robert W., 1957
V. radish mosaic
Tompkins, C.M., 1939
V. turnip mosaic
Tompkins, C.M., 1938, 1939
Tompkins, C.M. and H. Rex Thomas, 1938

RHOEO Hance 1853 (Commelinaceae)
R. discolor, Hance
V. tulip breaking
Brierley, Philip and Floyd F. Smith, 1944
V. wheat streak mosaic
Sill, W.H., Jr. and Patrick C. Agusiobo, 1955

RICINODENDRON Muell. 1864-65 (Euphorbiaceae)
R. africanus, Muell. Arg.
V. cacao swollen shoot
Posnette, A.F., N.F. Robertson and J. McA.
Todd, 1950
R. heudelotii, Pierre ex Pax
V. cacao swollen shoot
Tinsley, T.W. and A.L. Wharton, 1958

RICINUS ((Tourn.)) L. 1735 (Euphorbiaceae)
R. communis, L.
V. beet curly top
Giddings, N.J., C.W. Bennett and A.L. Harrison,
1951
V. cabbage black ring spot
Tompkins, C.M., M.W. Gardner and H. Rex
Thomas, 1938
V. cucumber mosaic
Bennett, C.W., 1944
Wellman, F.L., 1935
V. euphorbia mosaic
Costa, A.S. and C.W. Bennett, 1950
V. pea mosaic
Murphy, D.M. and W.H. Pierce, 1937
V. primula mosaic
Tompkins, C.M. and John T. Middleton, 1941
V. radish mosaic
Tompkins, C.M., 1939
V. squash mosaic
Freitag, J.H., 1956
V. tobacco etch
Holmes, Francis O., 1946
V. tobacco mosaic
Holmes, Francis O., 1946
V. turnip mosaic
Tompkins, C.M., 1938, 1939
Tompkins, C.M. and H. Rex Thomas, 1938

RIVINA Plum. ex L. 1735 (Phytolaccaceae)
R. humilis, L., var. aurantica *
V. cucumber mosaic
Adsuar, Jose and A. Cruz Miret, 1950
V. papaw mosaic
Adsuar, Jose, 1950

ROBINIA L. 1737 (Leguminosae)
R. pseudoacacia, L.
V. lucerne witches' broom
Menzies, J.D., 1946

RORIPPA Scop. 1760 (Cruciferae
(RORIPA) Scop. 1760
R. nasturtium, Rusby
  V. cauliflower mosaic
    Tompkins, C.M., 1937
R. palustris, (L.) Bess.
  V. muskmelon mosaic
    Rader, Wm. E., Hugh F. Fitzpatrick and E.M.
    Hildebrand, 1947

ROSA Tourn. ex L. 1735 (Rosaceae)
R. californica, Cham. & Schlecht.
  V. peach western X disease
    Rawlins, T.E. and H. Earl Thomas, 1941
R. chinensis, Jacq.
  V. beet curly top
    Giddings, N.J., 1944
(R. chinensis x R. moschata, Merrm.) x R. foetida,   Herrm.
  V. rose mosaic
    White, R.P., 1930
R. chinensis var. manetti, Dipp.
  V. rose streak
    Brierley, Philip and Floyd F. Smith, 1940
R. dilecta, Rehd.
  V. cucumber mosaic
    Wellman, F.L., 1935
R. hugonis, Hemsl.
  V. rose streak
    Brierley, Philip and Floyd F. Smith, 1940
R. laevigata, Michx.
  V. cucumber mosaic
    Wellman, F.L., 1935
R. odorata, Sweet
  V. rose mosaic
    White, R.P., 1930
  V. tobacco etch
    Holmes, Francis O., 1946
  V. tobacco mosaic
    Holmes, Francis O., 1946
R. polyantha, Hort.
  V. rose mosaic
    White, R.P., 1930
R. spp.
  V. aster yellows
    Brierley, Philip and Floyd F. Smith, 1940
  V. black raspberry necrosis
    Brierley, Philip and Floyd F. Smith, 1940
  V. strawberry crinkle
    Brierley, Philip and Floyd F. Smith, 1940
  V. tobacco ring spot
    Wingard, S.A., 1928

RUBUS ((Tourn.)) L. 1735 (Rosaceae)
R. loganobaccus, Bailey
  V. orchid (cymbidium) mosaic
    Jensen, D.D., 1951
R. occidentalis, L.
  V. raspberry alpha leaf curl
    Bennett, C.W., 1930
    Rankin, W. Howard, 1931

RUDBECKIA L. 1735 (Compositae)
R. hirta, L.
  V. muskmelon mosaic
    Rader, Wm. E., Hugh F. Fitzpatrick and E.M.
    Hildebrand, 1947
  V. tobacco etch
    Holmes, Francis O., 1946
  V. tobacco mosaic
    Holmes, Francis O., 1938
R. serotina, Nutt.
  V. chrysanthemum stunt
    Brierley, Philip, 1953
  V. dahlia mosaic
    Brierley, Philip and Floyd F. Smith, 1950
R. serotina f. pulcherrima, (Farw.) Fern & Schub. *
  V. dahlia mosaic
    Brierley, Philip and Floyd F. Smith, 1950

RUELLIA Plum. ex L. 1735 (Acanthaceae)
R. tuberosa, L.
  V. cucumber mosaic
    Adsuar, Jose and A. Cruz Miret, 1950

R. tuberosa, L. (cont.)
  V. papaw mosaic
    Adsuar, Jose, 1950

RUMEX L. 1735 (Polygonaceae)
R. abyssinicus, Jacq.
  V. tobacco ring spot
    Wingard, S.A., 1928
R. acetosa, L.
  V. beet yellows
    Roland, G. and J. Tahon, 1961
  V. pea mosaic
    Murphy, D.M. and W.H. Pierce, 1937
  V. squash mosaic
    Freitag, J.H., 1956
R. acetosella, L.
  V. beet mosaic
    Bennett, C.W., 1949
    Severin, Henry H.P. and Roger M. Drake, 1947
  V. beet yellows
    Roland, G. and J. Tahon, 1961
  V. pea mottle
    Johnson, Folke, 1942
  V. pea wilt
    Johnson, Folke, 1942
  V. tobacco mosaic
    Holmes, Francis O., 1938
  V. tomato ring spot
    Samson, R.W. and E.P. Imle, 1942
R. aquaticus, L.
  V. beet yellows
    Roland, G. and J. Tahon, 1961
R. britannica, L.
  V. stone fruit *
    Boyle, J.S., J. Duain Moore and G.W. Keitt, 1954
R. conglomeratus, Murr.
  V. beet yellows
    Roland, G. and J. Tahon, 1961
R. crispus, L.
  V. beet curly top
    Carsner, E., 1919
  V. beet mosaic
    Severin, Henry H.P. and Roger M. Drake, 1947
  V. beet yellow net
    Sylvester, Edward S., 1948
  V. beet yellows
    Roland, G. and J. Tahon, 1961
  V. stone fruit *
    Boyle, J.S., J. Duain Moore and G.W. Keitt, 1954
  V. tobacco etch
    Holmes, Francis O., 1946
  V. tobacco mosaic
    Stover, W.G. and M.T. Vermillion, 1933
R. domesticus, Hartm.
  V. beet yellows
    Roland, G. and J. Tahon, 1961
R. obtusifolius, L.
  V. beet yellows
    Roland, G. and J. Tahon, 1961
  V. tobacco etch
    Holmes, Francis O., 1946
  V. tobacco ring spot
    Fenne, S.B., 1931
R. occidentalis, S. Wats.
  V. beet mosaic
    Pound, Glenn S., 1947
  V. cucumber mosaic
    Nienow, Inez, 1948
R. patientia, L.
  V. tobacco ring spot
    Wingard, S.A., 1928
R. persicarioides, L.
  V. beet yellows
    Roland, G. and J. Tahon, 1961
R. pulcher, L.
  V. beet mosaic
    Severin, Henry H.P. and Roger M. Drake, 1947
  V. beet yellows
    Roland, G. and J. Tahon, 1961

RUTA ((Tourn.)) L. 1735 (Rutaceae)
R. chalepensis, L.
  V. citrus tristeza
    Knorr, L.C., 1956

Ruta graveolens, L.
V. citrus tristeza
Knorr, L.C., 1956
R. spp.
V. citrus tristeza
Bennett, C.W. and A.S. Costa, 1949

SACCHARUM L. 1737 (Gramineae)
S. officinarum, L.
V. cucumber mosaic
Wellman, F.L., 1935
V. maize leaf fleck
Stoner, Warren N., 1952
V. sugarcane mosaic
Storey, H.H., 1929
V. tulip breaking
Brierley, Philip and Floyd F. Smith, 1944
V. wheat streak mosaic
Sill, W.H., Jr. and Patrick C. Agusiobo, 1955

SAGITTARIA Rupp. ex L. 1735 (Alismaceae)
S. montevidensis, Cham. & Schlecht.
V. wheat streak mosaic
Sill, W.H., Jr. and Patrick C. Agusiobo, 1955

SAINTPAULIA H. Wendl. 1893 (Gesneriaceae)
S. ionantha, Wendl.
V. chrysanthemum B (mild mosaic) *
Hollings, M., 1957
V. tobacco etch
Holmes, Francis O., 1946
V. tobacco mosaic
Holmes, Francis O., 1946
V. tomato aspermy
Brierley, Philip, Floyd F. Smith and S.P.
Doolittle, 1955
S. spp.
V. beet yellows
Roland, G. and J. Tahon, 1961

SALPIGLOSSIS Ruiz & Pav. 1794 (Solanaceae)
S. sinuata, Ruiz & Pav.
V. cauliflower mosaic
Walker, J.C., Francis J. LeBeau and Glenn S.
Pound, 1945
V. chrysanthemum B (mild mosaic) *
Hollings, M., 1957
V. cucumber mosaic
Wellman, F.L., 1935
V. prunus A *
Fulton, Robert W., 1957
V. prunus G *
Fulton, Robert W., 1957
V. squash mosaic
Freitag, J.H., 1956
V. tomato ring spot
Samson, R.W. and E.P. Imle, 1942

SALVIA ((Tourn.)) L. 1735 (Labiatae)
S. azurea, Lam.
V. tobacco etch
Holmes, Francis O., 1946
S. farinacea, Benth.
V. cabbage black ring spot
Tompkins, C.M., M.W. Gardner and H. Rex
Thomas, 1938
V. radish mosaic
Tompkins, C.M., 1939
V. tobacco etch
Holmes, Francis O., 1946
V. turnip mosaic
Tompkins, C.M., 1938, 1939
Tompkins, C.M. and H. Rex Thomas, 1938
S. patens, Cav.
V. tobacco etch
Holmes, Francis O., 1946
S. splendens, Ker-Gawl.
V. anemone mosaic *
Hollings, M., 1957
V. beet mosaic
Pound, Glenn S., 1947
V. beet yellows
Roland, G. and J. Tahon, 1961

S. splendens, Ker-Gawl. (cont.)
V. chrysanthemum B (mild mosaic) *
Hollings, M., 1957
V. cucumber mosaic
Wellman, F.L., 1935
V. tobacco etch
Holmes, Francis O., 1946
V. tomato aspermy
Brierley, Philip, Floyd F. Smith and S.P.
Doolittle, 1955

SAMOLUS ((Tourn.)) L. 1735 (Primulaceae)
S. floribundus, H. B. & K.
V. beet curly top
Costa, A.S., 1952
S. parviflorus, Raf.
V. beet yellows
Roland, G. and J. Tahon, 1961

SANGUISORBA Rupp. ex L. 1735 (Rosaceae)
S. minor, Scop.
V. beet yellows
Roland, G. and J. Tahon, 1961

SANICULA ((Tourn.)) L. 1735 (Umbelliferae)
S. canadensis, L.
V. tobacco mosaic
Holmes, Francis O., 1938

SANSEVIERIA Thunb. 1794 (Liliaceae)
S. thyrsiflora, Thunb.
V. cucumber mosaic
Wellman, F.L., 1935
V. wheat streak mosaic
Sill, W.H., Jr. and Patrick C. Agusiobo, 1955
S. zeylanica, Willd.
V. cucumber mosaic
Brierley, Philip and Floyd F. Smith, 1944
V. lily symptomless
Brierley, Philip and Floyd F. Smith, 1944
V. tulip breaking
Brierley, Philip and Floyd F. Smith, 1944

SANVITALIA Gualt. in Lam. 1792 (Compositae)
S. procumbens, Lam.
V. tobacco etch
Holmes, Francis O., 1946
V. tomato aspermy
Brierley, Philip, Floyd F. Smith and S.P.
Doolittle, 1955

SAPONARIA L. 1735 (Caryophyllaceae)
S. vaccaria, L.
V. pea mosaic
Murphy, D.M. and W.H. Pierce, 1937

SCABIOSA ((Tourn.)) L. 1735 (Dipsaceae)
S. atropurpurea, L.
V. beet mosaic
Pound, Glenn S., 1947
V. cauliflower mosaic
Walker, J.C., Francis J. LeBeau and Glenn S.
Pound, 1945
V. pea mosaic
Murphy, D.M. and W.H. Pierce, 1937
V. radish mosaic
Tompkins, C.M., 1939
V. tobacco etch
Holmes, Francis O., 1946
V. tobacco mosaic
Holmes, Francis O., 1946
V. tomato aspermy
Hollings, M., 1955
V. tomato ring spot
Samson, R.W. and E.P. Imle, 1942
V. turnip mosaic
Tompkins, C.M., 1938, 1939
Tompkins, C.M. and H. Rex Thomas, 1938
S. caucasica, Bieb.
V. tobacco etch
Holmes, Francis O., 1946
V. tobacco mosaic
Holmes, Francis O., 1946

SCAPHOPETALUM Mast. 1869 (Sterculiaceae)
S. amoenum, A. Chev.
    V. cacao swollen shoot
        Tinsley, T.W. and A.L. Wharton, 1958

SCHIZANTHUS Ruiz & Pav. 1794 (Solanaceae)
S. pinnatus, Ruiz & Pav.
    V. chrysanthemum B (mild mosaic) *
        Hollings, M., 1957
    V. cucumber mosaic
        Wellman, F.L., 1935
S. retusus, Hook
    V. potato Y
        Smith, Kenneth M. and R.W.G. Dennis, 1940

SCILLA L. 1735 (Liliaceae)
S. hispanica, Mill. (S. campanulata, Ait.)
    V. tulip breaking
        Brierley, Philip and Floyd F. Smith, 1944
S. peruviana, L.
    V. ornithogalum mosaic
        Smith, Floyd F. and Philip Brierley, 1944

SCYTOPETALUM Pierre 1897 (Scytopetalaceae)
S. tieghemii, Hutchinson & Dalziel
    V. cacao swollen shoot
        Tinsley, T.W. and A.L. Wharton, 1958

SECALE ((Tourn.)) L. 1735 (Gramineae)
S. cereale, L.
    V. aster yellows
        Black, L.M., 1941
    V. barley yellow dwarf
        Bruehl, G.W. and H.V. Toko, 1955
    V. muskmelon mosaic
        Rader, Wm. E., Hugh F. Fitzpatrick and E.M.
        Hildebrand, 1947
    V. panicum mosaic *
        Sill, W.H., Jr. and R.C. Pickett, 1957
    V. sugarcane mosaic
        Brandes, E.W. and Peter J. Klaphaak, 1923
    V. tobacco etch
        Holmes, Francis O., 1946
    V. tobacco mosaic
        Holmes, Francis O., 1946
    V. tulip breaking
        Brierley, Philip and Floyd F. Smith, 1944
    V. wheat spot mosaic *
        Slykhuis, John T., 1956
    V. wheat streak mosaic
        Slykhuis, J.T., 1952
S. montanum, Guss.
    V. barley yellow dwarf
        Bruehl, G.W. and H.V. Toko, 1957

SECHIUM P. Br. 1756 (Cucurbitaceae)
S. edule, (Jacq.) Sw.
    V. cucumber mosaic
        Adsuar, Jose and A. Cruz Miret, 1950
    V. papaw mosaic
        Adsuar, Jose, 1950

SENECIO ((Tourn.)) L. 1735 (Compositae)
S. cruentus, (Mass.) DC.
    V. beet yellows
        Roland, G. and J. Tahon, 1961
    V. cabbage ring necrosis
        Larson, R.H. and J.C. Walker, 1941
    V. cauliflower mosaic
        Walker, J.C., Francis J. LeBeau and Glenn S.
        Pound, 1945
    V. chrysanthemum ring spot
        Brierley, Philip and Floyd F. Smith, 1955
    V. cucumber mosaic
        Govier, D.A., 1957
        Wellman, F.L., 1935
    V. primula mosaic
        Tompkins, C.M. and John T. Middleton, 1941
    V. radish mosaic
        Tompkins, C.M., 1939
    V. turnip mosaic
        Tompkins, C.M., 1938, 1939
        Tompkins, C.M. and H. Rex Thomas, 1938

S. douglasii, DC.
    V. beet curly top
        Severin, Henry H.P., 1939
S. elegans, L.
    V. chrysanthemum stunt
        Brierley, Philip, 1953
S. macrophyllus, Bieb.
    V. beet yellows
        Roland, G. and J. Tahon, 1961
S. mikanioides, Otto
    V. tomato aspermy
        Brierley, Philip, Floyd F. Smith and S.P.
        Doolittle, 1955
S. vulgaris, L.
    V. anemone brown ring *
        Hollings, M., 1958

SESAMUM L. 1737 (Pedaliaceae)
S. indicum, L.
    V. nothoscordum mosaic
        McKinney, H.H., 1950

SESBANIA Scop. 1777 (Leguminosae)
S. exaltata, (Raf.) Cory
    V. bean yellow stipple
        Zaumeyer, W.J. and H. Rex Thomas, 1950
    V. tobacco streak
        Thomas, H. Rex and W.J. Zaumeyer, 1950
S. macrocarpa, Muhl. ex Raf.
    V. tobacco ring spot
        Cooper, W.E., 1949
S. sesban, Merr.
    V. prunus G *
        Fulton, Robert W., 1957
S. speciosa, Taub. ex Engl.
    V. cowpea mosaic
        Capoor, S.P. and P.M. Varma, 1956

SETARIA Beauv. 1807 (Gramineae)
(CHAETOCHLOA) Scribn. 1897
S. italica, (L.) Beauv.
    V. agropyron mosaic
        Slykhuis, J.T., 1952
S. lutescens, (Weigel) F.T. Hubb (erroneously as S.
glauca, (L.) Beauv., a synonym of Pennisetum glaucum,
(L.) R. Br.)
    V. agropyron mosaic
        Slykhuis, J.T., 1952
    V. barley stripe mosaic
        Slykhuis, J.T., 1952
    V. onion yellow dwarf
        Henderson, W.J., 1935
    V. pea mosaic
        Murphy, D.M. and W.H. Pierce, 1937
    V. wheat streak mosaic
        Slykhuis, J.T., 1952, 1955
S. verticillata, (L.) Beauv.
    V. agropyron mosaic
        Slykhuis, J.T., 1952
S. virdis, (L.) Beauv.
    V. agropyron mosaic
        Slykhuis, J.T., 1952
    V. barley yellow dwarf
        Bruehl, G.W. and H.V. Toko, 1957
        Oswald, John W. and Byron R. Houston, 1953
    V. sugarcane mosaic
        Brandes, E.W. and Peter J. Klaphaak, 1923

SEVERINIA Tenore 1840 (Rutaceae)
S. buxifolia, Ten.
    V. citrus tristeza
        Knorr, L.C., 1956
S. disticha, (Blanco) Swingle
    V. citrus tristeza
        Knorr, L.C., 1956

SICANA Naud. 1862 (Cucurbitaceae)
S. odorifera, Naud.
    V. papaw mosaic
        Adsuar, Jose, 1950

SIDA L. 1735 (Malvaceae)
S. carpinifolia, L. f.
    V. cucumber mosaic
        Adsuar, Jose and A. Cruz Miret, 1950
    V. papaw mosaic
        Adsuar, Jose, 1950
S. fallax, Walp.
    V. hibiscus yellows *
        Hendrix, J. Walter, 1950
S. hederacea, (Dougl.) Torr.
    V. beet curly top
        Severin, Henry H.P., 1939
S. rhombifolia, L.
    V. abutilon infectious variegation
        Silberschmidt, Karl M., 1948
    V. beet curly top
        Bennett, C.W. and A.S. Costa, 1949
    V. euphorbia mosaic
        Costa, A.S. and C.W. Bennett, 1950
    V. hibiscus yellow vein mosaic
        Capoor, S.P. and P.M. Varma, 1950
S. spp.
    V. cowpea mosaic
        Anderson, C.W., 1955

SILENE L. 1735 (Caryophyllaceae)
S. compacta, Fisch.
    V. bean pod mottle
        Zaumeyer, W.J. and H. Rex Thomas, 1948
    V. hydrangea ring spot
        Brierley, Philip and Paul Lorentz, 1957
    V. peony leaf curl *
        Brierley, Philip and Paul Lorentz, 1957
    V. tomato aspermy
        Brierley, Philip, Floyd F. Smith and S.P.
        Doolittle, 1955
S. dichotoma, Ehrh.
    V. beet yellows
        Roland, G. and J. Tahon, 1961
S. nutans, L.
    V. beet yellows
        Roland, G. and J. Tahon, 1961
S. pendula, L.
    V. euphorbia mosaic
        Costa, A.S. and C.W. Bennett, 1950
    V. tobacco etch
        Holmes, Francis O., 1946
S. verecunda, S. Wats.
    V. beet yellows
        Roland, G. and J. Tahon, 1961
S. vulgaris, Garcke
    V. beet yellows
        Roland, G. and J. Tahon, 1961

SILYBUM Vaill. ex Adans. 1763 (Compositae)
S. marianum, Gaertn.
    V. red currant ring spot
        Klesser, P.J., 1951

SINNINGIA Nees 1825 (Gesneriaceae)
S. speciosa, Benth. & Hook.
    V. tobacco etch
        Holmes, Francis O., 1946

SISYMBRIUM ((Tourn.)) L. 1735 (Cruciferae)
S. alliaria, Scop.
    V. cauliflower mosaic
        Caldwell, John and Ian W. Prentice, 1942
S. altissimum, L.
    V. beet yellows
        Roland, G. and J. Tahon, 1961
S. irio, (L.) Britt.
    V. beet mosaic
        Bennett, C.W., 1949
    V. beet yellows
        Roland, G. and J. Tahon, 1961
    V. dodder latent mosaic
        Bennett, C.W., 1944
S. officinale, (L.) Scop.
    V. beet yellows
        Roland, G. and J. Tahon, 1961
    V. stone fruit *
        Boyle, J.S., J. Duain Moore and G.W. Keitt, 1954

SMILACINA Desf. 1807 (Liliaceae)
S. racemosa, (L.) Desf.
    V. cucumber mosaic
        Brierley, Philip and Floyd F. Smith, 1944
    V. lily symptomless
        Brierley, Philip and Floyd F. Smith, 1944
    V. tulip breaking
        Brierley, Philip and Floyd F. Smith, 1944
S. spp.
    V. wheat streak mosaic
        Sill, W.H., Jr. and Patrick C. Agusiobo, 1955

SMILAX ((Tourn.)) L. 1735 (Liliaceae)
S. spp.
    V. cucumber mosaic
        Brierley, Philip and Floyd F. Smith, 1944
    V. lily symptomless
        Brierley, Philip and Floyd F. Smith, 1944
    V. tulip breaking
        Brierley, Philip and Floyd F. Smith, 1944

SOLANUM ((Tourn.)) L. 1735 (Solanaceae)
S. andigenum, Juz. & Buk. *
    V. potato A
        MacLachlan, D.S., R.H. Larson and J.C. Walker,
        1953
S. antipoviczii, Buk.
    V. potato Y
        Easton, G.D., R.H. Larson and R.W. Hougas,
        1958
S. aviculare, Forst.
    V. cabbage black ring spot
        Tompkins, C.M., M.W. Gardner and H. Rex
        Tohmas, 1938
    V. radish mosaic
        Tompkins, C.M., 1939
    V. turnip mosaic
        Tompkins, C.M., 1938, 1939
        Tompkins, C.M. and H. Rex Thomas, 1938
S. capsicastrum, Link
    V. red currant ring spot
        Klesser, P.J., 1951
S. capsicum, L. *
    V. red currant ring spot
        Klesser, P.J., 1951
S. caribaeum, Dun.
    V. cucumber mosaic
        Adsuar, Jose and A. Cruz Miret, 1950
    V. papaw mosaic
        Adsuar, Jose, 1950
S. carolinense, L.
    V. potato A
        MacLachlan, D.S., R.H. Larson and J.C. Walker,
        1953
    V. potato Y
        Johnson, E.M., 1930
        Koch, K.L., 1933
    V. tobacco coarse etch
        Johnson, E.M., 1930
    V. tobacco ring spot
        Henderson, R.G. and S.A. Wingard, 1931
        Johnson, E.M., 1930
S. chacoense, Bitt.
    V. potato A
        MacLachlan, D.S., R.H. Larson and J.C. Walker,
        1953
S. commersonii, Dun.
    V. potato A
        MacLachlan, D.S., R.H. Larson and J.C. Walker,
        1953
(S. demissum, Lindl. x S. goniocalyx, Lanza) x (S.
stoloniferum, Schlecht. & Bouche)
    V. potato Y
        Easton, G.D., R.H. Larson and R.W. Hougas,
        1958
(S. demissum x S. rybinii, Juz. & Buk.) x (S.
stoloniferum, Schlecht. & Bouche)
    V. potato Y
        Easton, G.D., R.H. Larson and R.W. Hougas,
        1958
(S. demissum x S. soukupii, G. Hawkes) x (S.
stoloniferum, Schlecht. & Bouche)
    V. potato Y
        Easton, G.D., R.H. Larson and R.W. Hougas,
        1958

Solanum dulcamara, L.
  V. beet yellows
    Roland, G. and J. Tahon, 1961
  V. cauliflower mosaic
    Walker, J.C., Jrancis J. LeBeau and Glenn S.
    Pound, 1945
  V. cucumber mosaic
    Govier, D.A., 1957
  V. henbane mosaic
    Hamilton, Marion A., 1932
  V. potato A
    MacLachlan, D.S., R.H. Larson and J.C. Walker,
    1953
  V. potato X
    Dykstra, T.P., 1933
  V. potato Y
    Dykstra, T.P., 1933
  V. tobacco etch
    Holmes, Francis O., 1946
  V. tobacco ring spot
    Fenne, S.B., 1931
    Wingard, S.A., 1928
  V. tomato aspermy
    Hollings, M., 1955
  V. turnip mosaic
    Walker, J.C., Francis J. LeBeau and Glenn S.
    Pound, 1945
S. elaeagnifolium, Cav.
  V. beet yellows
    Roland, G. and J. Tahon, 1961
S. gilo, Raddi
  V. dodder latent mosaic
    Bennett, C.W., 1944
S. integrifolium, Poir.
  V. beet mosaic
    Pound, Glenn S., 1947
  V. cauliflower mosaic
    Alvarez-Garcia, L.A., 1951
    Walker, J.C., Francis J. LeBeau and Glenn S.
    Pound, 1945
  V. dodder latent mosaic
    Bennett, C.W., 1944
  V. potato A
    MacLachlan, D.S., R.H. Larson and J.C. Walker,
    1953
  V. turnip mosaic
    Pound, Glenn S., 1948
    Walker, J.C., Francis J. LeBeau and Glenn S.
    Pound, 1945
S. longipedicellatum, Bitter
  V. potato A
    MacLachlan, D.S., R.H. Larson and J.C. Walker,
    1953
S. lycopersicum, L.
  V. potato spindle tuber
    Goss, R.W., 1931
S. melongena, L.
  V. bayberry yellows
    Raychaudhuri, S.P., 1953
  V. beet curly top
    Costa, A.S., 1952
  V. beet mosaic
    Pound, Glenn S., 1947
  V. cabbage ring necrosis
    Larson, R.H. and J.C. Walker, 1941
  V. cauliflower mosaic
    Alvarez-Garcia, L.A., 1951
  V. chilli (pepper) mosaic
    Dale, W.T., 1954
    Ferguson, I.A.C., 1951
    Jha, Ashrafi and S.P. Raychaudhuri, 1956
  V. cowpea mosaic
    Capoor, S.P. and P.M. Varma, 1956
    Yu, T.F., 1946
  V. cucumber mosaic
    Adsuar, Jose and A. Cruz Miret, 1950
    Burnett, G., 1934
    Johnson, J., 1926
  V. datura distortion mosaic
    Capoor, S.P. and P.M. Varma, 1952
  V. henbane mosaic
    Hamilton, Marion A., 1932
  V. hibiscus yellow vein mosaic
    Capoor, S.P. and P.M. Varma, 1950

S. melongena, L. (cont.)
  V. lucerne mosaic
    Zaumeyer, W.J., 1938
  V. muskmelon mosaic
    Rader, Wm. E., Hugh F. Fitzpatrick and E.M.
    Hildebrand, 1947
  V. papaw mosaic
    Adsuar, Jose, 1950
  V. pea streak
    Zaumeyer, W.J., 1938
  V. petunia mosaic
    Johnson, J., 1926
  V. potato leaf roll
    Webb, R.E., R.H. Larson and J.C. Walker, 1952
  V. potato paracrinkle
    Bagnall, R.H. and R.H. Larson, 1957
    Bagnall, R.H., R.H. Larson and J.C. Walker,
    1956
  V. potato Y
    Koch, K.L., 1933
  V. tobacco etch
    Bawden, F.C. and B. Kassanis, 1941
  V. tobacco leaf curl
    Bird, Julio, 1957
  V. tobacco mosaic
    Johnson, J., 1926
  V. tobacco streak
    Johnson, J., 1936
  V. tobacco stunt *
    Hidaka, Zyun, Tetsuo Uozumi and Chuji Hiruki,
    1956
  V. tomato twisted leaf
    Ferguson, I.A.C., 1951
S. melongena var. esculentum, Nees
  V. cabbage black ring spot
    Tompkins, C.M., M.W. Gardner and H. Rex
    Thomas, 1938
  V. celery mosaic
    Freitag, Julius H. and Henry H.P. Severin, 1945
  V. potato X
    Smith, J. Henderson, 1928
  V. tobacco etch
    Johnson, E.M., 1930
  V. tobacco ring spot
    Johnson, E.M., 1930
S. nigrum, L.
  V. beet curly top
    Bennett, C.W. and A.S. Costa, 1949
    Carsner, E., 1919
    Costa, A.S., 1952
  V. beet mosaic
    Severin, Henry H.P. and Roger M. Drake, 1947
  V. beet yellows
    Roland, G. and J. Tahon, 1961
  V. cabbage ring necrosis
    Larson, R.H. and J.C. Walker, 1941
  V. cauliflower mosaic
    Alvarez-Garcia, L.A., 1951
  V. cowpea mosaic
    Capoor, S.P. and P.M. Varma, 1956
  V. cucumber green mottle mosaic
    Ainsworth, G.C., 1935
  V. datura distortion mosaic
    Capoor, S.P. and P.M. Varma, 1952
  V. hibiscus yellow vein mosaic
    Capoor, S.P. and P.M. Varma, 1950
  V. pea mosaic
    Murphy, D.M. and W.H. Pierce, 1937
  V. pea mottle
    Johnson, Folke, 1942
  V. pea wilt
    Johnson, Folke, 1942
  V. pokeweed mosaic *
    Allard, H.A., 1918
  V. potato A
    MacLachlan, D.S., R.H. Larson and J.C. Walker,
    1953
    Vasudeva, R. Sahai and C.S. Ramamoorthy, 1946
  V. potato Y
    Easton, G.D., R.H. Larson and R.W. Hougas,
    1958
  V. stone fruit *
    Boyle, J.S., J. Duain Moore and G.W. Keitt, 1954

Solanum nigrum, L. (cont.)
   V. tobacco ring spot
      Henderson, R.G. and S.A. Wingard, 1931
      Smith, Kenneth M., 1929
   V. tomato aspermy
      Blencowe, J.W. and John Waldwell, 1949
S. nodiflorum, Jacq.
   V. chilli (pepper) mosaic
      Jha, Ashrafi and S.P. Raychaudhuri, 1956
   V. datura distortion mosaic
      Capoor, S.P. and P.M. Varma, 1952
   V. henbane mosaic
      Hamilton, Marion A., 1932
   V. potato A
      Vasudeva, R. Sahai and C.S. Ramamoorthy, 1946
   V. potato Y
      Roque, Arturo and Jose Adsuar, 1941
      Smith, Kenneth M. and R.W.G. Dennis, 1940
   V. tobacco etch
      Bawden, F.C. and B. Kassanis, 1941
   V. tomato aspermy
      Blencowe, J.W. and John Caldwell, 1949
S. polyadenium, Greenm.
   V. potato A
      MacLachlan, D.S., R.H. Larson and J.C. Walker, 1953
S. pseudocapsicum, L.
   V. cauliflower mosaic
      Walker, J.C., Francis J. LeBeau and Glenn S. Pound, 1945
   V. cucumber mosaic
      Burnett, G., 1934
      Wellman, F.L., 1935
   V. potato A
      MacLachlan, D.S., R.H. Larson and J.C. Walker, 1953
   V. turnip mosaic
      Walker, J.C., Francis J. LeBeau and Glenn S. Pound, 1945
S. rostratum, Dun.
   V. cauliflower mosaic
      Walker, J.C., Francis J. LeBeau and Glenn S. Pound, 1945
S. saltense, Hawkes
   V. potato A
      MacLachlan, D.S., R.H. Larson and J.C. Walker, 1953
S. sanitwongsei, Craib
   V. tobacco etch
      Holmes, Francis O., 1946
S. schickii, Juz. & Buk.
   V. potato A
      MacLachlan, D.S., R.H. Larson and J.C. Walker, 1953
S. torvum, Sw.
   V. papaw mosaic
      Adsuar, Jose, 1950
S. tuberosum, L.
   V. anemone mosaic *
      Hollings, M., 1957
   V. bayberry yellows
      Raychaudhuri, S.P., 1953
   V. beet curly top
      Bennett, C.W. and A.S. Costa, 1949
   V. beet mosaic
      Pound, Glenn S., 1947
   V. beet yellows
      Roland, G. and J. Tahon, 1961
   V. cabbage black ring spot
      Tompkins, C.M., M.W. Gardner and H. Rex Thomas, 1938
   V. cabbage ring necrosis
      Larson, R.H. and J.C. Walker, 1941
   V. celery mosaic
      Freitag, Julius H. and Henry H.P. Severin, 1945
   V. chilli (pepper) mosaic
      Jha, Ashrafi and S.P. Raychaudhuri, 1956
   V. chrysanthemum B (mild mosaic) *
      Hollings, M., 1957
   V. citrus tristeza
      Bennett, C.W. and A.S. Costa, 1949
   V. cucumber mosaic
      Bhargava, K.S., 1951
      Burnett, G., 1934

S. tuberosum, L. (cont.)
   V. cucumber mosaic
      Dykstra, T.P., 1939
      Nariani, T.K. and Nirmaljit Singh, 1952
      Wellman, F.L., 1935
   V. cowpea mosaic
      McLean, D.M., 1941
      Yu, T.F., 1946
   V. euphorbia mosaic
      Costa, A.S. and C.W. Bennett, 1950
   V. henbane mosaic
      Hamilton, Marion A., 1932
   V. lovage mosaic
      Smith, Kenneth M. and Roy Markham, 1944
   V. lucerne mosaic
      Thomas, H. Rex, 1951
   V. muskmelon mosaic
      Rader, Wm. E., Hugh F. Fitzpatrick and E.M. Hildebrand, 1947
   V. nicotiana glutinosa mosaic *
      Allard, H.A., 1916
   V. nicotiana glutinosa root necrosis *
      Cetas, Robert C. and A. Frank Ross, 1952
   V. papaw ring spot
      Jensen, D.D., 1949
   V. pea enation mosaic
      Osborn, H.T., 1938
   V. pea streak
      Zaumeyer, W.J., 1938
   V. physalis floridana yellow net
      Webb, R.E., 1955
   V. potato X
      Hamilton, Marion A., 1932
      Johnson, James, 1927
   V. potato Y
      Hamilton, Marion A., 1932
      Roque, Arturo and Jose Adsuar, 1941
   V. primula mosaic
      Tompkins, C.M. and John T. Middleton, 1941
   V. radish mosaic
      Tompkins, C.M., 1939
   V. red clover vein mosaic
      Hagedorn, D.J. and J.C. Walker, 1949
      Osborn, H.T., 1937
   V. spinach yellow dwarf
      Severin, Henry H.P. and Donald H. Little, 1947
   V. squash mosaic
      Freitag, J.H., 1956
   V. tobacco mosaic
      Allard, H.A., 1916
      Quanjer, H.M., 1920
      Schultz, E.S. and Donald Folsom, 1923
   V. tobacco ring spot
      Cheo, Pen Ching and W.J. Zaumeyer, 1952
      Grogan, R.G. and W.C. Schnathorst, 1955
      Wingard, S.A., 1928
   V. tobacco streak
      Johnson, J., 1936
   V. tobacco yellow dwarf
      Hill, A.V. and M. Mandryk, 1954
   V. tomato aspermy
      Brierley, Philip, Floyd F. Smith and S.P. Doolittle, 1955
      Hollings, M., 1955
   V. tomato yellow net
      Sylvester, Edward S., 1954
   V. turnip mosaic
      Schultz, E.S., 1921
      Tompkins, C.M., 1938, 1939
      Tompkins, C.M. and H. Rex Thomas, 1938
S. verrucosum, Schlecht.
   V. potato A
      MacLachlan, D.S., R.H. Larson and J.C. Walker, 1953

SOLIDAGO ((Vaill.)) L. 1735 (Compositae)
S. graminifolia, L.
   V. tobacco mosaic
      Holmes, Francis O., 1938
S. rugosa, Mill.
   V. tobacco etch
      Holmes, Francis O., 1946
   V. tobacco mosaic
      Holmes, Francis O., 1938, 1946

Solidago spp.
   V. prunus A *
     Fulton, Robert W., 1957
   V. prunus E *
     Fulton, Robert W., 1957
   V. prunus G *
     Fulton, Robert W., 1957
S. virgaurea, L.
   V. beet yellows
     Roland, G. and J. Tahon, 1961

SONCHUS ((Tourn.)) L. 1735 (Compositae)
S. arvensis, L.
   V. beet yellow net
     Sylvester, Edward S., 1948
   V. beet yellows
     Roland, G. and J. Tahon, 1961
   V. lettuce mosaic
     Ainsworth, G.C. and L. Ogilvie, 1939
S. asper, (L.) Hill
   V. beet mosaic
     Bennett, C.W., 1949
     Severin, Henry H.P. and Roger M. Drake, 1947
   V. beet yellows
     Roland, G. and J. Tahon, 1961
S. oleraceus, L.
   V. beet mosaic
     Severin, Henry H.P. and Roger M. Drake, 1947
   V. beet yellows
     Roland, G. and J. Tahon, 1961
   V. cucumber mosaic
     Wellman, F.L., 1935
   V. dandelion yellow mosaic
     Kassanis, B., 1947
   V. lettuce mosaic
     Ainsworth, G.C. and L. Ogilvie, 1939
   V. stone fruit *
     Boyle, J.S., J. Duain Moore and G.W. Keitt, 1954
S. spp.
   V. hibiscus yellow vein mosaic
     Capoor, S.P. and P.M. Varma, 1950

SORGHASTRUM Nash 1901 (Gramineae)
S. nutans, (L.) Nash
   V. sugarcane mosaic
     Brandes, E.W. and Peter J. Klaphaak, 1923
   V. wheat streak mosaic
     Will, W.H., Jr. and Patrick C. Agusiobo, 1955

SORGHUM L. 1735 (Gramineae)
S. almum, L. Parodi
   V. wheat streak mosaic
     Sill, W.H., Jr. and Patrick C. Agusiobo, 1955
S. halepense, (L.) Pers.
   V. beet yellows
     Roland, G. and J. Tahon, 1961
   V. wheat streak mosaic
     Sill, W.H., Jr. and Patrick C. Agusiobo, 1955
S. versicolor, Anderss.
   V. wheat streak mosaic
     Sill, W.H., Jr. and Patrick C. Agusiobo, 1955
S. vulgare, Pers.
   V. agropyron mosaic
     Slykhuis, J.T., 1952
   V. barley stripe mosaic
     Sill, W.H., Jr. and E.D. Hansing, 1955
     Slykhuis, J.T., 1952
   V. barley yellow dwarf
     Oswald, John W. and Byron R. Houston, 1953
   V. beet yellows
     Roland, G. and J. Tahon, 1961
   V. cucumber mosaic
     McWhorter, F.P. and H.H. Millsap, 1954
   V. maize leaf fleck
     Stoner, Warren N., 1952
   V. panicum mosaic *
     Sill, W.H., Jr. and R.C. Pickett, 1957
   V. wheat streak mosaic
     Sill, W.H., Jr. and Patrick C. Agusiobo, 1955
     Slykhuis, J.T., 1952
S. vulgare var. saccharatum, (L.) Boerl.
   V. wheat streak mosaic
     Finley, A.M., 1957

S. vulgare var. sudanense, (Piper) Hitchc.
   V. maize leaf fleck
     Stoner, Warren N., 1952
   V. wheat streak mosaic
     Sill, W.H., Jr. and Patrick C. Agusiobo, 1955

SPARAXIS Ker-Gawl. 1804 (Iridaceae)
S. tricolor, Ker-Gawl.
   V. nothoscordum mosaic
     McKinney, H.H., 1950
   V. tomato aspermy
     Brierley, Philip, Floyd F. Smith and S.P.
     Doolittle, 1955

SPINACIA ((Tourn.)) L. 1735 (Chenopodiaceae)
S. oleracea, L.
   V. anemone brown ring *
     Hollings, M., 1958
   V. anemone mosaic *
     Hollings, M., 1957
   V. aster yellows
     Severin, H.H.P., 1928
   V. bean yellow mosaic
     Thomas, H. Rex and W.J. Zaumeyer, 1953
   V. beet curly top
     Costa, A.S., 1952
   V. beet rosette *
     Bennett, C.W. and James E. Duffus, 1957
   V. beet yellow net
     McLean, D.M., 1952
     Sylvester, Edward S., 1948
   V. cauliflower mosaic
     Alvarez-Garcia, L.A., 1951
     Berkeley, G.H. and J.H. Tremaine, 1954
     Tompkins, C.M., 1937
     Walker, J.C., Francis J. LeBeau and Glenn S.
     Pound, 1945
   V. chrysanthemum B (mild mosaic) *
     Hollings, M., 1957
   V. chrysanthemum latent *
     Hollings, M., 1957
   V. citrus tristeza
     Bennett, C.W. and A.S. Costa, 1949
   V. cowpea mosaic
     Capoor, S.P. and P.M. Varma, 1956
   V. cucumber mosaic
     Burnett, G., 1934
   V. datura distortion mosaic *
     Capoor, S.P. and P.M. Varma, 1952
   V. filaree red leaf
     Frazier, Norman W., 1951
   V. lucerne mosaic
     Kreitlow, K.W. and W.C. Price, 1949
     Thomas, H.R., 1953
   V. malva yellow vein mosaic *
     Costa, A.S. and James E. Duffus, 1957
   V. muskmelon mosaic
     Rader, Wm. E., Hugh F. Fitzpatrick and E.M.
     Hildebrand, 1947
   V. pea wilt
     Johnson, Folke, 1942
   V. primula mosaic
     Tompkins, C.M. and John T. Middleton, 1941
   V. squash mosaic
     Freitag, J.H., 1956
   V. stone fruit *
     Boyle, J.S., J. Duain Moore and G.W. Keitt, 1954
   V. tobacco etch
     Holmes, Francis O., 1946
   V. tobacco ring spot
     Smith, Kenneth M., 1929
     Wingard, S.A., 1928
   V. tobacco streak
     Thomas, H. Rex and W.J. Zaumeyer, 1950
   V. tomato spotted wilt
     Smith, Kenneth M., 1931
   V. turnip mosaic
     LeBeau, Francis J. and J.C. Walker, 1945
     Tompkins, C.M., 1938, 1939
     Tompkins, C.M. and H. Rex Thomas, 1938
S. oleracea var. inermis, Peterm. *
   V. celery mosaic
     Freitag, Julius H. and Henry H.P. Severin, 1945

SPREKELIA Heist. 1748 (Amaryllidaceae)
S. formosissima, Herb.
    V. narcissus mosaic
      Haasis, Frank A., 1939

STACHYS ((Tourn.)) L. 1735 (Labiatae)
S. arvensis, L.
    V. beet yellows
      Roland, G. and J. Tahon, 1961

STANLEYA Nutt. 1818 (Cruciferae)
S. pinnata, (Pursh) Britt.
    V. cauliflower mosaic
      Tompkins, C.M., 1937

STELLARIA L. 1753 (Caryophyllaceae)
S. media, (L.) Cyr.
    V. anemone brown ring *
      Hollings, M., 1958
    V. beet curly top
      Costa, A.S., 1952
    V. beet yellow net
      McLean, D.M., 1952
    V. cauliflower mosaic
      Walker, J.C., Francis J. LeBeau and Glenn S.
      Pound, 1945
    V. chrysanthemum B (mild mosaic) *
      Hollings, M., 1957
    V. chrysanthemum latent *
      Hollings, M., 1957
    V. citrus tristeza
      Bennett, C.W. and A.S. Costa, 1949
    V. dodder latent mosaic
      Bennett, C.W., 1944
    V. pea wilt
      Johnson, Folke, 1942
    V. tobacco etch
      Holmes, Francis O., 1946
    V. tobacco mosaic
      Holmes, Francis O., 1938
    V. tobacco ring spot
      Wingard, S.A., 1928

STENOTAPHRUM Trin. 1820 (Gramineae)
S. secundatum, (Walt.) Kuntze
    V. cucumber mosaic
      Wellman, F.L., 1935

STERCULIA L. 1747 (Sterculiaceae)
S. foetida, L.
    V. cacao swollen shoot
      Tinsley, T.W. and A.L. Wharton, 1958
S. oblonga, Mast.
    V. cacao swollen shoot
      Tinsley, T.W. and A.L. Wharton, 1958
S. rhinopetala, K. Schum.
    V. cacao swollen shoot
      Posnette, A.F., N.F. Robertson and J. McA.
      Todd, 1950
      Tinsley, T.W. and A.L. Wharton, 1958
S. tragacantha, Lindl.
    V. cacao swollen shoot
      Posnette, A.F., N.F. Robertson and J. McA.
      Todd, 1950
      Tinsley, T.W. and A.L. Wharton, 1958

STIPA L. 1753 (Gramineae)
S. cernua, Stebbins & Love
    V. barley yellow dwarf
      Oswald, John W. and Byron R. Houston, 1953

STOKESIA L'Herit. 1788 (Compositae)
S. laevis, (Hill) Greene
    V. chrysanthemum stunt
      Brierley, Philip, 1953

SWAINSONA Salisb. 1805 (Leguminosae)
S. salsula, Taub.
    V. lucerne witches' broom
      Klostermeyer, E.C. and J.D. Menzies, 1951

SWINGLEA Merrill 1927 (Rutaceae)
S. glutinosa, Merrill
    V. citrus tristeza
      Knorr, L.C., 1956

SYMPLOCARPUS Salisb. ex Nutt. 1818 (Araceae)
S. foetidus, (L.) Nutt.
    V. tobacco etch
      Holmes, Francis O., 1946
    V. tobacco mosaic
      Holmes, Francis O., 1946

TAGETES L. 1737 (Compositae)
T. signata, Bartl.
    V. tobacco etch
      Holmes, Francis O., 1946
    V. tomato ring spot
      Samson, R.W. and E.P. Imle, 1942
T. spp.
    V. euphorbia mosaic
      Costa, A.S. and C.W. Bennett, 1950
T. erecta, L.
    V. chilli (pepper) mosaic
      Jha, Ashrafi and S.P. Raychaudhuri, 1956
    V. chrysanthemum B (mild mosaic) *
      Hollings, M., 1957
    V. chrysanthemum stunt
      Brierley, Philip, 1953
    V. datura distortion mosaic
      Capoor, S.P. and P.M. Varma, 1952
    V. radish mosaic
      Tompkins, C.M., 1939
    V. squash mosaic
      Freitag, J.H., 1956
    V. tomato aspermy
      Brierley, Philip, Floyd F. Smith and S.P.
      Doolittle, 1955
    V. tobacco etch
      Holmes, Francis O., 1946
    V. tomato ring spot
      Samson, R.W. and E.P. Imle, 1942
    V. turnip mosaic
      Tompkins, C.M., 1938, 1939
      Tompkins, C.M. and H. Rex Thomas, 1938
T. patula, L.
    V. beet mosaic
      Pound, Glenn S., 1947
    V. cabbage ring necrosis
      Larson, R.H. and J.C. Walker, 1941
    V. cabbage black ring spot
      Tompkins, C.M., M.W. Gardner and H. Rex
      Thomas, 1938
    V. cauliflower mosaic
      Walker, J.C., Francis J. LeBeau and Glenn S.
      Pound, 1945
    V. primula mosaic
      Tompkins, C.M. and John T. Middleton, 1941
    V. radish mosaic
      Tompkins, C.M., 1939
    V. squash mosaic
      Freitag, J.H., 1956
    V. tobacco etch
      Holmes, Francis O., 1946
    V. turnip mosaic
      Tompkins, C.M., 1938, 1939
      Tompkins, C.M. and H. Rex Thomas, 1938
      Walker, J.C., Francis J. LeBeau and Glenn S.
      Pound, 1945

TANACETUM Tourn. ex L. 1735 (Compositae)
T. vulgare, L.
    V. beet yellows
      Roland, G. and J. Tahon, 1961

TARAXACUM L. 1735 (Compositae)
T. megalorrhizon, Hand.-Mazz.
    V. beet yellows
      Roland, G. and J. Tahon, 1961
T. officinale, Weber
    V. beet yellows
      Roland, G. and J. Tahon, 1961
    V. cabbage black ring spot
      Tompkins, C.M., M.W. Gardner and H. Rex
      Thomas, 1938
    V. cabbage ring necrosis
      Larson, R.H. and J.C. Walker, 1941
    V. chrysanthemum B (mild mosaic) *
      Hollings, M., 1957
    V. lettuce mosaic
      Ainsworth, G.C. and L. Ogilvie, 1939

Taraxacum officinale, Weber
  V. pea mottle
    Johnson, Folke, 1942
  V. pea wilt
    Johnson, Folke, 1942
  V. radish mosaic
    Tompkins, C.M., 1939
  V. stone fruit *
    Boyle, J.S., J. Duain Moore and G.W. Keitt, 1954
  V. tobacco etch
    Holmes, Francis O., 1946
  V. tobacco mosaic
    Holmes, Francis O., 1938, 1946
  V. turnip mosaic
    Tompkins, C.M., 1938, 1939
    Tompkins, C.M. and H. Rex Thomas, 1938

TARRIETIA Blume 1825 (Sterculiaceae)
T. utilis, (Sprague) Sprague *
  V. cacao swollen shoot
    Tinsley, T.W. and A.L. Wharton, 1958

TETRAGONIA L. 1735 (Aizoaceae)
T. expansa, Thunb.
  V. lucerne dwarf
    Freitag, J.H., 1951
  V. pelargonium ring spot *
    Hollings, M., 1957
  V. spinach yellow dwarf
    Severin, Henry H.P. and Donald H. Little, 1947
  V. tomato ring spot
    Samson, R.W. and E.P. Imle, 1942
  V. tomato spotted wilt
    Sakimura, K., 1940
    Smith, Kenneth M., 1931
  V. turnip yellow mosaic
    Broadbent, L. and G.D. Heathcote, 1958

THELESPERMA Less. 1831 (Compositae)
T. hybridum, Voss
  V. tobacco etch
    Holmes, Francis O., 1946
  V. tobacco mosaic
    Holmes, Francis O., 1946

THEOBROMA L. 1737 (Sterculiaceae)
T. angustifolia, ((Moc. & Sesse)) ex DC.
  V. cacao swollen shoot
    Tinsley, T.W. and A.L. Wharton, 1958
T. balaoense *
  V. cacao swollen shoot
    Posnette, A.F. and J. McA. Todd, 1951
T. bicolor, Humb. & Bonpl.
  V. cacao swollen shoot
    Tinsley, T.W. and A.L. Wharton, 1958
T. grandiflorum, K. Schum.
  V. cacao swollen shoot
    Tinsley, T.W. and A.L. Wharton, 1958
T. (Herrania) mariae, K. Schum.
  V. cacao swollen shoot
    Posnette, A.F. and J. McA. Todd, 1951
T. obovata, Klotzsch, ex Bern.
  V. cacao swollen shoot
    Tinsley, T.W. and A.L. Wharton, 1958
T. speciosa, Willd. ex Spreng.
  V. cacao swollen shoot
    Tinsley, T.W. and A.L. Wharton, 1958

THESPESIA Soland. ex Correa 1807 (Malvaceae)
T. lampas *
  V. cacao swollen shoot
    Posnette, A.F., N.F. Robertson and J. McA. Todd, 1950
T. populnea *
  V. cacao swollen shoot
    Tinsley, T.W. and A.L. Wharton, 1958
  V. hibiscus yellows *
    Hendrix, J. Walter, 1950

THLASPI ((Tourn.)) L. 1737 (Cruciferae)
T. arvense, L.
  V. beet mosaic
    Pound, Glenn S., 1947

T. arvense, L. (cont.)
  V. cauliflower mosaic
    Caldwell, John and Ian W. Prentice, 1942
  V. stone fruit *
    Boyle, J.S., J. Duain Moore and G.W. Keitt, 1954

THUNBERGIA Retz. 1776 (Acanthaceae)
T. alata, Bojer
  V. pea mosaic
    Murphy, D.M. and W.H. Pierce, 1937
  V. prunus A *
    Fulton, Robert W., 1957
  V. prunus E *
    Fulton, Robert W., 1957
  V. tobacco etch
    Holmes, Francis O., 1946
  V. tobacco mosaic
    Holmes, Francis O., 1946

THYSANOCARPUS Hook 1829 (Cruciferae)
T. radians, Benth.
  V. cauliflower mosaic
    Tompkins, C.M., 1937

TIGRIDIA Juss. 1789 (Iridaceae)
T. pavonia, Ker-Gawl.
  V. cucumber mosaic
    Brierley, Philip and Floyd F. Smith, 1944
  V. lily symptomless
    Brierley, Philip and Floyd F. Smith, 1944
  V. tulip breaking
    Brierley, Philip and Floyd F. Smith, 1944
T. spp.
  V. beet yellows
    Roland, G. and J. Tahon, 1961

TILIA ((Tourn.)) L. 1735 (Tiliaceae)
T. platyphyllos, Scop.
  V. cacao swollen shoot
    Tinsley, T.W. and A.L. Wharton, 1958

TILLANDSIA L. 1735 (Bromeliaceae)
T. fasciculata, Swartz
  V. cucumber mosaic
    Wellman, F.L., 1935

TITHONIA Desf. ex Juss. 1789 (Compositae)
T. rotundifolia, (Mill.) Blake
  V. dahlia mosaic
    Brierley, Philip and Floyd F. Smith, 1950
  V. tobacco mosaic
    Cook, M.T., 1936
  V. tomato aspermy
    Brierley, Philip, Floyd F. Smith and S.P. Doolittle, 1955
T. speciosa, Hook.
  V. prunus A *
    Fulton, Robert W., 1957
  V. prunus E *
    Fulton, Robert W., 1957
  V. prunus G *
    Fulton, Robert W., 1957

TRACHYMENE Rudge 1811 (Umbelliferae)
T. caerulea, R. Graham
  V. cucumber mosaic
    Wellman, F.L., 1935
  V. squash mosaic
    Freitag, J.H., 1956
  V. tobacco etch
    Holmes, Francis O., 1946
  V. tobacco mosaic
    Holmes, Francis O., 1946

TRADESCANTIA Rupp. ex L. 1735 (Commelinaceae)
T. fluminensis, Vell.
  V. tobacco ring spot
    Wingard, S.A., 1928

TRAGOPOGON ((Tourn.)) L. 1735 (Compositae)
T. porrifolius, L.
  V. chrysanthemum stunt
    Brierley, Philip, 1953

Tragopogon porrifolius, L. (cont.)
  V. cucumber mosaic
    Wellman, F.L., 1935
  V. tobacco ring spot
    Wingard, S.A., 1928

TREMA Lour. 1790 (Ulmaceae)
T. guineensis, Priemer
  V. cacao swollen shoot
    Tinsley, T.W. and A.L. Wharton, 1958

TRIBULUS Tourn. ex L. 1735 (Zygophyllaceae)
T. terrestris, L.
  V. beet yellows
    Roland, G. and J. Tahon, 1961

TRICHOLAENA Schrad. 1824 (Gramineae)
T. repens, (Willd.) Hitchc. (T. rosea, Nees)
  V. cucumber mosaic
    Wellman, F.L., 1935

TRICYRTIS Wall. 1826 (Liliaceae)
T. hirta, Hook.
  V. cucumber mosaic
    Brierley, Philip and Floyd F. Smith, 1944
  V. lily symptomless
    Brierley, Philip and Floyd F. Smith, 1944
  V. tulip breaking
    Brierley, Philip and Floyd F. Smith, 1944

TRIFOLIUM ((Tourn.)) L. 1735 (Leguminosae)
T. alexandrinum, L.
  V. chilli (pepper) mosaic
    Jha, Ashrafi and S.P. Raychaudhuri, 1956
  V. tobacco mosaic
    Das, C.R. and S.P. Raychaudhuri, 1953
T. fragiferum, L.
  V. lucerne witches' broom
    Menzies, J.D., 1946
T. hybridum, L.
  V. bean Montana *
    Afanasiev, M.M. and H.E. Morris, 1946
  V. bean yellow mosaic
    Afanasiev, M.M. and H.E. Morris, 1952
  V. cucumber mosaic
    Harter, L.L., 1938
  V. lucerne witches' broom
    Menzies, J.D., 1946
  V. pea enation mosaic
    Hagedorn, D.J. and J.C. Walker, 1954
    McEwen, F.L. and W.T. Schroeder, 1956
    Osborn, H.T., 1938
    Simons, John N., 1954
    Stubbs, M.W., 1937
  V. pea mosaic
    Hagedorn, D.J. and J.C. Walker, 1954
    Stubbs, M.W., 1937
  V. potato A
    MacLachlan, D.S., R.H. Larson and J.C. Walker,
    1953
  V. tobacco ring spot
    Fenne, S.B., 1931
    Stubbs, M.W., 1937
T. incarnatum, L.
  V. bayberry yellows
    Raychaudhuri, S.P., 1953
  V. bean pod mottle
    Zaumeyer, W.J. and H. Rex Thomas, 1948
  V. bean southern mosaic
    Zaumeyer, W.J. and L.L. Harter, 1943
  V. bean yellow mosaic
    Zaumeyer, W.J., 1952
    Zaumeyer, W.J. and H.H. Fisher, 1953
  V. bean yellow stipple
    Zaumeyer, W.J. and H. Rex Thomas, 1950
  V. beet yellows
    Roland, G. and J. Tahon, 1961
  V. cucumber mosaic
    Bridgmon, G.H. and J.C. Walker, 1952
  V. lucerne witches' broom
    Menzies, J.D., 1946
  V. orchid (cymbidium) mosaic
    Jensen, D.D., 1951

T. incarnatum, L. (cont.)
  V. orchid (odontoglossum) ring spot
    Jensen, D.D. and A. Herbert Gold, 1951
  V. potato A
    MacLachlan, D.S., R.H. Larson and J.C. Walker,
    1953
  V. soybean mosaic
    Conover, Robert A., 1948
  V. squash mosaic
    Freitag, J.H., 1956
  V. stone fruit *
    Boyle, J.S., J. Duain Moore and G.W. Keitt, 1954
  V. tobacco etch
    Holmes, Francis O., 1946
  V. tobacco mosaic
    Costa, A.S., 1944
    Holmes, Francis O., 1946
  V. tobacco ring spot
    Bridgmon, G.H. and J.C. Walker, 1952
T. medium, L.
  V. pea mosaic
    Murphy, D.M. and W.H. Pierce, 1937
  V. tobacco ring spot
    Fenne, S.B., 1931
T. pratense, L.
  V. alsike clover mosaic
    Zaumeyer, W.J., 1940
  V. bean common mosaic
    Ainsworth, G.C., 1940
    Snyder, W.C., 1942
    Zaumeyer, W.J. and B.L. Wade, 1935
  V. bean Montana *
    Afanasiev, M.M. and H.E. Morris, 1946
  V. bean southern mosaic
    Zaumeyer, W.J. and L.L. Harter, 1943
  V. bean yellow mosaic
    Afanasiev, M.M. and H.E. Morris, 1952
    Ainsworth, G.C., 1940
    Baggett, James R., 1957
    Grogan, Raymond G. and J.C. Walker, 1948
    Thomas, H. Rex and W.J. Zaumeyer, 1953
    Zaumeyer, W.J., 1940, 1952
    Zaumeyer, W.J. and H.H. Fisher, 1953
  V. bean yellow stipple
    Zaumeyer, W.J. and H. Rex Thomas, 1950
  V. beet curly top
    Giddings, N.J., 1944
  V. beet mosaic
    Bennett, C.W., 1949
  V. beet yellows
    Roland, G. and J. Tahon, 1961
  V. cowpea mosaic
    Yu, T.F., 1946
  V. cucumber mosaic
    Bridgmon, G.H. and J.C. Walker, 1952
    Costa, A.S., 1944
    Doolittle, S.P. and W.J. Zaumeyer, 1953
  V. filaree red leaf
    Frazier, Norman W., 1951
  V. gladiolus *
    Snow, Gordon F., 1955
  V. hibiscus yellow vein mosaic
    Capoor, S.P. and P.M. Varma, 1950
  V. kaimi clover disease *
    Murakishi, Harry H., 1952
  V. lettuce mosaic
    Ainsworth, G.C., 1940
  V. lucerne mosaic
    Zaumeyer, W.J., 1953
  V. muskmelon mosaic
    Rader, Wm. E., Hugh F. Fitzpatrick and E.M.
    Hildebrand, 1947
  V. onion yellow dwarf
    Henderson, W.J., 1935
  V. pea enation mosaic
    Ainsworth, G.C., 1940
    Chaudhuri, R.P., 1950
    Hagedorn, D.J. and J.C. Walker, 1954
    Johnson, Folke and Leon K. Jones, 1937
    McEwen, F.L. and W.T. Schroeder, 1956
    Osborn, H.T., 1938
    Pierce, W.H., 1935
    Simons, John N., 1954
    Stubbs, M.W., 1936, 1937

Trifolium pratense, L. (cont.)
V. pea mosaic
    Ainsworth, G.C., 1940
    Chaudhuri, R.P., 1950
    Hagedorn, D.J. and J.C. Walker, 1954
    Stubbs, M.W., 1936, 1937
    Zaumeyer, W.J. and B.L. Wade, 1935
V. potato A
    MacLachlan, D.S., R.H. Larson and J.C. Walker, 1953
V. soybean mosaic
    Kendrick, James B. and Max W. Gardner, 1924
    Pierce, W.H., 1935
V. squash mosaic
    Freitag, J.H., 1956
V. tobacco etch
    Holmes, Francis O., 1946
V. tobacco mosaic
    Holmes, Francis O., 1946
V. tobacco ring spot
    Bridgmon, G.H. and J.C. Walker, 1952
    Cheo, Pen Ching and W.J. Zaumeyer, 1952
    Fenne, S.B., 1931
    Stubbs, M.W., 1937
T. procumbens, L.
V. lucerne mosaic
    Kreitlow, K.W. and W.C. Price, 1949
V. orchid (cymbidium) mosaic
    Jensen, D.D., 1951
T. repens, L.
V. alsike clover mosaic
    Zaumeyer, W.J., 1940
V. anemone brown ring *
    Hollings, M., 1958
V. anemone mosaic *
    Hollings, M., 1957
V. bean common mosaic
    Ainsworth, G.C., 1940
    Snow, Gordon F., 1955
    Snyder, W.C., 1942
    Zaumeyer, W.J. and B.L. Wade, 1935
V. bean Montana *
    Afanasiev, M.M. and H.E. Morris, 1946
V. bean southern mosaic
    Zaumeyer, W.J. and L.L. Harter, 1943
V. bean yellow mosaic
    Afanasiev, M.M. and H.E. Morris, 1952
    Baggett, James R., 1957
    Elliott, J.A., 1921
    Grogan, Raymond G. and J.C. Walker, 1948
    Hagedorn, D.J. and J.C. Walker, 1950, 1954
    Pierce, W.H., 1935
    Zaumeyer, W.J., 1940, 1952
    Zaumeyer, W.J. and H.H. Fisher, 1953
    Zaumeyer, W.J. and B.L. Wade, 1935
V. bean yellow stipple
    Zaumeyer, W.J. and H. Rex Thomas, 1950
V. beet curly top
    Giddings, N.J., 1944
V. beet mosaic
    Bennett, C.W., 1949
V. chrysanthemum B (mild mosaic) *
    Hollings, M., 1957
V. cowpea mosaic
    Yu, T.F., 1946
V. cucumber mosaic
    Doolittle, S.P. and W.J. Zaumeyer, 1953
    Wellman, F.L., 1935
    Whipple, O.C. and J.C. Walker, 1941
V. filaree red leaf
    Frazier, Norman W., 1951
V. kaimi clover disease *
    Murakishi, Harry H., 1952
V. lettuce mosaic
    Ainsworth, G.C., 1940
V. lucerne mosaic
    Zaumeyer, W.J. and B.L. Wade, 1935
V. pea enation mosaic
    Ainsworth, G.C., 1940
    Chaudhuri, R.P., 1950
    Hagedorn, D.J. and J.C. Walker, 1954
    Johnson, Folke and Leon K. Jones, 1937
    Osborn, H.T., 1938
    Pierce, W.H., 1935

T. repens, L. (cont.)
V. pea enation mosaic
    Simons, John N., 1954
    Stubbs, M.W., 1937
V. pea mosaic
    Ainsworth, G.C., 1940
    Chaudhuri, R.P., 1950
    Hagedorn, D.J. and J.C. Walker, 1954
    Murphy, D.M. and W.H. Pierce, 1937
    Osborn, H.T., 1937
    Pierce, W.H., 1935
    Stubbs, M.W., 1937
V. pea yellow mosaic *
    Ainsworth, G.C., 1940
V. potato A
    MacLachlan, D.S., R.H. Larson and J.C. Walker, 1953
V. prunus E *
    Fulton, Robert W., 1957
V. prunus G *
    Fulton, Robert W., 1957
V. red clover mosaic *
    Elliott, J.A., 1921
    Zaumeyer, W.J. and B.L. Wade, 1935
V. red clover vein mosaic
    Graves, Clinton H., Jr. and D.J. Hagedorn, 1956
    Hagedorn, D.J. and J.C. Walker, 1949
V. soybean mosaic
    Pierce, W.H., 1935
V. squash mosaic
    Freitag, J.H., 1956
V. tobacco etch
    Holmes, Francis O., 1946
V. tobacco mosaic
    Holmes, Francis O., 1938, 1946
V. tobacco ring spot
    Fenne, S.B., 1931
    Grogan, R.G. and W.C. Schnathorst, 1955
    Stubbs, M.W., 1937
V. tobacco streak
    Thomas, H. Rex and W.J. Zaumeyer, 1950
V. Wisconsin pea streak
    Hagedorn, D.J. and J.C. Walker, 1949, 1954
T. repens var. latum, McCarthy *
V. squash mosaic
    Freitag, J.H., 1956
T. spp.
V. lucerne witches' broom
    Menzies, J.D., 1944
T. subterraneum, L.
V. bean yellow mosaic
    Baggett, James R., 1957
V. (cucumber) O.S.C. isolate 606 *
    Porter, Clark A. and Frank P. McWhorter, 1951
V. pea enation mosaic
    Chaudhuri, R.P., 1950

TRILLIUM L. 1753 (Liliaceae)
T. spp.
V. cucumber mosaic
    Brierley, Philip and Floyd F. Smith, 1944
V. lily symptomless
    Brierley, Philip and Floyd F. Smith, 1944
V. tulip breaking
    Brierley, Philip and Floyd F. Smith, 1944

TRIPHASIA Lour. 1790 (Rutaceae)
T. trifolia, P. Wilson
V. citrus tristeza
    Knorr, L.C., 1956

TRIPLOCHITON K. Schum. * (Sterculiaceae)
T. scleroxylon, K. Schum. *
V. cacao swollen shoot
    Posnette, A.F., N.F. Robertson and J. McA. Todd, 1950
    Tinsley, T.W. and A.L. Wharton, 1958

TRIPSACUM L. 1759 (Gramineae)
T. dactyloides, L.
V. sugarcane mosaic
    Brandes, E.W. and Peter J. Klaphaak, 1923

TRITICUM L. 1735 (Gramineae)
T. aestivum, L.
  V. cucumber mosaic
    McWhorter, F.P. and H.H. Millsap, 1954
  V. muskmelon mosaic
    Rader, Wm. E., Hugh F. Fitzpatrick and E.M.
    Hildebrand, 1947
  V. nothoscordum mosaic
    McKinney, H.H., 1950
  V. panicum mosaic *
    Sill, W.H., Jr. and R.C. Pickett, 1957
  V. sugarcane mosaic
    Brandes, E.W. and Peter J. Klaphaak, 1923
  V. tobacco etch
    Holmes, Francis O., 1946
  V. tobacco mosaic
    Holmes, Francis O., 1946
T. vulgare, Vill.
  V. maize leaf fleck
    Stoner, Warren N., 1952
  V. rice and corn leaf-gall *
    Agati, Julian A. and Carlos A. Calica, 1950
  V. tobacco ring spot
    Wingard, S.A., 1928

TRITONIA Ker-Gawl. 1802 (Iridaceae)
T. crocata, Ker-Gawl.
  V. cucumber mosaic
    Brierley, Philip and Floyd F. Smith, 1944
  V. lily symptomless
    Brierley, Philip and Floyd F. Smith, 1944
  V. ornithogalum mosaic
    Smith, Floyd F. and Philip Brierley, 1944
  V. tulip breaking
    Brierley, Philip and Floyd F. Smith, 1944

TRIUMFETTA Plum. ex L. 1737 (Tiliaceae)
T. lappula, L.
  V. abutilon infectious variegation
    Bird, Julio, 1958
T. semitriloba, Jacq.
  V. abutilon infectious variegation
    Bird, Julio, 1958

TROPAEOLUM L. 1737 (Tropaeolaceae)
T. majus, L.
  V. anemone brown ring *
    Hollings, M., 1958
  V. anemone mosaic *
    Hollings, M., 1957
  V. bean yellow stipple
    Zaumeyer, W.J. and H. Rex Thomas, 1950
  V. beet curly top
    Carsner, E., 1919
  V. cabbage black ring spot
    Tompkins, C.M., M.W. Gardner and H. Rex
    Thomas, 1938
  V. cabbage ring necrosis
    Larson, R.H. and J.C. Walker, 1941
  V. (cattleya) mosaic
    Jensen, D.D., 1949
  V. cauliflower mosaic
    Tompkins, C.M., 1937
  V. chrysanthemum B (mild mosaic) *
    Hollings, M., 1957
  V. cowpea mosaic
    Capoor, S.P. and P.M. Varma, 1956
  V. euphorbia mosaic
    Costa, A.S. and C.W. Bennett, 1950
  V. muskmelon mosaic
    Rader, Wm. E., Hugh F. Fitzpatrick and E.M.
    Hildebrand, 1947
  V. orchid (cymbidium) mosaic
    Jensen, D.D., 1951
  V. orchid (odontoglossum) ring spot
    Jensen, D.D. and A. Herbert Gold, 1951
  V. orchid (vanda) mosaic
    Murakishi, Harry H., 1952
  V. panax ring spot
    Aragaki, M., H. Murakishi and J.W. Hendrix, 1953
  V. pea mosaic
    Murphy, D.M. and W.H. Pierce, 1937
  V. primula mosaic
    Tompkins, C.M. and John T. Middleton, 1941

T. majus, L. (cont.)
  V. radish mosaic
    Tompkins, C.M., 1939
  V. red currant ring spot
    Klesser, P.J., 1951
  V. squash mosaic
    Freitag, J.H., 1956
  V. tobacco etch
    Holmes, Francis O., 1946
  V. tobacco necrosis
    Fulton, Robert W., 1950
  V. tobacco ring spot
    Wingard, S.A., 1928
  V. tobacco streak
    Thomas, H. Rex and W.J. Zaumeyer, 1950
  V. tomato aspermy
    Brierley, Philip, Floyd F. Smith and S.P.
    Doolittle, 1955
    Hollings, M., 1955
  V. tomato ring spot
    Samson, R.W. and E.P. Imle, 1942
  V. tulip breaking
    McWhorter, F.P., 1935
  V. turnip mosaic
    Tompkins, C.M., 1938, 1939
    Tompkins, C.M. and H. Rex Thomas, 1938
T. majus var. nanum, Hort.
  V. chrysanthemum stunt
    Keller, John R., 1953
T. peregrinum, L.
  V. beet yellows
    Roland, G. and J. Tahon, 1961

TULIPA L. 1735 (Liliaceae)
T. gesneriana, L.
  V. cucumber mosaic
    Wellman, F.L., 1935
  V. iris mosaic
    Brierley, Philip and Frank P. McWhorter, 1936
  V. narcissus mosaic
    Haasis, Frank A., 1939
  V. onion yellow dwarf
    Henderson, W.J., 1935
  V. ornithogalum mosaic
    Smith, Floyd F. and Philip Brierley, 1944
T. silvestris, L.
  V. beet yellows
    Roland, G. and J. Tahon, 1961
T. spp.
  V. wheat streak mosaic
    Sill, W.H., Jr. and Patrick C. Agusiobo, 1955

TUSSILAGO ((Tourn.)) L. 1735 (Compositae)
T. farfara, L.
  V. beet yellows
    Roland, G. and J. Tahon, 1961

TYPHA L. 1735 (Typhaceae)
T. angustifolia, L.
  V. cucumber mosaic
    Wellman, F.L., 1935
T. latifolia, L.
  V. wheat streak mosaic
    Sill, W.H., Jr. and Patrick C. Agusiobo, 1955

URENA Dill. ex L. 1935 (Malvaceae)
U. lobata, L.
  V. cacao swollen shoot
    Tinsley, T.W. and A.L. Wharton, 1958

URTICA ((Tourn.)) L. 1735 (Urticaceae)
U. californica, Greene
  V. beet yellows
    Roland, G. and J. Tahon, 1961
U. dioica, L.
  V. beet yellows
    Roland, G. and J. Tahon, 1961
U. urens, L.
  V. beet yellows
    Roland, G. and J. Tahon, 1961

UVULARIA L. 1737 (Liliaceae)
U. sessilifolia, L.
	V. cucumber mosaic
		Brierley, Philip and Floyd F. Smith, 1944
	V. lily symptomless
		Brierley, Philip and Floyd F. Smith, 1944
	V. tulip breaking
		Brierley, Philip and Floyd F. Smith, 1944

VACCINIUM L. 1735 (Ericaceae)
V. corymbosum, L.
	V. bayberry yellows
		Raychaudhuri, S.P., 1953
V. macrocarpon, Ait. (Oxycoccus macrocarpon, (Ait.)
	V. bayberry yellows					Pers.)
		Raychaudhuri, S.P., 1953

VALERIANA Tourn. ex L. 1735 (Valerianaceae)
V. officinalis, L.
	V. cabbage black ring spot
		Tompkins, C.M., M.W. Gardner and H. Rex
		Thomas, 1938

VALERIANELLA Tourn. ex Hall. 1742 (Valerianaceae)
V. olitoria, (L.) Poll.
	V. pea mosaic
		Murphy, D.M. and W.H. Pierce, 1937

VALERIANOIDES Medic. 1789 (Verbenaceae)
V. jamaicensis, Medic.
	V. cucumber mosaic
		Adsuar, Jose and A. Cruz Miret, 1950
	V. papaw mosaic
		Adsuar, Jose, 1950

VALLOTA Herb. 1821 (Amaryllidaceae)
V. purpurea, Herb.
	V. cucumber mosaic
		Brierley, Philip and Floyd F. Smith, 1944
	V. lily symptomless
		Brierley, Philip and Floyd F. Smith, 1944
	V. tulip breaking
		Brierley, Philip and Floyd F. Smith, 1944

VERBASCUM Tourn. ex L. 1737 (Scrophulariaceae)
V. blattaria, L.
	V. muskmelon mosaic
		Rader, Wm. E., Hugh F. Fitzpatrick and E.M.
		Hildebrand, 1947
V. phoeniceum, L.
	V. tobacco etch
		Holmes, Francis O., 1946
V. thapsus, L.
	V. dodder latent mosaic
		Bennett, C.W., 1944
	V. muskmelon mosaic
		Rader, Wm. E., Hugh F. Fitzpatrick and E.M.
		Hildebrand, 1947
	V. pea mosaic
		Murphy, D.M. and W.H. Pierce, 1937
	V. prunus A *
		Fulton, Robert W., 1957
	V. prunus E *
		Fulton, Robert W., 1957
	V. stone fruit *
		Boyle, J.S., J. Duain Moore and G.W. Keitt, 1954
	V. tomato ring spot
		Samson, R.W. and E.P. Imle, 1942

VERBENA L. 1737 (Verbenaceae)
V. canadensis, (L.) Britton
	V. tobacco etch
		Holmes, Francis O., 1946
V. hybrida, Voss
	V. anemone brown ring *
		Hollings, M., 1958
	V. cauliflower mosaic
		Walker, J.C., Francis J. LeBeau and Glenn S.
		Pound, 1945
	V. chrysanthemum B (mild mosaic) *
		Hollings, M., 1957
	V. cucumber mosaic
		Wellman, F.L., 1935

V. hybrida, Voss (cont.)
	V. primula mosaic
		Tompkins, C.M. and John T. Middleton, 1941
	V. radish mosaic
		Tompkins, C.M., 1939
	V. turnip mosaic
		Tompkins, C.M., 1939
		Tompkins, C.M. and H. Rex Thomas, 1938
V. prostrata, R. Br.
	V. beet curly top
		Carsner, E., 1919
V. urticifolia, L.
	V. tobacco mosaic
		Holmes, Francis O., 1938
V. venosa, Gill. & Hook.
	V. tobacco etch
		Holmes, Francis O., 1946
	V. tobacco mosaic
		Holmes, Francis O., 1946

VERBESINA L. 1735 (Compositae)
V. encelioides, (Cav.) Benth. & Hook.
	V. beet yellow net
		McLean, D.M., 1952
	V. peony leaf curl *
		Brierley, Philip and Paul Lorentz, 1957

VERNONIA Schreb. 1791 (Compositae)
V. anthelmintica, Willd.
	V. hibiscus yellow vein mosaic
		Capoor, S.P. and P.M. Varma, 1950

VERONICA ((Tourn.)) L. 1735 (Scrophulariaceae)
V. agrestis, L.
	V. beet yellows
		Roland, G. and J. Tahon, 1961
V. arvensis, L.
	V. beet yellows
		Roland, G. and J. Tahon, 1961
V. hederaefolia, L.
	V. beet yellows
		Roland, G. and J. Tahon, 1961
V. longifolia, L.
	V. tobacco etch
		Holmes, Francis O., 1946
V. officinalis, L.
	V. tobacco etch
		Holmes, Francis O., 1946
	V. tobacco mosaic
		Holmes, Francis O., 1938
V. peregrina, L.
	V. beet yellows
		Roland, G. and J. Tahon, 1961
	V. tobacco etch
		Holmes, Francis O., 1946
	V. tobacco mosaic
		Holmes, Francis O., 1938

VICIA Tourn. ex L. 1735 (Leguminosae)
V. americana, Muhl.
	V. bean common mosaic
		Zaumeyer, W.J. and B.L. Wade, 1935
	V. bean yellow mosaic
		Zaumeyer, W.J. and B.L. Wade, 1935
V. angustifolia, L.
	V. red clover vein mosaic
		Graves, Clinton H., Jr. and D.J. Hagedorn, 1956
V. atropurpurea, Desf.
	V. bean yellow mosaic
		Grogan, Raymond G. and J.C. Walker, 1948
V. cylindrica, L. *
	V. bean southern mosaic
		Zaumeyer, W.J. and L.L. Harter, 1943
V. faba, L.
	V. anemone brown ring *
		Hollings, M., 1958
	V. bayberry yellows
		Raychaudhuri, S.P., 1953
	V. bean common mosaic
		Zaumeyer, W.J. and B.L. Wade, 1935
	V. bean pod mottle
		Zaumeyer, W.J. and H. Rex Thomas, 1948
	V. bean southern mosaic
		Zaumeyer, W.J. and L.L. Harter, 1943

Vicia faba, L. (cont.)
- V. bean yellow mosaic
  Grogan, Raymond G. and J.C. Walker, 1948
- V. bean yellow stipple
  Zaumeyer, W.J. and H. Rex Thomas, 1950
- V. beet mosaic
  Severin, Henry H.P. and Roger M. Drake, 1948
- V. beet yellows
  Roland, G. and J. Tahon, 1961
- V. cabbage black ring spot
  Tompkins, C.M., M.W. Gardner and H. Rex Thomas, 1938
- V. cabbage ring necrosis
  Larson, R.H. and J.C. Walker, 1941
- V. canna mosaic
  Brierley, Philip and Floyd F. Smith, 1948
  Castillo, B.S., C.E. Yarwood and A.H. Gold, 1956
- V. cauliflower mosaic
  Tompkins, C.M., 1937
- V. chilli (pepper) mosaic
  Jha, Ashrafi and S.P. Raychaudhuri, 1956
- V. cowpea mosaic
  Capoor, S.P. and P.M. Varma, 1956
  McLean, D.M., 1941
  Yu, T.F., 1946
- V. cucumber mosaic
  Adsuar, Jose and A. Cruz Miret, 1950
  Anderson, C.W., 1951
  Harter, L.L., 1936
  Whipple, O.C. and J.C. Walker, 1941
- V. (cucumber) O.S.C. isolate 606 *
  Porter, Clark A. and Frank P. McWhorter, 1951
- V. datura distortion mosaic
  Capoor, S.P. and P.M. Varma, 1952
- V. filaree red leaf
  Frazier, Norman W., 1951
- V. gladiolus *
  Snow, Gordon F., 1955
- V. pea enation mosaic
  Chaudhuri, R.P., 1950
  Johnson, Folke and Leon K. Jones, 1937
  Simons, John N., 1954
- V. pelargonium ring spot *
  Hollings, M., 1957
- V. primula mosaic
  Tompkins, C.M. and John T. Middleton, 1941
- V. potato Y
  Bald, J.G. and D.O. Norris, 1945
- V. radish mosaic
  Tompkins, C.M., 1939
- V. red clover vein mosaic
  Hagedorn, D.J. and J.C. Walker, 1949
- V. red currant ring spot
  Klesser, P.J., 1951
- V. soybean mosaic
  Conover, Robert A., 1948
- V. squash mosaic
  Freitag, J.H., 1956
- V. squash mosaic (southern)
  Anderson, C.W., 1951
- V. tobacco etch
  Holmes, Francis O., 1946
- V. tobacco mosaic
  Holmes, Francis O., 1946
- V. turnip crinkle
  Broadbent, L. and G.D. Heathcote, 1958
- V. turnip mosaic
  Tompkins, C.M., 1938, 1939
  Tompkins, C.M. and H. Rex Thomas, 1938
- V. turnip rosette *
  Boradbent, L. and G.D. Heathcote, 1958
- V. turnip yellow mosaic
  Broadbent, L. and G.D. Heathcote, 1958

V. faba var. minor *
- V. soybean mosaic
  Pierce, W.H., 1935
- V. Wisconsin pea streak
  Hagedorn, D.J. and J.C. Walker, 1949

V. faba var. major *
- V. Wisconsin pea streak
  Hagedorn, D.J. and J.C. Walker, 1949

V. sativa, L.
- V. alsike clover mosaic
  Zaumeyer, W.J., 1940

V. sativa, L. (cont.)
- V. bean southern mosaic
  Zaumeyer, W.J. and L.L. Harter, 1943
- V. bean yellow mosaic
  Grogan, Raymond G. and J.C. Walker, 1948
  Zaumeyer, W.J., 1940
- V. beet yellows
  Roland, G. and J. Tahon, 1961
- V. broad bean mottle
  Bawden, F.C., R.P. Chaudhuri and B. Kassanis, 1951
- V. cowpea mosaic
  Yu, T.F., 1946
- V. cucumber mosaic
  Harter, L.L., 1938
- V. pea enation mosaic
  Chaudhuri, R.P., 1950
  Johnson, Folke and Leon K. Jones, 1937
- V. tobacco etch
  Holmes, Francis O., 1946
- V. tobacco mosaic
  Holmes, Francis O., 1946
- V. Wisconsin pea streak
  Hagedorn, D.J. and J.C. Walker, 1949, 1954

V. variabilis, Freyn & Sint. ex Freyn
- V. lucerne witches' broom
  Klostermeyer, E.C. and J.D. Menzies, 1951

V. villosa, Roth
- V. bean southern mosaic
  Zaumeyer, W.J. and L.L. Harter, 1943
- V. bean yellow mosaic
  Baggett, James R., 1957
- V. cowpea mosaic
  Yu, T.F., 1946
- V. cucumber mosaic
  Harter, L.L., 1938
- V. filaree red leaf
  Frazier, Norman W., 1951
- V. pea enation mosaic
  Simons, John N., 1954
- V. pea mosaic
  Murphy, D.M. and W.H. Pierce, 1937
- V. pea streak
  Zaumeyer, W.J., 1938
- V. red clover vein mosaic
  Hagedorn, D.J. and J.C. Walker, 1949, 1954
- V. tobacco ring spot
  Cooper, W.E., 1949

VIGNA Savi 1826? (Leguminosae)
V. cylindrica, (L.) Skeels (V. catjang, Walp.)
- V. bean common mosaic
  Snyder, W.C., 1942
V. sesquipedalis, (L.) Fruwirth
- V. bean common mosaic
  Zaumeyer, W.J. and B.L. Wade, 1935
- V. bean pod mottle
  Zaumeyer, W.J. and H. Rex Thomas, 1948
- V. bean southern mosaic
  Zaumeyer, W.J. and L.L. Harter, 1943
- V. bean yellow mosaic
  Conover, Robert A., 1948
  Zaumeyer, W.J. and B.L. Wade, 1935
- V. lucerne mosaic
  Zaumeyer, W.J. and B.L. Wade, 1935
- V. pea streak
  Zaumeyer, W.J., 1938
- V. red clover mosaic *
  Zaumeyer, W.J. and B.L. Wade, 1935
- V. soybean mosaic
  Conover, Robert A., 1948
- V. squash mosaic
  Freitag, J.H., 1956
V. sinensis, (Torner) Savi
- V. anemone brown ring *
  Hollings, M., 1958
- V. anemone mosaic *
  Hollings, M., 1957
- V. bean common mosaic
  Reddick, D. and V.B. Stewart, 1919
  Zaumeyer, W.J. and B.L. Wade, 1935
- V. bean pod mottle
  Zaumeyer, W.J. and H. Rex Thomas, 1948

Vigna sinensis, (Torner) Savi (cont.)
   V. bean southern mosaic
      Zaumeyer, W.J. and L.L. Harter, 1943
   V. bean yellow mosaic
      Conover, Robert A., 1948
      Hagedorn, D.J. and J.C. Walker, 1950, 1954
      Zaumeyer, W.J., 1952
      Zaumeyer, W.J. and B.L. Wade, 1935
   V. beet mosaic
      Pound, Glenn S., 1947
   V. beet yellows
      Roland, G. and J. Tahon, 1961
   V. broad bean mottle
      Yu, T.F., 1939
   V. cacao swollen shoot
      Tinsley, T.W. and A.L. Wharton, 1958
   V. canna mosaic
      Castillo, B.S., C.E. Yarwood and A.H. Gold, 1956
   V. cauliflower mosaic
      Alvarez-Garcia, L.A., 1951
      Walker, J.C., Francis J. LeBeau and Glenn S. Pound, 1945
   V. chilli veinbanding
      Simons, John N., 1956
   V. chrysanthemum B (mild mosaic) *
      Hollings, M., 1957
   V. citrus tristeza
      Bennett, C.W. and A.S. Costa, 1949
   V. cucumber green mottle mosaic
      Vasudeva, R.S., S.P. Raychaudhuri and Jagannath Singh, 1949
   V. cucumber mosaic
      Anderson, C.W., 1951
      Govier, D.A., 1957
      Lindberg, G.D., D.H. Hall and J.C. Walker, 1956
      Simons, John N., 1957
      Wellman, F.L., 1934, 1935
   V. datura distortion mosaic
      Capoor, S.P. and P.M. Varma, 1952
   V. filaree red leaf
      Frazier, Norman W., 1951
   V. hibiscus yellow vein mosaic
      Capoor, S.P. and P.M. Varma, 1950
   V. lucerne mosaic
      Zaumeyer, W.J. and B.L. Wade, 1935
   V. muskmelon mosaic
      Lindberg, G.D., D.H. Hall and J.C. Walker, 1956
      Rader, Wm. E., Hugh F. Fitzpatrick and E.M. Hildebrand, 1947
   V. nicotiana glutinosa root necrosis *
      Cetas, Robert C. and A. Frank Ross, 1952
   V. orchid (odontoglossum) ring spot
      Jensen, D.D. and A. Herbert Gold, 1951
   V. orchid (vanda) mosaic
      Murakishi, Harry H., 1952
   V. pea enation mosaic
      Hagedorn, D.J. and J.C. Walker, 1954
      Stubbs, M.W., 1937
   V. pea mosaic
      Hagedorn, D.J. and J.C. Walker, 1954
      Murphy, D.M. and W.H. Pierce, 1937
      Stubbs, M.W., 1937
   V. pea mottle
      Johnson, Folke, 1942
   V. pea streak
      Zaumeyer, W.J., 1938
   V. pelargonium ring spot *
      Hollings, M., 1957
   V. potato A
      MacLachlan, D.S., R.H. Larson and J.C. Walker, 1953
   V. potato Y
      Alvarez-Garcia, L.A. and Jose Adsuar, 1943
      Bald, J.G. and D.O. Norris, 1945
   V. potato yellow dwarf
      Hougas, R.W., 1951
   V. primula mosaic
      Tompkins, C.M. and John T. Middleton, 1941
   V. red clover mosaic *
      Zaumeyer, W.J. and B.L. Wade, 1935
   V. red clover vein mosaic
      Hagedorn, D.J. and E.W. Hanson, 1951
      Hagedorn, D.J. and J.C. Walker, 1949, 1954
      Roberts, D.A., 1957

V. sinensis, (Torner) Savi (cont.)
   V. soybean mosaic
      Conover, Robert A., 1948
      Kendrick, James B. and Max W. Gardner, 1924
   V. squash mosaic
      Freitag, J.H., 1956
      Lindberg, G.D., D.H. Hall and J.C. Walker, 1956
   V. squash mosaic (southern)
      Anderson, C.W., 1951
   V. stone fruit *
      Boyle, J.S., J. Duain Moore and G.W. Keitt, 1954
   V. sweet potato feathery mottle
      Webb, Raymon E., 1954
   V. tobacco etch
      Anderson, C.W., 1954
      Holmes, Francis O., 1946
   V. tobacco mosaic
      Holmes, Francis O., 1946
      Smith, Kenneth M., 1935
   V. tobacco ring spot
      Stubbs, M.W., 1937
   V. turnip mosaic
      Walker, J.C., Francis J. LeBeau and Glenn S. Pound, 1945
   V. watermelon mosaic
      Lindberg, G.D., D.H. Hall and J.C. Walker, 1956
   V. Wisconsin pea streak
      Hagedorn, D.J. and J.C. Walker, 1949, 1954
V. unguiculata, Walp.
   V. chilli (pepper) mosaic
      Dale, W.T., 1954
      Ferguson, I.A.C., 1951
   V. cucumber mosaic
      Adsuar, Jose and A. Cruz Miret, 1950
      Vasudeva, R. Sahai and T.B. Lal, 1943
   V. papaw mosaic
      Adsuar, Jose, 1950
   V. turnip mosaic
      Dale, W.T., 1948
V. vexillata, A. Rich.
   V. bean yellow stipple
      Zaumeyer, W.J. and H. Rex Thomas, 1950

VINCA L. 1735 (Apocynaceae)
V. minor, L.
   V. cauliflower mosaic
      Walker, J.C., Francis J. LeBeau and Glenn S. Pound, 1945
V. rosea, L.
   V. bean pod mottle
      Zaumeyer, W.J. and H. Rex Thomas, 1948
   V. beet curly top
      Bennett, C.W. and A.S. Costa, 1949
   V. beet yellows
      Roland, G. and J. Tahon, 1961
   V. chilli (pepper) mosaic
      Jha, Ashrafi and S.P. Raychaudhuri, 1956
   V. euphorbia mosaic
      Costa, A.S. and C.W. Bennett, 1950
   V. muskmelon mosaic
      Rader, Wm. E., Hugh F. Fitzpatrick and E.M. Hildebrand, 1947
   V. panicum mosaic *
      Sill, W.H., Jr. and R.C. Pickett, 1957
   V. prunus E *
      Fulton, Robert W., 1957
   V. squash mosaic
      Freitag, J.H., 1956
   V. tobacco etch
      Holmes, Francis O., 1946
   V. tobacco mosaic
      Holmes, Francis O., 1946
   V. tomato aspermy
      Brierley, Philip, Floyd F. Smith and S.P. Doolittle, 1955
   V. tomato ring spot
      Samson, R.W. and E.P. Imle, 1942

VIOLA Tourn. ex L. 1735 (Violaceae)
V. arvensis, Murr.
   V. beet yellows
      Roland, G. and J. Tahon, 1961
   V. tobacco etch
      Holmes, Francis O., 1946

Viola arvensis, Murr. (cont.)
V. tobacco mosaic
Holmes, Francis O., 1946
V. cornuta, L.
V. turnip mosaic
Tompkins, C.M., 1939
V. floridana, Brainerd
V. cucumber mosaic
Wellman, F.L., 1935
V. odorata, L.
V. cucumber mosaic
Wellman, F.L., 1935
V. datura distortion mosaic
Capoor, S.P. and P.M. Varma, 1952
V. papilionacea, Pursh
V. tobacco mosaic
Holmes, Francis O., 1938
V. primulifolia, L.
V. cucumber mosaic
Wellman, F.L., 1935
V. sagittata, Ait.
V. tobacco mosaic
Holmes, Francis O., 1938
V. spp.
V. orchid (cymbidium) mosaic
Jensen, D.D., 1951
V. tricolor, L.
V. beet yellows
Roland, G. and J. Tahon, 1961
V. cabbage black ring spot
Tompkins, C.M., M.W. Gardner and H. Rex
Thomas, 1938
V. cabbage ring necrosis
Larson, R.H. and J.C. Walker, 1941
V. cucumber mosaic
Burnett, G., 1934
Govier, D.A., 1957
Wellman, F.L., 1935
V. euphorbia mosaic
Costa, A.S. and C.W. Bennett, 1950
V. primula mosaic
Tompkins, C.M. and John T. Middleton, 1941
V. radish mosaic
Tompkins, C.M., 1939
V. tomato aspermy
Brierley, Philip, Floyd F. Smith and S.P.
Doolittle, 1955
V. tomato ring spot
Samson, R.W. and E.P. Imle, 1942
V. turnip mosaic
Tompkins, C.M., 1938
Tompkins, C.M. and H. Rex Thomas, 1938
V. tricolor var. hortensis, (Murr.) DC.
V. pea mosaic
Murphy, D.M. and W.H. Pierce, 1937
V. turnip crinkle
Broadbent, L. and G.D. Heathcote, 1958
V. turnip yellow mosaic
Broadbent, L. and G.D. Heathcote, 1958

VITIS ((Tourn.)) L. 1735 (Vitaceae)
V. californica, Benth.
V. filaree red leaf
Frazier, Norman W., 1951
V. spp.
V. beet yellows
Roland, G. and J. Tahon, 1961

WALTHERIA L. 1737 (Bombacaceae)
W. indica, L.
V. cacao swollen shoot
Tinsley, T.W. and A.L. Wharton, 1958
W. lanceolata, R. Br. ex Mast.
V. cacao swollen shoot
Tinsley, T.W. and A.L. Wharton, 1958

XANTHIUM ((Tourn.)) L. 1735 (Compositae)
X. americanum, Walt.
V. tobacco ring spot
Henderson, R.G. and S.A. Wingard, 1931
X. echinatum, Murr.
V. stone fruit *
Boyle, J.S., J. Duain Moore and G.W. Keitt, 1954

XANTHOSOMA Schott 1832 (Araceae)
X. sagittaefolium, (L.) Schott
V. cacao swollen shoot
Posnette, A.F., N.F. Robertson and J. McA.
Todd, 1950
X. spp.
V. cucumber mosaic
Wellman, F.L., 1935

XANTHOXALIS Small 1903 (Oxalidaceae)
X. corniculata, Small
V. cucumber mosaic
Wellman, F.L., 1935

XERANTHEMUM Tourn. ex L. 1735 (Compositae)
X. annuum, L.
V. chrysanthemum stunt
Brierley, Philip, 1953

YUCCA Dill. ex L. 1737 (Liliaceae)
Y. baccata, Torr.
V. cucumber mosaic
Brierley, Philip and Floyd F. Smith, 1944
V. lily symptomless
Brierley, Philip and Floyd F. Smith, 1944
V. tulip breaking
Brierley, Philip and Floyd F. Smith, 1944
Y. flaccida, Haw.
V. cucumber mosaic
Brierley, Philip and Floyd F. Smith, 1944
V. lily symptomless
Brierley, Philip and Floyd F. Smith, 1944
V. tulip breaking
Brierley, Philip and Floyd F. Smith, 1944
Y. glauca, Nutt.
V. wheat streak mosaic
Sill, W.H., Jr. and Patrick C. Agusiobo, 1955
Y. gloriosa, L.
V. cucumber mosaic
Wellman, F.L., 1935

ZANTEDESCHIA Spreng. 1826 (Araceae)
Z. aethiopica, Spreng.
V. maize leaf fleck
Stoner, Warren N., 1952
V. tulip breaking
Brierley, Philip and Floyd F. Smith, 1944

ZEA L. 1737 (Gramineae)
Z. indentata, Sturtev.
V. onion yellow dwarf
Henderson, W.J., 1935
Z. mays, L.
V. agropyron mosaic
Slykhuis, J.T., 1952
V. barley yellow dwarf
Oswald, John W. and Byron R. Houston, 1953
V. beet yellows
Roland, G. and J. Tahon, 1961
V. cabbage black ring spot
Tompkins, C.M., M.W. Gardner and H. Rex
Thomas, 1938
V. cucumber mosaic
Adsuar, Jose and A. Cruz Miret, 1950
Harter, L.L., 1938
V. muskmelon mosaic
Rader, Wm. E., Hugh F. Fitzpatrick and E.M.
Hildebrand, 1947
V. nothoscordum mosaic
McKinney, H.H., 1950
V. orchid (cymbidium) mosaic
Jensen, D.D., 1951
V. orchid (odontoglossum) ring spot
Jensen, D.D. and A. Herbert Gold, 1951
V. orchid (vanda) mosaic
Murakishi, Harry H., 1952
V. panicum mosaic *
Sill, W.H., Jr. and R.C. Pickett, 1957
V. papaw mosaic
Adsuar, Jose, 1950
V. pea mottle
Johnson, Folke, 1942
V. pea wilt
Johnson, Folke, 1942

Zea mays, L. (cont.)
    V. primula mosaic
        Tompkins, C.M. and John T. Middleton, 1941
    V. radish mosaic
        Tompkins, C.M., 1939
    V. soil-borne oat mosaic
        McKinney, H.H., 1946
    V. squash mosaic
        Freitag, J.H., 1956
    V. tobacco etch
        Holmes, Francis O., 1946
    V. tobacco mosaic
        Holmes, Francis O., 1946
    V. tobacco ring spot
        Cheo, Pen Ching and W.J. Zaumeyer, 1952
    V. tomato aspermy
        Brierley, Philip, Floyd F. Smith and S.P.
        Doolittle, 1955
    V. tulip breaking
        Brierley, Philip and Floyd F. Smith, 1944
    V. turnip mosaic
        Tompkins, C.M., 1938, 1939
        Tompkins, C.M. and H. Rex Thomas, 1938
    V. wheat streak mosaic
        Sill, W.H., Jr. and Patrick C. Agusiobo, 1955
        Slykhuis, J.T., 1952

ZEBRINA Schnizl. 1849 (Commelinaceae)
Z. pendula, Schnizl.
    V. muskmelon mosaic
        Rader, Wm. E., Hugh F. Fitzpatrick and E.M.
        Hildebrand, 1947
    V. tobacco ring spot
        Wingard, S.A., 1928
    V. wheat streak mosaic
        Sill, W.H., Jr. and Patrick C. Agusiobo, 1955

ZEPHYRANTHES Herb. 1821 (Amaryllidaceae)
Z. candida, Herb.
    V. narcissus mosaic
        Haasis, Frank A., 1939
Z. spp.
    V. ornithogalum mosaic
        Smith, Floyd F. and Philip Brierley, 1944
    V. tulip breaking
        Brierley, Philip and Floyd F. Smith, 1944

ZINNIA L. 1759 (Compositae)
Z. elegans, Jacq.
    V. abutilon infectious variegation
        Bird, Julio, 1958
    V. anemone brown ring *
        Hollings, M., 1958
    V. bean yellow mosaic
        Thomas, H. Rex and W.J. Zaumeyer, 1953
    V. beet curly top
        Costa, A.S., 1952
    V. beet mosaic
        Bennett, C.W., 1949
    V. beet yellow net
        McLean, D.M., 1952
    V. beet yellows
        Roland, G. and J. Tahon, 1961
    V. cauliflower mosaic
        Alvarez-Garcia, L.A., 1951
        Berkeley, G.H. and J.H. Tremaine, 1954
    V. celery mosaic
        Freitag, Julius H. and Henry H.P. Severin, 1945
    V. chilli (pepper) mosaic
        Dale, W.T., 1954
        Jha, Ashrafi and S.P. Raychaudhuri, 1956
    V. chrysanthemum B (mild mosaic) *
        Hollings, M., 1957
    V. chrysanthemum ring spot
        Brierley, Philip and Floyd F. Smith, 1955
    V. cowpea mosaic
        Capoor, S.P. and P.M. Varma, 1956
        McLean, D.M., 1941
        Yu, T.F., 1946
    V. cucumber mosaic
        Lindberg, G.D., D.H. Hall and J.C. Walker, 1956
    V. (cucumber) O.S.C. isolate 606 *
        Porter, Clark A. and Frank P. McWhorter, 1951

Z. elegans, Jacq. (cont.)
    V. datura distortion mosaic
        Capoor, S.P. and P.M. Varma, 1952
    V. eggplant mosaic
        Dale, W.T., 1954
    V. euphorbia mosaic
        Costa, A.S. and C.W. Bennett, 1950
    V. gladiolus *
        Snow, Gordon F., 1955
    V. hibiscus yellow vein mosaic
        Capoor, S.P. and P.M. Varma, 1950
    V. hydrangea ring spot
        Brierley, Philip and Paul Lorentz, 1957
    V. lucerne mosaic
        Johnson, E.M., 1946
        Zaumeyer, W.J., 1938
    V. muskmelon mosaic
        Anderson, C.W., 1954
        Lindberg, G.D., D.H. Hall and J.C. Walker, 1956
        Rader, Wm. E., Hugh F. Fitzpatrick and E.M.
        Hildebrand, 1947
    V. nicotiana glutinosa root necrosis *
        Cetas, Robert C. and A. Frank Ross, 1952
    V. orchid (vanda) mosaic
        Murakishi, Harry H., 1952
    V. pea mottle
        Johnson, Folke, 1942
    V. pea streak
        Zaumeyer, W.J., 1938
    V. pea wilt
        Johnson, Folke, 1942
    V. pelargonium ring spot *
        Hollings, M., 1957
    V. potato Y
        Bald, J.G. and D.O. Norris, 1945
    V. prunus A *
        Fulton, Robert W., 1957
    V. prunus E *
        Fulton, Robert W., 1957
    V. squash mosaic
        Freitag, J.H., 1956
        Lindberg, G.D., D.H. Hall and J.C. Walker, 1956
    V. squash mosaic (southern)
        Anderson, C.W., 1951
    V. stone fruit *
        Boyle, J.S., J. Duain Moore and G.W. Keitt, 1954
    V. tobacco mosaic
        Das, C.R. and S.P. Raychaudhuri, 1953
    V. tobacco ring spot
        Cooper, W.E., 1949
    V. tobacco streak
        Thomas, H. Rex and W.J. Zaumeyer, 1950
    V. tomato ring spot
        Samson, R.W. and E.P. Imle, 1942
    V. watermelon mosaic
        Anderson, C.W., 1954
        Lindberg, G.D., D.H Hall and J.C. Walker, 1956
Z. haageana, Regel
    V. tobacco etch
        Holmes, Francis O., 1946
Z. linearis, Benth.
    V. potato A
        MacLachlan, D.S., R.H. Larson and J.C. Walker,
        1953
Z. multiflora, L.
    V. bayberry yellows
        Raychaudhuri, S.P., 1953
Z. spp.
    V. citrus tristeza
        Knorr, L.C., 1956
    V. orchid (odontoglossum) ring spot
        Jensen, D.D. and A. Herbert Gold, 1951

ZYGOCACTUS K. Schum. * (Cactaceae)
Z. truncatus, Schum.
    V. beet yellows
        Roland, G. and J. Tahon, 1961

VIRUS

V. ABACA BUNCHY TOP Ocfemia 1930
Musa paradisiaca var. cinerea
Ocfemia, Gerardo Offimaria, 1930
Musa paradisiaca var. lacatan
Ocfemia, Gerardo Offimaria, 1930
Musa paradisiaca var. suaveolens
Ocfemia, Gerardo Offimaria, 1930
Musa textilis
Calinisan, Melanio R., 1931
Calinisan, Melanio R. and Crispiniano C.
Hernandez, 1936
Ocfemia, G.O., 1926, 1930
Ocfemia, G.O. and Gabino G. Buhay, 1934
Ocfemia, G.O., Martin S. Celino and Feliciano J.
Garcia, 1947
Musa textilis x M. balbisiana
Bernardo, Fernando A. and Dioscoro L. Umali,
1956

V. ABUTILON INFECTIOUS VARIEGATION ((Morren
1869)) Brierley 1944
Abutilon mulleri friderici
Keur, John Y., 1933
Abutilon regnellii
Keur, John Y., 1933
Abutilon striatum, clone thompsonii
Keur, John Y., 1933, 1934
Althaea rosea
Bird, Julio, 1958
Gossypium spp.
Crandall, Bowen S., 1954
Hibiscus cannabinus
Crandall, Bowen S., 1954
Malvastrum coromandelianum
Crandall, Bowen S., 1954
Mucuna pruriens
Crandall, Bowen S., 1954
Mucuna spp.
Crandall, Bowen S., 1954
Nicandra physalodes
Silberschmidt, K. and L.R. Tommasi, 1956
Nicotiana tabacum
Bird, Julio, 1958
Phenax sonneratii
Silberschmidt, Karl M., 1948
Sida carpinifolia
Bird, Julio, 1958
Sida rhombifolia
Bird, Julio, 1958
Costa, A.S. and C.W. Bennett, 1950
Kunkel, L.O., 1930
Silberschmidt, K. and L.R. Tommasi, 1956
Solanum tuberosum
(K.M. Smith, 1957) R.E. Fitzpatrick, et al., 1958

V. AGROPYRON MOSAIC McKinney 1944
Agropyron elongatum
Slykhuis, J.T., 1952
Agropyron inerme
Slykhuis, J.T., 1952
Agropyron intermedium
Slykhuis, J.T., 1952
Agropyron junceum
Slykhuis, J.T., 1952
Agropyron pertenue
Slykhuis, J.T., 1952
Agropyron repens
Slykhuis, J.T., 1952
Agropyron rigidum
Slykhuis, J.T., 1952
Festuca rubra
Slykhuis, J.T., 1952
Secale cereale
Slykhuis, J.T., 1952
Triticum durum
Slykhuis, J.T., 1952
Triticum vulgare
Slykhuis, J.T., 1952

V. ALMOND BUD FAILURE Wilson and Stout 1951
Prunus amygdalus
(K.M. Smith, 1957) R.E. Fitzpatrick, et al., 1958

VIRUS

V. ALMOND CALICO Thomas and Rawlins 1939
Prunus amygdalus
(K.M. Smith, 1957) R.E. Fitzpatrick, et al., 1958
Prunus avium
Thomas, H. Earl and T.E. Rawlins, 1939
Prunus communis
Thomas, H. Earl and T.E. Rawlins, 1939
Prunus persica
Thomas, H. Earl and T.E. Rawlins, 1939

V. ALSIKE CLOVER MOSAIC Zaumeyer and Wade 1935
Crotalaria spectabilis
Zaumeyer, W.J., 1940
Crotalaria striata
Zaumeyer, W.J., 1940
Lupinus albus
Zaumeyer, W.J., 1940
Lupinus angustifolius
Zaumeyer, W.J., 1940
Medicago sativa
(K.M. Smith, 1957) R.E. Fitzpatrick, et al., 1958
Zaumeyer, W.J., 1940
Melilotus alba
Zaumeyer, W.J., 1940
Phaseolus vulgaris
Harrison, Arthur L., 1935
Zaumeyer, W.J., 1933, 1940
Zaumeyer, W.J. and B.L. Wade, 1935, 1936
Pisum sativum
Wade, B.L. and W.J. Zaumeyer, 1938
Zaumeyer, W.J., 1940
Zaumeyer, W.J. and B.L. Wade, 1936
Trifolium hybridum
Wade, B.L. and W.J. Zaumeyer, 1938
Zaumeyer, W.J. and B.L. Wade, 1935
Trifolium incarnatum
Zaumeyer, W.J., 1940
Trifolium pratense
Hanson, E.W. and D.J. Hagedorn, 1952
Vicia faba
Wade, B.L. and W.J. Zaumeyer, 1938
Zaumeyer, W.J., 1940
Zaumeyer, W.J. and B.L. Wade, 1936

V. ANEMONE BROWN RING *
Amaranthus caudatus
Hollings, M., 1958
Anemone coronaria
Hollings, M., 1958
Aquilegia caerulea
Hollings, M., 1958
Chenopodium amaranticolor
Hollings, M., 1957, 1958
Gomphrena globosa
Hollings, M., 1958
Lathyrus odoratus
Hollings, M., 1958
Lycopersicon esculentum
Hollings, M., 1958
Portulaca oleracea
Hollings, M., 1958
Tetragonia expansa
Hollings, M., 1958

V. ANEMONE LATENT *
Chenopodium amaranticolor
(K.M. Smith, 1957) R.E. Fitzpatrick, et al., 1958
Delphinium spp.
(K.M. Smith, 1957) R.E. Fitzpatrick, et al., 1958
Nicotiana tabacum
(K.M. Smith, 1957) R.E. Fitzpatrick, et al., 1958

V. ANEMONE MOSAIC *
Ageratum conyzioides
Hollings, M., 1957
Alonsoa warscewiczii
Hollings, M., 1957
Amaranthus caudatus
Hollings, M., 1957
Anemone coronaria
Hollings, M., 1957
Anemone nemorosa
Hollings, M., 1957

VIRUS
V. ANEMONE MOSAIC * (cont.)
Aquilegia caerulea
Hollings, M., 1957
Brassica hirta (Brassica alba)
Hollings, M., 1957
Brassica napus
Hollings, M., 1957
Brassica oleracea var. capitata
Hollings, M., 1957
Brassica pekinensis
Hollings, M., 1957
Brassica rapa
Hollings, M., 1957
Capsella bursa-pastoris
Hollings, M., 1957
Cerastium vulgatum
Hollings, M., 1957
Chenopodium album
Hollings, M., 1957
Chenopodium amaranticolor
Hollings, M., 1956, 1957
Chrysanthemum carinatum
Hollings, M., 1957
Convolvulus tricolor
Hollings, M., 1957
Delphinium grandiflorum
Hollings, M., 1957
Fumaria officinalis
Hollings, M., 1957
Galium aparine
Hollings, M., 1957
Geum chiloense
Hollings, M., 1957
Gomphrena globosa
Hollings, M., 1957
Lactuca muralis
Hollings, M., 1957
Lavatera trimestris
Hollings, M., 1957
Malcomia maritima
Hollings, M., 1957
Matthiola incana var. annua
Hollings, M., 1957
Mimulus luteus
Hollings, M., 1957
Nicotiana glutinosa
Hollings, M., 1957
Nicotiana rustica
Hollings, M., 1957
Nicotiana tabacum
Hollings, M., 1957
Papaver rhoeas
Hollings, M., 1957
Papaver somniferum
Hollings, M., 1957
Passiflora caerulea
Hollings, M., 1957
Petunia hybrida
Hollings, M., 1957
Physalis peruviana
Hollings, M., 1957
Primula sinensis
Hollings, M., 1957
Ranunculus spp.
Hollings, M., 1957
Saintpaulia ionantha
Hollings, M., 1957
Salpiglossis sinuata
Hollings, M., 1957
Schizanthus pinnatus
Hollings, M., 1957
Senecio vulgaris
Hollings, M., 1957
Sisymbrium officinale
Hollings, M., 1957
Tagetes erecta
Hollings, M., 1957
Tetragonia expansa
Hollings, M., 1957
Thlaspi arvense
Hollings, M., 1957
Verbena hybrida
Hollings, M., 1957

VIRUS
V. ANEMONE MOSAIC * (cont.)
Vicia faba
Hollings, M., 1957
Zinnia elegans
Hollings, M., 1957

V. APPLE *
Amelanchier spp.
Millikan, D.F. and H.W. Guengerich, 1956
Datura inoxia
Hilborn, M.T. and Reiner Bonde, 1956
Malus sylvestris
Hilborn, M.T. and Reiner Bonde, 1956
Millikan, D.F. and H.W. Guengerich, 1956

V. APPLE DWARF FRUIT Cation and Gibson 1952
Malus coronaria
Cation, Donald and Roy E. Gibson, 1952
Malus sylvestris
Cation, Donald and Roy E. Gibson, 1952

V. APPLE FALSE STING Hockey 1943
Malus spp.
(K.M. Smith, 1957) R.E. Fitzpatrick, et al., 1958
Malus sylvestris
Hockey, J.F., 1941, 1943

V. APPLE GREEN MOTTLE Palmiter and Parker 1955
Malus sylvestris
Palmiter, D.H. and K.G. Parker, 1955

V. APPLE MOSAIC Khristov 1934 ((May be identical with V. Plum line pattern, Gilmer 1956
Cotoneaster spp.
(K.M. Smith, 1957) R.E. Fitzpatrick, et al., 1958
Cucumis sativus
Yarwood, C.E., 1955
Yarwood, C.E. and H.E. Thomas, 1954
Cyamopsis tetragonoloba
Yarwood, C.E., 1955
Eriobotrya spp.
(K.M. Smith, 1957) R.E. Fitzpatrick, et al., 1958
Fragaria vesca var. alpina *
Yarwood, C.E., 1955
Gomphrena globosa
Yarwood, C.E., 1955
Lycopersicon esculentum
Yarwood, C.E., 1955
Yarwood, C.E. and H.E. Thomas, 1954
Malus baccata
Hockey, J.F., 1943
Malus spectabis
Thomas, H. Earl and L.M. Massey, 1939
Malus spp.
(K.M. Smith, 1957) R.E. Fitzpatrick, et al., 1958
Malus sylvestris
Blodgett, F.M., 1938
Fulton, Robert W., 1956
Gilmer, R.M., 1956
Hockey, J.F., 1943
Hunter, J.A., E.E. Chamberlain and J.D. Atkinson, 1958
Kirkpatrick, Hugh C., 1955
Posnette, A.F. and R. Cropley, 1956
Posnette, A.F. and Christina E. Ellenberger, 1957
Yarwood, C.E., 1955, 1957
Yarwood, C.E. and H.E. Thomas, 1954
Nicotiana glutinosa
Yarwood, C.E., 1955
Nicotiana tabacum
Fulton, Robert W., 1956
Yarwood, C.E., 1955, 1957
Yarwood, C.E. and H.E. Thomas, 1954
Phaseolus vulgaris
Yarwood, C.E., 1955
Yarwood, C.E. and H.E. Thomas, 1954
Photinia spp.
(K.M. Smith, 1957) R.E. Fitzpatrick, et al., 1958
Phytolacca americana
Yarwood, C.E., 1955
Prunus americana x P. salicina
Gilmer, R.M., 1956

VIRUS
V. APPLE MOSAIC (cont.)
  Prunus americana x P. salicina
    Posnette, A.F. and Christina E. Ellenberger,
    1957
  Prunus avium
    Posnette, A.F. and Christina E. Ellenberger,
    1957
  Prunus cerasifera
    Posnette, A.F. and Christina E. Ellenberger,
    1957
  Prunus domestica
    Posnette, A.F. and Christina E. Ellenberger,
    1957
  Prunus gigantea *
    Posnette, A.F. and Christina E. Ellenberger,
    1957
  Prunus insititia
    Posnette, A.F. and Christina E. Ellenberger,
    1957
  Prunus persica
    Kirkpatrick, Hugh C., 1955
    Posnette, A.F. and Christina E. Ellenberger,
    1957
  Rosa hybrid
    Thomas, H. Earl and L.M. Massey, 1939
  Sorbus sitchensis
    Thomas, H. Earl and L.M. Massey, 1939
  Vicia faba
    Yarwood, C.E., 1955
    Yarwood, C.E. and H.E. Thomas, 1954
  Vigna sinensis
    Yarwood, C.E., 1955
    Yarwood, C.E. and H.E. Thomas, 1954

V. APPLE RING SPOT Atkinson et al. 1954
  Malus spp.
    (K.M. Smith, 1957) R.E. Fitzpatrick, et al., 1958

V. APPLE ROSETTE Van Katwijk 1953
  Malus spp.
    (K.M. Smith, 1957) R.E. Fitzpatrick, et al., 1958

V. APPLE ROUGH SKIN Van Katwijk 1955
  Malus spp.
    (K.M. Smith, 1957) R.E. Fitzpatrick, et al., 1958

V. APPLE RUBBERY WOOD Prentice 1950
  Malus spp.
    (K.M. Smith, 1957) R.E. Fitzpatrick, et al., 1958

V. APPLE STEM PITTING *
  Malus sylvestris on M. angustifolia
    Guengerick, H.W. and D.F. Millikan, 1956

V. APPLE WITCHES' BROOM Rui 1950
  Malus spp.
    (K.M. Smith, 1957) R.E. Fitzpatrick, et al., 1958

V. APRICOT MOORPARK MOTTLE Chamberlain et al.
  Prunus armeniaca   1954
    (K.M. Smith, 1957) R.E. Fitzpatrick, et al., 1958
  Prunus cerasifera
    (K.M. Smith, 1957) R.E. Fitzpatrick, et al., 1958
  Prunus persica
    (K.M. Smith, 1957) R.E. Fitzpatrick, et al., 1958

V. APRICOT RING POX Reeves 1943
  Phaseolus vulgaris
    Yarwood, C.E., 1957
  Prunus armeniaca
    Reeves, E.L. and Philip W. Cheney, 1956
    Simonds, Austin O., 1951
  Prunus domestica
    Simonds, Austin O., 1951
  Prunus persica
    Simonds, Austin O., 1951
    Yarwood, C.E., 1957

V. ARABIS MOSAIC Smith and Markham 1944
  Arabis hirsuta
    Smith, Kenneth M. and Roy Markham, 1944
  Cucumis sativus
    Smith, Kenneth M. and Roy Markham, 1944

VIRUS
V. ARABIS MOSAIC (cont.)
  Nicotiana glutinosa
    Smith, Kenneth M. and Roy Markham, 1944
  Nicotiana tabacum
    Smith, Kenneth M. and Roy Markham, 1944
  Phaseolus vulgaris
    Smith, Kenneth M. and Roy Markham, 1944
  Solanum nodiflorum
    Smith, Kenneth M. and Roy Markham, 1944

V. ASCLEPIAS YELLOWS *
  Asclepias syriaca
    Kunkel, L.O., 1950
  Daucus carota var. sativa
    Kunkel, L.O., 1950
  Lycopersicon esculentum
    Kunkel, L.O., 1950
  Vinca rosea
    Kunkel, L.O., 1950

V. ASH INFECTIOUS VARIEGATION Atanasoff 1935
  Pyrus aucuparia
    (K.M. Smith, 1957) R.E. Fitzpatrick, et al., 1958

V. ASH WITCHES' BROOM Plakidas 1949
  Fraxinus berlandieriana
    Plakidas, A.G., 1949

V. ASTER YELLOWS Kunkel 1926, 1936
  Adonis aestivalis
    (K.M. Smith, 1957) R.E. Fitzpatrick, et al., 1958
  Allium ascalonicum
    Smith, Floyd F. and Philip Brierley, 1948
  Allium cepa
    Severin, Henry H.P. and Julius H. Freitag, 1945
  Alyssum compactum var. procumbens *
    Kunkel, L.O., 1926
  Amaranthus auroro or aurora *
    Kunkel, L.O., 1926
  Amaranthus caudatus
    Kunkel, L.O., 1926
  Amaranthus retroflexus
    Frazier, Norman W. and Henry H.P. Severin, 1945
  Ambrosia artemisiifolia
    Kunkel, L.O., 1926
    Younkin, S.G., 1943
  Ambrosia trifida
    Kunkel, L.O., 1926
  Ammobium alatum
    Kunkel, L.O., 1926
  Anagallis arvensis
    Frazier, Norman W. and Henry H.P. Severin, 1945
  Anemone coronaria
    Severin, Henry H.P. and Julius H. Freitag, 1945
  Anethum graveolens
    Kunkel, L.O., 1926
  Anthemis cotula
    Frazier, Norman W. and Henry H.P. Severin, 1945
  Apium graveolens
    George, J.A. and J.K. Ricahrdson, 1957
    Raymer, W.B. and Clark R. Amen, 1954
  Apium graveolens var. dulce
    Freitag, J.H., 1956
    Magie, R.O., Floyd F. Smith and Philip Brierley,
    1952
    Raymer, W.B., 1956
    Severin, H.H.P., 1928, 1929, 1930, 1932, 1934
    Severin, Henry H.P. and Julius H. Freitag, 1945
    Severin, Henry H.P. and Sidney J. Oliver, 1939
    Smith, Floyd F. and Philip Brierley, 1953
  Apium graveolens var. rapaceum
    Severin, Henry H.P., 1929, 1932
    Severin, Henry H.P. and Julius H. Freitag, 1945
  Asclepias nivea
    Kunkel, L.O., 1926
  Aster chilensis
    Frazier, Norman W. and Henry H.P. Severin, 1945
  Aster novae-angliae
    George, J.A. and J.K. Richardson, 1957
  Begonia semperflorens
    Kunkel, L.O., 1926
  Bellis perennis
    Kunkel, L.O., 1926

VIRUS
V. ASTER YELLOWS (cont.)
Bidens frondosa
  Frazier, Norman W. and Henry H.P. Severin, 1945
Bidens pilosa
  Frazier, Norman W. and Henry H.P. Severin, 1945
Brachycome iberidifolia
  Kunkel, L.O., 1926
  Severin, Henry H.P. and Julius H. Freitag, 1945
Brassica campestris
  Frazier, Norman W. and Henry H.P. Severin, 1945
Brassica hirta (Brassica alba)
  Severin, Henry H.P., 1934
Brassica oleracea var. botrytis
  Severin, Henry H.P. and Julius H. Freitag, 1945
Brassica oleracea var. capitata
  Severin, Henry H.P. and Julius H. Freitag, 1945
Brassica oleracea var. italica
  Severin, Henry H.P. and Julius H. Freitag, 1945
Browallia americana (Browallia demissa)
  (K.M. Smith, 1957) R.E. Fitzpatrick, et al., 1958
Calandrinia grandiflora
  Kunkel, L.O., 1926
Calceolaria crenatiflora
  Kunkel, L.O., 1926
Calendula officinalis
  Kunkel, L.O., 1926
  Severin, Henry H.P. and Julius H. Freitag, 1945
Calendula spp.
  Severin, Henry H.P., 1934
Callistephus chinensis
  Black, L.M., 1941
  Brierley, Philip and Floyd F. Smith, 1957
  Freitag, Julius H., 1956
  Johnson, Folke, 1941
  Kunkel, L.O., 1924, 1926
  Magie, R.O., Floyd F. Smith and Philip Brierley, 1952
  Maramorosch, Karl, 1952, 1955
  Raymer, W.B., 1956
  Raymer, W.B. and Clark R. Amen, 1954
  Severin, Henry H.P., 1929, 1932, 1934, 1940
  Severin, Henry H.P. and Julius H. Freitag, 1945
  Smith, Floyd F. and Philip Brierley, 1948, 1951, 1953
  Younkin, S.G., 1943
Canna generalis
  Smith, Floyd F. and Philip Brierley, 1951
Capsella bursa-pastoris
  Frazier, Norman W. and Henry H.P. Severin, 1945
Centaurea americana
  Severin, Henry H.P. and Julius H. Freitag, 1945
Centaurea cyanus
  Frazier, Norman W. and Henry H.P. Severin, 1945
  Severin, Henry H.P. and Julius H. Freitag, 1945
Centaurea imperialis
  Kunkel, L.O., 1926, 1928
Centaurea margaritacea
  Kunkel, L.O., 1926
Centaurea melitensis
  Frazier, Norman W. and Henry H.P. Severin, 1945
Cheiranthus allionii
  (K.M. Smith, 1957) R.E. Fitzpatrick, et al., 1958
Cheiranthus cheiri
  Severin, Henry H.P. and Julius H. Freitag, 1945
Chrysanthemum carinatum
  Severin, Henry H.P. and Julius H. Freitag, 1945
Chrysanthemum coronarium
  Kunkel, L.O., 1926
Chrysanthemum frutescens
  Kunkel, L.O., 1926
  Severin, Henry H.P. and Julius H. Freitag, 1945
Chrysanthemum hortorum
  Smith, Floyd F. and Philip Brierley, 1948
Chrysanthemum leucanthemum
  Kunkel, L.O., 1926
Chrysanthemum leucanthemum var. maximum *
  Kunkel, L.O., 1926
Chrysanthemum maximum
  Kunkel, L.O., 1926
Chrysanthemum morifolium
  Brierley, Philip and Floyd F. Smith, 1957
  Smith, Floyd F. and Philip Brierley, 1953

VIRUS
V. ASTER YELLOWS (cont.)
Chrysanthemum segetum
  Severin, Henry H.P. and Julius H. Freitag, 1934, 1945
Chrysanthemum segetum x C. carinatum
  Severin, Henry H.P. and Julius H. Freitag, 1945
Chrysanthemum spp.
  Kunkel, L.O., 1926
Cichorium endivia
  Linn, M.B., 1940
  Severin, Henry H.P. and Julius H. Freitag, 1945
Cichorium intybus
  Severin, Henry H.P. and Julius H. Freitag, 1945
Clarkia elegans
  Severin, Henry H.P. and Julius H. Freitag, 1945
Coreopsis drummondii
  Severin, Henry H.P. and Julius H. Freitag, 1945
Coreopsis grandiflora
  Severin, Henry H.P. and Julius H. Freitag, 1945
Coreopsis tinctoria
  Kunkel, L.O., 1926
Cosmidium burridgeanum
  Kunkel, L.O., 1926
Cosmos bipinnatus
  Severin, Henry H.P. and Julius H. Freitag, 1945
Cotula australis
  Frazier, Norman W. and Henry H.P. Severin, 1945
Cucumis melo
  Freitag, Julius H., 1956
Cucumis sativus
  Freitag, J.H., 1956
Cucurbita maxima
  Freitag, J.H., 1956
Cucurbita mixta
  Freitag, J.H., 1956
Cucurbita moschata
  Freitag, J.H., 1956
Cucurbita pepo
  Freitag, J.H., 1956
Dahlia variabilis
  Smith, Floyd F. and Philip Brierley, 1953
Datura stramonium
  Frazier, Norman W. and Henry H.P. Severin, 1945
  Raymer, W.B., 1956
Daucus carota
  George, J.A. and J.K. Richardson, 1957
Daucus carota var. sativa
  Hervey, G.E.R. and W.T. Schroeder, 1949
  Severin, H.H.P., 1930, 1932, 1934
  Severin, Henry H.P. and Julius H. Freitag, 1945
Delphinium ajacis
  Severin, Henry H.P. and Julius H. Freitag, 1945
Delphinium cultorum
  Severin, Henry H.P. and Julius H. Freitag, 1945
  Severin, Henry H.P. and Sidney J. Oliver, 1939
Delphinium grandiflorum var. album
  Severin, Henry H.P., 1942
Delphinium hybrid
  Severin, Henry H.P., 1942
Delphinium spp.
  Severin, Henry H.P., 1942
Dianthus barbatus
  Kunkel, L.O., 1926
  Severin, Henry H.P. and Julius H. Freitag, 1945
Dianthus caryophyllus
  Brierley, Philip and Floyd F. Smith, 1957
  Jones, Leon K., 1945
  Thomas, W.D., Jr., 1953
Didiscus caeruleus
  Kunkel, L.O., 1926
Dimorphotheca aurantiacum
  Kunkel, L.O., 1926
Diplacus aurantiacus
  Frazier, Norman W. and Henry H.P. Severin, 1945
Dipsacus fullonum
  Frazier, Norman W. and Henry H.P. Severin, 1945
Epilobium californicum
  Frazier, Norman W. and Henry H.P. Severin, 1945
Epilobium paniculatum
  Frazier, Norman W. and Henry H.P. Severin, 1945
Erigeron annuus
  Kunkel, L.O., 1926

VIRUS
V. ASTER YELLOWS (cont.)

Erigeron canadensis
Frazier, Norman W. and Henry H. P. Severin, 1945
Kunkel, L. O., 1926
McClintock, J. A., 1931
Erigeron linifolius
Frazier, Norman W. and Henry H. P. Severin, 1945
Erodium cicutarium
Frazier, Norman W. and Henry H. P. Severin, 1945
Erodium moschatum
Frazier, Norman W. and Henry H. P. Severin, 1945
Eschscholtzia californica
Kunkel, L. O., 1926
Severin, Henry H. P. and Julius H. Freitag, 1934, 1945
Fagopyrum esculentum
Kunkel, L. O., 1926
Fragaria bracteata
Frazier, Norman W. and Harold E. Thomas, 1953
Fragaria californica
Frazier, Norman W. and Henry H. P. Severin, 1945
Fragaria chiloensis var. ananassa
Frazier, Norman W. and Harold E. Thomas, 1953
Fulton, J. P., 1957
Fragaria vesca
Fulton, J. P., 1957
Fragaria vesca var. americana
Frazier, Norman W. and Harold E. Thomas, 1953
Gaillardia aristata
Kunkel, L. O., 1926
Gaillardia pulchella var. picta
Severin, Henry H. P. and Julius H. Freitag, 1945
Gaura lindheimeri
Severin, Henry H. P. and Julius H. Freitag, 1945
Geranium dissectum
Frazier, Norman W. and Henry H. P. Severin, 1945
Geum chiloense
Severin, Henry H. P. and Julius H. Freitag, 1945
Gilia capitata var. achilleaefolia
Severin, Henry H. P. and Julius H. Freitag, 1945
Gladiolus hortulanus
Magie, R. O., Floyd F. Smith and Philip Brierley, 1952
Smith, Floyd F. and Philip Brierley, 1953
Gladiolus spp.
Smith, Floyd F. and Philip Brierley, 1948
Gnaphalium decurrens var. californicum
Frazier, Norman W. and Henry H. P. Severin, 1945
Gnaphalium ramosissimum
Frazier, Norman W. and Henry H. P. Severin, 1945
Godetia grandiflora
Severin, Henry H. P. and Julius H. Freitag, 1934, 1945
Gysophila paniculata
Kunkel, L. O., 1926
Severin, Henry H. P. and Julius H. Freitag, 1945
Helenium puberulum
Frazier, Norman W. and Henry H. P. Severin, 1945
Helichrysum arenarium
Kunkel, L. O., 1926
Helichrysum bracteatum
Severin, Henry H. P. and Julius H. Freitag, 1934, 1945
Hemizonia corymbosa
Frazier, Norman W. and Henry H. P. Severin, 1945
Hydrangea macrophylla
Brierley, Philip and Floyd F. Smith, 1954
Ilysanthes dubia
Frazier, Norman W. and Henry H. P. Severin, 1945
Lactuca altaica
Tompson, Ross C., 1944
Lactuca canadensis
Tompson, Ross C., 1944
Lactuca floridana
Tompson, Ross C., 1944
Lactuca graminifolia
Tompson, Ross C., 1944
Lactuca indica
Tompson, Ross C., 1944
Lactuca laciniata
Tompson, Ross C., 1944
Lactuca muralis
Tompson, Ross C., 1944

VIRUS
V. ASTER YELLOWS (cont.)

Lactuca muralis
Tompson, Ross C., 1944
Lactuca perennis
Tompson, Ross C., 1944
Lactuca raddeana
Tompson, Ross C., 1944
Lactuca saligna
Tompson, Ross C., 1944
Lactuca sativa
Brierley, Philip and Floyd F. Smith, 1944
Kunkel, L. O., 1926
Lee, P. E. and A. G. Robinson, 1958
Linn, M. B., 1940
Raymer, W. B. and Clark R. Amen, 1954
Severin, H. H. P., 1928, 1929
Severin, Henry H. P. and Julius H. Freitag, 1945
Smith, Floyd F. and Philip Brierley, 1951
Tompson, Ross C., 1944
Lactuca sativa var. longifolia
Severin, Henry H. P. and Julius H. Freitag, 1945
Lactuca scariola var. integrata
Frazier, Norman W. and Henry H. P. Severin, 1945
Lactuca serriola
Tompson, Ross C., 1944
Lactuca spicata
Tompson, Ross C., 1944
Lactuca squarrosa
Tompson, Ross C., 1944
Lactuca virosa
Tompson, Ross C., 1944
Lamium amplexicaule
Frazier, Norman W. and Henry H. P. Severin, 1945
Lavandula officinalis
Kunkel, L. O., 1926
Limonium sinuatum
Severin, Henry H. P. and Julius H. Freitag, 1945
Linaria bipartita
Severin, Henry H. P. and Julius H. Freitag, 1945
Linaria canadensis
Frazier, Norman W. and Henry H. P. Severin, 1945
Linum usitatissimum
Severin, Henry H. P. and Byron R. Houston, 1945
Lotus salsuginosus
Frazier, Norman W. and Henry H. P. Severin, 1945
Lycopersicon esculentum
Kunkel, L. O., 1930
Raymer, W. B., 1956
Madia sativa
Frazier, Norman W. and Henry H. P. Severin, 1945
Malcomia maritima
(K. M. Smith, 1957) R. E. Fitzpatrick, et al., 1958
Malva nicaeensis
Frazier, Norman W. and Henry H. P. Severin, 1945
Malva parviflora
Frazier, Norman W. and Henry H. P. Severin, 1945
Malva rotundifolia
Frazier, Norman W. and Henry H. P. Severin, 1945
Martynia louisiana
Kunkel, L. O., 1926
Matricaria alba
Kunkel, L. O., 1926
Matricaria suaveolens
Frazier, Norman W. and Henry H. P. Severin, 1945
Medicago hispida
Frazier, Norman W. and Henry H. P. Severin, 1945
Melilotus alba
Frazier, Norman W. and Henry H. P. Severin, 1945
Mimulus cardinalis
Severin, Henry H. P. and Julius H. Freitag, 1945
Mimulus guttatus
Frazier, Norman W. and Henry H. P. Severin, 1945
Severin, Henry H. P. and Julius H. Freitag, 1945
Mimulus luteus
Kunkel, L. O., 1926
Myosotis scorpioides
Kunkel, L. O., 1926
Severin, Henry H. P. and Julius H. Freitag, 1945
Nemesia strumosa
Kunkel, L. O., 1926
Nemophila maculata
Kunkel, L. O., 1926

VIRUS
V. ASTER YELLOWS (cont.)
Nicotiana rustica
Johnson, Folke, 1941
Kunkel, L.O., 1930
Raymer, W.B., 1956
Self, R.L. and H.M. Darling, 1949
Younkin, S.G., 1943
Nigella damascena
Severin, Henry H.P. and Julius H. Freitag, 1945
Pastinaca sativa
Severin, Henry H.P., 1932, 1934
Severin, Henry H.P. and Julius H. Freitag, 1945
Petroselinum crispum
Severin, H.H.P., 1930
Severin, Henry H.P. and Julius H. Freitag, 1945
Petroselinum hortense
Severin, Henry H.P., 1932, 1934
Petroselinum hortense var. crispum *
Severin, Henry H.P., 1932
Petroselinum hortense var. radicosum *
Severin, Henry H.P., 1932, 1934
Petunia hybrida
Severin, Henry H.P. and Julius H. Freitag, 1945
Phlox drummondii
Kunkel, L.O., 1926
Severin, Henry H.P., 1943
Severin, Henry H.P. and Julius H. Freitag, 1945
Phlox paniculata
Kunkel, L.O., 1926
Picris echioides
Frazier, Norman W. and Henry H.P. Severin, 1945
Pimpinella anisum
Kunkel, L.O., 1926
Plantago major
Frazier, Norman W. and Harold E. Thomas, 1953
Freitag, J.H., 1956
Kunkel, L.O., 1926, 1928
Severin, Henry H.P., 1929, 1934
Polygonum aviculare
Frazier, Norman W. and Henry H.P. Severin, 1945
Polygonum convolvulus
Frazier, Norman W. and Henry H.P. Severin, 1945
Portulaca grandiflora
Kunkel, L.O., 1926
Portulaca oleracea
Frazier, Norman W. and Henry H.P. Severin, 1945
Primula elatior
Kunkel, L.O., 1926
Primula obconica
Severin, Henry H.P. and C.M. Tompkins, 1950
Primula polyantha
Severin, Henry H.P. and Julius H. Freitag, 1945
Pyrethrum spp.
Kunkel, L.O., 1926
Ranunculus asiaticus
Severin, Henry H.P. and Julius H. Freitag, 1934, 1945
Raphanus sativus
Frazier, Norman W. and Henry H.P. Severin, 1945
Severin, Henry H.P. and Julius H. Freitag, 1945
Reseda odorata
Kunkel, L.O., 1926
Rorippa curvisiliqua
Frazier, Norman W. and Henry H.P. Severin, 1945
Rorippa sylvestris
(K.M. Smith, 1957) R.E. Fitzpatrick, et al., 1958
Rudbeckia hirta
Severin, Henry H.P. and Julius H. Freitag, 1945
Rumex acetosella
Frazier, Norman W. and Henry H.P. Severin, 1945
Salpiglossis sinuata
Kunkel, L.O., 1926
Severin, Henry H.P. and Julius H. Freitag, 1945
Salvia azurea var. pitcheri
Severin, Henry H.P. and Julius H. Freitag, 1945
Satureia hortensis
Kunkel, L.O., 1926
Scabiosa atropurpurea
Kunkel, L.O., 1926
Severin, Henry H.P. and Julius H. Freitag, 1945
Schizanthus pinnatus
Kunkel, L.O., 1926

VIRUS
V. ASTER YELLOWS (cont.)
Scorzonera hispanica
Severin, Henry H.P. and Julius H. Freitag, 1945
Scrophularia californica
Frazier, Norman W. and Henry H.P. Severin, 1945
Senecio hybridus
(K.M. Smith, 1957) R.E. Fitzpatrick, et al., 1958
Senecio vulgaris
Frazier, Norman W. and Henry H.P. Severin, 1945
Silene pendula
Kunkel, L.O., 1926
Sinningia speciosa
Kunkel, L.O., 1926
Solanum nigrum
Frazier, Norman W. and Henry H.P. Severin, 1945
Solanum tuberosum
Bonde, Reiner and E.S. Schultz, 1947
Burke, O.D., 1941
Jensen, James H. and H. Douglas Tate, 1947
Leach. J.G. and C. Franklin Bishop, 1944
Milbrath, J.A. and W.H. English, 1948, 1949
Raymer, W.B , 1956
Raymer, W.B. and Clark R. Amen, 1954
Self, R.L. and H.M. Darling, 1949
Severin, Henry H.P., 1940
Severin, Henry H.P. and Julius H. Freitag, 1945
Severin, Henry H.P. and Frank A. Haasis, 1934
Younkin, S.G., 1943
Sonchus arvensis
Kunkel, L.O., 1926
Sonchus asper
Frazier, Norman W. and Henry H.P. Severin, 1945
Sonchus oleraceus
Frazier, Norman W. and Henry H.P. Severin, 1945
Kunkel, L.O., 1926
Spergula arvensis
Frazier, Norman W. and Henry H.P. Severin, 1945
Spinacia oleracea
Kunkel, L.O., 1926
Severin, Henry H.P. and Julius H. Freitag, 1945
Stellaria media
Frazier, Norman W. and Henry H.P. Severin, 1945
Tagetes erecta
Kunkel, L.O., 1926
Severin, Henry H.P., 1929
Severin, Henry H.P. and Julius H. Freitag, 1934, 1945
Tagetes patula
Severin, Henry H.P. and Julius H. Freitag, 1934, 1945
Taraxacum officinale
Kunkel, L.O., 1926
Trachymene caerulea
Severin, Henry H.P. and Julius H. Freitag, 1945
Tragopogon porrifolius
Kunkel, L.O., 1926
Severin, Henry H.P., 1934
Trifolium hybridum
Raymer, W.B., 1956
Trifolium incarnatum
Raymer, W.B., 1956
Trifolium pratense
Raymer, W.B., 1956
Trifolium repens
Raymer, W.B., 1956
Raymer, W.B. and Clark R. Amen, 1954
Webb, R.E. and E.S. Schultz, 1955
Tropaeolum majus
Severin, Henry H.P. and Julius H. Freitag, 1945
Urtica californica
Frazier, Norman W. and Henry H.P. Severin, 1945
Veronica americana
Frazier, Norman W. and Henry H.P. Severin, 1945
Veronica buxbaumii
Frazier, Norman W. and Henry H.P. Severin, 1945
Veronica peregrina
(K.M. Smith, 1957) R.E. Fitzpatrick, et al., 1958
Vinca rosea
Brierley, Philip and Floyd F. Smith, 1957
Fulton, J.P., 1957
Maramorosch, Karl, 1957
Viola tricolor
Brierley, Philip and Floyd F. Smith, 1954

VIRUS

V. ASTER YELLOWS (cont.)
  Zinnia elegans
    George, J.A. and J.K. Richardson, 1957
    Magie, R.O., Floyd F. Smith and Philip Brierley,
    1952
    Severin, Henry H.P., 1929, 1934
    Severin, Henry H.P. and Julius H. Freitag, 1934,
    1945
    Smith, Floyd F. and Philip Brierley, 1953
  Zinnia haageana
    Severin, Henry H.P., 1934

V. ATROPA BELLADONNA MOSAIC Smith 1943
  Atropa belladonna
    R.A.M. 22:451, 1943
  Datura stramonium
    (K.M. Smith, 1957) R.E. Fitzpatrick, et al., 1958
  Hyocyamus niger
    (K.M. Smith, 1957) R.E. Fitzpatrick, et al., 1958
  Nicotiana glutinosa
    (K.M. Smith, 1957) R.E. Fitzpatrick, et al., 1958
  Nicotiana tabacum
    (K.M. Smith, 1957) R.E. Fitzpatrick, et al., 1958
  Phaseolus vulgaris
    (K.M. Smith, 1957) R.E. Fitzpatrick, et al., 1958
  Solanum nigrum
    (K M. Smith, 1957) R.E. Fitzpatrick, et al., 1958

V. AVOCADO PEAR SUN BLOTCH Horne and Parker
  Persea americana   1930
    Horne, W.T. and E.R. Parker, 1931
    Stevens, H.E., 1939

V. BABIANA MOSAIC Smith and Brierley 1944
  Babiana spp.
    Smith, Floyd F. and Philip Brierley, 1944
  Tritonia crocata
    Smith, Floyd F. and Philip Brierley, 1944

V. BANANA BUNCHY TOP Magee 1927
  Musa fehi
    (K.M. Smith, 1957) R.E. Fitzpatrick, et al., 1958
  Musa spp.
    Magee, C.J.P., 1940, 1948

V. BARLEY STRIPE MOSAIC McKinney 1953; Hagborg
  Agropyron hybrid   1954
    Sill, W.H., Jr., 1956
  Avena sativa
    McKinney, H.H., 1953
    Sill, W.H., Jr. and E.D. Hansing, 1955
  Bromus inermis
    McKinney, H.H., 1951, 1953
  Bromus japonicus
    Slykhuis, J.T., 1952
  Bromus secalinus
    Slykhuis, J.T., 1952
  Bromus tectorum
    Slykhuis, J.T., 1952
  Chenopodium album
    Sill, W.H., Jr. and E.D. Hansing, 1955
  Chenopodium amaranticolor
    Hollings, M., 1957
  Digitaria ischaemum
    McKinney, H.H., 1951, 1953
  Digitaria sanguinalis
    Slykhuis, J.T., 1952
  Echinochloa crus-galli
    Slykhuis, J.T., 1952
  Eragrostis cilianensis
    Slykhuis, J.T., 1952
  Hordeum jubatum
    Slykhuis, J.T., 1952
  Hordeum vulgare
    Afanasiev, M.M., 1956
    Eslick, R.F. and M.M. Afanasiev, 1955
    Fitzgerald, Paul J., Harland Stevens and R.G.
    Timian, 1957
    Hagborg, W.A.F., 1954
    McKinney, H.H., 1951, 1953, 1954, 1956
    Sill, W.H., Jr. and E.D. Hansing, 1955
    Sisler, W.W. and R.G. Timian, 1956
    Slykhuis, J.T., 1952

VIRUS

V. BARLEY STRIPE MOSAIC (cont.)
  Hordeum vulgare
    Timian, R.G. and W.W. Sisler, 1955
    Wadsworth, D.F., 1949
  Nicotiana tabacum
    McKinney, H.H., 1951
  Oryza sativa
    Kahn, Robert P. and Ottie J. Dickerson, 1957
    McKinney, H.H., 1951
  Panicum capillare
    Slykhuis, J.T., 1952
  Panicum miliaceum
    Slykhuis, J.T., 1952
  Secale cereale
    Sill, W.H., Jr. and E.D. Hansing, 1955
    Slykhuis, J.T., 1952
  Setaria italica
    Slykhuis, J.T., 1952
  Setaria verticillata
    Slykhuis, J.T., 1952
  Setaria virdis
    Slykhuis, J.T., 1952
  Triticum aestivum
    Fitzgerald, Paul J., Harland Stevens and R.G.
    Timian, 1957
    Lal, S.B. and W.H. Sill, Jr., 1957
    McKinney, H.H., 1951, 1953, 1956
    McNeal, F.H. and M.M. Afanasiev, 1955, 1956
    Sill, W.H., Jr. and E.D. Hansing, 1955
  Triticum durum
    Slykhuis, J.T., 1952
  Triticum vulgare
    Slykhuis, J.T., 1952
  Zea mays
    McKinney, H.H., 1951
    Sill, W.H., Jr., 1956
    Sill, W.H., Jr. and E.D. Hansing, 1955
    Slykhuis, J.T., 1952
  Zea mays var. saccharata
    McKinney, H.H., 1951, 1953

V. BARLEY YELLOW DWARF Oswald and Houston
  Aegilops triuncialis   1951
    Oswald, John W. and Byron R. Houston, 1953
  Agropyron inerme
    Bruehl, G.W. and H.V. Toko, 1957
  Agropyron intermedium
    Bruehl, G.W. and H.V. Toko, 1957
  Agropyron trachycaulum
    Oswald, John W. and Byron R. Houston, 1953
  Andropogon barbinodis
    Oswald, John W. and Byron R. Houston, 1953
  Anthoxanthum odoratum
    Oswald, John W. and Byron R. Houston, 1953
  Aristida oligantha
    Oswald, John W. and Byron R. Houston, 1953
  Avena barbata
    Oswald, John W. and Byron R. Houston, 1953
  Avena fatua
    Bruehl, G.W. and H.V. Toko, 1957
    Oswald, John W. and Byron R. Houston, 1952, 1953
  Avena sativa
    Allen, Thomas C., Jr., 1956, 1957
    Allen, Thomas C., Jr. and Byron R. Houston, 1956
    Bruehl, G.W. and H. Toko, 1955, 1957
    Endo, R.M., 1957
    Moore, M.B., 1952
    Oswald, John W. and Byron R. Houston, 1951,
    1952, 1953
    Oswald, John W. and T.H. Thung, 1955
    Takeshita, R.M., 1956
    Toko, H.V. and G.W. Bruehl, 1957
    Watson, Marion A. and T. Mulligan, 1957
    Wilson, V.E. and H.C. Murphy, 1953
  Avena strigosa
    Endo, R.M., 1957
  Beckmannia syzigachne
    Bruehl, G.W. and H.V. Toko, 1957
  Bouteloua curtipendula
    Oswald, John W. and Byron R. Houston, 1953
  Bromus brizaeformis
    Bruehl, G.W. and H.V. Toko, 1957

VIRUS
V. BARLEY YELLOW DWARF (cont.)
Bromus carinatus
    Bruehl, G.W. and H.V. Toko, 1957
Bromus catharticus
    Bruehl, G.W. and H.V. Toko, 1957
    Oswlad, John W. and Byron R. Houston, 1953
Bromus commutatus
    Bruehl, G.W. and H.V. Toko, 1957
Bromus erectus
    Bruehl, G.W. and H.V. Toko, 1957
Bromus inermis
    Oswald, John W. and Byron R. Houston, 1953
Bromus japonicus
    Bruehl, G.W. and H.V. Toko, 1957
Bromus mollis
    Bruehl, G.W. and H.V. Toko, 1957
    Oswald, John W. and Byron R. Houston, 1953
Bromus racemosus
    Bruehl, G.W. and H.V. Toko, 1957
Bromus rigidus
    Allen, Thomas C., Jr. and Byron R. Houston, 1956
    Bruehl, G.W. and H.V. Toko, 1957
    Oswald, John W. and Byron R. Houston, 1953
Bromus rubens
    Oswald, John W. and Byron R. Houston, 1953
Bromus secalinus
    Bruehl, G.W. and H.V. Toko, 1957
Bromus spp.
    Oswald, John W. and Byron R. Houston, 1952
Bromus sterilis
    Bruehl, G.W. and H.V. Toko, 1957
Bromus tectorum
    Bruehl, G.W. and H.V. Toko, 1957
    Oswald, John W. and Byron R. Houston, 1953
Bromus tomentellus
    Bruehl, G.W. and H.V. Toko, 1957
Chloris gayana
    Oswald, John W. and Byron R. Houston, 1953
Cynodon dactylon
    Oswald, John W. and Byron R. Houston, 1953
Cynosurus echinatus
    Oswald, John W. and Byron R. Houston, 1953
Dactylis glomerata
    Bruehl, G.W. and H.V. Toko, 1957
    Oswald, John W. and Byron R. Houston, 1953
Deschampsia caespitosa
    Bruehl, G.W. and H.V. Toko, 1957
Deschampsia danthonioides
    Bruehl, G.W. and H.V. Toko, 1957
Elymus caput-medusae
    Bruehl, G.W. and H.V. Toko, 1957
    Oswald, John W. and Byron R. Houston, 1953
Elymus condensatus
    Bruehl, G.W. and H.V. Toko, 1957
Elymus triticoides
    Oswald, John W. and Byron R. Houston, 1953
Festuca arundinacea
    Bruehl, G.W. and H.V. Toko, 1957
    Oswald, John W. and Byron R. Houston, 1953
Festuca elatior
    Bruehl, G.W. and H.V. Toko, 1957
Festuca idahoensis
    Bruehl, G.W. and H.V. Toko, 1957
Festuca myuros
    Oswald, John W. and Byron R. Houston, 1953
Festuca ovina
    Bruehl, G.W. and H.V. Toko, 1957
Festuca reflexa
    Bruehl, G.W. and H.V. Toko, 1957
    Oswald, John W. and Byron R. Houston, 1953
Festuca rubra
    Bruehl, G.W. and H.V. Toko, 1957
Festuca spp.
    Oswald, John W. and Byron R. Houston, 1952
Gastridium ventricosum
    Oswald, John W. and Byron R. Houston, 1953
Hordeum brachyantherum
    Oswald, John W. and Byron R. Houston, 1953
Hordeum brevisubulatum
    Bruehl, G.W. and H.V. Toko, 1957
Hordeum bulbosum
    Bruehl, G.W. and H.V. Toko, 1957

VIRUS
V. BARLEY YELLOW DWARF (cont.)
Hordeum hystrix
    Oswald, John W. and Byron R. Houston, 1953
Hordeum leporinum
    Bruehl, G.W. and H.V. Toko, 1957
    Oswald, John W. and Byron R. Houston, 1953
Hordeum spp.
    Oswald, John W. and Byron R. Houston, 1952
Hordeum vulgare
    Allen, Thomas C., Jr., 1956, 1957
    Allen, Thomas C., Jr. and Byron R. Houston, 1956
    Bruehl, G.W. and H. Toko, 1955, 1957
    Oswald, John W. and Byron R. Houston, 1951, 1952,
    1953
    Oswald, John W. and T.H. Thung, 1955
    Takeshita, R.M., 1956
    Toko, H.V. and G.W. Bruehl, 1957
    Watson, Marion A. and T. Mulligan, 1957
Loeleria cristata
    Bruehl, G.W. and H.V. Toko, 1957
Lolium multiflorum
    Bruehl, G.W. and H.V. Toko, 1957
    Oswald, John W. and Byron R. Houston, 1953
Lolium perenne
    Bruehl, G.W. and H.V. Toko, 1957
    Watson, Marion A. and T. Mulligan, 1957
Lolium remotum
    Bruehl, G.W. and H.V. Toko, 1957
Lolium temulentum
    Bruehl, G.W. and H.V. Toko, 1957
Panicum capillare
    Oswald, John W. and Byron R. Houston, 1953
Phalaris arundinacea
    Bruehl, G.W. and H.V. Toko, 1957
Phalaris paradoxa
    Oswald, John W. and Byron R. Houston, 1953
Phalaris spp.
    Oswald, John W. and Byron R. Houston, 1952
Phalaris tuberosa
    Oswald, John W. and Byron R. Houston, 1953
Phleum pratense
    Bruehl, G.W. and H.V. Toko, 1957
    Watson, Marion A. and T. Mulligan, 1957
Poa ampla
    Bruehl, G.W. and H.V. Toko, 1957
    Oswald, John W. and Byron R. Houston, 1953
Poa canbyi
    Bruehl, G.W. and H.V. Toko, 1957
Poa pratensis
    Bruehl, G.W. and H.V. Toko, 1957
    Oswald, John W. and Byron R. Houston, 1953
Secale cereale
    Allen, Thomas C., Jr., 1957
    Allen, Thomas C., Jr. and Byron R. Houston, 1956
    Takeshita, R.M., 1956
Setaria lutescens
    Bruehl, G.W. and H.V. Toko, 1957
Sitanion hystrix
    Bruehl, G.W. and H.V. Toko, 1957
    Oswald, John W. and Byron R. Houston, 1953
Sitanion jubatum
    Bruehl, G.W. and H.V. Toko, 1957
Sorghum vulgare
    Oswald, John W. and Byron R. H uston, 1953
Sorghum vulgare var. sudanense
    Oswald, John W. and Byron R. Houston, 1953
Stipa comata
    Bruehl, G.W. and H.V. Toko, 1957
Triticum aestivum
    Allen, Thomas C., Jr., 1957
    Allen, Thomas C., Jr. and Byron R. Houston, 1956
    Bruehl, G.W. and H. Toko, 1955, 1957
    Oswald, John W. and Byron R. Houston, 1951, 1952,
    1953
    Takeshita, R.M., 1956
    Toko, H.V. and G.W. Bruehl, 1957
Zea mays
    Allen, Thomas C., Jr., 1957

V. BAYBERRY YELLOWS Raychaudhuri 1953
Allium cepa
    Raychaudhuri, S.P., 1953

VIRUS
V. BAYBERRY YELLOWS (cont.)
Apium graveolens
  (K.M. Smith, 1957) R.E. Fitzpatrick, et al., 1958
Beta vulgaris
  Raychaudhuri, S.P., 1953
Cuscuta campestris
  (K.M. Smith, 1957) R.E. Fitzpatrick, et al., 1958
Cuscuta subinclusa
  (K.M. Smith, 1957) R.E. Fitzpatrick, et al., 1958
Daucus carota
  Raychaudhuri, S.P., 1953
Daucus carota var. sativa
  Raychaudhuri, S.P., 1952
Myrica carolinensis
  Raychaudhuri, S.P., 1952, 1953
Petunia hybrida var. nana compacta *
  Raychaudhuri, S.P., 1953
Tagetes signata var. pumila
  (K.M. Smith, 1957) R.E. Fitzpatrick, et al., 1958
Vinca minor
  Raychaudhuri, S.P., 1952
Vinca rosea
  Raychaudhuri, S.P., 1953

V. BEAN COMMON MOSAIC
Lespedeza striata
  Pierce, W.H., 1934
Melilotus alba
  Harrison, Arthur L., 1935
Phaseolus aconitifolius
  Nelson, Ray, 1932
Phaseolus acutifolius var. latifolius
  Nelson, Ray, 1932
  Pierce, W.H., 1934
  Reddick, D. and V.B. Stewart, 1919
Phaseolus angularis
  Nelson, Ray, 1932
Phaseolus aureus
  Pierce, W.H., 1934
Phaseolus calcaratus
  Nelson, Ray, 1932
  Pierce, W.H., 1934
Phaseolus coccineus
  Nelson, Ray, 1932
Phaseolus limensis
  Nelson, Ray, 1932
Phaseolus lunatus
  Nelson, Ray, 1932
  Pierce, W.H., 1934
Phaseolus lunatus f. macrocarpus
  Pierce, W.H., 1934
  Reddick, D. and V.B. Stewart, 1919
Phaseolus mungo
  Nelson, Ray, 1932
Phaseolus radiatus var. aurea *
  Matsumoto, T., 1922
Phaseolus vulgaris
  Ainsworth, G.C., 1940
  Bridgmon, G.H. and J.C. Walker, 1951
  Dean, Leslie L. and C.W. Hungerford, 1946, 1954
  Fajardo, T.G., 1928, 1930
  Fernow, Karl Hermann, 1925
  (K.M. Smith, 1957) R.E. Fitzpatrick, et al., 1958
  Fulton, Robert W., 1941
  Grogan, Raymond G. and J.C. Walker, 1948
  Harrison, Arthur L., 1935
  Jenkins, Wilbert A., 1940
  Mackie, W.W. and Katherine Esau, 1932
  Murphy, Donald M., 1940
  Murphy, Donald M. and W.H. Pierce, 1938
  Nelson, Ray, 1932
  Parker, M.C., 1936
  Pierce, W.H., 1934, 1935, 1937
  Pierce, W.H. and C.W. Hungerford, 1929
  Reddick, D. and V.B. Stewart, 1918, 1919
  Richards, B. Lorin and Walter H. Burkholder,
    1943
  Smith, Francis L. and Wm. B. Hewitt, 1938
  Snyder, W.C., 1942
  Stewart, V.B. and Donald Reddick, 1917
  Thomas, H. Rex and W.J. Zaumeyer, 1953
  Wade, B.L. and C.F. Andrus, 1941
  Walker, J.C. and J.P. Jolivette, 1943

VIRUS
V. BEAN COMMON MOSAIC (cont.)
Phaseolus vulgaris
  Yerkes, William D., Jr. and Alfonso Crispin
    Medina, 1957
  Zaumeyer, W.J. and H.H. Fisher, 1951
  Zaumeyer, W.J. and H. Rex Thomas, 1947, 1948
  Zaumeyer, W.J. and B.L. Wade, 1933, 1935
Phaseolus vulgaris var. humulis *
  Nelson, Ray, 1932
Vicia faba
  Nelson, Ray, 1932
  Reddick, D. and V.B. Stewart, 1919
Vicia faba var. minor
  Pierce, W.H., 1934
Vicia lathyroides
  (K.M. Smith, 1957) R.E. Fitzpatrick, et al., 1958
Vicia sativa
  Pierce, W.H., 1934
Vigna sesquipedalis
  Nelson, Ray, 1932
  Snyder, W.C., 1942
Vigna sinensis
  Snyder, W.C., 1942

V. BEAN DOUBLE YELLOW MOSAIC   K.M. Smith 1957
Phaseolus aureus
  (K.M. Smith, 1957) R.E. Fitzpatrick, et al., 1958
Phaseolus limensis
  (K.M. Smith, 1957) R.E. Fitzpatrick, et al., 1958
Phaseolus lunatus
  (K.M. Smith, 1957) R.E. Fitzpatrick, et al., 1958
Phaseolus vulgaris
  (K.M. Smith, 1957) R.E. Fitzpatrick, et al., 1958

V. BEAN LEAF WILT J. Johnson 1942
Lathyrus pusillus
  Johnson, James, 1942
Phaseolus vulgaris
  Johnson, James, 1942

V. BEAN MONTANA *
Melilotus alba
  Afanasiev, M.M. and H.E. Morris, 1946
Melilotus officinalis
  Afanasiev, M.M. and H.E. Morris, 1946
Phaseolus vulgaris
  Afanasiev, M.M. and H.E. Morris, 1946

V. BEAN MOSAIC 3 *
Phaseolus vulgaris
  Zaumeyer, W.J. and B.L. Wade, 1933, 1935

V. BEAN POD MOTTLE Zaumeyer and Thomas 1948
Glycine max
  Zaumeyer, W.J. and H. Rex Thomas, 1948
Phaseolus lunatus
  Zaumeyer, W.J. and H. Rex Thomas, 1948
Phaseolus lunatus x P. lunatus f. macrocarpus
  Zaumeyer, W.J. and H. Rex Thomas, 1948
Phaseolus vulgaris
  Thomas, H. Rex and W.J. Zaumeyer, 1950
  Zaumeyer, W.J. and H. Rex Thomas, 1948, 1950

V. BEAN SOUTHERN MOSAIC
Glycine max
  Zaumeyer, W.J. and L.L. Harter, 1943
  Zaumeyer, W.J. and H. Rex Thomas, 1948
Phaseolus lunatus
  Zaumeyer, W.J. and L.L. Harter, 1943
Phaseolus lunatus x P. lunatus f. macrocarpus
  Zaumeyer, W.J. and L.L. Harter, 1943
Phaseolus vulgaris
  Bain, Douglas C., 1950
  Bridgmon, G.H., 1951
  Bridgmon, G.H. and J.C. Walker, 1951
  Mitchell, J.W., W.H. Preston, Jr. and J.M. Beal,
    1956
  Price, W.C. and Betty R. Holt, 1948
  Zaumeyer, W.J. and H.H. Fisher, 1951
  Zaumeyer, W.J. and L.L. Harter, 1942, 1943,
    1944
  Zaumeyer, W.J. and H. Rex Thomas, 1948, 1950

VIRUS
V. BEAN YELLOW MOSAIC Pierce 1934
   Cajanus indicus
      Zaumeyer, W.J. and B.L. Wade, 1935
   Canavalia ensiformis
      Thomas, H. Rex and W.J. Zaumeyer, 1953
   Cassia tora
      Corbett, M.K., 1957
   Chenopodium amaranticolor
      Hollings, M., 1957
   Cicer arietinum
      Snyder, William C., A.O. Paulus and A.H. Gold, 1956
      Zaumeyer, W.J. and B.L. Wade, 1935
   Crotalaria retusa
      Zaumeyer, W.J., 1940
   Crotalaria spectabilis
      Corbett, M.K., 1957
      Hungerford, C.W. and Irvin G. Hillyer, 1954
      Zaumeyer, W.J., 1940
   Crotalaria striata
      Zaumeyer, W.J., 1940
   Cyamopsis tetragonoloba
      Thomas, H. Rex and W.J. Zaumeyer, 1953
   Dolichos biflorus
      (K.M. Smith, 1957) R.E. Fitzpatrick, et al., 1958
   Freesia spp.
      (K.M. Smith, 1957) R.E. Fitzpatrick, et al., 1958
   Gladiolus gandavensis
      McWhorter, Frank P., 1949
   Gladiolus hortulanus
      Berkeley, G.H., 1953
      Bridgmon, G.H., 1951
      Bridgmon, G.H. and J.C. Walker, 1952
      Brierley, Philip, 1952
      Brierley, Philip and Floyd F. Smith, 1948
      Dosdall, Louise, 1928
   Gladiolus spp.
      Smith, Floyd F. and Philip Brierley, 1944
   Glycine max
      Afanasiev, M.M. and H.E. Morris, 1952
      Conover, Robert A., 1948
      Grogan, Raymond G. and J.C. Walker, 1948
      Hagedorn, D.J., 1952
      Hagedorn, D.J. and J.C. Walker, 1949, 1950, 1954
      Pierce, W.H., 1934, 1935
      Thomas, H. Rex and W.J. Zaumeyer, 1953
      Zaumeyer, W.J. and H.H. Fisher, 1953
   Lathyrus hirsutus
      Hagedorn, D.J. and J.C. Walker, 1950, 1954
   Lathyrus odoratus
      Ainsworth, G.C., 1940
      Hagedorn, D.J. and J.C. Walker, 1950, 1954
      Zaumeyer, W.J. and B.L. Wade, 1933, 1935
   Lens esculenta
      Zaumeyer, W.J. and B.L. Wade, 1935
   Lespedeza striata
      Pierce, W.H., 1934
   Lupinus albus
      Pierce, W.H., 1934
      Zaumeyer, W.J., 1940
   Lupinus angustifolius
      Hagedorn, D.J. and J.C. Walker, 1950, 1954
      Zaumeyer, W.J., 1940
   Lupinus densiflorus
      Hungerford, C.W. and Irvin G. Hillyer, 1954
   Lycopersicon esculentum
      Osborn, H.T., 1938
   Medicago arabica
      Elliott, J.A., 1921
   Medicago lupulina
      Hungerford, C.W. and Irvin G. Hillyer, 1954
   Medicago orbicularis
      Hagedorn, D.J. and J.C. Walker, 1950, 1954
   Medicago sativa
      McWhorter, Frank P., 1949
      Zaumeyer, W.J., 1940
   Melilotus alba
      Afanasiev, M.M. and H.E. Morris, 1952
      Conover, Robert A., 1948
      Diachun, Stephen and Lawrence Henson, 1956
      Elliott, J.A., 1921
      Grogan, Raymond G. and J.C. Walker, 1948
      Hagedorn, D.J. and J.C. Walker, 1950

VIRUS
V. BEAN YELLOW MOSAIC (cont.)
   Melilotus alba
      Hagedorn, D.J. and J.C. Walker, 1954
      Hanson, E.W. and D.J. Hagedorn, 1954, 1956
      Hungerford, C.W. and Irvin G. Hillyer, 1954
      McWhorter, Frank P., 1949
      Pierce, W.H., 1934, 1937
      Thomas, H. Rex and W.J. Zaumeyer, 1953
      Zaumeyer, W.J., 1940, 1952
      Zaumeyer, W.J. and H.H. Fisher, 1953
      Zaumeyer, W.J. and B.L. Wade, 1935
   Melilotus indica
      Hagedorn, D.J. and E.W. Hanson, 1953
   Melilotus officinalis
      Afanasiev, M.M. and H.E. Morris, 1952
      Baggett, James R., 1957
      Conover, Robert A., 1948
      Grogan, Raymond G. and J.C. Walker, 1948
      Hagedorn, D.J. and E.W. Hanson, 1957
      Hagedorn, D.J. and J.C. Walker, 1950, 1954
      Pierce, W.H., 1935
      Zaumeyer, W.J. and B.L. Wade, 1935
   Melilotus spp.
      McLarty, H.R., 1920
   Nicotiana rustica
      Thomas, H. Rex and W.J. Zaumeyer, 1953
      Zaumeyer, W.J., 1952
      Zaumeyer, W.J. and H.H. Fisher, 1953
   Nicotiana sylvestris
      Thomas, H. Rex and W.J. Zaumeyer, 1953
   Nicotiana tabacum
      Thomas, H. Rex and W.J. Zaumeyer, 1953
      Zaumeyer, W.J., 1952
      Zaumeyer, W.J. and H.H. Fisher, 1953
   Phaseolus aconitifolius
      Thomas, H. Rex and W.J. Zaumeyer, 1953
   Phaseolus acutifolius var. latifolius
      Pierce, W.H., 1934
      Thomas, H. Rex and W.J. Zaumeyer, 1953
      Zaumeyer, W.J. and H.H. Fisher, 1953
   Phaseolus angularis
      Zaumeyer, W.J. and B.L. Wade, 1935
   Phaseolus aureus
      Osborn, H.T., 1938
      Pierce, W.H., 1934
      Zaumeyer, W.J. and H.H. Fisher, 1953
      Zaumeyer, W.J. and B.L. Wade, 1935
   Phaseolus limensis
      (K.M. Smith, 1957) R.E. Fitzpatrick, et al., 1958
   Phaseolus lunatus
      Zaumeyer, W.J. and H.H. Fisher, 1953
   Phaseolus vulgaris
      Afanasiev, M.M. and H.E. Morris, 1952
      Ainsworth, G.C., 1940
      Baggett, James R., 1956, 1957
      Berkeley, G.H., 1953
      Bridgmon, G.H. and J.C. Walker, 1952
      Brierley, Philip, 1952
      Conover, Robert A., 1948
      Grogan, Ray G., 1948
      Grogan, Raymond G. and J.C. Walker, 1948
      Hagedorn, D.J. and J.C. Walker, 1949, 1950, 1954
      Harrison, Arthur L., 1935
      Houston, Byron R. and John W. Oswald, 1953
      Hungerford, C.W. and Irvin G. Hillyer, 1954
      Johnson, James, 1942
      McWhorter, Frank P., 1949
      Murphy, Donald M., 1940
      Osborn, H.T., 1938
      Pierce, W.H., 1934, 1935, 1937
      Thomas, H.R., 1953
      Thomas, H. Rex and W.J. Zaumeyer, 1953
      Yerkes, William D., Jr. and Alfonso Crispin Medina, 1957
      Zaumeyer, W.J., 1933, 1940, 1952
      Zaumeyer, W.J. and H.H. Fisher, 1953
      Zaumeyer, W.J. and B.L. Wade, 1933, 1935, 1936
   Phaseolus vulgaris x P. coccineus
      Baggett, James R., 1956
   Pisum sativum
      Ainsworth, G.C., 1940
      Baggett, James R., 1957
      Berkeley, G.H., 1953

VIRUS
V. BEAN YELLOW MOSAIC (cont.)
Pisum sativum
Conover, Robert A., 1948
Corbett, M.K., 1957
Grogan, Raymond G. and J.C. Walker, 1948
Hagedorn, D.J., 1951, 1952
Hagedorn, D.J. and J.C. Walker, 1949, 1950, 1954
Hanson, E.W. and D.J. Hagedorn, 1954
Hungerford, C.W. and Irvin G. Hillyer, 1954
Johnson, James, 1942
McWhorter, Frank P., 1949
Osborn, H.T., 1935
Oshima, Nagayoshi and M.F. Kernkamp, 1957
Pierce, W.H., 1935, 1937
Thomas, H. Rex and W.J. Zaumeyer, 1953
Zaumeyer, W.J., 1940
Zaumeyer, W.J. and B.L. Wade, 1933, 1935, 1936
Pisum sativum var. arvense
Grogan, Raymond G. and J.C. Walker, 1948
Hagedorn, D.J. and J.C. Walker, 1950, 1954
Pisum sativum var. saccharatum
Pierce, W.H., 1935
Sesbania macrocarpa
Johnson, James, 1942
Trifolium hybridum
Baggett, James R., 1957
Grogan, Raymond G. and J.C. Walker, 1948
Hagedorn, D.J. and E.W. Hanson, 1953, 1957
Hagedorn, D.J. and J.C. Walker, 1950, 1954
Hanson, E.W. and D.J. Hagedorn, 1954, 1956
Hungerford, C.W. and Irvin G. Hillyer, 1954
Trifolium incarnatum
Baggett, James R., 1957
Conover, Robert A., 1948
Diachun, Stephen and Lawrence Henson, 1956
Grogan, Raymond G. and J.C. Walker, 1948
Hagedorn, D.J., 1948, 1952
Hagedorn, D.J. and E.W. Hanson, 1953, 1957
Hagedorn, D.J. and J.C. Walker, 1950, 1954
Hanson, E.W. and D.J. Hagedorn, 1954, 1956
Pierce, W.H., 1934
Thomas, H. Rex and W.J. Zaumeyer, 1953
Zaumeyer, W.J., 1940
Trifolium pratense
Diachun, Stephen and Lawrence Henson, 1953, 1956, 1957
Elliott, J.A., 1921
Hagedorn, D.J., 1948, 1952
Hagedorn, D.J. and E.W. Hanson, 1953, 1957
Hagedorn, D.J. and J.C. Walker, 1950, 1954
Hanson, E.W. and D.J. Hagedorn, 1952, 1954, 1956
McWhorter, Frank P., 1949
Oshima, Nagayoshi and M.F. Kernkamp, 1957
Pierce, W.H., 1935, 1937
Zaumeyer, W.J., 1940
Zaumeyer, W.J. and B.L. Wade, 1935
Trifolium repens
Ainsworth, G.C., 1940
Houston, Byron R. and John W. Oswald, 1953
Kreitlow, K.W., O.J. Hunt and H.L. Wilkins, 1957
Trifolium repens f. giganteum *
Thomas, H. Rex and W.J. Zaumeyer, 1953
Trifolium subterraneum
Hutton, E.M. and J.W. Peak, 1954
McWhorter, Frank P. and John R. Hardison, 1949
Trigonella foenum-graecum
Grogan, Raymond G. and J.C. Walker, 1948
Hagedorn, D.J., 1948, 1952
Hagedorn, D.J. and J.C. Walker, 1950, 1954
Vicia americana
Zaumeyer, W.J. and B.L. Wade, 1935
Vicia atropurpurea
Grogan, Raymond G. and J.C. Walker, 1948
Hagedorn, D.J. and J.C. Walker, 1950, 1954
Vicia faba
Afanasiev, M.M. and H.E. Morris, 1952
Ainsworth, G.C., 1940
Baggett, James R., 1957
Brierley, Philip and Floyd F. Smith, 1948
Conover, Robert A., 1948
Elliott, J.A., 1921
Grogan, Raymond G. and J.C. Walker, 1948
Houston, Byron R. and John W. Oswald, 1953

VIRUS
V. BEAN YELLOW MOSAIC (cont.)
Vicia faba
McWhorter, Frank P., 1949
McWhorter, Frank P. and John R. Hardison, 1949
Osborn, H.T., 1938
Thomas, H. Rex and W.J. Zaumeyer, 1953
Zaumeyer, W.J., 1940, 1952
Zaumeyer, W.J. and H.H. Fisher, 1953
Zaumeyer, W.J. and B.L. Wade, 1935, 1936
Vicia faba var. major *
Hagedorn, D.J. and J.C. Walker, 1950, 1954
Vicia faba var. minor *
Hagedorn, D.J. and J.C. Walker, 1950, 1954
Pierce, W.H., 1934, 1935
Vicia grandiflora
Hagedorn, D.J. and J.C. Walker, 1950, 1954
Vicia lathyroides
(K.M. Smith, 1957) R.E. Fitzpatrick, et al., 1958
Vicia monantha
Grogan, Raymond G. and J.C. Walker, 1948
Hagedorn, D.J. and J.C. Walker, 1950, 1954
Vicia sativa
Grogan, Raymond G. and J.C. Walker, 1948
Hagedorn, D.J. and J.C. Walker, 1950, 1954
Pierce, W.H., 1934
Vicia villosa
Grogan, Raymond G. and J.C. Walker, 1948
Hagedorn, D.J. and J.C. Walker, 1950, 1954
Hungerford, C.W. and Irvin G. Hillyer, 1954
Vigna sesquipedalis
Thomas, H. Rex and W.J. Zaumeyer, 1953
Zaumeyer, W.J. and H.H. Fisher, 1953
Vigna sinensis
Osborn, H.T., 1938
Zaumeyer, W.J. and H.H. Fisher, 1953

V. BEAN YELLOW STIPPLE Zaumeyer and Thomas
Cyamopsis tetragonoloba   1950
Zaumeyer, W.J. and H. Rex Thomas, 1950
Glycine max
Zaumeyer, W.J. and H. Rex Thomas, 1950
Phaseolus acutifolius var. latifolius
Zaumeyer, W.J. and H. Rex Thomas, 1950
Phaseolus calcaratus
Zaumeyer, W.J. and H. Rex Thomas, 1950
Phaseolus coccineus
Zaumeyer, W.J. and H. Rex Thomas, 1950
Phaseolus mungo
Zaumeyer, W.J. and H. Rex Thomas, 1950
Phaseolus vulgaris
Zaumeyer, W.J. and H. Rex Thomas, 1950
Pisum sativum
Zaumeyer, W.J. and H. Rex Thomas, 1950
Vigna sinensis
Zaumeyer, W.J. and H. Rex Thomas, 1950

V. BEET CURLY TOP ((Ball 1909; Boucquet and
Hartung 1915)) Carsner 1919; Severin 1919
Acanthospermum hispidum
Bennett, C.W. and A.S. Costa, 1949
Amaranthus aurora or auroro *
Freitag, Julius H. and Henry H.P. Severin, 1936
Amaranthus caudatus
Freitag, Julius H. and Henry H.P. Severin, 1936
Amaranthus deflexus
Severin, Henry H.P., 1934
Amaranthus gangeticus
Freitag, Julius H. and Henry H.P. Severin, 1936
Amaranthus graecizans
Carsner, E., 1919
Severin, Henry H.P., 1934
Amaranthus retroflexus
Severin, Henry H.P., 1934
Anagallis arvensis
Severin, Henry H.P., 1934
Anchusa azurea
Freitag, Julius H. and Henry H.P. Severin, 1936
Anemone coronaria
Freitag, Julius H. and Henry H.P. Severin, 1936
Anethum graveolens
Severin, Henry H.P., 1929
Anthemis cotula
Severin, Henry H.P., 1934

VIRUS
V. BEET CURLY TOP (cont.)

Anthriscus cerefolium
  Severin, Henry H.P., 1929
Apium graveolens var. dulce
  Severin, H.H.P., 1928, 1929
Arctotis stoechadifolia
  Freitag, Julius H. and Henry H.P. Severin, 1936
Armoracia rusticana
  Severin, Henry H.P., 1929
Atriplex argentea subsp. expansa
  Severin, Henry H.P., 1934
  Severin, Henry H.P. and Charles F. Henderson,
    1928
  Severin, Henry H.P. and Byron R. Houston, 1945
Atriplex argentea var. hillmanii
  Severin, Henry H.P., 1934
Atriplex bracteosa
  Severin, Henry H.P., 1934
  Severin, Henry H.P. and Charles F. Henderson,
    1928
  Severin, Henry H.P. and Byron R. Houston, 1945
Atriplex cordulata
  Severin, Henry H.P., 1934
  Severin, Henry H.P. and Charles F. Henderson,
    1928
Atriplex coronata
  Severin, Henry H.P., 1934
  Severin, Henry H.P. and Charles F. Henderson,
    1928
Atriplex fruticulosa
  Severin, Henry H.P., 1934
  Severin, Henry H.P. and Charles F. Henderson,
    1928
Atriplex hortensis var. rubra *
  Severin, Henry H.P., 1934
Atriplex lentiformis
  Severin, Henry H.P., 1934
  Severin, Henry H.P. and Charles F. Henderson,
    1928
Atriplex parishii
  Severin, Henry H.P., 1934
  Severin, Henry H.P. and Charles F. Henderson,
    1928
Atriplex patula var. hastata
  Severin, Henry H.P., 1934
  Severin, Henry H.P. and Charles F. Henderson,
    1928
Atriplex phyllostegia
  Severin, Henry H.P., 1934
  Severin, Henry H.P. and Charles F. Henderson,
    1928
Atriplex rosea
  Severin, Henry H.P., 1934
  Severin, Henry H.P. and Charles F. Henderson,
    1928
Atriplex semibaccata
  Severin, Henry H.P., 1934
  Severin, Henry H.P. and Charles F. Henderson,
    1928
Atriplex tularensis
  Severin, Henry H.P., 1934
  Severin, Henry H.P. and Charles F. Henderson,
    1928
Baeria uliginosa
  Severin, Henry H.P., 1934
Barbarea vulgaris
  Severin, Henry H.P., 1929
Bellis perennis
  Freitag, Julius H. and Henry H.P. Severin, 1936
Beta macrocarpa
  Bennett, C.W. and Aziz Tanrisever, 1957
  Costa, A.S., 1952
  Giddings, N.J., 1944
Beta maritima
  Severin, Henry H.P. and Charles F. Henderson,
    1928
Beta patellaris
  Costa, A.S., 1952
  Giddings, N.J., 1944
Beta patula
  Costa, A.S., 1952
Beta trigyna
  Giddings, N.J., 1944

VIRUS
V. BEET CURLY TOP (cont.)

Beta vulgaris
  Bennett, C.W., 1934, 1937, 1944, 1951, 1955
  Bennett, C.W., Eubanks Carsner, G.H. Coons and
    E.W. Brandes, 1946
  Bennett, C.W. and A.S. Costa, 1949
  Bennett, C.W. and Aziz Tanrisever, 1957
  Carsner, E., 1919, 1926, 1938
  Carsner, Eubanks and C.F. Stahl, 1924
  Costa, A.S., 1952
  Esau, Katherine, 1930
  Fawcett, G.L., 1927
  Giddings, N.J., 1938, 1940, 1941, 1944, 1946, 1952,
    1954
  Johnson, Folke, 1941
  Jones, Leon K., 1931
  Lackey, C.F., 1932, 1937, 1941, 1942, 1951
  Menzies, J.D. and N.J. Giddings, 1953
  Mumford, Edward Philpott, 1930
  Owen, F.V., Albert M. Murphy and Bion Tolman,
    1942
  Severin, Henry H.P. and Charles F. Henderson,
    1928
  Severin, Henry H.P. and Byron R. Houston, 1945
  Smith, R.E. and P.A. Boncquet, 1915
  Thornberry, H.H. and R.M. Takeshita, 1954
Beta vulgaris var. cicla
  Bennett, C.W., Eubanks Carsner, F.H. Coons and
    E.W. Brandes, 1946
  Severin, Henry H.P. and Charles F. Henderson,
    1928
Beta vulgaris var. macrorhiza *
  Bennett, C.W., Eubanks Carsner, G.H. Coons and
    E.W. Brandes, 1946
  Severin, Henry H.P. and Charles F. Henderson,
    1928
Borago officinalis
  Severin, Henry H.P., 1929
Brachycome iberidifolia
  Freitag, Julius H. and Henry H.P. Severin, 1936
Brassica hirta (Brassica alba)
  Severin, Henry H.P., 1929
Brassica kaber (Brassica arvensis)
  Severin, Henry H.P., 1929, 1934
Brassica oleracea var. acephala
  Severin, Henry H.P., 1929
Brassica oleracea var. botrytis
  Severin, Henry H.P., 1929
Brassica oleracea var. capitata
  Severin, Henry H.P., 1929
Brassica pekinensis
  Costa, A.S., 1952
Brassica rapa
  Severin, Henry H.P., 1929
Browallia speciosa
  Freitag, Julius H. and Henry H.P. Severin, 1936
Calandrinia grandiflora
  Freitag, Julius H. and Henry H.P. Severin, 1936
Calandrinia menziesii
  Carsner, Eubanks and C.F. Stahl, 1924
Calendula officinalis
  Freitag, Julius H. and Henry H.P. Severin, 1936
Capsella bursa-pastoris
  Severin, Henry H.P., 1929, 1934
Capsicum frutescens (Capsicum annuum)
  Costa, A.S., 1952
  Kendrick, J.B., Jr., L.D. Anderson and R.C.
    Dickson, 1951
  Severin, Henry H.P., 1929
Capsicum frutescens var. grossum
  Costa, A.S., 1952
Cardiospermum halicacabum
  Freitag, Julius H. and Henry H.P. Severin, 1936
Celosia argentea
  Freitag, Julius H. and Henry H.P. Severin, 1936
Celosia argentea var. cristata
  (K.M. Smith, 1957) R.E. Fitzpatrick, et al., 1958
  Severin, Henry H.P. and Julius H. Freitag, 1934
Centaurea americana
  Freitag, Julius H. and Henry H.P. Severin, 1936
Centaruea cyanus
  Freitag, Julius H. and Henry H.P. Severin, 1936

VIRUS
V. BEET CURLY TOP (cont.)
  Centaurea moschata
    Freitag, Julius H. and Henry H.P. Severin, 1936
  Chenopodium album
    Bennett, C.W. and Aziz Tanrisever, 1957
    Carsner, E., 1919
    Lackey, C.F., 1929
    Severin, Henry H.P., 1934
    Severin, Henry H.P. and Charles F. Henderson,
    1928
  Chenopodium album var. viride
    Lackey, C.F., 1929
  Chenopodium amaranticolor
    Bennett, C.W. and Aziz Tanrisever, 1957
  Chenopodium ambrosioides
    (K.M. Smith, 1957) R.E. Fitzpatrick, et al., 1958
    Severin, Henry H.P., 1934
    Severin, Henry H.P. and Charles F. Henderson,
    1928
  Chenopodium californicum
    Severin, Henry H.P., 1934
    Severin, Henry H.P. and Charles F. Henderson,
    1928
  Chenopodium leptophyllum
    Severin, Henry H.P., 1934
    Severin, Henry H.P. and Charles F. Henderson,
    1928
  Chenopodium murale
    Bennett, C.W. and Aziz Tanrisever, 1957
    Carsner, E., 1925
    Carsner, E. and C.F. Stahl, 1924
    Giddings, N.J., 1944
    Lackey, C.F., 1932, 1937
    Severin, Henry H.P., 1934
    Severin, Henry H.P. and Charles F. Henderson,
    1928
  Chrysanthemum coronarium
    Freitag, Julius H. and Henry H.P. Severin, 1936
  Chrysanthemum frutescens
    Freitag, Julius H. and Henry H.P. Severin, 1936
  Chrysanthemum parthenium
    Freitag, Julius H. and Henry H.P. Severin, 1936
  Cicer arietinum
    Severin, Henry H.P. and Charles F. Henderson,
    1928
  Citrullus vulgaris
    Lackey, C.F., 1929
    Severin, Henry H.P. and Charles F. Henderson,
    1928
  Citrullus vulgaris var. citroides
    Severin, Henry H.P. and Charles F. Henderson,
    1928
  Clarkia elegans
    Freitag, Julius H. and Henry H.P. Severin, 1936
  Cleome spinosa
    Freitag, Julius H. and Henry H.P. Severin, 1936'
  Cobaea scandens
    Freitag, Julius H. and Henry H.P. Severin, 1936
  Coreopsis tinctoria
    Freitag, Julius H. and Henry H.P. Severin, 1936
    Severin, Henry H.P. and Julius H. Freitag, 1934
  Coriandrum sativum
    Severin, Henry H.P., 1929
  Cosmos bipinnatus
    Freitag, Julius H. and Henry H.P. Severin, 1936
    Severin, Henry H.P. and Julius H. Freitag, 1934
  Cosmos hybridus
    Freitag, Julius H. and Henry H.P. Severin, 1936
  Cucumis anguria
    Severin, Henry H.P. and Charles F. Henderson,
    1928
  Cucumis melo
    Giddings, N.J., 1948
  Cucumis melo var. cantalupensis
    Severin, Henry H.P. and Charles F. Henderson,
    1928
  Cucumis melo var. inodorus
    Severin, Henry H.P. and Charles F. Henderson,
    1928
  Cucumis melo var. reticulatus
    Severin, Henry H.P. and Charles F. Henderson,
    1928

VIRUS
V. BEET CURLY TOP (cont.)
  Cucumis sativus
    Severin, Henry H.P. and Charles F. Henderson,
    1928
  Cucurbita maxima
    Bennett, C.W., 1934
    Dana, B.F., 1938
    Lackey, C.F., 1929
    McKay, M.B. and T.P. Dykstra, 1927
    Severin, Henry H.P. and Charles F. Henderson,
    1928
  Cucurbita moschata
    Dana, B.F., 1941
    Severin, Henry H.P. and Charles F. Henderson,
    1928
  Cucurbita pepo
    Dana, B.F., 1941
    Severin, Henry H.P. and Charles F. Henderson,
    1928
  Cucurbita pepo var. ovifera
    Freitag, Julius H. and Henry H.P. Severin, 1936
  Cymbalaria muralis
    Freitag, Julius H. and Henry H.P. Severin, 1936
  Cynoglossum amabile
    Freitag, Julius H. and Henry H.P. Severin, 1936
  Datura stramonium
    Adsuar, J., 1955
    Bennett, C.W. and A.S. Costa, 1949
    Bennett, C.W. and Aziz Tanrisever, 1957
    Costa, A.S., 1952
    Fulton, Robert W., 1955
    Giddings, N.J., 1944, 1954
    Giddings, N.J., C.W. Bennett and A.L. Harrison,
    1951
    Severin, Henry H.P., 1929, 1934
  Delphinium nudicaule
    Freitag, Julius H. and Henry H.P. Severin, 1936
    Severin, Henry H.P., 1942
  Delphinium spp.
    Severin, Henry H.P., 1942
  Dianthus barbatus
    Freitag, Julius H. and Henry H.P. Severin, 1936
  Dianthus caryophyllus
    Freitag, Julius H. and Henry H.P. Severin, 1936
    Severin, Henry H.P. and Julius H. Freitag, 1934
  Dianthus chinensis
    Freitag, Julius H. and Henry H.P. Severin, 1936
  Dianthus chinensis var. heddewigii
    Freitag, Julius H. and Henry H.P. Severin, 1936
  Dianthus plumarius
    Freitag, Julius H. and Henry H.P. Severin, 1936
    Severin, Henry H.P., 1939
    Severin, Henry H.P. and Julius H. Freitag, 1934
  Digitalis ambigua
    Freitag, Julius H. and Henry H.P. Severin, 1936
  Dimorphotheca aurantiaca
    Freitag, Julius H. and Henry H.P. Severin, 1936
  Erodium botrys
    Severin, Henry H.P., 1934
  Erodium cicutarium
    Carsner, E., 1919
    Carsner, Eubanks and C.F. Stahl, 1924
    Giddings, N.J., 1944
    Lackey, C.F., 1937
    Severin, Henry H.P., 1934
  Erodium macrophyllum
    Severin, Henry H.P., 1934
  Erodium moschatum
    Carsner, E., 1919
    Severin, Henry H.P., 1934
  Erysimum repandum
    Giddings, N.J., 1944
  Eschscholtzia californica
    Giddings, N.J., 1944
  Euphorbia marginata
    Freitag, Julius H. and Henry H.P. Severin, 1936
  Euphorbia peplus
    Severin, Henry H.P., 1934
  Euphorbia prunifolia
    Bennett, C.W. and A.S. Costa, 1949
    Costa, A.S., 1952
  Fagopyrum esculentum
    Bennett, C.W. and A.S. Costa, 1949

VIRUS
V. BEET CURLY TOP (cont.)
 Fagopyrum esculentum
  Carsner, E., 1919
  Costa, A.S., 1952
  Severin, Henry H.P., 1929
 Foeniculum vulgare var. dulce
  Severin, Henry H.P., 1929
 Gnaphalium chilense
  Severin, Henry H.P., 1934
 Gomphrena globosa
  Freitag, Julius H. and Henry H.P. Severin, 1936
 Gypsophila paniculata
  Freitag, Julius H. and Henry H.P. Severin, 1936
 Helianthus debilis
  Freitag, Julius H. and Henry H.P. Severin, 1936
 Helianthus decapetalus var. multiflorus
  Freitag, Julius H. and Henry H.P. Severin, 1936
 Helichrysum bracteatum
  Freitag, Julius H. and Henry H.P. Severin, 1936
  Severin, Henry H.P. and Julius H. Freitag, 1934
 Heliotropium peruvianum
  Freitag, Julius H. and Henry H.P. Severin, 1936
 Helipterum roseum
  Freitag, Julius H. and Henry H.P. Severin, 1936
 Hesperis matronalis
  Freitag, Julius H. and Henry H.P. Severin, 1936
 Hibiscus esculentus
  Severin, Henry H.P., 1929
 Humulus japonicus
  Freitag, Julius H. and Henry H.P. Severin, 1936
 Iberis umbellata
  Freitag, Julius H. and Henry H.P. Severin, 1936
 Ipomoea setosa
  Freitag, Julius H. and Henry H.P. Severin, 1936
 Kochia scoparia var. trichophylla
  Freitag, Julius H. and Henry H.P. Severin, 1936
  Severin, Henry H.P. and Julius H. Freitag, 1934
 Lactuca sativa
  Giddings, N.J., 1944
 Lagenaria siceraria (Lagenaria leucantha)
  Freitag, Julius H. and Henry H.P. Severin, 1936
 Lathyrus odoratus
  Giddings, N.J., 1944
 Lavatera trimestris
  Freitag, Julius H. and Henry H.P. Severin, 1936
 Lepidium lasiocarpum
  Giddings, N.J., 1944
 Lepidium nitidum
  Giddings, N.J., 1938, 1944
  Lackey, C.F., 1937
  Severin, Henry H.P., 1934
 Limonium sinuatum
  Freitag, Julius H. and Henry H.P. Severin, 1936
 Linum flavum
  Giddings, N.J., 1947, 1948
 Linum grandiflorum var. rubrum *
  Giddings, N.J., 1947, 1948
 Linum lewisii
  Bennett, C.W. and A.S. Costa, 1949
  Giddings, N.J., 1947, 1948
 Linum perenne
  Giddings, N.J., 1947, 1948
 Linum usitatissimum
  Atkins, I.M., M.C. Futrell and O.G. Merkle,
   1957
  Bennett, C.W. and A.S. Costa, 1949
  Giddings, N.J., 1948
  Severin, Henry H.P., 1929
  Severin, Henry H.P. and Byron R. Houston, 1945
 Lobelia cardinalis
  Freitag, Julius H. and Henry H.P. Severin, 1936
 Lobelia erinus var. speciosa *
  Freitag, Julius H. and Henry H.P. Severin, 1936
 Lotus americanus
  Severin, Henry H.P., 1934
 Lotus strigosus
  Severin, Henry H.P., 1934
 Luffa aegyptiaca (Luffa cylindrica)
  Freitag, Julius H. and Henry H.P. Severin, 1936
 Lunaria annua
  Freitag, Julius H. and Henry H.P. Severin, 1936
 Lychnis chalcedonica
  Freitag, Julius H. and Henry H.P. Severin, 1936

VIRUS
V. BEET CURLY TOP (cont.)
 Lychnis haageana
  Freitag, Julius H. and Henry H.P. Severin, 1936
 Lycopersicon esculentum
  Adsuar, J., 1955
  Bennett, C.W., 1944, 1951
  Bennett, C.W. and A.S. Costa, 1949
  Bennett, C.W. and Aziz Tanrisever, 1957
  Carsner, Eubanks and C.F. Stahl, 1924
  Costa, A.S., 1952
  Fulton, Robert W., 1955
  Giddings, N.J., 1938, 1944, 1952, 1954
  Giddings, N.J., C.W. Bennett and A.L. Harrison,
   1951
  Lackey, C.F., 1929
  Lesley, J.W., 1931
  Lesley, J.W. and J.M. Wallace, 1938
  McKay, M.B. and T.P. Dykstra, 1927
  Menzies, J.D. and N.J. Giddings, 1952, 1953
  Severin, Henry H.P., 1928
  Shapovalov, M., 1927, 1931
  Virgin, Walter J., 1940
  Wallace, J.M. and J.W. Lesley, 1944
  Watson, R.D. and J.E. Kraus, 1949
 Lycopersicon hirsutum
  Giddings, N.J., C.W. Bennett and A.L. Harrison,
   1951
 Lycopersicon pimpinellifolium
  Costa, A.S., 1952
  Lesley, J.W. and J.M. Wallace, 1938
 Malcomia maritima
  Giddings, N.J., 1944
 Malva parviflora
  Bennett, C.W. and Aziz Tanrisever, 1957
  Carsner, E., 1919
  Severin, Henry H.P., 1929, 1934
 Malva rotundifolia
  Severin, Henry H.P., 1929, 1934
 Matricaria inodora
  Freitag, Julius H. and Henry H.P. Severin, 1936
 Matthiola incana
  Severin, Henry H.P. and Julius H. Freitag, 1934
 Matthiola incana var. annua
  Freitag, Julius H. and Henry H.P. Severin, 1936
  Severin, Henry H.P. and Julius H. Freitag, 1934
 Medicago hispida
  Carsner, E., 1919
  Giddings, N.J., 1944
  Severin, Henry H.P., 1934
  Severin, Henry H.P. and Charles F. Henderson,
   1928
 Medicago sativa
  Severin, Henry H.P. and Charles F. Henderson,
   1928
 Melilotus alba
  Severin, Henry H.P. and Charles F. Henderson,
   1928
 Melilotus indica
  Giddings, N.J., 1944
  Severin, Henry H.P. and Charles F. Henderson,
   1928
 Microseris douglasii
  Severin, Henry H.P., 1934
 Mimulus luteus
  Freitag, Julius H. and Henry H.P. Severin, 1936
 Mirabilis jalapa
  Freitag, Julius H. and Henry H.P. Severin, 1936
  Severin, Henry H.P. and Julius H. Freitag, 1934
 Modiola caroliniana
  Severin, Henry H.P., 1934, 1939
 Monolepsis nuttalliana
  Severin, Henry H.P., 1934
 Myosotis scorpioides
  Freitag, Julius H. and Henry H.P. Severin, 1936
 Nemesia strumosa
  Freitag, Julius H. and Henry H.P. Severin, 1936
 Nemophila maculata
  Freitag, Julius H. and Henry H.P. Severin, 1936
  Giddings, N.J., 1944
 Nicotiana alata var. grandiflora
  Freitag, Julius H. and Henry H.P. Severin, 1936
 Nicotiana glauca
  Bennett, C.W., 1934, 1937

VIRUS
V. BEET CURLY TOP (cont.)

Nicotiana glauca
  Bennett, C.W. and Aziz Tanrisever, 1957
  Costa, A.S., 1952
  Giddings, N.J., 1944
  Severin, Henry H.P., 1934, 1939

Nicotiana glutinosa
  Bennett, C.W. and A.S. Costa, 1949
  Bennett, C.W. and Aziz Tanrisever, 1957
  Costa, A.S., 1952
  Fulton, Robert W., 1955
  Giddings, N.J., 1944, 1947, 1954

Nicotiana rustica
  Fulton, Robert W., 1955
  Lackey, C.F., 1929
  Severin, Henry H.P., 1929

Nicotiana tabacum
  Bennett, C.W., 1934, 1937, 1944, 1951
  Bennett, C.W. and A.S. Costa, 1949
  Bennett, C.W. and Aziz Tanrisever, 1957
  Costa, A.S., 1952
  Fulton, Robert W., 1955
  Giddings, N.J., 1938, 1944, 1947, 1954
  Lackey, C.F., 1941
  Price, W.C., 1943
  Severin, Henry H.P., 1929

Nigella damascena
  Freitag, Julius H. and Henry H.P. Severin, 1936

Nitrophila occidentalis
  Severin, Henry H.P. and Charles F. Henderson, 1928

Oxalis corniculata
  Severin, Henry H.P., 1934

Oxalis corniculata var. atropurpurea
  Severin, Henry H.P., 1934

Oxalis spp.
  Bennett, C.W. and A.S. Costa, 1949

Oxalis stricta
  Starrett, Ruth C., 1929

Papaver nudicaule
  Freitag, Julius H. and Henry H.P. Severin, 1936

Papaver orientale
  Freitag, Julius H. and Henry H.P. Severin, 1936

Pelargonium hortorum (X P. zonale)
  Freitag, Julius H. and Henry H.P. Severin, 1936
  Severin, Henry H.P., 1939
  Severin, Henry H.P. and Julius H. Freitag, 1934

Petroselinum hortense
  Severin, Henry H.P., 1929

Petunia hybrida
  Bennett, C.W., Eubanks Carsner, F.H. Coons and E.W. Brandes, 1946
  Bennett, C.W. and Aziz Tanrisever, 1957
  Costa, A.S., 1952
  Freitag, Julius H. and Henry H.P. Severin, 1936
  Fulton, Robert W., 1955
  Severin, Henry H.P. and Julius H. Freitag, 1934

Phacelia ramosissima
  Severin, Henry H.P., 1934, 1939

Phaseolus lunatus
  Severin, Henry H.P. and Charles F. Henderson, 1928

Phaseolus vulgaris
  Bennett, C.W., 1934
  Carsner, E., 1925, 1926
  Dana, B.F., 1940
  Dean, Leslie L. and C.W. Hungerford, 1954
  Giddings, N.J., 1938, 1944
  Lackey, C.F., 1942
  Mackie, W.W. and Katherine Esau, 1932
  Murphy, Donald M., 1940
  Pierce, W.H., 1937
  Severin, Henry H.P. and Charles F. Henderson, 1928

Phlox drummondii
  Freitag, Julius H. and Henry H.P. Severin, 1936

Phyllanthus corcovadensis
  Bennett, C.W. and A.S. Costa, 1949

Physalis spp.
  Bennett, C.W., Eubanks Carsner, F.H. Coons and E.W. Brandes, 1946

Physalis wrightii
  Severin, Henry H.P., 1929, 1934

VIRUS
V. BEET CURLY TOP (cont.)

Plantago erecta
  Giddings, N.J., 1938, 1944
  Severin, Henry H.P., 1934

Plantago major
  Giddings, N.J., 1944
  Severin, Henry H.P., 1934

Polygonum amphibian var. hartwrightii
  Severin, Henry H.P., 1929, 1934

Polygonum aviculare
  Carsner, E., 1919
  Severin, Henry H.P., 1929, 1934

Polygonum lapathifolium
  Severin, Henry H.P., 1929, 1934

Polygonum muhlengergii
  Severin, Henry H.P., 1929, 1934

Polygonum persicaria
  Severin, Henry H.P., 1929, 1934

Portulaca grandiflora
  Freitag, Julius H. and Henry H.P. Severin, 1936

Portulaca oleracea
  Severin, Henry H.P., 1934

Primula elatior
  Freitag, Julius H. and Henry H.P. Severin, 1936

Primula obconica
  Freitag, Julius H. and Henry H.P. Severin, 1936

Primula saxatalis
  Freitag, Julius H. and Henry H.P. Severin, 1936

Primula veris
  Freitag, Julius H. and Henry H.P. Severin, 1936

Quamoclit lobata
  Freitag, Julius H. and Henry H.P. Severin, 1936

Raphanus sativus
  Severin, Henry H.P., 1929, 1934

Reseda odorata
  Freitag, Julius H. and Henry H.P. Severin, 1936

Rheum rhaponticum
  Severin, Henry H.P., 1929

Rumex crispus
  Carsner, E., 1925
  Severin, Henry H.P., 1929, 1934

Rumex scutatus
  Severin, Henry H.P., 1929

Salpiglossis sinuata
  Freitag, Julius H. and Henry H.P. Severin, 1936

Salsola kali var. tenuifolia
  Carsner, E., 1919
  Severin, Henry H.P., 1934
  Severin, Henry H.P. and Charles F. Henderson, 1928
  Severin, Henry H.P. and Byron R. Houston, 1945

Salvia splendens
  Freitag, Julius H. and Henry H.P. Severin, 1936

Samolus floribundus
  Costa, A.S., 1952

Samolus parviflorus
  Bennett, C.W., 1952, 1955
  Giddings, N.J., 1944

Scabiosa atropurpurea
  Severin, Henry H.P. and Julius H. Freitag, 1934

Schizanthus wisetonensis
  Freitag, Julius H. and Henry H.P. Severin, 1936

Senecio vulgaris
  Severin, Henry H.P., 1934

Silene pendula
  Freitag, Julius H. and Henry H.P. Severin, 1936

Solanum andigenum * or Solanum tuberosum
  Watson, R.D. and T.E. Randall, 1951

Solanum antipoviczii
  Watson, R.D. and T.E. Randall, 1951

Solanum antipoviczii or Solanum neo-antipoviczii
  Watson, R.D. and T.E. Randall, 1951

Solanum demissum
  Watson, R.D. and T.E. Randall, 1951

Solanum douglasii
  Severin, Henry H.P., 1934

Solanum nigrum
  Costa, A.S., 1952

Solanum nigrum var. douglassi *
  Severin, Henry H.P., 1929

Solanum polyadenium
  Watson, R.D. and T.E. Randall, 1951

VIRUS
V. BEET CURLY TOP (cont.)
  Solanum simplicifolium
    Watson, R.D. and T.E. Randall, 1951
  Solanum spp.
    Watson, R.D. and T.E Randall, 1951
  Solanum tuberosum
    Giddings, N.J., 1944, 1947, 1952, 1953, 1954
    Jones, Leon K., C.L. Vincent and Earl F. Burk, 1940
    Menzies, J.D. and N.J. Giddings, 1952, 1953
    Milbrath, J.A., 1946
    Severin, Henry H.P., 1929
  Sonchus asper
    Severin, Henry H.P., 1934
  Sonchus oleraceus
    Severin, Henry H.P., 1934
  Spinacia oleracea
    Carsner, E., 1919
    Costa, A.S., 1952
    Giddings, N.J., 1944
    Lackey, C.F., 1929
    Severin, H.H.P., 1928
    Severin, Henry H.P. and Charles F. Henderson, 1928
  Stellaria media
    Bennett, C.W., Eubanks Carsner, F.H. Coons and E.W. Brandes, 1946
    Bennett, C.W. and A.S. Costa, 1949
    Bennett, C.W. and Aziz Tanrisever, 1957
    Carsner, E., 1919
    Carsner, Eubanks and C.F. Stahl, 1924
    Costa, A.S., 1952
    Lackey, C.F., 1932, 1937
    Severin, Henry H.P., 1934
  Suaeda moquini
    Carsner, E., 1925
    Severin, Henry H.P., 1939
  Tagetes erecta
    Freitag, Julius H. and Henry H.P. Severin, 1936
  Tagetes patula
    Freitag, Julius H. and Henry H.P. Severin, 1936
  Thelypodium lasiophyllum
    Severin, Henry H.P., 1934
  Thunbergia alata
    Freitag, Julius H. and Henry H.P. Severin, 1936
  Trachymene caerulea
    Freitag, Julius H. and Henry H.P. Severin, 1936
  Trichosanthes anguina
    Freitag, Julius H. and Henry H.P. Severin, 1936
  Trifolium hybridum
    Giddings, N.J., 1944
    Severin, Henry H.P. and Charles F. Henderson, 1928
  Trifolium incarnatum
    Giddings, N.J., 1944
    Severin, Henry H.P. and Charles F. Henderson, 1928
  Trifolium pratense
    Severin, Henry H.P. and Charles F. Henderson, 1928
  Trifolium pratense var. perenne
    Severin, Henry H.P. and Charles F. Henderson, 1928
  Trifolium repens
    Giddings, N.J., 1944
    Severin, Henry H.P. and Charles F. Henderson, 1928
  Tropaeolum majus
    Severin, Henry H.P. and Julius H. Freitag, 1934
  Tropaeolum peregrinum
    Freitag, Julius H. and Henry H.P. Severin, 1936
  Urtica urens
    Carsner, E., 1919
    Severin, Henry H.P., 1934
  Valerianella olitoria
    Severin, Henry H.P., 1929
  Vicia atropurpurea
    Severin, Henry H.P. and Charles F. Henderson, 1928
  Vicia faba
    Severin, Henry H.P. and Charles F. Henderson, 1928

VIRUS
V. BEET CURLY TOP (cont.)
  Vicia sativa
    Severin, Henry H.P. and Charles F. Henderson, 1928
  Vicia villosa
    Severin, Henry H.P. and Charles F. Henderson, 1928
  Vigna sinensis
    Severin, Henry H.P. and Charles F. Henderson, 1928
  Vinca rosea
    Freitag, Julius H. and Henry H.P. Severin, 1936
  Viola cornuta
    Freitag, Julius H. and Henry H.P. Severin, 1936
    Severin, Henry H.P. and Julius H. Freitag, 1934
  Viola tricolor
    Dana, B.F. and F.P. McWhorter, 1935
  Viola tricolor var. hortensis
    Severin, Henry H.P. and Julius H. Freitag, 1934
  Xanthium spinosum
    Severin, Henry H.P., 1934
  Zinnia elegans
    Bennett, C.W., Eubanks Carsner, F.H. Coons and E.W. Brandes, 1946
    Bennett, C.W. and A.S. Costa, 1949
    Bennett, C.W. and Aziz Tanrisever, 1957
    Freitag, Julius H. and Henry H.P. Severin, 1936
    Severin, Henry H.P., 1934
    Severin, Henry H.P. and Julius H. Freitag, 1934
  Zinnia haageana
    Freitag, Julius H. and Henry H.P. Severin, 1936
    Severin, Henry H.P., 1934

V. BEET LEAF CURL ((Wille 1928))
  Ambrosia artemisiifolia
    (K.M. Smith, 1957) R.E. Fitzpatrick, et al., 1958
  Beta vulgaris
    Boncquet, P.A., 1923
    Coons, G.H., J.E. Kotila and D. Stewart, 1937
    Hildebrand, A.A. and L.W. Koch, 1942
    Severin, H.H.P., 1924
  Chenopodium album
    (K.M. Smith, 1957) R.E. Fitzpatrick, et al., 1958
  Phaseolus vulgaris
    (K.M. Smith, 1957) R.E. Fitzpatrick, et al., 1958
  Spinacia oleracea
    (K.M. Smith, 1957) R.E. Fitzpatrick, et al., 1958

V. BEET MOSAIC Robbins 1921; Hoggan 1933
  Amaranthus caudatus
    (K.M. Smith, 1957) R.E. Fitzpatrick, et al., 1958
  Amaranthus retroflexus
    Bennett, C.W., 1949
    Pound, Glenn S., 1947
  Aster amellus
    Pound, Glenn S., 1947
  Atriplex bracteosa
    Severin, Henry H.P. and Roger M. Drake, 1947
  Atriplex hortensis
    Pound, Glenn S., 1947
  Atriplex patula var. hastata
    Severin, Henry H.P. and Roger M. Drake, 1947
  Atriplex rosea
    Severin, Henry H.P. and Roger M. Drake, 1947
  Beta maritima
    Severin, Henry H.P. and Roger M. Drake, 1948
  Beta patellaris
    Bennett, C.W., 1949
  Beta vulgaris
    Bawden, F.C., Brenda M.G. Hamlyn and Marion A. Watson, 1954
    Bennett, C.W., 1944
    Doncaster, J.P. and B. Kassanis, 1946
    Hale, J.B., M.A. Watson and R. Hull, 1946
    Hoggan, I.A., 1933
    Jones, Leon K., 1931
    McLean, D.M., 1952
    Pound, Glenn S., 1947
    Robbins, W.W., 1921
    Severin, Henry H.P. and Roger M. Drake, 1948
    Sylvester, E.S., 1947, 1949, 1950, 1952
    Watson, Marion A., R. Hull, J.W. Blencowe and Brenda M.G. Hamlyn, 1951

VIRUS

V. BEET MOSAIC (cont.)

Beta vulgaris var. cicla
McLean, D.M., 1952
Pound, Glenn S., 1947
Severin, Henry H.P. and Roger M. Drake, 1948
Beta vulgaris var. macrorhiza *
Severin, Henry H.P. and Roger M. Drake, 1948
Browallia speciosa
Bennett, C.W., 1949
Capsella bursa-pastoris
Pound, Glenn S., 1947
Chenopodium album
Pound, Glenn S., 1947
Severin, Henry H.P. and Roger M. Drake, 1947
Chenopodium amaranticolor
Hollings, M., 1957
Chenopodium murale
Severin, Henry H.P. and Roger M. Drake, 1947
Iodanthus pinnatifidus
Pound, Glenn S., 1947
Kochia scoparia var. trichophylla
Severin, Henry H.P. and Roger M. Drake, 1948
Melilotus indica
Bennett, C.W., 1949
Nicotiana clevelandi
Bennett, C.W., 1949
Nicotiana multivalvis
Bennett, C.W., 1949
Nicotiana quadrivalvis
Bennett, C.W., 1949
Nicotiana tabacum
Hoggan, Isme A., 1934
Severin, Henry H.P. and Roger M. Drake, 1948
Phacelia campanularia
Bennett, C.W., 1949
Pisum sativum
Bennett, C.W., 1949
Salsola kali var. tenuifolia
Severin, Henry H.P. and Roger M. Drake, 1947
Samolus parviflorus
Bennett, C.W., 1949
Sonchus arvensis
(K.M. Smith, 1957) R.E. Fitzpatrick, et al., 1958
Spinacia oleracea
Hoggan, I.A., 1933
McLean, D.M., 1952
Pound, Glenn S., 1947
Severin, Henry H.P., 1948
Severin, Henry H.P. and Roger M. Drake, 1948
Stellaria media
Pound, Glenn S., 1947
Tetragonia expansa
Pound, Glenn S., 1947
Severin, Henry H.P. and Roger M. Drake, 1948
Trifolium incarnatum
Bennett, C.W., 1949
Verbena hybrida
Pound, Glenn S., 1947
Viola tricolor var. hortensis
Pound, Glenn S., 1947
Zinnia elegans
McLean, D.M., 1952
Pound, Glenn S., 1947

V. BEET RING SPOT *

Avena sativa
Harrison, B.D., 1957
Beta vulgaris
Harrison, B.D., 1957
Brassica campestris var. napobrassica
Harrison, B.D., 1957
Brassica rapa
Harrison, B.D., 1957
Capsella bursa-pastoris
Harrison, B.D., 1957
Chenopodium amaranticolor
Harrison, B.D., 1957
Cucumis sativus
Harrison, B.D., 1957
Datura stramonium
Harrison, B.D., 1957
Fragaria vesca
Harrison, B.D., 1957

VIRUS

V. BEET RING SPOT * (cont.)

Heracleum sphondylium
Harrison, B.D., 1957
Lycopersicon esculentum
Harrison, B.D., 1957
Lycopsis arvensis
Harrison, B.D., 1957
Myosotis arvensis
Harrison, B.D., 1957
Nicotiana glutinosa
Harrison, B.D., 1957
Nicotiana rustica
Harrison, B.D., 1957
Nicotiana tabacum
Harrison, B.D., 1957
Petunia hybrida
Harrison, B.D., 1957
Phaseolus vulgaris
Harrison, B.D., 1957
Polygonum aviculare
Harrison, B.D., 1957
Polygonum convolvulus
Harrison, B.D., 1957
Polygonum persicaria
Harrison, B.D., 1957
Senecio vulgaris
Harrison, B.D., 1957
Solanum tuberosum
Harrison, B.D., 1957
Sonchus asper
Harrison, B.D., 1957
Stellaria media
Harrison, B.D., 1957
Taraxacum officinale
Harrison, B.D., 1957
Triticum aestivum
Harrison, B.D., 1957
Tussilago farfara
Harrison, B.D., 1957
Urtica urens
Harrison, B.D., 1957
Veronica persica
Harrison, B.D., 1957

V. BEET ROSETTE *

Beta vulgaris
Bennett, C.W. and James E. Duffus, 1957

V. BEET YELLOW NET Sylvester 1948

Beta vulgaris
Bennett, C.W., 1944, 1956
McLean, D.M., 1952
Sylvester, Edward S., 1948, 1949, 1950
Beta vulgaris var. cicla
McLean, D.M., 1952
Sylvester, Edward S., 1948

V. BEET YELLOW WILT Bennett and Munck 1946

Beta vulgaris
Bennett, C.W. and Carlos Munck, 1946
Beta vulgaris var. cicla
(K.M. Smith, 1957) R.E. Fitzpatrick, et al., 1958

V. BEET YELLOWS Watson 1942; Petherbridge and Stirrup 1935

Achyranthes aspera
Roland, G. and J. Tahon, 1961
Aizoon spp.
Roland, G. and J. Tahon, 1961
Amaranthus albus
Roland, G. and J. Tahon, 1961
Amaranthus aureus
Roland, G. and J. Tahon, 1961
Amaranthus caracu
Roland, G. and J. Tahon, 1961
Amaranthus carneus
Roland, G. and J. Tahon, 1961
Amaranthus caudatus
Roland, G. and J. Tahon, 1961
Amaranthus cruentus
Roland, G. and J. Tahon, 1961
Amaranthus deflexus
Roland, G. and J. Tahon, 1961

VIRUS
V. BEET YELLOWS (cont.)

Amaranthus gangeticus
  Roland, G. and J. Tahon, 1961
Amaranthus graecizans
  Roland, G. and J. Tahon, 1961
Amaranthus palmeri
  Roland, G. and J. Tahon, 1961
Amaranthus paniculatus
  Roland, G. and J. Tahon, 1961
Amaranthus patulus
  Roland, G. and J. Tahon, 1961
Amaranthus retroflexus
  Roland, G. and J. Tahon, 1961
Atriplex bracteosa
  Roland, G. and J. Tahon, 1961
Atriplex canescens
  Roland, G. and J. Tahon, 1961
Atriplex coronata
  Roland, G. and J. Tahon, 1961
Atriplex coulteri
  Roland, G. and J. Tahon, 1961
Atriplex elegans
  Roland, G. and J. Tahon, 1961
Atriplex expansa
  Roland, G. and J. Tahon, 1961
Atriplex hortensis
  Roland, G. and J. Tahon, 1961
Atriplex microcarpa
  Roland, G. and J. Tahon, 1961
Atriplex nitens
  (K.M. Smith, 1957) R.E. Fitzpatrick, et al., 1958
  Roland, G. and J. Tahon, 1961
Atriplex patula
  Roland, G. and J. Tahon, 1961
Atriplex patula var. hastata
  Roland, G. and J. Tahon, 1961
Atriplex rosea
  Roland, G. and J. Tahon, 1961
Atriplex semibaccatus
  Roland, G. and J. Tahon, 1961
Atriplex siberica
  Roland, G. and J. Tahon, 1961
Atriplex spongiosa
  Roland, G. and J. Tahon, 1961
Bassia hyssopifolia
  Roland, G. and J. Tahon, 1961
Beta atriplicifolia
  Roland, G. and J. Tahon, 1961
Beta cicla viridis *
  Roland, G. and J. Tahon, 1961
Beta hybrida
  Roland, G. and J. Tahon, 1961
Beta lomatogona
  Roland, G. and J. Tahon, 1961
Beta macrocarpa
  .Costa, A.S. and C.W. Bennett, 1955
  Roland, G. and J. Tahon, 1961
Beta maritima
  Costa, A.S. and C.W. Bennett, 1955
  Roland, G. and J. Tahon, 1961
Beta patellaris
  Roland, G. and J. Tahon, 1961
Beta patula
  Roland, G. and J. Tahon, 1961
Beta procumbens
  Costa, A.S. and C.W. Bennett, 1955
  Roland, G. and J. Tahon, 1961
Beta trigyna
  Roland, G. and J. Tahon, 1961
Beta vulgaris
  Bawden, F.C., Brenda M.G. Hamlyn and Marion
  A. Watson, 1954
  Coons, G.H., 1952
  Costa, A.S. and C.W. Bennett, 1955
  Doncaster, J.P. and B. Kassanis, 1946
  Dufrenoy, Jean, 1940
  Hale, J.B., M.A. Watson and R. Hull, 1946
  Kassanis, B., 1949
  McLean, D.M., 1952, 1953
  Roland, G. and J. Tahon, 1961
  Watson, M.A., 1942
  Watson, Marion A., R. Hull, J.W. Blencowe and
  Brenda M.G. Hamlyn, 1951

VIRUS
V. BEET YELLOWS (cont.)

Beta vulgaris
  Watson, Marion A. and G.E. Russell, 1956
Beta vulgaris var. cicla
  McLean, D.M., 1953
Beta webbiana
  Roland, G. and J. Tahon, 1961
Capsella bursa-pastoris
  (K.M. Smith, 1957) R.E. Fitzpatrick, et al., 1958
  Roland, G. and J. Tahon, 1961
Celosia argentea
  Roland, G. and J. Tahon, 1961
Celosia argentea var. cristata
  Roland, G. and J. Tahon, 1961
Cerastium viscosum
  Roland, G. and J. Tahon, 1961
Chenopodium album
  (K.M. Smith, 1957) R.E. Fitzpatrick, et al., 1958
  Roland, G. and J. Tahon, 1961
Chenopodium amaranticolor
  Roland, G. and J. Tahon, 1961
Chenopodium ambrosioides
  Roland, G. and J. Tahon, 1961
Chenopodium bonus henricus
  Roland, G. and J. Tahon, 1961
Chenopodium botrys
  Roland, G. and J. Tahon, 1961
Chenopodium capitatum
  Roland, G. and J. Tahon, 1961
Chenopodium ficifolium
  Roland, G. and J. Tahon, 1961
Chenopodium foliosum
  Roland, G. and J. Tahon, 1961
Chenopodium giganteum
  Roland, G. and J. Tahon, 1961
Chenopodium glaucum
  Roland, G. and J. Tahon, 1961
Chenopodium hybridum
  Roland, G. and J. Tahon, 1961
Chenopodium leptophyllum
  Roland, G. and J. Tahon, 1961
Chenopodium murale
  Costa, A.S. and C.W. Bennett, 1955
  Roland, G. and J. Tahon, 1961
Chenopodium opulifolium
  Roland, G. and J. Tahon, 1961
Chenopodium polyspermum
  Roland, G. and J. Tahon, 1961
Chenopodium quinoa
  Roland, G. and J. Tahon, 1961
Chenopodium rubrum
  Roland, G. and J. Tahon, 1961
Chenopodium spp.
  (K.M. Smith, 1957) R.E. Fitzpatrick, et al., 1958
Chenopodium suecicum
  Roland, G. and J. Tahon, 1961
Chenopodium urbicum
  Roland, G. and J. Tahon, 1961
Chenopodium vulvaria foetidum *
  Roland, G. and J. Tahon, 1961
Chenopodium watsonii
  Roland, G. and J. Tahon, 1961
Claytonia perfoliata
  Roland, G. and J. Tahon, 1961
Convolvulus occidentalis
  Roland, G. and J. Tahon, 1961
Convolvulus tricolor
  Roland, G. and J. Tahon, 1961
Cuscuta californica
  Roland, G. and J. Tahon, 1961
Cuscuta campestris
  Roland, G. and J. Tahon, 1961
Cuscuta gronovii
  Roland, G. and J. Tahon, 1961
Cycloloma atriplicifolium
  Roland, G. and J. Tahon, 1961
Dianthus deltoides
  Roland, G. and J. Tahon, 1961
Gomphrena globosa
  Roland, G. and J. Tahon, 1961
Gypsophila elegans
  Roland, G. and J. Tahon, 1961

VIRUS
V. BEET YELLOWS (cont.)
  Kochia childsii
    Roland, G. and J. Tahon, 1961
  Kochia scoparia
    Roland, G. and J. Tahon, 1961
  Lychnis coronaria
    Roland, G. and J. Tahon, 1961
  Melilotus indica
    Roland, G. and J. Tahon, 1961
  Mesembryanthemum crystallinum
    Roland, G. and J. Tahon, 1961
  Monolepis nuttalliana
    Roland, G. and J. Tahon, 1961
  Monolepis trifida
    Roland, G. and J. Tahon, 1961
  Nicotiana bigelovii
    Roland, G. and J. Tahon, 1961
  Nicotiana clevelandii
    Roland, G. and J. Tahon, 1961
  Papaver dubium
    Roland, G. and J. Tahon, 1961
  Papaver rhoeas
    (K.M. Smith, 1957) R.E. Fitzpatrick, et al., 1958
    Roland, G. and J. Tahon, 1961
  Pectocarya pusilla
    Roland, G. and J. Tahon, 1961
  Plantago erecta
    Roland, T. and J. Tahon, 1961
  Plantago insularis
    Roland, G. and J. Tahon, 1961
  Plantago lanceolata
    Roland, G. and J. Tahon, 1961
  Plantago major
    Roland, G. and J. Tahon, 1961
  Plantago rumosa *
    Roland, G. and J. Tahon, 1961
  Polygonum convolvulus
    (K.M. Smith, 1957) R.E. Fitzpatrick, et al., 1958
    Roland, G. and J. Tahon, 1961
  Polygonum persicaria
    Roland, G. and J. Tahon, 1961
  Reseda odorata
    Roland, G. and J. Tahon, 1961
  Rhagodia nutans
    Roland, G. and J. Tahon, 1961
  Salsola kali
    Roland, G. and J. Tahon, 1961
  Senecio vulgaris
    (K.M. Smith, 1957) R.E. Fitzpatrick, et al., 1958
    Roland, G. and J. Tahon, 1961
  Silene armeria
    Roland, G. and J. Tahon, 1961
  Silene gallica
    Roland, G. and J. Tahon, 1961
  Spergula arvensis
    Roland, G. and J. Tahon, 1961
  Spinacia oleracea
    Bennett, C.W. and A.S. Costa, 1949
    McLean, D.M., 1953
    Roland, G. and J. Tahon, 1961
  Spinacia tetranda
    Roland, G. and J. Tahon, 1961
  Stellaria media
    (K.M. Smith, 1957) R.E. Fitzpatrick, et al., 1958
    Roland, G. and J. Tahon, 1961
  Suaeda fruticosa
    Roland, G. and J. Tahon, 1961
  Suaeda moquini
    Roland, G. and J. Tahon, 1961
  Suaeda splendens
    Roland, G. and J. Tahon, 1961
  Tetragonia echinata
    Roland, G. and J. Tahon, 1961
  Tetragonia expansa
    Roland, G. and J. Tahon, 1961
  Thlaspi arvense
    (K.M. Smith, 1957) R.E. Fitzpatrick, et al., 1958
    Roland, G. and J. Tahon, 1961
  Trianthema portulacastrum
    Roland, G. and J. Tahon, 1961

VIRUS
V. BLACKBERRY DWARF Zeller 1927
  Rubus fruticosus
    (K.M. Smith, 1957) R.E. Fitzpatrick, et al., 1958
  Rubus loganobaccus
    Zeller, S.M., 1925
  Rubus spp.
    Zeller, S.M., 1927

V. BLACKBERRY DWARFING Wilhelm et al. 1948
  Rubus alleghaniensis
    Wilhelm, Stephen, H.E. Thomas and D.D. Jensen,
    1948
  Rubus ursinus
    Wilhelm, Stephen, H.E. Thomas and D.D. Jensen,
    1948

V. BLACKBERRY VARIEGATION Horn 1948
  Rubus alleghaniensis
    Horn, Norman L., 1948
  Rubus idaeus
    (K.M. Smith, 1957) R.E. Fitzpatrick, et al., 1958
  Rubus occidentalis
    Horn, Norman L., 1948

V. BLACK CURRANT REVERSION ((Lees 1920; Amos
and Hatton 1927)) Amos et al. 1928
  Ribes nigrum
    Lees, A.H., 1925

V. BLACK CURRANT VEIN PATTERN Posnette 1952
  Ribes nigrum
    (K.M. Smith, 1957) R.E. Fitzpatrick, et al., 1958

V. BLACK RASPBERRY NECROSIS Stace-Smith 1955
  Rubus albescens
    (K.M. Smith, 1957) R.E. Fitzpatrick, et al., 1958
  Rubus henryi
    Cadman, C.H., 1951
  Rubus idaeus
    Cadman, C.H., 1951, 1954
  Rubus idaeus var. strigosus
    Bennett, C.W., 1927, 1932
    Schwartze, C.D. and Glenn A. Huber, 1939
    Wilcox, R.B. and F.F. Smith, 1924
  Rubus laciniatus
    Bennett, C.W., 1932
  Rubus macropetalus
    Bennett, C.W., 1932
  Rubus neglectus
    Bennett, C.W., 1927, 1932
    Cooley, L.M., 1936
  Rubus occidentalis
    Bennett, C.W., 1927, 1932
    Cadman, C.H., 1951, 1954
    Cooley, L.M., 1936
    Rankin, W.H., 1930, 1931
    Wilcox, R.B. and F.F. Smith, 1924
  Rubus procerus
    (K.M. Smith, 1957) R.E. Fitzpatrick, et al., 1958
  Rubus saxatilis
    Cadman, C.H., 1951
  Rubus strigosus
    Huber, Glenn A. and C.D. Schwartze, 1938

V. BROAD BEAN MOTTLE Bawden et al. 1951
  Chenopodium amaranticolor
    Hollings, M., 1957
  Glycine max
    Bawden, F.C., R.P. Chaudhuri and B. Kassanis,
    1951
  Lathyrus odoratus
    Bawden, F.C., R.P. Chaudhuri and B. Kassanis,
    1951
    Yu, T.F., 1939
  Medicago sativa
    Yu, T.F., 1939
  Melilotus alba
    Yu, T.F., 1939
  Phaseolus vulgaris
    Bawden, F.C., R.P. Chaudhuri and B. Kassanis,
    1951

VIRUS
V. BROAD BEAN MOTTLE (cont.)
Pisum sativum
Bawden, F.C., R.P. Chaudhuri and B. Kassanis,
1951
Pisum sativum var. arvense
Yu, T.F., 1939
Trifolium incarnatum
Bawden, F.C., R.P. Chaudhuri and B. Kassanis,
1951
Trifolium pratense
Bawden, F.C., R.P. Chaudhuri and B. Kassanis,
1951
Yu, T.F., 1939
Trifolium repens
Yu, T.F., 1939
Trifolium subterraneum
Bawden, F.C., R.P. Chaudhuri and B. Kassanis,
1951
Vicia faba
Bawden, F.C., R.P. Chaudhuri and B. Kassanis,
1951
Yu, T.F., 1939
Vicia sativa
Yu, T.F., 1939
Vicia tetrasperma
Yu, T.F., 1939
Vicia villosa
Yu, T.F., 1939

V. BROME MOSAIC McKinney 1944
Agropyron hybrid
Sill, W.H., Jr., 1956
Avena byzantina
(K.M. Smith, 1957) R.E. Fitzpatrick, et al., 1958
Avena sativa
McKinney, H.H., 1944, 1953
McKinney, H.H., H. Fellows and C.O. Johnston,
1942
· Beta vulgaris
McKinney, H.H., 1953
Beta vulgaris var. cicla
McKinney, H.H., 1953
Bromus inermis
McKinney, H.H., 1953
McKinney, H.H., H. Fellows and C.O. Johnston,
1942
Chenopodium album
McKinney, H.H., 1953
Cucumis sativus
McKinney, H.H., 1944, 1953
Digitaria ischaemum
McKinney, H.H., 1953
Euchlaena mexicana
McKinney, H.H., 1944
Euchlaena perennis
(K.M. Smith, 1957) R.E. Fitzpatrick, et al., 1958
Hordeum vulgare
McKinney, H.H., 1944, 1953, 1956
Nicotiana tabacum
McKinney, H.H., 1944, 1953
Oryza sativa
Kahn, Robert P. and Ottie J. Dickerson, 1957
Phaseolus vulgaris
McKinney, H.H., 1944, 1953
Secale cereale
McKinney, H.H., 1944
Sorghum halepense
McKinney, H.H., 1944
Sorghum vulgare
McKinney, H.H., 1944
Sorghum vulgare var. sudanense
McKinney, H.H., 1944
Triticum aestivum
Lal, S.B. and W.H. Sill, Jr., 1957
McKinney, H.H., 1944, 1953, 1956
McKinney, H.H., H. Fellows and C.O. Johnston,
1942
Zea mays
McKinney, H.H., 1944
Sill, W.H., Jr., 1956
Zea mays var. saccharata
McKinney, H.H., 1953

VIRUS
V. CABBAGE BLACK RING SPOT Smith 1935 ((? a
strain of V. turnip mosaic (q.v.).))
Alonsoa warscewiczii
Hollings, M., 1957
Amaranthus caudatus
Hollings, M., 1957
Anchusa capensis
(K.M. Smith, 1957) R.E. Fitzpatrick, et al., 1958
Anchusa spp.
(K.M. Smith, 1957) R.E. Fitzpatrick, et al., 1958
Anemone nemorosa
Hollings, M., 1957
Barbarea vulgaris
(K.M. Smith, 1957) R.E. Fitzpatrick, et al., 1958
Begonia semperflorens
Tompkins, C.M., M.W. Gardner and H. Rex
Thomas, 1938
Brassica adpressa
Tompkins, C.M., M.W. Gardner and H. Rex
Thomas, 1938
Brassica campestris var. napobrassica
Tompkins, C.M., M.W. Gardner and H.R.
Thomas, 1937, 1938
Brassica chinensis
Hamlyn, Brenda M.G., 1953
Brassica hirta (Brassica alba)
Hamlyn, Brenda M.G., 1953
Hollings, M., 1957
Tompkins, C.M., M.W. Gardner and H. Rex
Thomas, 1938
Brassica juncea (Brassica japonica)
Tompkins, C.M., M.W. Gardner and H. Rex
Thomas, 1938
Brassica kaber (Brassica arvensis)
Tompkins, C.M., M.W. Gardner and H.R.
Thomas, 1937, 1938
Brassica muralis
Hamlyn, Brenda M.G., 1953
Brassica napus
Hollings, M., 1957
Tompkins, C.M., M.W. Gardner and H. Rex
Thomas, 1938
Brassica oleracea var. acephala
Broadbent, L., 1954
Hamlyn, Brenda M.G., 1953
Tompkins, C.M., M.W. Gardner and H. Rex
Thomas, 1938
Brassica oleracea var. botrytis
Broadbent, L., 1954
Broadbent, L. and T.W. Tinsley, 1953
Hamlyn, Brenda M.G., 1953
Tompkins, C.M., M.W. Gardner and H.R.
Thomas, 1937, 1938
Brassica oleracea var. bullata *
Hamlyn, Brenda M.G., 1953
Brassica oleracea var. capitata
Hamlyn, Brenda M.G., 1953
Hollings, M., 1957
Pound, Glenn S., 1952
Pound, Glenn S. and J.C. Walker, 1951
Tompkins, C.M., M.W. Gardner and H.R.
Thomas, 1937, 1938
Brassica oleracea var. caulorapa
Hamlyn, Brenda M.G., 1953
Tompkins, C.M., M.W. Gardner and H. Rex
Thomas, 1938
Brassica oleracea var. gemmifera
Broadbent, L., 1954
Hamlyn, Brenda M.G., 1953
Tompkins, C.M., M.W. Gardner and H.R.
Thomas, 1937, 1938
Brassica oleracea var. gongylodes
Tompkins, C.M., M.W. Gardner and H.R.
Thomas, 1937
Brassica oleracea var. italica *
Hamlyn, Brenda M.G., 1953
Brassica oleracea var. viridis
Tompkins, C.M., M.W. Gardner and H.R.
Thomas, 1937
Brassica pekinensis
Hamlyn, Brenda M.G., 1953
Hollings, M., 1957

VIRUS
V. CABBAGE BLACK RING SPOT (cont.)
Brassica pekinensis
Tompkins, C.M., M.W. Gardner and H. Rex
Thomas, 1938
Brassica rapa
Bawden, F.C., Brenda M.G. Hamlyn and Marion
A. Watson, 1954
Hamlyn, Brenda M.G., 1953
Hollings, M., 1957
Tompkins, C.M., M.W. Gardner and H.R.
Thomas, 1937, 1938
Camelina sativa
(K.M. Smith, 1957) R.E. Fitzpatrick, et al., 1958
Canna indica
Hollings, M., 1957
Capsella bursa-pastoris
Hamlyn, Brenda M.G., 1953
Hollings, M., 1957
Tompkins, C.M., M.W. Gardner and H. Rex
Thomas, 1938
Cardamine hirsuta
(K.M. Smith, 1957) R.E. Fitzpatrick, et al., 1958
Cheiranthus cheiri
(K.M. Smith, 1957) R.E. Fitzpatrick, et al., 1958
Hollings, M., 1957
Tompkins, C.M., M.W. Gardner and H.R.
Thomas, 1937, 1938
Chenopodium album
Hollings, M., 1957
Tompkins, C.M., M.W. Gardner and H.R.
Thomas, 1937, 1938
Chenopodium amaranticolor
Hollings, M., 1956, 1957
Chenopodium murale
Tompkins, C.M., M.W. Gardner and H.R.
Thomas, 1937, 1938
Chrysanthemum carinatum
Hollings, M., 1957
Chrysanthemum coronarium
Tompkins, C.M., M.W. Gardner and H. Rex
Thomas, 1938
Cichorium endivia
Hamlyn, Brenda M.G., 1953
Cochlearia armoracia
(K.M. Smith, 1957) R.E. Fitzpatrick, et al., 1958
Datura ferox
(K.M. Smith, 1957) R.E. Fitzpatrick, et al., 1958
Datura stramonium
(K.M. Smith, 1957) R.E. Fitzpatrick, et al., 1958
Dimorphotheca aurantiaca
Tompkins, C.M., M.W. Gardner and H. Rex
Thomas, 1938
Echium vulgare
Hollings, M., 1957
Gomphrena globosa
Hollings, M., 1957
Hesperis matronalis
Tompkins, C.M., M.W. Gardner and H.R.
Thomas, 1937, 1938
Isatis tinctoria
(K.M. Smith, 1957) R.E. Fitzpatrick, et al., 1958
Lepidium campestre
(K.M. Smith, 1957) R.E. Fitzpatrick, et al., 1958
Lunaria annua
Tompkins, C.M., M.W. Gardner and H.R.
Thomas, 1937, 1938
Lycium halimifolium
Hamlyn, Brenda M.G., 1953
Malcomia maritima
Hollings, M., 1957
Tompkins, C.M., M.W. Gardner and H.R.
Thomas, 1937, 1938
Matthiola bicornis
Tompkins, C.M., M.W. Gardner and H. Rex
Thomas, 1938
Matthiola incana
(K.M. Smith, 1957) R.E. Fitzpatrick, et al., 1958
Tompkins, C.M., M.W. Gardner and H. Rex
Thomas, 1938
Matthiola incana var. annua
Hamlyn, Brenda M.G., 1953
Hollings, M., 1957

VIRUS
V. CABBAGE BLACK RING SPOT (cont.)
Matthiola incana var. annua
Tompkins, C.M., M.W. Gardner and H.R.
Thomas, 1937, 1938
Mimulus luteus
Hollings, M., 1957
Myosotis alpestris
Tompkins, C.M., M.W. Gardner and H. Rex
Thomas, 1938
Nasturtium officinale (Rorippa nasturtium-aquaticum)
Tompkins, C.M., M.W. Gardner and H.R.
Thomas, 1937
Nicotiana glutinosa
Hamlyn, Brenda M.G., 1953
Hollings, M., 1957
Tompkins, C.M., M.W. Gardner and H.R.
Thomas, 1937, 1938
Nicotiana langsdorffii
(K.M. Smith, 1957) R.E. Fitzpatrick, et al., 1958
Tompkins, C.M., M.W. Gardner and H. Rex
Thomas, 1938
Nicotiana rustica
Hamlyn, Brenda M.G., 1953
Nicotiana tabacum
Bawden, F.C., Brenda M.G. Hamlyn and Marion
A. Watson, 1954
Broadbent, L., 1954
(K.M. Smith, 1957) R.E. Fitzpatrick, et al., 1958
Hamlyn, Brenda M.G., 1953
Hollings, M., 1957
Pound, Glenn S., 1952
Tompkins, C.M., M.W. Gardner and H.R.
Thomas, 1937, 1938
Papaver nudicaule
Hamlyn, Brenda M.G., 1953
Tompkins, C.M., M.W. Gardner and H. Rex
Thomas, 1938
Papaver rhoeas
Hamlyn, Brenda M.G., 1953
Papaver somniferum
Hamlyn, Brenda M.G., 1953
Hollings, M., 1957
Passiflora caerulea
Hollings, M., 1957
Petunia hybrida
Hamlyn, Brenda M.G., 1953
Hollings, M., 1957
Tompkins, C.M., M.W. Gardner and H. Rex
Thomas, 1938
Physalis peruviana
Hollings, M., 1957
Radicula nasturtium-aquaticum
Tompkins, C.M., M.W. Gardner and H. Rex
Thomas, 1938
Raphanus raphanistrum
(K.M. Smith, 1957) R.E. Fitzpatrick, et al., 1958
Raphanus sativus var. longipinnatus *
Tompkins, C.M., M.W. Gardner and H.R.
Thomas, 1937, 1938
Reseda odorata
Tompkins, C.M., M.W. Gardner and H. Rex
Thomas, 1938
Rheum rhaponticum
Tompkins, C.M., M.W. Gardner and H.R.
Thomas, 1937, 1938
Salpiglossis sinuata
Hollings, M., 1957
Scabiosa atropurpurea
Tompkins, C.M., M.W. Gardner and H. Rex
Thomas, 1938
Schizanthus pinnatus
Hollings, M., 1957
Senecio cruentus
Tompkins, C.M., M.W. Gardner and H. Rex
Thomas, 1938
Sisymbrium officinale
Hollings, M., 1957
Spinacia oleracea
Tompkins, C.M., M.W. Gardner and H.R.
Thomas, 1937, 1938
Stellaria media
Tompkins, C.M., M.W. Gardner and H.R.
Thomas, 1937, 1938

VIRUS
V. CABBAGE BLACK RING SPOT (cont.)
   Tetragonia expansa
     Hollings, M., 1957
   Thlaspi arvense
     Hollings, M., 1957
   Tropaeolum majus
     (K.M. Smith, 1957) R.E. Fitzpatrick, et al., 1958
   Verbena hybrida
     Hamlyn, Brenda M.G., 1953
     Hollings, M., 1957
     Tompkins, C.M., M.W. Gardner and H. Rex
     Thomas, 1938
   Vicia faba
     Hollings, M., 1957
   Vinca rosea
     (K.M. Smith, 1957) R.E. Fitzpatrick, et al., 1958
   Zinnia elegans
     Hamlyn, Brenda M.G., 1953
     Hollings, M., 1957
     Tompkins, C.M., M.W. Gardner and H. Rex
     Thomas, 1938

V. CABBAGE RING NECROSIS Larson and Walker 1941
   Berteroa incana
     Larson, R.H. and J.C. Walker, 1941
   Beta vulgaris
     Larson, R.H. and J.C. Walker, 1940, 1941
   Beta vulgaris var. cicla
     Larson, R.H. and J.C. Walker, 1940, 1941
   Beta vulgaris var. macrorhiza *
     Larson, R.H. and J.C. Walker, 1941
   Brassica campestris var. napobrassica
     Larson, R.H. and J.C. Walker, 1941
   Brassica hirta (Brassica alba)
     Larson, R.H. and J.C. Walker, 1941
   Brassica juncea (Brassica japonica)
     Larson, R.H. and J.C. Walker, 1941
   Brassica napus
     Larson, R.H. and J.C. Walker, 1941
   Brassica nigra
     Larson, R.H. and J.C. Walker, 1941
   Brassica oleracea var. botrytis
     Larson, R.H. and J.C. Walker, 1941
   Brassica oleracea var. capitata
     Larson, R.H. and J.C. Walker, 1940, 1941
   Brassica oleracea var. gemmifera
     Larson, R.H. and J.C. Walker, 1941
   Brassica oleracea var. gongylodes
     Larson, R.H. and J.C. Walker, 1941
   Brassica oleracea var. viridis
     Larson, R.H. and J.C. Walker, 1941
   Brassica pekinensis
     Larson, R.H. and J.C. Walker, 1941
   Brassica rapa
     Larson, R.H. and J.C. Walker, 1941
   Brassica spp.
     (K.M. Smith, 1957) R.E. Fitzpatrick, et al., 1958
   Calendula officinalis
     Larson, R.H. and J.C. Walker, 1940, 1941
   Capsella bursa-pastoris
     Larson, R.H. and J.C. Walker, 1941
   Cheiranthus allionii
     Larson, R.H. and J.C. Walker, 1941
   Cucumis sativus
     Larson, R.H. and J.C. Walker, 1940, 1941
   Hesperis matronalis
     Larson, R.H. and J.C. Walker, 1941
   Lepidium sativum
     Larson, R.H. and J.C. Walker, 1941
   Lepidium virginicum
     Larson, R.H. and J.C. Walker, 1941
   Matthiola incana var. annua
     Larson, R.H. and J.C. Walker, 1941
   Neslia paniculata
     Larson, R.H. and J.C. Walker, 1941
   Nicotiana glutinosa
     Larson, R.H. and J.C. Walker, 1940, 1941
   Nicotiana langsdorffii
     Larson, R.H. and J.C. Walker, 1940, 1941
   Nicotiana repanda
     Larson, R.H. and J.C. Walker, 1940, 1941
   Nicotiana rustica
     Larson, R.H. and J.C. Walker, 1940, 1941

VIRUS
V. CABBAGE RING NECROSIS (cont.)
   Nicotiana tabacum
     Larson, R.H. and J.C. Walker, 1940, 1941
   Petunia hybrida
     Larson, R.H. and J.C. Walker, 1940, 1941
   Raphanus sativus
     Larson, R.H. and J.C. Walker, 1941
   Sisymbrium altissimum
     Larson, R.H. and J.C. Walker, 1941
   Sisymbrium officinale
     Larson, R.H. and J.C. Walker, 1941
   Spinacia oleracea
     Larson, R.H. and J.C. Walker, 1940, 1941
   Thlaspi arvense
     Larson, R.H. and J.C. Walker, 1941
   Zinnia elegans
     Larson, R.H. and J.C. Walker, 1940, 1941

V. CACAO SWOLLEN SHOOT (((W.F. Stevens) 1937))
   Abroma augusta   Posnette 1940
     Tinsley, T.W. and A.L. Wharton, 1958
   Adansonia digitata
     Attafuah, A. and T.W. Tinsley, 1958
     Posnette, A.F., N.F. Robertson and J. McA.
     Todd, 1950
     Tinsley, T.W. and A.L. Wharton, 1958
   Bombax buonopozense
     Attafuah, A. and T.W. Tinsley, 1958
     Posnette, A.F., N.F. Robertson and J. McA.
     Todd, 1950
     Tinsley, T.W. and A.L. Wharton, 1958
   Bombax malabaricum
     Tinsley, T.W. and A.L. Wharton, 1958
   Ceiba cordifolia *
     (K.M. Smith, 1957) R.E. Fitzpatrick, et al., 1958
   Ceiba pentandra
     Attafuah, A. and T.W. Tinsley, 1958
     Posnette, A.F., N.F. Robertson and J. McA.
     Todd, 1950
     Tinsley, T.W. and A.L. Wharton, 1958
   Cola chlamydantha
     Tinsley, T.W. and A.L. Wharton, 1958
   Cola cordifolia
     Posnette, A.F., N.F. Robertson and J. McA.
     Todd, 1950
   Cola gigantea var. glabrescens *
     Tinsley, T.W. and A.L. Wharton, 1958
   Cola lateritia var. maclaudi *
     Tinsley, T.W. and A.L. Wharton, 1958
   Corchorus aestuans
     Tinsley, T.W. and A.L. Wharton, 1958
   Corchorus olitorius
     Tinsley, T.W. and A.L. Wharton, 1958
   Corchorus tridens
     Tinsley, T.W. and A.L. Wharton, 1958
   Corchorus trilocularis
     Tinsley, T.W. and A.L. Wharton, 1958
   Erythropsis barteri
     Posnette, A.F., N.F. Robertson and J. McA.
     Todd, 1950
   Heliocarpus popayanensis
     Tinsley, T.W. and A.L. Wharton, 1958
   Herrania balaensis
     Tinsley, T W. and A.L. Wharton, 1958
   Herrania spp.
     Tinsley, T.W. and A.L. Wharton, 1958
   Hildegardia barteri
     Tinsley, T.W. and A.L. Wharton, 1958
   Pterygota macrocarpa
     Tinsley, T.W. and A.L. Wharton, 1958
   Sterculia laevis
     Tinsley, T.W. and A.L. Wharton, 1958
   Sterculia rhinopetala
     Posnette, A.F., N.F. Robertson and J. McA.
     Todd, 1950
     Tinsley, T.W. and A.L. Wharton, 1958
   Sterculia setigera
     Tinsley, T.W. and A.L. Wharton, 1958
   Sterculia tragacantha
     Posnette, A.F., N.F. Robertson and J. McA.
     Todd, 1950
     Tinsley, T.W. and A.L. Wharton, 1958

VIRUS
V. CACAO SWOLLEN SHOOT (cont.)
  Theobroma angustifolia
    Tinsley, T.W. and A.L. Wharton, 1958
  Theobroma bicolor
    Posnette, A.F., N.F. Robertson and J. McA.
      Todd, 1950
    Posnette, A.F. and J. McA. Todd, 1951
    Tinsley, T.W. and A.L. Wharton, 1958
  Theobroma cacao
    Attafuah, A. and T.W. Tinsley, 1958
    Baker, R.E.D. and W.T. Dale, 1947
    Crowdy, S.H. and A.F. Posnette, 1947
    Goodall, D.W., 1949
    Hanna, A.F. and W. Heatherington, 1957
    Posnette, A.F., 1947, 1950
    Posnette, A.F. and N.F. Robertson, 1950
    Posnette, A.F., N.F. Robertson and J. McA.
      Todd, 1950
    Posnette, A.F. and A.H. Strickland, 1948
    Posnette, A.F. and J. McA. Todd, 1951, 1955
    Tinsley, T.W. and A.L. Wharton, 1958
  Theobroma grandiflorum
    Tinsley, T.W. and A.L. Wharton, 1958
  Theobroma microcarpa
    Tinsley, T.W. and A.L. Wharton, 1958
  Theobroma obovata
    Tinsley, T.W. and A.L. Wharton, 1958
  Theobroma speciosa
    Tinsley, T.W. and A.L. Wharton, 1958

V. CAMELLIA YELLOW MOTTLE LEAF Milbrath and
  Camellia japonica   McWhorter 1946
    Milbrath, J.A. and F.P. McWhorter, 1940
    Plakidas, A.G., 1953, 1954
  Camellia sasanqua
    Plakidas, A.G., 1953, 1954

V. CANNA MOSAIC Fukushi 1932
  Canna edulis
    Celino, M.S. and G.O. Ocfemia, 1941
  Canna generalis
    Brierley, Philip and Floyd F. Smith, 1948
    Castillo, B.S., C.E. Yarwood and A.H. Gold,
      1956
  Canna glauca
    Brierley, Philip and Floyd F. Smith, 1948
    Castillo, B.S., C.E. Yarwood and A.H. Gold,
      1956
  Canna indica
    Brierley, Philip and Floyd F. Smith, 1948
    Castillo, B.S., C.E. Yarwood and A.H. Gold,
      1956
    Ocfemia, G.O., Isidro S. Macaspac and Hsieh Feng
      Yuan, 1941
  Musa textilis
    Juliano, Jorge P., 1951
    Ocfemia, G.O., Isidro S. Macaspac and Hsieh Feng
      Yuan, 1941
  Phaseolus vulgaris
    Castillo, B.S., C.E. Yarwood and A.H. Gold,
      1956
  Zea mays
    Castillo, B.S., C.E. Yarwood and A.H. Gold,
      1956

V. CARDAMOM MOSAIC Uppal et al. 1945
  Elettaria cardamomum
    (K.M. Smith, 1957) R.E. Fitzpatrick, et al., 1958

V. CARNATION MOSAIC Creager 1943
  Asclepias syriaca
    Gasiorkiewicz, E.C., 1954
  Beta vulgaris
    Brierley, Philip and Floyd F. Smith, 1957
  Chenopodium album
    Brierley, Philip and Floyd F. Smith, 1957
    Gasiorkiewicz, E.C., 1956
  Chenopodium amaranticolor
    Brierley, Philip and Floyd F. Smith, 1957
  Dianthus barbatus
    Ames, Ralph W. and H.H. Thornberry, 1952
    Ames, Ralph W., A.E. Vatter, John J. Scholz and
      H.H. Thornberry, 1951

VIRUS
V. CARNATION MOSAIC (cont.)
  Dianthus barbatus
    Brierley, Philip and Floyd F. Smith, 1955, 1957
    Gasiorkiewicz, E.C., 1954, 1956
    Rumley, Gail E. and W.D. Thomas, Jr., 1951
    Thomas, W.D., Jr. and R.R. Baker, 1952
    Wright, Charles M., 1951
  Dianthus caryophyllus
    Ames, Ralph W. and H.H. Thornberry, 1952
    Ames, Ralph W., A.E. Vatter, John J. Scholz and
      H.H. Thornberry, 1951
    Brierley, Philip and Floyd F. Smith, 1955, 1957
    Creager, D.B., 1943
    Gasiorkiewicz, E.C., 1954, 1956
    Jones, Leon K., 1945
    Rumley, Gail E. and W.D. Thomas, Jr., 1951
    Thomas, W.D., Jr. and R.R. Baker, 1952
    Wright, Charles M., 1951
  Dianthus chinensis
    Brierley, Philip and Floyd F. Smith, 1957
  Dianthus deltoides
    Brierley, Philip and Floyd F. Smith, 1957
  Dianthus giganteus
    Brierley, Philip and Floyd F. Smith, 1957
  Dianthus latifolius
    Brierley, Philip and Floyd F. Smith, 1957
  Dianthus plumarius
    Brierley, Philip and Floyd F. Smith, 1957
  Dianthus superbus
    Brierley, Philip and Floyd F. Smith, 1957
  Gomphrena globosa
    Brierley, Philip and Floyd F. Smith, 1957
    Gasiorkiewicz, E.C., 1954
    Wright, Charles M., 1951
  Helichrysum bracteatum
    Gasiorkiewicz, E.C., 1954
  Lycopersicon esculentum
    Wright, Charles M., 1951
  Silene compacta
    Brierley, Philip and Floyd F. Smith, 1957
  Tunica saxifraga
    Brierley, Philip and Floyd F. Smith, 1957

V. CARNATION MOTTLE Kassanis 1955
  Chenopodium amaranticolor
    Brierley, Philip and Floyd F. Smith, 1957
    Hollings, M., 1956
  Dianthus barbatus
    Brierley, Philip and Floyd F. Smith, 1957
    Kassanis, B., 1955
  Dianthus caryophyllus
    Brierley, Philip and Floyd F. Smith, 1957
    Kassanis, B., 1955
  Dianthus superbus
    Brierley, Philip and Floyd F. Smith, 1957
  Gomphrena globosa
    Brierley, Philip and Floyd F. Smith, 1957
  Silene compacta
    Brierley, Philip and Floyd F. Smith, 1957

V. CARNATION RING SPOT Kassanis 1955
  Althaea rosea
    Brierley, Philip and Floyd F. Smith, 1957
  Antirrhinum majus
    Brierley, Philip and Floyd F. Smith, 1957
  Arenaria montana
    Brierley, Philip and Floyd F. Smith, 1957
  Beta vulgaris
    Brierley, Philip and Floyd F. Smith, 1957
  Calendula officinalis
    Brierley, Philip and Floyd F. Smith, 1957
  Callistephus chinensis
    Brierley, Philip and Floyd F. Smith, 1955, 1957
  Celosia argentea var. cristata
    Brierley, Philip and Floyd F. Smith, 1957
  Chenopodium album
    Brierley, Philip and Floyd F. Smith, 1957
  Chenopodium amaranticolor
    Brierley, Philip and Floyd F. Smith, 1957
    Hollings, M., 1956
  Cucumis sativus
    Brierley, Philip and Floyd F. Smith, 1955, 1957

VIRUS

V. CARNATION RING SPOT (cont.)
  Datura inoxia
    Brierley, Philip and Floyd F. Smith, 1957
  Datura stramonium
    Brierley, Philip and Floyd F. Smith, 1957
  Dianthus arenarius
    Brierley, Philip and Floyd F. Smith, 1957
  Dianthus barbatus
    Brierley, Philip and Floyd F. Smith, 1957
    Kassanis, B., 1955
  Dianthus caesius
    Brierley, Philip and Floyd F. Smith, 1957
  Dianthus caryophyllus
    Brierley, Philip and Floyd F. Smith, 1955, 1957
    Kassanis, B., 1955
  Dianthus deltoides
    Brierley, Philip and Floyd F. Smith, 1957
  Dianthus plumarius
    Brierley, Philip and Floyd F. Smith, 1957
  Dianthus superbus
    Brierley, Philip and Floyd F. Smith, 1957
  Glycine max
    Brierley, Philip and Floyd F. Smith, 1957
  Gomphrena globosa
    Brierley, Philip and Floyd F. Smith, 1955, 1957
    Kassanis, B., 1955
  Gypsophila elegans
    Kassanis, B., 1955
  Lathyrus odoratus
    Brierley, Philip and Floyd F. Smith, 1957
  Lychnis alba
    Kassanis, B., 1955
  Nicotiana glutinosa
    Kassanis, B., 1955
  Nicotiana tabacum
    Brierley, Philip and Floyd F. Smith, 1955, 1957
    Kassanis, B., 1955
  Phaseolus vulgaris
    Brierley, Philip and Floyd F. Smith, 1955, 1957
    Kassanis, B., 1955
  Saponaria ocymoides
    Brierley, Philip and Floyd F. Smith, 1957
  Silene compacta
    Brierley, Philip and Floyd F. Smith, 1957
  Spinacia oleracea
    Brierley, Philip and Floyd F. Smith, 1957
  Tagetes patula
    Brierley, Philip and Floyd F. Smith, 1957
  Tunica saxifraga
    Brierley, Philip and Floyd F. Smith, 1957
  Ulmus americana
    Brierley, Philip and Floyd F. Smith, 1957

V. CARNATION VEIN MOTTLE Kassanis 1955
  Chenopodium amaranticolor
    Hollings, M., 1956
  Dianthus barbatus
    Kassanis, B., 1955
  Dianthus caryophyllus
    Kassanis, B., 1955

V. CARROT MOTLEY DWARF Stubbs 1948
  Apium leptophyllum
    Stubbs, L.L., 1955
  Capsicum frutescens (Capsicum annuum)
    (K.M. Smith, 1957) R.E. Fitzpatrick, et al., 1958
  Datura stramonium
    (K.M. Smith, 1957) R.E. Fitzpatrick, et al., 1958
  Daucus carota var. sativa
    Stubbs, L.L., 1956
  Nemesia spp.
    (K.M. Smith, 1957) R.E. Fitzpatrick, et al., 1958
  Nicotiana tabacum
    (K.M. Smith, 1957) R.E. Fitzpatrick, et al., 1958
  Petunia spp.
    (K.M. Smith, 1957) R.E. Fitzpatrick, et al., 1958

V. CASSAVA BROWN STREAK Storey 1936
  Manihot esculenta (Manihot utilissima)
    (K.M. Smith, 1957) R.E. Fitzpatrick, et al., 1958

VIRUS

V. (CASSAVA) GREEN MOSAIC *
  Manihot spp.
    McKinney, H.H., 1929

V. CASSAVA MOSAIC Lefevre 1935; Storey and Nichols
  Manihot esculenta (Manihot utilissima)   1938
    Chant, S.R., 1958
    McKinney, H.H., 1928
    Storey, H.H. and R.F.W. Nichols, 1938
  Manihot palmata
    (K.M. Smith, 1957) R.E. Fitzpatrick, et al., 1958

V. CAULIFLOWER MOSAIC Tompkins 1934
  Barbarea verna
    (K.M. Smith, 1957) R.E. Fitzpatrick, et al., 1958
  Barbarea vulgaris
    (K.M. Smith, 1957) R.E. Fitzpatrick, et al., 1958
  Brassica adpressa
    Tompkins, C.M., 1937
    Tompkins, C.M. and H. Rex Thomas, 1938
  Brassica campestris
    Tompkins, C.M., 1937
    Walker, J.C., Francis J. LeBeau and Glenn S.
    Pound, 1945
  Brassica campestris var. napobrassica
    Alvarez-Garcia, L.A., 1951
    Berkeley, G.H. and J.H. Tremaine, 1954
    Caldwell, John and Ian W. Prentice, 1942
    Tompkins, C.M., 1937
  Brassica hirta (Brassica alba)
    Tompkins, C.M., 1937
    Walker, J.C., Francis J. LeBeau and Glenn S.
    Pound, 1945
  Brassica juncea (Brassica japonica)
    Tompkins, C.M., 1937
    Walker, J.C., Francis J. LeBeau and Glenn S.
    Pound, 1945
  Brassica kaber (Brassica arvensis)
    Caldwell, John and Ian W. Prentice, 1942
    Tompkins, C.M., 1937
  Brassica kaber var. pinnatifida
    Walker, J.C., Francis J. LeBeau and Glenn S.
    Pound, 1945
  Brassica muralis
    (K.M. Smith, 1957) R.E. Fitzpatrick, et al., 1958
  Brassica napus
    Berkeley, G.H. and J.H. Tremaine, 1954
    Caldwell, John and Ian W. Prentice, 1942
    Tompkins, C.M., 1937
    Tompkins, C.M. and H. Rex Thomas, 1938
    Walker, J.C., Francis J. LeBeau and Glenn S.
    Pound, 1945
  Brassica nigra
    Tompkins, C.M., 1937
    Walker, J.C., Francis J. LeBeau and Glenn S.
    Pound, 1945
  Brassica oleracea var. acephala
    Alvarez-Garcia, L.A., 1951
    Caldwell, John and Ian W. Prentice, 1942
    Tompkins, C.M., 1934, 1937
  Brassica oleracea var. botrytis
    Alvarez-Garcia, L.A., 1951
    Berkeley, G.H. and J.H. Tremaine, 1954
    Broadbent, L., 1954
    Broadbent, L. and T.W. Tinsley, 1953
    Caldwell, John and Ian W. Prentice, 1942
    Jenkinson, J.G., 1955
    Severin, Henry H.P. and C.M. Tompkins, 1948
    Tompkins, C.M., 1934, 1937
    Walker, J.C., Francis J. LeBeau and Glenn S.
    Pound, 1945
  Brassica oleracea var. capitata
    Alvarez-Garcia, L.A., 1951
    Berkeley, G.H. and J.H. Tremaine, 1954
    Caldwell, John and Ian W. Prentice, 1942
    Natti, J.J., 1956
    Pound, Glenn S., 1946, 1947, 1952
    Pound, Glenn S. and J.C. Walker, 1951
    Tompkins, C.M., 1934, 1937
    Walker, J.C., Francis J. LeBeau and Glenn S.
    Pound, 1945

VIRUS

V. CAULIFLOWER MOSAIC (cont.)

Brassica oleracea var. caulorapa
Caldwell, John and Ian W. Prentice, 1942
Tompkins, C.M., 1937

Brassica oleracea var. gemmifera
Alvarez-Garcia, L.A., 1951
Berkeley, G.H. and J.H. Tremaine, 1954
Caldwell, John and Ian W. Prentice, 1942
Severin, Henry H.P. and C.M. Tompkins, 1948
Tompkins, C.M., 1937
Walker, J.C., Francis J. LeBeau and Glenn S.
Pound, 1945

Brassica oleracea var. gongylodes
Alvarez-Garcia, L.A., 1951
Berkeley, G.H. and J.H. Tremaine, 1954
Walker, J.C., Francis J. LeBeau and Glenn S.
Pound, 1945

Brassica oleracea var. italica *
(K.M. Smith, 1957) R.E. Fitzpatrick, et al., 1958

Brassica oleracea var. subauda *
Caldwell, John and Ian W.Prentice, 1942

Brassica oleracea var. viridis
Berkeley, G.H. and J.H. Tremaine, 1954
Walker, J.C., Francis J. LeBeau and Glenn S.
Pound, 1945

Brassica pekinensis
Alvarez-Garcia, L.A., 1951
Berkeley, G.H. and J.H. Tremaine, 1954
Tompkins, C.M., 1937
Walker, J.C., Francis J. LeBeau and Glenn S.
Pound, 1945

Brassica rapa
Alvarez-Garcia, L.A., 1951
Hamlyn, Brenda M.G., 1955
Tompkins, C.M., 1937
Walker, J.C., Francis J. LeBeau and Glenn S.
Pound, 1945

Camelina sativa
(K.M. Smith, 1957) R.E. Fitzpatrick, et al., 1958

Capsella bursa-pastoris
Tompkins, C.M., 1937
Walker, J.C., Francis J. LeBeau and Glenn S.
Pound, 1945

Cheiranthus cheiri
Berkeley, G.H. and J.H. Tremaine, 1954

Cochlearia armoracia
(K.M. Smith, 1957) R.E. Fitzpatrick, et al., 1958

Crambe maritima
(K.M. Smith, 1957) R.E. Fitzpatrick, et al., 1958

Diplotaxis tenuifolia
(K.M. Smith, 1957) R.E. Fitzpatrick, et al., 1958

Iberis amara
Tompkins, C.M., 1937

Isatis tinctoria
(K.M. Smith, 1957) R.E. Fitzpatrick, et al., 1958

Lepidium campestre
(K.M. Smith, 1957) R.E. Fitzpatrick, et al., 1958

Lepidium sativum
Tompkins, C.M., 1937
Walker, J.C., Francis J. LeBeau and Glenn S.
Pound, 1945

Lepidium virginicum
Walker, J.C., Francis J. LeBeau and Glenn S.
Pound, 1945

Lunaria annua
Tompkins, C.M., 1937

Matthiola incana
Berkeley, G.H. and J.H. Tremaine, 1954
Tompkins, C.M., 1934

Matthiola incana var. annua
Severin, Henry H.P. and C.M. Tompkins, 1948
Tompkins, C.M., 1937
Walker, J.C., Francis J. LeBeau and Glenn S.
Pound, 1945

Neslia paniculata
Walker, J.C., Francis J. LeBeau and Glenn S.
Pound, 1945

Nicotiana tabacum
Broadbent, L., 1954
Pound, Glenn S., 1952

Raphanus raphanistrum
Tompkins, C.M., 1937

VIRUS

V. CAULIFLOWER MOSAIC (cont.)

Raphanus sativus
Alvarez-Garcia, L.A., 1951
Berkeley, G.H. and J.H. Tremaine, 1954
Caldwell, John and Ian W. Prentice, 1942
Tompkins, C.M., 1937
Tompkins, C.M. and H. Rex Thomas, 1938
Walker, J.C., Francis J. LeBeau and Glenn S.
Pound, 1945

Sisymbrium altissimum
Walker, J.C., Francis J. LeBeau and Glenn S.
Pound, 1945

Sisymbrium officinale
(K.M. Smith, 1957) R.E. Fitzpatrick, et al., 1958

Thlaspi arvense
Walker, J.C., Francis J. LeBeau and Glenn S.
Pound, 1945

V. CELERY MOSAIC Holmes 1939

Anethum graveolens
Freitag, Julius H. and Henry H.P. Severin, 1945
Severin, Henry H.P. and Julius H. Freitag, 1938

Anthriscus cerefolium
Freitag, Julius H. and Henry H.P. Severin, 1945
Severin, Henry H.P. and Julius H. Freitag, 1938

Apium graveolens
Doolittle, S.P. and F.L. Wellman, 1934

Apium graveolens var. dulce
Bardin, Roy, 1947
Freitag, Julius H. and Henry H.P. Severin, 1939,
1945
Poole, R.F., 1922
Severin, H.H.P. and J.H. Freitag, 1935, 1938

Apium graveolens var. rapaceum
Freitag, Julius H. and Henry H.P. Severin, 1945
Severin, Henry H.P. and Julius H. Freitag, 1938

Carum carvi
Freitag, Julius H. and Henry H.P. Severin, 1945
Severin, Henry H.P. and Julius H. Freitag, 1938

Commelina communis
Price, W.C., 1935

Commelina nudiflora
Doolittle, S.P., 1931
Doolittle, S.P. and F.L. Wellman, 1934

Coriandrum sativum
Freitag, Julius H. and Henry H.P. Severin, 1945
Severin, Henry H.P. and Julius H. Freitag, 1938

Cucumis sativus
Doolittle, S.P., 1931
Doolittle, S.P. and F.L. Wellman, 1934

Daucus carota var. sativa
Freitag, Julius H. and Henry H.P. Severin, 1945
Severin, Henry H.P. and Julius H. Freitag, 1938

Lilium longiflorum
Price, W.C., 1937

Lycopersicon esculentum
Doolittle, S.P., 1931
Doolittle, S.P. and F.L. Wellman, 1934

Nicotiana tabacum
Doolittle, S.P., 1931
Doolittle, S.P. and F.L. Wellman, 1934
Nolla, J.A.B., 1934
Price, W.C., 1936

Pastinaca sativa
Freitag, Julius H. and Henry H.P. Severin, 1945

Petroselinum crispum var. latifolium *
Freitag, Julius H. and Henry H.P. Severin, 1945

Petroselinum hortense
Severin, Henry H.P. and Julius H. Freitag, 1938

Physalis lagascae
Doolittle, S.P. and F.L. Wellman, 1934

Physalis pubescens
Doolittle, S.P., 1931
Doolittle, S.P. and F.L. Wellman, 1934

Pimpinella anisum
Freitag, Julius H. and Henry H.P. Severin, 1945

Vigna sinensis
Price, W.C., 1935

Zea mays
Price, W.C., 1935

Zinnia elegans
Price, W.C., 1935

VIRUS
V. (CELERY) PSEUDO-CALICO *
    Apium graveolens var. dulce
        Freitag, Julius H. and Henry H.P. Severin, 1939

V. CELERY YELLOW SPOT   Freitag and Severin 1945
    Apium graveolens var. dulce
        Freitag, Julius H. and Henry H.P. Severin, 1939,
        1945
    Conium maculatum
        Freitag, Julius H. and Henry H.P. Severin, 1945
    Pastinaca sativa
        Freitag, Julius H. and Henry H.P. Severin, 1945

V. (CEREAL) CALIFORNIA MOSAIC DISEASE *
    Hordeum vulgare
        Houston, Byron R. and John W. Oswald, 1952
    Triticum aestivum
        Houston, Byron R. and John W. Oswald, 1952

V. (CEREAL) ENANISMO DISEASE *
    Hordeum vulgare
        Gibler, John W., 1957
    Triticum aestivum
        Gibler, John W., 1957

V. CHERRY ALBINO   Zeller et al. 1944
    Prunus avium
        Zeller, S.M., J.A. Milbrath and C.B. Cordy, 1944

V. CHERRY BARK SPLITTING *
    Prunus armeniaca
        Cameron, H. Ronald, 1954
    Prunus cerasus
        Cameron, H. Ronald, 1954
        Milbrath, J.A., 1957

V. CHERRY BLACK CANKER   Zeller et al. 1947
    Prunus avium
        (K.M. Smith, 1957) R.E. Fitzpatrick, et al., 1958

V. CHERRY BUD ABORTION DISEASE *
    Prunus avium
        Milbrath, J.A. and H.E. Williams, 1956
    Prunus cerasus
        Milbrath, J.A. and H.E. Williams, 1956

V. CHERRY CHLOROSIS *
    Prunus mahaleb
        Keitt, G.W. and C.N. Clayton, 1941
    Prunus virginiana
        Keitt, G.W. and C.N. Clayton, 1941

V. CHERRY DUSTY YELLOWS   Posnette 1954
    Prunus avium
        Posnette, A.F., 1954
    Prunus cerasus
        Posnette, A.F., 1954
    Prunus persica
        Posnette, A.F., 1954

V. CHERRY FRECKLE FRUIT DISEASE *
    Prunus avium
        Williams, H.E. and J.A. Milbrath, 1955

V. CHERRY (FROGMORE) CANKER *
    Prunus avium
        Posnette, A.F. and R. Cropley, 1957

V. CHERRY GREEN RING MOTTLE *
    Prunus cerasus
        Fink, Harry C., 1955
        Gilmer, R.M., K.D. Brase and K.G. Parker, 1957
        Parker, K.G. and E.J. Klos, 1953
    Prunus tomentosa
        Fink, Harry C., 1955

V. CHERRY LITTLE CHERRY   Foster and Lott 1947
    Prunus avium
        Blodgett, E.C., E.L. Reeves, C.M. Wright and
        H.E. Williams, 1948
        Foster, W.R. and T.B. Lott, 1947
        Milbrath, J.A. and H.E. Williams, 1956
        Reeves, E.L. and Philip W. Cheney, 1956

VIRUS
V. CHERRY LITTLE CHERRY   (cont.)
    Prunus avium
        Welsh, Maurice F., 1952
        Wilks, Jack M. and J.A. Milbrath, 1956
        Wilks, J.M. and M.F. Welsh, 1955
    Prunus cerasus
        Milbrath, J.A. and H.E. Williams, 1956
        Wilks, Jack M. and J.A. Milbrath, 1956
    Prunus mollis
        Wilks, J.M. and M.F. Welsh, 1955
    Prunus serrulata
        Milbrath, J.A. and H.E. Williams, 1956

V. CHERRY MIDLEAF NECROSIS *
    Prunus avium
        Milbrath, J.A., 1957
    Prunus cerasus
        Milbrath, J.A., 1957
    Prunus serrulata
        Milbrath, J.A., 1957

V. CHERRY MORA   Milbrath 1952
    Prunus avium
        Milbrath, J.A., 1952

V. CHERRY MOTTLE *
    Prunus avium
        Hildebrand, E.M., 1944
    Prunus domestica
        Hildebrand, E.M., 1944

V. CHERRY MOTTLE LEAF   Zeller 1934; Reeves 1941
    Prunus avium
        Lott, T.B., 1945
        Reeves, E.L., 1941
        Richards, B.L. and L.C. Cochran, 1956
        Zeller, S.M. and A.W. Evans, 1941
    Prunus avium x Prunus cerasus
        Reeves, E.L., 1941
    Prunus cerasus
        Reeves, E.L., 1941
        Richards, B.L. and L.C. Cochran, 1956
    Prunus emarginata
        Reeves, E.L., 1941
        Richards, B.L. and L.C. Cochran, 1956
    Prunus mahaleb
        Reeves, E.L., 1941
    Prunus persica
        Richards, B.L. and L.C. Cochran, 1956

V. CHERRY NECROTIC ETCH *
    Prunus avium
        Posnette, A.F., 1954
    Prunus persica
        Posnette, A.F., 1954

V. CHERRY NECROTIC LINE PATTERN   Posnette 1954
    Prunus avium
        Posnette, A.F. and R. Cropley, 1956

V. CHERRY NECROTIC RUSTY MOTTLE   Richards and
    Prunus avium   Reeves 1951
        Afanasiev, M.M. and H.E. Morris, 1954
        (K.M. Smith, 1957) R.E. Fitzpatrick, et al., 1958
        Lott, T.B., 1945
        Reeves, E.L. and B.L. Richards, 1946
        Richards, B.L. and L.C. Cochran, 1956
        Richards, B.L. and Bryce N. Wadley, 1950
    Prunus avium x Prunus cerasus
        Richards, B.L. and L.C. Cochran, 1956
    Prunus cerasus
        Richards, B.L. and L.C. Cochran, 1956
        Richards, B.L. and Bryce N. Wadley, 1950
    Prunus persica
        Richards, B.L. and L.C. Cochran, 1956
        Richards, B.L. and Bryce N. Wadley, 1950
    Prunus virginiana var. demissa
        Richards, B.L. and L.C. Cochran, 1956

V. CHERRY PINTO LEAF   Kienholz 1947
    Prunus avium
        Kienholz, J.R., 1947

VIRUS
V. CHERRY RASP LEAF Bodine and Newton 1942
  Prunus armeniaca
    Posnette, A.F., 1954
  Prunus avium
    Blodgett, Earle C., 1943
    Bodine, E.W. and J.H. Newton, 1942
    Milbrath, J.A., 1954
    Posnette, A.F., 1954
    Posnette, A.F. and R. Cropley, 1956
    Richards, B.L. and L.C. Cochran, 1956
  Prunus cerasifera
    Posnette, A.F., 1954
  Prunus cerasus
    Blodgett, Earle C., 1943
    Posnette, A.F., 1954
    Richards, B.L. and L.C. Cochran, 1956
  Prunus cerasus var. umbraculifera *
    Milbrath, J.A., 1954
  Prunus mahaleb
    Posnette, A.F., 1954
  Prunus persica
    Posnette, A.F., 1954

V. CHERRY RUGOSE MOSAIC Thomas and Rawlins 1951
  Prunus amygdalus
    Nyland, George, 1954
  Prunus avium
    Berkeley, G.H., 1950
    Nyland, George, 1954
    Posnette, A.F., 1954
    Posnette, A.F. and R. Cropley, 1956
    Richards, B.L. and L.C. Cochran, 1956
    Thomas, H. Earl and T.E. Rawlins, 1939
  Prunus cerasifera
    Posnette, A.F., 1954
  Prunus cerasus
    Berkeley, G.H., 1950
    Hildebrand, E.M., 1944
    Posnette, A.F., 1954
    Richards, B.L. and L.C. Cochran, 1956
  Prunus domestica
    Nyland, George, 1954
  Prunus mahaleb
    Berkeley, G.H., 1950
    Thomas, H. Earl and T.E. Rawlins, 1939
  Prunus persica
    Berkeley, G.H., 1950
    Nyland, George, 1954
    Posnette, A.F., 1954
    Thomas, H. Earl and T.E. Rawlins, 1939

V. CHERRY RUSTY MOTTLE Reeves 1940
  Prunus armeniaca
    Posnette, A.F., 1954
  Prunus avium
    Posnette, A.F., 1954
    Posnette, A.F. and R. Cropley, 1956
    Reeves, E.L., 1940
    Zeller, S.M. and J.A. Milbrath, 1947
  Prunus cerasus
    Posnette, A.F., 1954
    Zeller, S.M. and J.A. Milbrath, 1947
  Prunus domestica
    Zeller, S.M. and J.A. Milbrath, 1947
  Prunus mahaleb
    Zeller, S.M. and J.A. Milbrath, 1947
  Prunus persica
    Posnette, A.F., 1954
    Zeller, S.M. and J.A. Milbrath, 1947
  Prunus serrulata
    Zeller, S.M. and J.A. Milbrath, 1947

V. CHERRY SUNKEN MOTTLE *
  Prunus avium
    Posnette, A.F., 1954
  Prunus persica
    Posnette, A.F., 1954

V. CHERRY TWISTED LEAF Lott 1943
  Prunus avium
    Lott, T.B., 1943
    Reeves, E.L. and Philip W. Cheney, 1956

VIRUS
V. CHERRY TWISTED LEAF (cont.)
  Prunus persica
    (K.M. Smith, 1957) R.E. Fitzpatrick, et al., 1958

V. CHERRY VEIN CLEARING *
  Prunus avium
    Zeller, S.M. and A.W. Evans, 1941
  Prunus serrulata
    Zeller, S.M. and A.W. Evans, 1941

V. CHILLI (PEPPER) MOSAIC Ferguson 1951
  Capsicum frutescens (Capsicum annuum)
    Dale, W.T., 1954
    Ferguson, I.A.C., 1951
    Jha, Ashrafi and S.P. Raychaudhuri, 1956
  Capsicum frutescens var. grossum
    Dale, W.T., 1954
    Ferguson, I.A.C., 1951
  Capsicum frutescens var. minimum *
    Dale, W.T., 1954
    Ferguson, I.A.C., 1951
  Carthamus tinctorius
    Jha, Ashrafi and S.P. Raychaudhuri, 1956
  Cucumis melo var. utilissimus *
    Jha, Ashrafi and S.P. Raychaudhuri, 1956
  Cucumis sativus
    Jha, Ashrafi and S.P. Raychaudhuri, 1956
  Datura stramonium
    Jha, Ashrafi and S.P. Raychaudhuri, 1956
  Nicotiana alata var. grandiflora
    Dale, W.T., 1954
  Nicotiana chinensis
    Dale, W.T., 1954
  Nicotiana glutinosa
    Dale, W.T., 1954
    Jha, Ashrafi and S.P. Raychaudhuri, 1956
  Nicotiana rustica
    Dale, W.T., 1954
  Nicotiana sanderae
    Dale, W.T., 1954
  Nicotiana sylvestris
    Dale, W.T., 1954
  Nicotiana tabacum
    Dale, W.T., 1954
    Ferguson, I.A.C., 1951
    Jha, Ashrafi and S.P. Raychaudhuri, 1956
  Nicotiana tabacum var. macrophylla
    Dale, W.T., 1954
    Ferguson, I.A.C., 1951
  Nicotiana tomentosiformis
    Adsuar, J. and L. Lopez Matos, 1955
  Nicotiana undulata
    Adsuar, J. and L. Lopez Matos, 1955
  Nicotiana velutina
    Adsuar, J. and L. Lopez Matos, 1955
  Petunia hybrida
    Dale, W.T., 1954
    Jha, Ashrafi and S.P. Raychaudhuri, 1956
  Physalis floridana
    Dale, W.T., 1954
  Solanum nigrum
    Jha, Ashrafi and S.P. Raychaudhuri, 1956
  Solanum tuberosum
    Jha, Ashrafi and S.P. Raychaudhuri, 1956

V. CHILLI VEINBANDING Simons 1956
  Capsicum frutescens (Capsicum annuum)
    Simons, J.N., 1956, 1957
  Capsicum frutescens var. longum
    Simons, John N., 1956
  Lycopersicon esculentum
    Simons, John N., 1956
  Lycopersicon esculentum var. cerasiforme
    Simons, John N., 1956
  Nicotiana glutinosa
    Simons, John N., 1956
  Nicotiana tabacum
    Simons, John N., 1956
  Physalis peruviana
    Simons, John N., 1956
  Portulaca oleracea
    Simons, John N., 1956

VIRUS

V. CHILLI VEINBANDING (cont.)
Solanum elaeagnifolium
Simons, John N., 1956
Solanum gracile *
Simons, John N., 1956, 1957
Solanum melongena
Simons, John N., 1956
Zinnia elegans
Simons, John N., 1956

V. CHRYSANTHEMUM B (MILD MOSAIC) *
Aster amellus
Hollings, M., 1957
Chrysanthemum carinatum
Hollings, M., 1957
Chrysanthemum morifolium
Hollings, M., 1957
Nicotiana affinis
Hollings, M., 1957
Nicotiana glutinosa
Hollings, M., 1957
Nicotiana rustica
Hollings, M., 1957
Passiflora caerulea
Hollings, M., 1957
Petunia hybrida
Hollings, M., 1957
Senecio cruentus
Hollings, M., 1957
Tetragonia expansa
Hollings, M., 1957
Vicia faba
Hollings, M., 1957

V. CHRYSANTHEMUM D *
Chenopodium amaranticolor
Hollings, M., 1956

V. CHRYSANTHEMUM LATENT *
Amaranthus caudatus
Hollings, M., 1957
Antirrhinum majus
Hollings, M., 1957
Celosia argentea
Hollings, M., 1957
Chenopodium amaranticolor
Hollings, M., 1957
Chrysanthemum morifolium
Hollings, M., 1957
Gomphrena globosa
Hollings, M., 1957
Helichrysum bracteatum
Hollings, M., 1957
Nicotiana glutinosa
Hollings, M., 1957
Nicotiana rustica
Hollings, M., 1957
Nicotiana tabacum
Hollings, M., 1957
Papaver somniferum
Hollings, M., 1957
Taraxacum officinale
Hollings, M., 1957
Tetragonia expansa
Hollings, M., 1957
Thlaspi arvense
Hollings, M., 1957

V. CHRYSANTHEMUM Q Keller 1950
Antirrhinum spp.
(K.M. Smith, 1957) R.E. Fitzpatrick, et al., 1958
Calendula officinalis
(K.M. Smith, 1957) R.E. Fitzpatrick, et al., 1958
Callistephus chinensis
(K.M. Smith, 1957) R.E. Fitzpatrick, et al., 1958
Chrysanthemum hortorum
Graham, D.C., 1957
Chrysanthemum indicum
(K.M. Smith, 1957) R.E. Fitzpatrick, et al., 1958
Chrysanthemum morifolium
Brierley, Philip, 1955
Brierley, Philip and Floyd F. Smith, 1953
Holmes, Francis O., 1956

VIRUS

V. CHRYSANTHEMUM Q (cont.)
Chrysanthemum morifolium
Keller, John R., 1951, 1953
Petunia hybrida
Brierley, Philip, 1955
Brierley, Philip and Floyd F. Smith, 1953

V. CHRYSANTHEMUM RING SPOT Brierley and Smith
Chrysanthemum indicum   1955
(K.M. Smith, 1957) R.E. Fitzpatrick, et al., 1958
Chrysanthemum morifolium
Brierley, Philip and Floyd F. Smith, 1955
Senecio cruentus
Brierley, Philip and Floyd F. Smith, 1955

V. CHRYSANTHEMUM ROSETTE Brierley and Smith
Chrysanthemum indicum   1951
(K.M. Smith, 1957) R.E. Fitzpatrick, et al., 1958

V. CHRYSANTHEMUM STUNT Brierley and Smith 1949
Achillea millefolium
Brierley, Philip, 1953
Achillea ptarmica
Brierley, Philip, 1950, 1953
Keller, John R., 1953
Ambrosia trifida
Brierley, Philip, 1953
Anthemis tinctoria
Brierley, Philip, 1950, 1953
Centaurea cyanus
Brierley, Philip, 1950, 1953
Keller, John R., 1953
Chrysanthemum carinatum
Brierley, Philip, 1950, 1953
Chrysanthemum cinerariaefolium
Brierley, Philip, 1953
Chrysanthemum coccineum
Brierley, Philip, 1950, 1953
Chrysanthemum coronarium
Brierley, Philip, 1950, 1953
Chrysanthemum corymbosum
Brierley, Philip, 1953
Chrysanthemum frutescens
Brierley, Philip, 1953
Chrysanthemum hortorum
Brierley, Philip, 1950
Chrysanthemum indicum
(K.M. Smith, 1957) R.E. Fitzpatrick, et al., 1958
Chrysanthemum lacustre
Brierley, Philip, 1953
Chrysanthemum leucanthemum
Brierley, Philip, 1953
Chrysanthemum majus
Brierley, Philip, 1953
Chrysanthemum maximum
Brierley, Philip, 1953
Chrysanthemum morifolium
Brierley, Philip, 1953
Brierley, Philip and Floyd F. Smith, 1949, 1955
Keller, John R., 1951, 1953
Welsh, Maurice F., 1948
Chrysanthemum myconis
Brierley, Philip, 1953
Chrysanthemum nivellei
Brierley, Philip, 1953
Chrysanthemum parthenium
Brierley, Philip, 1953
Chrysanthemum parthenium f. flosculosum *
Brierley, Philip, 1953
Chrysanthemum praealtum
Brierley, Philip, 1950, 1953
Chrysanthemum spp.
Brierley, Philip, 1953
Chrysanthemum viscosum
Brierley, Philip, 1953
Dahlia pinnata
Brierley, Philip, 1953
Dahlia spp.
Keller, John R., 1953
Dahlia variabilis
Brierley, Philip, 1950
Echinacea purpurea
Brierley, Philip, 1950, 1953

VIRUS

V. CHRYSANTHEMUM STUNT (cont.)
Echinacea purpurea
 Keller, John R., 1953
Emilia sagittata
 Brierley, Philip, 1950, 1953
 Keller, John R., 1953
Heliopsis helianthoides var. pitcheriana
 Brierley, Philip, 1953
Liatris pycnostachya
 Brierley, Philip, 1953
Liatris spicata
 Brierley, Philip, 1950
 Keller, John R., 1953
Sanvitalia procumbens
 Brierley, Philip, 1953
Senecio cruentus
 Brierley, Philip, 1950, 1953
 Keller, John R., 1953
Senecio glastifolium
 Brierley, Philip, 1953
Senecio mikanioides
 Brierley, Philip, 1953
Tanacetum boreale
 Brierley, Philip, 1953
Tanacetum camphoratum
 Brierley, Philip, 1953
Tanacetum vulgare
 Brierley, Philip, 1953
Tithonia rotundifolia
 Brierley, Philip, 1953
 Keller, John R., 1953
Venidium fastuosum
 Brierley, Philip, 1953
Verbesina encelioides
 Brierley, Philip, 1953
Zinnia elegans
 Brierley, Philip, 1953

V. CHRYSANTHEMUM VEIN MOTTLE *
Chrysanthemum morifolium
 Hollings, M., 1957
Petunia hybrida
 Hollings, M., 1957

V. CINERARIA MOSAIC Jones 1942
Cineraria cruenta
 Jones, Leon K., 1944

V. CITRUS CONVEX GUM *
Citrus spp.
 (K.M. Smith, 1957) R.E. Fitzpatrick, et al., 1958

V. CITRUS EXOCORTIS Moreira 1955
Citrus paradisi on Citrus aurantifolia
 Olson, E.O. and A.V. Shull, 1956
Citrus paradisi on (Citrus sinensis x Poncirus trifoliata)
 Olson, E.O. and A.V. Shull, 1956
Citrus sinensis on Citrus aurantifolia
 Olson, E.O. and A.V. Shull, 1956

V. CITRUS GROWTH-RETARDING *
Citrus limon
 Calavan, E.C., J.M. Wallace and L.G. Weathers, 1954

V. CITRUS PSOROSIS ((Swingle and Weber 1896))
Citrus aurantifolia   Fawcett 1936
 Wallace, J.M., 1951
 Weathers, L.G., E.C. Calavan and J.M. Wallace, 1956
Citrus limon
 Fawcett, H.S. and A.A. Bitancourt, 1943
 Weathers, L.G., E.C. Calavan and J.M. Wallace, 1956
Citrus maxima
 Weathers, L.G., E.C. Calavan and J.M. Wallace, 1956
Citrus paradisi
 Fawcett, H.S., 1938
 Weathers, L.G., E.C. Calavan and J.M. Wallace, 1956
Citrus reticulata
 Fawcell, H.S., 1938

VIRUS

V. CITRUS PSOROSIS (cont.)
Citrus sinensis
 Fawcett, H.S., 1933, 1934, 1938
 Fawcett, H.S. and A.A. Bitancourt, 1943
 Fawcett, H.S. and L.C. Cochran, 1941, 1942
 Rhoads, Authur S., 1942
 Wallace, James M., 1945
Citrus spp.
 Bennett, C.W., 1944

V. CITRUS STUBBORN DISEASE Fawcett 1946
Citrus sinensis
 Fawcett, H.S., 1946

V. CITRUS TRISTEZA Meneghini 1946
Aeglopsis chevalieri
 Hughes, W.A. and C.A. Lister, 1953
 Knorr, L.C., 1956
Afraegle paniculata
 Hughes, W.A. and C.A. Lister, 1953
 Knorr, L.C., 1956
Arracacha esculenta
 Costa, A.S. and T.J. Grant, 1951
Citropsis articulata
 Hughes, W.A. and C.A. Lister, 1953
Citrus aurantifolia
 Dickson, R.C., Metta McD. Johnson, R.A. Flock and Edward F. Laird, Jr., 1956
 Grant, Theodore J. and Henry Schneider, 1953
 Hughes, W.A. and C.A. Lister, 1953
 Knorr, L.C., 1956
 Olson, Edward O., 1956
 Wallace, J.M., 1951, 1957
 Wallace, J.M., P.C.J. Oberholzer and J.D.J. Hofmeyer, 1956
 Wallace, J.M., I. Reichert, A. Bental and E. Winocour, 1956
Citrus aurantium
 Costa, A.S. and T.J. Grant, 1951
 Grant, Theodore J. and A.S. Costa, 1951
 Hughes, W.A. and C.A. Lister, 1953
 Olson, Edward O., 1956
Citrus combava
 Knorr, L.C., 1956
Citrus grandis
 Carpenter, J.B., 1957
 Wallace, James M., 1957
Citrus grandis on Citrus aurantium
 Bennett, C.W. and A.S. Costa, 1949
Citrus hystrix
 Knorr, L.C., 1956
Citrus limon
 Bennett, C.W. and A.S. Costa, 1949
 Carpenter, J.B., 1956, 1957
 Grant, Theodore J. and Richard P. Higgins, 1957
 Hughes, W.A. and C.A. Lister, 1953
 Olson, Edward O. and James R. McDonald, 1954
 Schneider, Henry, 1957
 Wallace, James M., 1957
 Wallace, J.M., P.C.J. Oberholzer and J.D.J. Hofmeyer, 1956
 Wallace, J.M., I. Reichert, A. Bental and E. Winocour, 1956
Citrus limon on Citrus aurantium
 Bennett, C.W. and A.S. Costa, 1949
Citrus limon x Citrus sinensis
 Olson, Edward O., 1956
Citrus limon on Poncirus trifoliata
 Olson, Edward O. and James R. McDonald, 1954
Citrus medica
 Hughes, W.A. and C.A. Lister, 1953
Citrus nobilis var. unshiu
 Hughes, W.A. and C.A. Lister, 1953
 Olson, Edward O. and James R. McDonald, 1954
 Wallace, James M., 1957
Citrus nobilis var. unshiu on Citrus paradisi x Poncirus trifoliata
 Olson, Edward O. and James R. McDonald, 1954
Citrus nobilis var. unshiu on Citrus sinensis x Poncirus trifoliata
 Olson, Edward O. and James R. McDonald, 1954
Citrus nobilis var. unshiu on Poncirus trifoliata
 Olson, Edward O. and James R. McDonald, 1954

VIRUS
V. CITRUS TRISTEZA (cont.)
  Citrus paradisi
    Carpenter, J.B., 1957
    Hughes, W.A. and C.A. Lister, 1953
    Knorr, L.C., 1956
    Olson, Edward O., 1956
    Wallace, James M., 1957
    Wallace, J.M., P.C.J. Oberholzer and J.D.J.
    Hofmeyer, 1956
  Citrus paradisi on Citrus aurantium
    Bennett, C.W. and A.S. Costa, 1949
  Citrus paradisi x Citrus reticulata
    Costa, A.S. and T.J. Grant, 1951
    Hughes, W.A. and C.A. Lister, 1953
  Citrus paradisi x Citrus reticulata on Citrus aurantium
    Bennett, C.W. and A.S. Costa, 1949
  Citrus reticulata
    Bennett, C.W. and A.S. Costa, 1949
    Carpenter, J.B., 1957
    Hughes, W.A. and C.A. Lister, 1953
    Olson, Edward O., 1956
    Wallace, James M., 1957
  Citrus reticulata on Citrus aurantium
    Bennett, C.W. and A.S. Costa, 1949
  Citrus sinensis
    Carpenter, J.B., 1957
    Costa, A.S. and T.J. Grant, 1951
    Dickson, R.C., Metta McD. Johnson, R.A. Flock
    and Edward F. Laird, Jr., 1956
    Grant, Theodore J. and A.S. Costa, 1951
    Grant, Theodore J. and Henry Schneider, 1953
    Hughes, W.A. and C.A. Lister, 1953
    Knorr, L.C., 1956
    Schneider, Henry, J.M. Wallace and J.E. Dimitman,
    1950
    Wallace, J.M., 1949, 1957
  Citrus sinensis on Citrus aurantifolia
    Bennett, C.W. and A.S. Costa, 1949
  Citrus sinensis on Citrus aurantium
    Bennett, C.W. and A.S. Costa, 1949
    Schneider, Henry, 1954
  Citrus sinensis on Citrus paradisi
    Bennett, C.W. and A.S. Costa, 1949
  Clausena anisata
    Hughes, W.A. and C.A. Lister, 1953
  Pamburus missiones
    Knorr, L.C., 1956

V. CITRUS VEIN ENATION Wallace and Drake 1953
  Citrus spp.
    (K.M. Smith, 1957) R.E. Fitzpatrick, et al., 1958

V. CITRUS VEIN-YELLOWING DISEASE *
  Citrus aurantifolia
    Weathers, L.G., 1957
  Citrus aurantifolia x Fortunella margarita
    Weathers, L.G., 1957
  Citrus limon
    Weathers, L.G., 1957
  Citrus mitis
    Weathers, L.G., 1957
  Citrus paradisi x Citrus reticulata
    Weathers, L.G., 1957
  Fortunella margarita
    Weathers, L.G., 1957

V. CITRUS XYLOPOROSIS Reichert and Perlberger 1934
  Citrus aurantifolia
    Childs, J.F.L., 1956
  Citrus paradisi on Citrus aurantifolia
    Olson, E.O. and A.V. Shull, 1956
  Citrus paradisi on (Citrus paradisi x Citrus reticulata)
    Olson, E.O. and A.V. Shull, 1956
  Citrus paradisi x Citrus reticulata
    Childs, J.F.L., 1956
  Citrus sinensis
    Childs, J.F.L., 1956
  Citrus sinensis x Citrus reticulata
    Childs, J.F.L., 1956

V. CLOVE SUDDEN DEATH DISEASE *
  Eugenia caryophyllata
    Nutman, F.J. and F.M.L. Sheffield, 1949

VIRUS
V. CLOVER BIG VEIN Black 1944
  Anagallis linifolia
    Black, L.M., 1945
  Anthemis cotula
    Black, L.M., 1945
  Barbarea vulgaris
    Black, L.M., 1945
  Brachycome iberidifolia
    Black, L.M., 1945
  Capsella bursa-pastoris
    Black, L.M., 1945
    Lee, C.L., 1956
  Chrysanthemum leucanthemum var. pinnatifidum
    Black, L.M., 1945
  Collinsia bicolor
    Black, L.M., 1945
  Dianthus armeria
    Black, L.M., 1945
  Dianthus barbatus
    Black, L.M., 1945
  Heliophila linearifolia
    Black, L.M., 1945
  Heliotropium peruvianum
    Black, L.M., 1945
  Kochia scoparia var. trichophylla
    Black, L.M., 1945
  Lepidium campestre
    Black, L.M., 1945
  Lepidium virginicum
    Black, L.M., 1945
  Linaria maroccana
    Black, L.M., 1945
  Linum grandiflorum
    Black, L.M., 1945
  Lobelia erinus
    Black, L.M., 1945
  Lychnis alba
    Black, L.M., 1945
  Matthiola bicornis
    Black, L.M., 1945
  Melilotus alba
    Black, L.M., 1945, 1951
  Melilotus altissima
    Black, L.M., 1951
  Melilotus dentata
    Black, L.M., 1951
  Melilotus indica
    Black, L.M., 1951
  Melilotus officinalis
    Black, L.M., 1951
  Melilotus polonica
    Black, L.M., 1951
  Melilotus suaveolens
    Black, L.M., 1951
  Melilotus taurica
    Black, L.M., 1951
  Melilotus tommasinii
    Black, L.M., 1951
  Melilotus wolgica
    Black, L.M., 1951
  Nicotiana tabacum
    (K.M. Smith, 1957) R.E. Fitzpatrick, et al., 1958
  Nierembergia frutescens
    Black, L.M., 1945
  Nolana atriplicifolia
    Black, L.M., 1945
  Phacelia campanularia
    Black, L.M., 1945
  Portulaca grandiflora
    Black, L.M., 1945
  Portulaca oleracea
    Black, L.M., 1945
  Reseda odorata
    Black, L.M., 1945
  Rheum rhaponticum
    Black, L.M., 1945
  Rudbeckia bicolor
    Black, L.M., 1945
  Rudbeckia hirta
    Black, L.M., 1945
  Rumex acetosa
    Black, L.M., 1945

VIRUS
V. CLOVER BIG VEIN (cont.)
  Rumex acetosella
    Black, L.M., 1945
  Rumex crispus
    Black, L.M., 1945
  Rumex obtusifolius
    Black, L.M., 1945
  Scabiosa atropurpurea
    Black, L.M., 1945
  Schizanthus wisetonensis
    Black, L.M., 1945
  Silene latifolia
    Black, L.M., 1945
  Tetragonia expansa
    Black, L.M., 1945
  Torenia fournieri
    Black, L.M., 1945
  Trifolium incarnatum
    Black, L.M., 1945, 1953
    Black, L.M. and M.K. Brakke, 1952
    Maramorosch, Karl, 1950
  Trifolium pratense
    Black, L.M., 1945
  Trigonella caerulea
    Black, L.M., 1951
  Venidium fastuosum
    Black, L.M., 1945
  Verbena hybrida
    Black, L.M., 1945
  Vinca rosea
    Black, L.M., 1945

V. CLOVER CLUB LEAF Black 1944
  Trifolium incarnatum
    Black, L.M., 1948, 1949

V. CLOVER DISEASE, EUROPEAN LEAFHOPPER-
  Trifolium incarnatum   BORNE *
    Maramorosch, Karl, 1953, 1954

V. CLOVER ENATION *
  Prunus avium
    (K.M. Smith, 1957) R.E. Fitzpatrick, et al., 1958
  Trifolium incarnatum
    (K.M. Smith, 1957) R.E. Fitzpatrick, et al., 1958

V. CLOVER WITCHES' BROOM *
  Anthemis cotula
    Frazier, N.W. and A.F. Posnette, 1957
  Apium graveolens
    Frazier, N.W. and A.F. Posnette, 1957
  Daucus carota
    Frazier, N.W. and A.F. Posnette, 1957
  Duchesnea indica
    Frazier, N.W. and A.F. Posnette, 1957
  Fragaria vesca
    Frazier, N.W. and A.F. Posnette, 1957
  Lycopersicon esculentum
    Frazier, N.W. and A.F. Posnette, 1957
  Plantago major
    Frazier, N.W. and A.F. Posnette, 1957
  Solanum tuberosum
    Frazier, N.W. and A.F. Posnette, 1957
  Trifolium incarnatum
    Frazier, N.W. and A.F. Posnette, 1957
  Trifolium pratense
    Frazier, N.W. and A.F. Posnette, 1957
  Trifolium repens
    Frazier, N.W. and A.F. Posnette, 1957

V. COCKSFOOT STREAK Smith 1952
  Dactylis gloverata
    Smith, Kenneth M., 1952

V. (COCONUT) CADANG-CADANG DISEASE *
  Cocos nucifera
    Celino, M.S., 1947

V. COFFEE HOT AND COLD DISEASE *
  Coffea arabica
    (K.M. Smith, 1957) R.E. Fitzpatrick, et al., 1958

VIRUS
V. COFFEE RING SPOT *
  Coffea arabica
    (K.M. Smith, 1957) R.E. Fitzpatrick, et al., 1958

V. COLEUS MOSAIC Creager 1945
  Coleus blumei
    Creager, D.B., 1945

V. CORN NEW MOSAIC *
  Hordeum vulgare
    Finley, A.M., 1954
  Setaria virdis
    Finley, A.M., 1954
  Triticum aestivum
    Finley, A.M., 1954

V. COTTON LEAF CRUMPLE Dickson et al. 1954
  Gossypium hirsutum
    Dickson, R.C., M. McD. Johnson and Edward F.
    Laird, 1954

V. COTTON LEAF CURL Bailey 1934; Kirkpatrick 1931
  Abutilon spp.
    (K.M. Smith, 1957) R.E. Fitzpatrick, et al., 1958
  Althaea rosea
    (K.M. Smith, 1957) R.E. Fitzpatrick, et al., 1958
  Gossypium hirsutum
    (K.M. Smith, 1957) R.E. Fitzpatrick, et al., 1958
  Gossypium peruvianum
    (K.M. Smith, 1957) R.E. Fitzpatrick, et al., 1958
  Gossypium peruvianum x Gossypium barbadense
    (K.M. Smith, 1957) R.E. Fitzpatrick, et al., 1958
  Gossypium vitifolium
    (K.M. Smith, 1957) R.E. Fitzpatrick, et al., 1958
  Hibiscus cannabinus
    (K.M. Smith, 1957) R.E. Fitzpatrick, et al., 1958
  Hibiscus esculentus
    (K.M. Smith, 1957) R.E. Fitzpatrick, et al., 1958
  Hibiscus sabdariffa
    (K.M. Smith, 1957) R.E. Fitzpatrick, et al., 1958
  Sida spp.
    (K.M. Smith, 1957) R.E. Fitzpatrick, et al., 1958
  Urena lobata
    (K.M. Smith, 1957) R.E. Fitzpatrick, et al., 1958
  Zinnia elegans
    Mathur, R.N., 1933

V. COTTON SMALL LEAF *
  Gossypium arboreum var. typicum f. indica *
    (K.M. Smith, 1957) R.E. Fitzpatrick, et al., 1958

V. COTTON TEXAS *
  Gossypium hirsutum
    Rosberg, David W., 1957

V. COTTON VEINAL MOSAIC *
  Gossypium barbadense
    (K.M. Smith, 1957) R.E. Fitzpatrick, et al., 1958
  Gossypium hirsutum
    (K.M. Smith, 1957) R.E. Fitzpatrick, et al., 1958
  Gossypium klotzchianum
    (K.M. Smith, 1957) R.E. Fitzpatrick, et al., 1958
  Gossypium punctatum
    (K.M. Smith, 1957) R.E. Fitzpatrick, et al., 1958
  Gossypium trilobum
    (K.M. Smith, 1957) R.E. Fitzpatrick, et al., 1958

V. COWPEA MOSAIC
  Canavalia ensiformis
    Anderson, C.W., 1955
    Capoor, S.P. and P.M. Varma, 1956
    Dale, W.T., 1949
  Canavalia gladiata
    Anderson, C.W., 1955
  Cassia tora
    Anderson, C.W., 1954, 1955
  Chenopodium ambrosioides var. anthelminticum
    Anderson, C.W., 1955
  Crotalaria juncea
    Capoor, S.P. and P.M. Varma, 1956
    Dale, W.T., 1949
  Crotalaria mucronata
    Anderson, C.W., 1955

VIRUS

V. COWPEA MOSAIC (cont.)

Crotalaria spectabilis
  Anderson, C.W., 1955
Cyamopsis tetragonoloba
  Capoor, S.P. and P.M. Varma, 1956
Desmodium frutescens
  Dale, W.T., 1949
Desmodium incanum
  Anderson, C.W., 1955
Dolichos lablab
  Anderson, C.W., 1955
  Dale, W.T., 1949
Glycine max
  Anderson, C.W., 1955
  Capoor, S.P. and P.M. Varma, 1956
  Dale, W.T., 1949
Phaseolus angularis
  Yu, T.F., 1946
Phaseolus aureus
  Dale, W.T., 1949
Phaseolus limensis
  Anderson, C.W., 1955
Phaseolus lunatus
  Dale, W.T., 1949
Phaseolus lunatus f. macrocarpus
  Capoor, S.P. and P.M. Varma, 1956
  Dale, W.T., 1949
  McLean, D.M., 1941
  Yu, T.F., 1946
Phaseolus mungo
  Dale, W.T., 1949
Phaseolus trinervius
  Dale, W.T., 1949
Psophocarpus tetragonolobus
  Dale, W.T., 1949
Sesbania speciosa
  Dale, W.T., 1949
Vicia faba
  Anderson, C.W., 1955
Vigna cylindrica (Vigna catjang)
  Capoor, S.P. and P.M. Varma, 1956
  Vasudeva, R. Sahai, 1942
Vigna sesquipedalis
  Capoor, S.P. and P.M. Varma, 1956
Vigna sinensis
  Anderson, C.W., 1955, 1957
  Capoor, S.P. and P.M. Varma, 1956
  Dale, W.T., 1953
  McLean, D.M., 1941
  Yu, T.F., 1946
Vigna unguiculata
  Dale, W.T., 1949
Vigna vexillata
  Dale, W.T., 1949
Zinnia elegans
  Anderson, C.W., 1955

V. CROTALARIA MOSAIC Johnson and Lefebvre 1938

Crotalaria incana
  Jensen, D.D., 1949, 1950
  Johnson, H.W. and C.L. Lefebvre, 1938
Crotalaria intermedia
  Johnson, H.W. and C.L. Lefebvre, 1938
Crotalaria juncea
  (K.M. Smith, 1957) R.E. Fitzpatrick, et al., 1958
Crotalaria lanceolata
  Johnson, H.W. and C.L. Lefebvre, 1938
Crotalaria maxillaris
  Johnson, H.W. and C.L. Lefebvre, 1938
Crotalaria mucronata
  Jensen, D.D., 1949
Crotalaria retusa
  Johnson, H.W. and C.L. Lefebvre, 1938
Crotalaria spectabilis
  Johnson, H.W. and C.L. Lefebvre, 1938
Crotalaria striata
  Cook, Melville T., 1931
  Johnson, H.W. and C.L. Lefebvre, 1938
Crotalaria usaramoensis
  Johnson, H.W. and C.L. Lefebvre, 1938
Vicia faba
  Johnson, H.W. and C.L. Lefebvre, 1938

VIRUS

V. CRUCIFER RING SPOT *

Brassica oleracea var. acephala
  Smith, Kenneth M., 1935
Brassica oleracea var. capitata
  Smith, Kenneth M., 1935
Brassica oleracea var. gemmifera
  Smith, Kenneth M., 1935
Nicotiana glutinosa
  Smith, Kenneth M., 1935
Nicotiana langsdorffii
  Smith, Kenneth M., 1935
Nicotiana tabacum
  Smith, Kenneth M., 1935

V. CUCUMBER GREEN MOTTLE MOSAIC Ainsworth 1935 ((This virus is serologically related to V. tobacco mosaic and is generally regarded as a strain of it, but see Knight 1955))

Citrullus vulgaris
  Ainsworth, G.C., 1935
Colocynthis vulgaris
  Vasudeva, R.S., S.P. Raychaudhuri and Jagannath Singh, 1949
Cucumis anguria
  Ainsworth, G.C., 1935
Cucumis maderaspatanus
  Ainsworth, G.C., 1935
Cucumis melo
  Ainsworth, G.C., 1935
  Azad, R.N., 1956
Cucumis melo var. utilissimus *
  Azad, R.N., 1956
Cucumis sativus
  Ainsworth, G.C., 1935
  Fulton, Robert W., 1950
  Johnson, Folke, 1941
  Vasudeva, R.S. and T.K. Nariani, 1952
  Vasudeva, R.S., S.P. Raychaudhuri and Jagannath Singh, 1949
Cucurbita moschata
  Vasudeva, R.S. and T.K. Nariani, 1952
  Vasudeva, R.S., S.P. Raychaudhuri and Jagannath Singh, 1949
Cucurbita pepo
  Ainsworth, G.C., 1935
  Storey, I.F., 1939
Datura stramonium
  Ainsworth, G.C., 1935
  Vasudeva, R.S. and T.K. Nariani, 1952
  Vasudeva, R.S., S.P. Raychaudhuri and Jagannath Singh, 1949
Lagenaria siceraria (Lagenaria leucantha)
  Azad, R.N., 1956
  Vasudeva, R.S. and T.K. Nariani, 1952
  Vasudeva, R.S., S.P. Raychaudhuri and Jagannath Singh, 1949
Luffa acutangula
  Vasudeva, R.S., S.P. Raychaudhuri and Jagannath Singh, 1949
Lycopersicon esculentum
  Ainsworth, G.C., 1935
Momordica charantia
  Vasudeva, R.S., S.P. Raychaudhuri and Jagannath Singh, 1949
Nicotiana tabacum
  Ainsworth, G.C., 1935
  Storey, I.F., 1939
  Vasudeva, R.S. and T.K. Nariani, 1952
Solanum nigrum
  Vasudeva, R.S. and T.K. Nariani, 1952
Solanum nodiflorum
  Vasudeva, R.S. and T.K. Nariani, 1952
Spinacia oleracea
  Storey, I.F., 1939
Trichosanthes anguina
  Azad, R.N., 1956

V. CUCUMBER MOSAIC Doolittle 1916, 1920

Adenia spp.
  Nattrass, R.M., 1944
Allium cepa
  Wellman, F.L., 1935

VIRUS

V. CUCUMBER MOSAIC (cont.)

Alternanthera ficoidea
  Dale, W.T., 1954
Amaranthus caudatus
  Fulton, Joseph P., 1950
  Pound, Glenn S. and J.C. Walker, 1948
  Price, W.C., 1940
Amaranthus tricolor
  Price, W.C., 1940
Ambrosia artemisiifolia var. elatior
  Wellman, F.L., 1935
Ananas comosus
  Carter, W., 1935
Anethum graveolens
  Wellman, F.L., 1935
Anthemis cotula
  Burnett, G., 1934
Anthriscus cerefolium
  Price, W.C., 1940
Antirrhinum majus
  Berkeley, G.H., 1951, 1953
  Brierley, Philip, 1952
  Doolittle, S.P. and W.J. Zaumeyer, 1953
  Hollings, M., 1955
  Nienow, Inez, 1948
  Pound, Glenn S. and J.C. Walker, 1948
  Wellman, F.L., 1935
Apium graveolens
  Anderson, C.W., 1955
  Bhargava, K.S., 1951
  Doolittle, S.P. and F.L. Wellman, 1934
  Doolittle, S.P. and W.J. Zaumeyer, 1953
  Fulton, Robert W., 1941
  Wellman, F.L., 1935
Apium graveolens var. dulce
  Anderson, C.W., 1951
  Severin, Henry H.P., 1950
  Simons, John N., 1955, 1957
  Wellman, F.L., 1934
  Whipple, O.C. and J.C. Walker, 1941
Apium graveolens var. rapaceum
  Wellman, F.L., 1935
Aquilegia vulgaris
  (K.M. Smith, 1957) R.E. Fitzpatrick, et al., 1958
Asclepias curassavica
  Silberschmidt, K., 1955
Aster amellus
  Pound, Glenn S. and J.C. Walker, 1948
Atropa belladonna
  Wellman, F.L., 1935
Barbarea vulgaris
  Pound, Glenn S. and J.C. Walker, 1948
Benincasa hispida
  Jagger, I.C., 1918
Berberis thunbergii
  Wilkinson, R.E., 1953
Beta vulgaris
  Anderson, C.W., 1951
  Bennett, C.W., 1944
  Berkeley, G.H. and J.H. Tremaine, 1954
  Bhargava, K.S., 1951
  Fulton, Joseph P., 1950
  Harrison, B.D., 1958
  Hoggan, I.A., 1933
  Johnson, E.M., 1930
  Severin, Henry H.P., 1948
  Wellman, F.L., 1934, 1935
Beta vulgaris var. cicla
  Berkeley, G.H. and J.H. Tremaine, 1954
  Bhargava, K.S., 1951
  Fulton, Joseph P., 1950
  Nienow, Inez, 1948
  Simons, John N., 1955, 1957
  Wellman, F.L., 1935
Brassica campestris var. napobrassica
  Berkeley, G.H. and J.H. Tremaine, 1954
Brassica juncea (Brassica japonica)
  Pound, Glenn S. and J.C. Walker, 1948
Brassica kaber (Brassica arvensis)
  Pound, Glenn S. and J.C. Walker, 1948
Brassica napus
  Berkeley, G.H. and J.H. Tremaine, 1954
  Pound, Glenn S. and J.C. Walker, 1948

VIRUS

V. CUCUMBER MOSAIC (cont.)

Brassica nigra
  Pound, Glenn S. and J.C. Walker, 1948
Brassica oleracea var. acephala
  Pound, Glenn S. and J.C. Walker, 1948
Brassica oleracea var. botrytis
  Pound, Glenn S. and J.C. Walker, 1948
Brassica oleracea var. capitata
  Pound, Glenn S. and J.C. Walker, 1948
Brassica oleracea var. gemmifera
  Pound, Glenn S. and J.C. Walker, 1948
Brassica oleracea var. gongylodes
  Pound, Glenn S. and J.C. Walker, 1948
Brassica pekinensis
  Pound, Glenn S. and J.C. Walker, 1948
Brassica rapa
  Wellman, F.L., 1935
Browallia speciosa
  Price, W.C., 1940
Bryonia dioica
  Ainsworth, G.C., 1935
Buddleia spp.
  (K.M. Smith, 1957) R.E. Fitzpatrick, et al., 1958
Cajanus indicus
  Dale, W.T., 1949
Calendula officinalis
  Nienow, Inez, 1948
  Pound, Glenn S. and J.C. Walker, 1948
  Price, W.C., 1940
Callistephus hortensis
  Govier, D.A., 1957
Calochortus spp.
  Brierley, Philip and Floyd F. Smith, 1944
Canna indica
  Celino, Martin S., 1940
  Celino, M.S. and Aureo L. Martinez, 1956
  Magee, C.J.P., 1940
Canna spp.
  Ocfemia, G.O. and Martin S. Celino, 1938
Capsella bursa-pastoris
  Burnett, G., 1934
  Pound, Glenn S. and J.C. Walker, 1948
Capsicum frutescens (Capsicum annuum)
  Adsuar, Jose and A. Cruz Miret, 1950
  Anderson, C.W., 1951, 1955, 1957
  Anderson, C.W. and M.K. Corbett, 1957
  Berkeley, G.H., 1951, 1953
  Doolittle, S.P., 1931
  Doolittle, S.P. and W.J. Zaumeyer, 1952, 1953
  Fulton, Robert W., 1941
  Harter, L.L., 1938
  Hoggan, Isme A., 1927
  Hollings, M., 1955
  Johnson, E.M., 1930
  Johnson, J., 1926, 1927
  Nariani, T.K. and Nirmaljit Singh, 1952
  Simons, John N., 1955, 1957
  Wellman, F.L., 1935
  Whipple, O.C. and J.C. Walker, 1941
Capsicum frutescens var. cerasiforme
  Pound, Glenn S. and J.C. Walker, 1948
Capsicum frutescens var. conoides
  Wellman, F.L., 1934
Capsicum frutescens var. grossum
  Wellman, F.L., 1934, 1935
Catharanthus roseus
  Adsuar, Jose and A. Cruz Miret, 1950
Celeri graveolens
  Adsuar, Jose and A. Cruz Miret, 1950
Celosia argentea var. cristata
  Price, W.C., 1940
Centaurea moschata
  Price, W.C., 1940
Chayota edulis
  Wellman, F.L., 1935
Cheiranthus allionii
  Pound, Glenn S. and J.C. Walker, 1948
Cheiranthus cheiri
  Berkeley, G.H. and J.H. Tremaine, 1954
Chenopodium album
  Fulton, Joseph P., 1950
Chenopodium amaranticolor
  Harrison, B.D., 1958

VIRUS
V. CUCUMBER MOSAIC (cont.)
    Chenopodium amaranticolor
        Hollings, M., 1955, 1956
    Chenopodium hybridum
        Roberts, Daniel A., 1952
        Roberts, Daniel A., R.E. Wilkinson and A. Frank
        Ross, 1951
    Chenopodium murale
        Wellman, F.L., 1935
    Chrysanthemum carinatum
        Govier, D.A., 1957
    Chrysanthemum hortorum
        Graham, D.C., 1957
    Chrysanthemum morifolium
        Hollings, M., 1955
        Whipple, O.C. and J.C. Walker, 1941
    Chrysanthemum segetum
        Govier, D.A., 1957
    Chrysanthemum spp.
        Govier, D.A., 1957
        Price, W.C., 1940
    Cichorium endivia
        Price, W.C., 1940
    Citrullus citrullus
        Adsuar, Jose and A. Cruz Miret, 1950
    Citrullus vulgaris
        Anderson, C.W., 1951
        Aycock, Robert, 1951
        Bhargava, K.S., 1951
        Jagger, I.C., 1918
        Lindberg, G.D., D.H. Hall and J.C. Walker, 1956
        Porter, R.H., 1930
        Pound, Glenn S. and J.C. Walker, 1948
        Vasudeva, R. Sahai and T.B. Lal, 1943
        Wellman, F.L., 1934, 1935
        Whipple, O.C. and J.C. Walker, 1941
    Citrus medica
        Porter, R.H., 1930
    Clarkia elegans
        Price, W.C., 1940
    Cleome spinosa
        Adsuar, Jose and A. Cruz Miret, 1950
        Faan, Hwei Chung and James Johnson, 1951
        Price, W.C., 1940
    Colchicum autumnale
        Brierley, Philip and Floyd F. Smith, 1944
    Coleus blumei
        Price, W.C., 1940
    Coleus lanuginosus
        Adsuar, Jose and A. Cruz Miret, 1950
    Commelina communis
        Price, W.C., 1935
        Wellman, F.L., 1935
    Commelina diffusa
        Dale, W.T., 1954
    Commelina elegans
        Anderson, C.W., 1952
        Dale, W.T., 1954
    Commelina erecta
        Wellman, F.L., 1935
    Commelina gigas
        Anderson, C.W., 1951, 1952
    Commelina nudiflora
        Anderson, C.W., 1952
        Price, W.C., 1941
        Wellman, F.L., 1934, 1935
    Commelina spp.
        Simons, John N., 1957
    Convolvulus spp.
        Wellman, F.L., 1935
    Crassina elegans
        Adsuar, Jose and A. Cruz Miret, 1950
    Crotalaria intermedia
        Price, W.C., 1940
    Crotalaria mucronata
        Anderson, C.W., 1955
    Cucumis anguria
        Jagger, I.C., 1918
        Rader, Wm. E., Hugh F. Fitzpatrick and E.M.
        Hildebrand, 1947
        Wellman, F.L., 1935
    Cucumis melo
        Adsuar, Jose, 1955

VIRUS
V. CUCUMBER MOSAIC (cont.)
    Cucumis melo
        Adsuar, Jose and A. Cruz Miret, 1950
        Doolittle, S.P., 1916
        Jagger, I.C., 1918
        Lindberg, G.D., D.H. Hall and J.C. Walker, 1956
        Pound, Glenn S. and J.C. Walker, 1948
        Vasudeva, R. Sahai and T.B. Lal, 1943
        Wellman, F.L., 1934, 1935
    Cucumis melo var. chito
        Rader, Wm. E., Hugh F. Fitzpatrick and E.M.
        Hildebrand, 1947
    Cucumis melo var. conomon
        Rader, Wm. E., Hugh F. Fitzpatrick and E.M.
        Hildebrand, 1947
        Whitaker, Thomas W. and G.W. Bohn, 1954
    Cucumis melo var. flexuosus
        Rader, Wm. E., Hugh F. Fitzpatrick and E.M.
        Hildebrand, 1947
    Cucumis melo var. inodorus
        Rader, Wm. E., Hugh F. Fitzpatrick and E.M.
        Hildebrand, 1947
        Whipple, O.C. and J.C. Walker, 1941
    Cucumis melo var. reticulatus
        Anderson, C.W., 1952
        Aycock, Robert, 1951
        Freitag, J.H., 1952
        Rader, Wm. E., Hugh F. Fitzpatrick and E.M.
        Hildebrand, 1947
        Whipple, O.C. and J.C. Walker, 1941
    Cucumis sativus
        Adsuar, Jose and A. Cruz Miret, 1950
        Ainsworth, G.C., 1938, 1940
        Anderson, C.W., 1951, 1952, 1955
        Aycock, Robert, 1951
        Berkeley, G.H., 1951, 1953
        Bhargava, K.S., 1951
        Brierley, Philip, 1939
        Burnett, G., 1934
        Cook, M.T., 1937
        Dale, W.T., 1954
        Diachun, Stephen, 1952
        Doolittle, S.P., 1916
        Doolittle, S.P. and M.N. Walker, 1928
        Doolittle, S.P. and W.J. Zaumeyer, 1952, 1953
        Elmer, O.H., 1927
        Freitag, J.H., 1952
        Fulton, Joseph P., 1950
        Fulton, Robert W., 1941
        Govier, D.A., 1957
        Hagedorn, D.J. and J.C. Walker, 1954
        Harrison, B.D., 1958
        Harter, L.L., 1936, 1938
        Hoggan, Isme A., 1933, 1935
        Hollings, M., 1955
        Jagger, I.C., 1916, 1918
        Johnson, E.M., 1930
        Larsh, Howard W. and J.R. Shay, 1945
        Lindberg, G.D., D.H. Hall and J.C. Walker, 1956
        Magee, C.J.P., 1940
        Milbrath, J.A. and Roy A. Young, 1956
        Nariani, T.K. and Nirmaljit Singh, 1952
        Nienow, Inez, 1948
        Porter, Clark A., 1954
        Porter, R.H., 1928, 1929, 1930
        Pound, Glenn S. and J.C. Walker, 1948
        Price, W.C., 1934, 1937, 1941
        Rader, Wm. E., Hugh F. Fitzpatrick and E.M.
        Hildebrand, 1947
        Shifriss, Oved, C.H. Myers and Charles Chupp,
        1942
        Silberschmidt, K., 1955
        Sill, Webster H., Jr., 1951
        Sill, W.H., Jr. and J.C. Walker, 1952
        Simons, John N., 1955, 1957
        Sinclair, J.B. and J.C. Walker, 1956
        Smith, Floyd F. and Philip Brierley, 1944
        Storey, I.F., 1939
        Valleau, W.D., 1932
        Varney, E.H. and J. Duain Moore, 1951
        Vasudeva, R. Sahai and T.B. Lal, 1943
        Walker, M.N., 1926
        Wellman, F.L., 1934, 1935

VIRUS
V. CUCUMBER MOSAIC (cont.)
Cucumis sativus
  Whipple, O.C. and J.C. Walker, 1938, 1941
Cucurbita lagenaria
  Adsuar, Jose and A. Cruz Miret, 1950
Cucurbita maxima
  Anderson, C.W., 1952
  Aycock, Robert, 1951
  Jagger, I.C., 1918
  Lindberg, G.D., D.H. Hall and J.C. Walker, 1956
  Magee, C.J.P., 1940
  Pound, Glenn S. and J.C. Walker, 1948
  Rader, Wm. E., Hugh F. Fitzpatrick and E.M.
    Hildebrand, 1947
  Wellman, F.L., 1935
Cucurbita moschata
  Adsuar, Jose and A. Cruz Miret, 1950
  Jagger, I.C., 1918
  Lindberg, G.D., D.H. Hall and J.C. Walker, 1956
  Rader, Wm. E., Hugh F. Fitzpatrick and E.M.
    Hildebrand, 1947
Cucurbita pepo
  Adsuar, Jose and A. Cruz Miret, 1950
  Jagger, I.C., 1916, 1918
  Lindberg, G.D., D.H. Hall and J.C. Walker, 1956
  Pound, Glenn S. and J.C. Walker, 1948
  Rader, Wm. E., Hugh F. Fitzpatrick and E.M.
    Hildebrand, 1947
  Vasudeva, R. Sahai and T.B. Lal, 1943
  Wellman, F.L., 1935
  Whipple, O.C. and J.C. Walker, 1941
Cucurbita pepo var. melopepo
  Anderson, C.W., 1951
  Jagger, I.C., 1916
  Wellman, F.L., 1934, 1935
Cucurbita pepo var. ovifera
  Jagger, I.C., 1916
Cuscuta campestris
  Costa, A.S., 1944
Cuscuta subinclusa
  Bennett, C.W., 1940
Cymbalaria muralis
  Price, W.C., 1940
Cynoglossum amabile
  Fulton, Robert W., 1941
  Wellman, F.L., 1935
Dahlia pinnata
  Pound, Glenn S. and J.C. Walker, 1948
Dahlia variabilis
  Brierley, Philip, 1951
Daphne mezereum
  (K.M. Smith, 1957) R.E. Fitzpatrick, et al., 1958
Daphne odora
  Milbrath, J.A. and Roy A. Young, 1956
Datura metel
  Pound, Glenn S. and J.C. Walker, 1948
Datura meteloides
  Wellman, F.L., 1935
Datura stramonium
  Berkeley, G.H., 1951, 1953
  Bhargava, K.S., 1951
  Doolittle, S.P. and W.J. Zaumeyer, 1953
  Govier, D.A., 1957
  Hagedorn, D.J. and J.C. Walker, 1954
  Harrison, B.D., 1958
  Hollings, M., 1955
  Johnson, E.M., 1930
  Lindberg, G.D., D.H. Hall and J.C. Walker, 1956
  Nariani, T.K. and Nirmaljit Singh, 1952
  Nienow, Inez, 1948
  Smith, Kenneth M., 1935
  Wellman, F.L., 1934, 1935
  Whipple, O.C. and J.C. Walker, 1941
Daucus carota
  Wellman, F.L., 1935
Delphinium ajacis
  Nienow, Inez, 1948
Delphinium consolida
  Wellman, F.L., 1935
Delphinium cultorum
  Valleau, W.D., 1932
Delphinium formosum
  Severin, Henry H.P., 1942

VIRUS
V. CUCUMBER MOSAIC (cont.)
Delphinium hybrid
  Severin, Henry H.P., 1942
Delphinium parryi var. maritimum
  Severin, Henry H.P., 1942
Delphinium spp.
  Burnett, G., 1934
Dipsacus spp.
  (K.M. Smith, 1957) R.E. Fitzpatrick, et al., 1958
Dolichos lablab
  Anderson, C.W., 1955
Echinocystis lobata
  Doolittle, S.P. and W.W. Gilbert, 1918
Emilia sagittata
  Wellman, F.L., 1934, 1935
Ensete glaucum
  Bernardo, Fernando A. and Dioscoro L. Umali,
    1956
Eryngium aquaticum
  Johnson, James, 1946
  Johnson, James and Edith M. Hein, 1948
Erysimum cheiranthoides
  Pound, Glenn S. and J.C. Walker, 1948
Euchlaena mexicana
  Wellman, F.L., 1934, 1935
Euphorbia corollata
  Faan, Hwei-Chung and James Johnson, 1951
Euphorbia splendens
  (K.M. Smith, 1957) R.E. Fitzpatrick, et al., 1958
Fagopyrum esculentum
  Fulton, Robert W., 1941
  Wellman, F.L., 1935
Foeniculum vulgare
  Wellman, F.L., 1935
Fritillaria pudica
  Brierley, Philip and Floyd F. Smith, 1944
Geranium carolinianum
  Wellman, F.L., 1935
Gilia capitata
  Wellman, F.L., 1935
Gilia liniflora
  Price, W.C., 1940
Gladiolus hortulanus
  Berkeley, G.H., 1951, 1953
  Bridgmon, G.H., 1951
  Brierley, Philip, 1952
Gladiolus spp.
  Faan, Hwei-Chung and James Johnson, 1951
Gloriosa rothschildiana
  Brierley, Philip and Floyd F. Smith, 1944
Glycine max
  Hagedorn, D.J., 1950, 1952
  Hagedorn, D.J. and J.C. Walker, 1954
Godetia amoena
  Price, W.C., 1940
Gomphrena globosa
  Berkeley, G.H. and J.H. Tremaine, 1954
  Doolittle, S.P. and W.J. Zaumeyer, 1953
Helianthus debilis
  Jagger, I.C., 1918
Helichrysum bracteatum
  Govier, D.A., 1957
  Price, W.C., 1940
Heliotropium corymbosum
  Price, W.C., 1940
Heliotropium peruvianum
  Price, W.C., 1940
Hesperis matronalis
  Berkeley, G.H. and J.H. Tremaine, 1954
  Pound, Glenn S. and J.C. Walker, 1948
Hibiscus esculentus
  Fulton, Robert W., 1941
Hibiscus manihot
  Price, W.C., 1940
Holcus sorghum
  Wellman, F.L., 1934, 1935
Hyacinthus orientalis
  Ainsworth, G.C., 1938
Hyoscyamus niger
  Govier, D.A., 1957
  Hoggan, Isme A., 1927
  Johnson, James, 1927

VIRUS
V. CUCUMBER MOSAIC (cont.)

Impatiens balsamina
  Price, W.C., 1940
Impatiens sultani (or sometimes Impatiens holstii)
  Adsuar, Jose, 1955
Ipomoea batata
  Wellman, F.L., 1935
Ipomoea purpurea
  Pound, Glenn S. and J.C. Walker, 1948
  Wellman, F.L., 1935
Lactuca sativa
  Anderson, C.W., 1955
  Hollings, M., 1955
  Kassanis, B., 1947
  Price, W.C., 1940
Lactuca scariola
  Burnett, G., 1934
Lagenaria vulgaris
  Jagger, I.C., 1918
  Vasudeva, R. Sahai and T.B. Lal, 1943
Lathyrus odoratus
  Ainsworth, G.C., 1940
  Doolittle, S.P. and W.J. Zaumeyer, 1952, 1953
Lavatera trimestris
  Price, W.C., 1940
Leonurus cardiaca
  Faan, Hwei-Chung and James Johnson, 1951
Ligustrum spp.
  (K.M. Smith, 1957) R.E. Fitzpatrick, et al., 1958
Lilium auratum
  Brierley, Philip, 1940
  Guterman, C.E.F., 1928
  Wellman, F.L., 1935
Lilium brownii
  Brierley, Philip, 1940
Lilium canadense
  Brierley, Philip, 1940
Lilium candidum
  Brierley, Philip, 1940
Lilium croceum
  Brierley, Philip, 1940
Lilium formosanum *
  Brierley, Philip, 1939
  Brierley, Philip and S.P. Doolittle, 1940
  Brierley, Philip and Floyd F. Smith, 1944
Lilium harrisi (Lilium longiflorum var. eximium)
  Ainsworth, G.C., 1938
  Ogilvie, L. and C.E.F. Guterman, 1929
Lilium longiflorum
  Brierley, Philip, 1939
  Brierley, Philip and S.P. Doolittle, 1940
  McWhorter, F.P. and H.H. Millsap, 1954
  Porter, Clark A., 1954
  Price, W.C., 1937
  Smith, Floyd F. and Philip Brierley, 1948
  Wellman, F.L., 1935
Lilium longiflorum var. formosum
  Ainsworth, G.C., 1938
Lilium monadelphum
  Brierley, Philip, 1940
Lilium regale
  Brierley, Philip, 1940
Lilium sargentiae
  Brierley, Philip, 1940
Lilium speciosum
  Brierley, Philip, 1940
  Brierley, Philip and S.P. Doolittle, 1940
Lilium speciosum var. rubrum
  McWhorter; F.P. and H.H. Millsap, 1954
Lilium spp.
  (K.M. Smith, 1957) R.E. Fitzpatrick, et al., 1958
Lilium superbum
  Brierley, Philip, 1940
Lilium tigrinum
  Brierley, Philip, 1940
  Brierley, Philip and Floyd F. Smith, 1944
Lilium umbellatum
  Brierley, Philip, 1940
Lilium wallacei
  Brierley, Philip, 1940
Lobelia gracilis
  Jagger, I.C., 1918

VIRUS
V. CUCUMBER MOSAIC (cont.)

Lobelia tenuior
  Price, W.C., 1940
Lobularia maritima
  Pound, Glenn S. and J.C. Walker, 1948
  Price, W.C., 1940
Luffa acutangula
  Adsuar, Jose and A. Cruz Miret, 1950
Luffa spp.
  Jagger, I.C., 1918
Lupinus angustifolius
  Whipple, O.C. and J.C. Walker, 1941
Lupinus hartwegii
  Whipple, O.C. and J.C. Walker, 1941
Lychnis alba
  Faan, Hwei-Chung and James Johnson, 1951
  Price, W.C., 1940
Lychnis chalcedonica
  Price, W.C., 1940
Lychnis viscaria
  Wellman, F.L., 1935
Lycopersicon esculentum
  Ainsworth, G.C., 1940
  Anderson, C.W., 1951, 1955
  Berkeley, G.H., 1951, 1953
  Bhargava, K.S., 1951
  Bridgmon, G.H. and J.C. Walker, 1952
  Burnett, G., 1934
  Doolittle, S.P. and L.J. Alexander, 1936, 1951
  Doolittle, S.P. and W.J. Zaumeyer, 1953
  Fulton, Joseph P., 1950
  Fulton, Robert W., 1941
  Govier, D.A., 1957
  Harrison, B.D., 1958
  Harter, L.L., 1938
  Heuberger, J.W. and J.B.S. Norton, 1933
  Hoggan, Isme A., 1927, 1935
  Hollings, M., 1955
  Johnson, E.M., 1930
  Johnson, J., 1926, 1927
  Johnson, James and Edith M. Hein, 1948
  Larsh, Howard W. and J.R. Shay, 1945
  Magee, C.J.P., 1940
  Mogendorff, N., 1930
  Nariani, T.K. and Nirmaljit Singh, 1952
  Nienow, Inez, 1948
  Pound, Glenn S. and J.C. Walker, 1948
  Price, W.C., 1934
  Selman, Ireson W., 1941
  Severin, Henry H.P., 1950
  Simons, John N., 1955
  Storey, I.F., 1939
  Valleau, W.D., 1932
  Valleau, W.D. and E.M. Johnson, 1930
  Wellman, F.L., 1934, 1935
  Whipple, O.C. and J.C. Walker, 1941
Lycopersicon esculentum var. grandifolium
  Mogendorff, N., 1930
Lycopersicon lycopersicon *
  Adsuar, Jose and A. Cruz Miret, 1950
Lythrum salicaria
  Price, W.C., 1940
Maranta arundinaceae
  Celino, M.S. and Aureo L. Martinez, 1956
Marrubium vulgare
  Burnett, G., 1934
Matthiola incana
  Berkeley, G.H. and J.H. Tremaine, 1954
Matthiola incana var. annua
  Pound, Glenn S. and J.C. Walker, 1948
Melilotus alba
  Doolittle, S.P. and W.J. Zaumeyer, 1952, 1953
Melilotus officinalis
  Hagedorn, D.J., 1950
  Hagedorn, D.J. and J.C. Walker, 1954
  Whipple, O.C. and J.C. Walker, 1941
Melothria guadalupensis
  Adsuar, Jose and A. Cruz Miret, 1950
Melothria scabra
  Jagger, I.C., 1918
Mertensia virginica
  Nienow, Inez, 1948

VIRUS
V. CUCUMBER MOSAIC (cont.)
  Mesembryanthemum crystallinum
    Wellman, F.L., 1935
  Mimulus moschatus
    Price, W.C., 1940
  Mollugo verticillata
    Faan, Hwei-Chung and James Johnson, 1951
  Momordica balsamina
    Jagger, I.C., 1918
  Momordica charianta
    Simons, John N., 1957
    Vasudeva, R. Sahai and T.B. Lal, 1943
  Musa banksii
    Bernardo, Fernando A. and Dioscoro L. Umali, 1956
  Musa cavendishii
    Magee, C.J.P., 1940
    Wellman, F.L., 1934, 1935
  Musa ensete
    Magee, C.J.P., 1940
  Musa paradisiaca subsp. sapientum
    Castillo, Bernardo S., 1952
    Magee, C.J.P., 1940
    Wellman, F.L., 1934, 1935
  Musa textilis
    Bernardo, Fernando A. and Dioscoro L. Umali, 1956
    Calinisan, Melanio R., 1938, 1940
    Celino, M.S. and Aureo L. Martinez, 1955, 1956
    Lawas, Orencio M. and William L. Fernandez, 1949
    Magee, C.J.P., 1940
    Ocfemia, G.O. and Martin S. Celino, 1938
    Ocfemia, G.O., Martin S. Celino and Feliciano J. Garcia, 1947
  Musa textilis x Musa balbisiana
    Bernardo, Fernando A. and Dioscoro L. Umali, 1956
  Musa textilis x Musa banksii
    Bernardo, Fernando A. and Dioscoro L. Umali, 1956
  Myosotis sylvatica
    Price, W.C., 1940
  Nasturtium officinale (Rorippa nasturtium-aquaticum)
    (K.M. Smith, 1957) R.E. Fitzpatrick, et al., 1958
  Nemesia strumosa
    Price, W.C., 1940
  Nicandra physalodes
    Burnett, G., 1934
    Hoggan, Isme A., 1927
    Johnson, E.M., 1930
    Pound, Glenn S. and J.C. Walker, 1948
    Wellman, F.L., 1935
  Nicotiana affinis
    Govier, D.A., 1957
  Nicotiana alata
    Price, W.C., 1941
  Nicotiana bigelovii var. quadrivalvis *
    Price, W.C., 1940, 1941
  Nicotiana glauca
    Hoggan, Isme A., 1927
    Johnson, J., 1926, 1927
    Nariani, T.K. and Nirmaljit Singh, 1952
    Price, W.C., 1941
  Nicotiana glutinosa
    Adsuar, Jose and A. Cruz Miret, 1950
    Ainsworth, G.C., 1935, 1940
    Anderson, C.W., 1951, 1955
    Anderson, C.W. and M.K. Corbett, 1957
    Berkeley, G.H., 1951, 1953
    Berkeley, G.H. and J.H. Tremaine, 1954
    Bhargava, K.S., 1951
    Black, L.M. and W.C. Price, 1940
    Bridgmon, G.H. and J.C. Walker, 1952
    Costa, A.S., 1944
    Doolittle, S.P. and W.J. Zaumeyer, 1953
    Fulton, Robert W., 1941
    Govier, D.A., 1957
    Hagedorn, D.J. and J.C. Walker, 1954
    Hoggan, Isme A., 1927, 1935
    Johnson, J., 1926, 1927
    Lindberg, G.D., D.H. Hall and J.C. Walker, 1956
    Nariani, T.K. and Nirmaljit Singh, 1952

VIRUS
V. CUCUMBER MOSAIC (cont.)
  Nicotiana glutinosa
    Nienow, Inez, 1948
    Pound, Glenn S. and J.C. Walker, 1948
    Price, W.C., 1934, 1941
    Roberts, Daniel A., 1952
    Silberschmidt, K., 1955
    Sill, W.H., Jr. and J.C. Walker, 1952
    Simons, John N., 1955, 1957
    Smith, Kenneth M., 1935
    Storey, I.F., 1939
    Wellman, F.L., 1934, 1935
    Whipple, O.C. and J.C. Walker, 1941
  Nicotiana langsdorffii
    Price, W.C., 1934
    Smith, Kenneth M., 1935
  Nicotiana paniculata
    Govier, D.A., 1957
  Nicotiana repanda
    Nienow, Inez, 1948
  Nicotiana rustica
    Doolittle, S.P. and W.J. Zaumeyer, 1953
    Govier, D.A., 1957
    Johnson, E.M., 1930
    Johnson, J., 1926, 1927
    Lindberg, G.D., D.H. Hall and J.C. Walker, 1956
    Pound, Glenn S. and J.C. Walker, 1948
  Nicotiana sanderae
    Wellman, F.L., 1935
  Nicotiana sylvestris
    Govier, D.A., 1957
    Nienow, Inez, 1948
    Wellman, F.L., 1935
  Nicotiana tabacum
    Adsuar, Jose and A. Cruz Miret, 1950
    Ainsworth, G.C., 1938, 1940
    Anderson, C.W., 1951, 1955
    Bennett, C.W., 1944
    Berkeley, G.H., 1951, 1953
    Berkeley, G.H. and J.H. Tremaine, 1954
    Bhargava, K.S., 1951
    Black, L.M. and W.C. Price, 1940
    Bridgmon, G.H. and J.C. Walker, 1952
    Brierley, Philip, 1939, 1940, 1951
    Brierley, Philip and S.P. Doolittle, 1940
    Burnett, G., 1934
    Costa, A.S., 1944
    Diachun, Stephen, 1952
    Doncaster, J.P. and B. Kassanis, 1946
    Doolittle, S.P. and W.J. Zaumeyer, 1952, 1953
    Dykstra, T.P., 1939
    Fulton, Joseph P., 1950
    Fulton, Robert W., 1941, 1953
    Govier, D.A., 1957
    Hagedorn, D.J. and J.C. Walker, 1954
    Harrison, B.D., 1958
    Harter, L.L., 1936, 1938
    Hoggan, Isme A., 1927, 1930, 1933, 1934, 1935
    Johnson, E.M., 1930
    Johnson, J., 1926, 1927, 1933
    Kassanis, B., 1947
    Larsh, Howard W. and J.R. Shay, 1945
    Lindberg, G.D., D.H Hall and J.C. Walker, 1956
    Magee, C.J.P., 1940
    McKinney, H.H., 1943
    Nariani, T.K. and Nirmaljit Singh, 1952
    Nienow, Inez, 1948
    Nolla, J.A.B., 1934
    Pound, Glenn S. and J.C. Walker, 1948
    Price, W.C., 1934, 1936, 1937, 1941
    Silberschmidt, K., 1955
    Sill, Webster H., Jr., 1951
    Sill, W.H., Jr. and J.C. Walker, 1952
    Simons, John N., 1955, 1957
    Smith, Floyd F. and Philip Brierley, 1944
    Smith, Kenneth M., 1935
    Valleau, W.D., 1935
    Wellman, F.L., 1934, 1935
    Whipple, O.C. and J.C. Walker, 1938, 1941
    Wilkinson, R.E., 1953
  Nicotiana tabacum x Nicotiana glutinosa
    Bridgmon, G.H. and J.C. Walker, 1952
    Sill, W.H., Jr. and J.C. Walker, 1952

VIRUS
V. CUCUMBER MOSAIC (cont.)
  Passiflora alba
    McKinght, T., 1953
  Passiflora caerulea
    Nattrass, R.M., 1944
  Passiflora edulis
    McKnight, T., 1953
    Nattrass, R.M., 1944
  Passiflora edulis f. flavicarpa *
    McKnight, T., 1953
  Passiflora foetida
    McKnight, T., 1953
  Passiflora ligularis
    Nattrass, R.M., 1944
  Passiflora suberosa
    McKnight, T., 1953
  Passiflora subpeltata
    Nattrass, R.M., 1944
  Pastinaca sativa
    Wellman, F.L., 1935
  Pelargonium hortorum (X P. zonale)
    Wellman, F.L., 1935
  Penstemon spp.
    (K.M. Smith, 1957) R.E. Fitzpatrick, et al., 1958
  Petroselinum hortense
    Wellman, F.L., 1935
  Petunia hybrida
    Berkeley, G.H., 1953
    Berkeley, G.H. and J.H. Tremaine, 1954
    Burnett, G., 1934
    Dale, W.T., 1954
    Doolittle, S.P. and W.J. Zaumeyer, 1953
    Govier, D.A., 1957
    Harrison, B.D., 1958
    Harter, L.L., 1938
    Nariani, T.K. and Nirmaljit Singh, 1952
    Nienow, Inez, 1948
    Pound, Glenn S. and J.C. Walker, 1948
    Wellman, F.L., 1935
  Petunia violacea
    Hoggan, Isme A., 1927
    Johnson, J., 1926, 1927
  Phacelia tanacetifolia
    Wellman, F.L., 1935
  Phacelia whitlavia (Whitlavia grandiflora)
    Wellman, F.L., 1934, 1935
  Phaseolus acutifolius var. latifolius
    Doolittle, S.P. and W.J. Zaumeyer, 1953
  Phaseolus aureus
    Price, W.C., 1940
  Phaseolus calcaratus
    Doolittle, S.P. and W.J. Zaumeyer, 1953
  Phaseolus limensis
    Anderson, C.W., 1955
    Harter, L.L., 1936
    Thomas, H. Rex, W.J. Zaumeyer and Hans
    Jorgensen, 1951
  Phaseolus lunatus
    Doolittle, S.P. and W.J. Zaumeyer, 1953
    Whipple, O.C. and J.C. Walker, 1941
  Phaseolus lunatus f. macrocarpus
    Harter, L.L., 1938
    Pryor, Dean E. and Robert E. Wester, 1946
  Phaseolus vulgaris
    Anderson, C.W., 1955
    Berkeley, G.H., 1951
    Bhargava, K.S., 1951
    Doolittle, S.P. and W.J. Zaumeyer, 1952, 1953
    Fulton, Joseph P., 1950
    Hagedorn, D.J., 1950
    Hagedorn, D.J. and J.C. Walker, 1954
    Harrison, B.D., 1958
    Hollings, M., 1955
    Silberschmidt, K., 1955
    Thomas, H. Rex and W.J. Zaumeyer, 1953
    Whipple, O.C. and J.C. Walker, 1938, 1941
  Phlox drummondii
    Faan, Hwei-Chung and James Johnson, 1951
    Govier, D.A., 1957
    Pound, Glenn S. and J.C. Walker, 1948
    Wellman, F.L., 1935
  Phlox paniculata
    Faan, Hwei-Chung and James Johnson, 1951

VIRUS
V. CUCUMBER MOSAIC (cont.)
  Physalis alkekengi
    Wellman, F.L., 1935
  Physalis angulata
    Adsuar, Jose and A. Cruz Miret, 1950
    Wellmna, F.L., 1935
  Physalis floridana
    Ross, A. Frank, 1950, 1953
  Physalis franchetti
    Hoggan, Isme A., 1927
  Physalis heterophylla
    Walker, M.N., 1925
  Physalis heterophylla var. nyctaginea
    Johnson, E.M., 1930
  Physalis lagascae
    Wellman, F.L., 1934, 1935
  Physalis peruviana
    Govier, D.A., 1957
    Holmes, Francis O., 1942
    Simons, John N., 1957
    Wellman, F.L., 1935
  Physalis pubescens
    Hoggan, Isme A., 1927
    Johnson, E.M., 1930
    Johnson, J., 1926, 1927
    Pound, Glenn S. and J.C. Walker, 1948
    Walker, M.N., 1925, 1926
    Wellman, F.L., 1934, 1935
  Physalis spp.
    Wellman, F.L., 1935
  Physalis subglabrata
    Walker, M.N., 1925
  Phytolacca americana
    Harter, L.L., 1938
    Wellman, F.L., 1935
  Phytolacca decandra
    Diachun, Stephen, 1952
    Hoggan, Isme A., 1935
    Johnson, E.M., 1930
    Johnson, J., 1926, 1927
  Phytolacca esculenta
    Bhargava, K.S., 1951
  Phytolacca rigida
    Wellman, F.L., 1935
  Pisum sativum
    Ainsworth, G.C., 1940
    Anderson, C.W., 1955
    Berkeley, G.H., 1951
    Bhargava, K.S., 1951
    Doolittle, S.P. and W.J. Zaumeyer, 1953
    Fulton, Joseph P., 1950
    Hagedorn, D.J., 1950, 1952
    Hagedorn, D.J. and J.C. Walker, 1954
    Pound, Glenn S. and J.C. Walker, 1948
    Whipple, O.C. and J.C. Walker, 1938, 1941
  Polanisia trachysperma
    Price, W.C., 1940
  Polemonium caeruleum
    Faan, Hwei-Chung and James Johnson, 1951
  Portulaca grandiflora
    Price, W.C., 1940
  Primula obconica
    (K.M. Smith, 1957) R.E. Fitzpatrick, et al., 1958
    Govier, D.A., 1957
    Severin, Henry H.P. and C.M. Tompkins, 1950
    Smith, Kenneth M., 1935
  Primula sinensis
    Govier, D.A., 1957
    Smith, Kenneth M., 1935
  Rubus idaeus
    Harrison, B.D., 1958
  Raphanus sativus
    Berkeley, G.H. and J.H. Tremaine, 1954
  Reseda odorata
    Pound, Glenn S. and J.C. Walker, 1948
  Rheum rhaponticum
    Price, W.C., 1940
  Rudbeckia spp.
    Faan, Hwei-Chung and James Johnson, 1951
  Ruellia tuberosa
    Adsuar, Jose and A. Cruz Miret, 1950
  Rumex crispus
    Price, W.C., 1940

VIRUS
V. CUCUMBER MOSAIC (cont.)
    Salpiglossis sinuata
        Price, W.C., 1940
    Salvia patens
        Faan, Hwei-Chung and James Johnson, 1951
    Salvia splendens
        Price, W.C., 1940
    Scabiosa atropurpurea
        Wellman, F.L., 1935
    Scabiosa japonica
        Price, W.C., 1940
    Schizanthus wisetonensis
        Price, W.C., 1940
    Secale cereale
        Wellman, F.L., 1934, 1935
    Sicana odorifera
        Adsuar, Jose and A. Cruz Miret, 1950
    Sisymbrium officinale
        Pound, Glenn S. and J.C. Walker, 1948
    Solanum atropurpureum *
        Hoggan, Isme A., 1927
    Solanum aviculare
        Wellman, F.L., 1935
    Solanum caribaeum
        Adsuar, Jose and A. Cruz Miret, 1950
    Solanum carolinense
        Johnson, E.M., 1930
    Solanum gracile *
        Anderson, C.W., 1955
        Simons, John N., 1957
    Solanum integrifolium
        Pound, Glenn S. and J.C. Walker, 1948
    Solanum laciniatum
        Hoggan, Isme A., 1927
    Solanum melongena
        Adsuar, Jose and A. Cruz Miret, 1950
        Doolittle, S.P. and W.J. Zaumeyer, 1953
        Fulton, Robert W., 1941
        Harter, L.L., 1938
        Hoggan, Isme A., 1935
        Nariani, T.K. and Nirmaljit Singh, 1952
        Simons, John N., 1957
        Wellman, F.L., 1935
    Solanum melongena var. esculentum
        Johnson, E.M., 1930
    Solanum miniatum
        Hoggan, Isme A., 1927
    Solanum nigrum
        Burnett, G., 1934
        Fulton, Robert W., 1941
        Govier, D.A., 1957
        Hoggan, Isme A., 1935
        Johnson, J., 1926
        Nariani, T.K. and Nirmaljit Singh, 1952
        Wellman, F.L., 1935
    Solanum nodiflorum
        Govier, D.A., 1957
        Nariani, T.K. and Nirmaljit Singh, 1952
        Price, W.C., 1940
    Solanum torvum
        Adsuar, Jose and A. Cruz Miret, 1950
    Solanum triflorum
        Pound, Glenn S. and J.C. Walker, 1948
    Solanum tuberosum
        Johnson, James, 1927
    Sparaxis spp.
        Smith, Floyd F. and Philip Brierley, 1944
    Spinacia oleracea
        Berkeley, G.H. and J.H. Tremaine, 1954
        Bridgmon, G.H. and J.C. Walker, 1952
        Cheo, Pen-Ching and Glenn S. Pound, 1952
        Doolittle, S.P. and W.J. Zaumeyer, 1952, 1953
        Fulton, Joseph P., 1950
        Fulton, Robert W., 1941
        Govier, D.A., 1957
        Hoggan, I.A., 1930, 1933, 1935
        Larsh, Howard W. and J.R. Shay, 1945
        McClintock, J.A. and Loren B. Smith, 1918
        Nienow, Inez, 1948
        Pound, Glenn S. and Pen-Ching Cheo, 1952
        Price, W.C., 1934
        Wellman, F.L., 1935
        Whipple, O.C. and J.C. Walker, 1941

VIRUS
V. CUCUMBER MOSAIC (cont.)
    Stellaria media
        Burnett, G., 1934
    Tacsonia spp.
        Nattrass, R.M., 1944
    Tagetes erecta
        Wellman, F.L., 1935
    Tagetes patula
        Nienow, Inez, 1948
        Wellman, F.L., 1934, 1935
    Tetragonia expansa
        Hollings, M., 1955
        Wellman, F.L., 1935
    Thlaspi arvense
        Pound, Glenn S. and J.C. Walker, 1948
    Tradescantia spp.
        Wellman, F.L., 1935
    Trichosanthes anguina
        Jagger, I.C., 1918
        Nariani, T.K. and Nirmaljit Singh, 1952
    Trifolium hybridum
        Hagedorn, D.J., 1950
        Hagedorn, D.J. and J.C. Walker, 1954
    Trifolium incarnatum
        Brierley, Philip and Floyd F. Smith, 1944
        Doolittle, S.P. and W.J. Zaumeyer, 1952, 1953
        Hagedorn, D.J., 1950, 1952
        Hagedorn, D.J. and J.C. Walker, 1954
        Price, W.C., 1940
    Trifolium pratense
        Hagedorn, D.J., 1950, 1952
        Hagedorn, D.J. and J.C. Walker, 1954
    Trifolium repens
        Hagedorn, D.J., 1950
        Hagedorn, D.J. and J.C. Walker, 1954
    Trigonella foenum-graecum
        Hagedorn, D.J., 1952
    Triticum aestivum
        Wellman, F.L., 1934, 1935
    Tropaeolum majus
        Govier, D.A., 1957
        Wellman, F.L., 1935
    Tulipa gesneriana
        Ainsworth, G.C., 1938
        Brierley, Philip, 1941
        Brierley, Philip and S.P. Doolittle, 1940, 1944
        Porter, Clark A., 1954
        Smith, Floyd F. and Philip Brierley, 1944
    Valeriana officinalis
        Faan, Hwei-Chung and James Johnson, 1951
    Verbascum phoeniceum
        Price, W.C., 1940
    Verbesina encelioides
        Brierley, Philip, 1951
    Veronica longifolia
        Price, W.C., 1940
    Vicia faba
        Anderson, C.W., 1955
        Costa, A.S., 1944
        Doolittle, S.P. and W.J. Zaumeyer, 1953
        Hagedorn, D.J., 1950
        Harter, L.L., 1938
        Milbrath, J.A. and Roy A. Young, 1956
        Porter, Clark A., 1954
        Wellman, F.L., 1934, 1935
        Whipple, O.C. and J.C. Walker, 1941
    Vicia faba var. minor
        Hagedorn, D.J. and J.C. Walker, 1954
    Vigna sesquipedalis
        Doolittle, S.P. and W.J. Zaumeyer, 1953
    Vigna sinensis
        Anderson, C.W., 1955, 1957
        Anderson, C.W. and M.K. Corbett, 1957
        Bhargava, K.S., 1951
        Bridgmon, G.H. and J.C. Walker, 1952
        Costa, A.S., 1944
        Diachun, Stephen, 1952
        Doolittle, S.P. and W.J. Zaumeyer, 1952, 1953
        Fulton, Joseph P., 1950
        Hagedorn, D.J., 1950
        Hagedorn, D.J. and J.C. Walker, 1954
        Harter, L.L., 1938
        Hollings, M., 1955

VIRUS

V. CUCUMBER MOSAIC (cont.)

Vigna sinensis
    Lindberg, G.D., D.H. Hall and J.C. Walker, 1956
    Milbrath, J.A. and Roy A. Young, 1956
    Nienow, Inez, 1948
    Price, W.C., 1934, 1935
    Silberschmidt, K., 1955
    Sill, Webster H., Jr., 1951
    Sill, W.H., Jr. and J.C. Walker, 1952
    Sinclair, J.B. and J.C. Walker, 1954, 1955, 1956
    Smith, Kenneth M., 1935
    Whipple, O.C. and J.C. Walker, 1941
Vigna unguiculata
    Adsuar, Jose and A. Cruz Miret, 1950
Vinca rosea
    Anderson, C.W. and M.K. Corbett, 1957
    Fulton, Robert W., 1953
    Wellman, F.L., 1935
Viola cornuta
    Severin, Henry H.P., 1947
Viola tricolor var. hortensis
    Severin, Henry H.P., 1947
Zaluzianskya villosa
    Price, W.C., 1940
Zea mays
    Bhargava, K.S., 1951
    Bridgmon, G.H., 1951
    Bridgmon, G.H. and J.C. Walker, 1952
    Celino, M.S. and Aureo L. Martinez, 1955, 1956
    Celino, M.S. and G.O. Ocfemia, 1941
    Doolittle, S.P. and W.J. Zaumeyer, 1953
    Lawas, Orencio M. and William L. Fernandez, 1949
    McWhorter, F.P. and H.H. Millsap, 1954
    Price, W.C., 1935
    Wellman, F.L., 1934, 1935
Zea mays var. everta
    Harter, L.L., 1938
Zea mays var. rugosa *
    Fulton, Joseph P., 1950
    Pound, Glenn S. and J.C. Walker, 1948
Zebrina pendula
    Wellman, F.L., 1935
Zinnia elegans
    Ainsworth, G.C., 1938
    Anderson, C.W., 1951, 1955
    Berkeley, G.H. and J.H. Tremaine, 1954
    Bridgmon, G.H. and J.C. Walker, 1952
    Brierley, Philip, 1951, 1952
    Burnett, G., 1934
    Doolittle, S.P. and W.J. Zaumeyer, 1952, 1953
    Fulton, Joseph P., 1950
    Fulton, Robert W., 1941
    Harter, L.L., 1938
    Lindberg, G.D., D.H. Hall and J.C. Walker, 1956
    Nienow, Inez, 1948
    Pound, Glenn S. and J.C. Walker, 1948
    Price, W.C., 1935, 1937, 1939, 1941
    Simons, John N., 1957
    Sinclair, J.B. and J.C. Walker, 1956
    Smith, Floyd F. and Philip Brierley, 1944
    Wellman, F.L., 1934, 1935
    Whipple, O.C. and J.C. Walker, 1941
Zinnia elegans var. dahliiflora *
    Govier, D.A., 1957

V. (CUCUMBER O.S.C. ISOLATE 606 *

Cucumis sativus
    Porter, Clark A. and Frank P. McWhorter, 1951
Echinocystis oregana
    Porter, Clark A. and Frank P. McWhorter, 1951
Lilium longiflorum
    Porter, Clark A. and Frank P. McWhorter, 1951

V. CUCUMBER WESTERN MOSAIC *

Apium graveolens var. dulce
    Severin, Henry H.P., 1950
    Severin, Henry H.P. and Julius H. Freitag, 1948
Beta vulgaris
    Severin, Henry H.P. and Julius H. Freitag, 1948
Beta vulgaris var. cicla
    Severin, Henry H.P. and Julius H. Freitag, 1948
Cucumis anguria
    Severin, Henry H.P. and Julius H. Freitag, 1948

VIRUS

V. CUCUMBER WESTERN MOSAIC * (cont.)

Cucumis melo var. inodorus
    Severin, Henry H.P. and Julius H. Freitag, 1948
Cucumis sativus
    Severin, Henry H.P. and Julius H. Freitag, 1948
Cucurbita maxima
    Freitag, J.H., 1941
Delphinium cardinale
    Severin, Henry H.P., 1942
Delphinium formosum
    Severin, Henry H.P., 1942
Delphinium grandiflorum var. album
    Severin, Henry H.P., 1942
Delphinium hybrid
    Severin, Henry H.P., 1942
Delphinium spp.
    Severin, Henry H.P., 1942
Delphinium zalil
    Severin, Henry H.P., 1942
Lactuca sativa
    Severin, Henry H.P. and Julius H. Freitag, 1948
Lycopersicon esculentum
    Severin, Henry H.P., 1950
    Severin, Henry H.P. and Julius H. Freitag, 1948
Phlox drummondii
    Severin, Henry H.P., 1943
Primula obconica
    Severin, Henry H.P. and C.M. Tompkins, 1950
Spinacia oleracea
    Severin, Henry H.P., 1948
    Severin, Henry H.P. and Julius H. Freitag, 1948
Tetragonia expansa
    Severin, Henry H.P., 1948
Viola cornuta
    Severin, Henry H.P., 1947
Viola tricolor var. hortensis
    Severin, Henry H.P., 1947

V. CUCURBIT MOSAIC *

Amaranthus retroflexus
    Doolittle, S.P., 1921
    Doolittle, S.P. and M.N. Walker, 1925
Asclepias syriaca
    Doolittle, S.P., 1921
    Doolittle, S.P. and M.N. Walker, 1922, 1924, 1925
Benincasa cerifera
    Doolittle, S.P. and M.N. Walker, 1925
Benincasa hispida
    Doolittle, S.P. and M.N. Walker, 1925
Bryonopsis laciniosa
    Doolittle, S.P. and M.N. Walker, 1925
Capsicum frutescens (Capsicum annuum)
    Doolittle, S.P., 1921
    Doolittle, S.P. and M.N. Walker, 1925
Citrullus vulgaris
    Doolittle, S.P. and M.N. Walker, 1925
Cucumis anguria
    Doolittle, S.P. and M.N. Walker, 1925
Cucumis ficifolius
    Doolittle, S.P. and M.N. Walker, 1925
Cucumis grossulariaeformis *
    Doolittle, S.P. and M.N. Walker, 1925
Cucumis melo
    Doolittle, S.P. and M.N. Walker, 1925
    Kendrick, J.B., 1934
Cucumis melo var. dudaim
    Doolittle, S.P. and M.N. Walker, 1925
Cucumis melo var. glexuosus
    Doolittle, S.P. and M.N. Walker, 1925
Cucumis melo var. utilissimus *
    Doolittle, S.P. and M.N. Walker, 1925
Cucumis metuliferus
    Doolittle, S.P. and M.N. Walker, 1925
Cucumis odoratissimus
    Doolittle, S.P. and M.N. Walker, 1925
Cucumis sativus
    Doolittle, S.P. and M.N. Walker, 1925
Cucurbita maxima
    Doolittle, S.P. and M.N. Walker, 1925
Cucurbita moschata
    Doolittle, S.P. and M.N. Walker, 1925
Cucurbita pepo
    Doolittle, S.P. and M.N. Walker, 1925

VIRUS
V. CUCURBIT MOSAIC * (cont.)
   Cucurbita pepo var. melopepo
      Doolittle, S.P. and M.N. Walker, 1925
      Kendrick, J.B., 1934
   Cucurbita pepo var. ovifera
      Doolittle, S.P. and M.N. Walker, 1925
   Ecballium elaterium
      Doolittle, S.P. and M.N. Walker, 1925
   Echinocystis lobata
      Doolittle, S.P., 1921
      Doolittle, S.P. and W.W. Gilbert, 1919
      Doolittle, S.P. and M.N. Walker, 1924, 1925
   Lagenaria siceraria (Lagenaria leucantha)
      Doolittle, S.P. and M.N. Walker, 1925
   Lagenaria vulgaris
      Doolittle, S.P. and M.N. Walker, 1925
   Luffa acutangula
      Doolittle, S.P. and M.N. Walker, 1925
   Luffa aegyptiaca (Luffa cylindrica)
      Doolittle, S.P. and M.N. Walker, 1925
   Martynia louisiana
      Doolittle, S.P., 1921
      Doolittle, S.P. and M.N. Walker, 1925
   Momordica charantia
      Doolittle, S.P. and M.N. Walker, 1925
   Momordica involucrata
      Doolittle, S.P. and M.N. Walker, 1925
   Nepeta cataria
      Doolittle, S.P. and M.N. Walker, 1925
   Physalis heterophylla
      Walker, M.N., 1924
   Physalis pubescens
      Walker, M.N., 1924
   Physalis spp.
      Doolittle, S.P. and M.N. Walker, 1924
   Physalis subglabrata
      Walker, M.N., 1924
   Phytolacca americana
      Doolittle, S.P. and M.N. Walker, 1922
   Phytolacca decandra
      Doolittle, S.P. and M.N. Walker, 1924, 1925
   Sicyos angulatus
      Doolittle, S.P. and M.N. Walker, 1925
   Solanum tuberosum
      Doolittle, S.P. and M.N. Walker, 1922
   Trichosanthes anguina
      Doolittle, S.P. and M.N. Walker, 1925

V. CUCURBIT RING MOSAIC *
   Cucurbita maxima
      Freitag, J.H., 1941

V. CYNARUS CURLY DWARF
   Centaurea cyanus
      Morton, Donald J., 1957
   Cynara cardunculus
      Leach, L.D. and J.W. Oswald, 1950
   Cynara scolymus
      Leach, L.D. and J.W. Oswald, 1950
      Morton, Donald J., 1957
   Silybum marianum
      Leach, L.D. and J.W. Oswald, 1950
   Zinnia elegans
      Leach, L.D. and J.W. Oswald, 1950
      Morton, Donald J., 1957

V. DAHLIA MOSAIC Brierley 1933
   Coreopsis douglasii
      Brierley, Philip and Floyd F. Smith, 1950
   Dahlia variabilis
      Brierley, Philip, 1933, 1951
      Brierley, Philip and Floyd F. Smith, 1950
   Sanvitalia procumbens
      Brierley, Philip and Floyd F. Smith, 1950
   Verbesina encelioides
      Brierley, Philip, 1951
      Brierley, Philip and Floyd F. Smith, 1950
   Zinnia elegans
      Brierley, Philip, 1951
      Brierley, Philip and Floyd F. Smith, 1950

VIRUS
V. DANDELION YELLOW MOSAIC Kassanis 1944
   Chenopodium amaranticolor
      Hollings, M., 1956
   Lactuca sativa
      Doncaster, J.P. and B. Kassanis, 1946
      Kassanis, B., 1947
   Lactuca serriola
      Kassanis, B., 1947
   Lactuca virosa
      Kassanis, B., 1947
   Taraxacum officinale
      Kassanis, B., 1947

V. DATURA DISTORTION MOSAIC Capoor and Varma
   Capsicum frutescens (Capsicum annuum)   1952
      Capoor, S.P. and P.M. Varma, 1952
   Datura chlorantha
      Capoor, S.P. and P.M. Varma, 1952
   Datura inoxia
      Capoor, S.P. and P.M. Varma, 1952
   Datura metel
      Capoor, S.P. and P.M. Varma, 1952
   Datura metel var. fastuosa *
      Capoor, S.P. and P.M. Varma, 1952
   Datura stramonium
      Capoor, S.P. and P.M. Varma, 1952
   Lycopersicon esculentum
      Capoor, S.P. and P.M. Varma, 1952
   Nicotiana glauca
      Capoor, S.P. and P.M. Varma, 1952
   Nicotiana glutinosa
      Capoor, S.P. and P.M. Varma, 1952
   Nicotiana rustica
      Capoor, S.P. and P.M. Varma, 1952
   Nicotiana sylvestris
      Capoor, S.P. and P.M. Varma, 1952
   Nicotiana tabacum
      Capoor, S.P. and P.M. Varma, 1952
   Nicotiana tabacum x Nicotiana glutinosa
      Capoor, S.P. and P.M. Varma, 1952
   Petunia hybrida
      Capoor, S.P. and P.M. Varma, 1952
   Tetragonia expansa
      Capoor, S.P. and P.M. Varma, 1952

V. DATURA RUGOSE LEAF CURL Grylls 1954; K.M.
   Crotalaria spp.   Smith 1957
      (K.M. Smith, 1957) R.E. Fitzpatrick, et al., 1958
   Datura stramonium
      (K.M. Smith, 1957) R.E. Fitzpatrick, et al., 1958
   Datura stramonium var. tatula
      (K.M. Smith, 1957) R.E. Fitzpatrick, et al., 1958
   Daucus carota var. sativa
      (K.M. Smith, 1957) R.E. Fitzpatrick, et al., 1958
   Lycopersicon esculentum
      (K.M. Smith, 1957) R.E. Fitzpatrick, et al., 1958
   Malva parviflora
      Grylls, N.E., 1955
   Medicago lupulina
      (K.M. Smith, 1957) R.E. Fitzpatrick, et al., 1958
   Medicago sativa
      (K.M. Smith, 1957) R.E. Fitzpatrick, et al., 1958
   Nicandra physalodes
      (K.M. Smith, 1957) R.E. Fitzpatrick, et al., 1958
   Pastinaca sativa
      (K.M. Smith, 1957) R.E. Fitzpatrick, et al., 1958
   Physalis floridana
      (K.M. Smith, 1957) R.E. Fitzpatrick, et al., 1958
   Polygonum aviculare
      (K.M. Smith, 1957) R.E. Fitzpatrick, et al., 1958
   Sanguisorba minor
      (K.M. Smith, 1957) R.E. Fitzpatrick, et al., 1958
   Sonchus oleraceus
      (K.M. Smith, 1957) R.E. Fitzpatrick, et al., 1958
   Trifolium pratense
      Grylls, N.E., 1955
   Trifolium repens
      Grylls, N.E., 1955
   Urtica urens
      (K.M. Smith, 1957) R.E. Fitzpatrick, et al., 1958

VIRUS

V. DELPHINIUM DISEASE *
Nicotiana tabacum
Valleau, W.D., 1932

V. DELPHINIUM RING SPOT Severin and Dickson 1942
Beta vulgaris
Severin, Henry H.P. and R.C. Dickson, 1942
Cucumis sativus
Severin, Henry H.P. and R.C. Dickson, 1942
Datura stramonium
Severin, Henry H.P. and R.C. Dickson, 1942
Delphinium hybrid
Severin, Henry H.P. and R.C. Dickson, 1942
Gossypium hirsutum
Severin, Henry H.P. and R.C. Dickson, 1942
Nicotiana alata var. grandiflora
Severin, Henry H.P. and R.C. Dickson, 1942
Nicotiana glutinosa
Severin, Henry H.P. and R.C. Dickson, 1942
Nicotiana rustica var. humilis *
Severin, Henry H.P. and R.C. Dickson, 1942
Nicotiana tabacum
Severin, Henry H.P. and R.C. Dickson, 1942
Petunia hybrida
Severin, Henry H.P. and R.C. Dickson, 1942
Ranunculus asiaticus
Severin, Henry H.P. and R.C. Dickson, 1942

V. DOCK MOSAIC Grainger and Cockerham 1930
Chenopodium amaranticolor
Hollings, M., 1956
Rumex lanceolatus
(K.M. Smith, 1957) R.E. Fitzpatrick, et al., 1958
Rumex obtusifolius
Fernow, Karl Hermann, 1925
Rumex sanguineus
(K.M. Smith, 1957) R.E. Fitzpatrick, et al., 1958

V. DODDER LATENT MOSAIC Bennett 1944
Apium graveolens
Bennett, C.W., 1944, 1949
Beta vulgaris
Bennett, C.W., 1944, 1949
Brassica adpressa
Bennett, C.W., 1949
Brassica incana *
Bennett, C.W., 1944
Chenopodium album
Bennett, C.W., 1944
Chenopodium murale
Bennett, C.W., 1944
Cucumis melo
Bennett, C.W., 1949
Cucumis melo var. rockyford
Bennett, C.W., 1944
Cuscuta californica
Bennett, C.W., 1944, 1949
Cuscuta campestris
Bennett, C.W., 1944, 1949
Cuscuta subinclusa
Bennett, C.W., 1944
Fagopyrum esculentum
Bennett, C.W., 1944
Lycopersicon esculentum
Bennett, C.W., 1944, 1949
Nicotiana glauca
Bennett, C.W., 1944, 1949
Nicotiana glutinosa
Bennett, C.W., 1949
Nicotiana palmeri
Bennett, C.W., 1944
Nicotiana rustica
Bennett, C.W., 1944, 1949
Nicotiana rustica var. jamaicensis *
Bennett, C.W., 1944
Nicotiana rustica var. pumila *
Bennett, C.W., 1944
Nicotiana tabacum
Bennett, C.W., 1944, 1949
Phytolacca americana
Bennett, C.W., 1944, 1949
Plantago major
Bennett, C.W., 1944

VIRUS

V. DODDER LATENT MOSAIC (cont.)
Polygonum pensylvanicum
Bennett, C.W., 1944
Samolus floribundus
Bennett, C.W., 1944
Solanum tuberosum
Bennett, C.W., 1944, 1949

V. EGGPLANT MOSAIC Ferguson 1951
Capsicum frutescens (Capsicum annuum)
Dale, W.T., 1954
Ferguson, I.A.C., 1951
Chenopodium hybridum
Dale, W.T., 1954
Cucumis sativus
Dale, W.T., 1954
Lycopersicon esculentum
Dale, W.T., 1954
Ferguson, I.A.C., 1951
Lycopersicon pimpinellifolium
Dale, W.T., 1954
Ferguson, I.A.C., 1951
Nicotiana glutinosa
Dale, W.T., 1954
Ferguson, I.A.C., 1951
Nicotiana tabacum
Dale, W.T., 1954
Petunia hybrida
Dale, W.T., 1954
Physalis floridana
Dale, W.T., 1954
Solanum melongena
Dale, W.T., 1954
Ferguson, I.A.C., 1951
Solanum tuberosum
Dale, W.T., 1954
Ferguson, I.A.C., 1951
Vigna unguiculata
Dale, W.T., 1954

V. ELM MOSAIC Swingle et al. 1941
Cucumis sativus
Varney, E.H. and J. Duain Moore, 1952
Nepeta cataria
Varney, E.H. and J. Duain Moore, 1952
Nicotiana tabacum
Moore, J. Duain and E.H. Varney, 1954
Varney, E.H. and J. Duain Moore, 1952
Phaseolus vulgaris
Varney, E.H. and J. Duain Moore, 1952
Physalis heterophylla
Varney, E.H. and J. Duain Moore, 1952
Pisum sativum
Varney, E.H. and J. Duain Moore, 1952
Prunus avium
Callahan, Kemper L. and J. Duain Moore, 1957
Prunus besseyi
Callahan, Kemper L. and J. Duain Moore, 1957
Prunus cerasus
Callahan, Kemper L. and J. Duain Moore, 1957
Prunus domestica
Callahan, Kemper L. and J. Duain Moore, 1957
Prunus mahaleb
Callahan, Kemper L. and J. Duain Moore, 1957
Prunus pensylvanica
Callahan, Kemper L. and J. Duain Moore, 1957
Prunus persica
Moore, J. Duain and E.H. Varney, 1954
Prunus serotina
Callahan, Kemper L. and J. Duain Moore, 1957
Ulmus americana
Bretz, T.W., 1950
Callahan, Kemper L., 1957
Moore, J. Duain and E.H. Varney, 1954
Swingle, R.U., P.E. Tilford and Charles F.
Irish, 1941, 1943
Varney, E.H. and J. Duain Moore, 1952
Vigna sinensis
Varney, E.H. and J. Duain Moore, 1952

V. ELM PHLOEM NECROSIS Swingle 1938
Ulmus americana
McLean, D.M., 1944

VIRUS
V. ELM PHLOEM NECROSIS (cont.)
    Ulmus americana
        Swingle, Roger U., 1938, 1940
        Swingle, Roger U., B.S. Meyer and Curtis May,
        1945
    Ulmus fulva x Ulmus pumila
        Swingle, Roger U., B.S. Meyer and Curtis May,
        1945

V. ELM ZONATE CANKER Swingle and Bretz 1950
    Ulmus americana
        Swingle, Roger U. and T.W. Bretz, 1950

V. ERYNGIUM CHLOROSIS *
    Nicotiana tabacum
        Johnson, James, 1946

V. ERYNGIUM YELLOW MOSAIC *
    Eryngium aquaticum
        Johnson, James, 1946
        Johnson, James and Edith M. Hein, 1948
    Nicotiana tabacum
        Johnson, James and Edith M. Hein, 1948

V. EUONYMUS INFECTIOUS VARIEGATION Brierley
    Euonymus fortunei var. radicans   1944
        Woods, M.W. and H.G. DuBuy, 1943

V. EUPHORBIA MOSAIC Costa and Bennett 1950
    Datura stramonium
        Costa, A.S. and C.W. Bennett, 1950
    Euphorbia prunifolia
        Costa, A.S. and C.W. Bennett, 1950
    Fagopyrum esculentum
        Costa, A.S. and C.W. Bennett, 1950
    Nicandra physalodes
        Costa, A.S. and C.W. Bennett, 1950
    Oxalis spp.
        Costa, A.S. and C.W. Bennett, 1950
    Phyllanthus corcovadensis
        Costa, A.S. and C.W. Bennett, 1950

V. FIG MOSAIC Condit and Horne 1933
    Ficus altissima
        (K.M. Smith, 1957) R.E. Fitzpatrick, et al., 1958
    Ficus carica
        Condit, I.J. and W.T. Horne, 1933, 1941, 1943
        Flock, R.A. and J.M. Wallace, 1955
    Ficus carica var. sylvestris *
        Condit, Ira J. and W.T. Horne, 1943
    Ficus krishna
        (K.M. Smith, 1957) R.E. Fitzpatrick, et al., 1958
    Ficus pseudocarica
        Condit, I.J. and W.T. Horne, 1933
    Ficus tsida *
        (K.M. Smith, 1957) R.E. Fitzpatrick, et al., 1958

V. FILAREE RED LEAF Frazier 1951
    Erodium botrys
        Frazier, Norman W., 1951
    Erodium chamaedryoides var. roseum *
        Anderson, Chris W., 1952
    Erodium cicutarium
        Anderson, Chris W., 1951
        Frazier, Norman W., 1951
    Erodium moschatum
        Anderson, Chris W., 1951
        Frazier, Norman W., 1951
    Fragaria bracteata
        Anderson, Chris W., 1952
    Geranium dissectum
        Frazier, Norman W., 1951
    Geranium molle
        Anderson, Chris W., 1952
    Pelargonium domesticum
        Anderson, Chris W., 1952
    Trifolium incarnatum
        Anderson, Chris W., 1952
    Zea mays
        Anderson, Chris W., 1952

VIRUS
V. (FLOWERING) CHERRY ROUGH BARK Milbrath and
    Prunus avium   Zeller 1942
        Nichols, Carl W. and R.L. McClain, 1957
    Prunus persica
        Nichols, Carl W. and R.L. McClain, 1957
    Prunus serrulata
        Milbrath, J.A. and S.M. Zeller, 1942
        Nichols, Carl W. and R.L. McClain, 1957

V. FREESIA MOSAIC Woodward in K.M. Smith 1957
    Freesia spp.
        (K.M. Smith, 1957) R.E. Fitzpatrick, et al., 1958

V. GLADIOLUS *
    Gladiolus hortulanus
        Snow, Gordon F., 1955
    Phaseolus vulgaris
        Snow, Gordon F., 1955
    Trifolium hybridum
        Snow, Gordon F., 1955
    Trifolium subterraneum
        Snow, Gordon F., 1955
    Vicia faba
        Snow, Gordon F., 1955

V. GOOSEBERRY VEINBANDING Posnette 1952
    Ribes grossularia
        (K.M. Smith, 1957) R.E. Fitzpatrick, et al., 1958

V. GRASS NATAL MOSAIC *
    Saccharum officinarum
        Storey, H.H., 1929
    Setaria sulcata
        Storey, H.H., 1929
    Sorghum arundinaceum
        Storey, H.H., 1929
    Zea mays
        Storey, H.H., 1929

V. GRASS ORCHARD MOSAIC *
    Avena sativa
        McKinney, H.H., 1956
    Dactylis glomerata
        McKinney, H.H., 1956

V. GROUNDNUT MOSAIC Thung 1947
    Arachis hypogaea
        Cooper, W.E., 1950

V. GROUNDNUT ROSETTE Storey and Bottomley 1928
    Arachis hypogaea
        Evans, A.C., 1954
        McKinney, H.H., 1929
        Storey, H.H. and A.M. Bottomley, 1928
        Storey, H.H. and A.K. Ryland, 1955, 1957
    Brachystegia burttii
        Evans, A.C., 1954
    Cajanus cajan
        Evans, A.C., 1954
    Cassia absus
        Evans, A.C., 1954
    Crotalaria fwamboensis
        Evans, A.C., 1954
    Crotalaria intermedia
        Evans, A.C., 1954
    Crotalaria kirkii
        Evans, A.C., 1954
    Dalbergia melanoxylon
        Evans, A.C., 1954
    Dichrostachys nyassana
        Evans, A.C., 1954
    Dolichos fulcatus *
        Evans, A.C., 1954
    Dolichos malosanus
        Evans, A.C., 1954
    Indigofera rhynchocarpa
        Evans, A.C., 1954
    Millettia makondensis
        Evans, A.C., 1954
    Rhynchosia resinosa
        Evans, A.C., 1954

VIRUS

V. GROUNDNUT ROSETTE (cont.)
Strychnos subifera
Evans, A.C., 1954
Talinum caffrum
Evans, A.C., 1954
Vigna reticulata
Evans, A.C., 1954
Vigna triloba
Evans, A.C., 1954
Vigna unguiculata
Evans, A.C., 1954

V. GROUNDNUT WITCHES' BROOM Thung 1947
Arachis hypogaea
(K.M. Smith, 1957) R.E. Fitzpatrick, et al., 1958

V. HENBANE MOSAIC K.M. Smith 1957
Atropa belladonna
(K.M. Smith, 1957) R.E. Fitzpatrick, et al., 1958
Chenopodium amaranticolor
Hollings, M., 1956
Datura stramonium
Bradley, R.H.E., 1952
Hamilton, Marion A., 1932
Hyoscyamus niger
Hamilton, Marion A., 1932
Watson (Hamilton), Marion A., 1937
Lycopersicon esculentum
Hamilton, Marion A., 1932
Nicotiana glauca
Hamilton, Marion A., 1932
Nicotiana glutinosa
Hamilton, Marion A., 1932
Hollings, M., 1955
Nicotiana rustica
Bradley, R.H.E., 1952
Nicotiana tabacum
Bawden, F.C., Brenda M.G. Hamlyn and Marion
A. Watson, 1954
Bradley, R.H.E., 1952
Doncaster, J.P. and B. Kassanis, 1946
Hamilton, Marion A., 1932
Sheffield, F.M.L., 1936, 1938
Watson (Hamilton), Marion A., 1937
Petunia spp.
Hamilton, Marion A., 1932

V. HIBISCUS RING SPOT *
Hibiscus rosa-sinensis
Jensen, D.D., 1949

V. HIBISCUS YELLOW VEIN MOSAIC Capoor and Varma
Althaea rosea   1950
Capoor, S.P. and P.M. Varma, 1950
Hibiscus abelmoschus
Capoor, S.P. and P.M. Varma, 1950
Hibiscus cannabinus
Capoor, S.P. and P.M. Varma, 1950
Hibiscus esculentus
Capoor, S.P. and P.M. Varma, 1950
Varma, P.M., 1952
Hibiscus palustris (Hibiscus moscheutos)
Capoor, S.P. and P.M. Varma, 1950
Hibiscus sabdariffa
Capoor, S.P. and P.M. Varma, 1950
Hibiscus tetraphyllus
Capoor, S.P. and P.M. Varma, 1950

V. HIBISCUS YELLOWS *
Hibiscus abelmoschus
Hendrix, J. Walter, 1950
Hibiscus arnottianus
Hendrix, J. Walter, 1950
Hibiscus rosa-sinensis
Hendrix, J. Walter, 1950

V. HOLLYHOCK MOSAIC K.M. Smith 1957
Althaea rosea
(K.M. Smith, 1957) R.E. Fitzpatrick, et al., 1958
Malva spp.
(K.M. Smith, 1957) R.E. Fitzpatrick, et al., 1958

VIRUS

V. HOLODISCUS WITCHES' BROOM K.M. Smith 1957
Holodiscus discolor
Zeller, S.M., 1931

V. (HONEYSUCKLE) MOTTLE *
Lonicera brachypoda var. foliis aureo-reticulatis *
Corp, V.H., 1949
Lonicera japonica
Corp, V.H., 1949

V. HOP CHLOROTIC DISEASE Salmon and Ware 1930
Humulus lupulus
Salmon, E.S. and W.M. Ware, 1930, 1932, 1935

V. HOP MOSAIC Salmon 1923
Humulus lupulus
Cheal, W.F., 1929
Mackenzie, D., E.S. Salmon, W.M. Ware and R.
Williams, 1929
Salmon, E.S. and W.M. Ware, 1928, 1932
Thrupp, T.C., 1927

V. HOP NETTLE HEAD ((Duffield 1925)) Salmon and
Humulus lupulus   Ware 1930
Blattny, C. and V. Vukolov
Keyworth, W.G. and D.L.G. Davies, 1946

V. HOP SPLIT LEAF BLOTCH Keyworth 1951
Humulus lupulus
Keyworth, W.G., 1951

V. HYDRANGEA *
Hydrangea macrophylla
Brierley, Philip, 1954

V. HYDRANGEA DIE BACK *
Hydrangea macrophylla
Brierley, Philip and Floyd F. Smith, 1952

V. HYDRANGEA RING SPOT Brierley and Smith 1952
Amaranthus retroflexus
Brierley, Philip and Paul Lorentz, 1956, 1957
Antirrhinum majus
Brierley, Philip and Paul Lorentz, 1956, 1957
Beta vulgaris
Brierley, Philip and Paul Lorentz, 1956, 1957
Callistephus chinensis
Brierley, Philip and Floyd F. Smith, 1952
Chenopodium album
Brierley, Philip and Paul Lorentz, 1957
Chenopodium amaranticolor
Brierley, Philip and Paul Lorentz, 1956, 1957
Hollings, M., 1957
Cucumis sativus
Brierley, Philip and Paul Lorentz, 1957
Brierley, Philip and Floyd F. Smith, 1952
Dianthus barbatus
Brierley, Philip and Paul Lorentz, 1956, 1957
Gomphrena globosa
Brierley, Philip and Paul Lorentz, 1956, 1957
Hydrangea macrophylla
Brierley, Philip, 1957
Brierley, Philip and Paul Lorentz, 1956, 1957
Brierley, Philip and Floyd F. Smith, 1952
Nicotiana tabacum
Brierley, Philip and Floyd F. Smith, 1952
Zinnia elegans
Brierley, Philip and Floyd F. Smith, 1952

V. (IPOMOEA) MOSAIC *
Ipomoea nil
Cook, Melville T., 1931

V. IRIS BEARDED MOSAIC *
Belamcanda chinensis
Brierley, Philip and Floyd F. Smith, 1948
Travis, R.V., 1957
Gladiolus hortulanus
Brierley, Philip and Floyd F. Smith, 1948

V. IRIS BEARDLESS MOSAIC *
Belamcanda chinensis
Travis, R.V., 1957

VIRUS

V. IRIS FULVA MOSAIC *
  Belamcanda chinensis
    Travis, R.V., 1957

V. IRIS MOSAIC Brierley and McWhorter 1936
  Chenopodium amaranticolor
    Hollings, M., 1956
  Gladiolus hortulanus
    Brierley, Philip and Floyd F. Smith, 1948
  Iris filifolia
    Brierley, Philip and Frank P. McWhorter, 1936
  Iris ricardi *
    Brierley, Philip and Frank P. McWhorter, 1936
  Iris tingitana
    Brierley, Philip and Frank P. McWhorter, 1936
  Iris unguicularis var. alba
    Brierley, Philip and Frank P. McWhorter, 1936
  Iris xiphioides
    Brierley, P. and F.P. McWhorter, 1934
  Iris xiphium
    Brierley, Philip and Frank P. McWhorter, 1936
  Iris xiphium praecox *
    Brierley, Philip and Frank P. McWhorter, 1936

V. IRIS RING SPOT *
  Amaranthus retroflexus
    Travis, R.V., 1957
  Chenopodium amaranticolor
    Travis, R.V., 1957
  Cyamopsis tetragonoloba
    Travis, R.V., 1957
  Gomphrena globosa
    Travis, R.V., 1957
  Nicotiana tabacum
    Travis, R.V., 1957
  Phaseolus vulgaris
    Travis, R.V., 1957
  Physalis angulata
    Travis, R.V., 1957

V. IRIS SPURIA MOSAIC *
  Belamcanda chinensis
    Brierley, Philip and Floyd F. Smith, 1948
  Iris aurea
    Brierley, Philip and Floyd F. Smith, 1948
  Iris spuria
    Brierley, Philip and Floyd F. Smith, 1948

V. IXIA MOSAIC Smith and Brierley 1944
  Ixia spp.
    Smith, Floyd F. and Philip Brierley, 1944
  Tritonia crocata
    Smith, Floyd F. and Philip Brierley, 1944

V. JATROPHA MOSAIC *
  Jatropha gossypifolia
    Bird, Julio, 1957
  Jatropha multifida
    Bird, Julio, 1957
  Nicotiana tabacum
    Bird, Julio, 1957

V. JIMSONWEED MOSAIC *
  Datura meteloides
    Fernow, Karl Hermann, 1925
  Datura stramonium
    Fernow, Karl Hermann, 1925

V. KAIMI CLOVER DISEASE *
  Crotalaria spp.
    Murakishi, Harry H., 1952
  Desmodium canum
    Murakishi, Harry H., 1952
  Glycine max
    Murakishi, Harry H., 1952
  Phaseolus lunatus
    Murakishi, Harry H., 1952
  Phaseolus vulgaris
    Murakishi, Harry H., 1952
  Trifolium subterraneum
    Murakishi, Harry H., 1952
  Vigna sinensis
    Murakishi, Harry H., 1952

VIRUS

V. LABURNUM INFECTIOUS VARIEGATION Brierley
  Laburnum anagyroides   1944
    (K.M. Smith, 1957) R.E. Fitzpatrick, et al., 1958
  Laburnum vosii *
    (K.M. Smith, 1957) R.E. Fitzpatrick, et al., 1958
  Laburnum vulgare
    (K.M. Smith, 1957) R.E. Fitzpatrick, et al., 1958
  Lespedeza formosa
    (K.M. Smith, 1957) R.E. Fitzpatrick, et al., 1958

V. LABURNUM VEIN MOSAIC *
  Gladiolus hortulanus
    Brierley, Philip and Floyd F. Smith, 1954
  Laburnum alpinum
    Brierley, Philip and Floyd F. Smith, 1954
  Laburnum watereri
    Brierley, Philip and Floyd F. Smith, 1954
  Nicotiana tabacum
    Brierley, Philip and Floyd F. Smith, 1954
  Phaseolus vulgaris
    Brierley, Philip and Floyd F. Smith, 1954

V. (LEGUME) LITTLE LEAF DISEASE *
  Aeschynomene falcata
    Hutton, E.M. and N.E. Grylls, 1956
  Astragalus glycyphyllus
    Hutton, E.M. and N.E. Grylls, 1956
  Cajanus cajan
    Hutton, E.M. and N.E. Grylls, 1956
  Crotalaria goreensis
    Hutton, E.M. and N.E. Grylls, 1956
  Crotalaria grahamiana
    Hutton, E.M. and N.E. Grylls, 1956
  Crotalaria intermedia
    Hutton, E.M. and N.E. Grylls, 1956
  Crotalaria juncea
    Hutton, E.M. and N.E. Grylls, 1956
  Crotalaria orixensis
    Hutton, E.M. and N.E. Grylls, 1956
  Crotalaria pumila
    Hutton, E.M. and N.E. Grylls, 1956
  Crotalaria retusa
    Hutton, E.M. and N.E. Grylls, 1956
  Crotalaria sericea
    Hutton, E.M. and N.E. Grylls, 1956
  Datura stramonium
    Hutton, E.M. and N.E. Grylls, 1956
  Daucus carota
    Hutton, E.M. and N.E. Grylls, 1956
  Desmodium batocaulon
    Hutton, E.M. and N.E. Grylls, 1956
  Desmodium canum
    Hutton, E.M. and N.E. Grylls, 1956
  Desmodium gangeticum
    Hutton, E.M. and N.E. Grylls, 1956
  Desmodium scorpiurus
    Hutton, E.M. and N.E. Grylls, 1956
  Desmodium uncinatum
    Hutton, E.M. and N.E. Grylls, 1956
  Dolichos striatus
    Hutton, E.M. and N.E. Grylls, 1956
  Indigofera endecaphylla
    Hutton, E.M. and N.E. Grylls, 1956
  Indigofera retroflexa
    Hutton, E.M. and N.E. Grylls, 1956
  Indigofera spp.
    Hutton, E.M. and N.E. Grylls, 1956
  Indigofera subulata
    Hutton, E.M. and N.E. Grylls, 1956
  Indigofera tettensis
    Hutton, E.M. and N.E. Grylls, 1956
  Lathyrus sylvestris
    Hutton, E.M. and N.E. Grylls, 1956
  Lotononis bainesii
    Hutton, E.M. and N.E. Grylls, 1956
  Lycopersicon esculentum
    Hutton, E.M. and N.E. Grylls, 1956
  Malva parviflora
    Hutton, E.M. and N.E. Grylls, 1956
  Medicago sativa
    Hutton, E.M. and N.E. Grylls, 1956
  Rhynchosia hagenbeckii
    Hutton, E.M. and N.E. Grylls, 1956

VIRUS

V. (LEGUME) LITTLE LEAF DISEASE * (cont.)
Rhynchosia minima
   Hutton, E.M. and N.E. Grylls, 1956
Stylosanthes bojeri
   Hutton, E.M. and N.E. Grylls, 1956
Stylosanthes erecta
   Hutton, E.M. and N.E. Grylls, 1956
Stylosanthes gracilis
   Hutton, E.M. and N.E. Grylls, 1956
Stylosanthes guianensis
   Hutton, E.M. and N.E. Grylls, 1956
Stylosanthes leiocarpa
   Hutton, E.M. and N.E. Grylls, 1956
Stylosanthes montevidensis
   Hutton, E.M. and N.E. Grylls, 1956
Stylosanthes spp.
   Hutton, E.M. and N.E. Grylls, 1956
Stylosanthes sundaica
   Hutton, E.M. and N.E. Grylls, 1956
Tephrosia spp.
   Hutton, E.M. and N.E. Grylls, 1956
Trifolium pratense
   Hutton, E.M. and N.E. Grylls, 1956
Trifolium repens
   Hutton, E.M. and N.E. Grylls, 1956
Trifolium subterraneum
   Hutton, E.M. and N.E. Grylls, 1956

V. (LEGUME) WESTERN RING SPOT *
Pisum sativum
   McWhorter, Frank P., 1954

V. LEMON WOOD POCKET *
Citrus limon
   Fawcett, H.S. and E.C. Calavan, 1947

V. LETTUCE BIG VEIN Jagger and Chandler 1934
Lactuca sativa
   Allen, M.W., 1948
   Doolittle, S.P. and Ross C. Thompson, 1945
   Pryor, Dean E., 1946
   Thompson, Ross C., S.P. Doolittle and Floyd F.
   Smith, 1944

V. LETTUCE MOSAIC Jagger 1921 Ainsworth and
Chenopodium amaranticolor   Ogilvie 1939
   Hollings, M., 1957
Chenopodium urbicum
   Wilkinson, R.E. and Ursula Hirsch, 1952
Cichorium intybus
   Grogan, R.G., J.E. Welch and Roy Bardin, 1952
Gomphrena globosa
   Couch, Houston B., 1954, 1955
   Wilkinson, R.E. and Ursula Hirsch, 1952
Lactuca sativa
   Ainsworth, G.C. and L. Ogilvie, 1939
   Broadbent, L., T.W. Tinsley, W. Buddin and E.T.
   Roberts, 1951
   Couch, Houston B., 1954, 1955
   Doncaster, J.P. and B. Kassanis, 1946
   Grogan, R.G., J.E. Welch and Roy Bardin, 1952
   Jagger, Ivan C., 1920-21
   Jones, Leon K., 1944
   Kassanis, B., 1947
   Newhall, A.G., 1923
   Selman, Ireson W., 1945
   Sylvester, Edward S., 1954, 1955
Lactuca sativa var. capitata
   Ainsworth, G.C., 1940
   Ainsworth, G.C. and L. Ogilvie, 1939
Lactuca sativa var. romana
   Ainsworth, G.C. and L. Ogilvie, 1939
Lactuca serriola
   Grogan, R.G., J.E. Welch and Roy Bardin, 1952
   Kassanis, B., 1947
Lactuca virosa
   Kassanis, B., 1947
Lathyrus odoratus
   Ainsworth, G.C., 1940
   Ainsworth, G.C. and L. Ogilvie, 1939
Pisum sativum
   Ainsworth, G.C., 1940
   Ainsworth, G.C. and L. Ogilvie, 1939

VIRUS

V. LETTUCE MOSAIC (cont.)
Rumex britannica
   Newhall, A.G., 1923
Senecio vulgaris
   Ainsworth, G.C. and L. Ogilvie, 1939
Sonchus asper
   Ainsworth, G.C. and L. Ogilvie, 1939
Tagetes erecta
   (K.M. Smith, 1957) R.E. Fitzpatrick, et al., 1958
Zinnia elegans
   Grogan, R.G., J.E. Welch and Roy Bardin, 1952

V. LILAC RING MOSAIC Protsenko et al. 1950
Syringa vulgaris
   Beale, J.H. and Helen Purdy Beale, 1952

V. LILAC WITCHES' BROOM Lorentz and Brierley 1953
Ligustrum obtusifolium var. regelianum
   Lorentz, Paul and Philip Brierley, 1953
Syringa japonica
   Brierley, Philip, 1955
   Lorentz, Paul and Philip Brierley, 1953
Syringa vulgaris
   Brierley, Philip, 1955
   Lorenta, Paul and Philip Brierley, 1953
Vinca rosea
   Brierley, Philip, 1955

V. LILY COLOR ADDING *
Lilium henryi x Lilium myriophyllum var. superbum *
   McWhorter, Frank P., 1956
Narcissus poeticus
   McWhorter, F.P., 1932

V. LILY COLOR REMOVING *
Lilium henryi x Lilium myriophyllum var. superbum *
   McWhorter, Frank P., 1956
Narcissus poeticus
   McWhorter, F.P., 1932

V. LILY RING SPOT Smith 1950 ((May be V. cucumber
Lilium regale   mosaic (str).))
   (K.M. Smith, 1957) R.E. Fitzpatrick, et al., 1958
Lilium tigrinum
   (K.M. Smith, 1957) R.E. Fitzpatrick, et al., 1958
Nicotiana glutinosa
   (K.M. Smith, 1957) R.E. Fitzpatrick, et al., 1958

V. LILY ROSETTE Ogilvie 1928
Lilium batemaniae
   (K.M. Smith, 1957) R.E. Fitzpatrick, et al., 1958
Lilium brownii var. leucanthemum
   Brierley, Philip and Floyd F. Smith, 1945
Lilium dauricum
   Brierley, Philip and Floyd F. Smith, 1945
Lilium davidi
   Brierley, Philip and Floyd F. Smith, 1945
Lilium davidi var. willmottiae *
   Brierley, Philip and Floyd F. Smith, 1945
Lilium elegans
   Brierley, Philip and Floyd F. Smith, 1945
Lilium formosanum *
   Brierley, Philip and Floyd F. Smith, 1945
Lilium harrisi
   Ogilvie, Lawrence, 1928
Lilium henryi
   Brierley, Philip and Floyd F. Smith, 1945
Lilium longiflorum
   Brierley, Philip and Floyd F. Smith, 1944, 1945,
   1954
   Smith, Floyd F. and Philip Brierley, 1948
Lilium longiflorum var. takesima
   Ogilvie, Lawrence, 1928
Lilium myriophyllum var. superbum *
   Brierley, Philip and Floyd F. Smith, 1945
Lilium regale
   Brierley, Philip and Floyd F. Smith, 1945
Lilium sargentiae
   Brierley, Philip and Floyd F. Smith, 1945
Lilium speciosum
   Brierley, Philip and Floyd F. Smith, 1945
Lilium umbellatum
   Brierley, Philip and Floyd F. Smith, 1945

VIRUS
V. LILY SYMPTOMLESS Brierley and Smith 1944
   Lilium formosanum
      Brierley, Philip, 1940
   Lilium longiflorum
      Brierley, Philip, 1940
      Brierley, Philip and S.P. Doolittle, 1940, 1944
      Porter, Clark A., 1954
   Tulipa gesneriana
      Brierley, Philip, 1940, 1941

V. LOVAGE MOSAIC Smith and Markham 1944
   Arabis hirsuta
      Smith, Kenneth M. and Roy Markham, 1944
   Capsicum frutescens (Capsicum annuum)
      Smith, Kenneth M. and Roy Markham, 1944
   Cucumis sativus
      Smith, Kenneth M. and Roy Markham, 1944
   Datura stramonium
      Smith, Kenneth M. and Roy Markham, 1944
   Lavatera trimestris
      Smith, Kenneth M. and Roy Markham, 1944
   Ligusticum scothicum
      Smith, Kenneth M. and Roy Markham, 1944
   Lycopersicon esculentum
      Smith, Kenneth M. and Roy Markham, 1944
   Nicotiana glutinosa
      Smith, Kenneth M. and Roy Markham, 1944
   Nicotiana langsdorffii
      Smith, Kenneth M. and Roy Markham, 1944
   Nicotiana rustica
      Smith, Kenneth M. and Roy Markham, 1944
   Nicotiana sylvestris
      Smith, Kenneth M. and Roy Markham, 1944
   Nicotiana tabacum
      Smith, Kenneth M. and Roy Markham, 1944
   Phaseolus vulgaris
      Smith, Kenneth M. and Roy Markham, 1944
   Pisum sativum
      Smith, Kenneth M. and Roy Markham, 1944

V. LUCERNE DWARF
   Acacia longifolia
      Freitag, J.H., 1951
   Amsinckia douglasiana
      Freitag, J.H., 1951
   Artemisia vulgaris var. heterophylla
      Freitag, J.H., 1951
   Avena fatua
      Freitag, J.H., 1951
   Baccharis pilularis
      Freitag, J.H., 1951
   Bromus catharticus
      Freitag, J.H., 1951
   Bromus rigidus
      Freitag, J.H., 1951
   Bromus spp.
      Freitag, J.H., 1951
   Callistephus chinensis
      Freitag, J.H., 1951
   Canna spp.
      Freitag, J.H., 1951
   Chenopodium ambrosioides
      Freitag, J.H., 1951
   Coprosma baueri
      Freitag, J.H., 1951
   Cotoneaster rotundifolia var. lanata
      Freitag, J.H., 1951
   Crotalaria intermedia
      Price, W.C., 1940
   Cynodon dactylon
      Freitag, J.H., 1951
   Cyperus esculentus
      Freitag, J.H., 1951
   Cytisus scoparius
      Freitag, J.H., 1951
   Daucus carota var. sativa
      Freitag, J.H., 1951
   Digitaria sanguinalis
      Freitag, J.H., 1951
   Echinochloa crus-galli
      Freitag, J.H., 1951
   Epilobium californicum
      Freitag, J.H., 1951

VIRUS
V. LUCERNE DWARF (cont.)
   Epilobium paniculatum
      Freitag, J.H., 1951
   Eragrostis diffusa
      Freitag, J.H., 1951
   Erodium cicutarium
      Freitag, J.H., 1951
   Escallonia montevidensis
      Freitag, J.H., 1951
   Eugenia myrtifolia
      Freitag, J.H., 1951
   Festuca megalura
      Freitag, J.H., 1951
   Franseria acanthicarpa
      Freitag, J.H., 1951
   Fraxinus dipetala
      Freitag, J.H., 1951
   Fuchsia magellanica
      Freitag, J.H., 1951
   Godetia grandiflora
      Freitag, J.H., 1951
   Hedera helix
      Freitag, J.H., 1951
   Holcus halepensis
      Freitag, J.H., 1951
   Holcus sudanensis
      Freitag, J.H., 1951
   Hordeum murinum
      Freitag, J.H., 1951
   Hordeum vulgare
      Freitag, J.H., 1951
   Hydrangea paniculata
      Freitag, J.H., 1951
   Lactuca scariola
      Freitag, J.H., 1951
   Lathyrus cicera
      Freitag, J.H., 1951
   Lathyrus clymenum
      Freitag, J.H., 1951
   Lathyrus sativus
      Freitag, J.H., 1951
   Lolium multiflorum
      Freitag, J.H., 1951
   Lolium temulentum
      Freitag, J.H., 1951
   Lonicera japonica
      Freitag, J.H., 1951
   Majorana hortensis
      Freitag, J.H., 1951
   Medicago falcata
      Houston, Byron R. and Ernest H. Stanford, 1954
   Medicago glutinosa
      Houston, Byron R. and Ernest H. Stanford, 1954
   Medicago hispida
      Freitag, J.H., 1951
   Medicago sativa
      Frazier, Norman W. and J.H. Freitag, 1946
      Freitag, J.H., 1951
      Freitag, J.H. and Norman W. Frazier, 1954
      Freitag, J.H., N.W. Frazier and R.A. Flock, 1952
      Hewitt, Wm. B., Byron R. Houston, Norman W.
      Frazier and J.H. Freitag, 1946
      Houston, Byron R., Katherine Esau and Wm. B.
      Hewitt, 1946
      Houston, Byron R., N.W. Frazier and Wm. B.
      Hewitt, 1942
      Houston, Byron R. and Ernest H. Stanford, 1954
      Severin, Henry H.P., 1949
      Stoner, Warren N., 1953
      Weimer, J.L., 1936
   Melilotus alba
      Freitag, J.H., 1951
   Melilotus alba var. annua
      Freitag, J.H., 1951
   Melilotus indica
      Freitag, J.H., 1951
   Melilotus officinalis
      Freitag, J.H., 1951
   Melissa officinalis
      Freitag, J.H., 1951
   Mentha spp.
      Freitag, J.H., 1951

VIRUS

V. LUCERNE DWARF (cont.)

Oenanthe sarmentosa
    Freitag, J.H., 1951
Oenothera hookeri
    Freitag, J.H., 1951
Parthenocissus tricuspidata
    Freitag, J.H., 1951
Paspalum dilatatum
    Freitag, J.H., 1951
Pelargonium hortorum
    Freitag, J.H., 1951
Pennisetum clandestimum
    Freitag, J.H., 1951
Phalaris minor
    Freitag, J.H., 1951
Phalaris paradoxa
    Freitag, J.H., 1951
Phleum pratense
    Freitag, J.H., 1951
Photinia arbutifolia
    Freitag, J.H., 1951
Pittosporum crassifolium
    Freitag, J.H., 1951
Poa annua
    Freitag, J.H., 1951
Polygonum convolvulus
    Freitag, J.H., 1951
Polygonum persicaria
    Freitag, J.H., 1951
Reseda odorata
    Freitag, J.H., 1951
Rheum rhaponticum
    Freitag, J.H., 1951
Rhus diversiloba
    Freitag, J.H., 1951
Rosa californica
    Freitag, J.H., 1951
Rosmarinus officinalis
    Freitag, J.H., 1951
Rubus ursinus var. vitifolius
    Freitag, J.H., 1951
Rumex crispus
    Freitag, J.H., 1951
Salix spp.
    Freitag, J.H., 1951
Sambucus caerulea
    Freitag, J.H., 1951
Setaria lutescens
    Freitag, J.H., 1951
Sonchus asper
    Freitag, J.H., 1951
Symphoricarpos albus
    Freitag, J.H., 1951
Syringa vulgaris
    Freitag, J.H., 1951
Trifolium fragiferum
    Freitag, J.H., 1951
Trifolium hybridum
    Freitag, J.H., 1951
Trifolium incarnatum
    Freitag, J.H., 1951
Trifolium pratense
    Freitag, J.H., 1951
Trifolium repens
    Freitag, J.H., 1951
Trifolium repens var. latum *
    Freitag, J.H., 1951
Urtica gracilis var. holosericea
    Freitag, J.H., 1951
Veronica spp.
    Freitag, J.H., 1951
Vicia monantha
    Freitag, J.H., 1951
Vinca major
    Freitag, J.H., 1951
Vitis californica
    Freitag, J.H., 1951
    Severin, Henry H.P., 1949
Vitis vinifera
    Crall, J.M. and L.H. Stover, 1957
    Frazier, Norman W. and J.H. Freitag, 1946
    Freitag, J.H., 1951
    Freitag, J.H. and Norman W. Frazier, 1954

VIRUS

V. LUCERNE DWARF (cont.)

Vitis vinifera
    Freitag, J.H., N.W. Frazier and R.A. Flock, 1952
    Hewitt, Wm. B., 1939
    Hewitt, Wm. B., N.W. Frazier and Byron R. Houston, 1942
    Hewitt, Wm. B., Byron R. Houston, Norman W. Frazier and J.H. Freitag, 1946
    Houston, Byron R., Katherine Esau and Wm. B. Hewitt, 1946
    Severin, Henry H.P., 1949
    Stoner, Warren N., 1953
Xanthium canadense
    Freitag, J.H., 1951

V. LUCERNE MOSAIC

Amaranthus caudatus
    Price, W.C., 1940
Anthriscus cerefolium
    Price, W.C., 1940
Antirrhinum majus
    Berkeley, G.H., 1947
    Kreitlow, K.W. and W.C. Price, 1948, 1949
    Price, W.C., 1940
    Zaumeyer, W.J., 1953
Apium graveolens
    Berkeley, G.H., 1947
    Houston, Byron R. and John W. Oswald, 1953
    Richardson, D.E. and T.W. Tinsley, 1956
    Snyder, William C. and Saul Rich, 1942
Apium graveolens var. dulce
    Houston, Byron R. and John W. Oswald, 1951
    Oswald, John W., 1950
    Severin, Henry H.P., 1950
    Severin, H.H.P. and J.H. Freitag, 1935
    Swenson, K.G., 1952
Aquilegia caerulea
    Price, W.C., 1940
Beta vulgaris
    Price, W.C., 1940
    Richardson, D.E. and T.W. Tinsley, 1956
    Severin, Henry H.P., 1948
Calendula officinalis
    Richardson, D.E. and T.W. Tinsley, 1956
Capsicum frutescens (Capsicum annuum)
    Berkeley, G.H., 1947
    Dykstra, T.P., 1939
    Houston, Byron R. and John W. Oswald, 1953
    Johnson, E.M., 1946
    Kreitlow, K.W. and W.C. Price, 1948, 1949
    Oswald, John W., 1948, 1950
    Porter, D.R., 1935
    Price, W.C., 1940
    Swenson, K.G., 1952
Celosia argentea var. cristata
    Kreitlow, K.W. and W.C. Price, 1949
Chenopodium amaranticolor
    Hollings, M., 1957
Chrysanthemum spp.
    Price, W.C., 1940
Cicer arietinum
    Zaumeyer, W.J., 1938
Cichorium endivia
    Price, W.C., 1940
Cleome spinosa
    Price, W.C., 1940
Coleus blumei
    Price, W.C., 1940
Crotalaria spectabilis
    Thomas, H. Rex, 1951
Cucumis sativus
    Berkeley, G.H., 1947
    Black, L.M. and W.C. Price, 1940
    Johnson, E.M., 1946
    Oswald, John W., 1950
    Richardson, D.E. and T.W. Tinsley, 1956
    Severin, Henry H.P., 1942
    Thomas, H. Rex, 1951, 1953
    Zaumeyer, W.J., 1938
Cyamopsis tetragonoloba
    Thomas, H. Rex, 1951
Cymbalaria muralis
    Price, W.C., 1940

VIRUS
V. LUCERNE MOSAIC (cont.)
Cynoglossum amabile
   Price, W.C., 1940
Daphne odora
   Milbrath, J.A. and Roy A. Young, 1956
Datura stramonium
   Berkeley, G.H., 1947
   Oswald, John W., 1950
   Porter, D.R., 1935
   Richardson, D.E. and T.W. Tinsley, 1956
   Thomas, H. Rex, 1951, 1953
   Zaumeyer, W.J., 1938, 1953
Daucus carota var. sativa
   Price, W.C., 1940
Delphinium cultorum
   Price, W.C., 1940
Delphinium formosum
   Severin, Henry H.P., 1942
Delphinium grandiflorum var. album
   Severin, Henry H.P., 1942
Delphinium hybrid
   Severin, Henry H.P., 1942
Delphinium parryi var. maritimum
   Severin, Henry H.P., 1942
Delphinium spp.
   Severin, Henry H.P., 1942
Delphinium zalil
   Severin, Henry H.P., 1942
Dolichos lablab
   Pierce, W.H., 1934
   Zaumeyer, W.J., 1953
Eschscholtzia californica
   Price, W.C., 1940
Gilia liniflora
   Price, W.C., 1940
Glycine max
   Berkeley, G.H., 1947
   Kreitlow, K.W. and W.C. Price, 1948, 1949
   Pierce, W.H., 1934
   Snyder, William C. and Saul Rich, 1942
   Thomas, H. Rex, 1951
   Zaumeyer, W.J., 1938, 1953
Godetia amoena
   Price, W.C., 1940
Gomphrena globosa
   Richardson, D.E. and T.W. Tinsley, 1956
   Thomas, H. Rex, 1951
Hyoscyamus albus
   Price, W.C., 1940
Hyoscyamus niger
   Price, W.C., 1940
Impatiens balsamina
   Price, W.C., 1940
Impatiens sultani (or sometimes Impatiens holstii)
   Kreitlow, K.W. and W.C. Price, 1949
   Zaumeyer, W.J., 1953
Lathyrus odoratus
   Berkeley, G.H., 1947
   Kreitlow, K.W. and W.C. Price, 1949
   Snyder, William C. and Saul Rich, 1942
   Zaumeyer, W.J., 1938
   Zaumeyer, W.J. and B.L. Wade, 1935
Lavatera trimestris
   Price, W.C., 1940
Lens esculenta
   Zaumeyer, W.J., 1938
Lespedeza striata
   Zaumeyer, W.J., 1938
Limonium sinuatum
   Price, W.C., 1940
Linaria macedonica
   Price, W.C., 1940
Lobelia tenuior
   Price, W.C., 1940
Lupinus albus
   Thomas, H. Rex, 1951
   Zaumeyer, W.J., 1938, 1953
Lupinus luteus
   Zaumeyer, W.J., 1938
Lycopersicon esculentum
   Berkeley, G.H., 1947
   Johnson, E.M., 1946
   Milbrath, J.A. and F.P. McWhorter, 1953

VIRUS
V. LUCERNE MOSAIC (cont.)
Lycopersicon esculentum
   Porter, D.R., 1935
   Severin, Henry H.P., 1942, 1950
Medicago arabica
   Kreitlow, K.W. and W.C. Price, 1949
Medicago hispida
   Kreitlow, K.W. and W.C. Price, 1949
Medicago obscura
   Kreitlow, K.W. and W.C. Price, 1949
Medicago orbicularis
   Kreitlow, K.W. and W.C. Price, 1949
Medicago sativa
   Diachun, Stephen and Lawrence Henson, 1957
   Henson, Lawrence and Stephen Diachun, 1957
   Houston, Byron R. and John W. Oswald, 1951, 1953
   Johnson, E.M., 1946
   McWhorter, Frank P., 1949
   Oswald, J hn W., 1950
   Pierce, W.H., 1934, 1937
   Snyder, William C. and Saul Rich, 1942
   Swenson, K.G., 1952
   Thomas, H. Rex, 1951
   Weimer, J.L., 1931, 1934
   Zaumeyer, W.J., 1938, 1953
   Zaumeyer, W.J. and B.L. Wade, 1935
Melilotus alba
   Hanson, E.W. and D.J. Hagedorn, 1954, 1956
   Kreitlow, K.W. and W.C. Price, 1949
   Pierce, W.H., 1934, 1937
   Thomas, H. Rex, 1951
   Zaumeyer, W.J., 1938, 1953
   Zaumeyer, W.J. and B.L. Wade, 1935
Melilotus indica
   Hagedorn, D.J. and E.W. Hanson, 1953
   Kreitlow, K.W. and W.C. Price, 1949
   Snyder, William C. and Saul Rich, 1942
Melilotus officinalis
   Hagedorn, D.J. and E.W. Hanson, 1957
   Kreitlow, K.W. and W.C. Price, 1949
Melilotus spp.
   Kreitlow, K.W. and W.C. Price, 1948
Melilotus suaveolens
   Kreitlow, K.W. and W.C. Price, 1949
Mimulus moschatus
   Price, W.C., 1940
Mirabilis jalapa
   Price, W.C., 1940
Nemesia strumosa
   Price, W.C., 1940
Nemophila menziesii subsp. insignis
   Price, W.C., 1940
Nicandra physalodes
   Price, W.C., 1940
Nicotiana alata
   Price, W.C., 1940
Nicotiana glutinosa
   Berkeley, G.H., 1947
   Black, L.M. and W.C. Price, 1940
   Dykstra, T.P., 1939
   Houston, Byron R. and John W. Oswald, 1953
   Kreitlow, K.W. and W.C. Price, 1948, 1949
   Oswald, John W., 1950
   Pierce, W.H., 1934
   Severin, Henry H.P., 1942
   Thomas, H. Rex, 1951
   Zaumeyer, W.J., 1953
Nicotiana langsdorffii
   Price, W.C., 1940
   Severin, Henry H.P., 1942
Nicotiana longiflora
   Price, W.C., 1940
Nicotiana palmeri
   Price, W.C., 1940
Nicotiana paniculata
   Price, W.C., 1940
Nicotiana rustica
   Berkeley, G.H., 1947
   Kreitlow, K.W. and W.C. Price, 1948, 1949
   Oswald, John W., 1950
   Price, W.C., 1940
   Thomas, H. Rex, 1951
   Zaumeyer, W.J., 1953

VIRUS
V. LUCERNE MOSAIC (cont.)
Nicotiana sanderae
Price, W.C., 1940
Nicotiana sylvestris
Dykstra, T.P., 1939
Price, W.C., 1940
Nicotiana tabacum
Berkeley, G.H., 1947
Black, L.M. and W.C. Price, 1940
Houston, Byron R. and John W. Oswald, 1951, 1953
Johnson, E.M., 1946
Kreitlow, K.W. and W.C. Price, 1948, 1949
Oswald, John W., 1950
Pierce, W.H., 1934
Richardson, D.E. and T.W. Tinsley, 1956
Severin, Henry H.P., 1942
Swenson, K.G., 1952
Thomas, H. Rex, 1951, 1953
Thomas, H. Rex and W.J. Zaumeyer, 1950
Zaumeyer, W.J., 1938, 1953
Pentstemon spp.
Price, W.C., 1940
Petunia hybrida
Berkeley, G.H., 1947
Kreitlow, K.W. and W.C. Price, 1948, 1949
Pierce, W.H., 1934
Richardson, D.E. and T.W. Tinsley, 1956
Severin, Henry H.P., 1942
Snyder, William C. and Saul Rich, 1942
Zaumeyer, W.J., 1938
Petunia spp.
Porter, D.R., 1935
Phacelia campanularia
Price, W.C., 1940
Phaseolus aconitifolius
Thomas, H. Rex, 1951
Phaseolus acutifolius var. latifolius
Thomas, H.R., 1953
Zaumeyer, W.J., 1953
Phaseolus angularis
Pierce, W.H., 1934
Thomas, H. Rex, 1951
Zaumeyer, W.J., 1938
Zaumeyer, W.J. and B.L. Wade, 1935
Phaseolus aureus
Pierce, W.H., 1934
Thomas, H. Rex, 1951
Zaumeyer, W.J., 1938
Zaumeyer, W.J. and B.L. Wade, 1935
Phaseolus calcaratus
Pierce, W.H., 1934
Thomas, H. Rex, 1951
Zaumeyer, W.J. and B.L. Wade, 1935
Phaseolus coccineus
Thomas, H. Rex, 1951
Phaseolus lunatus
Kreitlow, K.W. and W.C. Price, 1948, 1949
Thomas, H. Rex, 1951
Zaumeyer, W.J., 1938, 1953
Phaseolus mungo
Thomas, H. Rex, 1951
Zaumeyer, W.J., 1938
Zaumeyer, W.J. and B.L. Wade, 1935
Phaseolus vulgaris
Berkeley, G.H., 1947
Black, L.M. and W.C. Price, 1940
Houston, Byron R. and John W. Oswald, 1951, 1953
Johnson, E.M., 1946
Kreitlow, K.W. and W.C. Price, 1948, 1949
McWhorter, Frank P., 1949
Milbrath, J.A., 1952
Oswald, John W., 1950
Pierce, W.H., 1934, 1937
Richardson, D.E. and T.W. Tinsley, 1956
Thomas, H. Rex, 1951, 1953
Zaumeyer, W.J., 1938, 1952, 1953
Zaumeyer, W.J. and B.L. Wade, 1933, 1935
Phlox drummondii
Price, W.C., 1940
Physalis peruviana
Price, W.C., 1940
Phytolacca americana
Johnson, E.M., 1946

VIRUS
V. LUCERNE MOSAIC (cont.)
Phytolacca decandra
Price, W.C., 1940
Pisum sativum
Berkeley, G.H., 1947
Hanson, E.W. and D.J. Hagedorn, 1954
Johnson, E.M., 1946
Kreitlow, K.W. and W.C. Price, 1948, 1949
McWhorter, Frank P., 1949, 1954
Oswald, John W., 1950
Pierce, W.H., 1934
Richardson, D.E. and T.W. Tinsley, 1956
Thomas, H. Rex, 1951, 1953
Zaumeyer, W.J., 1937, 1938, 1953
Zaumeyer, W.J. and B.L. Wade, 1936
Primula obconica
Price, W.C., 1940
Severin, Henry H.P. and C.M. Tompkins, 1950
Rheum rhaponticum
Price, W.C., 1940
Rumex crispus
Price, W.C., 1940
Salpiglossis sinuata
Price, W.C., 1940
Sesbania spp.
Thomas, H. Rex, 1951
Sinningia speciosa
Price, W.C., 1940
Solanum melongena
Berkeley, G.H., 1947
Porter, D.R., 1935
Solanum nodiflorum
Price, W.C., 1940
Solanum tuberosum
Black, L.M. and W.C. Price, 1940
Dykstra, T.P., 1939
Folsom, Donald, 1953
Hoggan, Isme A., 1927
Houston, Byron R. and John W. Oswald, 1951, 1953
McKay, M.B. and T.P. Dykstra, 1932
Milbrath, J.A., 1952
Oswald, John W., 1950
Poster, D.R., 1931, 1935
Richardson, D.E. and T.W. Tinsley, 1956
Spinacia oleracea
Price, W.C., 1940
Severin, Henry H.P., 1948
Tetragonia expansa
Price, W.C., 1940
Thunbergia alata
Price, W.C., 1940
Trifolium alexandrinum
Kreitlow, K.W. and W.C. Price, 1949
Trifolium dubium
Kreitlow, K.W. and W.C. Price, 1949
Trifolium fragiferum
Kreitlow, K.W. and W.C. Price, 1949
Trifolium giganteum *
(K.M. Smith, 1957) R.E. Fitzpatrick, et al., 1958
Trifolium glomeratum
Kreitlow, K.W. and W.C. Price, 1949
Trifolium hirtum
Kreitlow, K.W. and W.C. Price, 1949
Trifolium hybridum
Hagedorn, D.J. and E.W. Hanson, 1953, 1957
Hanson, E.W. and D.J. Hagedorn, 1954, 1956
Kreitlow, K.W. and W.C. Price, 1949
Trifolium incarnatum
Black, L.M. and W.C. Price, 1940
Hagedorn, D.J. and E.W. Hanson, 1953, 1957
Hanson, E.W. and D.J. Hagedorn, 1954, 1956
Kreitlow, K.W. and W.C. Price, 1949
Pierce, W.H., 1934
Thomas, H. Rex, 1951
Zaumeyer, W.J., 1938, 1953
Trifolium pratense
Berkeley, G.H., 1947
Black, L.M. and W.C. Price, 1940
Hagedorn, D.J. and E.W. Hanson, 1953, 1957
Hanson, E.W. and D.J. Hagedorn, 1952, 1954, 1956
Johnson, E.M., 1946
Kreitlow, K.W. and W.C. Price, 1949
Pierce, W.H., 1934, 1937

VIRUS
V. LUCERNE MOSAIC (cont.)
  Trifolium pratense
    Thomas, H. Rex, 1951
    Zaumeyer, W.J., 1938
    Zaumeyer, W.J. and B.L. Wade, 1935
  Trifolium repens
    Black, L.M. and W.C. Price, 1940
    Houston, Byron R. and John W. Oswald, 1953
    Johnson, E.M., 1946
    Kreitlow, K.W., O.J. Hunt and H.L. Wilkins, 1957
    Kreitlow, K.W. and W.C. Price, 1949
    Pierce, W.H., 1934
    Roberts, D.A., 1956
    Snyder, William C. and Saul Rich, 1942
    Zaumeyer, W.J., 1938, 1953
  Trifolium repens var. giganteum *
    Kreitlow, K.W. and W.C. Price, 1948
    Thomas, H. Rex, 1951
  Trifolium repens var. latum *
    Houston, Byron R. and John W. Oswald, 1951
  Trifolium resupinatum
    Kreitlow, K.W. and W.C. Price, 1949
  Trifolium spp.
    Kreitlow, K.W. and W.C. Price, 1948
  Trifolium subterraneum
    Kreitlow, K.W. and W.C. Price, 1949
  Verbascum phoeniceum
    Price, W.C., 1940
  Veronica longifolia
    Price, W.C., 1940
  Vicia americana
    Zaumeyer, W.J. and B.L. Wade, 1935
  Vicia faba
    Berkeley, G.H., 1947
    Black, L.M. and W.C. Price, 1940
    Houston, Byron R. and John W. Oswald, 1953
    Richardson, D.E. and T.W. Tinsley, 1956
    Snyder, William C. and Saul Rich, 1942
    Swenson, K.G., 1952
    Thomas, H. Rex, 1951
    Zaumeyer, W.J., 1938, 1953
    Zaumeyer, W.J. and B.L. Wade, 1935
  Vicia faba var. minor
    Pierce, W.H., 1934, 1938
  Vicia sativa
    Pierce, W.H., 1934
    Zaumeyer, W.J., 1938
  Vicia villosa
    Zaumeyer, W.J., 1938
  Vigna sesquipedalis
    Pierce, W.H., 1934
    Snyder, William C. and Saul Rich, 1942
    Zaumeyer, W.J., 1938
  Vigna sinensis
    Black, L.M. and W.C. Price, 1940
    Kreitlow, K.W. and W.C. Price, 1949
    Milbrath, J.A. and F.P. McWhorter, 1954
    Oswald, John W., 1950
    Snyder, William C. and Saul Rich, 1942
    Thomas, H. Rex, 1951, 1953
    Zaumeyer, W.J., 1938, 1953
  Vinca rosea
    Kreitlow, K.W. and W.C. Price, 1948, 1949
    Price, W.C., 1940
  Viola cornuta
    Severin, Henry H.P., 1947
  Viola tricolor var. hortensis
    Severin, Henry H.P., 1947
  Zaluzianskya villosa
    Price, W.C., 1940
  Zinnia elegans
    Berkeley, G.H., 1947
    (K.M. Smith, 1957) R.E. Fitzpatrick, et al., 1958
    Johnson, E.M., 1946
    Kreitlow, K.W. and W.C. Price, 1948, 1949
    Richardson, D.E. and T.W. Tinsley, 1956
    Swenson, K.G., 1952
    Thomas, H. Rex, 1951, 1953
    Zaumeyer, W.J., 1938, 1953

VIRUS
V. LUCERNE WITCHES' BROOM Edwards 1936
  Astragalus chinensis
    Klostermeyer, E.C. and J.D. Menzies, 1951
  Astragalus falcatus
    Klostermeyer, E.C. and J.D. Menzies, 1951
  Astragalus mortoni
    Klostermeyer, E.C. and J.D. Menzies, 1951
  Calendula officinalis
    Helms, Katie, 1957
  Crotalaria goreensis
    Helms, Katie, 1957
  Datura stramonium
    Helms, Katie, 1957
  Datura stramonium var. tatula
    Helms, Katie, 1957
  Daucus carota
    Helms, Katie, 1957
  Daucus carota var. sativa
    Kunkel, L.O., 1952
  Hedysarum coronarium
    Klostermeyer, E.C. and J.D. Menzies, 1951
  Lactuca sativa
    Helms, Katie, 1957
  Lathyrus latifolius
    Klostermeyer, E.C. and J.D. Menzies, 1951
  Lotus corniculatus
    Klostermeyer, E.C. and J.D. Menzies, 1951
  Lycopersicon esculentum
    Helms, Katie, 1957
    Kunkel, L.O., 1952
  Medicago falcata
    Klostermeyer, E.C. and J.D. Menzies, 1951
  Medicago hispida
    Klostermeyer, E.C. and J.D. Menzies, 1951
    Menzies, J.D., 1944, 1946
  Medicago lupulina
    Klostermeyer, E.C. and J.D. Menzies, 1951
    Menzies, J.D., 1944, 1946
  Medicago ruthenica
    Klostermeyer, E.C. and J.D. Menzies, 1951
  Medicago sativa
    Helms, Katie, 1957
    Kunkel, L.O., 1952
    Menzies, J.D., 1944, 1946
    Menzies, J.D. and F.D. Heald, 1942
  Melilotus alba
    Klostermeyer, E.C. and J.D. Menzies, 1951
  Nicotiana glutinosa
    Helms, Katie, 1957
  Nicotiana rustica
    Helms, Katie, 1957
  Nicotiana tabacum
    Helms, Katie, 1957
  Nicotiana tabacum var. atropurpurea *
    Helms, Katie, 1957
  Petunia spp.
    Helms, Katie, 1957
  Solanum tuberosum
    Helms, Katie, 1957
    Kunkel, L.O., 1952
  Trifolium pratense
    Klostermeyer, E.C. and J.D. Menzies, 1951
    Menzies, J.D., 1946
  Trifolium repens
    Klostermeyer, E.C. and J.D. Menzies, 1951
    Menzies, J.D., 1946
  Trifolium subterraneum
    Klostermeyer, E.C. and J.D. Menzies, 1951
  Vinca rosea
    Kunkel, L.O., 1952
  Vinca rosea var. alba
    Helms, Katie, 1957
  Vinca rosea var. oculata *
    Helms, Katie, 1957

V. LUPINE DISEASE *
  Capsicum frutescens (Capsicum annuum)
    Weimer, J.L., 1950
  Cucumis sativus
    Weimer, J.L., 1950
  Lupinus angustifolius
    Weimer, J.L., 1950

VIRUS
V. MAIZE LEAF FLECK Stoner 1952
Phalaris tuberosa var. stenoptera
Stoner, Warren N., 1952
Zea mays
Stoner, Warren N., 1952

V. MAIZE MOSAIC Kunkel 1923
Musa textilis
Juliano, Jorge P., 1951
Saccharum officinarum
Brandes, E.W., 1920
Zea mays
Brandes, E.W., 1920
Kunkel, L.O., 1927

V. MAIZE STREAK Storey 1925
Avena sativa
(K.M. Smith, 1957) R.E. Fitzpatrick, et al., 1958
Chloris virgata
(K.M. Smith, 1957) R.E. Fitzpatrick, et al., 1958
Digitaria horizontalis
Storey, H.H. and A.P.D. McClean, 1930
Eleusine indica
Storey, H.H. and A.P.D. McClean, 1930
Eragrostis abyssinica
(K.M. Smith, 1957) R.E. Fitzpatrick, et al., 1958
Eragrostis aspera
(K.M. Smith, 1957) R.E. Fitzpatrick, et al., 1958
Eragrostis curvula
(K.M. Smith, 1957) R.E. Fitzpatrick, et al., 1958
Euchlaena mexicana
(K.M. Smith, 1957) R.E. Fitzpatrick, et al., 1958
Hordeum vulgare
(K.M. Smith, 1957) R.E. Fitzpatrick, et al., 1958
Lolium subulatum
(K.M. Smith, 1957) R.E. Fitzpatrick, et al., 1958
Saccharum officinarum
(K.M. Smith, 1957) R.E. Fitzpatrick, et al., 1958
Saccharum spp.
Storey, H.H. and A.P.D. McClean, 1930
Secale cereale
(K.M. Smith, 1957) R.E. Fitzpatrick, et al., 1958
Triticum aestivum
(K.M. Smith, 1957) R.E. Fitzpatrick, et al., 1958
Urochloa panicoides
(K.M. Smith, 1957) R.E. Fitzpatrick, et al., 1958
Zea mays
Finley, A.M., 1954
McKinney, H.H., 1929
Storey, H.H., 1925, 1928, 1932, 1937
Storey, H.H. and A.P.D. McClean, 1930

V. MAIZE STUNT Kunkel 1946
Zea mays
Hildebrand, E.M., 1949
Maramorosch, Karl, 1951, 1955, 1956, 1957
Niederhauser, John S. and Javier Cervantes, 1950

V. MAIZE WALLABY EAR Schindler 1942
Zea mays
(K.M. Smith, 1957) R.E. Fitzpatrick, et al., 1958

V. MALVA YELLOW VEIN MOSAIC *
Lavatera assurgentiflora
Costa, A.S. and James E. Duffus, 1957
Malva parviflora
Costa, A.S. and James E. Duffus, 1957
Malva rotundifolia
Costa, A.S. and James E. Duffus, 1957
Malva sylvestris
Costa, A.S. and James E. Duffus, 1957

V. MILKWEED MOSAIC *
Asclepias syriaca
Newhall, A.G., 1923

V. MOUNTAIN ASH INFECTIOUS VARIEGATION
Sorbus aucuparia
(K.M. Smith, 1957) R.E. Fitzpatrick, et al., 1958

V. MUSKMELON MOSAIC Rader et al. 1947
Citrullus vulgaris
Anderson, C.W., 1954

VIRUS
V. MUSKMELON MOSAIC (cont.)
Citrullus vulgaris
Lindberg, G.D., D.H. Hall and J.C. Walker, 1956
Citrullus vulgaris var. citroides
Anderson, C.W., 1954
Cucumis anguria
Rader, Wm. E., Hugh F. Fitzpatrick and E.M.
Hildebrand, 1947
Cucumis melo
Anderson, C.W., 1954
Freitag, J.H., 1952
Lindberg, G.D., D.H. Hall and J.C. Walker, 1956
Cucumis melo var. chito
Rader, Wm. E., Hugh F. Fitzpatrick and E.M.
Hildebrand, 1947
Cucumis melo var. conomon *
Rader, Wm. E., Hugh F. Fitzpatrick and E.M.
Hildebrand, 1947
Cucumis melo var. flexuosus
(K.M. Smith, 1957) R.E. Fitzpatrick, et al., 1958
Rader, Wm. E., Hugh F. Fitzpatrick and E.M.
Hildebrand, 1947
Cucumis melo var. inodorus
Rader, Wm. E., Hugh F. Fitzpatrick and E.M.
Hildebrand, 1947
Cucumis melo var. reticulatus
Rader, Wm. E., Hugh F. Fitzpatrick and E.M.
Hildebrand, 1947
Cucumis sativus
Anderson, C.W., 1954
Lindberg, G.D., D.H. Hall and J.C. Walker, 1956
Rader, Wm. E., Hugh F. Fitzpatrick and E.M.
Hildebrand, 1947
Cucurbita maxima
Lindberg, G.D., D.H. Hall and J.C. Walker, 1956
Rader, Wm. E., Hugh F. Fitzpatrick and E.M.
Hildebrand, 1947
Cucurbita moschata
Anderson, C.W., 1954
Lindberg, G.D., D.H. Hall and J.C. Walker, 1956
Rader, Wm. E., Hugh F. Fitzpatrick and E.M.
Hildebrand, 1947
Cucurbita okeechobeensis
Anderson, C.W., 1954
Cucurbita pepo
Lindberg, G.D., D.H. Hall and J.C. Walker, 1956
Rader, Wm. E., Hugh F. Fitzpatrick and E.M.
Hildebrand, 1947
Cucurbita pepo var. medullosa *
Anderson, C.W., 1954
Cucurbita pepo var. melopepo
Anderson, C.W., 1954
Cyclanthera pedata
Anderson, C.W., 1954
Lagenaria siceraria (Lagenaria leucantha)
Anderson, C.W., 1954
Luffa aegyptiaca (Luffa cylindrica)
Anderson, C.W., 1954
Melothria pendula
Anderson, C.W., 1954
Momordica charantia
Anderson, C.W., 1954

V. MUSKMELON VEIN NECROSIS Freitag 1952
Cucumis melo
Freitag, J.H., 1952

V. MUSTARD (BLACK) RING SPOT *
Brassica spp.
(K.M. Smith, 1957) R.E. Fitzpatrick, et al., 1958

V. NARCISSUS MOSAIC McWhorter and Weiss 1932;
Narcissus pseudo-narcissus   Haasis 1939
Haasis, Frank A., 1939
Narcissus spp.
Blanton, F.S. and F.A. Haasis, 1942
Haasis, Frank A., 1939
McWhorter, Frank P. and Freeman Weiss, 1932

V. NARCISSUS STRIPE *
Chenopodium amaranticolor
Hollings, M., 1957

VIRUS

V. NARCISSUS STRIPE * (cont.)
Narcissus pallida praecox *
    Caldwell, John and Ian W. Prentice, 1943
Narcissus spp.
    Caldwell, John and Ian W. Prentice, 1943
    Hawker, Lilian E., 1943
Narcissus triandrus
    Caldwell, John and Ian W. Prentice, 1943

V. NICOTIANA GLAUCA LIGHT GREEN MOSAIC *
Nicotiana glauca
    McKinney, H.H., 1929
Nicotiana tabacum
    McKinney, H.H., 1929

V. NICOTIANA GLAUCA MILD DARK GREEN MOSAIC *
Nicotiana tabacum
    McKinney, H.H., 1929

V. NICOTIANA GLAUCA YELLOW MOSAIC *
Nicotiana tabacum
    McKinney, H.H., 1929

V. NICOTIANA GLUTINOSA MOSAIC *
Datura fastuosa
    Allard, H.A., 1916
Lycopersicon esculentum
    Walker, M.N., 1925
Nicotiana glutinosa
    Allard, H.A., 1916
    Fernow, Karl Hermann, 1925
Nicotiana tabacum
    Walker, M.N., 1925
Nicotiana tabacum x Nicotiana glutinosa
    Allard, H.A., 1916

V. NICOTIANA GLUTINOSA ROOT NECROSIS *
Nicotiana glutinosa
    Cetas, Robert C. and A. Frank Ross, 1952
Nicotiana repanda
    Cetas, Robert C. and A. Frank Ross, 1952
Physalis floridana
    Cetas, Robert C. and A. Frank Ross, 1952
Physalis peruviana
    Cetas, Robert C. and A. Frank Ross, 1952

V. NOTHOSCORDUM MOSAIC McKinney 1950
Nothoscordum fragrans
    McKinney, H.H., 1950

V. (OAT) BLUE DWARF *
Avena sativa
    Moore, M.B., 1952

V. OAT PSEUDO-ROSETTE Grebennikov 1941
Agropyron repens
    (K.M. Smith, 1957) R.E. Fitzpatrick, et al., 1958
Avena byzantina
    (K.M. Smith, 1957) R.E. Fitzpatrick, et al., 1958
Avena festuca *
    (K.M. Smith, 1957) R.E. Fitzpatrick, et al., 1958
Avena sativa
    (K.M. Smith, 1957) R.E. Fitzpatrick, et al., 1958
Avena sterilis
    (K.M. Smith, 1957) R.E. Fitzpatrick, et al., 1958
Avena strigosa
    (K.M. Smith, 1957) R.E. Fitzpatrick, et al., 1958
Bromus inermis
    (K.M. Smith, 1957) R.E. Fitzpatrick, et al., 1958
Echinochloa crus-galli
    (K.M. Smith, 1957) R.E. Fitzpatrick, et al., 1958
Hordeum vulgare
    (K.M. Smith, 1957) R.E. Fitzpatrick, et al., 1958
Oryza sativa
    (K.M. Smith, 1957) R.E. Fitzpatrick, et al., 1958
Panicum miliaceum
    (K.M. Smith, 1957) R.E. Fitzpatrick, et al., 1958
Secale cereale
    (K.M. Smith, 1957) R.E. Fitzpatrick, et al., 1958
Setaria virdis
    (K.M. Smith, 1957) R.E. Fitzpatrick, et al., 1958
Triticum aestivum
    (K.M. Smith, 1957) R.E. Fitzpatrick, et al., 1958

VIRUS

V. OAT PSEUDO-ROSETTE (cont.)
Zea mays
    (K.M. Smith, 1957) R.E. Fitzpatrick, et al., 1958

V. ONION MOSAIC Vovk 1944
Allium canadense
    McKinney, H.H., 1928
Allium cepa
    Brierley, Philip and Floyd F. Smith, 1944
Allium neopolitanum
    Brierley, Philip and Floyd F. Smith, 1944
Allium sativum
    Brierley, Philip and Floyd F. Smith, 1944
Allium vineale
    Brierley, Philip and Floyd F. Smith, 1944

V. ONION YELLOW DWARF Melhus et al. 1929; Drake,
Harris, and Tate 1932
Allium ascalonicum
    Henderson, D.M., 1953
    Henderson, W.J., 1935
Allium cepa
    Brierley, Philip and Floyd F. Smith, 1946
    Henderson, D.M., 1953
    Henderson, W.J., 1932, 1935
    Melhus, I.E. and W.J. Henderson, 1929
    Melhus, I.E., C.S. Reddy, W.J. Henderson and E.
    Vestal, 1929
Allium cepa var. solaninum
    Brierley, Philip and Floyd F. Smith, 1944
Allium cepa var. viviparum
    Brierley, Philip and Floyd F. Smith, 1944
Allium porrum
    (K.M. Smith, 1957) R.E. Fitzpatrick, et al., 1958
Allium sativum
    (K.M. Smith, 1957) R.E. Fitzpatrick, et al., 1958
Allium vineale
    Brierley, Philip and Floyd F. Smith, 1944
Narcissus jonquilla
    Henderson, W.J., 1935
Narcissus tazetta
    Henderson, W.J., 1935

V. ORCHID *
Spathoglottis spp.
    Murakishi, H. and M. Ishii, 1954

V. ORCHID (CATTLEYA) MOSAIC Jensen 1949
Cattleya mossiae
    Jensen, D.D., 1949
Cattleya spp.
    Murakishi, Harry H., 1952
Cattleya trianae
    Jensen, D.D., 1949

V. ORCHID (CYMBIDIUM) MOSAIC Jensen 1950
Angraecum eburneum
    Jensen, D.D. and A.H. Gold, 1955
Brassocattleya dietrichiana *
    Jensen, D.D. and A.H. Gold, 1955
Cattleya spp.
    Murakishi, H. and M. Ishii, 1954
Cattleya trianaei
    Jensen, D.D. and A.H. Gold, 1955
Cattleya waltersiana *
    Jensen, D.D. and A.H. Gold, 1955
Chenopodium amaranticolor
    Hollings, M., 1956
Cymbidium insigne
    Jensen, D.D., 1951
Cymbidium lowianum
    Jensen, D.D., 1951
Cymbidium spp.
    Jensen, D.D., 1950
    Jensen, D.D. and A.H. Gold, 1955
    Murakishi, H. and M. Ishii, 1954
    White, N.H. and D.J. Goodchild, 1955
Datura stramonium
    Jensen, D.D. and A.H. Gold, 1955
    White, N.H. and D.J. Goodchild, 1955
Epidendrum spp.
    Jensen, D.D. and A.H. Gold, 1955

VIRUS
V. ORCHID (CYMBIDIUM) MOSAIC (cont.)
Laelia anceps
    Jensen, D.D. and A.H. Gold, 1955
Laeliocattleya lustre plumosa *
    Jensen, D.D. and A.H. Gold, 1955
Laeliocattleya pasadena *
    Jensen, D.D. and A.H. Gold, 1955
Laeliocattleya proca *
    Jensen, D.D. and A.H. Gold, 1955
Laeliocattleya sargon *
    Jensen, D.D. and A.H. Gold, 1955
Laeliocattleya shoshone *
    Jensen, D.D. and A.H. Gold, 1955
Oncidium spp.
    Jensen, D.D. and A.H. Gold, 1955
Zygopetalum spp.
    Jensen, D.D. and A.H. Gold, 1955

V. ORCHID (DENDROBIUM) MOSAIC *
Dendrobium superbun
    Murakishi, Harry H., 1952
    Murakishi, H. and M. Ishii, 1954

V. ORCHID (LAELIA ANCEPS) *
Cymbidium spp.
    Jensen, D.D. and A. Herbert Gold, 1952
Laelia anceps
    Jensen, D.D. and A. Herbert Gold, 1952

V. ORCHID (ODONTOGLOSSUM) RING SPOT Jensen and
Cattleya spp.   Gold 1951
    Jensen, D.D. and A. Herbert Gold, 1952
Cymbidium spp.
    Jensen, D.D. and A. Herbert Gold, 1952
Odontoglossum grande
    Jensen, D.D. and A. Herbert Gold, 1951, 1952
Zinnia elegans
    Jensen, D.D. and A. Herbert Gold, 1952

V. ORCHID (ONCIDIUM ROGERS) *
Cymbidium spp.
    Jensen, D.D. and A. Herbert Gold, 1952
Oncidium rogers *
    Jensen, D.D. and A. Herbert Gold, 1952

V. ORCHID (VANDA) MOSAIC Murakishi 1950
Aranda spp.
    Murakishi, Harry H., 1952
Vanda boschii *
    Murakishi, Harry H., 1952
Vanda cooperii *
    Murakishi, Harry H., 1952
Vanda spp.
    Murakishi, Harry H., 1952
    Murakishi, H. and M. Ishii, 1954

V. ORNITHOGALUM MOSAIC Smith and Brierley 1944
Eucomis spp.
    (K.M. Smith, 1957) R.E. Fitzpatrick, et al., 1958
Ornithogalum thyrsoides
    Smith, Floyd F. and Philip Brierley, 1944

V. PANAX RING SPOT Aragaki et al. 1953
Nothopanax guilfoylei
    Aragaki, M. and H. Murakishi, and J.W. Hendrix,
    1953

V. PANICUM MOSAIC *
Digitaria sanguinalis
    Sill, W.H., Jr., 1957
    Sill, W.H., Jr. and R.C. Pickett, 1957
Echinochloa crus-galli
    Sill, W.H., Jr., 1957
    Sill, W.H., Jr. and R.C. Pickett, 1957
Panicum capillare
    Sill, W.H., Jr. and R.C. Pickett, 1957
Panicum hallii
    Sill, W.H., Jr. and R.C. Pickett, 1957
Panicum miliaceum
    Sill, W.H., Jr. and R.C. Pickett, 1957
Panicum scribnerianum
    Sill, W.H., Jr. and R.C. Pickett, 1957

VIRUS
V. PANICUM MOSAIC * (cont.)
Panicum virgatum
    Sill, W.H., Jr., 1957
    Sill, W.H., Jr. and R.C. Pickett, 1957
Setaria italica
    Sill, W.H., Jr., 1957
    Sill, W.H., Jr. and R.C. Pickett, 1957

V. PAPAW BUNCHY TOP Bird and Adsuar 1952
Carica papaya
    Bird, Julio and Jose Adsuar, 1952

V. PAPAW MOSAIC Capoor and Varma 1948
Carica papaya
    Adsuar, Jose, 1946, 1947
Melothria guadalupensis
    Adsuar, Jose, 1950

V. PAPAW RING SPOT Jensen 1947
Carica papaya
    Holmes, F.O., J.W. Hendrix, W. Ikeda, D.D.
    Jensen, R.C. Lindner and W.B. Storey, 1948
    Jensen, D.D., 1949

V. PASSIFLORA FOETIDA MOSAIC *
Passiflora foetida
    Jensen, D.D., 1949

V. PASSIFLORA PFORDTI MOSAIC *
Passiflora pfordtii
    Jensen, D.D., 1949

V. PEA DIE BACK *
Cucumis sativus
    Zaumeyer, W.J., 1939
Nicotiana tabacum
    Zaumeyer, W.J., 1939
Petunia hybrida
    Zaumeyer, W.J., 1939
Phaseolus lunatus
    Zaumeyer, W.J., 1939
Pisum sativum
    Zaumeyer, W.J., 1939
Vicia faba
    Zaumeyer, W.J., 1939

V. PEA ENATION MOSAIC Pierce 1935
Astragalus rubyi
    Hagedorn, D.J., 1957
Cicer arietinum
    Hagedorn, D.J., 1957
Glycine max
    Chaudhuri, R.P., 1950
    Hagedorn, D.J., 1952
    Hagedorn, D.J. and J.C. Walker, 1954
    Pierce, W.H., 1935
    Simons, John N., 1954
    Stubbs, M.W., 1936, 1937
Lathyrus cicera
    Hagedorn, D.J., 1957
Lathyrus hirsutus
    McEwen, F.L. and W.T. Schroeder, 1956
Lathyrus latifolius
    Johnson, Folke and Leon K. Jones, 1937
Lathyrus odoratus
    Ainsworth, G.C., 1940
    Chaudhuri, R.P., 1950
    Hagedorn, D.J. and J.C. Walker, 1954
    Johnson, Folke and Leon K. Jones, 1937
    Osborn, H.T., 1938
    Simons, John N., 1954
    Stubbs, M.W., 1936, 1937
Lathyrus tingitanus
    Hagedorn, D.J., 1957
Lupinus albus
    Hagedorn, D.J., 1957
Lupinus angustifolius
    Hagedorn, D.J., 1957
Medicago arabica
    Simons, John N., 1954
Medicago hispida
    Simons, John N., 1954

VIRUS
V. PEA ENATION MOSAIC (cont.)
    Medicago sativa
        Johnson, Folke and Leon K. Jones, 1937
        McEwen, F.L. and W.T. Schroeder, 1956
    Melilotus alba
        McEwen, F.L. and W.T. Schroeder, 1956
    Melilotus officinalis
        Hagedorn, D.J. and J.C. Walker, 1954
        McEwen, F.L. and W.T. Schroeder, 1956
        Stubbs, M.W., 1936, 1937
    Phaseolus vulgaris
        Johnson, Folke and Leon K. Jones, 1937
    Pisum sativum
        Ainsworth, G.C., 1940
        Chaudhuri, R.P., 1950
        Hagedorn, D.J., 1952
        Hagedorn, D.J. and J.C. Walker, 1954
        Johnson, Folke and Leon K. Jones, 1937
        McEwen, F.L. and W.T. Schroeder, 1956
        McWhorter, Frank P., 1954
        Osborn, H.T., 1938
        Pierce, W.H., 1935, 1937
        Simons, John N., 1954
        Stubbs, M.W., 1936, 1937
    Pisum sativum var. arvense
        Osborn, H.T., 1938
    Pisum sativum var. saccharatum
        Pierce, W.H., 1935
    Trifolium glomeratum
        Hagedorn, D.J., 1957
    Trifolium hybridum
        Johnson, Folke and Leon K. Jones, 1937
    Trifolium incarnatum
        Chaudhuri, R.P., 1950
        Hagedorn, D.J., 1952
        Hagedorn, D.J. and J.C. Walker, 1954
        McEwen, F.L. and W.T. Schroeder, 1956
        Osborn, H.T., 1938
        Simons, John N., 1954
        Stubbs, M.W., 1937
    Trifolium pratense
        Hagedorn, D.J., 1952
    Trifolium repens
        McEwen, F.L. and W.T. Schroeder, 1956
    Trifolium resupinatum
        Hagedorn, D.J., 1957
    Trifolium subterraneum
        Hagedorn, D.J., 1957
    Trigonella foenum-graecum
        Hagedorn, D.J., 1952
    Vicia dasycarpa
        Hagedorn, D.J., 1957
    Vicia faba
        Ainsworth, G.C., 1940
        McEwen, F.L. and W.T. Schroeder, 1956
        Osborn, H.T., 1934, 1935, 1938
        Stubbs, M.W., 1936
    Vicia faba var. minor
        Hagedorn, D.J. and J.C. Walker, 1954
        Pierce, W.H., 1935
        Stubbs, M.W., 1937
    Vicia pannonica
        Hagedorn, D.J., 1957
    Vicia sativa
        McEwen, F.L. and W.T. Schroeder, 1956
    Vicia villosa
        McEwen, F.L. and W.T. Schroeder, 1956

V. PEA LEAF ROLL Quantz and Volk 1954
    Medicago sativa
        (K.M. Smith, 1957) R.E. Fitzpatrick, et al., 1958
    Pisum sativum
        (K.M. Smith, 1957) R.E. Fitzpatrick, et al., 1958

V. PEA MOSAIC Doolittle and Jones 1925; Chamberlain
    Chenopodium amaranticolor   1936, 1937
        Hollings, M., 1957
    Cicer arietinum
        Murphy, D.M. and W.H. Pierce, 1937
        Zaumeyer, W.J. and B.L. Wade, 1935
    Desmodium canadense
        Murphy, D.M. and W.H. Pierce, 1937

VIRUS
V. PEA MOSAIC (cont.)
    Lathyrus hirsutus
        Hagedorn, D.J., 1948
    Lathyrus odoratus
        Ainsworth, G.C., 1940
        Chaudhuri, R.P., 1950
        Doolittle, S.P. and F.R. Jones, 1925
        Hagedorn, D.J. and J.C. Walker, 1954
        Murphy, D.M. and W.H. Pierce, 1937
        Osborn, H.T., 1934, 1935
        Stubbs, M.W., 1936, 1937
    Lathyrus sativus
        Murphy, D.M. and W.H. Pierce, 1937
    Lupinus albus
        Hagedorn, D.J. and J.C. Walker, 1954
        Murphy, D.M. and W.H. Pierce, 1937
        Pierce, W.H., 1937
        Stubbs, M.W., 1936, 1937
    Lupinus angustifolius
        Murphy, D.M. and W.H. Pierce, 1937
    Lupinus densiflorus
        Murphy, D.M. and W.H. Pierce, 1937
    Lupinus hartwegii
        Murphy, D.M. and W.H. Pierce, 1937
    Lupinus luteus
        Steveninck, R.F.M. Van, 1957
    Lupinus nanus
        Murphy, D.M. and W.H. Pierce, 1937
    Medicago arabica
        Murphy, D.M. and W.H. Pierce, 1937
    Medicago hispida
        Murphy, D.M. and W.H. Pierce, 1937
    Medicago sativa
        Johnson, F. and L.K. Jones, 1936
    Melilotus alba
        Hagedorn, D.J., 1948
        Murphy, D.M. and W.H. Pierce, 1937
        Osborn, H.T., 1937
        Pierce, W.H., 1937
        Zaumeyer, W.J. and B.L. Wade, 1935
    Melilotus alba var. annua
        Murphy, D.M. and W.H. Pierce, 1937
    Melilotus indica
        Murphy, D.M. and W.H. Pierce, 1937
    Melilotus officinalis
        Hagedorn, D.J., 1948
        Hagedorn, D.J. and J.C. Walker, 1954
        Murphy, D.M. and W.H. Pierce, 1937
        Pierce, W.H., 1935
        Stubbs, M.W., 1936, 1937
    Phaseolus acutifolius var. latifolius
        Murphy, D.M. and W.H. Pierce, 1937
    Phaseolus vulgaris
        Hagedorn, D.J., 1948
        Johnson, F. and L.K. Jones, 1936
        Osborn, H.T., 1937
        Zaumeyer, W.J., 1933
        Zaumeyer, W.J. and B.L. Wade, 1933
    Pisum sativum
        Ainsworth, G.C., 1940
        Chaudhuri, R.P., 1950
        Doolittle, S.P. and F.R. Jones, 1925
        Hagedorn, D.J., 1948
        Hagedorn, D.J. and J.C. Walker, 1954
        Johnson, F. and L.K. Jones, 1936
        Murphy, D.M. and W.H. Pierce, 1937
        Osborn, H.T., 1934, 1935
        Oshima, Nagayoshi and M.F. Kernkamp, 1957
        Pierce, W.H., 1935, 1937
        Snyder, W.C., 1934
        Stubbs, M.W., 1936, 1937
        Yen, D.E. and P.R. Fry, 1956
        Zaumeyer, W.J. and B.L. Wade, 1936
    Pisum sativum var. arvense
        Hagedorn, D.J., 1948
        Murphy, D.M. and W.H. Pierce, 1937
        Osborn, H.T., 1934, 1935
    Pisum sativum var. saccharatum
        Pierce, W.H., 1935
    Trifolium agrarium
        Murphy, D.M. and W.H. Pierce, 1937
    Trifolium carolinianum
        Murphy, D.M. and W.H. Pierce, 1937

VIRUS
V. PEA MOSAIC (cont.)
    Trifolium dubium
        Murphy, D.M. and W.H. Pierce, 1937
    Trifolium glomeratum
        Murphy, D.M. and W.H. Pierce, 1937
    Trifolium hybridum
        Johnson, F. and L.K. Jones, 1936
        Murphy, D.M. and W.H. Pierce, 1937
        Pierce, W.H., 1937
    Trifolium incarnatum
        Chaudhuri, R.P., 1950
        Hagedorn, D.J., 1948
        Hagedorn, D.J. and J.C. Walker, 1954
        Murphy, D.M. and W.H. Pierce, 1937
        Osborn, H.T., 1935, 1937
        Stubbs, M.W., 1936, 1937
    Trifolium pratense
        Doolittle, S.P. and F.R. Jones, 1925
        Hagedorn, D.J., 1948
        Hanson, E.W. and D.J. Hagedorn, 1952
        Murphy, D.M. and W.H. Pierce, 1937
        Osborn, H.T., 1937
        Oshima, Nagayoshi and M.F. Kernkamp, 1957
        Pierce, W.H., 1935, 1937
    Trifolium procumbens
        Murphy, D.M. and W.H. Pierce, 1937
    Trifolium reflexum
        Murphy, D.M. and W.H. Pierce, 1937
    Trifolium suaveolens
        Murphy, D.M. and W.H. Pierce, 1937
    Trifolium subterranean
        Chaudhuri, R.P., 1950
    Trigonella foenum-graecum
        Hagedorn, D.J., 1948
    Vicia faba
        Ainsworth, G.C., 1940
        Chaudhuri, R.P., 1950
        Hagedorn, D.J., 1948
        Johnson, F. and L.K. Jones, 1936
        Osborn, H.T., 1937
        Stubbs, M.W., 1936
    Vicia faba var. major *
        Murphy, D.M. and W.H. Pierce, 1937
    Vicia faba var. minor
        Hagedorn, D.J. and J.C. Walker, 1954
        Murphy, D.M. and W.H. Pierce, 1937
        Pierce, W.H., 1935
        Stubbs, M.W., 1937
    Vicia sativa
        Chaudhuri, R.P., 1950
        Murphy, D.M. and W.H. Pierce, 1937

V. PEA MOTTLE F. Johnson 1942
    Antirrhinum majus
        Johnson, Folke, 1942
    Cucumis sativus
        Johnson, Folke, 1942
    Lathyrus latifolius
        Johnson, Folke and Leon K. Jones, 1937
    Lathyrus odoratus
        Johnson, Folke, 1942
        Johnson, Folke and Leon K. Jones, 1937
    Lens culinaris
        Johnson, F. and L.K. Jones, 1936
    Lens esculenta
        Johnson, Folke, 1942
        Johnson, Folke and Leon K. Jones, 1937
    Lupinus albus
        Johnson, Folke, 1942
    Lupinus hirsutus
        Johnson, Folke, 1942
    Medicago lupulina
        Johnson, Folke, 1942
        Johnson, Folke and Leon K. Jones, 1937
    Medicago sativa
        Johnson, Folke, 1942
        Johnson, F. and L.K. Jones, 1936, 1937
    Melilotus alba
        Johnson, Folke, 1942
        Johnson, F. and L.K. Jones, 1936
    Melilotus officinalis
        Johnson, Folke and Leon K. Jones, 1937

VIRUS
V. PEA MOTTLE (cont.)
    Pisum sativum
        Johnson, Folke, 1942
        Johnson, F. and L.K. Jones, 1936, 1937
    Phaseolus aureus
        Johnson, Folke, 1942
    Phaseolus vulgaris
        Johnson, Folke, 1942
        Johnson, F. and L.K. Jones, 1936, 1937
    Spinacia oleracea
        Johnson, Folke, 1942
    Stellaria media
        Johnson, Folke, 1942
    Trifolium hybridum
        Johnson, Folke, 1942
        Johnson, F. and L.K. Jones, 1936, 1937
    Trifolium incarnatum
        Johnson, Folke, 1942
    Trifolium pratense
        Johnson, Folke, 1942
        Johnson, F. and L.K. Jones, 1936, 1937
    Trifolium repens
        Johnson, Folke, 1942
        Johnson, F. and L.K Jones, 1936, 1937
        Zaumeyer, W.J. and B.L. Wade, 1935
    Vicia faba
        Johnson, Folke, 1942
        Johnson, F. and L.K. Jones, 1936, 1937
    Vicia sativa
        Johnson, Folke, 1942
        Johnson, F. and L.K. Jones, 1936, 1937

V. PEA STEM STREAK *
    Cucumis sativus
        Zaumeyer, W.J., 1939
    Nicotiana tabacum
        Zaumeyer, W.J., 1939
    Petunia hybrida
        Zaumeyer, W.J., 1939
    Phaseolus lunatus
        Zaumeyer, W.J., 1939
    Pisum sativum
        Zaumeyer, W.J., 1939
    Vicia faba
        Zaumeyer, W.J., 1939

V. PEA STREAK Zaumeyer and Wade 1938
    Cicer arietinum
        Zaumeyer, W.J., 1938
    Glycine max
        Kim, Woon S. and D.J. Hagedorn, 1957
        Zaumeyer, W.J., 1938
    Lathyrus hirsutus
        Hagedorn, D.J., 1948
    Lens esculenta
        Zaumeyer, W.J., 1938
    Medicago sativa
        Zaumeyer, W.J., 1938
    Melilotus alba
        Hagedorn, D.J., 1948
        Zaumeyer, W.J., 1938
    Nicotiana tabacum
        Kim, Woon S. and D.J. Hagedorn, 1957
    Phaseolus vulgaris
        Kim, Woon S. and D.J. Hagedorn, 1957
    Pisum sativum
        Kim, Woon S. and D.J. Hagedorn, 1957
        Linford, M.B., 1931
        Oshima, Nagayoshi and M.F. Kernkamp, 1957
        Zaumeyer, W.J., 1937, 1938
        Zaumeyer, W.J. and B.L. Wade, 1937
    Trifolium hybridum
        Hagedorn, D.J., 1948
    Trifolium incarnatum
        Hagedorn, D.J., 1948
        Zaumeyer, W.J., 1938
    Trifolium pratense
        Hagedorn, D.J., 1948
        Oshima, Nagayoshi and M.F. Kernkamp, 1957
        Zaumeyer, W.J., 1938
    Trifolium repens
        Zaumeyer, W.J., 1938

VIRUS
V. PEA STREAK (cont.)
Vicia faba
Zaumeyer, W.J., 1938
Vicia faba var. minor
Zaumeyer, W.J., 1938
Vicia sativa
Zaumeyer, W.J., 1938
Vigna sinensis
Kim, Woon S. and D.J. Hagedorn, 1957
Zinnia elegans
Kim, Woon S. and D.J. Hagedorn, 1957

V. PEA WILT F. Johnson 1942
Glycine max
Pierce, W.H., 1935
Lathyrus odoratus
Johnson, Folke, 1942
Lens esculenta
Johnson, Folke, 1942
Lupinus albus
Johnson, Folke, 1942
Medicago lupulina
Johnson, Folke, 1942
Melilotus alba
Johnson, Folke, 1942
Phaseolus aureus
Johnson, Folke, 1942
Phaseolus vulgaris
Johnson, Folke, 1942
Pisum sativum
Johnson, Folke, 1942
Pierce, W.H., 1935
Pisum sativum var. saccharatum
Pierce, W.H., 1935
Trifolium hybridum
Johnson, Folke, 1942
Trifolium incarnatum
Johnson, Folke, 1942
Trifolium pratense
Johnson, Folke, 1942
Trifolium repens
Johnson, Folke, 1942
Vicia faba
Johnson, Folke, 1942
Vicia faba var. minor
Pierce, W.H., 1935
Vicia sativa
Johnson, Folke, 1942
Vigna sinensis
Johnson, Folke, 1942

V. PEA YELLOW MOSAIC *
Lathyrus odoratus
Ainsworth, G.C., 1940
Pisum sativum
Ainsworth, G.C., 1940
Trifolium pratense
Ainsworth, G.C., 1940
Vicia faba
Ainsworth, G.C., 1940

V. PEACH ASTEROID SPOT Cochran and C.O. Smith
Prunus amygdalus   1938
Richards, B.L. and L.C. Cochran, 1956
Prunus armeniaca
Richards, B.L. and L.C. Cochran, 1956
Prunus avium
Richards, B.L. and L.C. Cochran, 1956
Prunus domestica
Richards, B.L. and L.C. Cochran, 1956
Prunus mume
Richards, B.L. and L.C. Cochran, 1956
Prunus persica
Clayton, C.N., 1949
Cochran, L.C. and Clayton O. Smith, 1938
Richards, B.L. and L.C. Cochran, 1956
Prunus persica var. nectarina
(K.M. Smith, 1957) R.E. Fitzpatrick, et al., 1958
Prunus salicina
Richards, B.L. and L.C. Cochran, 1956

VIRUS
V. PEACH BLOTCH Willison 1946
Prunus persica
Willison, R.S., 1946

V. PEACH CALICO Blodgett 1942
Prunus calico
Blodgett, Earle C., 1944

V. PEACH LITTLE PEACH E.F. Smith 1891 ((This virus is related to the longer known V. Peach yellows (q.v.).))
Prunus armeniaca
Manns, T.F., 1942
Prunus cerasifera
Manns, T.F., 1942
Prunus cerasifera var. pissardii
Manns, T.F., 1942
Prunus communis
Manns, T.F., 1942
Prunus domestica
Manns, T.F., 1942
Prunus insititia
Manns, T.F., 1942
Prunus munsoniana
Manns, T.F., 1942
Prunus munsoniana x Prunus salicina
Manns, T.F., 1942
Prunus persica
Cook, M.T., 1922
Kunkel, L.O., 1936, 1938
Manns, T.F., 1936, 1942
Prunus salicina
Manns, T.F., 1936, 1942
Prunus simonii
Manns, T.F., 1942

V. PEACH MOSAIC Hutchins 1932
Prunus americana
Richards, B.L. and L.C. Cochran, 1956
Prunus amygdalus
Cochran, L.C. and L.M. Hutchins, 1937, 1938
Prunus angustifolia
(K.M. Smith, 1957) R.E. Fitzpatrick, et al., 1958
Prunus armeniaca
Bodine, E.W. and L.W. Durrell, 1941
Cochran, L.C. and L.M. Hutchins, 1937, 1938
Thomas, H. Earl and T.E. Rawlins, 1939
Prunus avium x Prunus cerasus
Bodine, E.W. and L.W. Durrell, 1941
Prunus besseyi
(K.M. Smith, 1957) R.E. Fitzpatrick, et al., 1958
Prunus cerasifera
(K.M. Smith, 1957) R.E. Fitzpatrick, et al., 1958
Prunus communis
Bodine, E.W. and L.W. Durrell, 1941
Prunus davidiana (Amygdalus davidiana)
(K.M. Smith, 1957) R.E. Fitzpatrick, et al., 1958
Prunus domestica
Bodine, E.W., 1937
Bodine, E.W. and L.W. Durrell, 1941
Cochran, L.C. and L.M. Hutchins, 1937, 1938
Prunus insititia
Bodine, E.W. and L.W. Durrell, 1941
Prunus mexicana
(K.M. Smith, 1957) R.E. Fitzpatrick, et al., 1958
Prunus mume
(K.M. Smith, 1957) R.E. Fitzpatrick, et al., 1958
Prunus munsoniana
Richards, B.L. and L.C. Cochran, 1956
Prunus persica
Bennett, C.W., 1944
Bodine, E.W., 1937, 1942
Bodine, E.W. and L.W. Durrell, 1941
Cation, D., 1934
Cochran, L.C. and L.M. Hutchins, 1937, 1938
Cochran, L.C. and John L. Rue, 1944, 1946
Hutchins, L.M., 1933
Hutchins, Lee M. and L.C. Cochran, 1940
Kunkel, L.O., 1938
Richards, B.L. and L.C. Cochran, 1956
Stout, Gilbert L., 1939
Wilson, Norton S., Laurence S. Jones and L.C. Cochran, 1955

VIRUS
V. PEACH MOSAIC (cont.)
   Prunus persica var. nectarina
      (K.M. Smith, 1957) R.E. Fitzpatrick, et al., 1958
   Prunus salicina
      Bodine, E.W. and L.W. Durrell, 1941
      Richards, B.L. and L.C. Cochran, 1956
   Prunus salicina x Prunus simonii
      Bodine, E.W. and L.W. Durrell, 1941
   Prunus tangutica
      (K.M. Smith, 1957) R.E. Fitzpatrick, et al., 1958
   Prunus tomentosa
      (K.M. Smith, 1957) R.E. Fitzpatrick, et al., 1958

V. PEACH MOTTLE Blodgett 1941
   Prunus avium
      Blodgett, Earle C., 1941
   Prunus cerasus
      Blodgett, Earle C., 1941
   Prunus persica
      Blodgett, Earle C., 1941

V. PEACH NECROTIC LEAF SPOT Cation 1942
   Prunus avium
      Cation, Donald, 1942
      Richards, B.L. and L.C. Cochran, 1956
   Prunus besseyi
      Fridlund, Paul R., 1954
   Prunus besseyi x Prunus hortulana
      Fridlurnd, Paul R., 1954
   Prunus besseyi x Prunus salicina
      Fridlund, Paul R., 1954
   Prunus cerasus
      Richards, B.L. and L.C. Cochran, 1956
   Prunus persica
      Cation, Donald, 1942
      Richards, B.L. and L.C. Cochran, 1956
   Prunus persica var. nectarina
      Richards, B.L. and L.C. Cochran, 1956
   Rosa spp.
      (K.M. Smith, 1957) R.E. Fitzpatrick, et al., 1958

V. PEACH RED SUTURE Bennett 1926 ((This virus is related to the longer known V. Peach yellows (q.v.).))
   Prunus persica
      (K.M. Smith, 1957) R.E. Fitzpatrick, et al., 1958

V. PEACH RING SPOT Cochran and Hutchins 1941
   Cucumis sativus
      Boyle, J.S., J. Duain Moore and G.W. Keitt, 1949
      Fulton, Robert W., 1956
      Gilmer, R.M., 1955
      Gilmer, R.M., K.D. Brase and K.G. Parker, 1957
      Hobbs, Gordon A., 1951
      Milbrath, J.A., 1953
      Tomlinson, N., 1955
      Willison, R.S., 1951
   Cucurbita maxima
      Milbrath, J.A., 1957
   Cucurbita pepo
      Hobbs, Gordon A., 1951
   Cyamopsis tetragonaloba
      Fulton, Robert W., 1956
   Malus sylvestris
      Cochran, L.C., 1950
   Phaseolus vulgaris
      Yarwood, C.E., 1957
   Prunus alabamensis
      Gilmer, R.M., 1955
   Prunus alleghaniensis
      Gilmer, R.M., 1955
   Prunus americana
      Gilmer, R.M., 1954, 1955
      Moore, J. Duain and G.W. Keitt, 1946
   Prunus amygdalus
      Cochran, L.C. and Lee M. Hutchins, 1941
   Prunus andersoni
      Gilmer, R.M., 1955
   Prunus angustifolia
      Gilmer, R.M., 1955
   Prunus apetala
      Gilmer, R.M., 1954, 1955
   Prunus armeniaca
      Gilmer, R.M., 1954, 1955

VIRUS
V. PEACH RING SPOT (cont.)
   Prunus armeniaca
      Posnette, A.F., 1954
      Yarwood, C.E., 1957 .
   Prunus armeniaca var. mandshurica
      Gilmer, R.M., 1955
   Prunus avium
      Cation, Donald, 1952
      Cochran, L.C. and Lee M. Hutchins, 1941
      Gilmer, R.M., 1954, 1955
      Gilmer, R.M., K.D. Brase and K.G. Parker, 1957
      Hildebrand, E.M., 1944
      Milbrath, J.A., 1950
      Millikan, D.F., 1953, 1955
      Posnette, A.F., 1954
      Posnette, A.F. and R. Cropley, 1956
      Tomlinson, N., 1955
      Willison, R.S. and G.H. Berkeley, 1946
   Prunus besseyi
      Gilmer, R.M., 1954, 1955
      Moore, J. Duain and G.W. Keitt, 1946
   Prunus blirieana
      Gilmer, R.M., 1954, 1955
   Prunus bokhariensis
      Gilmer, R.M., 1955
   Prunus bucharica
      Gilmer, R.M., 1955
   Prunus campanulata
      Gilmer, R.M., 1955
   Prunus canescens
      Gilmer, R.M., 1954, 1955
   Prunus caroliniana
      Gilmer, R.M., 1954, 1955
   Prunus cerasifera
      Cochran, L.C. and Lee M. Hutchins, 1941
      Gilmer, R.M., 1954, 1955
      Posnette, A.F., 1954
      Willison, R.S. and G.H. Berkeley, 1946
   Prunus cerasifera var. pissardii
      Gilmer, R.M., 1954
   Prunus cerasoides
      Gilmer, R.M., 1955
   Prunus cerasus
      Berkeley, G.H. and R.S. Willison, 1948
      Cation, Donald, 1949, 1952
      Fink, Harry C., 1950, 1955
      Fulton, Robert W., 1956
      Gilmer, R.M., 1954, 1955
      Gilmer, R.M., K.D. Brase and K.G. Parker, 1957
      Hildebrand, E.M., 1944
      Milbrath, J.A., 1950, 1952, 1957
      Millikan, D.F. and A.D. Hibbard, 1952
      Moore, J. Duain and G.W. Keitt, 1944, 1946
      Moore, J. Duain and D.A. Slack, 1952
      Nyland, George, 1952
      Parker, K.G. and L.C. Cochran, 1951
      Posnette, A.F., 1954
      Willison, R.S. and G.H. Berkeley, 1946
   Prunus cistena *
      Gilmer, R.M., 1954, 1955
      Young, H.C., Jr., 1951
   Prunus communis
      Gilmer, R.M., 1954, 1955
   Prunus conradinae
      Gilmer, R.M., 1955
   Prunus cyclamina
      Gilmer, R.M., 1955
   Prunus dasycarpa
      Gilmer, R.M., 1955
   Prunus davidiana (Amygdalus davidiana)
      Gilmer, R.M., 1955
   Prunus demissa
      Gilmer, R.M., 1955
   Prunus dielsiana *
      Gilmer, R.M., 1955
   Prunus domestica
      Berkeley, G.H., 1947
      Berkeley, G.H. and R.S. Willison, 1948
      Gilmer, R.M., 1954, 1955
      Gilmer, R.M., K.D. Brase and K.G. Parker, 1957
      Moore, J. Duain, 1951
      Willison, R.S. and G.H. Berkeley, 1946

VIRUS
V. PEACH RING SPOT (cont.)
  Prunus dropmoreana *
    Gilmer, R.M., 1954, 1955
  Prunus dunbarii
    Gilmer, R.M., 1954, 1955
  Prunus effusa *
    Gilmer, R.M., 1955
  Prunus emarginata
    Gilmer, R.M., 1955
  Prunus fasciculata
    Gilmer, R.M., 1955
  Prunus fenzliana
    Gilmer, R.M., 1955
  Prunus fontanesiana
    Gilmer, R.M., 1955
  Prunus fremonti
    Gilmer, R.M., 1955
  Prunus fruticosa
    Gilmer, R.M., 1954, 1955
  Prunus gigantea *
    Gilmer, R.M., 1955
  Prunus glandulifolia
    Gilmer, R.M., 1955
  Prunus glandulosa
    Gilmer, R.M., 1954, 1955
  Prunus gracilis
    Gilmer, R.M., 1955
  Prunus gravesii
    Gilmer, R.M., 1955
  Prunus grayana
    Gilmer, R.M., 1955
  Prunus hillieri *
    Gilmer, R.M., 1955
  Prunus hortulana
    Gilmer, R.M., 1955
  Prunus ilicifolia
    Gilmer, R.M., 1954, 1955
  Prunus incana
    Gilmer, R.M., 1955
  Prunus incisa
    Gilmer, R.M., 1955
  Prunus insititia
    Gilmer, R.M., 1955
  Prunus jacquemontii
    Gilmer, R.M., 1955
  Prunus japonica
    Gilmer, R.M., 1954, 1955
  Prunus juddii
    Gilmer, R.M., 1955
  Prunus kansuensis
    Gilmer, R.M., 1955
  Prunus lanata
    Gilmer, R.M., 1955
  Prunus lannesiana
    Gilmer, R.M., 1955
  Prunus laucheana
    Gilmer, R.M., 1955
  Prunus laurocerasus
    Gilmer, R.M., 1954, 1955
  Prunus lobulata
    Gilmer, R.M., 1955
  Prunus lusitanica
    Gilmer, R.M., 1955
  Prunus lycioides
    Gilmer, R.M., 1955
  Prunus lyoni
    Gilmer, R.M., 1954, 1955
  Prunus maackii
    Gilmer, R.M., 1954, 1955
  Prunus mahaleb
    Berkeley, G.H. and R.S. Willison, 1948
    Cation, Donald, 1949, 1952
    Cochran, L.C. and Lee M. Hutchins, 1941
    Fink, Harry C., 1950, 1955
    Gilmer, R.M., 1954, 1955
    Milbrath, J.A., 1957
    Posnette, A.F., 1954
    Willison, R.S. and G.H. Berkeley, 1946
  Prunus maritima
    Gilmer, R.M., 1954, 1955
  Prunus maximowiczi
    Gilmer, R.M., 1955

VIRUS
V. PEACH RING SPOT (cont.)
  Prunus mexicana
    Gilmer, R.M., 1955
  Prunus meyeri
    Gilmer, R.M., 1955
  Prunus mira
    Gilmer, R.M., 1955
  Prunus monticola
    Gilmer, R.M., 1955
  Prunus mugus
    Gilmer, R.M., 1955
  Prunus mume
    Gilmer, R.M., 1955
  Prunus munsoniana
    Gilmer, R.M., 1955
  Prunus nana
    Gilmer, R.M., 1954, 1955
  Prunus newporti
    Gilmer, R.M., 1954, 1955
  Prunus nigra
    Gilmer, R.M., 1955
  Prunus nipponica
    Gilmer, R.M., 1955
  Prunus nipponica var. kurilensis
    Gilmer, R.M., 1955
  Prunus padus
    Gilmer, R.M., 1954, 1955
  Prunus padus var. cornuta
    Gilmer, R.M., 1955
  Prunus pensylvanica
    Gilmer, R.M., 1954, 1955
  Prunus persica
    Berkeley, G.H., 1947
    Berkeley, G.H. and R.S. Willison, 1948
    Cation, Donald, 1949
    Cochran, L.C., 1950, 1952
    Cochran, L.C. and Lee M. Hutchins, 1941
    Cochran, L.C. and R.L. McClain, 1951
    Fink, Harry C., 1950, 1955
    Gilmer, R.M., 1954, 1955, 1956
    Gilmer, R.M., K.D. Brase and K.G. Parker, 1957
    Hildebrand, E.M., 1944
    Moore, J. Duain and G.W. Keitt, 1944
    Posnette, A.F., 1954
    Willison, R.S. and G.H. Berkeley, 1946
    Yarwood, C.E., 1957
    Young, H.C., Jr., 1951
  Prunus petunnikowi
    Gilmer, R.M., 1955
  Prunus pilosiuscula
    Gilmer, R.M., 1955
  Prunus pleiocerasus
    Gilmer, R.M., 1955
  Prunus potanini *
    Gilmer, R.M., 1955
  Prunus pumila
    Gilmer, R.M., 1955
    Moore, J. Duain and G.W. Keitt, 1946
  Prunus reverchoni
    Gilmer, R.M., 1955
  Prunus rufa
    Gilmer, R.M., 1955
  Prunus salicina
    Gilmer, R.M., 1953, 1954, 1955
    Willison, R.S. and G.H. Berkeley, 1946
  Prunus sargenti
    Gilmer, R.M., 1955
  Prunus scopulorum
    Gilmer, R.M., 1955
  Prunus serotina
    Fink, Harry C., 1950, 1955
    Gilmer, R.M., 1954, 1955
  Prunus serrula
    Gilmer, R.M., 1955
  Prunus serrulata
    Gilmer, R.M., 1954, 1955
    Gilmer, R.M., K.D. Brase and K.G. Parker, 1957
    Milbrath, J.A., 1952
    Tomlinson, N., 1955
  Prunus setulosa
    Gilmer, R.M., 1955
  Prunus sibirica
    Gilmer, R.M., 1955

VIRUS
V. PEACH RING SPOT (cont.)
  Prunus sieboldi
    Gilmer, R.M., 1954, 1955
  Prunus simonii
    Gilmer, R.M., 1955
  Prunus skinneri
    Gilmer, R.M., 1955
  Prunus slavinii
    Gilmer, R.M., 1955
  Prunus spinosa
    Gilmer, R.M., 1955
  Prunus ssiori ·
    Gilmer, R.M., 1955
  Prunus subcordata
    Gilmer, R.M., 1955
  Prunus subhirtella
    Gilmer, R.M., 1955
  Prunus sultana
    Gilmer, R.M., 1955
  Prunus tenella (Amygdalus nana)
    Gilmer, R.M., 1954, 1955
  Prunus tomentosa
    Fink, Harry C., 1950, 1955
    Gilmer, R.M., 1954, 1955, 1956
    Gilmer, R.M., K.D. Brase and K.G. Parker, 1957
    Young, H.C., Jr., 1951
  Prunus triloba
    Gilmer, R.M., 1954, 1955
  Prunus umbellata
    Gilmer, R.M., 1955
  Prunus ursina
    Gilmer, R.M., 1955
  Prunus ussuriensis
    Gilmer, R.M., 1955
  Prunus venulosa
    Gilmer, R.M., 1955
  Prunus virginiana
    Gilmer, R.M., 1955
    Moore, J. Duain and G.W. Keitt, 1946
  Prunus virginiana var. demissa
    Gilmer, R.M., 1954
  Prunus yedoensis
    Gilmer, R.M., 1955
  Rosa multiflora
    Gilmer, R.M., 1956
  Rosa spp.
    Cochran, L.C., 1950
  Vigna sinensis
    Milbrath, J.A., 1953
    Thornberry, H.H., 1957

V. PEACH ROSETTE ((E.F. Smith 1891)) McClintock
  Prunus amygdalus   1923
    McClintock, J.A., 1923
  Prunus angustifolia
    McClintock, J.A., 1923
  Prunus armeniaca
    McClintock, J.A., 1923
  Prunus avium
    McClintock, J.A., 1923
  Prunus domestica
    McClintock, J.A., 1923, 1931
  Prunus persica
    KenKnight, Glenn, 1957
    Kunkel, L.O., 1936, 1938
    McClintock, J.A., 1923, 1931
  Prunus pumila
    McClintock, J.A., 1931

V. PEACH ROSETTE MOSAIC Cation 1933
  Prunus cerasus
    Fink, Harry C., 1955
  Prunus domestica
    Cation, Donald, 1942
  Prunus insititia
    (K.M. Smith, 1957) R.E. Fitzpatrick, et al., 1958
  Prunus persica
    Cation, Donald, 1942
    Hildebrand, E.M., 1941
  Prunus salicina
    (K.M. Smith, 1957) R.E. Fitzpatrick, et al., 1958
  Prunus tomentosa
    Fink, Harry C., 1955

VIRUS
V. PEACH STUNT *
  Cucurbita maxima
    Milbrath, J.A., 1956
  Prunus cerasus
    Milbrath, J.A., 1957

V. PEACH WART Blodgett 1943
  Prunus avium
    Zeller, S.M. and J.A. Milbrath, 1945
  Prunus persica
    Blodgett, Earle C., 1941, 1943, 1946
    Zeller, S.M. and J.A. Milbrath, 1945

V. PEACH WESTERN X DISEASE Reeves and Hutchins
  Apium graveolens var. dulce   1941
    Jensen, D.D., 1955, 1957
  Daucus carota var. sativa
    Weathers, Lewis G. and George W. Cochran, 1950
  Petroselinum crispum
    Weathers, Lewis G. and George W. Cochran, 1950
  Prunus americana var. mollis
    Schneider, Henry, 1945
  Prunus armeniaca
    Rawlins, T.E. and H. Earl Thomas, 1941
  Prunus avium
    Jensen, D.D. and H. Earl Thomas, 1954, 1955
    Kaloostian, George H., 1951
    Kaloostian, George H., Mervin W. Nielson and L.S.
    Jones, 1951
    Lott, T.B., 1950
    Rawlins, T.E., 1939
    Rawlins, T.E. and W.T. Horne, 1931
    Rawlins, T.E. and K.G. Parker, 1934
    Rawlins, T.E. and H. Earl Thomas, 1941
    Richards, B.L., L.M. Hutchins and E.L. Reeves,
    1949
    Richards, B.L., E.L. Reeves and Lee M.
    Hutchins, 1946
    Schneider, Henry, 1945
    Thomas, H. Earl, 1940
    Thomas, H. Earl and T.E. Rawlins, 1941
    Wadley, Bryce N., 1952
    Wilks, Jack M. and J.A. Milbrath, 1956
    Zeller, S.M. and J.A. Milbrath, 1948, 1950
  Prunus avium on Prunus avium
    Richards, B.L. and L.C. Cochran, 1956
  Prunus avium on Prunus mahaleb
    Richards, B.L. and L.C. Cochran, 1956
  Prunus besseyi
    Richards, B.L. and L.C. Cochran, 1956
  Prunus cerasus
    Kaloostian, George H., 1951
    Nielson, Mervin W. and Laurence S. Jones, 1954
    Rawlins, T.E. and K.G. Parker, 1934
    Rawlins, T.E. and H. Earl Thomas, 1941
    Richards, B.L., L.M. Hutchins and E.L. Reeves,
    1949
    Richards, B.L., E.L. Reeves and Lee M. Hutchins,
    1946
    Schneider, Henry, 1945
    Wilks, Jack M. and J.A. Milbrath, 1956
    Zeller, S.M. and J.A. Milbrath, 1948, 1950
  Prunus cerasus on Prunus avium
    Richards, B.L. and L.C. Cochran, 1956
  Prunus cerasus on Prunus mahaleb
    Richards, B.L. and L.C. Cochran, 1956
  Prunus communis
    Rawlins, T.E. and H. Earl Thomas, 1941
  Prunus communis x Prunus fenzliana
    Rawlins, T.E. and H. Earl Thomas, 1941
  Prunus davidiana (Amygdalus davidiana)
    Rawlins, T.E. and H. Earl Thomas, 1941
  Prunus davidiana x Prunus communis
    Rawlins, T.E. and H. Earl Thomas, 1941
  Prunus demissa
    Richards, B.L. and Lee M. Hutchins, 1941
    Richards, B.L., L.M. Hutchins and E.L. Reeves,
    1949
    Wilks, Jack M. and J.A. Milbrath, 1956
    Zeller, S.M. and J.A. Milbrath, 1950
  Prunus fenzliana
    Rawlins, T.E. and H. Earl Thomas, 1941

VIRUS

V. PEACH WESTERN X DISEASE (cont.)

Prunus mahaleb
Rawlins, T.E. and H. Earl Thomas, 1941
Schneider, Henry, 1945

Prunus mira
Rawlins, T.E. and H. Earl Thomas, 1941

Prunus mira x Prunus persica
Rawlins, T.E. and H. Earl Thomas, 1941

Prunus persica
Jensen, D.D., 1953, 1955, 1957
Jensen, D.D. and H. Earl Thomas, 1954, 1955
Kaloostian, George H., 1951
Keener, Paul D., 1953
Nielson, Mervin W. and Laurence S. Jones, 1954
Nyland, George, 1955
Nyland, George and Archie Schlocker, 1951
Rawlins, T.E. and H. Earl Thomas, 1941
Richards, B.L. and L.C. Cochran, 1956
Richards, B.L. and Lee M. Hutchins, 1941
Richards, B.L., L.M. Hutchins and E.L. Reeves, 1949
Schneider, Henry, 1945
Thomas, H. Earl, 1940
Thomas, H. Earl and T.E. Rawlins, 1941
Thomas, H. Earl, T.E. Rawlins and K.G. Parker, 1940
Wadley, Bryce N., 1952
Weathers, Lewis G. and George W. Cochran, 1950
Wilks, Jack M. and J.A. Milbrath, 1956
Wolfe, H.R., 1955
Wolfe, H.R., E.W. Anthon and L.S. Jones, 1950
Zeller, S.M. and J.A. Milbrath, 1948, 1950

Prunus persica var. nectarina
Richards, B.L. and L.C. Cochran, 1956

Prunus tomentosa
Richards, B.L. and L.C. Cochran, 1956

Prunus virginiana
Rawlins, T.E. and H. Earl Thomas, 1941
Richards, B.L. and L.C. Cochran, 1956
Richards, B.L., L.M. Hutchins and E.L. Reeves, 1949
Richards, B.L., E.L. Reeves and Lee M. Hutchins, 1946
Zeller, S.M. and J.A. Milbrath, 1948

Prunus virginiana var. demissa
Kaloostian, George H., 1951
Richards, B.L. and L.C. Cochran, 1956

Vinca minor
Weathers, Lewis G. and George W. Cochran, 1950

V. PEACH X DISEASE Stoddard 1938

Datura stramonium
Slack, Derald A., 1952

Daucus carota var. sativa
Kunkel, L.O., 1944
Slack, Derald A., 1952

Fragaria vesca
Slack, Derald A., 1952

Lycopersicon esculentum
Hildebrand, E.M., 1953
Kunkel, L.O., 1944

Petroselinum crispum
Kunkel, L.O., 1944
Slack, Derald A., 1952

Prunus americana
Gilmer, R.M., J. Duain Moore and G.W. Keitt, 1954
Hildebrand, E.M., 1953

Prunus amygdalus
Palmiter, D.H. and E.M. Hildebrand, 1943

Prunus armeniaca
Palmiter, D.H. and E.M. Hildebrand, 1943

Prunus armeniaca var. mandshurica
Hildebrand, E.M., 1953

Prunus avium
(K.M. Smith, 1957) R.E. Fitzpatrick, et al., 1958
Gilmer, R.M., J. Duain Moore and G.W. Keitt, 1954

Prunus besseyi
Fridlund, Paul R., 1954
Gilmer, R.M., J. Duain Moore and G.W. Keitt, 1954
Hildebrand, E.M., 1943, 1953

VIRUS

V. PEACH X DISEASE (cont.)

Prunus cerasus
Fridlund, Paul R., 1954
Gilmer, R.M., J. Duain Moore and G.W. Keitt, 1954
Hildebrand, E.M., 1953
Palmiter, D.H. and K.G. Parker, 1948
Parker, K.G. and D.H. Palmiter, 1948

Prunus communis
Hildebrand, E.M., 1953

Prunus demissa var. melanocarpa
Hildebrand, E.M., 1953

Prunus domestica
(K.M. Smith, 1957) R.E. Fitzpatrick, et al., 1958
Gilmer, R.M., 1951
Gilmer, R.M., J. Duain Moore and G.W. Keitt, 1954

Prunus dunbarii
(K.M. Smith, 1957) R.E. Fitzpatrick, et al., 1958
Gilmer, R.M., 1951
Gilmer, R.M., J. Duain Moore and G.W. Keitt, 1954

Prunus glandulosa
(K.M. Smith, 1957) R.E. Fitzpatrick, et al., 1958
Gilmer, R.M., 1951
Gilmer, R.M., J. Duain Moore and G.W. Keitt, 1954

Prunus hortulana
Hildebrand, E.M., 1953

Prunus japonica
Fridlund, Paul R., 1954
Gilmer, R.M., J. Duain Moore and G.W. Keitt, 1954
Hildebrand, E.M., 1953

Prunus lannesiana
Gilmer, R.M., J. Duain Moore and G.W. Keitt, 1954

Prunus maackii
Gilmer, R.M., 1951
Gilmer, R.M., J. Duain Moore and G.W. Keitt, 1954

Prunus mahaleb
Gilmer, R.M., J. Duain Moore and G.W. Keitt, 1954

Prunus makii *
(K.M. Smith, 1957) R.E. Fitzpatrick, et al., 1958

Prunus maritima
Gilmer, R.M., 1951
Gilmer, R.M., J. Duain Moore and G.W. Keitt, 1954

Prunus munsoniana
(K.M. Smith, 1957) R.E. Fitzpatrick, et al., 1958

Prunus newporti
Gilmer, R.M., J. Duain Moore and G.W. Keitt, 1954

Prunus padus
(K.M. Smith, 1957) R.E. Fitzpatrick, et al., 1958
Gilmer, R.M., 1951
Gilmer, R.M., J. Duain Moore and G.W. Keitt, 1954

Prunus pensylvanica
(K.M. Smith, 1957) R.E. Fitzpatrick, et al., 1958
Gilmer, R.M., 1951
Gilmer, R.M., J. Duain Moore and G.W. Keitt, 1954

Prunus persica
Fridlund, Paul R., 1954
Gilmer, R.M., J. Duain Moore and G.W. Keitt, 1954
Hildebrand, E.M., 1943, 1953
Hildebrand, E.M. and D.H. Palmiter, 1940
Kunkel, L.O., 1944
Palmiter, D.H. and E.M. Hildebrand, 1943
Palmiter, D.H. and K.G. Parker, 1948
Parker, K.G. and D.H. Palmiter, 1948
Slack, Derald A., 1952
Stoddard, E.M., 1938, 1947
Thornberry, H.H., 1954

Prunus persica var. nectarina
Palmiter, D.H. and E.M. Hildebrand, 1943

Prunus persica var. nucipersica
Hildebrand, E.M., 1953

VIRUS

V. PEACH X DISEASE (cont.)

Prunus pumila
Gilmer, R.M., 1951
Gilmer, R.M., J. Duain Moore and G.W. Keitt, 1954
Slack, Derald A., 1952

Prunus salicina
Gilmer, R.M., J. Duain Moore and G.W. Keitt, 1954

Prunus serotina
Hildebrand, E.M., 1953

Prunus serrulata
Gilmer, R.M., J. Duain Moore and G.W. Keitt, 1954

Prunus sieboldi
Gilmer, R.M., J. Duain Moore and G.W. Keitt, 1954

Prunus spinosa
Gilmer, R.M., J. Duain Moore and G.W. Keitt, 1954

Prunus tomentosa
(K.M. Smith, 1957) R.E. Fitzpatrick, et al., 1958
Gilmer, R.M., 1951
Gilmer, R.M., J. Duain Moore and G.W. Keitt, 1954

Prunus virginiana
Fridlund, Paul R., 1954
Gilmer, R.M., 1951, 1954
Gilmer, R.M., J. Duain Moore and G.W. Keitt, 1954
Hildebrand, E.M., 1953
Hildebrand, E.M. and D.H. Palmiter, 1940
Palmiter, D.H. and E.M. Hildebrand, 1943
Palmiter, D.H. and K.G. Parker, 1948
Parker, K.G. and D.H. Palmiter, 1948
Stoddard, E.M., 1947
Thornberry, H.H., 1946, 1954

Vinca minor
Kunkel, L.O., 1944
Slack, Derald A., 1952

Vinca rosea
(K.M. Smith, 1957) R.E. Fitzpatrick, et al., 1958

V. PEACH YELLOW BUD MOSAIC Thomas et al. 1944

Cucumis sativus
Yarwood, C.E., 1956

Cyamopsis tetragonoloba
Yarwood, C.E., 1956

Erodium cicutarium
Karle, Harry P., 1957

Kerria japonica
Thomas, H. Earl and T.E. Rawlins, 1939

Lactuca virosa
Karle, Harry P., 1957

Nicotiana tabacum
Karle, Harry P., 1957
Yarwood, C.E., 1956

Phaseolus vulgaris
Karle, Harry P., 1957
Yarwood, C.E., 1956
Yarwood, C.E. and H.E. Thomas, 1954

Prunus amygdalus
Thomas, H. Earl, 1940
Thomas, H. Earl, C. Emlen Scott, E.E. Wilson and J.H. Freitag, 1944

Prunus andersoni
Thomas, H. Earl, 1940
Thomas, H. Earl and T.E. Rawlins, 1939

Prunus armeniaca
Schlocker, Archie, H. Keith Wagnon and James R. Breece, 1957
Thomas, H. Earl and T.E. Rawlins, 1939
Thomas, H. Earl, C. Emlen Scott, E.E. Wilson and J.H. Freitag, 1944

Prunus avium
Thomas, H. Earl, 1940
Thomas, H. Earl and T.E. Rawlins, 1939

Prunus communis
Thomas, H. Earl and T.E. Rawlins, 1939

Prunus lusitanica
Thomas, H. Earl, 1940

Prunus mume
Thomas, H. Earl and T.E. Rawlins, 1939

VIRUS

V. PEACH YELLOW BUD MOSAIC (cont.)

Prunus persica
Alcorn, Stanley M., Stephen Wilhelm and H. Earl Thomas, 1955
Schlocker, Archie, H. Keith Wagnon and James R. Breece, 1957
Thomas, H. Earl, 1940
Thomas, H. Earl and T.E. Rawlins, 1939
Thomas, H. Earl, C. Emlen Scott, E.E. Wilson and J.H. Freitag, 1944
Wagnon, H. Keith and James R. Breece, 1955
Yarwood, C.E., 1956, 1957
Yarwood, C.E. and H.E. Thomas, 1954

Prunus salicina x Prunus simonii
Schlocker, Archie, H. Keith Wagnon and James R. Breece, 1957

Prunus tomentosa
Schlocker, Archie, H. Keith Wagnon and James R. Breece, 1957

Rosa odorata
Thomas, H. Earl and L.M. Massey, 1939

Rosa spp.
Thomas, H. Earl and L.M. Massey, 1939
Thomas, H. Earl and T.E. Rawlins, 1939

Rubus idaeus
Alcorn, Stanley M., Stephen Wilhelm and H. Earl Thomas, 1955

Rubus procerus
Alcorn, Stanley M., Stephen Wilhelm and H. Earl Thomas, 1955

Rubus spp.
Alcorn, Stanley M., Stephen Wilhelm and H. Earl Thomas, 1955

Rubus ursinus
Alcorn, Stanley M., Stephen Wilhelm and H. Earl Thomas, 1955

Stellaria media
Karle, Harry P., 1957

Vigna sinensis
Karle, Harry P., 1957
Yarwood, C.E., 1956, 1957
Yarwood, C.E. and H.E. Thomas, 1954

V. PEACH YELLOWS ((E.F. Smith 1888)) Kunkel 1933

Prunus armeniaca
Manns, T.F., 1942

Prunus cerasifera
Manns, T.F., 1942

Prunus cerasifera var. pissardii
Manns, T.F., 1942

Prunus communis
Manns, T.F., 1942

Prunus domestica
Manns, T.F., 1942

Prunus insititia
Manns, T.F., 1942

Prunus munsoniana
Manns, T.F., 1942

Prunus munsoniana x Prunus salicina
Manns, T.F., 1942

Prunus persica
Blake, M.A., Mel. T. Cook and C.H. Connors, 1921
Cook, M.T., 1922
Kunkel, L.O., 1936, 1938
Manns, T.F., 1936, 1942

Prunus persica var. nectarina
(K.M. Smith, 1957) R.E. Fitzpatrick, et al., 1958

Prunus salicina
Manns, T.F., 1936, 1942

Prunus simonii
Manns, T.F., 1942

V. PEAR MOSAIC Khristov 1935

Cydonia oblonga
Posnette, A.F., 1957

Pyrus communis
Posnette, A.F., 1957

V. PEAR RED MOTTLE *

Cydonia oblonga
Posnette, A.F., 1957

Pyrus communis
Posnette, A.F., 1957

VIRUS
V. PEAR STONY PIT Kienholz 1939
   Pyrus communis
      Kienholz, J.R., 1939

V. PEAR VEIN YELLOWS *
   Pyrus communis
      Posnette, A.F., 1957

V. (PECAN) BUNCH *
   Carya illinoensis
      Cole, J.R., 1937
   (Hicoria) aquatica
      Cole, J.R., 1937

V. PELARGONIUM LEAF CURL Pape 1927
   Antirrhinum majus
      McWhorter, Frank P., 1957
   Chenopodium amaranticolor
      Hollings, M., 1956
   Pelargonium hederaceum *
      (K.M. Smith, 1957) R.E. Fitzpatrick, et al., 1958
   Pelargonium hortorum
      (K.M. Smith, 1957) R.E. Fitzpatrick, et al., 1958
      Jones, L.K., 1938, 1940
   Pelargonium spp.
      McWhorter, Frank P., 1957

V. PELARGONIUM MOSAIC Jones 1940
   Pelargonium hortorum
      Jones, L.K., 1938, 1940

V. PELARGONIUM RING SPOT *
   Pelargonium hortorum
      Hollings, M., 1957
   Pelargonium peltatum
      Hollings, M., 1957

V. PEONY LEAF CURL *
   Paeonia officinalis
      Brierley, Philip and Paul Lorentz, 1957

V. PEONY RING SPOT Dufrenoy 1934; Green 1935
   Paeonia spp.
      (K.M. Smith, 1957) R.E. Fitzpatrick, et al., 1958

V. PETUNIA MOSAIC Johnson 1926
   Lycopersicon esculentum
      Johnson, J., 1926, 1927
   Nicotiana glauca
      Johnson, J., 1926, 1927
   Nicotiana glutinosa
      Johnson, J., 1926, 1927
   Nicotiana rustica
      Johnson, J., 1926, 1927
   Nicotiana tabacum
      Johnson, J., 1926, 1927
   Petunia violacea
      Johnson, J., 1926, 1927
   Physalis pubescens
      Johnson, J., 1926, 1927
   Phytolacca decandra
      Johnson, J., 1926, 1927
   Solanum nigrum
      Johnson, J., 1926

V. PHORMIUM YELLOW LEAF Boyce et al. 1951
   Phormium tenax
      Boyce, W.R., 1958

V. PHYSALIS FLORIDANA YELLOW NET Webb 1955
   Datura stramonium
      Webb, R.E., 1955
   Physalis angulata
      Webb, R.E., 1955
   Physalis floridana
      Webb, R.E., 1955

V. PHYSALIS HETEROPHYLLA MOSAIC *
   Physalis heterophylla
      Walker, M.N., 1925
   Physalis pubescens
      Walker, M.N., 1925

VIRUS
V. (PHYSALIS LONGIFOLIA) MOSAIC *
   Physalis longifolia
      Melhus, I.E., 1922

V. (PHYSALIS) MOSAIC *
   Capsicum frutescens (Capsicum annuum)
      Melhus, I.E., 1922
   Cucumis sativus
      Walker, M.N., 1925, 1926
   Lycopersicon esculentum
      Melhus, I.E., 1922
      Walker, M.N., 1926
   Nicandra physalodes
      Fernow, K.H., 1923
   Petunia hybrida
      Melhus, I.E., 1922
   Physalis pubescens
      Walker, M.N., 1926
   Solanum melongena
      Melhus, I.E., 1922
   Solanum tuberosum
      Melhus, I.E., 1922

V. PHYSALIS PUBESCENS MOSAIC *
   Nicotiana glutinosa
      Walker, M.N., 1925

V. PHYSALIS SUBGLABRATA MOSAIC *
   Cucumis sativus
      Walker, M.N., 1925
   Physalis pubescens
      Walker, M.N., 1925
   Physalis subglabrata
      Walker, M.N., 1925

V. PIGEON PEA STERILITY MOSAIC Capoor 1952
   Cajanus cajan
      Capoor, S.P., 1952

V. PLANTAGO MOSAIC Gol'din 1953 ((Distinct from
V. Tobacco mosaic.))
   Nicotiana tabacum
      McKinney, H.H., 1943

V. PLUM BARK SPLIT Posnette 1953
   Prunus cerasifera
      Posnette, A.F. and Christina E. Ellenberger, 1957
   Prunus domestica
      Posnette, A.F. and Christina E. Ellenberger, 1957

V. PLUM FRUIT CRINKLE *
   Prunus spp.
      Chamberlain, E.E., J.D. Atkinson and J.A.
      Hunter, 1959

V. PLUM LINE PATTERN Cation 1941 ((May be identi-
cal with V. Apple mosaic Gilmer 1956.))
   Prunus armeniaca
      Bodine, E.W. and L.W. Durrell, 1941
      Willison, R.S., 1945
   Prunus avium
      Gilmer, R.M., K.D. Brase and K.G. Parker, 1957
      Richards, B.L. and L.C. Cochran, 1956
      Willison, R.S., 1945
      Zeller, S.M. and J.A. Milbrath, 1942
   Prunus cerasifera
      Cochran, L.C. and L.M. Hutchins, 1937
      Gilmer, R.M., K.D. Brase and K.G. Parker, 1957
      Richards, B.L. and L.C. Cochran, 1956
      Thomas, H. Earl and T.E. Rawlins, 1939
      Willison, R.S., 1945
   Prunus cerasus
      Gilmer, R.M., K.D. Brase and K.G. Parker, 1957
      Richards, B.L. and L.C. Cochran, 1956
      Willison, R.S., 1945
   Prunus domestica
      Bodine, E.W. and L.W. Durrell, 1941
      Cochran, L.C. and L.M. Hutchins, 1937, 1938
      Gilmer, R.M., K.D. Brase and K.G. Parker, 1957
      Moore, J. Duain and H.R. Cameron, 1956
      Willison, R.S., 1945
   Prunus hybrid
      Richards, B.L. and L.C. Cochran, 1956

VIRUS

V. PLUM LINE PATTERN (cont.)
Prunus mahaleb
Cation, Donald, 1941
Willison, R.S., 1945
Prunus persica (Amygdalus persica)
Cation, Donald, 1941
Cochran, L.C. and L.M. Hutchins, 1937, 1938
Richards, B.L. and L.C. Cochran, 1956
Willison, R.S., 1945
Prunus salicina
Bodine, E.W. and L.W. Durrell, 1941
Cation, Donald, 1941
Gilmer, R.M., K.D. Brase and K.G. Parker, 1957
Willison, R.S., 1945
Prunus serrulata
Richards, B.L. and L.C. Cochran, 1956
Zeller, S.M. and J.A. Milbrath, 1942

V. PLUM WHITE SPOT Thomas and Rawlins 1951
Prunus americana x Prunus salicina
Valleau, W.D., 1932
Prunus domestica
Valleau, W.D., 1932
Prunus persica
Thomas, H. Earl and T.E. Rawlins, 1939
Valleau, W.D., 1932
Prunus salicina
Thomas, H. Earl and T.E. Rawlins, 1939
Valleau, W.D., 1932

V. POISON HEMLOCK RING SPOT Freitag and Severin
Anethum graveolens   1945
Freitag, Julius H. and Henry H.P. Severin, 1945
Anthriscus cerefolium
Freitag, Julius H. and Henry H.P. Severin, 1945
Apium graveolens var. dulce
Freitag, Julius H. and Henry H.P. Severin, 1939,
1945
Apium graveolens var. rapaceum
Freitag, Julius H. and Henry H.P. Severin, 1945
Conium maculatum
Freitag, Julius H. and Henry H.P. Severin, 1945
Coriandrum sativum
Freitag, Julius H. and Henry H.P. Severin, 1945
Daucus carota var. sativa
Freitag, Julius H. and Henry H.P. Severin, 1945
Pastinaca sativa
Freitag, Julius H. and Henry H.P. Severin, 1945
Petroselinum crispum
Freitag, Julius H. and Henry H.P. Severin, 1939,
1945
Petroselinum crispum var. latifolium *
Freitag, Julius H. and Henry H.P. Severin, 1945
Petroselinum hortense var. radicosum *
Freitag, Julius H. and Henry H.P. Severin, 1945

V. POKEWEED MOSAIC *
Physalis pubescens
Walker, M.N., 1924, 1925
Phytolacca decandra
Allard, H.A., 1918
Fernow, Karl Hermann, 1925

V. PHONY PEACH ((Neal 1921)) Hutchins 1930
Prunus amygdalus
(K.M. Smith, 1957) R.E. Fitzpatrick, et al., 1958
Prunus angustifolia
Bruer, H.L. and C.E. Shepard, 1952
Bruer, H.L., C.E. Shepard and T.D. Persons,
1951
Cochran, L.C., J.H. Weinberger and W.F. Turner,
1951
Hutchins, Lee M., L.C. Cochran, W.F. Turner
and J.H. Weinberger, 1953
Hutchins, Lee M. and John L. Rue, 1949
KenKnight, Glenn, H.L. Bruer and C.E. Shepard,
1951
Prunus armeniaca
Hutchins, Lee M. and John L. Rue, 1949
Prunus davidiana (Amygdalus davidiana)
(K.M. Smith, 1957) R.E. Fitzpatrick, et al., 1958
Prunus hortulana
Hutchins, Lee M., L.C. Cochran, W.F. Turner
and J.H. Weinberger, 1953

VIRUS

V. PHONY PEACH (cont.)
Prunus hortulana
Hutchins, Lee M. and John L. Rue, 1949
Prunus mexicana
Hutchins, Lee M., L.C. Cochran, W.F. Turner
and J.H. Weinberger, 1953
Hutchins, Lee M. and John L. Rue, 1949
Prunus mume
Hutchins, Lee M. and John L. Rue, 1949
Prunus munsoniana
Bruer, H.L. and C.E. Shepard, 1952
Prunus persica
Hutchins, L.M., 1929, 1939
Hutchins, Lee M., L.C. Cochran, W.F. Turner
and J.H. Weinberger, 1953
Hutchins, Lee M. and John L. Rue, 1949
KenKnight, Glenn, 1957
Prunus persica var. nectarina
(K.M. Smith, 1957) R.E. Fitzpatrick, et al., 1958
Prunus umbellata
Bruer, H.L. and C.E. Shepard, 1952
Bruer, H.L., C.E. Shepard and T.D. Persons,
1951
Prunus umbellata var. injucunda
Bruer, H.L. and C.E. Shepard, 1952
Bruer, H.L., C.E. Shepard and T.D. Persons,
1951

V. POTATO A Murphy and McKay 1932
Lycium barbarum
MacLachlan, D.S. and R.H. Larson, 1953
MacLachlan, D.S., R.H. Larson and J.C. Walker,
1953
Lycium halimifolium
MacLachlan, D.S. and R.H. Larson, 1953
MacLachlan, D.S., R.H. Larson and J.C. Walker,
1953
Lycium rhombifolium
MacLachlan, D.S. and R.H. Larson, 1953
MacLachlan, D.S., R.H. Larson and J.C. Walker,
1953
Lycopersicon esculentum
Doolittle, S.P., 1928
Jarrett, Phyllis H., 1930
Krantz, F.A. and G.R. Bisby, 1921
Quanjer, H.M., 1920
Schultz, E.S. and Donald Folsom, 1923
Smith, J. Henderson, 1928
Stover, W.G., 1928
Lycopersicon pimpinellifolium
MacLachlan, D.S. and R.H. Larson, 1953
MacLachlan, D.S., R.H. Larson and J.C. Walker,
1953
Nicandra physalodes
Bagnall, R.H., R.H. Larson and J.C. Walker,
1956
MacLachlan, D.S. and R.H. Larson, 1953
MacLachlan, D.S., R.H. Larson and J.C. Walker,
1953
Nicotiana glutinosa
Vasudeva, R. Sahai and C.S. Ramamoorthy, 1946
Nicotiana sylvestris
Bagnall, R.H., R.H. Larson and J.C. Walker,
1956
Dykstra, T.P., 1939
MacLachlan, D.S., R.H. Larson and J.C. Walker,
1953
Nicotiana tabacum
Bagnall, R.H., R.H. Larson and J.C. Walker,
1956
Bawden, F.C., 1936
Bawden, F.C. and F.M.L. Sheffield, 1944
Dykstra, T.P., 1936, 1939
Dykstra, T.P. and W.C. Whitaker, 1938
MacLachlan, D.S., R.H. Larson and J.C. Walker,
1953
Valleau, W.D. and E.M. Johnson, 1930
Vasudeva, R. Sahai and C.S. Ramamoorthy, 1946
Petunia hybrida
MacLachlan, D.S., R.H. Larson and J.C. Walker,
1953
Solanum demissum
MacLachlan, D.S., R.H. Larson and J.C. Walker,
1953

VIRUS
V. POTATO A (cont.)
  Solanum demissum x Solanum tuberosum var. aquila *
    Raymer, W.B. and J.A. Milbrath, 1957
  Solanum nigrum
    Schultz, E.S. and Donald Folsom, 1923
  Solanum tuberosum
    Abbott, E.V., 1929
    Bawden, F.C., 1936
    Cockerham, George, 1943
    Dykstra, T.P., 1935, 1936, 1939
    Dykstra, T.P. and W.C. Whitaker, 1938
    Goss, R.W., 1929
    Hoggan, Isme A., 1927
    Johnson, James, 1929
    Koch, Karl and James Johnson, 1935
    MacLachlan, D.S. and R.H. Larson, 1953
    MacLachlan, D.S., R.H. Larson and J.C. Walker, 1953
    McKay, M.B. and T.P. Dykstra, 1932
    Peterson, Paul D. and H.H. McKinney, 1938
    Porter, D.R., 1935
    Schultz, E.S., C.F. Clark, R. Bonde, W.P. Raleigh and F.J. Stevenson, 1934
    Schultz, E.S., C.F. Clark, W.P. Raleigh, F.J. Stevenson, R. Bonde and J.H. Beaumont, 1937
    Schultz, E.S., C.F. Clark and F.J. Stevenson, 1940
    Schultz, E.S. and Donald Folsom, 1923, 1925
    Schultz, E.S. and W.P. Raleigh, 1936
    Valleau, W.D. and E.M. Johnson, 1930
    Vasudeva, R. Sahai and C.S. Ramamoorthy, 1946
    Young, P.A., 1930
    Young, P.A. and H.E. Morris, 1930

V. POTATO ANECROTIC MOSAIC *
  Solanum tuberosum
    Quanjer, H.M., 1931

V. POTATO AUCUBA MOSAIC Quanjer 1931
  Capsicum frutescens (Capsicum annuum)
    Bagnall, R.H., R.H. Larson and J.C. Walker, 1956
    Dennis, R.W.G., 1939
  Chenopodium amaranticolor
    Hollings, M., 1957
  Datura stramonium
    Bagnall, R.H., R.H. Larson and J.C. Walker, 1956
    Dennis, R.W.G., 1939
  Datura stramonium var. tatula
    Bagnall, R.H., R.H. Larson and J.C. Walker, 1956
  Lycopersicon esculentum
    (K.M. Smith, 1957) R.E. Fitzpatrick, et al., 1958
  Nicotiana glutinosa
    Bagnall, R.H., R.H. Larson and J.C. Walker, 1956
    Black, L.M. and W.C. Price, 1940
    Dykstra, T.P., 1939
  Nicotiana sylvestris
    Dykstra, T.P., 1939
  Nicotiana tabacum
    Bagnall, R.H., R.H. Larson and J.C. Walker, 1956
    Black, L.M. and W.C. Price, 1940
    Dennis, R.W.G., 1939
    Dykstra, T.P., 1939
  Petunia spp.
    (K.M. Smith, 1957) R.E. Fitzpatrick, et al., 1958
  Physalis peruviana
    Holmes, Francis O., 1942
  Solanum nodiflorum
    (K.M. Smith, 1957) R.E. Fitzpatrick, et al., 1958
  Solanum tuberosum
    Atanasoff, D., 1926
    Dennis, R.W.G., 1939
    Dykstra, T.P., 1939
    Quanjer, H.M., 1931

V. POTATO BUNCH TOP DISEASE *
  Lycopersicon esculentum
    Menzies, J.D., 1950

VIRUS
V. (POTATO) GIANT HILL *
  Solanum tuberosum
    Porter, D.R., 1935

V. POTATO LEAF ROLL Appell 1907
  Amaranthus graecizans
    (K.M. Smith, 1957) R.E. Fitzpatrick, et al., 1958
  Amaranthus retroflexus
    (K.M. Smith, 1957) R.E. Fitzpatrick, et al., 1958
  Capsicum frutescens (Capsicum annuum)
    Dykstra, T.P., 1930
  Celosia argentea var. cristata
    (K.M. Smith, 1957) R.E. Fitzpatrick, et al., 1958
  Datura aegyptiaca
    Webb, R.E., R.H. Larson and J.C. Walker, 1952
  Datura chlorantha
    Webb, R.E., R.H. Larson and J.C. Walker, 1952
  Datura fastuosa
    Webb, R.E., R.H. Larson and J.C. Walker, 1952
  Datura metel
    Webb, R.E., R.H. Larson and J.C. Walker, 1952
  Datura stramonium
    Dykstra, T.P., 1930, 1933
    Kassanis, B., 1952
    Kirkpatrick, Hugh C. and A. Frank Ross, 1952
    Webb, R.E., 1956
    Williams, W. Llewelyn and A. Frank Ross, 1957
  Datura stramonium var. tatula
    Dykstra, T.P., 1930, 1933
    Kassanis, B., 1952
    Webb, R.E., R.H. Larson and J.C. Walker, 1952
  Gomphrena globosa
    (K.M. Smith, 1957) R.E. Fitzpatrick, et al., 1958
  Lycopersicon esculentum
    Burnett, Grover and Leon K. Jones, 1931
    Dykstra, T.P., 1930, 1933
    MacCarthy, H.R., 1954
    Natti, John J., 1953
    Stover, W.G., 1928
  Lycopersicon pimpinellifolium
    MacCarthy, H.R., 1954
  Nicandra physalodes
    Webb, R.E., R.H. Larson and J.C. Walker, 1952
  Nicotiana glutinosa
    Webb, R.E., R.H. Larson and J.C. Walker, 1952
  Nicotiana rustica
    Webb, R.E., R.H. Larson and J.C. Walker, 1952
  Nicotiana tabacum
    Webb, R.E., R.H. Larson and J.C. Walker, 1952
  Nolana lanceolata
    (K.M. Smith, 1957) R.E. Fitzpatrick, et al., 1958
  Petunia hybrida
    Webb, R.E., R.H. Larson and J.C. Walker, 1952
  Physalis angulata
    Hovey, Charles and Reiner Bonde, 1948
    Kirkpatrick, Hugh C. and A. Frank Ross, 1952
    Klostermeyer, E.C., 1953
    MacCarthy, H.R., 1954
    Webb, R.E., R.H. Larson and J.C. Walker, 1952
    Williams, W. Llewelyn and A. Frank Ross, 1957
  Physalis floridana
    Kirkpatrick, Hugh C. and A. Frank Ross, 1952
    Klostermeyer, E.C., 1953
    MacCarthy, H.R., 1954
    Webb, R.E. and R.H. Larson, 1952
    Webb, R.E., R.H. Larson and J.C. Walker, 1952
    Webb, R.E. and E.S. Schultz, 1954
    Williams, W. Llewelyn and A. Frank Ross, 1957
  Physalis philadelphica
    MacCarthy, H.R., 1954
  Solanum dulcamara
    Dykstra, T.P., 1930, 1933
  Solanum nigrum
    Dykstra, T.P., 1930
    Webb, R.E., R.H. Larson and J.C. Walker, 1952
  Solanum nigrum var. villosum
    Dykstra, T.P., 1933
  Solanum tuberosum
    Abbott, E.V., 1929
    Artschwager, Ernest F., 1918
    Atanasoff, D., 1924
    Bald, J.G. and E.M. Hutton, 1950
    Barton-Wright, Eustace and Alan McBain, 1933

VIRUS
V. POTATO LEAF ROLL (cont.)
Solanum tuberosum
Bawden, F.C. and B. Kassanis, 1946
Broadbent, L., 1946
Broadbent, L., R.P. Chaudhuri and L. Kapica, 1950
Broadbent, L. and T.W. Tinsley, 1951
Davidson, T.R., 1955
Davidson, T.R. and G.B. Sanford, 1955
Dennis, R.W.G., 1939
Dykstra, T.P., 1933
Dykstra, T.P. and W.C. Whitaker, 1938
Elze, D.L., 1931
Folsom, Donald, 1921
Gardner, Max W. and James B. Kendrick, 1924
Gilbert, Alfred H., 1923, 1928
Gilbert, G.H., 1929
Goss, R.W., 1929
Hoggan, Isme A., 1927
Jones, Leon K., 1944
Kassanis, B., 1952
Kendrick, James B., Sr., 1952
Kirkpatrick, Hugh C. and A. Frank Ross, 1952
Klostermeyer, E.C., 1953
Koch, Karl and James Johnson, 1935
Link, G.K.K., 1923
Locke, Seth Barton, 1947
MacCarthy, H.R., 1954
McKay, M.B. and T.P. Dykstra, 1932
Porter, D.R., 1935
Quanjer, H.M., 1920, 1931
Quanjer, H.M. and D.L. Elze, 1930
Rich, Avery E., 1949, 1951
Schultz, E.S. and R. Bonde, 1929
Schultz, E.S., C.F. Clark, R. Bonde, W.P. Raleigh and F.J. Stevenson, 1934
Schultz, E.S., C.F. Clark, W.P. Raleigh, F.J. Stevenson, R. Bonde and J.H. Beaumont, 1937
Schultz, E.S. and Donald Folsom, 1921, 1923, 1925
Sheffield, F.M.L., 1943
Smith, Kenneth M., 1929, 1931
Stewart, F.C. and Hugh Glasgow, 1930, 1931
Webb, R.E., 1956
Webb, R.E., R.H. Larson and J.C. Walker, 1952
Webb, R.E. and E.S. Schultz, 1954
Whitehead, T., 1924, 1931
Whitehead, T. and J.F. Currie, 1931
Whitehead, T., J.F. Currie and W. Maldwyn Davies, 1932
Young, P.A., 1930
Young, P.A. and H.E. Morris, 1930
Vicia faba
(K.M. Smith, 1957) R.E. Fitzpatrick, et al., 1958

V. POTATO LEAF ROLLING MOSAIC ((Schultz and Folsom 1923)) Folsom 1926; J. Johnson 1929
Amaranthus caudatus
(K.M. Smith, 1957) R.E. Fitzpatrick, et al., 1958
Solanum tuberosum
Dykstra, T.P., 1935, 1936
Dykstra, T.P. and W.C. Whitaker, 1938
Hoggan, Isme A., 1927
Johnson, James, 1929
McKay, M.B. and T.P. Dykstra, 1932
Porter, D.R., 1935
Schultz, E.S. and Donald Folsom, 1923, 1925
Young, P.A., 1930
Young, P.A. and H.E. Morris, 1930

V. POTATO M *
Browallia elata
Bagnall, R.H., R.H. Larson and J.C. Walker, 1956
Chenopodium album
Bagnall, R.H., R.H. Larson and J.C. Walker, 1956
Cyamopsis tetragonoloba
Bagnall, R.H. and R.H. Larson, 1957
Bagnall, R.H., R.H. Larson and J.C. Walker, 1956
Datura bernhardii
Bagnall, R.H., R.H. Larson and J.C. Walker, 1956

VIRUS
V. POTATO M * (cont.)
Datura metel
Bagnall, R.H. and R.H. Larson, 1957
Bagnall, R.H., R.H. Larson and J.C. Walker, 1956
Lycopersicon esculentum
Bagnall, R.H. and R.H. Larson, 1957
Bagnall, R.H., R.H. Larson and J.C. Walker, 1956
Nicotiana debneyi
Bagnall, R.H. and R.H. Larson, 1957
Bagnall, R.H., R.H. Larson and J.C. Walker, 1956
Physalis philadelphica
Bagnall, R.H. and R.H. Larson, 1957
Physalis pubescens
Bagnall, R.H., R.H. Larson and J.C. Walker, 1956
Saracha umbellata *
Bagnall, R.H., R.H. Larson and J.C. Walker, 1956
Solanum melongena
Bagnall, R.H. and R.H. Larson, 1957
Bagnall, R.H., R.H. Larson and J.C. Walker, 1956
Solanum nigrum var. villosum
Bagnall, R.H. and R.H. Larson, 1957
Bagnall, R.H., R.H. Larson and J.C. Walker, 1956
Solanum rostratum
Bagnall, R.H. and R.H. Larson, 1957
Bagnall, R.H., R.H. Larson and J.C. Walker, 1956
Solanum sisymbrifolium
Bagnall, R.H., R.H. Larson and J.C. Walker, 1956
Solanum tuberosum
Bagnall, R.H. and R.H. Larson, 1957
Vigna sinensis
Bagnall, R.H. and R.H. Larson, 1957
Bagnall, R.H., R.H. Larson and J.C. Walker, 1956

V. POTATO NECROTIC *
Datura stramonium
Schultz, E.S. and W.P. Raleigh, 1933
Lycopersicon esculentum
Schlutz, E.S. and W.P. Raleigh, 1933
Nicotiana tabacum
Schultz, E.S. and W.P. Raleigh, 1933
Solanum tuberosum
Schultz, E.S. and W.P. Raleigh, 1933

V. POTATO PARACRINKLE Salaman and LePelley 1930
Beta vulgaris
Kassanis, B., 1955
Browallia elata
Bagnall, R.H., R.H. Larson and J.C. Walker, 1956
Chenopodium album
Bagnall, R.H. and R.H. Larson, 1957
Bagnall, R.H., R.H. Larson and J.C. Walker, 1956
Chenopodium amaranticolor
Hollings, M., 1956
Cyamopsis tetragonoloba
Bagnall, R.H. and R.H. Larson, 1957
Bagnall, R.H., R.H. Larson and J.C. Walker, 1956
Yarwood, C.E. and A.H. Gold, 1955
Datura bernhardii
Bagnall, R.H., R.H. Larson and J.C. Walker, 1956
Datura metel
Bagnall, R.H. and R.H. Larson, 1957
Bagnall, R.H., R.H. Larson and J.C. Walker, 1956
Dianthus barbatus
Kassanis, B., 1955
Dianthus caryophyllus
Kassanis, B., 1955
Lycopersicon esculentum
Dykstra, T.P., 1939

VIRUS
V. POTATO PARACRINKLE (cont.)
  Nicotiana debneyi
      Bagnall, R.H. and R.H. Larson, 1957
      Bagnall, R.H., R.H. Larson and J.C. Walker,
      1956
  Physalis philadelphica
      Bagnall, R.H. and R.H. Larson, 1957
      Bagnall, R.H., R.H. Larson and J.C. Walker,
      1956
  Physalis pubescens
      Bagnall, R.H., R.H. Larson and J.C. Walker,
      1956
  Saracha umbellata *
      Bagnall, R.H. and R.H. Larson, 1957
      Bagnall, R.H., R.H. Larson and J.C. Walker,
      1956
  Solanum nigrum var. villosum
      Bagnall, R.H. and R.H. Larson, 1957
      Bagnall, R.H., R.H. Larson and J.C. Walker,
      1956
  Solanum rostratum
      Bagnall, R.H. and R.H. Larson, 1957
      Bagnall, R.H., R.H. Larson and J.C. Walker,
      1956
  Solanum sisymbrifolium
      Bagnall, R.H., R.H. Larson and J.C. Walker,
      1956
  Solanum tuberosum
      Alfieri, S.A. and R.F. Stouffer, 1957
      Bagnall, R.H. and R.H. Larson, 1957
      Bagnall, R.H., R.H. Larson and J.C. Walker,
      1956
      Barton-Wright, Eustace and Alan McBain, 1933
      Dykstra, T.P., 1936, 1939
      (K.M. Smith, 1957) R.E. Fitzpatrick, et al., 1958
      Kassanis, B., 1955
      Whitehead, T., 1937
  Vigna sinensis
      Bagnall, R.H., R.H. Larson and J.C. Walker,
      1956

V. POTATO ROSETTE Hutton and Oldaker
  Lycopersicon esculentum
      Hutton, E.M. and C.E.W. Oldaker, 1949
  Nicotiana tabacum
      Hutton, E.M. and C.E.W. Oldaker, 1949
  Solanum tuberosum
      Hutton, E.M. and C.E.W. Oldaker, 1949

V. POTATO SPINDLE TUBER K.M. Smith 1957
  Lycopersicon esculentum
      Stover, W.G., 1928
  Solanum tuberosum
      Abbott, E.V., 1929
      Bald, J.G., D.O. Norris and B.T. Dickson, 1941
      Fernow, K.H., 1923
      Folsom, Donald, 1923
      Folsom Donald and E.S. Schultz, 1924
      Goss, R.W., 1926, 1928, 1929, 1930, 1931
      McKay, M.B. and T.P. Dykstra, 1932
      Porter, D.R., 1935
      Schultz, E.S., C.F. Clark, R. Bonde, W.P.
      Raleigh and F.J. Stevenson, 1934
      Schultz, E.S., C.F. Clark, W.P. Raleigh, F.J.
      Stevenson, R. Bonde and J.H. Beaumont, 1937
      Schultz, E.S. and D. Folsom, 1922, 1923, 1925
      Werner, H.O., 1926
      Young, P.A., 1930
      Young, P.A. and H.E. Morris, 1930

V. POTATO STEM MOTTLE Rozendaal 1947
  Callistephus chinensis
      Van der Want, J.P.H., 1955
  Cuscuta campestris
      Van der Want, J.P.H., 1955
  Nicotiana glauca
      (K.M. Smith, 1957) R.E. Fitzpatrick, et al., 1958
  Nicotiana glutinosa
      (K.M. Smith, 1957) R.E. Fitzpatrick, et al., 1958
  Nicotiana otophora
      (K.M. Smith, 1957) R.E. Fitzpatrick, et al., 1958
  Nicotiana tabacum
      Harrison, B.D., 1957

VIRUS
V. POTATO STEM MOTTLE (cont.)
  Nicotiana tabacum
      Van der Want, J.P.H., 1955
  Nicotiana tomentosa
      (K.M. Smith, 1957) R.E. Fitzpatrick, et al., 1958
  Nicotiana tomentosiformis
      (K.M. Smith, 1957) R.E. Fitzpatrick, et al., 1958
  Solanum tuberosum
      (K.M. Smith, 1957) R.E. Fitzpatrick, et al., 1958

V. (POTATO) STEM-END BROWNING *
  Solanum tuberosum
      Ross, A. Frank, 1946

V. POTATO STUNT Cockerham and McGhee 1953
  Capsicum frutescens (Capsicum annuum)
      (K.M. Smith, 1957) R.E. Fitzpatrick, et al., 1958
  Lycopersicon esculentum
      (K.M. Smith, 1957) R.E. Fitzpatrick, et al., 1958
  Nicotiana rustica
      (K.M. Smith, 1957) R.E. Fitzpatrick, et al., 1958
  Nicotiana tabacum
      (K.M. Smith, 1957) R.E. Fitzpatrick, et al., 1958
  Physalis floridana
      (K.M. Smith, 1957) R.E. Fitzpatrick, et al., 1958
  Solanum demissum
      (K.M. Smith, 1957) R.E. Fitzpatrick, et al., 1958
  Solanum nodiflorum
      (K.M. Smith, 1957) R.E. Fitzpatrick, et al., 1958
  Solanum tuberosum
      (K.M. Smith, 1957) R.E. Fitzpatrick, et al., 1958

V. POTATO WITCHES' BROOM Hungerford and Dana
  Lycopersicon esculentum   1924
      Young, P.A. and H.E. Morris, 1928
  Nicotiana tabacum
      (K.M. Smith, 1957) R.E. Fitzpatrick, et al., 1958
      Young, P.A., 1929
  Solanum tuberosum
      Kunkel, L.O., 1952
      McKay, M.B. and T.P. Dykstra, 1932
      Porter, D.R., 1935
      Young, P.A., 1930
      Young, P.A. and H.E. Morris, 1928, 1930

V. POTATO X K.M. Smith 1931
  Amaranthus gangeticus
      Hutton, E.M., 1949
  Amaranthus retroflexus
      Dykstra, T.P., 1939
      Larson, R.H., 1944
  Atropa belladonna
      Larson, R.H., 1944
  Beta vulgaris
      Johnson, E.M., 1930
  Browallia speciosa
      Dennis, R.W.G., 1939
  Capsicum frutescens (Capsicum annuum)
      Bagnall, R.H., R.H. Larson and J.C. Walker,
      1956
      Blodgett, F.M., 1927
      Cockerham, George, 1943
      Dennis, R.W.G., 1939
      Hoggan, Isme A., 1927
      Hoyman, Wm. G., 1951
      Johnson, E.M., 1930
      Johnson, James, 1925, 1927
      Larson, R.H., 1947
      Smith, J. Henderson, 1928
      Vasudeva, R. Sahai and T.B. Lal, 1944
  Chenopodium album
      Thompson, A.D., 1956
  Chenopodium amaranticolor
      Hollings, M., 1956
  Chenopodium spp.
      (K.M. Smith, 1957) R.E. Fitzpatrick, et al., 1958
  Cucumis sativus
      Matthews, R.E.F., 1949
  Cyphomandra betacea
      Larson, R.H., 1947
      Matthews, R.E.F., 1949
      Thompson, A.D., 1956

VIRUS
V. POTATO X (cont.)
 Datura metel
  Larson, R.H., 1947
 Datura meteloides
  Fernow, Karl Hermann, 1925
 Datura stramonium
  Ainsworth, G.C., 1933, 1934
  Ainsworth, G.C., G.H. Berkeley and J. Caldwell,
  1934
  Bagnall, R.H., R.H. Larson and J.C. Walker,
  1956
  Bawden, F.C., 1936
  Bawden, F.C. and F.M.L. Sheffield, 1944
  Cockerham, George, 1943
  Dennis, R.W.G., 1939
  Dykstra, T.P., 1933, 1939
  Fernow, Karl Hermann, 1925
  Folsom, Donald and Reiner Bonde, 1937
  Goss, R.W., 1931
  Hutton, E.M., 1949
  Jarrett, Phyllis H., 1930
  Johnson, E.M., 1930
  Johnson, James, 1925
  Roberts, F.M., 1948
  Samson, R.W., 1930
  Schultz, E.S., C.F. Clark, W.P. Raleigh, F.J.
  Stevenson, R. Bonde and J.H. Beaumont, 1937
  Schultz, E.S. and W.P. Raleigh, 1936
  Smith, J. Henderson, 1928
  Thompson, A.D., 1956
  Vasudeva, R. Sahai and T.B. Lal, 1944
 Datura stramonium var. tatala
  Dykstra, T.P., 1933
  Larson, R.H., 1947
  Matthews, R.E.F., 1949
  Timian, Roland G., W.J. Hooker and C.E.
  Peterson, 1955
 Digitalis lanata
  Larson, R.H., 1944
 Gomphrena globosa
  Bagnall, R.H., R.H. Larson and J.C. Walker,
  1956
  Hoyman, Wm. G., 1951
  Roberts, Daniel A., 1952
  Thompson, A.D., 1956
  Timian, Roland G., W.J. Hooker and C.E.
  Peterson, 1955
  Wilkinson, R.E. and F.M. Blodgett, 1948
  Wilkinson, R.E. and A. Frank Ross, 1949
 Hyoscyamus niger
  Cockerham, George, 1943
  Dennis, R.W.G., 1939
  Hamilton, Marion A., 1932
  Hoggan, Isme A., 1927
  Johnson, James, 1927
  Smith, J. Henderson, 1928
 Lamium hybridum
  Larson, R.H., 1947
 Lamium purpureum
  (K.M. Smith, 1957) R.E. Fitzpatrick, et al., 1958
 Lycium barbarum
  Dennis, R.W.G., 1939
 Lycopersicon esculentum
  Ainsworth, G.C., 1933, 1934
  Ainsworth, G.C., G.H. Berkeley and J. Caldwell,
  1934
  Bawden, F.C. and F.M.L. Sheffield, 1944
  Burnett, Grover and Leon K. Jones, 1931
  Cockerham, George, 1943
  Dennis, R.W.G., 1939
  Dykstra, T.P., 1933, 1935
  Fernow, Karl Hermann, 1925
  Folsom, Donald and Reiner Bonde, 1937
  Fulton, Robert W., 1941
  Goss, R.W., 1931
  Hamilton, Marion A., 1932
  Hoggan, Isme A., 1927
  Johnson, E.M., 1930
  Johnson, James, 1925, 1927
  Jones, Leon K. and Grover Burnett, 1935
  MacNeill, Blair H., 1955
  Matthews, R.E.F., 1949
  Samson, R.W., 1930

VIRUS
V. POTATO X (cont.)
 Lycopersicon esculentum
  Smith, Kenneth M., 1929
  Valleau, W.D. and E.M. Johnson, 1930
  Vasudeva, R. Sahai and T.B. Lal, 1944
 Lycopersicon esculentum f. pyriforme
  Dennis, R.W.G., 1939
 Lycopersicon racemigerum
  Dennis, R.W.G., 1939
 Nicandra physalodes
  Dennis, R.W.G., 1939
  Fernow, K.H., 1923, 1925
  Folsom, Donald and Reiner Bonde, 1937
  Goss, R.W., 1931
  Hoggan, Isme A., 1927
  Johnson, E.M., 1930
  Larson, R.H., 1947
  Smith, J. Henderson, 1928
 Nicotiana affinis
  Smith, J. Henderson, 1928
 Nicotiana alata
  Dennis, R.W.G., 1939
 Nicotiana glauca
  Hoggan, Isme A., 1927
 Nicotiana glutinosa
  Ainsworth, G.C., 1933, 1934
  Ainsworth, G.C., G.H. Berkeley and J. Caldwell,
  1934
  Black, L.M. and W.C. Price, 1940
  Cockerham, George, 1943
  Dennis, R.W.G., 1939
  Fernow, Karl Hermann, 1925
  Fulton, Robert W., 1941
  Hoggan, Isme A., 1927
  Johnson, James, 1927
  Larson, R.H., 1944, 1947
  Matthews, R.E.F., 1949
  Roberts, Daniel A., 1952
  Thompson, A.D., 1956
  Timian, Roland G., W.J. Hooker and C.E.
  Peterson, 1955
  Vasudeva, R. Sahai and T.B. Lal, 1944
 Nicotiana rustica
  Larson, R.H., 1943, 1944, 1947
  Larson, R.H. and R.C. Ladeburg, 1949
  Thompson, A.D., 1956
  Timian, Roland G., W.J. Hooker and C.E.
  Peterson, 1955
  Vasudeva, R. Sahai and T.B. Lal, 1944
 Nicotiana sanderae
  Smith, J. Henderson, 1928
 Nicotiana sylvestris
  Dennis, R.W.G., 1939
  Vasudeva, R. Sahai and T.B. Lal, 1944
 Nicotiana tabacum
  Ainsworth, G.C., 1933, 1934
  Bagnall, R.H., R.H. Larson and J.C. Walker,
  1956
  Bawden, F.C., 1936
  Bawden, F.C. and F.M.L. Sheffield, 1944
  Black, L.M. and W.C. Price, 1940
  Blodgett, F.M., 1927
  Burnett, Grover and Leon K. Jones, 1931
  Cockerham, George, 1943
  Dennis, R.W.G., 1939
  Dykstra, T.P., 1939
  Folsom, Donald and Reiner Bonde, 1937
  Fulton, Robert W., 1941
  Hamilton, Marion A., 1932
  Hoggan, Isme A., 1927
  Hollings, M., 1955
  Johnson, E.M., 1930
  Johnson, James, 1925, 1926, 1927
  Koch, K.L., 1933
  Koch, Karl and James Johnson, 1935
  Larson, R.H., 1943, 1944, 1947
  Larson, R.H. and R.C. Ladebrug, 1949
  Matthews, R.E.F., 1949
  Nolla, J.A.B., 1934
  Price, W.C., 1936
  Quanjer, H.M., 1933
  Roberts, Daniel A., 1952
  Roberts, F.M., 1948

VIRUS
V. POTATO X (cont.)
  Nicotiana tabacum
    Smith, J. Henderson, 1928
    Smith, Kenneth M., 1930
    Thompson, A.D., 1956
    Timian, Roland G., W.J. Hooker and C.E.
    Peterson, 1955
    Valleau, W.D. and E.M. Johnson, 1930
    Vasudeva, R. Sahai and T.B. Lal, 1944
    Walters, H.J., 1952
  Petunia hybrida
    Dykstra, T.P., 1933
  Petunia nyctaginiflora
    Dennis, R.W.G., 1939
  Petunia violacea
    Hoggan, Isme A., 1927
    Johnson, James, 1925, 1927
    Smith, J. Henderson, 1928
  Physalis floridana
    Ross, A. Frank, 1950, 1953
  Physalis franchetti
    Hoggan, Isme A., 1927
  Physalis heterophylla
    Goss, R.W., 1931
  Physalis heterophylla var. nyctaginea
    Johnson, E.M., 1930
  Physalis pubescens
    Fernow, K.H., 1923
    Folsom, Donald and Reiner Bonde, 1937
    Hoggan, Isme A., 1927
    Johnson, E.M., 1930
    Johnson, James, 1925, 1927
  Physalis spp.
    Dykstra, T.P., 1933
  Phytolacca decandra
    Johnson, E.M., 1930
  Salpiglossis sinuata
    Smith, J. Henderson, 1928
  Salpiglossis variabilis
    Dennis, R.W.G., 1939
  Schizanthus retusus
    Larson, R.H., 1947
  Solanum aculeatissimum
    Fernow, Karl Hermann, 1925
    Larson, R.H., 1947
  Solanum atropurpureum *
    Fernow, Karl Hermann, 1925
    Hoggan, Isme A., 1927
  Solanum carolinense
    Fernow, Karl Hermann, 1925
    Johnson, E.M., 1930
  Solanum demissum x Solanum tuberosum var. aquila *
    Raymer, W.B. and J.A. Milbrath, 1957
  Solanum dulcamara
    Smith, J. Henderson, 1928
    Thompson, A.D., 1956
  Solanum laciniatum
    Hoggan, Isme A., 1927
    Thompson, A.D., 1956
  Solanum melongena
    Fulton, Robert W., 1941
    Johnson, James, 1925
  Solanum melongena var. esculentum
    Johnson, E.M., 1930
  Solanum miniatum
    Hoggan, Isme A., 1927
  Solanum nigrum
    Dennis, R.W.G., 1939
    Folsom, Donald and Reiner Bonde, 1937
    Fulton, Robert W., 1941
    Johnson, James, 1925
    Smith, J. Henderson, 1928
    Thompson, A.D., 1956
  Solanum nigrum var. villosum
    Dykstra, T.P., 1933
    Smith, J. Henderson, 1928
  Solanum nodiflorum
    Cockerham, George, 1943
    Dennis, R.W.G., 1939
    Smith, J. Henderson, 1928
    Thompson, A.D., 1956
    Vasudeva, R. Sahai and T.B. Lal, 1944

VIRUS
V. POTATO X (cont.)
  Solanum rostratum
    Johnson, James, 1925
  Solanum tuberosum
    Ainsworth, G.C., G.H. Berkeley and J. Caldwell,
    1934
    Atanasoff, D., 1924
    Bagnall, R.H., R.H. Larson and J.C. Walker,
    1956
    Bald, J.G., 1945
    Bawden, F.C., 1936
    Bawden, F.C. and F.M.L. Sheffield, 1944
    Blodgett, F.M., 1927
    Burnett, Grover and Leon K. Jones, 1931
    Cockerham, George, 1943
    Dennis, R.W.G., 1939
    Dykstra, T.P., 1933, 1935, 1936, 1939
    Fernow, Karl Hermann, 1925
    Folsom, Donald, 1920
    Folsom, Donald and Reiner Bonde, 1937
    Folsom, Donald and E.S. Schultz, 1924
    Gilbert, Alfred H., 1923
    Goss, R.W., 1931
    Gussow, H.T., 1918
    Hoyman, Wm. G., 1951
    Jones, Leon K. and C.L. Vincent, 1937
    Jones, Leon K., C.L. Vincent and Earl F. Burk,
    1940
    Koch, K.L., 1933
    Koch, Karl and James Johnson, 1935
    Krantz, F.A. and G.R. Bisby, 1921
    Ladeburg, R.C. and R.H. Larson, 1949
    Larson, R.H., 1943, 1944, 1947
    Larson, R.H. and R.C. Ladeburg, 1949
    Link, G.K.K., 1923
    Matthews, R.E.F., 1949
    McKay, M.B. and T.P. Dykstra, 1932
    McKinney, H.H., 1928
    Norris, D.O., 1953, 1954
    Quanjer, H.M., 1931
    Roberts, F.M., 1948
    Ross, A. Frank, 1950
    Schultz, E.S., 1951
    Schultz, E.S., C.F. Clark, R. Bonde, W.P.
    Raleigh and F.J. Stevenson, 1934
    Schultz, E.S., C.F. Clark, W.P. Raleigh, F.J.
    Stevenson, R. Bonde and J.H. Beaumont, 1937
    Schultz, E.S., C.F. Clark and F.J. Stevenson,
    1940
    Schultz, E.S. and Donald Folsom, 1920
    Schultz, E.S., Donald Folsom, F. Merrill
    Hildebrandt and Lon A. Hawkins, 1919
    Schultz, E.S. and W.P. Raleigh, 1933, 1936
    Smith, J. Henderson, 1928
    Smith, Kenneth M., 1927, 1929, 1930
    Thompson, A.D., 1956
    Timian, Roland G., W.J. Hooker and C.E.
    Peterson, 1955
    Tompkins, C.M., 1926
    Valleau, W.D. and E.M. Johnson, 1930
    Vasudeva, R. Sahai and T.B. Lal, 1944
    Whitehead, T., 1937
    Whitehead, T. and J.F. Currie, 1931
    Whitehead, T., J.F. Currie and W. Maldwyn
    Davies, 1932
  Veronica agrestis
    (K.M. Smith, 1957) R.E. Fitzpatrick, et al., 1958

V. POTATO Y Smith 1931
  Capsicum frutescens (Capsicum annuum)
    Alvarez-Garcia, L.A. and Jose Adsuar, 1943
    Anderson, C.W. and M.K. Corbett, 1957
    Bald, J.G. and D.O. Norris, 1945
    Dennis, R.W.G., 1939
    Dykstra, T.P., 1939
    Easton, G.D., R.H. Larson and R.W. Hougas,
    1958
    Hoggan, Isme A., 1927
    Hutton, E.M. and J.W. Peak, 1952
    Johnson, E.M., 1930
    Johnson, James, 1927
    Roque, Arturo and Jose Adsuar, 1941
    Sakimura, K., 1953

VIRUS
V. POTATO Y (cont.)
  Capsicum frutescens (Capsicum annuum)
    Simons, J.N., Robert A. Conover and James M.
    Walter, 1956
  Cassia tora
    Anderson, C.W., 1954
  Chenopodium amaranticolor
    Hollings, M., 1956
  Chenopodium urbicum
    Darby, J.F., R.H. Larson and J.C. Walker, 1951
    Ross, A. Frank, 1948
  Cyphomandra betacea
    (K.M. Smith, 1957) R.E. Fitzpatrick, et al., 1958
  Dahlia spp.
    (K.M. Smith, 1957) R.E. Fitzpatrick, et al., 1958
  Datura metel
    Darby, J.F., R.H. Larson and J.C. Walker, 1951
    Easton, G.D., R.H. Larson and R.W. Hougas,
    1958
  Datura stramonium
    Bawden, F.C., 1936
    Bawden, F.C. and B. Kassanis, 1947
    Samson, R.W., 1930
  Hyoscyamus niger
    Cockerham, George, 1943
    Hamilton, Marion A., 1932
    Hoggan, Isme A., 1927
    Johnson, James, 1927
    Larson, R.H., 1947
    Smith, Kenneth M. and R.W.G. Dennis, 1940
    Watson (Hamilton), Marion A., 1937
  Indigofera hirsuta
    Anderson, C.W. and M.K. Corbett, 1957
  Lycium barbarum
    Darby, J.F., R.H. Larson and J.C. Walker, 1951
    Smith, Kenneth M. and R.W.G. Dennis, 1940
  Lycium chinense
    Ross, A. Frank, 1948
  Lycium halimifolium
    Hutton, E.M. and J.W. Peak, 1952
    Larson, R.H. and J.F. Darby, 1951
    Ross, A. Frank, 1948
  Lycium rhombifolium
    Darby, J.F., R.H. Larson and J.C. Walker, 1951
    Hutton, E.M. and J.W. Peak, 1952
    Larson, R.H. and J.F. Darby, 1951
  Lycopersicon esculentum
    Alvarez-Garcia, L.A. and Jose Adsuar, 1943
    Bawden, F.C. and B. Kassanis, 1951
    Bawden, F.C. and F.M.L. Sheffield, 1944
    Burnett, Grover and Leon K. Jones, 1931
    Cockerham, George, 1943
    Conover, Robert A. and Robert W. Fulton, 1953
    Dykstra, T.P., 1933, 1939
    Hoggan, Isme A., 1927
    Johnson, E.M., 1930
    Johnson, James, 1927
    Jones, Leon K. and C.L. Vincent, 1937
    Koch, K.L., 1933
    MacNeill, Blair H., 1955
    Roque, Arturo and Jose Adsuar, 1941
    Sakimura, K., 1953
    Samson, R.W., 1930
    Schultz, E.S. and Donald Folsom, 1923
    Simons, J.N., Robert A. Conover and James M.
    Walter, 1956
    Smith, Kenneth M. and R.W.G. Dennis, 1940
  Lycopersicon racemigerum
    Smith, Kenneth M. and R.W.G. Dennis, 1940
  Nicandra physalodes
    Bagnall, R.H., R.H. Larson and J.C. Walker,
    1956
    Hoggan, Isme A., 1927
    Koch, K.L., 1933
    Sakimura, K., 1953
  Nicotiana alata
    Smith, Kenneth M. and R.W.G. Dennis, 1940
  Nicotiana bigelovii var. multivalvis *
    Roque, Arturo and Jose Adsuar, 1941
  Nicotiana bigelovii var. quadrivalvis *
    Roque, Arturo and Jose Adsuar, 1941
  Nicotiana glauca
    Hoggan, Isme A., 1927

VIRUS
V. POTATO Y (cont.)
  Nicotiana glauca
    Johnson, James, 1927
  Nicotiana glutinosa
    Alvarez-Garcia, L.A. and Jose Adsuar, 1943
    Bald, J.G. and D.O. Norris, 1945
    Bawden, F.C. and B. Kassanis, 1951
    Cockerham, George, 1943
    Conover, Robert A. and Robert W. Fulton, 1953
    Corbett, M.K., 1955
    Darby, J.F., R.H. Larson and J.C. Walker, 1951
    Hamilton, Marion A., 1932
    Hoggan, Isme A., 1927
    Hutton, E.M. and J.W. Peak, 1952
    Johnson, James, 1927
    Koch, K.L., 1933
    Peterson, Paul D. and H.H. McKinney, 1938
    Roque, Arturo and Jose Adsuar, 1941
    Ross, A. Frank, 1948, 1949, 1950, 1953
    Sakimura, K., 1953
    Simons, J.N., Robert A. Conover and James M.
    Walter, 1956
    Smith, Kenneth M. and R.W.G. Dennis, 1940
    Vasudeva, R. Sahai and T.B. Lal, 1945
    Watson, Marion A., 1956
  Nicotiana langsdorffii
    Peterson, Paul D. and H.H. McKinney, 1938
    Smith, Kenneth M. and R.W.G. Dennis, 1940
  Nicotiana noctiflora
    Smith, Kenneth M. and R.W.G. Dennis, 1940
  Nicotiana rustica
    Johnson, E.M., 1930
    Johnson, James, 1927
    Koch, K.L., 1933
    Oswald, John W., 1948
    Roque, Arturo and Jose Adsuar, 1941
    Sakimura, K., 1953
    Smith, Kenneth M. and R.W.G. Dennis, 1940
    Vasudeva, R. Sahai and T.B. Lal, 1945
  Nicotiana sylvestris
    Dykstra, T.P., 1939
    Vasudeva, R. Sahai and T.B. Lal, 1945
  Nicotiana tabacum
    Alvarez-Garcia, L.A. and Jose Adsuar, 1943
    Bagnall, R.H., R.H. Larson and J.C. Walker,
    1956
    Bald, J.G. and D.O. Norris, 1945
    Bawden, F.C., 1936
    Bawden, F.C. and B. Kassanis, 1946, 1947, 1951
    Bawden, F.C. and F.M.L. Sheffield, 1944
    Burnett, Grover and Leon K. Jones, 1931
    Cockerham, George, 1943
    Conover, Robert A. and Robert W. Fulton, 1953
    Corbett, M.K., 1955
    Darby, J.F., R.H. Larson and J.C. Walker, 1951
    Doncaster, J.P. and B. Kassanis, 1946
    Dykstra, T.P., 1936, 1939
    Easton, G.D., R.H. Larson and R.W. Hougas,
    1958
    Hamilton, Marion A., 1932
    Hoggan, Isme A., 1927
    Johnson, E.M., 1930
    Johnson, James, 1927
    Jones, Leon K. and C.L. Vincent, 1937
    Kassanis, B., 1942
    Koch, K.L., 1933
    Koch, Karl and James Johnson, 1935
    Larson, R.H., 1947
    Larson, R.H. and J.F. Darby, 1951
    McKinney, H.H., 1943
    Nolla, J.A.B., 1934
    Oswald, John W., 1948
    Peterson, Paul D. and H.H. McKinney, 1938
    Price, W.C., 1936
    Richardson, D.E., 1958
    Roque, Arturo and Jose Adsuar, 1941
    Ross, A. Frank, 1950, 1953
    Sakimura, K., 1953
    Simons, J.N., Robert A. Conover and James M.
    Walter, 1956
    Smith, Kenneth M. and R.W.G. Dennis, 1940
    Valleau, W.D. and E.M. Johnson, 1930
    Vasudeva, R. Sahai and T.B. Lal, 1945

VIRUS
V. POTATO Y (cont.)
    Nicotiana tabacum
        Watson, Marion A., 1937, 1956
    Petunia hybrida
        Dykstra, T.P., 1933, 1939
        Sakimura, K., 1953
        Vasudeva, R. Sahai and T.B. Lal, 1945
    Petunia nyctaginiflora
        Smith, Kenneth M. and R.W.G. Dennis, 1940
    Petunia violacea
        Hoggan, Isme A., 1927
        Johnson, James, 1927
    Physalis floridana
        Darby, J.F., R.H. Larson and J.C. Walker, 1951
        Easton, G.D., R.H. Larson and R.W. Hougas, 1958
        Hutton, E.M. and J.W. Peak, 1952
        Richardson, D.E., 1958
        Ross, A. Frank, 1948, 1949, 1950, 1953
    Physalis franchetti
        Hoggan, Isme A., 1927
    Physalis heterophylla
        Darby, J.F., R.H. Larson and J.C. Walker, 1951
        Larson, R.H., 1947
    Physalis heterophylla var. nyctaginea
        Johnson, E.M., 1930
    Physalis peruviana
        Larson, R.H. and J.F. Darby, 1951
        Sakimura, K., 1953
        Simons, J.N., Robert A. Conover and James M.
        Walter, 1956
    Physalis pubescens
        Hoggan, Isme A., 1927
        Johnson, James, 1927
        Koch, K.L., 1933
    Physalis spp.
        Dykstra, T.P., 1933
    Physalis turbinata
        Darby, J.F., R.H. Larson and J.C. Walker, 1951
    Physalis virginiana
        Darby, J.F., R.H. Larson and J.C. Walker, 1951
        Larson, R.H., 1947
    Salpiglossis variabilis
        Smith, Kenneth M. and R.W.G. Dennis, 1940
    Schizanthus retusus
        Smith, Kenneth M. and R.W.G. Dennis, 1940
    Solanum acaule
        Easton, G.D., R.H. Larson and R.W. Hougas, 1958
    Solanum ajuscoense
        Easton, G.D., R.H. Larson and R.W. Hougas, 1958
    Solanum atropurpureum *
        Hoggan, Isme A., 1927
    Solanum cardiophyllum
        Easton, G.D., R.H. Larson and R.W. Hougas, 1958
    Solanum cardiophyllum subsp. ehrenbergii
        Easton, G.D., R.H. Larson and R.W. Hougas, 1958
    Solanum chacoense
        Easton, G.D., R.H. Larson and R.W. Hougas, 1958
    (Solanum demissum x Solanum gibberulosum) x
    (Solanum stoloniferum)
        Easton, G.D., R.H. Larson and R.W. Hougas, 1958
    (Solanum demissum x Solanum saltense) x (Solanum
    stoloniferum)
        Easton, G.D., R.H. Larson and R.W. Hougas, 1958
    (Solanum demissum x Solanum schickii) x (Solanum
    stoloniferum)
        Easton, G.D., R.H. Larson and R.W. Hougas, 1958
    (Solanum demissum x Solanum simplicifolium) x
    (Solanum stoloniferum)
        Easton, G.D., R.H. Larson and R.W. Hougas, 1958
    Solanum dulcamara
        (K.M. Smith, 1957) R.E. Fitzpatrick, et al., 1958
    Solanum gibberulosum
        Easton, G.D., R.H. Larson and R.W. Hougas, 1958
    Solanum gigantophyllum
        Easton, G.D., R.H. Larson and R.W. Hougas, 1958
    Solanum gracile *
        Simons, J.N., Robert A. Conover and James M.
        Walter, 1956
    Solanum kesselbrenneri
        Easton, G.D., R.H. Larson and R.W. Hougas, 1958
    Solanum laciniatum
        Hoggan, Isme A., 1927

VIRUS
V. POTATO Y (cont.)
    Solanum melongena
        Roque, Arturo and Jose Adsuar, 1941
        Sakimura, K., 1953
    Solanum melongena var. esculentum
        Johnson, E.M., 1930
    Solanum miniatum
        Hoggan, Isme A., 1927
        Koch, K.L., 1933
    Solanum nigrum
        Koch, K.L., 1933
        Smith, Kenneth M. and R.W.G. Dennis, 1940
    Solanum nigrum var. villosum
        Dykstra, T.P., 1933
    Solanum nodiflorum
        Cockerham, George, 1943
        Sakimura, K., 1953
        Smith, Kenneth M. and R.W.G. Dennis, 1940
        Vasudeva, R. Sahai and T.B. Lal, 1945
    Solanum polyadenium
        Easton, G.D., R.H. Larson and R.W. Hougas, 1958
    Solanum rybinii
        Easton, G.D., R.H. Larson and R.W. Hougas, 1958
    Solanum saltense
        Easton, G.D., R.H. Larson and R.W. Hougas, 1958
    Solanum simplicifolium x Solanum rybinii
        Easton, G.D., R.H. Larson and R.W. Hougas, 1958
    Solanum simplicifolium x Solanum toralapanum
        Easton, G.D., R.H. Larson and R.W. Hougas, 1958
    Solanum stoloniferum
        Easton, G.D., R.H. Larson and R.W. Hougas, 1958
    Solanum tuberosum
        Atanasoff, D., 1924, 1925
        Bald, J.G., 1945
        Bald, J.G. and D.O. Norris, 1945
        Bawden, F.C., 1936
        Bawden, F.C. and B. Kassanis, 1946, 1947, 1951
        Bawden, F.C. and F.M.L. Sheffield, 1944
        Broadbent, L., 1946
        Broadbent, L., R.P. Chaudhuri and L. Kapica,
        1950
        Broadbent, L. and T.W. Tinsley, 1951
        Cockerham, George, 1943
        Corbett, M.K., 1955
        Darby, J.F., R.H. Larson and J.C. Walker, 1951
        Dennis, R.W.G., 1939
        Dykstra, T.P., 1933, 1936, 1939
        Easton, G.D., R.H. Larson and R.W. Hougas, 1958
        Hoggan, Isme A., 1927
        Hutton, E.M. and J.W. Peak, 1952
        Johnson, James, 1927
        Jones, Leon K. and C.L. Vincent, 1937
        Jones, Leon K., C.L. Vincent and Earl F. Buck,
        1940
        Kassanis, B., 1942
        Koch, K.L., 1933
        Koch, Karl and James Johnson, 1935
        Larson, R.H., 1947
        Larson, R.H. and J.F. Darby, 1951
        Oswald, John W., 1948
        Quanjer, H.M., 1931
        Richardson, D.E., 1958
        Ross, A. Frank, 1948, 1950
        Samson, R.W., 1930
        Schultz, E.S., C.F. Clark, R. Bonde, W.P.
        Raleigh and F.J. Stevenson, 1934
        Schultz, E.S., C.F. Clark, W.P. Raleigh, F.J.
        Stevenson, R. Bonde and J.H. Beaumont, 1937
        Schultz, E.S. and D. Folsom, 1922, 1923, 1925
        Smith, Kenneth M. and R.W.G. Dennis, 1940
        Valleau, W.D. and E.M. Johnson, 1930
        Vasudeva, R. Sahai and T.B. Lal, 1945
        Vincent, C.L. and L.K. Jones, 1936
        Watson, Marion A., 1956
        Whitehead, T., 1937
    Vigna chinensis *
        Darby, J.F., R.H. Larson and J.C. Walker, 1951
    Vigna sinensis
        Dykstra, T.P., 1939
        Ross, A. Frank, 1948
    Zinnia elegans
        Simons, J.N., Robert A. Conover and James M.
        Walter, 1956

VIRUS
V. POTATO YELLOW DWARF Barrus and Chupp 1922
  Barbarea vulgaris
    Hansing, E.D., 1942
  Callistephus chinensis
    Black, L.M., 1938
  Capsella bursa-pastoris
    Hansing, E.D., 1942
  Datura stramonium
    Hougas, R.W., 1951
  Hyoscyamus niger
    Black, L.M., 1937, 1938
  Kalanchoe diagremontiana
    Hansing, E.D., 1942
  Lycopersicon esculentum
    Black, L.M., 1937
    Hougas, R.W., 1951
  Medicago lupulina
    Hansing, E.D., 1942
  Nicotiana glauca
    Black, L.M., 1938
  Nicotiana glutinosa
    Black, L.M., 1938
  Nicotiana langsdorffii
    Black, L.M., 1938
  Nicotiana paniculata
    Black, L.M., 1938
  Nicotiana rustica
    Black, L.M., 1938, 1940, 1943
    Hougas, R.W., 1951
    Price, W.C. and L.M. Black, 1941
    Younkin, S.G., 1943
  Nicotiana rustica var. jamaicensis *
    Black, L.M., 1938
  Nicotiana rustica var. pumila *
    Black, L.M., 1938
  Nicotiana sanderae
    Black, L.M., 1938
  Nicotiana sylvestris
    Black, L.M., 1938
  Nicotiana tabacum
    Black, L.M., 1938
  Nicotiana undulata
    Black, L.M., 1938
  Physalis heterophylla
    Black, L.M., 1937
    Larson, R.H., 1947
  Physalis pubescens
    Black, L.M., 1938
  Physalis virginiana
    Larson, R.H., 1947
  Solanum acaule var. subexinterruptum
    Black, L.M., 1937
  Solanum ajuscoense
    Black, L.M., 1937
  Solanum antipoviczii
    Black, L.M., 1937
  Solanum cardiophyllum f. coyoacanum *
    Black, L.M., 1937
  Solanum melongena
    Black, L.M., 1938
  Solanum neo-antipoviczii
    Black, L.M., 1937
  Solanum tuberosum
    Black, L.M., 1937, 1938, 1940, 1943
    Hansing, E.D., 1942, 1943
    Hougas, R.W., 1951
    Koch, K., 1934
    Larson, R.H., 1945, 1947
    Muncie, J.H., 1935
    Walker, J.C. and R.H. Larson, 1939
  Solanum verrucosum
    Black, L.M., 1937
  Trifolium agrarium
    Black, L.M., 1937
  Trifolium hybridum
    Black, L.M., 1937
  Trifolium incarnatum
    Black, L.M., 1938, 1943, 1953
    Hougas, R.W., 1951
  Trifolium pratense
    Black, L.M., 1936, 1937
    Hansing, E.D., 1942

VIRUS
V. POTATO YELLOW DWARF (cont.)
  Trifolium repens
    Black, L.M., 1937
    Hansing, E.D., 1942
  Trifolium spp.
    Black, L.M., 1938
  Vicia faba
    Black, L.M., 1938
    Hougas, R.W., 1951

V. POTATO YELLOW SPOT Bonde and Merriam 1954
  Solanum tuberosum
    Bonde, Reiner and Donald Merriam, 1954

V. POTATO YELLOW VEIN K.M. Smith 1957
  Solanum tuberosum
    (K.M. Smith, 1957) R.E. Fitzpatrick, et al., 1958

V. PRIMULA MOSAIC
  Primula malacoides
    Tompkins, C.M. and John T. Middleton, 1941
  Primula obconica
    Severin, Henry H.P. and C.M. Tompkins, 1950
    Tompkins, C.M. and John T. Middleton, 1941
  Primula sinensis
    Tompkins, C.M. and John T. Middleton, 1941

V. PRUNE DIAMOND CANKER Smith 1941
  Cucumis sativus
    Yarwood, C.E. and H.E. Thomas, 1954
  Prunus domestica
    Smith, Ralph E., 1941
    Yarwood, C.E. and H.E. Thomas, 1954

V. PRUNE DWARF Thomas and Hildebrand 1936
  Cucumis sativus
    Willison, R.S., 1951
  Cucurbita maxima
    Milbrath, J.A., 1956
    Willison, R.S., 1951
  Prunus armeniaca
    Moore, J. Duain and H.R. Cameron, 1956
    Willison, R.S., 1944
  Prunus avium
    Gilmer, R.M., K.D. Brase and K.G. Parker, 1957
    Willison, R.S., 1944
  Prunus cerasifera
    Willison, R.S., 1944
  Prunus cerasus
    Fink, Harry C., 1955
    Gilmer, R.M., K.D. Brase and K.G. Parker, 1957
    Milbrath, J.A., 1957
    Moore, J. Duain and H.R. Cameron, 1956
    Willison, R.S., 1944
  Prunus domestica
    Cochran, L.C., 1956
    Gilmer, R.M., K.D. Brase and K.G. Parker, 1957
    Hildebrand, E.M., 1942
    Moore, J. Duain and H.R. Cameron, 1956
    Richards, B.L. and L.C. Cochran, 1956
    Thomas, H.E. and E.M. Hildebrand, 1936
    Willison, R.S., 1944
  Prunus insititia
    Hildebrand, E.M., 1942
  Prunus mahaleb
    Willison, R.S., 1944
  Prunus persica
    Hildebrand, E.M., 1942
    Richards, B.L. and L.C. Cochran, 1956
    Willison, R.S., 1944
  Prunus salicina
    Hildebrand, E.M., 1942
    Willison, R.S., 1944
  Prunus tomentosa
    Fink, Harry C., 1955

V. PRUNUS *
  Zinnia elegans
    Varney, E.H. and J. Duain Moore, 1954

V. PRUNUS A *
  Antirrhinum majus
    Fulton, Robert W., 1957

VIRUS

V. PRUNUS A * (cont.)

Apocynum androsaemifolium
 Fulton, Robert W., 1957
Asclepias syriaca
 Fulton, Robert W., 1957
Astragalus rubyi
 Fulton, Robert W., 1957
Carthamus tinctorius
 Fulton, Robert W., 1957
Cassia tora
 Fulton, Robert W., 1957
Centaurea imperialis
 Fulton, Robert W., 1957
Citrullus colocynthis
 Fulton, Robert W., 1957
Citrullus vulgaris
 Ehlers, Clifford G. and J. Duain Moore, 1957
 Fulton, Robert W., 1957
Citrullus vulgaris var. citroides
 Fulton, Robert W., 1957
Crotalaria intermedia
 Fulton, Robert W., 1957
Cucumis anguria
 Fulton, Robert W., 1957
Cucumis dipsaceus
 Fulton, Robert W., 1957
Cucumis melo
 Fulton, Robert W., 1957
Cucumis prophetarum
 Fulton, Robert W., 1957
Cucumis sativus
 Fulton, Robert W., 1957
Cucurbita ficifolia
 Fulton, Robert W., 1957
Cucurbita maxima
 Fulton, Robert W., 1957
Cucurbita moschata
 Fulton, Robert W., 1957
Cucurbita okeechobeensis
 Fulton, Robert W., 1957
Cucurbita pepo
 Fulton, Robert W., 1957
Cyamopsis tetragonoloba
 Ehlers, Clifford G. and J. Duain Moore, 1957
 Fulton, Robert W., 1957
Cyclanthera pedata
 Fulton, Robert W., 1957
Cynoglossum amabile
 Fulton, Robert W., 1957
Datura stramonium
 Vasudeva, R. Sahai and C.S. Ramamoorthy, 1946
Datura stramonium var. tatula
 MacLachlan, D.S., R.H. Larson and J.C. Walker, 1953
Echinocystis lobata
 Fulton, Robert W., 1957
Gomphrena globosa
 Fulton, Robert W., 1957
Gossypium hirsutum
 Fulton, Robert W., 1957
Hedysarum coronarium
 Fulton, Robert W., 1957
Ipomoea purpurea
 Fulton, Robert W., 1957
Lactuca sativa
 Fulton, Robert W., 1957
Melilotus alba
 Fulton, Robert W., 1957
Melothria pendula
 Fulton, Robert W., 1957
Momordica balsamina
 Fulton, Robert W., 1957
Nicotiana benthamiana
 Fulton, Robert W., 1957
Nicotiana tabacum
 Ehlers, Clifford G. and J. Duain Moore, 1957
 Fulton, Robert W., 1957
 Varney, E.H. and J. Duain Moore, 1954
Petunia hybrida
 Fulton, Robert W., 1957
Pisum sativum
 Fulton, Robert W., 1957

VIRUS

V. PRUNUS A * (cont.)

Prunus americana x Prunus salicina
 Ehlers, Clifford G. and J. Duain Moore, 1957
Prunus cerasus
 Ehlers, Clifford G. and J. Duain Moore, 1957
 Fulton, Robert W., 1957
Prunus mahaleb
 Fulton, Robert W., 1957
Prunus pensylvanica
 Fulton, Robert W., 1957
Prunus serotina
 Fulton, Robert W., 1957
Prunus virginiana
 Fulton, Robert W., 1957
Sesbania bispinosa
 Fulton, Robert W., 1957
Sesbania cannabina
 Fulton, Robert W., 1957
Sesbania cinerascens
 Fulton, Robert W., 1957
Sesbania exaltata
 Ehlers, Clifford G. and J. Duain Moore, 1957
 Fulton, Robert W., 1957
Sesbania paulensis
 Fulton, Robert W., 1957
Sesbania sesban
 Fulton, Robert W., 1957
Sesbania speciosa
 Fulton, Robert W., 1957
Sicana odorifera
 Fulton, Robert W., 1957
Trichosanthes anguina
 Fulton, Robert W., 1957
Trifolium repens
 Fulton, Robert W., 1957
Vinca rosea
 Fulton, Robert W., 1957

V. PRUNUS B *

Antirrhinum majus
 Fulton, Robert W., 1957
Apocynum androsaemifolium
 Fulton, Robert W., 1957
Astragalus rubyi
 Fulton, Robert W., 1957
Benincasa hispida
 Fulton, Robert W., 1957
Boltonia latisquama
 Fulton, Robert W., 1957
Browallia elata
 Fulton, Robert W., 1957
Callistephus chinensis
 Fulton, Robert W., 1957
Carthamus tinctorius
 Fulton, Robert W., 1957
Centaurea imperialis
 Fulton, Robert W., 1957
Citrullus colocynthis
 Fulton, Robert W., 1957
Citrullus vulgaris
 Ehlers, Clifford G. and J. Duain Moore, 1957
 Fulton, Robert W., 1957
Citrullus vulgaris var. citroides
 Fulton, Robert W., 1957
Coleus blumei
 Fulton, Robert W., 1957
Crotalaria capensis
 Fulton, Robert W., 1957
Crotalaria spectabilis
 Fulton, Robert W., 1957
Cucumis anguria
 Fulton, Robert W., 1957
Cucumis dipsaceus
 Fulton, Robert W., 1957
Cucumis melo
 Fulton, Robert W., 1957
Cucumis sativus
 Fulton, Robert W., 1957
Cucurbita ficifolia
 Fulton, Robert W., 1957
Cucurbita maxima
 Fulton, Robert W., 1957

VIRUS

V. PRUNUS B * (cont.)

Cucurbita moschata
Fulton, Robert W., 1957
Cucurbita okeechobeensis
Fulton, Robert W., 1957
Cucurbita pepo
Fulton, Robert W., 1957
Cyamopsis tetragonoloba
Ehlers, Clifford G. and J. Duain Moore, 1957
Cyclanthera pedata
Fulton, Robert W., 1957
Cynoglossum amabile
Fulton, Robert W., 1957
Datura stramonium
Fulton, Robert W., 1957
Echinocystis lobata
Fulton, Robert W., 1957
Gleditsia triacanthos
Fulton, Robert W., 1957
Gossypium hirsutum
Fulton, Robert W., 1957
Ipomoea purpurea
Fulton, Robert W., 1957
Lactuca sativa
Fulton, Robert W., 1957
Lagenaria siceraria (Lagenaria leucantha)
Fulton, Robert W., 1957
Melilotus alba
Fulton, Robert W., 1957
Melilotus indica
Fulton, Robert W., 1957
Melilotus officinalis
Fulton, Robert W., 1957
Melothria guadalupensis
Fulton, Robert W., 1957
Melothria pendula
Fulton, Robert W., 1957
Momordica balsamina
Fulton, Robert W., 1957
Momordica charantia
Fulton, Robert W., 1957
Nepeta cataria
Fulton, Robert W., 1957
Nicotiana benthamiana
Fulton, Robert W., 1957
Nicotiana spp.
Fulton, Robert W., 1957
Nicotiana tabacum
Ehlers, Clifford G. and J. Duain Moore, 1957
Fulton, Robert W., 1956, 1957
Nierembergia hippomanica
Fulton, Robert W., 1957
Petunia hybrida
Fulton, Robert W., 1957
Phlox drummondii
Fulton, Robert W., 1957
Physalis aequata
Fulton, Robert W., 1957
Plantago virginica
Fulton, Robert W., 1957
Prunus americana x Prunus salicina
Ehlers, Clifford G. and J. Duain Moore, 1957
Prunus cerasus
Ehlers, Clifford G. and J. Duain Moore, 1957
Fulton, Robert W., 1957
Prunus mahaleb
Fulton, Robert W., 1957
Prunus pensylvanica
Fulton, Robert W., 1957
Prunus serotina
Fulton, Robert W., 1957
Prunus virginiana
Fulton, Robert W., 1957
Salpiglossis sinuata
Fulton, Robert W., 1957
Sesbania bispinosa
Fulton, Robert W., 1957
Sesbania cannabina
Fulton, Robert W., 1957
Sesbania cinerascens
Fulton, Robert W., 1957
Sesbania exaltata
Ehlers, Clifford G. and J. Duain Moore, 1957

VIRUS

V. PRUNUS B * (cont.)

Sesbania exaltata
Fulton, Robert W., 1957
Sesbania paulensis
Fulton, Robert W., 1957
Sesbania sesban
Fulton, Robert W., 1957
Sesbania speciosa
Fulton, Robert W., 1957
Sicana odorifera
Fulton, Robert W., 1957
Solidago spp.
Fulton, Robert W., 1957
Tithonia speciosa
Fulton, Robert W., 1957
Thunbergia alata
Fulton, Robert W., 1957
Trichosanthes anguina
Fulton, Robert W., 1957
Trifolium repens
Fulton, Robert W., 1957
Verbascum thapsus
Fulton, Robert W., 1957
Vinca rosea
Fulton, Robert W., 1957
Zinnia elegans
Fulton, Robert W., 1957

V. PRUNUS E * (cont.)

Antirrhinum majus
Fulton, Robert W., 1957
Apocynum androsaemifolium
Fulton, Robert W., 1957
Benincasa hispida
Fulton, Robert W., 1957
Carthamus tinctorius
Fulton, Robert W., 1957
Cassia marilandica
Fulton, Robert W., 1957
Cassia tora
Fulton, Robert W., 1957
Centaurea imperialis
Fulton, Robert W., 1957
Citrullus vulgaris
Ehlers, Clifford G. and J. Duain Moore, 1957
Coleus blumei
Fulton, Robert W., 1957
Crotalaria intermedia
Fulton, Robert W., 1957
Crotalaria mucronata
Fulton, Robert W., 1957
Cucumis anguria
Fulton, Robert W., 1957
Cucumis dipsaceus
Fulton, Robert W., 1957
Cucumis melo
Fulton, Robert W., 1957
Cucumis prophetarum
Fulton, Robert W., 1957
Cucumis sativus
Fulton, Robert W., 1957
Cucurbita ficifolia
Fulton, Robert W., 1957
Cucurbita maxima
Fulton, Robert W., 1957
Cucurbita moschata
Fulton, Robert W., 1957
Cucurbita okeechobeensis
Fulton, Robert W., 1957
Cucurbita pepo
Fulton, Robert W., 1957
Cyamopsis tetragonoloba
Ehlers, Clifford G. and J. Duain Moore, 1957
Fulton, Robert W., 1957
Cyclanthera pedata
Fulton, Robert W., 1957
Echinocystis lobata
Fulton, Robert W., 1957
Gossypium hirsutum
Fulton, Robert W., 1957
Ipomoea purpurea
Fulton, Robert W., 1957

VIRUS
V. PRUNUS E * (cont.)
  Melothria guadalupensis
    Fulton, Robert W., 1957
  Melothria pendula
    Fulton, Robert W., 1957
  Momordica balsamina
    Fulton, Robert W., 1957
  Nicotiana benthamiana
    Fulton, Robert W., 1957
  Nicotiana tabacum
    Ehlers, Clifford G. and J. Duain Moore, 1957
  Petunia hybrida
    Fulton, Robert W., 1957
  Prunus americana x Prunus salicina
    Ehlers, Clifford G. and J. Duain Moore, 1957
  Prunus cerasus
    Ehlers, Clifford G. and J. Duain Moore, 1957
    Fulton, Robert W., 1957
  Prunus mahaleb
    Fulton, Robert W., 1957
  Prunus pensylvanica
    Fulton, Robert W., 1957
  Prunus serotina
    Fulton, Robert W., 1957
  Prunus virginiana
    Fulton, Robert W., 1957
  Sesbania bispinosa
    Fulton, Robert W., 1957
  Sesbania cannabina
    Fulton, Robert W., 1957
  Sesbania cinerascens
    Fulton, Robert W., 1957
  Sesbania exaltata
    Ehlers, Clifford G. and J. Duain Moore, 1957
    Fulton, Robert W., 1957
  Sesbania paulensis
    Fulton, Robert W., 1957
  Sesbania speciosa
    Fulton, Robert W., 1957
  Sicana odorifera
    Fulton, Robert W., 1957
  Trichosanthes anguina
    Fulton, Robert W., 1957

V. PRUNUS G *
  Antirrhinum majus
    Fulton, Robert W., 1957
  Apocynum androsaemifolium
    Fulton, Robert W., 1957
  Asclepias syriaca
    Fulton, Robert W., 1957
  Carthamus tinctorius
    Fulton, Robert W., 1957
  Cassia tora
    Fulton, Robert W., 1957
  Centaurea imperialis
    Fulton, Robert W., 1957
  Crotalaria intermedia
    Fulton, Robert W., 1957
  Crotalaria mucronata
    Fulton, Robert W., 1957
  Cucumis anguria
    Fulton, Robert W., 1957
  Cucumis dipsaceus
    Fulton, Robert W., 1957
  Cucumis melo
    Fulton, Robert W., 1957
  Cucumis prophetarum
    Fulton, Robert W., 1957
  Cucumis sativus
    Fulton, Robert W., 1957
  Cucurbita ficifolia
    Fulton, Robert W., 1957
  Cucurbita maxima
    Fulton, Robert W., 1957
  Cucurbita moschata
    Fulton, Robert W., 1957
  Cucurbita okeechobeensis
    Fulton, Robert W., 1957
  Cyamopsis tetragonoloba
    Fulton, Robert W., 1957
  Cyclanthera pedata
    Fulton, Robert W., 1957

VIRUS
V. PRUNUS G * (cont.)
  Echinocystis lobata
    Fulton, Robert W., 1957
  Gomphrena globosa
    Fulton, Robert W., 1957
  Hedysarum coronarium
    Fulton, Robert W., 1957
  Indigofera hirsuta
    Fulton, Robert W., 1957
  Ipomoea purpurea
    Fulton, Robert W., 1957
  Melilotus alba
    Fulton, Robert W., 1957
  Melothria guadalupensis
    Fulton, Robert W., 1957
  Momordica balsamina
    Fulton, Robert W., 1957
  Nicotiana tabacum
    Fulton, Robert W., 1957
  Petunia hybrida
    Fulton, Robert W., 1957
  Pisum sativum
    Fulton, Robert W., 1957
  Potentilla palustris
    Fulton, Robert W., 1957
  Prunus americana x Prunus salicina
    Ehlers, Clifford G. and J. Duain Moore, 1957
  Prunus cerasus
    Ehlers, Clifford G. and J. Duain Moore, 1957
    Fulton, Robert W., 1957
  Prunus mahaleb
    Fulton, Robert W., 1957
  Prunus pensylvanica
    Fulton, Robert W., 1957
  Prunus serotina
    Fulton, Robert W., 1957
  Prunus virginiana
    Fulton, Robert W., 1957
  Rheum rhaponticum
    Fulton, Robert W., 1957
  Sesbania bispinosa
    Fulton, Robert W., 1957
  Sesbania cannabina
    Fulton, Robert W., 1957
  Sesbania cinerascens
    Fulton, Robert W., 1957
  Sesbania exaltata
    Fulton, Robert W., 1957
  Sesbania paulensis
    Fulton, Robert W., 1957
  Sesbania speciosa
    Fulton, Robert W., 1957
  Sicana odorifera
    Fulton, Robert W., 1957
  Trichosanthes anguina
    Fulton, Robert W., 1957
  Verbascum thapsus
    Fulton, Robert W., 1957
  Vinca rosea
    Fulton, Robert W., 1957
  Zinnia elegans
    Fulton, Robert W., 1957

V. PRIVET MOSAIC *
  Chenopodium amaranticolor
    Hollings, M., 1956

V. PSORALEA BITUMINOSA MOSAIC *
  Psoralea bituminosa
    McKinney, H.H., 1928

V. QUINCE SOOTY RING SPOT *
  Cydonia oblonga
    Posnette, A.F., 1957
  Pyrus communis
    Posnette, A.F., 1957

V. QUINCE STUNT *
  Cydonia oblonga
    Posnette, A.F., 1957
  Pyrus communis
    Posnette, A.F., 1957

VIRUS
V. RADISH MOSAIC Tompkins 1939
  Brassica adpressa
    Tompkins, C.M., 1939
  Brassica campestris
    Raychaudhuri, S.P. and P.S. Pathanian, 1955
  Brassica hirta (Brassica alba)
    Raychaudhuri, S.P. and P.S. Pathanian, 1955
    Tompkins, C.M., 1939
  Brassica juncea (Brassica japonica)
    Raychaudhuri, S.P. and P.S. Pathanian, 1955
    Takahashi, William N., 1952
    Tompkins, C.M., 1939
  Brassica kaber (Brassica arvensis)
    Tompkins, C.M., 1939
  Brassica nigra
    Raychaudhuri, S.P. and P.S. Pathanian, 1955
    Tompkins, C.M., 1939
  Brassica oleracea
    Raychaudhuri, S.P. and P.S. Pathanian, 1955
  Brassica oleracea var. acephala
    Tompkins, C.M., 1939
  Brassica oleracea var. botrytis
    Raychaudhuri, S.P. and P.S. Pathanian, 1955
    Tompkins, C.M., 1939
  Brassica oleracea var. capitata
    Raychaudhuri, S.P. and P.S. Pathanian, 1955
    Tompkins, C.M., 1939
  Brassica oleracea var. caulorapa
    Tompkins, C.M., 1939
  Brassica oleracea var. gemmifera
    Tompkins, C.M., 1939
  Brassica pekinensis
    Tompkins, C.M., 1939
  Brassica rapa
    Raychaudhuri, S.P. and P.S. Pathanian, 1955
    Takahashi, William N., 1952
    Tompkins, C.M., 1939
  Capsella bursa-pastoris
    Tompkins, C.M., 1939
  Chenopodium album
    Tompkins, C.M., 1939
  Chenopodium murale
    Tompkins, C.M., 1939
  Delphinium ajacis
    Tompkins, C.M., 1939
  Malcomia maritima
    Tompkins, C.M., 1939
  Matthiola bicornis
    Tompkins, C.M., 1939
  Matthiola incana
    (K.M. Smith, 1957) R.E. Fitzpatrick, et al., 1958
  Nicotiana glutinosa
    Tompkins, C.M., 1939
  Nicotiana langsdorffii
    Tompkins, C.M., 1939
  Nicotiana rustica var. humulis *
    Tompkins, C.M., 1939
  Nicotiana tabacum
    Tompkins, C.M., 1939
  Raphanus sativus
    Raychaudhuri, S.P. and P.S. Pathanian, 1955
    Severin, Henry H.P. and C.M. Tompkins, 1950
    Takahashi, William N., 1952
    Tompkins, C.M., 1939
  Raphanus sativus var. longipinnatus *
    Tompkins, C.M., 1939
  Spinacia oleracea
    Tompkins, C.M., 1939

V. RANUNCULUS MOSAIC K.M. Smith 1957
  Cucumis sativus
    (K.M. Smith, 1957) R.E. Fitzpatrick, et al., 1958
  Gomphrena globosa
    (K.M. Smith, 1957) R.E. Fitzpatrick, et al., 1958
  Nicotiana glutinosa
    (K.M. Smith, 1957) R.E. Fitzpatrick, et al., 1958
  Nicotiana tabacum
    (K.M. Smith, 1957) R.E. Fitzpatrick, et al., 1958
  Phaseolus vulgaris
    Raabe, Robert D. and A. Herbert Gold, 1957
  Ranunculus asiasticus
    Raabe, Robert D. and A. Herbert Gold, 1957
  Tetragonia expansa
    (K.M. Smith, 1957) R.E. Fitzpatrick, et al., 1958

VIRUS
V. RAPE SAVOY F.O. Holmes 1939
  Brassica chinensis
    Ling, Lee and Juhwa Y. Yang, 1940
  Brassica juncea (Brassica japonica)
    Ling, Lee and Juhwa Y. Yang, 1940
  Brassica napus
    Ling, Lee and Juhwa Y. Yang, 1940
  Brassica pekinensis
    Ling, Lee and Juhwa Y. Yang, 1940
  Brassica rapa
    Ling, Lee and Juhwa Y. Yang, 1940
  Raphanus sativus var. longipinnatus *
    Ling, Lee and Juhwa Y. Yang, 1940

V. RASPBERRY ALPHA LEAF CURL
  Rubus allegheniensis
    Bennett, C.W., 1927
  Rubus idaeus var. strigosus
    Bennett, C.W., 1927, 1930
    Rankin, W.H., J.F. Hockey and J.B. McCurry,
    1922
  Rubus macropetalus
    Bennett, C.W., 1927
  Rubus occidentalis
    Rankin, W.H. and J.F. Hockey, 1922
  Rubus phoenicolasius
    Rankin, W.H. and J.F. Hockey, 1922
  Rubus strigosus
    Bennett, C.W., 1927
    Rankin, W.H. and J.F. Hockey, 1922

V. RASPBERRY BETA LEAF CURL
  Rubus idaeus var. strigosus
    Bennett, C.W., 1930
  Rubus neglectus
    Bennett, C.W., 1927
  Rubus occidentalis
    Bennett, C.W., 1927, 1930
    Rankin, W. Howard, 1931

V. RASPBERRY CURLY DWARF Prentice and Harris
  Rubus idaeus   1950
    (K.M. Smith, 1957) R.E. Fitzpatrick, et al., 1958

V. RASPBERRY LEAF SPOT Cadman 1952
  Rubus idaeus
    Cadman, C.H., 1952

V. RASPBERRY (MILD) YELLOWS Cadman 1952
  Rubus idaeus
    Cadman, C.H., 1952

V. RASPBERRY (MODERATE) VEIN CHLOROSIS Cadman
  Rubus idaeus   1952
    Cadman, C.H., 1952

V. RASPBERRY MOSAIC 2 *
  Rubus idaeus
    Cadman, C.H., 1952
    Harris, R.V., 1940
    Prentice, I.W. and R.V. Harris, 1950

V. RASPBERRY NECROTIC FERN LEAF MOSAIC
  Rubus idaeus   Chamberlain 1941
    Chamberlain, G.C., 1941
  Rubus occidentalis
    Chamberlain, G.C., 1941

V. RASPBERRY SCOTTISH LEAF CURL Harris et al.
  Beta vulgaris   1953
    Harrison, B.D., 1958
  Chenopodium amaranticolor
    Harrison, B.D., 1958
    Lister, R.M., 1958
  Cirsium arvense
    Harrison, B.D., 1958
  Cucumis sativus
    Harrison, B.D., 1958
    Lister, R.M., 1958
  Datura stramonium
    Cadman, C.H., 1956
    Harrison, B.D., 1958
    Lister, R.M., 1958

VIRUS

V. RASPBERRY SCOTTISH LEAF CURL (cont.)
Fragaria vesca
Lister, R.M., 1958
Vaughan, Edward K. and Harold W. Wiedman, 1955
Hyoscyamus niger
Cadman, C.H., 1956
Matricaria matricarioides
Harrison, B.D., 1958
Myosotis arvensis
Harrison, B.D., 1958
Nicotiana glutinosa
Cadman, C.H., 1956
Nicotiana rustica
Cadman, C.H., 1956
Harrison, B.D., 1958
Lister, R.M., 1958
Nicotiana tabacum
Cadman, C.H., 1956
Harrison, B.D., 1957, 1958
Lister, R.M., 1958
Petunia hybrida
Harrison, B.D., 1958
Lister, R.M., 1958
Petunia spp.
Cadman, C.H., 1956
Phaseolus vulgaris
Cadman, C.H., 1956
Harrison, B.D., 1958
Lister, R.M., 1958
Polygonum convolvulus
Harrison, B.D., 1958
Rubus idaeus
Cadman, C.H., 1956
Cadman, C.H. and R.V. Harris, 1952
Harrison, B.D., 1958
Spergula arvensis
Harrison, B.D., 1957, 1958
Stellaria media
Harrison, B.D., 1958
Veronica persica
Harrison, B.D., 1958

V. RASPBERRY STREAK Zeller 1923
Cuscuta subinclusa
(K.M. Smith, 1957) R.E. Fitzpatrick, et al., 1958
Rubus occidentalis
Bennett, C.W., 1927
Horn, Norman L., 1948
Horn, N.L. and M.W. Woods, 1949
Rankin, W. Howard, 1931

V. RASPBERRY VEINBANDING Cadman 1952
Rubus idaeus
Cadman, C.H., 1952
Harris, R.V., 1940
Prentice, I.W. and R.V. Harris, 1950
Rubus idaeus var. strigosus
Cadman, C.H., 1952
Rubus occidentalis
Cadman, C.H., 1952
Rubus occidentalis x Rubus idaeus
Cadman, C.H., 1952
Rubus saxatilis
Cadman, C.H., 1952

V. RASPBERRY YELLOW BLOTCH CURL Chamberlain
Fragaria vesca   1938
Vaughan, Edward K. and Harold W. Wiedman, 1955
Rubus idaeus
Cadman, C.H. and R.V. Harris, 1952
(K.M. Smith, 1957) R.E. Fitzpatrick, et al., 1958
Rubus idaeus var. strigosus
Zeller, S.M. and A.J. Braun, 1943

V. RASPBERRY YELLOW DWARF
Anagallis arvensis
Harrison, B.D., 1958
Beta vulgaris
Harrison, B.D., 1958
Brassica pekinensis
Harrison, B.D., 1958
Brassica rapa
Harrison, B.D., 1958

VIRUS

V. RASPBERRY YELLOW DWARF (cont.)
Cerastium spp.
Harrison, B.D., 1958
Chenopodium amaranticolor
Harrison, B.D., 1958
Lister, R.M., 1958
Cucumis sativus
Harrison, B.D., 1958
Datura stramonium
Harrison, B.D., 1958
Fragaria vesca
Harrison, B.D., 1958
Lister, R.M., 1958
Gomphrena globosa
Harrison, B.D., 1958
Kickxia spuria
Harrison, B.D., 1958
Lycopersicon esculentum
Harrison, B.D., 1958
Nicotiana glutinosa
Harrison, B.D., 1958
Nicotiana rustica
Harrison, B.D., 1958
Lister, R.M., 1958
Nicotiana tabacum
Harrison, B.D., 1958
Lister, R.M., 1958
Petunia hybrida
Harrison, B.D., 1958
Lister, R.M., 1958
Phaseolus vulgaris
Harrison, B.D., 1958
Lister, R.M., 1958
Plantago spp.
Harrison, B.D., 1958
Rubus idaeus
Harrison, B.D., 1958
Taraxacum officinale
Harrison, B.D., 1958
Trifolium spp.
Harrison, B.D., 1958

V. RASPBERRY YELLOW MOSAIC Bennett 1927
Rubus idaeus var. strigosus
Bennett, C.W., 1932
Rubus occidentalis
Bennett, C.W., 1927, 1932
Rankin, W. Howard, 1931

V. RED CLOVER MOSAIC *
Cicer arietinum
Zaumeyer, W.J. and B.L. Wade, 1935
Lathyrus odoratus
Doolittle, S.P. and F.R. Jones, 1925
Zaumeyer, W.J. and B.L. Wade, 1935
Lens esculenta
Zaumeyer, W.J. and B.L. Wade, 1935
Medicago arabica
Elliott, J.A., 1921
Medicago lupulina
Dickson, B.T., 1922
Melilotus alba
Elliott, J.A., 1921
Phaseolus aureus
Zaumeyer, W.J. and B.L. Wade, 1935
Phaseolus vulgaris
Harrison, Arthur L., 1935
Pisum sativum
Doolittle, S.P. and F.R. Jones, 1925
Zaumeyer, W.J. and B.L. Wade, 1933, 1935, 1936
Trifolium hybridum
Dickson, B.T., 1922
Trifolium incarnatum
Dickson, B.T., 1922
Trifolium pratense
Dickson, B.T., 1922
Dickson, B.T. and G.P. McRostie, 1922
Elliott, J.A., 1921
Zaumeyer, W.J. and B.L. Wade, 1935
Trifolium repens
Dickson, B.T., 1922
Vicia americana
Zaumeyer, W.J. and B.L. Wade, 1935

VIRUS
V. RED CLOVER MOSAIC * (cont.)
Vicia faba
Elliott, J.A., 1921
Zaumeyer, W.J. and B.L. Wade, 1935, 1936

V. RED CLOVER VEIN MOSAIC Osborn 1937
Glycine max
Hagedorn, D.J., 1952
Lathyrus hirsutus
Hagedorn, D.J. and J.C. Walker, 1949, 1954
Lathyrus odoratus
Hagedorn, D.J. and E.W. Hanson, 1951
Hagedorn, D.J. and J.C. Walker, 1949, 1954
Osborn, H.T., 1937
Roberts, D.A., 1957
Lupinus angustifolius
Hagedorn, D.J. and J.C. Walker, 1949, 1954
Medicago lupulina
Graves, Clinton H., Jr. and D.J. Hagedorn, 1956
Melilotus alba
Graves, Clinton H., Jr. and D.J. Hagedorn, 1956
Hagedorn, D.J. and E.W. Hanson, 1951
Hagedorn, D.J. and J.C. Walker, 1949, 1954
Hanson, E.W. and D.J. Hagedorn, 1954, 1956
Osborn, H.T., 1937
Melilotus indica
Hagedorn, D.J. and E.W. Hanson, 1953
Melilotus officinalis
Graves, Clinton H., Jr. and D.J. Hagedorn, 1956
Hagedorn, D.J. and E.W. Hanson, 1957
Hagedorn, D.J. and J.C. Walker, 1949, 1954
Phaseolus vulgaris
Graves, Clinton H., Jr. and D.J. Hagedorn, 1956
Pisum sativum
Graves, Clinton H., Jr. and D.J. Hagedorn, 1956
Hagedorn, D.J., 1952, 1954
Hagedorn, D.J. and E.W. Hanson, 1951
Hagedorn, D.J. and J.C. Walker, 1949, 1954
Hanson, E.W. and D.J. Hagedorn, 1954
Osborn, H.T., 1937
Roberts, D.A., 1957
Pisum sativum var. arvense
Hagedorn, D.J. and J.C. Walker, 1949, 1954
Osborn, H.T., 1937
Trifolium hybridum
Graves, Clinton H., Jr. and D.J. Hagedorn, 1956
Hagedorn, D.J. and E.W. Hanson, 1951, 1953, 1957
Hagedorn, D.J. and J.C. Walker, 1949, 1954
Hanson, E.W. and D.J. Hagedorn, 1954, 1956
Osborn, H.T., 1937
Trifolium incarnatum
Hagedorn, D.J., 1952
Hagedorn, D.J. and E.W. Hanson, 1951, 1953, 1957
Hagedorn, D.J. and J.C. Walker, 1949, 1954
Hanson, E.W. and D.J. Hagedorn, 1954, 1956
Osborn, H.T., 1937
Trifolium pratense
Graves, Clinton H., Jr. and D.J. Hagedorn, 1956
Hagedorn, D.J., 1952
Hagedorn, D.J. and E.W. Hanson, 1951, 1953, 1957
Hagedorn, D.J. and J.C. Walker, 1949, 1954
Hanson, E.W. and D.J. Hagedorn, 1952, 1954, 1956
Osborn, H.T., 1937, 1938
Trifolium repens
Hagedorn, D.J. and E.W. Hanson, 1951
Hagedorn, D.J. and J.C. Walker, 1954
Osborn, H.T., 1937
Roberts, D.A., 1957
Trifolium repens var. latum *
Graves, Clinton H., Jr. and D.J. Hagedorn, 1956
Trigonella feonum-graecum
Hagedorn, D.J., 1952
Hagedorn, D.J. and J.C. Walker, 1949, 1954
Vicia atropurpurea
Hagedorn, D.J. and J.C. Walker, 1949, 1954
Vicia faba
Hagedorn, D.J. and E.W. Hanson, 1951
Osborn, H.T., 1937
Roberts, D.A., 1957
Vicia faba var. minor *
Hagedorn, D.J. and J.C. Walker, 1954
Vicia grandiflora
Hagedorn, D.J. and J.C. Walker, 1949, 1954

VIRUS
V. RED CLOVER VEIN MOSAIC (cont.)
Vicia monantha
Hagedorn, D.J. and J.C. Walker, 1949, 1954
Vicia sativa
Hagedorn, D.J. and J.C. Walker, 1949, 1954

V. RED CURRANT MOSAIC Hildebrand 1939
Ribes rubrum
Hildebrand, E.M., 1939

V. RED CURRANT RING SPOT Klesser 1951
Amaranthus tricolor
Klesser, P.J., 1951
Cucumis sativus
Klesser, P.J., 1951
Datura stramonium
Klesser, P.J., 1951
Lycopersicon esculentum
Klesser, P.J., 1951
Nicandra physalodes
Klesser, P.J., 1951
Nicotiana glauca
Klesser, P.J., 1951
Nicotiana glutinosa
Klesser, P.J., 1951
Nicotiana rustica
Klesser, P.J., 1951
Nicotiana sylvestris
Klesser, P.J., 1951
Nicotiana tabacum
Klesser, P.J., 1951
Petunia hybrida
Klesser, P.J., 1951
Physalis angulata
Klesser, P.J., 1951
Ribes rubrum
Klesser, P.J., 1951
Solanum muricatum
Klesser, P.J., 1951
Solanum nigrum
Klesser, P.J., 1951
Solanum nodiflorum
Klesser, P.J., 1951
Spinacea oleracea
Klesser, P.J., 1951
Tetragonia expansa
Klesser, P.J., 1951
Zinnia elegans
Klesser, P.J., 1951

V. RED RASPBERRY MOTTLE MOSAIC *
Rubus idaeus
Vaughan, Edward K. and Harold W. Wiedman, 1955
Rubus idaeus var. strigosus
Vaughan, Edward K. and Harold W. Wiedman, 1955
Rubus occidentalis
Vaughan, Edward K. and Harold W. Wiedman, 1955

V. RHUBARB MOSAIC *
Rheum officinale
(K.M. Smith, 1957) R.E. Fitzpatrick, et al., 1958
Rumex obtusifolius
(K.M. Smith, 1957) R.E. Fitzpatrick, et al., 1958

V. RHUBARB RING SPOT *
Cucumis sativus
Vaughan, Edward K. and John W. Yale, Jr., 1953
Yale, John W., Jr. and Edward K. Vaughan, 1954
Dianthus barbatus
Vaughan, Edward K. and John W. Yale, Jr., 1953
Yale, John W., Jr. and Edward K. Vaughan, 1954
Fagopyrum esculentum
Vaughan, Edward K. and John W. Yale, Jr., 1953
Yale, John W., Jr. and Edward K. Vaughan, 1954
Phaseolus vulgaris
Vaughan, Edward K. and John W. Yale, Jr., 1953
Yale, John W., Jr. and Edward K. Vaughan, 1954
Rheum rhaponticum
Vaughan, Edward K. and John W. Yale, Jr., 1953
Yale, John W., Jr. and Edward K. Vaughan, 1954
Rumex crispus
Vaughan, Edward K. and John W. Yale, Jr., 1953
Yale, John W., Jr. and Edward K. Vaughan, 1954

VIRUS
V. RHUBARB RING SPOT * (cont.)
  Spinacia oleracea
    Vaughan, Edward K. and John W. Yale, Jr., 1953
    Yale, John W., Jr. and Edward K. Vaughan, 1954
  Vicia faba
    Vaughan, Edward K. and John W. Yale, Jr., 1953
    Yale, John W., Jr. and Edward K. Vaughan, 1954
  Zinnia elegans
    Vaughan, Edward K. and John W. Yale, Jr., 1953
    Yale, John W., Jr. and Edward K. Vaughan, 1954

V. RICE AND CORN LEAF GALL *
  Coix lachryma-jobi
    Agati, Julian A. and Carlos A. Calica, 1950
  Dactyloctenium aegyptium
    Agati, Julian A. and Carlos A. Calica, 1950
  Eleusine indica
    Agati, Julian A. and Carlos A. Calica, 1950
  Holcus halepensis
    Agati, Julian A. and Carlos A. Calica, 1950
  Ischaemum rogusum
    Agati, Julian A. and Carlos A. Calica, 1950
  Oryza minuta
    Agati, Julian A. and Carlos A. Calica, 1950
  Oryza sativa
    Agati, Julian A. and Carlos Calica, 1949
  Rottboellia exaltata
    Agati, Julian A. and Carlos Calica, 1950
  Saccharum officinarum
    Agati, Julian A. and Carlos A. Calica, 1950
  Sorghum vulgare
    Agati, Julian A. and Carlos A. Calica, 1950
  Zea mays
    Agati, Julian A. and Carlos Calica, 1949

V. RICE DWARF Fukushi 1931
  Alopecurus fulvus
    (K.M. Smith, 1957) R.E. Fitzpatrick, et al., 1958
  Avena sativa
    (K.M. Smith, 1957) R.E. Fitzpatrick, et al., 1958
  Echinochloa crus-galli var. edulis
    (K.M. Smith, 1957) R.E. Fitzpatrick, et al., 1958
  Oryza sativa
    Agati, Julian A., Pedro L. Sison and Roman
    Abalos, 1941
    Katsura, S., 1936
  Panicum miliaceum
    (K.M. Smith, 1957) R.E. Fitzpatrick, et al., 1958
  Poa pratensis
    (K.M. Smith, 1957) R.E. Fitzpatrick, et al., 1958
  Secale cereale
    (K.M. Smith, 1957) R.E. Fitzpatrick, et al., 1958
  Triticum aestivum
    (K.M. Smith, 1957) R.E. Fitzpatrick, et al., 1958

V. ROBINIA BROOMING K.M. Smith 1957
  Robinia pseudoacacia
    Grant, Theodore J., 1939
    Hartley, C. and L.W.R. Jackson, 1933
    Jackson, L.W.R. and C. Hartley, 1933

V. ROSE COWL FORMING Klastersky 1951
  Rosa spp.
    (K.M. Smith, 1957) R.E. Fitzpatrick, et al., 1958
  Tilia platyphyllos
    (K.M. Smith, 1957) R.E. Fitzpatrick, et al., 1958
  Tilia spp.
    (K.M. Smith, 1957) R.E. Fitzpatrick, et al., 1958

V. ROSE MOSAIC Weiss and McWhorter 1928
  Citrullus vulgaris
    Fulton, Robert W., 1952
  Convolvulus tricolor
    Fulton, Robert W., 1952
  Crotalaria intermedia
    Fulton, Robert W., 1952
  Cucumis sativus
    Fulton, Robert W., 1952
  Cucurbita maxima
    Fulton, Robert W., 1952
  Cucurbita pepo
    Fulton, Robert W., 1952

VIRUS
V. ROSE MOSAIC (cont.)
  Cyamopsis tetragonoloba
    Fulton, Robert W., 1952
  Cynara cardunculus
    Fulton, Robert W., 1952
  Dolichos biflorus
    Fulton, Robert W., 1952
  Fragaria spp.
    Fulton, Robert W., 1952
  Fragaria vesca
    Fulton, Robert W., 1952
  Nerium oleander
    Fulton, Robert W., 1952
  Nicotiana benthamiana
    Fulton, Robert W., 1952
  Nicotiana forgetiana
    Fulton, Robert W., 1952
  Nicotiana fragrans
    Fulton, Robert W., 1952
  Nicotiana glutinosa
    Fulton, Robert W., 1952
  Nicotiana occidentalis
    Fulton, Robert W., 1952
  Nicotiana rustica
    Fulton, Robert W., 1952
  Petunia hybrida
    Fulton, Robert W., 1952
  Phaseolus aconitifolius
    Fulton, Robert W., 1952
  Phaseolus aureus
    Fulton, Robert W., 1952
  Phaseolus vulgaris
    Fulton, Robert W., 1952
  Potentilla monspeliensis
    Fulton, Robert W., 1952
  Potentilla recta
    (K.M. Smith, 1957) R.E. Fitzpatrick, et al., 1958
    Fulton, Robert W., 1952
  Rosa canina
    Brierley, Philip and Floyd F. Smith, 1940
  Rosa chinensis var. manetti
    Brierley, Philip and Floyd F. Smith, 1940
    Nelson, R., 1930
    Thomas, H. Earl and L.M. Massey, 1939
    White, R.P., 1930, 1932
  (Rosa chinensis x Rosa moschata) x Rosa foetida
    Nelson, R., 1930
  Rosa hugonis
    Brierley, Philip and Floyd F. Smith, 1940
  Rosa hybrid
    Thomas, H. Earl and L.M. Massey, 1939
  Rosa multiflora
    Brierley, Philip and Floyd F. Smith, 1940
    Fulton, Robert W., 1952
    Thomas, H. Earl and L.M. Massey, 1939
    White, R.P., 1930, 1932
  Rosa multiflora x Rosa chinensis
    Brierley, Philip and Floyd F. Smith, 1940
  Rosa noisettiana
    Brierley, Philip and Floyd F. Smith, 1940
  Rosa nutkana
    Brierley, Philip and Floyd F. Smith, 1940
  Rosa odorata
    Brierley, Philip and Floyd F. Smith, 1940
    Nelson, R., 1930
    Thomas, H. Earl and L.M. Massey, 1939
    White, R.P., 1930, 1932, 1934
  Rosa setigera
    Fulton, Robert W., 1952
  Rosa spp.
    Brierley, Philip and Floyd F. Smith, 1940
    Thomas, H. Earl and L.M. Massey, 1939
    White, R.P., 1932
  Rosa wichuraiana
    Brierley, Philip and Floyd F. Smith, 1940
  Rubus parviflorus
    (K.M. Smith, 1957) R.E. Fitzpatrick, et al., 1958
  Vigna sinensis
    Fulton, Robert W., 1952
  Vinca rosea
    Fulton, Robert W., 1952

VIRUS
V. ROSE ROSETTE   Thomas and Scott   1953
   Rosa californica
      Thomas, H. Earl and C. Emlen Scott, 1953
   Rosa chinensis var. manetti
      Thomas, H. Earl and C. Emlen Scott, 1953
   Rosa multiflora
      Thomas, H. Earl and C. Emlen Scott, 1953
   Rosa nutkana
      Thomas, H. Earl and C. Emlen Scott, 1953
   Rosa odorata
      Thomas, H. Earl and C. Emlen Scott, 1953
   Rosa odorata var. gigantea
      Thomas, H. Earl and C. Emlen Scott, 1953
   Rosa pisocarpa
      Thomas, H. Earl and C. Emlen Scott, 1953
   Rosa rubrifolia
      Thomas, H. Earl and C. Emlen Scott, 1953
   Rosa spinosissima
      Thomas, H. Earl and C. Emlen Scott, 1953

V. ROSE STREAK   Brierley   1935
   Rosa canina
      Brierley, Philip and Floyd F. Smith, 1940
   Rosa hybrid
      Brierley, P., 1935
   Rosa multiflora
      Brierley, Philip and Floyd F. Smith, 1940
   Rosa multiflora x Rosa chinensis
      Brierley, Philip and Floyd F. Smith, 1940
   Rosa noisettiana
      Brierley, Philip and Floyd F. Smith, 1940
   Rosa nutkana
      Brierley, Philip and Floyd F. Smith, 1940
   Rosa odorata
      Brierley, Philip and Floyd F. Smith, 1940
   Rosa spp.
      Brierley, Philip and Floyd F. Smith, 1940
   Rosa wichuraiana
      Brierley, Philip and Floyd F. Smith, 1940

V. ROSE WILT   Grieve   1931
   Rosa spp.
      (K.M. Smith, 1957) R.E. Fitzpatrick, et al., 1958

V. ROSE YELLOW MOSAIC   Brierley   1935
   Rosa canina
      Brierley, Philip and Floyd F. Smith, 1940
   Rosa chinensis var. manetti
      Brierley, Philip and Floyd F. Smith, 1940
      Thomas, H. Earl and L.M. Massey, 1939
   Rosa hugonis
      Brierley, Philip and Floyd F. Smith, 1940
   Rosa hybrid
      Thomas, H. Earl and L.M. Massey, 1939
   Rosa multiflora
      Brierley, Philip and Floyd F. Smith, 1940
      Thomas, H. Earl and L.M. Massey, 1939
   Rosa multiflora x Rosa chinensis
      Brierley, Philip and Floyd F. Smith, 1940
   Rosa noisettiana
      Brierley, Philip and Floyd F. Smith, 1940
   Rosa nutkana
      Brierley, Philip and Floyd F. Smith, 1940
   Rosa odorata
      Brierley, Philip and Floyd F. Smith, 1940
      Thomas, H. Earl and L.M. Massey, 1939
   Rosa spp.
      Brierley, Philip and Floyd F. Smith, 1940
      Thomas, H. Earl and L.M. Massey, 1939
   Rosa wichuraiana
      Brierley, Philip and Floyd F. Smith, 1940

V. RUBUS STUNT   Prentice   1950
   Rubus fruticosus
      Prentice, I.W., 1951
   Rubus idaeus
      Prentice, I.W., 1951
   Rubus laciniatus
      Prentice, I.W., 1951
   Rubus loganobaccus
      Prentice, I.W., 1951

VIRUS
V. RUBUS YELLOW NET   Stace-Smith   1955
   Rubus albescens
      (K.M. Smith, 1957) R.E. Fitzpatrick, et al., 1958
   Rubus occidentalis
      (K.M. Smith, 1957) R.E. Fitzpatrick, et al., 1958
   Rubus procerus
      (K.M. Smith, 1957) R.E. Fitzpatrick, et al., 1958
   Rubus strigosus
      (K.M. Smith, 1957) R.E. Fitzpatrick, et al., 1958

V. RYEGRASS MOSAIC *
   Avena fatua
      Bruehl, G.W., H. Toko and H.H. McKinney, 1957
   Bromus commutatus
      Bruehl, G.W., H. Toko and H.H. McKinney, 1957
   Bromus mollis
      Bruehl, G.W., H. Toko and H.H. McKinney, 1957
   Bromus racemosus
      Bruehl, G.W., H. Toko and H.H. McKinney, 1957
   Bromus secalinus
      Bruehl, G.W., H. Toko and H.H. McKinney, 1957
   Bromus tectorum
      Bruehl, G.W., H. Toko and H.H. McKinney, 1957
   Dactylis glomerata
      Bruehl, G.W., H. Toko and H.H. McKinney, 1957
   Festuca elatior
      Bruehl, G.W., H. Toko and H.H. McKinney, 1957
   Hordeum leporinum
      Bruehl, G.W., H. Toko and H.H. McKinney, 1957
   Lolium multiflorum
      Bruehl, G.W., H. Toko and H.H. McKinney, 1957
   Lolium perenne
      Bruehl, G.W., H. Toko and H.H. McKinney, 1957
   Lolium remotum
      Bruehl, G.W., H. Toko and H.H. McKinney, 1957
   Lolium temulentum
      Bruehl, G.W., H. Toko and H.H. McKinney, 1957
   Triticum aestivum
      Bruehl, G.W., H. Toko and H.H. McKinney, 1957

V. SALVIA CHLOROSIS *
   Salvia coccinea
      Verma, G.S. and A.K. Bose, 1955

V. SANDAL LEAF CURL MOSAIC   Venkata Rao   1933
   Santalum album
      (K.M. Smith, 1957) R.E. Fitzpatrick, et al., 1958

V. SANDAL SPIKE
   Dodonaea viscosa
      (K.M. Smith, 1957) R.E. Fitzpatrick, et al., 1958
   Santalum album
      Iyengar, A.V. Varadaraja, 1938
      Narasimhan, M.J., 1928
   Stachytarpheta indica
      (K.M. Smith, 1957) R.E. Fitzpatrick, et al., 1958
   Vinca rosea
      (K.M. Smith, 1957) R.E. Fitzpatrick, et al., 1958
   Zizyphus oenoplia
      (K.M. Smith, 1957) R.E. Fitzpatrick, et al., 1958

V. SCAEVOLA FRUTESCENS RING SPOT *
   Scaevola frutescens
      Jensen, D.D., 1949

V. SESAMUM PHYLLODY *
   Sesamum indicum
      Pal, B.P. and Pushkar Nath, 1935
   Sesamum occidentale *
      Vasudeva, R.S. and H.S. Sahambi, 1955
   Sesamum orientale
      Vasudeva, R.S. and H.S. Sahambi, 1955

V. SOIL-BORNE OAT MOSAIC   McKinney   1946, 1953
   Avena byzantina
      McKinney, H.H., 1946
   Avena sativa
      Hadden, S.J. and H.F. Harrison, 1955
      McKinney, H.H., 1946
      Moseman, J.G., U.R. Gore and H.H. McKinney, 1953
   Triticum aestivum
      McKinney, H.H., 1946

VIRUS

V. SOIL-BORNE WHEAT MOSAIC McKinney 1925, 1953
  Hordeum sativum
    McKinney, H.H., 1930
  Hordeum vulgare
    McKinney, H.H., 1948
  Secale cereale
    McKinney, H.H., 1925, 1930
    Sill, W.J., Jr., 1955
  Triticum aestivum
    Bever, Wayne M. and J.W. Pendleton, 1954
    Koehler, Benjamin, W.M. Bever and O.T. Bonnett, 1952
    McKinney, H.H., 1925, 1947, 1948
    Moseman, J.G., H.H. McKinney and C.W. Roane, 1954
    Roane, C.W., T.M. Starling and H.H. McKinney, 1954
    Wadsworth, D.F. and H.C. Young, Jr., 1953
  Triticum compactum
    McKinney, H.H., 1930
  Triticum dicoccum
    McKinney, H.H., 1930
  Triticum durum
    McKinney, H.H., 1930
  Triticum monococcum
    McKinney, H.H., 1930
  Triticum polonicum
    McKinney, H.H., 1930
  Triticum spelta
    McKinney, H.H., 1930, 1953
    Wadsworth, D.F. and H.C. Young, Jr., 1953
  Triticum turgidum
    McKinney, H.H., 1930
  Triticum vulgare
    McKinney, H.H., 1930

V. (SOUR) CHERRY YELLOWS Keitt and Clayton 1939, 1943
  Cucumis sativus
    Gilmer, R.M., K.D. Brase and K.G. Parker, 1957
    Willison, R.S., 1951
  Cucurbita maxima
    Milbrath, J.A., 1956
  Prunus armeniaca
    Moore, J. Duain and H.R. Cameron, 1956
  Prunus avium
    Cation, Donald, 1952
    Richards, B.L. and L.C. Cochran, 1956
  Prunus cerasus
    Berkeley, G.H. and R.S. Willison, 1948
    Cation, Donald, 1952
    Fink, Harry C., 1955
    Fulton, Robert W., 1956
    Gilmer, R.M., K.D. Brase and K.G. Parker, 1957
    Hildebrand, E.M., 1942, 1943, 1944
    Hildebrand, E.M. and W.D. Mills, 1941
    Keitt, G.W. and C.N. Clayton, 1939, 1940, 1941, 1943
    Milbrath, J.A., 1957
    Moore, J. Duain and H.R. Cameron, 1956
    Moore, J. Duain and G.W. Keitt, 1944, 1946
    Moore, J. Duain and D.A. Slack, 1952
    Nyland, George, 1952
    Rasmussen, E.J. and Donald Cation, 1942
    Richards, B.L. and L.C. Cochran, 1956
  Prunus domestica
    Berkeley, G.H., 1947
    Berkeley, G.H. and R.S. Willison, 1948
    Hildebrand, E.M., 1944
    Moore, J. Duain, 1951
    Moore, J. Duain and H.R. Cameron, 1956
    Richards, B.L. and L.C. Cochran, 1956
  Prunus mahaleb
    Berkeley, G.H. and R.S. Willison, 1948
    Cation, Donald, 1949, 1952
    Keitt, G.W. and C.N. Clayton, 1943
    Rasmussen, E.J. and Donald Cation, 1942
    Richards, B.L. and L.C. Cochran, 1956
  Prunus pensylvanica
    Keitt, G.W. and C.N. Clayton, 1943
  Prunus persica
    Berkeley, G.H., 1947
    Berkeley, G.H. and R.S. Willison, 1948
    Cation, Donald, 1949
    Gilmer, R.M., K.D. Brase and K.G. Parker, 1957
    Hildebrand, E.M., 1942, 1943, 1944

VIRUS

V. (SOUR) CHERRY YELLOWS (cont.)
  Prunus persica
    Rasmussen, E.J. and Donald Cation, 1942
    Richards, B.L. and L.C. Cochran, 1956
    Young, H.C., Jr., 1951
  Prunus serotina
    Keitt, G.W. and C.N. Clayton, 1943
    Richards, B.L. and L.C. Cochran, 1956
  Prunus tomentosa
    Fink, Harry C., 1955
    Young, H.C., Jr., 1951
  Prunus virginiana
    Keitt, G.W. and C.N. Clayton, 1943
    Richards, B.L. and L.C. Cochran, 1956
  Sesbania exaltata
    Fulton, Robert W., 1956

V. SOYBEAN MOSAIC Gardner and Kendrick 1921
  Glycine max
    Conover, Robert A., 1948
    Gardner, Max W. and James B. Kendrick, 1921
    Kendrick, James B. and Max W. Gardner, 1924
    Pierce, W.H., 1935

V. SOYBEAN NEW DISEASE *
  Glycine max
    Dunleavy, John, 1957
  Melilotus alba
    Dunleavy, John, 1957
  Setaria virdis
    Dunleavy, John, 1957

V. SPARAXIS MOSAIC Smith and Brierley 1944
  Sparaxis spp.
    Smith, Floyd F. and Philip Brierley, 1944
  Tritonia crocata
    Smith, Floyd F. and Philip Brierley, 1944

V. SPINACH YELLOW DWARF Severin and Little 1947
  Spinacia oleracea
    Severin, Henry H.P. and Donald H. Little, 1947

V. SQUASH MOSAIC Middleton 1949
  Anthriscus cerefolium
    Freitag, J.H., 1956
  Citrullus vulgaris
    Lindberg, G.D., D.H. Hall and J.C. Walker, 1956
  Citrullus vulgaris var. citroides
    Freitag, J.H., 1956
  Coriandrum sativum
    Freitag, J.H., 1956
  Cucumis anguria
    Freitag, J.H., 1956
  Cucumis melo
    Freitag, J.H., 1956
    Lindberg, G.D., D.H. Hall and J.C. Walker, 1956
  Cucumis sativus
    Freitag, J.H., 1956
    Lindberg, G.D., D.H. Hall and J.C. Walker, 1956
  Cucurbita maxima
    Freitag, J.H., 1941, 1952, 1956
    Lindberg, G.D., D.H. Hall and J.C. Walker, 1956
  Cucurbita mixta
    Freitag, J.H., 1956
  Cucurbita moschata
    Freitag, J.H., 1956
    Lindberg, G.D., D.H. Hall and J.C. Walker, 1956
  Cucurbita pepo
    Freitag, J.H., 1956
    Lindberg, G.D., D.H. Hall and J.C. Walker, 1956
    Middleton, John T., 1944
  Cucurbita pepo var. melopepo
    Freitag, J.H., 1956
  Lagenaria siceraria (Lagenaria leucantha)
    Freitag, J.H., 1956
  Lathyrus odoratus
    Freitag, J.H., 1956
  Momordica charantia
    Freitag, J.H., 1956
  Phacelia campanularia
    Freitag, J.H., 1956
  Trichosanthes anguina
    Freitag, J.H., 1956

VIRUS
V. SQUASH MOSAIC (SOUTHERN) Anderson 1951
   Citrullus vulgaris
      Anderson, C.W., 1951
   Cucumis sativus
      Anderson, C.W., 1951
   Cucurbita moschata
      Anderson, C.W., 1951
   Pisum sativum
      Freitag, J.H., 1956

V. STACHYTARPHETA CAYENNENSIS MOSAIC *
   Stachytarpheta cayennensis
      Jensen, D.D., 1949

V. (STANDARD) PRUNE CONSTRICTING MOSAIC   Thomas
and Rawlins 1951
   Prunus domestica
      (K.M. Smith, 1957) R.E. Fitzpatrick, et al., 1958
      Thomas, H. Earl and T.E. Rawlins, 1939
   Prunus persica
      (K.M. Smith, 1957) R.E. Fitzpatrick, et al., 1958
      Thomas, H. Earl and T.E. Rawlins, 1939

V. STOCK MOSAIC Tompkins 1939
   Matthiola incana
      Tompkins, C.M., 1934

V. STONE FRUIT *
   Cucumis sativus
      Boyle, J.S., J. Duain Moore and G.W. Keitt, 1954
      Lindner, R.C., Hugh C. Kirkpatrick and T.E.
       Weeks, 1955
   Cucurbita maxima
      Boyle, J.S., J. Duain Moore and G.W. Keitt, 1954
   Plantago major
      Boyle, J.S., J. Duain Moore and G.W. Keitt, 1954
   Prunus americana
      Boyle, J.S., J. Duain Moore and G.W. Keitt, 1954
   Prunus avium
      Boyle, J.S., J. Duain Moore and G.W. Keitt, 1954
   Prunus cerasus
      Boyle, J.S., J. Duain Moore and G.W. Keitt, 1954
   Prunus domestica
      Boyle, J.S., J. Duain Moore and G.W. Keitt, 1954
   Prunus dunbarii
      Boyle, J.S., J. Duain Moore and G.W. Keitt, 1954
   Prunus glandulosa
      Boyle, J.S., J. Duain Moore and G.W. Keitt, 1954
   Prunus japonica
      Boyle, J.S., J. Duain Moore and G.W. Keitt, 1954
   Prunus maackii
      Boyle, J.S., J. Duain Moore and G.W. Keitt, 1954
   Prunus mahaleb
      Boyle, J.S., J. Duain Moore and G.W. Keitt, 1954
   Prunus padus
      Boyle, J.S., J. Duain Moore and G.W. Keitt, 1954
   Prunus pensylvanica
      Boyle, J.S., J. Duain Moore and G.W. Keitt, 1954
   Prunus pumila
      Boyle, J.S., J. Duain Moore and G.W. Keitt, 1954
   Prunus serotina
      Boyle, J.S., J. Duain Moore and G.W. Keitt, 1954
   Prunus virginiana
      Boyle, J.S., J. Duain Moore and G.W. Keitt, 1954

V. STONE FRUIT NECROTIC RING SPOT *
   Cucumis sativus
      Gilmer, R.M., 1956
   Cucurbita pepo
      Willison, R.S., 1951
   Prunus armeniaca
      Moore, J. Duain and H.R. Cameron, 1956
   Prunus cerasus
      Moore, J. Duain and H.R. Cameron, 1956
   Prunus domestica
      Fridlund, Paul R., 1954
      Moore, J. Duain and H.R. Cameron, 1956
   Prunus tomentosa
      Fridlund, Paul R., 1954
   Prunus virginiana
      Fridlund, Paul R., 1954

VIRUS
V. STONE FRUIT RING SPOT *
   Cucumis sativus
      Heinis, J.L., 1956
      Heinis, J.L. and J.A. Milbrath, 1954
   Cucurbita maxima
      Milbrath, J.A., 1956
   Prunus armeniaca
      Richards, B.L. and L.C. Cochran, 1956
   Prunus avium
      Heinis, Julius L., 1956
      Heinis, J.L. and J.A. Milbrath, 1954
      Richards, B.L. and L.C. Cochran, 1956
   Prunus besseyi
      Boyle, J.S., J. Duain Moore and G.W. Keitt, 1954
   Prunus cerasus
      Heinis, J.L. and J.A. Milbrath, 1954
      Millikan, D.F., 1955
      Richards, B.L. and L.C. Cochran, 1956
   Prunus domestica
      Richards, B.L. and L.C. Cochran, 1956
   Prunus mahaleb
      Heinis, J.L. and J.A. Milbrath, 1954
   Prunus persica
      Heinis, Julius L., 1956
      Heinis, J.L. and J.A. Milbrath, 1954
      Richards, B.L. and L.C. Cochran, 1956
   Prunus serrulata
      Heinis, Julius L., 1956
      Heinis, J.L. and J.A. Milbrath, 1954
      Richards, B.L. and L.C. Cochran, 1956

V. STRAWBERRY CRINKLE Zeller and Vaughan 1932
   Fragaria bracteata
      Frazier, Norman W., 1951
   Fragaria chiloensis
      Harris, R.V. and Mary E. King, 1942
      Miller, P.W., 1951
      Zeller, S.M., 1933
   Fragaria chiloensis var. ananassa
      Beaumont, A. and L.N. Staniland, 1945
      Miller, P.W., 1952
      Prentice, I.W., 1949, 1952
      Vaughan, E.K., 1933
      Zeller, S.M., 1933
   Fragaria cuneifolia
      Zeller, S.M., 1933
   Fragaria ovalis
      Miller, P.W., 1951
   Fragaria spp.
      Harris, R.V. and Mary E. King, 1942
      Massee, A.M., 1942
   Fragaria vesca
      Demaree, J.B. and C.P. Marcus, 1951
      Harris, R.V. and Mary E. King, 1942
      Massee, A.M., 1942
      Miller, P.W., 1951, 1952
      Prentice, I.W., 1949, 1952
      Prentice, I.W. and Tamsyn M. Woollcombe, 1951
      Smith, Harlan E., 1952
      Smith, Harlan E. and J. Duain Moore, 1952
   Fragaria vesca var. alpina *
      Miller, P.W., 1951

V. STRAWBERRY GREEN PETAL Posnette 1953
   Anagallis arvensis
      Frazier, N.W. and A.F. Posnette, 1957
   Anthemis cotula
      Frazier, N.W. and A.F. Posnette, 1957
   Callistephus chinensis
      Frazier, N.W. and A.F. Posnette, 1957
   Crotalaria juncea
      Rose, B.D. and S.D. Misra, 1938
   Duchesnea indica
      Frazier, N.W. and A.F. Posnette, 1957
   Erodium cicutarium
      Frazier, N.W. and A.F. Posnette, 1957
   Fragaria chiloensis var. ananassa
      Posnette, A.F., 1953
   Fragaria vesca
      Frazier, N.W. and A.F. Posnette, 1957
   Helenium spp.
      Frazier, N.W. and A.F. Posnette, 1957

VIRUS
V. STRAWBERRY GREEN PETAL (cont.)
  Phaseolus vulgaris
    Dana, B.F., 1947
  Solanum tuberosum
    Frazier, N.W. and A.F. Posnette, 1957
  Trifolium incarnatum
    Frazier, N.W. and A.F. Posnette, 1957
  Trifolium pratense
    Frazier, N.W. and A.F. Posnette, 1957
  Trifolium repens
    Frazier, N.W. and A.F. Posnette, 1957

V. STRAWBERRY, ISOLATE I, MILD MOTTLE *
  Fragaria chiloensis var. ananassa
    Rorie, Forest Gay, 1957
  Fragaria vesca
    Rorie, Forest Gay, 1957

V. STRAWBERRY, ISOLATE II *
  Fragaria chiloensis var. ananassa
    Rorie, Forest Gay, 1957
  Fragaria vesca
    Rorie, Forest Gay, 1957

V. STRAWBERRY LATENT Frazier 1953
  Fragaria bracteata
    Frazier, Norman W., 1953
  Fragaria chiloensis
    Miller, P.W., 1951
  Fragaria chiloensis var. ananassa
    McGrew, J.R., 1956
  Fragaria ovalis
    Miller, P.W., 1951
  Fragaria vesca
    Frazier, Norman W., 1953
    McGrew, J.R., 1956

V. STRAWBERRY LEAF BURN *
  Fragaria spp.
    (K.M. Smith, 1957) R.E. Fitzpatrick, et al., 1958

V. STRAWBERRY LEAF ROLL Berkeley and Plakidas
  Fragaria virginiana   1942
    Berkeley, G.H. and A.G. Plakidas, 1942

V. STRAWBERRY MILD MOTTLE *
  Fragaria chiloensis var. ananassa
    McGrew, J.R., 1956
  Fragaria vesca
    McGrew, J.R., 1956

V. STRAWBERRY MILD YELLOW EDGE Prentice 1948
  Fragaria chiloensis var. ananassa
    Prentice, I.W., 1952
  Fragaria vesca
    Prentice, I.W., 1952

V. STRAWBERRY MOSAIC Brandes 1920
  Fragaria spp.
    (K.M. Smith, 1957) R.E. Fitzpatrick, et al., 1958

V. STRAWBERRY MOTTLE Prentice 1952
  Asclepias syriaca
    Smith, Harlan E. and J. Duain Moore, 1952
  Fragaria chiloensis var. ananassa
    Mellor, Frances C. and R.E. Fitzpatrick, 1952
    Prentice, Ian W., 1948, 1952
    Scott, D.H., D.P. Ink, George M. Darrow and
    C.P. Marcus, 1952
  Fragaria vesca
    Demaree, J.B. and C.P. Marcus, 1951
    Prentice, Ian W., 1948, 1952
    Scott, D.H., D.P. Ink, George M. Darrow and
    C.P. Marcus, 1952
    Smith, Harlan E., 1952
    Smith, Harlan E. and J. Duain Moore, 1952
    Stubbs, L.L., 1957
  Fragaria vesca subsp. californica
    Thomas, Harold E., 1949
  Potentilla simplex
    Demaree, J.B. and C.P. Marcus, 1951

VIRUS
V. STRAWBERRY STUNT Zeller and Weaver 1941
  Fragaria chiloensis var. ananassa
    Skiles, R.L. and T.H. King, 1952
    Zeller, S.M. and L.E. Weaver, 1941
  Fragaria vesca
    Skiles, R.L. and T.H. King, 1952

V. STRAWBERRY, TYPE 2 *
  Fragaria chiloensis var. ananassa
    Braun, Alvin J., 1955
    Fulton, R.H., 1954
  Fragaria vesca
    Braun, Alvin J., 1955
    Demaree, J.B. and C.P. Marcus, 1951
    Fulton, R.H., 1954
    Smith, Harlan E., 1952
    Smith, Harlan E. and J. Duain Moore, 1952
  Fragaria vesca subsp. californica
    Thomas, Harold E., 1949
  Potentilla simplex
    Demaree, J.B. and C.P. Marcus, 1951

V. STRAWBERRY VEINBANDING Frazier 1955
  Fragaria californica
    Frazier, Norman W., 1955
  Fragaria chiloensis var. ananassa
    Frazier, Norman W., 1955
  Fragaria vesca
    Frazier, Norman W., 1955

V. STRAWBERRY VEIN CHLOROSIS Prentice 1952
  Fragaria chiloensis var. ananassa
    Prentice, I.W., 1952
  Fragaria vesca
    Prentice, I.W., 1952

V. STRAWBERRY WITCHES' BROOM Zeller 1927
  Fragaria chiloensis var. ananassa
    Mellor, Frances C. and R.E. Fitzpatrick, 1952
    Prentice, Ian W., 1948
    Zeller, S.M., 1927
  Fragaria vesca
    Prentice, Ian W., 1948

V. STREPTANTHERA MOSAIC Smith and Brierley 1944
  Streptanthera cuprea
    Smith, Floyd F. and Philip Brierley, 1944
  Tritonia crocata
    Smith, Floyd F. and Philip Brierley, 1944

V. SUBTERRANEAN CLOVER, APHID-TRANSMITTED *
  Trifolium subterraneum
    Grylls, N.E. and F.C. Butler, 1956

V. SUBTERRANEAN CLOVER MOSAIC Aitken and Grieve
  Glycine max   1943
    Aitken, Y. and B.J. Grieve, 1943
  Lathyrus odoratus
    Aitken, Y. and B.J. Grieve, 1943
  Lupinus angustifolius
    Aitken, Y. and B.J. Grieve, 1943
  Lupinus hirsutus
    Aitken, Y. and B.J. Grieve, 1943
  Lupinus luteus
    Aitken, Y. and B.J. Grieve, 1943
  Lupinus varius
    Aitken, Y. and B.J. Grieve, 1943
  Medicago arabica
    Aitken, Y. and B.J. Grieve, 1943
  Medicago hispida var. denticulata *
    Aitken, Y. and B.J. Grieve, 1943
  Medicago lupulina
    Aitken, Y. and B.J. Grieve, 1943
  Medicago tribuloides
    Aitken, Y. and B.J. Grieve, 1943
  Melilotus alba
    Aitken, Y. and B.J. Grieve, 1943
  Melilotus indica
    Aitken, Y. and B.J. Grieve, 1943
  Phaseolus lunatus f. macrocarpus
    Aitken, Y. and B.J. Grieve, 1943
  Phaseolus vulgaris
    Aitken, Y. and B.J. Grieve, 1943

VIRUS

V. SUBTERRANEAN CLOVER MOSAIC (cont.)
Pisum sativum
    Aitken, Y. and B.J. Grieve, 1943
Trifolium angustifolium
    Aitken, Y. and B.J. Grieve, 1943
Trifolium glomeratum
    Aitken, Y. and B.J. Grieve, 1943
Trifolium hybridum
    Aitken, Y. and B.J. Grieve, 1943
Trifolium incarnatum
    Aitken, Y. and B.J. Grieve, 1943
Trifolium minus
    Aitken, Y. and B.J. Grieve, 1943
Trifolium pratense
    Aitken, Y. and B.J. Grieve, 1943
Trifolium striatum
    Aitken, Y. and B.J. Grieve, 1943
Trigonella foenum-graecum
    Aitken, Y. and B.J. Grieve, 1943
Trigonella ornithopodioides
    Aitken, Y. and B.J. Grieve, 1943
Vicia faba var. major *
    Aitken, Y. and B.J. Grieve, 1943
Vicia faba var. minor *
    Aitken, Y. and B.J. Grieve, 1943

V. SUGARCANE CHLOROTIC STREAK Abbott and Ingram
Saccharum officinarum   1942
    Abbott, E.V., 1945, 1947
    Abbott, E.V. and J.W. Ingram, 1942
    Adsuar, Jose, 1946

V. SUGARCANE DWARF Bell 1932; Storey 1936
Saccharum officinarum
    (K.M. Smith, 1957) R.E. Fitzpatrick, et al., 1958

V. SUGARCANE FIJI DISEASE ((Muir 1910)) Kunkel
1924; Ocfemia 1932; Montgomery and Bell 1933
Saccharum officinarum
    Ocfemia, Gerardo Offimaria, 1934
    Ocfemia, Gerardo Offimaria and Martin S. Celino, 1939
    Ocfemia, G.O., Evaristo A. Hurtado and
    Crispiniano C. Hernandez, 1933

V. SUGARCANE GREEN MOSAIC *
Saccharum officinarum
    Forbes, I.L. and P.J. Mills, 1942

V. SUGARCANE MOSAIC Brandes 1920
Andropogon sorghum
    Lawas, Orencio M. and William L. Fernandez, 1949
Andropogon sorghum var. virgatus *
    (K.M. Smith, 1957) R.E. Fitzpatrick, et al., 1958
Brachiaria platyphylla
    Brandes, E.W. and Peter J. Klaphaak, 1923
Cymbopogon nardus
    Costa, A.S. and M.P. Penteado, 1951
    Lawas, Orencio M. and William L. Fernandez, 1949
Dactyloctenium aegyptium
    Lawas, Orencio M. and William L. Fernandez, 1949
Digitaria corymbosa
    Lawas, Orencio M. and William L. Fernandez, 1949
Digitaria sanguinalis
    Ingram, J.W. and E.M. Summers, 1938
Echinochloa colonum
    Chardon, C.E. and R.A. Veve, 1923
Echinochloa crus-galli
    Brandes, E.W. and Peter J. Klaphaak, 1923
Eleusine indica
    Chardon, C.E. and R.A. Veve, 1923
    Lawas, Orencio M. and William L. Fernandez, 1949
Eragrostis amabilis
    Lawas, Orencio M. and William L. Fernandez, 1949
Euchlaena mexicana
    Chona, B.L. and S.A. Rafay, 1950
Gynerium sagittatum
    Abbott, E.V., 1930
Holcus halepensis
    Lawas, Orencio M. and William L. Fernandez, 1949
Holcus sorghum
    Adsuar, Jose, 1950, 1954
    Brandes, E.W. and Peter J. Klaphaak, 1923

VIRUS

V. SUGARCANE MOSAIC (cont.)
Miscanthus sinensis
    Brandes, E.W. and Peter J. Klaphaak, 1923
Musa textilis
    Lawas, Orencio M. and William L. Fernandez, 1949
Panicum dichotomiflorum
    Brandes, E.W., 1920
    Brandes, E.W. and Peter J. Klaphaak, 1923
Paspalum boscianum
    Brandes, E.W. and Peter J. Klaphaak, 1923
Paspalum conjugatum
    Lawas, Orencio M. and William L. Fernandez, 1949
Pennisetum glaucum
    Brandes, E.W. and Peter J. Klaphaak, 1923
Pennisetum purpureum
    Bruehl, G.W., 1953
Saccharum narenga
    Brandes, E.W. and Peter J. Klaphaak, 1923
Saccharum officinarum
    Abbott, E.V., 1929, 1931, 1949, 1952
    Adsuar, Jose, 1950, 1954
    Brandes, E.W., 1920
    Brandes, E.W. and Peter J. Klaphaak, 1923
    Bruehl, George W., 1953, 1954
    Chardon, C.E. and R.A. Veve, 1923
    Chona, B.L. and S.A. Rafay, 1950
    Costa, A.S. and M.P. Penteado, 1951
    Edgerton, C.W., I.L. Forbes and P.J. Mills, 1937
    Edgerton, C.W. and W.G. Taggart, 1924
    Forbes, I.L. and Jean Dufrenoy, 1943
    Forbes, I.L. and P.J. Mills, 1943, 1945
    Gonzales-Rios, P. and J. Adsuar, 1953
    Ingram, J.W., 1936
    Ingram, J.W. and E.M. Summers, 1938
    Kunkel, L.O., 1927
    Luthra, Jai Chand and Abdus Sattar, 1935
    Matz, Julius, 1933, 1934
    McKinney, H.H., 1929
    Ocfemia, G.O., 1932
    Ocfemia, G.O., Evaristo A. Hurtado and
    Crispiniano C. Hernandez, 1933
    Sein, Francisco, Jr., 1930
    Storey, H.H., 1929
    Summers, E.M., 1934.
    Tate, H.D. and S.R. Vandenberg, 1939
    Tims, E.C., 1935
    Tims, E.C. and C.W. Edgerton, 1931, 1932
    Tims, E.C., P.J. Mills and C.W. Edgerton, 1935
Setaria lutescens
    Brandes, E.W., 1920
    Brandes, E.W. and Peter J. Klaphaak, 1923
Setaria sulcata
    (K.M. Smith, 1957) R.E. Fitzpatrick, et al., 1958
(Chaetochloa) magna
    Brandes, E.W. and Peter J. Klaphaak, 1923
Sorghum arundinaceum
    Storey, H.H., 1929
Sorghum spp.
    Storey, H.H., 1929
Sorghum vulgare
    Costa, A.S. and M.P. Penteado, 1951
    Chona, B.L. and S.A. Rafay, 1950
Sorghum vulgare var. saccharatum
    Brandes, E.W., 1920
    Matz, Julius, 1933
Syntherisma sanguinale
    Brandes, E.W., 1920
    Brandes, E.W. and Peter J. Klaphaak, 1923
    Chardon, C.E. and R.A. Veve, 1923
Tripsacum laxum
    (K.M. Smith, 1957) R.E. Fitzpatrick, et al., 1958
Zea mays
    Brandes, E.W., 1920
    Brandes, E.W. and Peter J. Klaphaak, 1923
    Chona, B.L. and S.A. Rafay, 1950
    Costa, A.S. and M.P. Penteado, 1951
    Lawas, Orencio M. and William L. Fernandez, 1949
    Storey, H.H., 1929
    Tims, E.C., P.J. Mills and C.W. Edgerton, 1935

VIRUS

V. SUGARCANE RATOON STUNTING Steindl and Hughes
Saccharum officinarum   1953
    Bruehl, G.W., 1955
    Steib, R.J., I.L. Forbes and S.J.P. Chilton, 1957

V. SUGARCANE SEREH DISEASE Kunkel 1928
Saccharum officinarum
    (K.M. Smith, 1957) R.E. Fitzpatrick, et al., 1958

V. SUGARCANE STREAK Storey 1925
Eleusine indica
    Storey, H.H. and A.P.D. McClean, 1930
Saccharum officinarum
    (K.M. Smith, 1957) R.E. Fitzpatrick, et al., 1958
Saccharum spp.
    Storey, H.H. and A.P.D. McClean, 1930
Zea mays
    Storey, H.H. and A.P.D. McClean, 1930

V. SUGARCANE YELLOW MOSAIC *
Saccharum officinarum
    Forbes, I.L. and P.J. Mills, 1942

V. SUNFLOWER MOSAIC Traversi 1949
Nicotiana tabacum
    (K.M. Smith, 1957) R.E. Fitzpatrick, et al., 1958
Zea mays
    (K.M. Smith, 1957) R.E. Fitzpatrick, et al., 1958

V. SWEET CLOVER NEW *
Nicotiana tabacum
    Henderson, R.G., 1934
Petunia hybrida
    Henderson, R.G., 1934

V. SWEET PEA MOSAIC *
Lathyrus odoratus
    Zaumeyer, W.J. and B.L. Wade, 1935
Phaseolus vulgaris
    Zaumeyer, W.J., 1933
    Zaumeyer, W.J. and B.L. Wade, 1933, 1935
Pisum sativum
    Doolittle, S.P. and F.R. Jones, 1925
Trifolium pratense
    Doolittle, S.P. and F.R. Jones, 1925

V. SWEET POTATO A
Ipomoea batata
    Sheffield, F.M.L., 1957

V. SWEET POTATO B, STRAINS 1,2,3,4,5 *
Ipomoea batata
    Sheffield, F.M.L., 1957

V. SWEET POTATO FEATHERY MOTTLE Doolittle and
Calonyction aculeatum   Harter 1945
    Webb, Raymon E., 1954
Ipomoea batata
    Webb, Raymon E., 1954
    Webb, R.E. and R.H. Larson, 1954
Ipomoea purpurea
    Webb, R.E., 1954
Merremia sibirica
    Webb, Raymon E., 1954
Quamoclit lobata
    Webb, Raymon E., 1954

V. SWEET POTATO FOLIAGE-SPOTTING DISEASE *
Calonyction aculeatum
    Holmes, Francis O., 1956
Ipomoea batata
    Holmes, Francis O., 1956
Ipomoea tricolor
    Holmes, Francis O., 1956

V. SWEET POTATO INTERNAL CORK Nusbaum 1947
Ipomoea batata
    Aycock, Robert and Morris B. Hughes, 1952
    Feazell, George D., 1953
    Hildebrand, E.M., 1956, 1957
    Hildebrand, E.M. and F.F. Smith, 1956
    Martin, W.J., 1950, 1955
    Nielsen, L.W., 1956

VIRUS

V. SWEET POTATO INTERNAL CORK (cont.)
Ipomoea batata
    Nielsen, L.W. and L.H. Person, 1954
    Nusbaum, C.J., 1947, 1950
    Rankin, H.W., 1950
    Williams, A.S., 1954
Ipomoea hederacea
    Hildebrand, E.M. and H.A. Borthwick, 1956
Ipomoea purpurea
    Hildebrand, E.M., 1956
    Hildebrand, E.M. and H.A. Borthwick, 1956
    Hildebrand, E.M. and F.F. Smith, 1956
Pharbitis diversifolia *
    Hildebrand, E.M. and H.A. Borthwick, 1956
    Hildebrand, E.M. and F.F. Smith, 1956
Pharbitis hederacea
    Hildebrand, E.M. and H.A. Borthwick, 1956

V. SWEET POTATO MOSAIC Sheffield 1953
Capsicum frutescens (Capsicum annuum)
    Elmer, O.H., 1957
Gomphrena globosa
    Elmer, O.H., 1957
Ipomoea batata
    Adsuar, Jose, 1955
    Borders, H.I. and T.J. Ratcliff, 1954
    Elmer, O.H., 1957
    Rosen, H.R., 1926
Ipomoea rubra
    Adsuar, Jose, 1955
Lycopersicon esculentum
    Elmer, O.H., 1957
Nicotiana glutinosa
    Elmer, O.H., 1957
Nicotiana rustica
    Elmer, O.H., 1957
Nicotiana tabacum
    Elmer, O.H., 1957
Petunia hybrida
    Elmer, O.H., 1957
Solanum melongena
    Elmer, O.H., 1957
Vinca minor
    Elmer, O.H., 1957
Zinnia elegans
    Elmer, O.H., 1957

V. TABEBUIA WITCHES' BROOM Cook 1938
Tabebuia pallida
    Cook, M.T., 1937, 1938

V. TEA PHLOEM NECROSIS Bond 1944
Camellia thea *
    Bond, T.E.T., 1944
Thea sinensis (Camellia sinensis)
    Bond, T.E.T., 1947

V. TEASEL MOSAIC Stoner 1951
Dipsacus fullonum
    Stoner, Warren N., 1951
Scabiosa atropurpurea
    Stoner, Warren N., 1951

V. TIGRIDIA MOSAIC Smith and Brierley 1944
Tigridia pavonia
    Smith, Floyd F. and Philip Brierley, 1944
Tritonia crocata
    Smith, Floyd F. and Philip Brierley, 1944

V. TITHONIA ROTUNDIFOLIA MOSAIC *
Tithonia rotundifolia
    Cook, M.T., 1936

V. TROPAEOLUM MOSAIC Jensen 1950
Nicotiana glutinosa
    Silberschmidt, Karl, 1953
Nicotiana tabacum
    Silberschmidt, Karl, 1953
Tropaeolum majus
    Jensen, D.D., 1950
    Silberschmidt, Karl, 1953
Zinnia elegans
    (K.M. Smith, 1957) R.E. Fitzpatrick, et al., 1958
    Silberschmidt, Karl, 1953

VIRUS

V. TROPAEOLUM RING SPOT K.M. Smith 1957
  Nicotiana glutinosa
    (K.M. Smith, 1957) R.E. Fitzpatrick, et al., 1958
  Nicotiana tabacum
    (K.M. Smith, 1957) R.E. Fitzpatrick, et al., 1958
  Petunia spp.
    (K.M. Smith, 1957) R.E. Fitzpatrick, et al., 1958
  Tropaeolum majus
    (K.M. Smith, 1957) R.E. Fitzpatrick, et al., 1958
  Vicia faba
    (K.M. Smith, 1957) R.E. Fitzpatrick, et al., 1958

V. (TUNG) ROUGH BARK *
  Aleurites fordii
    Large, John R., 1949

V. TOBACCO BERGERAC RING SPOT Smith 1937
  Datura stramonium
    (K.M. Smith, 1957) R.E. Fitzpatrick, et al., 1958
  Lycopersicon esculentum
    (K.M. Smith, 1957) R.E. Fitzpatrick, et al., 1958
  Nicotiana glutinosa
    (K.M. Smith, 1957) R.E. Fitzpatrick, et al., 1958
  Nicotiana tabacum
    (K.M. Smith, 1957) R.E. Fitzpatrick, et al., 1958
  Phaseolus vulgaris
    (K.M. Smith, 1957) R.E. Fitzpatrick, et al., 1958

V. TOBACCO BROAD RING SPOT J. Johnson and Fulton
  Acalypha virginica   1940
    Johnson, James and Robert W. Fulton, 1942
  Amaranthus paniculatus
    (K.M. Smith, 1957) R.E. Fitzpatrick, et al., 1958
  Amaranthus retroflexus
    Johnson, James and Robert W. Fulton, 1942
  Antirrhinum majus
    Johnson, James and Robert W. Fulton, 1942
  Apium graveolens
    Johnson, James and Robert W. Fulton, 1942
  Brassica kaber (Brassica arvensis)
    Johnson, James and Robert W. Fulton, 1942
  Brassica nigra
    Johnson, James and Robert W. Fulton, 1942
  Brassica oleracea
    Johnson, James and Robert W. Fulton, 1942
  Brassica oleracea var. capitata
    (K.M. Smith, 1957) R.E. Fitzpatrick, et al., 1958
  Calendula officinalis
    Johnson, James and Robert W. Fulton, 1942
  Callistephus chinensis
    Johnson, James and Robert W. Fulton, 1942
  Capsella bursa-pastoris
    (K.M. Smith, 1957) R.E. Fitzpatrick, et al., 1958
    Johnson, James and Robert W. Fulton, 1942
  Chenopodium album
    Johnson, James and Robert W. Fulton, 1942
  Chenopodium spp.
    (K.M. Smith, 1957) R.E. Fitzpatrick, et al., 1958
  Cucumis sativus
    Johnson, James and Robert W. Fulton, 1940, 1942
  Cucurbita maxima
    Johnson, James and Robert W. Fulton, 1942
  Cynoglossum amabile
    Johnson, James and Robert W. Fulton, 1942
  Datura stramonium
    Johnson, James and Robert W. Fulton, 1942
  Delphinium spp.
    Johnson, James and Robert W. Fulton, 1942
  Dolichos lablab
    Johnson, James and Robert W. Fulton, 1942
  Fagopyrum esculentum
    Johnson, James and Robert W. Fulton, 1942
  Hibiscus esculentus
    Johnson, James and Robert W. Fulton, 1942
  Lycopersicon esculentum
    Johnson, James and Robert W. Fulton, 1942
  Mollugo verticillata
    Holmes, Francis O., 1946
  Nicandra physalodes
    Johnson, James and Robert W. Fulton, 1942
  Nicotiana glutinosa
    Johnson, James and Robert W. Fulton, 1942
  Nicotiana rustica
    Johnson, James and Robert W. Fulton, 1942

VIRUS

V. TOBACCO BROAD RING SPOT (cont.)
  Nicotiana sylvestris
    Johnson, James and Robert W. Fulton, 1942
  Nicotiana tabacum
    Fulton, Robert W., 1941
    Johnson, James and Robert W. Fulton, 1940, 1942
  Nicotiana tabacum var. angustifolia
    Johnson, James and Robert W. Fulton, 1942
  Petunia violacea
    Johnson, James and Robert W. Fulton, 1942
  Phaseolus vulgaris
    Johnson, James and Robert W. Fulton, 1942
  Physalis spp.
    Johnson, James and Robert W. Fulton, 1942
  Pisum sativum
    Johnson, James and Robert W. Fulton, 1942
  Portulaca oleracea
    Johnson, James and Robert W. Fulton, 1942
  Rumex crispus
    Johnson, James and Robert W. Fulton, 1942
  Solanum melongena
    Johnson, James and Robert W. Fulton, 1942
  Solanum nigrum
    Johnson, James and Robert W. Fulton, 1942
  Solanum tuberosum
    Johnson, James and Robert W. Fulton, 1942
  Spinacia oleracea
    Johnson, James and Robert W. Fulton, 1942
  Trifolium incarnatum
    Johnson, James and Robert W. Fulton, 1942
  Tropaeolum majus
    Johnson, James and Robert W. Fulton, 1942
  Vigna sinensis
    Johnson, James and Robert W. Fulton, 1942
  Zinnia elegans
    Johnson, James and Robert W. Fulton, 1942

V. TOBACCO BROKEN RING SPOT Smith and Markham
  Cucumis sativus   1944
    Smith, Kenneth M. and Roy Markham, 1944
  Nicotiana glutinosa
    Smith, Kenneth M. and Roy Markham, 1944
  Nicotiana tabacum
    (K.M. Smith, 1957) R.E. Fitzpatrick, et al., 1958
    Smith, Kenneth M. and Roy Markham, 1944
  Phaseolus vulgaris
    Smith, Kenneth M. and Roy Markham, 1944

V. TOBACCO COARSE ETCH E.M. Johnson 1930
  Datura stramonium
    Johnson, E.M., 1930
  Nicandra physalodes
    Johnson, E.M., 1930
  Nicotiana rustica
    Johnson, E.M., 1930
  Nicotiana tabacum
    Johnson, E.M., 1930
  Physalis heterophylla var. nyctaginea
    Johnson, E.M., 1930
  Physalis pubescens
    Johnson, E.M., 1930
  Phytolacca decandra
    Johnson, E.M., 1930
  Solanum melongena var. esculentum
    Johnson, E.M., 1930

V. TOBACCO ETCH E.M. Johnson 1930
  Brachycome iberidifolia
    Holmes, Francis O., 1946
  Browallia speciosa
    Holmes, Francis O., 1946
  Callistephus chinensis
    Holmes, Francis O., 1946
  Campanula drabifolia
    Holmes, Francis O., 1946
  Capsicum frutescens (Capsicum annuum)
    Anderson, C.W., 1954
    Anderson, C.W. and M.K. Corbett, 1957
    Doolittle, S.P., 1946
    Greenleaf, W.H., 1953, 1956
    Holmes, Francis O., 1942, 1946
    Johnson, E.M., 1930

VIRUS
V. TOBACCO ETCH (cont.)
  Capsicum microcarpum
    Greenleaf, W.H., 1953
  Capsicum pendulum
    Greenleaf, W.H., 1953
  Cassia tora
    Anderson, C.W., 1954
  Celosia argentea
    Holmes, Francis O., 1946
  Charieis heterophylla
    Holmes, Francis O., 1946
  Chenopodium album
    Greenleaf, W.H., 1953
  Chenopodium amaranticolor
    Hollings, M., 1956
  Collinsia bicolor
    Holmes, Francis O., 1946
  Cuscuta californica
    (K.M. Smith, 1957) R.E. Fitzpatrick, et al., 1958
  Cymbalaria muralis
    Holmes, Francis O., 1946
  Datura ferox
    Greenleaf, W.H., 1956
  Datura meteloides
    Bennett, C.W., 1944
  Datura stramonium
    Anderson, C.W. and M.K. Corbett, 1957
    Bawden, F.C. and B. Kassanis, 1941
    Bennett, C.W., 1944
    Fulton, Robert W., 1941
    Greenleaf, W.H., 1956
    Holmes, Francis O., 1942, 1946
    Johnson, E.M., 1930
  Dimorphotheca aurantiaca
    Holmes, Francis O., 1946
  Emmenanthe penduliflora
    Holmes, Francis O., 1946
  Eupatorium lasseauxii
    Holmes, Francis O., 1946
  Gamolepis tagetes
    Holmes, Francis O., 1946
  Gomphrena globosa
    Greenleaf, W.H., 1953
  Gypsophila elegans
    Holmes, Francis O., 1946
  Helipterum humboldtianum
    Holmes, Francis O., 1946
  Hyoscyamus niger
    Bawden, F.C. and B. Kassanis, 1941
  Indigofera hirsuta
    Anderson, C.W. and M.K. Corbett, 1957
  Lamium amplexicaule
    Holmes, Francis O., 1946
  Linaria maroccana
    Holmes, Francis O., 1946
  Lobelia gracilis
    Holmes, Francis O., 1946
  Lobelia inflata
    Holmes, Francis O., 1946
  Lobelia tenuior
    Holmes, Francis O., 1946
  Lycium chinense
    Holmes, Francis O., 1946
  Lycopersicon esculentum
    Anderson, C.W., 1954
    Bawden, F.C. and B. Kassanis, 1941
    Bennett, C.W., 1944
    Doolittle, S.P. and L.J. Alexander, 1951
    Fulton, Robert W., 1941
    Holmes, Francis O., 1942, 1946
    Johnson, E.M., 1930
    MacNeill, Blair H., 1955
    Valleau, W.D. and E.M. Johnson, 1930
  Lycopersicon hirsutum
    Holmes, Francis O., 1946
  Lycopersicon peruvianum
    Holmes, Francis O., 1946
  Lycopersicon pimpinellifolium
    Holmes, Francis O., 1946
  Nemophila maculata
    Holmes, Francis O., 1946
  Nemophila menziesii subsp. insignis
    Holmes, Francis O., 1946

VIRUS
V. TOBACCO ETCH (cont.)
  Nicandra physalodes
    Fulton, Robert W., 1941
    Holmes, Francis O., 1946
    Johnson, E.M., 1930
  Nicotiana acuminata
    Holmes, Francis O., 1946
  Nicotiana alata
    Holmes, Francis O., 1946
  Nicotiana bigelovii
    Holmes, Francis O., 1946
  Nicotiana bonariensis
    Holmes, Francis O., 1946
  Nicotiana caudigera
    Holmes, Francis O., 1946
  Nicotiana clevelandi
    Holmes, Francis O., 1946
  Nicotiana digluta *
    Holmes, Francis O., 1946
  Nicotiana glauca
    Holmes, Francis O., 1946
  Nicotiana glutinosa
    Anderson, C.W., 1954
    Fulton, Robert W., 1941
    Holmes, Francis O., 1942, 1946
  Nicotiana langsdorffii
    Holmes, Francis O., 1946
  Nicotiana longiflora
    Holmes, Francis O., 1946
  Nicotiana nudicaulis
    Holmes, Francis O., 1946
  Nicotiana paniculata
    Holmes, Francis O., 1946
  Nicotiana plumbaginifolia
    Holmes, Francis O., 1946
  Nicotiana repanda
    Holmes, Francis O., 1946
  Nicotiana rustica
    Holmes, Francis O., 1946
    Johnson, E.M., 1930
  Nicotiana sanderae
    Holmes, Francis O., 1946
  Nicotiana solanifolia
    Holmes, Francis O., 1946
  Nicotiana spp.
    Bawden, F.C. and B. Kassanis, 1941
  Nicotiana sylvestris
    Holmes, Francis O., 1946
  Nicotiana tabacum
    Anderson, C.W., 1954
    Bawden, F.C. and B. Kassanis, 1941
    Bennett, C.W., 1944
    Doncaster, J.P. and B. Kassanis, 1946
    Fulton, Robert W., 1941
    Holmes, Francis O., 1941, 1942, 1946
    Johnson, E.M., 1930
    Price, W.C., 1936
    Stover, R.H., 1951
    Valleau, W.D., 1935
  Nicotiana tomentosa
    Holmes, Francis O., 1946
  Nicotiana trigonophylla
    Holmes, Francis O., 1946
  Nicotiana undulata
    Holmes, Francis O., 1946
  Nierembergia hippomanica
    Holmes, Francis O., 1946
  Nolana lanceolata
    Holmes, Francis O., 1946
  Penstemon grandiflorus
    Holmes, Francis O., 1946
  Petunia hybrida
    Holmes, Francis O., 1946
  Petunia violacea
    Fulton, Robert W., 1941
  Phacelia campanularia
    Holmes, Francis O., 1946
  Phacelia ciliata
    Holmes, Francis O., 1946
  Phacelia viscida
    Holmes, Francis O., 1946
  Phacelia whitlavia (Whitlavia grandiflora)
    Holmes, Francis O., 1946

VIRUS

V. TOBACCO ETCH (cont.)

Physalis alkekengi
    Holmes, Francis O., 1946
Physalis angulata
    Holmes, Francis O., 1946
Physalis floridana
    Greenleaf, W.H., 1953
Physalis heterophylla var. nyctaginea
    Johnson, E.M., 1930
Physalis ixocarpa
    Greenleaf, W.H., 1953
Physalis peruviana
    Anderson, C.W., 1954
    Costa, A.S., 1944
    Holmes, Francis O., 1941, 1942, 1946
Physalis pruinosa
    Anderson, C.W., 1954
Physalis pubescens
    Johnson, E.M., 1930
Physalis subglabrata
    Holmes, Francis O., 1943, 1946
Portulaca oleracea
    Holmes, Francis O., 1946
Primula malacoides
    Holmes, Francis O., 1946
Proboscidea louisiana
    Holmes, Francis O., 1946
Salpiglossis sinuata
    Holmes, Francis O., 1946
Schizanthus pinnatus
    Holmes, Francis O., 1946
Silene anglica
    Holmes, Francis O., 1946
Solanum capsicastrum
    Holmes, Francis O., 1946
Solanum carolinense
    Greenleaf, W.H., 1953
    Johnson, E.M., 1930
Solanum integrifolium
    Greenleaf, W.H., 1953
    Holmes, Francis O., 1946
Solanum melongena
    Holmes, Francis O., 1946
Solanum nigrum
    Anderson, C.W. and M.K. Corbett, 1957
    Fulton, Robert W., 1941
    Holmes, Francis O., 1946
Solanum pseudocapsicum
    Greenleaf, W.H., 1953
Solanum tuberosum
    Holmes, Francis O., 1946
Tetragonia expansa
    Holmes, Francis O., 1946
Torenia fournieri
    Holmes, Francis O., 1946
Verbena hybrida
    Holmes, Francis O., 1946
Zaluzianskya villosa
    Holmes, Francis O., 1946
Zinnia elegans
    Holmes, Francis O., 1946
    Price, W.C., 1935

V. TOBACCO GREEN MOSAIC McKinney 1929 ((A synonym of V. Tobacco mosaic K.M. Smith 1957.))

Capsicum frutescens (Capsicum annuum)
    Peterson, Paul D. and H.H. McKinney, 1938
Lycopersicon esculentum
    McKinney, H.H., 1929
Nicotiana glauca
    McKinney, H.H., 1929
Nicotiana langsdorffii
    Peterson, Paul D. and H.H. McKinney, 1938
Nicotiana rustica
    Peterson, Paul D. and H.H. McKinney, 1938
Nicotiana sylvestris
    Peterson, Paul D. and H.H. McKinney, 1938
Nicotiana tabacum
    Dufrenoy, J., 1933
    Peterson, Paul D. and H.H. McKinney, 1938

VIRUS

V. TOBACCO GREEN RING SPOT *

Nicotiana sylvestris
    Price, W.C., 1936
Nicotiana tabacum
    Price, W.C., 1936
    Valleau, W.D., 1935
Vigna sinensis
    Price, W.C., 1936

V. TOBACCO LEAF CURL Storey 1932

Ageratum conyzoides
    Pruthi, Hem Singh and C.K. Samuel, 1939
Althaea rosea
    (K.M. Smith, 1957) R.E. Fitzpatrick, et al., 1958
Carica papaya
    Goenaga, Alvaro, 1945
    Nariani, T.K., 1956
Crotalaria juncea
    Pruthi, Hem Singh and C.K. Samuel, 1937, 1939
Crotalaria usaramoensis
    (K.M. Smith, 1957) R.E. Fitzpatrick, et al., 1958
Datura stramonium
    Vasudeva, R.S. and J. Sam Raj, 1948
Euphorbia hirta
    Pruthi, Hem Singh and C.K. Samuel, 1941
Glycine max
    (K.M. Smith, 1957) R.E. Fitzpatrick, et al., 1958
Launea asplenifolia
    Pruthi, Hem Singh and C.K. Samuel, 1941
Lycopersicon esculentum
    Bird, Julio, 1957
    Nariani, T.K., 1956
    Pal, B.P. and R.K. Tandon, 1937
    Pruthi, Hem Singh and C.K. Samuel, 1941
    Vasudeva, R.S. and J. Sam Raj, 1948
Nicotiana glauca
    (K.M. Smith, 1957) R.E. Fitzpatrick, et al., 1958
Nicotiana glutinosa
    Pal, B.P. and R.K. Tandon, 1937
    Vasudeva, R.S. and J. Sam Raj, 1948
Nicotiana rustica
    Pal, B.P. and R.K. Tandon, 1937
Nicotiana sylvestris
    Vasudeva, R.S. and J. Sam Raj, 1948
Nicotiana tabacum
    Bird, Julio, 1957
    Kerling, L.C.P., 1933
    Nariani, T.K., 1956
    Nariani, T.K. and P.S. Pathanian, 1953
    Pal, B.P. and R.K. Tandon, 1937
    Pruthi, Hem Singh and C.K. Samuel, 1937, 1939, 1941
    Vasudeva, R.S. and J. Sam Raj, 1948
Petunia spp.
    Pal, B.P. and R.K. Tandon, 1937
Physalis angulata
    Bird, Julio, 1957
Physalis peruviana
    Nariani, T.K. and P.S. Pathanian, 1953
Scoparia dulcis
    Pruthi, Hem Singh and C.K. Samuel, 1941
Sida rhombifolia
    Pruthi, Hem Singh and C.K. Samuel, 1941
Solanum caribaeum
    Bird, Julio, 1957
Solanum nigrum
    Pal, B.P. and R.K. Tandon, 1937
    Pruthi, Hem Singh and C.K. Samuel, 1941
Solanum tuberosum
    Vasudeva, R.S. and J. Sam Raj, 1948
Synedrella nodiflora
    (K.M. Smith, 1957) R.E. Fitzpatrick, et al., 1958
Vernonia cinerea
    Pruthi, Hem Singh and C.K. Samuel, 1941
Zinnia elegans
    Kerling, L.C.P., 1933
    Pruthi, Hem Singh and C.K. Samuel, 1941

V. TOBACCO LEAF CURL-LIKE DISEASE *

Nicotiana tabacum
    Morgan, O.D. and H.H. McKinney, 1951

VIRUS
V. TOBACCO LEAF ROLL DISEASE *
Lycopersicon esculentum
Goenaga, Alvaro, 1945
Nicotiana tabacum
Goenaga, Alvaro, 1945
Solanum tuberosum
Goenaga, Alvaro, 1945

V. TOBACCO MOSAIC Allard 1914
Adlumia fungosa
Holmes, Francis O., 1946
Amaranthus graecizans
Holmes, Francis O., 1938
Amaranthus hybridus
Holmes, Francis O., 1938
Amaranthus tricolor
Holmes, Francis O., 1946
Ambrosia artemisiifolia
Boyle, John S. and David C. Wharton, 1957
Holmes, Francis O., 1938
Wingard, S.A., 1928
Ambrosia trifida
Holmes, Francis O., 1938, 1946
Anagallis arvensis
Holmes, Francis O., 1946
Anchusa azurea
Holmes, Francis O., 1946
Anchusa capensis
Holmes, Francis O., 1946
Antirrhinum majus
Berkeley, G.H., 1951
Grant, T.J., 1934
Holmes, Francis O., 1946
Apium graveolens
Holmes, Francis O., 1946
Arctium lappa
Holmes, Francis O., 1946
Aster dumosus
Holmes, Francis O., 1938
Bellis perennis
Holmes, Francis O., 1946
Beta vulgaris
Grant, T.J., 1934
Holmes, Francis O., 1946
Beta vulgaris var. cicla
Grant, T.J., 1934
Bidens frondosa
Holmes, Francis O., 1938, 1946
Brachycome iberidifolia
Holmes, Francis O., 1946
Brassica campestris var. napobrassica
Holmes, Francis O., 1946
Brassica hirta (Brassica alba)
Grant, T.J., 1934
Brassica rapa
Grant, T.J., 1934
Browallia americana (Browallia demissa)
Holmes, Francis O., 1946
Browallia speciosa
Holmes, Francis O., 1946
Browallia speciosa var. major
Holmes, Francis O., 1938
Calendula officinalis
Holmes, Francis O., 1946
Callistephus shinensis
Holmes, Francis O., 1946
Calonyction aculeatum
Holmes, Francis O., 1946
Campanula drabifolia
Holmes, Francis O., 1946
Capsella bursa-pastoris
Holmes, Francis O., 1938, 1946
Capsicum cerasiforme
Allard, H.A., 1916
Capsicum frutescens (Capsicum annuum)
Abbott, E.V., 1931
Ainsworth, G.C., 1933
Anderson, C.W. and M.K. Corbett, 1957
Berkeley, G.H., 1951
Cox, C.E. and L.O. Weaver, 1950
Dale, W.T., 1954
Desjardins, P.R., J.M. Wallace and R.J. Drake, 1954

VIRUS
V. TOBACCO MOSAIC (cont.)
Capsicum frutescens (Capsicum annuum)
Doolittle, S.P. and F.S. Beecher, 1942
Dykstra, T.P., 1939
Greenleaf, W.H., 1953
Heuberger, J.W., 1944
Hoggan, Isme A., 1927
Holmes, F.O., 1934, 1937, 1946
Jensen, D.D., 1949
Johnson, J., 1926, 1927
Kendrick, J.B., Jr., L.D. Anderson and R.C. Dickson, 1951
McKinney, H.H., 1929, 1952
Perez, J. Enrique, J. Adsuar and Orlando Sala, 1956
Schwarze, C.A., 1914
Stover, W.G. and M.T. Vermillion, 1933
Woods, M.W. and Richard V. Eck, 1948
Capsicum frutescens var. Golden Dawn x (var. Golden Dawn x var. minimum)
Holmes, F.O., 1934
Capsicum frutescens var. Golden Dawn x var. minimum
Holmes, F.O., 1934
Capsicum frutescens var. Tabasco x var. Ruby King
Holmes, F.O., 1934
Capsicum microcarpum
Greenleaf, W.H., 1953
Capsicum spp.
McKinney, H.H., 1928
Carica papaya
Holmes, Francis O., 1946
Cattleya spp.
Perez, J. Enrique, J. Adsuar and Orlando Sala, 1956
Celosia argentea
Holmes, Francis O., 1946
Centaurea americana
Holmes, Francis O., 1946
Centaurea montana
Holmes, Francis O., 1946
Cerastium vulgatum
Holmes, Francis O., 1938
Charieis heterophylla
Holmes, Francis O., 1946
Cheiranthus allionii
Holmes, Francis O., 1946
Cheiranthus cheiri
Holmes, Francis O., 1946
Chelidonium majus
Holmes, Francis O., 1938, 1946
Chenopodium album
Holmes, Francis O., 1938, 1946
Chenopodium amaranticolor
Hollings, M., 1956
Chenopodium ambrosioides
Holmes, Francis O., 1938, 1946
Chenopodium glaucum
Holmes, Francis O., 1946
Chenopodium hybridum
Benedict, W.G., 1955
Chenopodium rubrum
Holmes, Francis O., 1946
Chenopodium spp.
(K.M. Smith, 1957) R.E. Fitzpatrick, et al., 1958
Cichorium endivia
Holmes, Francis O., 1946
Cirsium arvense
Boyle, John S. and David C. Wharton, 1956
Citrullus vulgaris
McKinney, H.H. and Robert W. Fulton, 1949
Cleome spinosa
Holmes, Francis O., 1946
Coleus blumei
Holmes, Francis O., 1946
Collinsia bicolor
Holmes, Francis O., 1946
Coreopsis grandiflora
Holmes, Francis O., 1946
Cucumis melo
McKinney, H.H. and Robert W. Fulton, 1949
Cucumis sativus
Berkeley, G.H., 1951
Cox, C.E. and L.O. Weaver, 1950

VIRUS
V. TOBACCO MOSAIC (cont.)
  Cucumis sativus
    Fulton, Robert W., 1950
    McKinney, H.H., 1952
    McKinney, H.H. and Robert W. Fulton, 1949
    Walker, M.N., 1924, 1926
  Cucurbita pepo
    McKinney, H.H. and Robert W. Fulton, 1949
  Cymbalaria muralis
    Holmes, Francis O., 1946
  Cynoglossum amabile
    Fulton, Robert W., 1941
    Grant, T.J., 1934
    Holmes, Francis O., 1946
  Datura metel
    Perez, J. Enrique, J. Adsuar and Orlando Sala,
    1956
  Datura meteloides
    Keener, Paul D., 1954
  Datura stramonium
    Ainsworth, G.C., 1933, 1937
    Ainsworth, G.C., G.H. Berkeley and J. Caldwell,
    1934
    Allard, H.A., 1916
    Anderson, C.W. and M.K. Corbett, 1957
    Berkeley, G.H., 1951
    Caldwell, John, 1932
    Crawford, R.F., 1921
    Das, C.R. and S.P. Raychaudhuri, 1953
    Doolittle, S.P. and F.S. Beecher, 1942
    Holmes, F.O., 1934, 1946
    Jarrett, Phyllis H., 1930
    Johnson, E.M., 1930
    McKinney, H.H., 1952
    McKinney, H.H. and Robert W. Fulton, 1949
    Samson, R.W., 1930
  Daucus carota
    Holmes, Francis O., 1938, 1946
  Daucus carota var. sativa
    Grant, T.J., 1934
  Delphinium consolida
    Grant, T.J., 1934
  Delphinium hybrid
    Severin, Henry H.P., 1942
  Digitalis purpurea
    Grant, T.J., 1934
    Holmes, Francis O., 1946
  Dimorphotheca aurantiaca
    Grant, T.J., 1934
    Holmes, Francis O., 1946
  Echium vulgare
    Holmes, Francis O., 1946
  Emilia flammea
    Holmes, Francis O., 1946
  Emilia sagittata
    Grant, T.J., 1934
  Emmenanthe penduliflora
    Holmes, Francis O., 1946
  Erigeron annuus
    Holmes, Francis O., 1938, 1946
  Erigeron canadensis
    Holmes, Francis O., 1938
  Eryngium aquaticum
    Johnson, James, 1946
  Eupatorium lasseauxii
    Holmes, Francis O., 1946
  Fagopyrum esculentum
    Fulton, Robert W., 1941
    Grant, T.J., 1934
    Holmes, Francis O., 1946
  Galinsoga parviflora
    Holmes, Francis O., 1938, 1946
  Galium triflorum
    Holmes, Francis O., 1938
  Gamolepis tagetes
    Holmes, Francis O., 1946
  Geranium carolinianum
    Holmes, Francis O., 1938, 1946
  Gesneria spp.
    (K.M. Smith, 1957) R.E. Fitzpatrick, et al., 1958
  Gilia capitata
    Holmes, Francis O., 1946

VIRUS
V. TOBACCO MOSAIC (cont.)
  Gilia liniflora
    Holmes, Francis O., 1946
  Gladiolus hortulanus
    Berkeley, G.H., 1951
  Gomphrena globosa
    Desjardins, P.R., J.M. Wallace and R.J. Drake,
    1954
  Gypsophila elegans
    Holmes, Francis O., 1946
  Hedeoma pulegioides
    Holmes, Francis O., 1938
  Helichrysum bracteatum
    Holmes, Francis O., 1946
  Heliotropium corymbosum
    Holmes, Francis O., 1946
  Helipterum humboldtianum
    Holmes, Francis O., 1946
  Hieracium scabrum
    Holmes, Francis O., 1938
  Hyoscyamus niger
    Allard, H.A., 1916
    Hoggan, Isme A., 1927
    Jarrett, Phyllis H., 1930
    Johnson, James, 1927
    Sheffield, F.M.L., 1931, 1936
  Iberis gibraltarica
    Holmes, Francis O., 1946
  Iberis umbellata
    Holmes, Francis O., 1946
  Impatiens sultani (or sometimes Impatiens holstii)
    Holmes, Francis O., 1946
  Incarvillea variabilis
    Holmes, Francis O., 1946
  Ipomoea nil
    Holmes, Francis O., 1946
  Ipomoea tricolor
    Grant, T.J., 1934
    Holmes, Francis O., 1946
  Kalanchoe daigremontiana
    Holmes, Francis O., 1946
  Kochia scoparia
    Holmes, Francis O., 1946
  Lamium amplexicaule
    Holmes, Francis O., 1938, 1946
  Lepidium campestre
    Holmes, Francis O., 1938
  Lepidium ruderale
    Holmes, Francis O., 1938
  Leptosyne maritima
    Holmes, Francis O., 1946
  Limonium bonduelli
    Holmes, Francis O., 1946
  Limonium sinuatum
    Holmes, Francis O., 1946
  Linaria cymbalaria
    Grant, T.J., 1934
  Linaria maroccana
    Holmes, Francis O., 1946
  Linaria vulgaris
    Holmes, Francis O., 1938, 1946
  Lobelia erinus
    Holmes, Francis O., 1946
  Lobelia gracilis
    Holmes, Francis O., 1946
  Lobelia inflata
    Holmes, Francis O., 1938, 1946
  Lobelia tenuior
    Holmes, Francis O., 1946
  Lobularia maritima
    Holmes, Francis O., 1946
  Lunaria annua
    Holmes, Francis O., 1946
  Lychnis coeli-rosa
    Holmes, Francis O., 1946
  Lycium chinense
    Holmes, Francis O., 1946
  Lycium ferocissimum
    (K.M. Smith, 1957) R.E. Fitzpatrick, et al., 1958
  Lycopersicon chilense
    Holmes, Francis O., 1943, 1946
  Lycopersicon esculentum
    Abbott, E.V., 1929, 1931

VIRUS

V. TOBACCO MOSAIC (cont.)

Lycopersicon esculentum
    Ainsworth, G.C., 1933, 1937
    Ainsworth, G.C., G.H. Berkeley and J. Caldwell, 1934
    Ainsworth, G.C. and I.W. Selman, 1936
    Allard, H.A., 1916
    Berkeley, G.H., 1927, 1951
    Berkeley, G.H. and G.O. Madden, 1932, 1933
    Boyle, John S., 1956
    Boyle, John S. and David C. Wharton, 1956, 1957
    Brierley, W.B., 1916
    Burnett, Grover and Leon K. Jones, 1931
    Caldwell, John, 1932
    Cochran, G.W., 1946
    Conover, Robert A. and Robert W. Fulton, 1953
    Costa, A.S., 1944
    Cox, C.E. and L.O. Weaver, 1950
    Dale, W.T., 1954
    Das, C.R. and S.P. Raychaudhuri, 1953 .
    Desai, S.V., 1933
    Desjardins, P.R., J.M. Wallace and R.J. Drake, 1954
    Doering, G.R., W.C. Price and S.B. Fenne, 1957
    Doolittle, S.P., 1928
    Doolittle, S.P. and L.J. Alexander, 1936, 1951
    Doolittle, S.P. and F.S. Beecher, 1942
    Doolittle, S.P. and W.S. Porte, 1949
    Eckerson, Sophia H. and H.R. Karybill, 1927
    Fernow, Karl Hermann, 1925
    Fulton, Robert W., 1941
    Gardner, Max W., 1925
    Gardner, Max W. and James B. Kendrick, 1922
    Heuberger, J.W. and J.B.S. Norton, 1933
    Hoggan, Isme A., 1927
    Holmes, Francis O., 1941, 1943, 1946, 1950
    Jarrett, Phyllis H., 1930
    Jensen, J.H., 1933, 1936
    Johnson, E.M., 1930
    Johnson, J., 1926, 1927
    Jones, Leon K., 1940
    Jones, Leon K. and Grover Burnett, 1935
    Kunkel, L.O., 1932
    MacNeill, Blair H., 1955
    McKinney, H.H., 1929, 1952
    McRitchie, John J., 1957
    McRitchie, John J. and Leonard J. Alexander, 1957
    Mogendorff, N., 1930
    Norval, I.P., 1938
    Perez, J. Enrique, J. Adsuar and Orlando Sala, 1956
    Peterson, Paul D. and H.H. McKinney, 1938
    Price, W.C. and S.B. Fenne, 1951
    Quanjer, H.M., 1920
    Raychaudhuri, S.P., 1952
    Schultz, E.S. and Donald Folsom, 1923
    Selman, Ireson W., 1941, 1943
    Severin, Henry H.P., 1950
    Sheffield, F.M.L., 1931, 1936
    Smith, J. Henderson, 1928, 1933
    Smith, Kenneth M., 1935
    Stover, W.G., 1928
    Stover, W.G. and M.T. Vermillion, 1933
    Valleau, W.D. and E.M. Johnson, 1930, 1943
    Vanterpool, T.C., 1926
    Verwoerd, Len, 1929
    Walker, M.N., 1926
    Watson, R.D., E.C. Heinrich and W.R. Harvey, 1954
    Woods, M.W. and Richard V. Eck, 1948

Lycopersicon esculentum var. cerasiforme
    Gardner, Max W. and James B. Kendrick, 1922

Lycopersicon esculentum var. grandifolium
    Mogendorff, N., 1930

Lycopersicon esculentum var. Sioux x Lycopersicon hirsutum
    Watson, R.D. and E.C. Heinrich, 1951

Lycopersicon esculentum x Lycopersicon chilense
    Holmes, Francis O., 1943

Lycopersicon esculentum x Lycopersicon hirsutum
    Watson, R.D., E.C. Heinrich and W.R. Harvey, 1954

VIRUS

V. TOBACCO MOSAIC (cont.)

Lycopersicon glandulosum
    Doolittle, S.P. and F.S. Beecher, 1942

Lycopersicon hirsutum
    Doolittle, S.P. and F.S. Beecher, 1942
    Doolittle, S.P., W.S. Porte and F.S. Beecher, 1946
    Holmes, Francis O., 1946
    Porte, W.S., S.P. Doolittle and F.L. Wellman, 1939
    Watson, R.D., E.C. Heinrich and W.R. Harvey, 1954

Lycopersicon hirsutum f. glabratum *
    Doolittle, S.P. and F.S. Beecher, 1942

Lycopersicon hirsutum x Lycopersicon esculentum
    Doolittle, S.P. and W.S. Porte, 1949

Lycopersicon peruvianum
    Doolittle, S.P. and F.S. Beecher, 1942
    Holmes, Francis O., 1946
    Nagaich, B.B. and H.H. Thornberry, 1957

Lycopersicon peruvianum subsp. dentatum
    Doolittle, S.P. and F.S. Beecher, 1942

Lycopersicon pimpinellifolium
    Doolittle, S.P. and F.S. Beecher, 1942
    Gardner, Max W. and James B. Kendrick, 1922
    Holmes, Francis O., 1946

Lycopus rubellus
    Holmes, Francis O., 1938, 1946

Lycopus virginicus
    Holmes, Francis O., 1938

Marrubium vulgare
    Holmes, Francis O., 1946

Martynia louisiana
    Fernow, Karl Hermann, 1925
    Grant, T.J., 1934

Matthiola bicornis
    Holmes, Francis O., 1946

Melissa officinalis
    Holmes, Francis O., 1946

Mentha spicata
    Holmes, Francis O., 1946

Mesembryanthemum crystallinum
    Holmes, Francis O., 1946

Mesembryanthemum lineare
    Holmes, Francis O., 1946

Mimulus moschatus
    Holmes, Francis O., 1946

Mimulus tigrinus
    Holmes, Francis O., 1946

Mollugo verticillata
    Holmes, Francis O., 1938, 1946

Myosotis scorpioides
    Holmes, Francis O., 1946

Myosotis sylvatica
    Holmes, Francis O., 1946

Nemesia strumosa
    Holmes, Francis O., 1946

Nemophila maculata
    Holmes, Francis O., 1946

Nemophila menziesii subsp. insignis
    Holmes, Francis O., 1946

Nepeta cataria
    Holmes, Francis O., 1946

Nepeta mussini
    Holmes, Francis O., 1946

Nicandra physalodes
    Crawford, R.F., 1921
    Fulton, Robert W., 1941
    Hoggan, Isme A., 1927
    Holmes, Francis O., 1946
    Jarrett, Phyllis H., 1930
    Johnson, E.M., 1930

Nicotiana acuminata
    Adsuar, J. and L. Lopez Matos, 1955
    Caldwell, John, 1932
    Diachun, Stephen and W.D. Valleau, 1954
    Holmes, Francis O., 1929, 1934, 1946
    Jensen, J.H., 1933
    Kunkel, L.O., 1932

Nicotiana affinis
    Jarrett, Phyllis H., 1930
    McKinney, H.H., 1935

VIRUS
V. TOBACCO MOSAIC (cont.)
  Nicotiana alata
    Diachun, Stephen and W.D. Valleau, 1954
    Holmes, F.O., 1934, 1946
    Kunkel, L.O., 1932
    Weber, Paul V.V., 1951
  Nicotiana arentsii
    Diachun, Stephen and W.D. Valleau, 1954
  Nicotiana attenuata
    Diachun, Stephen and W.D. Valleau, 1954
  Nicotiana benavidesii
    Diachun, Stephen and W.D. Valleau, 1954
  Nicotiana benthamiana
    Adsuar, J. and L. Lopez Matos, 1955
    Diachun, Stephen and W.D. Valleau, 1954
  Nicotiana bigelovii
    Adsuar, J. and L. Lopez Matos, 1955
    Diachun, Stephen and W.D. Valleau, 1954
    Holmes, F.O., 1934, 1946
    Stover, R.H., 1951
  Nicotiana bigelovii var. quadrivalvis x glutinosa
    Holmes, F.O., 1934
  Nicotiana bigelovii var. quadrivalvis x sanderae
    Holmes, F.O., 1934
  Nicotiana bigelovii var. quadrivalvis x tabacum
    Holmes, F.O., 1934
  Nicotiana bonariensis
    Adsuar, J. and L. Lopez Matos, 1955
    Diachun, Stephen and W.D. Valleau, 1954
    Holmes, Francis O., 1946
  Nicotiana caudigera
    Holmes, Francis O., 1946
  Nicotiana caudigera x Nicotiana acuminata
    Holmes, F.O., 1934
  Nicotiana chinensis
    Ferguson, I.A.C., 1951
  Nicotiana clevelandi
    Adsuar, J. and L. Lopez Matos, 1955
    Diachun, Stepehn and W.D. Valleau, 1954
    Holmes, F.O., 1934, 1946
  Nicotiana cordifolia
    Diachun, Stephen and W.D. Valleau, 1954
  Nicotiana corymbosa
    Diachun, Stephen and W.D. Valleau, 1954
  Nicotiana debneyi
    Adsuar, J. and L. Lopez Matos, 1955
    Diachun, Stephen and W.D. Valleau, 1954
  Nicotiana digluta *
    Holmes, Francis O., 1938, 1946
  Nicotiana digluta x Nicotiana tabacum
    Holmes, Francis O., 1938
    Price, W.C. and S.B. Fenne, 1951
  Nicotiana exigua
    Diachun, Stephen and W.D. Valleau, 1954
  Nicotiana fragrans
    Diachun, Stephen and W.D. Valleau, 1954
  Nicotiana glauca
    Allard, H.A., 1917
    Diachun, Stephen and W.D. Valleau, 1954
    Doolittle, S.P. and F.S. Beecher, 1942
    Hoggan, Isme A., 1927
    Holmes, F.O., 1934, 1946
    Jensen, J.H., 1933
    Johnson, J., 1926, 1927
    Keener, Paul D., 1954
    McKinney, H.H., 1928, 1929, 1935, 1943, 1952
  Nicotiana glauca x Nicotiana langsdorffii
    Holmes, F.O., 1934
  Nicotiana glutinosa
    Adsuar, J. and L. Lopez Matos, 1955
    Ainsworth, G.C., 1933, 1937
    Ainsworth, G.C., G.H. Berkeley and J. Caldwell,
      1934
    Anderson, C.W. and M.K. Corbett, 1957
    Bawden, F.C. and F.M. Roberts, 1948
    Berkeley, G.H., 1951
    Best, Rupert J. and Geoffrey Samuel, 1936
    Boyle, John S. and David C. Wharton, 1956, 1957
    Caldwell, John, 1932
    Conover, Robert A. and Robert W. Fulton, 1953
    Costa, A.S., 1944
    Cox, C.E. and L.O. Weaver, 1950

VIRUS
V. TOBACCO MOSAIC (cont.)
  Nicotiana glutinosa
    Desjardins, P.R., J.M. Wallace and R.J. Drake,
      1954
    Diachun, Stephen and W.D. Valleau, 1954
    Doering, G.R., W.C. Price and S.B. Fenne, 1957
    Doolittle, S.P. and F.S. Beecher, 1942
    Dykstra, T.P., 1939
    Hoggan, Isme A., 1927
    Holmes, Francis O., 1929, 1934, 1936, 1941, 1946
    Jensen, J.H., 1933, 1936, 1937
    Johnson, J., 1926, 1927
    Kendrick, J.B., Jr., L.D. Anderson and R.C.
      Dickson, 1951
    Kunkel, L.O., 1932
    McKinney, H.H., 1935, 1943, 1952
    Nagaich, B.B. and H.H. Thornberry, 1957
    Nolla, J.A.B., 1934
    Norval, I.P., 1938
    Peterson, Paul D. and H.H. McKinney, 1938
    Pierce, W.H., 1934
    Price, W.C. and S.B. Fenne, 1951
    Raychaudhuri, S.P., 1952
    Roberts, Daniel A., 1952
    Sheffield, F.M.L., 1936
    Siegel, Albert and Sam G. Wildman, 1954
    Smith, Kenneth M., 1935
    Spencer, E.L., 1935
    Stover, R.H., 1951
    Walker, M.N., 1924, 1925
    Walters, H.J., 1952
    Weber, Paul V.V., 1951
    Woods, M.W. and Richard V. Eck, 1948
  Nicotiana glutinosa x Nicotiana langsdorffii
    Holmes, F.O., 1934
  Nicotiana glutinosa x Nicotiana tabacum
    Fulton, Robert W., 1941
  Nicotiana goodspeedii
    Adsuar, J. and L. Lopez Matos, 1955
    Diachun, Stephen and W.D. Valleau, 1954
  Nicotiana gossei
    Adsuar, J. and L. Lopez Matos, 1955
    Diachun, Stephen and W.D. Valleau, 1954
  Nicotiana knightiana
    Diachun, Stephen and W.D. Valleau, 1954
  Nicotiana langsdorffii
    Ainsworth, G.C., 1937
    Diachun, Stephen and W.D. Valleau, 1954
    Holmes, F.O., 1929, 1934, 1936, 1946
    Jensen, J.H., 1933, 1936
    Kunkel, L.O., 1932, 1934
    Peterson, Paul D. and H.H. McKinney, 1938
    Stover, R.H., 1951
  Nicotiana langsdorffii x Nicotiana sanderae
    Holmes, F.O., 1934
  Nicotiana longiflora
    Adsuar, J. and L. Lopez Matos, 1955
    Diachun, Stephen and W.D. Valleau, 1954
    Holmes, F.O., 1934, 1946
    Stover, R.H., 1951
    Weber, Paul V.V., 1951
  Nicotiana longiflora x Nicotiana alata
    Weber, Paul V.V., 1951
  Nicotiana maritima
    Adsuar, J. and L. Lopez Matos, 1955
    Diachun, Stephen and W.D. Valleau, 1954
  Nicotiana megalosiphon
    Adsuar, J. and L. Lopez Matos, 1955
    Diachun, Stephen and W.D. Valleau, 1954
  Nicotiana multivalis
    (K.M. Smith, 1957) R.E. Fitzpatrick, et al., 1958
  Nicotiana nesophila
    Diachun, Stephen and W.D. Valleau, 1954
  Nicotiana nudicaulis
    Diachun, Stephen and W.D. Valleau, 1954
    Holmes, Francis O., 1946
  Nicotiana occidentalis
    Adsuar, J. and L. Lopez Matos, 1955
    Diachun, Stephen and W.D. Valleau, 1954
  Nicotiana otophora
    Adsuar, J. and L. Lopez Matos, 1955
    Diachun, Stephen and W.D. Valleau, 1954
    Holmes, Francis O., 1946

VIRUS
V. TOBACCO MOSAIC (cont.)
    Nicotiana palmeri
        Adsuar, J. and L. Lopez Matos, 1955
        Diachun, Stephen and W.D. Valleau, 1954
        Holmes, F.O., 1934, 1946
    Nicotiana paniculata
        Adsuar, J. and L. Lopez Matos, 1955
        Diachun, Stephen and W.D. Valleau, 1954
        Doolittle, S.P. and F.S. Beecher, 1942
        Holmes, F.O., 1934, 1946
        Jensen, J.H., 1933
        Kunkel, L.O., 1932
        Woods, M.W. and Richard V. Eck, 1948
    Nicotiana paniculata x Nicotiana rustica
        Holmes, F.O., 1934
    Nicotiana pauciflora
        Diachun, Stephen and W.D. Valleau, 1954
    Nicotiana plumbaginafolia
        Boyle, John S. and David C. Wharton, 1956, 1957
        Diachun, Stephen and W.D. Valleau, 1954
        Holmes, Francis O., 1946
    Nicotiana quadrivalvis
        Doolittle, S.P. and F.S. Beecher, 1942
    Nicotiana raimondii
        Diachun, Stephen and W.D. Valleau, 1954
        Holmes, Francis O., 1946
    Nicotiana repanda
        Adsuar, J. and L. Lopez Matos, 1955
        Diachun, Stephen and W.D. Valleau, 1954
        Holmes, Francis O., 1946
    Nicotiana rotundifolia
        Diachun, Stephen and W.D. Valleau, 1954
    Nicotiana rusbyi
        Kunkel, L.O., 1932
    Nicotiana rustica
        Allard, H.A., 1914-15, 1916
        Boyle, John S. and David C. Wharton, 1956, 1957
        Caldwell, John, 1932
        Das, C.R. and S.P. Raychaudhuri, 1953
        Diachun, Stephen and W.D. Valleau, 1954
        Doolittle, S.P. and F.S. Beecher, 1942
        Fernow, Karl Hermann, 1925
        Holmes, Francis O., 1929, 1934, 1946
        Jensen, J.H., 1933
        Johnson, E.M., 1930
        Johnson, J., 1926, 1927
        Kunkel, L.O., 1932
        McKinney, H.H., 1935
        Peterson, Paul D. and H.H. McKinney, 1938
        Stover, R.H., 1951
    Nicotiana sanderae
        Holmes, Francis O., 1929, 1934, 1946
        Stover, R.H., 1951
    Nicotiana sanderae x Nicotiana langsdorffii
        Holmes, F.O., 1934
    Nicotiana sanderae x Nicotiana sanderae
        Holmes, F.O., 1934
    Nicotiana setchellii
        Diachun, Stephen and W.D. Valleau, 1954
    Nicotiana solanifolia
        Holmes, Francis O., 1946
    Nicotiana stocktoni
        Diachun, Stephen and W.D. Valleau, 1954
    Nicotiana suaveolens
        Diachun, Stephen and W.D. Valleau, 1954
        Holmes, F.O., 1934
        Kunkel, L.O., 1932
    Nicotiana sylvestris
        Boyle, John S. and David C. Wharton, 1956, 1957
        Conover, Robert A. and Robert W. Fulton, 1953
        Diachun, Stephen and W.D. Valleau, 1954
        Doolittle, S.P. and F.S. Beecher, 1942
        Dykstra, T.P., 1939
        Fulton, Robert W., 1951
        Holmes, F.O., 1934, 1941, 1946
        Jensen, J.H., 1933, 1936, 1937
        Kunkel, L.O., 1932, 1934
        McKinney, H.H., 1935, 1952
        Norval, I.P., 1938
        Peterson, Paul D. and H.H. McKinney, 1938
        Price, W.C. and S.B. Fenne, 1951
        Raychaudhuri, S.P., 1952
        Siegel, Albert and Sam G. Wildman, 1954

VIRUS
V. TOBACCO MOSAIC (cont.)
    Nicotiana sylvestris
        Stover, R.H., 1951
        Weber, Paul V.V., 1951
    Nicotiana tabacum
        Ainsworth, G.C., 1933, 1937
        Ainsworth, G.C., G.H. Berkeley and J. Caldwell, 1934
        Allard, H.A., 1914-15, 1915, 1916, 1917
        Bawden, F.C. and F.M. Roberts, 1948
        Beale, Helen P., 1933
        Bennett, C.W., 1944
        Berkeley, G.H., 1927, 1951
        Best, Rupert J. and Geoffrey Samuel, 1936
        Boyle, John S. and David C. Wharton, 1956, 1957
        Caldwell, John, 1932
        Conover, Robert A. and Robert W. Fulton, 1953
        Costa, A.S., 1944
        Cox, C.E. and L.O. Weaver, 1950
        Dale, W.T., 1954
        Das, C.R. and S.P. Raychaudhuri, 1953
        Diachun, Stephen and W.D. Valleau, 1954
        Doolittle, S.P. and F.S. Beecher, 1942
        Dufrenoy, J., 1933
        Fernow, Karl Hermann, 1925
        Fulton, Robert W., 1941
        Gutierrez, Mariano E., 1954
        Gutierrez, Mariano E., Julian Agati and Serapion Bayubay, 1950
        Henderson, R.G., 1950
        Hoggan, Isme A., 1927, 1934
        Holmes, F.O., 1934, 1936, 1941, 1946, 1953
        Jarrett, Phyllis H., 1930
        Jensen, J.H., 1933, 1936, 1937
        Johnson, E.M., 1930
        Johnson, Folke, 1941
        Johnson, J., 1926, 1927
        Jones, Leon K., 1940
        Kassanis, B. and Ireson W. Selman, 1947
        Kunkel, L.O., 1932
        McKinney, H.H., 1935, 1939, 1943, 1952
        McMurtrey, J.E., Jr., 1928, 1929
        Nagaich, B.B. and H.H. Thornberry, 1957
        Nolla, J.A.B., 1934
        Nolla, J.A.B., John Simon Guggenheim and Arturo Roque, 1933
        Norval, I.P., 1938
        Perez, J. Enrique, J. Adsuar and Orlando Sala, 1956
        Peterson, Paul D. and H.H. McKinney, 1938
        Pierce, W.H., 1934
        Price, W.C., 1936
        Price, W.C. and S.B. Fenne, 1951
        Purdy, Helen A., 1927
        Quanjer, H.M., 1920, 1933
        Raychaudhuri, S.P., 1952
        Roberts, Daniel A., 1952
        Schwarze, C.A., 1914
        Sheffield, F.M.L., 1931, 1936
        Siegel, Albert and Sam G. Wildman, 1954
        Smith, J. Henderson, 1933
        Smith, Kenneth M., 1935
        Spencer, E.L., 1935, 1937
        Stover, R.H., 1951
        Stover, W.G., 1928
        Stover, W.G. and M.T. Vermillion, 1933
        Valleau, W.D., 1935
        Valleau, W.D. and E.M. Johnson, 1935, 1943
        Vanterpool, T.C., 1926
        Walker, M.N., 1926
        Walters, H.J., 1952
        Weber, Paul V.V., 1951
        Woods, M.W. and Richard V. Eck, 1948
    Nicotiana tabacum var. angustifolia
        Adsuar, J. and L. Lopez Matos, 1955
    Nicotiana tabacum var. atropurpurea *
        Weber, Paul V.V., 1951
    Nicotiana tabacum var. macrophylla
        Ainsworth, G.C., 1933
        Kunkel, L.O., 1932
    Nicotiana tabacum var. purpurea *
        Kunkel, L.O., 1932

VIRUS

V. TOBACCO MOSAIC (cont.)

Nicotiana tabacum var. purpurea * x glutinosa
Holmes, F.O., 1934
Nicotiana tabacum x Nicotiana glutinosa
Costa, A.S., 1944
Fulton, Robert W., 1950
Holmes, F.O., 1934
Johnson, James, 1936, 1937
McKinney, H.H. and Robert W. Fulton, 1949
Walters, H.J., 1952
Nicotiana tabacum x Nicotiana longiflora
Weber, Paul V.V., 1951
Nicotiana tabacum x Nicotiana sylvestris
Weber, Paul V.V., 1951
Nicotiana tomentosa
Diachun, Stephen and W.D. Valleau, 1954
Holmes, Francis O., 1946
Weber, Paul V.V., 1951
Nicotiana tomentosiformis
Adsuar, J. and L. Lopez Matos, 1955
Diachun, Stephen and W.D. Valleau, 1954
Holmes, Francis O., 1946
Weber, Paul V.V., 1951
Nicotiana trigonophylla
Diachun, Stephen and W.D. Valleau, 1954
Holmes, F.O., 1934, 1946
Nicotiana undulata
Adsuar, J. and L. Lopez Matos, 1955
Diachun, Stephen and W.D. Valleau, 1954
Holmes, Francis O., 1946
Nicotiana velutina
Adsuar, J. and L. Lopez Matos, 1955
Diachun, Stephen and W.D. Valleau, 1954
Nicotiana wigandioides
Holmes, Francis O., 1946
Nierembergia hippomanica
Holmes, Francis O., 1946
Nolana lanceolata
Holmes, Francis O., 1946
Papaver nudicaule
Holmes, Francis O., 1946
Parthenium argentatum
Severin, Henry H.P., 1945
Penstemon barbatus
Grant, T.J., 1934
Penstemon grandiflorus
Holmes, Francis O., 1946
Petroselinum hortense
Holmes, Francis O., 1946
Petunia hybrida
Allard, H.A., 1916
Holmes, Francis O., 1946
Petunia spp.
Ainsworth, G.C., 1933
Das, C.R. and S.P. Raychaudhuri, 1953
Petunia violacea
Fulton, Robert W., 1941
Hoggan, Isme A., 1927
Jarrett, Phyllis H., 1930
Johnson, J., 1926, 1927
Phacelia campanularia
Grant, T.J., 1934
Holmes, Francis O., 1946
Phacelia ciliata
Holmes, Francis O., 1946
Phacelia parryi
Grant, T.J., 1934
Phacelia tanacetifolia
Grant, T.J., 1934
Phacelia viscida
Holmes, Francis O., 1946
Phacelia whitlavia (Whitlavia grandiflora)
Grant, T.J., 1934
Holmes, Francis O., 1946
Phaseolus vulgaris
Berkeley, G.H., 1951
Costa, A.S., 1944
Doolittle, S.P. and F.S. Beecher, 1942
(K.M. Smith, 1957) R.E. Fitzpatrick, et al., 1958
Grant, T.J., 1934
Holmes, F.O., 1934, 1941, 1946
McKinney, H.H., 1943
McKinney, H.H. and Robert W. Fulton, 1949

VIRUS

V. TOBACCO MOSAIC (cont.)

Phaseolus vulgaris
Nagaich, B.B. and H.H. Thornberry, 1957
Peterson, Paul D. and H.H. McKinney, 1938
Pierce, W.H., 1934
Price, W.C., 1930
Silberschmidt, K. and M. Kramer, 1941
Spencer, E.L., 1935
Zaumeyer, W.J. and B.L. Wade, 1935
Phlox drummondii
Grant, T.J., 1934
Holmes, Francis O., 1946
Physalis alkekengi
Doolittle, S.P. and F.S. Beecher, 1942
Hoggan, Isme A., 1927
Holmes, Francis O., 1946
Physalis angulata
Doolittle, S.P. and F.S. Beecher, 1942
Holmes, F.O., 1934, 1941, 1946
Jensen, J.H., 1933
Physalis elliottii
Anderson, C.W. and M.K. Corbett, 1957
Physalis floridana
Ross, A. Frank, 1953
Physalis franchetti
Hoggan, Isme A., 1927
Physalis heterophylla
Doolittle, S.P. and F.S. Beecher, 1942
Fernow, Karl Hermann, 1925
Gardner, Max W. and James B. Kendrick, 1922
Physalis heterophylla var. nyctaginea
Johnson, E.M., 1930
Physalis longifolia
Crawford, R.F., 1921
Physalis peruviana
Holmes, Francis O., 1942, 1946
Physalis pubescens
Ainsworth, G.C., 1933
Doolittle, S.P. and F.S. Beecher, 1942
Hoggan, Isme A., 1927
Johnson, E.M., 1930
Johnson, J., 1926, 1927
Walker, M.N., 1924, 1925, 1926
Physalis subglabrata
Fernow, Karl Hermann, 1925
Gardner, Max W. and James B. Kendrick, 1922
Holmes, Francis O., 1946
Physalis virginiana
Gardner, M.W. and J.B. Kendrick, 1922
Phytolacca decandra
Holmes, Francis O., 1938, 1946
Pisum sativum
Berkeley, G.H., 1951
Plantago lanceolata
Boyle, John S. and David C. Wharton, 1957
Harrison, B.C., 1955
Holmes, Francis O., 1938, 1941, 1946, 1950
McKinney, H.H., 1952
Plantago major
Boyle, John S. and David C. Wharton, 1956
Harrison, B.D., 1955
Holmes, Francis O., 1938, 1941, 1946, 1950
Valleau, W.D. and E.M. Johnson, 1943
Plantago rugelii
Boyle, John S. and David C. Wharton, 1957
Holmes, Francis O., 1938, 1946, 1950
McKinney, H.H., 1952
Polanisia trachysperma
Holmes, Francis O., 1946
Polygonum aviculare
Holmes, Francis O., 1938
Polygonum convolvulus
Holmes, Francis O., 1938
Polygonum erectum
Holmes, Francis O., 1938
Polygonum hydropiper
Holmes, Francis O., 1938, 1946
Polygonum persicaria
Holmes, Francis O., 1938
Portulaca oleracea
Holmes, Francis O., 1946
Primula malacoides
Holmes, Francis O., 1946

VIRUS
V. TOBACCO MOSAIC (cont.)
  Primula obconica
    Holmes, Francis O., 1946
    Severin, Henry H. P. and C. M. Tompkins, 1950
  Proboscidea louisiana
    Holmes, Francis O., 1946
  Prunella vulgaris
    Holmes, Francis O., 1938, 1946
  Quamoclit pennata
    Grant, T. J., 1934
  Radicula palustris
    Holmes, Francis O., 1938
  Rudbeckia hirta
    Holmes, Francis O., 1946
  Rumex acetosella
    Holmes, Francis O., 1938
  Rumex crispus
    Holmes, Francis O., 1938, 1946
  Rumex obtusifolius
    Holmes, Francis O., 1946
  Salpiglossis sinuata
    Holmes, Francis O., 1946
  Salvia azurea
    Holmes, Francis O., 1946
  Salvia farinacea
    Holmes, Francis O., 1946
  Salvia patens
    Holmes, Francis O., 1946
  Salvia splendens
    Holmes, Francis O., 1946
  Schizanthus pinnatus
    Holmes, Francis O., 1946
  Scrophularia marilandica
    Grant, T. J., 1934
  Silene anglica
    Holmes, Francis O., 1946
  Silene pendula
    Holmes, Francis O., 1946
  Sinningia speciosa
    Holmes, Francis O., 1946
  Sisymbrium officinale
    Holmes, Francis O., 1938
  Sisymbrium thalianum
    Holmes, Francis O., 1938
  Solanum aculeatissimum
    Fernow, Karl Hermann, 1925
  Solanum atropurpureum *
    Fernow, Karl Hermann, 1925
    Hoggan, Isme A., 1927
  Solanum cabiliense var. argenteum *
    Hoggan, Isme A., 1927
  Solanum capsicastrum
    Holmes, Francis O., 1946
  Solanum carolinense
    Boyle, John S. and David C. Wharton, 1956, 1957
    Fernow, Karl Hermann, 1925
    Gardner, Max W. and James B. Kendrick, 1922
    Johnson, E. M., 1930
  Solanum ciliatum
    Ainsworth, G. C., 1933
  Solanum dulcamara
    Crawford, R. F., 1921
    Gardner, Max W. and James B. Kendrick, 1922
    Holmes, Francis O., 1946
    Jarrett, Phyllis H., 1930
  Solanum integrifolium
    Gardner, Max W. and James B. Kendrick, 1922
    Holmes, Francis O., 1946
  Solanum laciniatum
    Hoggan, Isme A., 1927
  Solanum marginatum
    Hoggan, Isme A., 1927
  Solanum melongena
    Ainsworth, G. C., 1933
    Das, C. R. and S. P. Raychaudhuri, 1953
    Holmes, F. O., 1934, 1946
    Jensen, J. H., 1933
    Johnson, J., 1926
  Solanum melongena var. esculentum
    Johnson, E. M., 1930
  Solanum melongena var. Hangchow Long x var. Black
  Beauty
    Holmes, F. O., 1934

VIRUS
V. TOBACCO MOSAIC (cont.)
  Solanum melongena var. Peking Green x var. Black
  Beauty
    Holmes, F. O., 1934
  Solanum miniatum
    Hoggan, Isme A., 1927
  Solanum nigrum
    Caldwell, John, 1932
    Crawford, R. F., 1921
    Das, C. R. and S. P. Raychaudhuri, 1953
    Fernow, Karl Hermann, 1925
    Fulton, Robert W., 1941
    Hoggan, Isme A., 1927
    Holmes, Francis O., 1946
    Jarrett, Phyllis H., 1930
    Johnson, J., 1926
    Sheffield, F. M. L., 1931
    Stover, W. G., 1928
    Stover, W. G. and M. T. Vermillion, 1933
  Solanum nigrum var. nodiflorum *
    Holmes, F. O., 1934
  Solanum nigrum var. villosum
    Jarrett, Phyllis H., 1930
  Solanum nodiflorum
    Caldwell, John, 1932
    Jarrett, Phyllis H., 1930
    Sheffield, F. M. L., 1931, 1936
    Smith, J. Henderson, 1930
  Solanum pseudocapsicum
    Greenleaf, W. H., 1953
    Holmes, F. O., 1934
  Solanum pyracanthum
    Hoggan, Isme A., 1927
  Solanum sanitwongsei
    Holmes, Francis O., 1946
  Solanum tuberosum
    Berkeley, G. H., 1927
    Blodgett, F. M., 1927
    Fernow, Karl Hermann, 1925
    Hoggan, Isme A., 1927
    Holmes, Francis O., 1946
    Johnson, James, 1927, 1929
    Jones, Leon K., C. L. Vincent and Earl F. Burk,
    1940
    Quanjer, H. M., 1920
  Spinacia oleracea
    Fulton, Robert W., 1941
    Grant, T. J., 1934
    Holmes, Francis O., 1946
    Jones, L. K., 1934
  Stellaria media
    Holmes, Francis O., 1938, 1946
  Tagetes erecta
    Holmes, Francis O., 1946
  Tagetes patula
    Grant, T. J., 1934
    Holmes, Francis O., 1946
  Tagetes signata
    Holmes, Francis O., 1946
  Tetragonia expansa
    Grant, T. J., 1934
    Holmes, Francis O., 1946
  Torenia fournieri
    Holmes, Francis O., 1946
  Tropaeolum majus
    Holmes, Francis O., 1946
  Tulipa spp.
    (K. M. Smith, 1957) R. E. Fitzpatrick, et al., 1958
  Verbascum phoeniceum
    Holmes, Francis O., 1946
  Verbascum thapsus
    Grant, T. J., 1934
  Verbena canadensis
    Holmes, Francis O., 1946
  Verbena hybrida
    Holmes, Francis O., 1946
  Verbena urticifolia
    Holmes, Francis O., 1938
  Veronica longifolia
    Holmes, Francis O., 1946
  Veronica officinalis
    Holmes, Francis O., 1938, 1946

VIRUS

V. TOBACCO MOSAIC (cont.)
Veronica peregrina
Holmes, Francis O., 1938, 1946
Vigna sinensis
Nagaich, B.B. and H.H. Thornberry, 1957
Zaluzianskya villosa
Holmes, Francis O., 1946
Zinnia elegans
Grant, T.J., 1934
Holmes, Francis O., 1946
Price, W.C., 1935
Zinnia haageana
Holmes, Francis O., 1946

V. TOBACCO MOTTLE Smith 1945
Datura stramonium
(K.M. Smith, 1957) R.E. Fitzpatrick, et al., 1958
Lycopersicon esculentum
(K.M. Smith, 1957) R.E. Fitzpatrick, et al., 1958
Nicotiana glutinosa
(K.M. Smith, 1957) R.E. Fitzpatrick, et al., 1958
Nicotiana tabacum
(K.M. Smith, 1957) R.E. Fitzpatrick, et al., 1958

V. TOBACCO NECROSIS K.M. Smith and Bald 1935;
Price 1938
Ageratum spp.
Price, W.C., 1940
Amaranthus caudatus
Price, W.C., 1940
Anthriscus cerefolium
Price, W.C., 1940
Antirrhinum majus
Price, W.C., 1940
Arachis hypogaea
Fulton, Robert W., 1950
Avena sativa
Fulton, J.P., 1952
Bignonia capreolata
Price, W.C., 1940
Brassica oleracea var. capitata
Fulton, Robert W., 1950
Callistephus chinensis
(K.M. Smith, 1957) R.E. Fitzpatrick, et al., 1958
Campanula medium
Price, W.C., 1940
Capsicum frutescens (Capsicum annuum)
Price, W.C., 1940
Chenopodium amaranticolor
Hollings, M., 1957
Cichorium endivia
Price, W.C., 1940
Citrullus vulgaris
Fulton, Robert W., 1950
Clarkia elegans
Price, W.C., 1940
Cleome spinosa
Price, W.C., 1940
Coleus blumei
Price, W.C., 1940
Price, W.C., Frank P. McWhorter and Betty H.
Steranka, 1950
Convolvulus tricolor
Price, W.C., 1940
Crotalaria intermedia
Price, W.C., 1940
Cucumis melo
Fulton, Robert W., 1950
Cucumis melo var. reticulatus
Fulton, J.P., 1952
Cucumis sativus
Fulton, J.P., 1952
Price, W.C., Frank P. McWhorter and Betty H.
Steranka, 1950
Price, W.C. and Ralph W.G. Wyckoff, 1939
Cucurbita maxima
Fulton, J.P., 1952
Fulton, Robert W., 1950
Cucurbita pepo var. melopepo
Frazier, Norman W., 1955
Cyamopsis tetragonaloba
Fulton, Robert W., 1950
Cymbalaria muralis
Price, W.C., 1940

VIRUS

V. TOBACCO NECROSIS (cont.)
Eschscholtzia californica
Price, W.C., 1940
Fragaria californica
Frazier, Norman W., 1955
Fragaria chiloensis var. ananassa
Fulton, J.P., 1952
Fragaria vesca
Frazier, Norman W., 1955
Fulton, J.P., 1952
Gilia capitata
Price, W.C., 1940
Gilia liniflora
Price, W.C., 1940
Glycine max
Price, W.C., 1940
Godetia amoena
Price, W.C., 1940
Gomphrena globosa
Kassanis, B., 1955
Gypsophila elegans
Kassanis, B., 1955
Heliotropium corymbosum
Price, W.C., 1940
Hibiscus manihot
Price, W.C., 1940
Hordeum vulgare
Fulton, Robert W., 1950
Hyoscyamus albus
Price, W.C., 1940
Hyoscyamus niger
Price, W.C., 1940
Incarvillea delavayi
Price, W.C., 1940
Ipomoea setosa
Price, W.C., 1940
Ipomoea spp.
Price, W.C., 1940
Lactuca sativa
(K.M. Smith, 1957) R.E. Fitzpatrick, et al., 1958
Lathyrus odoratus
Price, W.C., 1940
Lavatera trimestris
Price, W.C., 1940
Limonium sinuatum
Price, W.C., 1940
Linaria macedonica
Price, W.C., 1940
Lobelia tenuior
Price, W.C., 1940
Lychnis alba
Kassanis, B., 1955
Lycopersicon esculentum
(K.M. Smith, 1957) R.E. Fitzpatrick, et al., 1958
Mimulus moschatus
Price, W.C., 1940
Mirabilis jalapa
Price, W.C., 1940
Nemesia strumosa
Price, W.C., 1940
Nemophila menziesii subsp. insignis
Price, W.C., 1940
Nicandra physalodes
Price, W.C., 1940
Nicotiana digluta * x Nicotiana tabacum
Price, W.C., 1938
Nicotiana glutinosa
Bawden, F.C. and B. Kassanis, 1947
Kassanis, B., 1949, 1955
Price, W.C., 1938
Price, W.C., Frank P. McWhorter and Betty H.
Steranka, 1950
Price, W.C. and Ralph W.G. Wyckoff, 1939
Nicotiana langsdorffii
Price, W.C., 1940
Nicotiana rustica
Price, W.C., 1938
Price, W.C., Frank P. McWhorter and Betty H.
Steranka, 1950
Nicotiana sylvestris
Price, W.C., 1940
Price, W.C., Frank P. McWhorter and Betty H.
Steranka, 1950

VIRUS
V. TOBACCO NECROSIS (cont.)
  Nicotiana tabacum
      Bawden, F.C. and B. Kassanis, 1947
      Bawden, F.C. and F.M. Roberts, 1948
      Frazier, Norman W., 1955
      Fulton, J.P., 1952
      Fulton, Robert W., 1950
      Kassanis, B., 1949, 1955
      Price, W.C., 1938
      Price, W.C., Frank P. McWhorter and Betty H.
      Steranka, 1950
      Price, W.C. and Ralph W.G. Wyckoff, 1939
  Papaver orientale
      Price, W.C., 1940
  Pelargonium hortorum
      (K.M. Smith, 1957) R.E. Fitzpatrick, et al., 1958
  Penstemon spp.
      Price, W.C., 1940
  Phacelia campanularia
      Price, W.C., 1940
  Phaseolus aureus
      Price, W.C., 1940
  Phaseolus vulgaris
      Bawden, F.C. and B. Kassanis, 1947
      Bawden, F.C. and F.M. Roberts, 1948
      Frazier, Norman W., 1955
      Fulton, J.P., 1952
      Fulton, Robert W., 1950
      Kassanis, B., 1949, 1955
      Price, W.C., 1938
      Price, W.C., Frank P. McWhorter and Betty H.
      Steranka, 1950
      Price, W.C. and Ralph W.G. Wyckoff, 1939
  Phlox drummondii
      Price, W.C., 1940
  Phytolacca decandra
      Price, W.C., 1940
  Pisum sativum
      Price, W.C., 1940
  Polanisia trachysperma
      Price, W.C., 1940
  Polyanthus spp.
      (K.M. Smith, 1957) R.E. Fitzpatrick, et al., 1958
  Portulaca grandiflora
      Price, W.C., 1940
  Primula malacoides
      Bawden, F.C. and B. Kassanis, 1947
      Price, W.C., Frank P. McWhorter and Betty H.
      Steranka, 1950
  Primula obconica
      Bawden, F.C. and B. Kassanis, 1947
      Price, W.C., Frank P. McWhorter and Betty H.
      Steranka, 1950
      Severin, Henry H.P. and C.M. Tompkins, 1950
  Primula vulgaris
      Bawden, F.C. and B. Kassanis, 1947
  Proboscidea louisiana
      Price, W.C., 1940
  Rheum rhaponticum
      Price, W.C., 1940
  Ricinus communis
      Price, W.C., 1940
  Rumex crispus
      Price, W.C., 1940
  Salpiglossis sinuata
      Price, W.C., 1940
      Price, W.C., Frank P. McWhorter and Betty H.
      Steranka, 1950
  Secale cereale
      Price, W.C., 1940
  Sinningia speciosa
      Price, W.C., 1940
      Price, W.C., Frank P. McWhorter and Betty H.
      Steranka, 1950
  Solanum nodiflorum
      Price, W.C., 1940
  Statice armeria
      Price, W.C., 1940
  Tetragonia expansa
      Price, W.C., 1940
  Trachymene caerulea
      Price, W.C., 1940

VIRUS
V. TOBACCO NECROSIS (cont.)
  Trifolium incarnatum
      Price, W.C., 1940
  Trifolium pratense
      Fulton, Robert W., 1950
  Trifolium repens
      Fulton, Robert W., 1950
  Triticum aestivum
      Price, W.C., 1940
  Tulipa gesneriana
      Fulton, Robert W., 1950
      Kassanis, B., 1949, 1954
  Verbascum phoeniceum
      Price, W.C., 1940
  Veronica longifolia
      Price, W.C., 1940
  Vigna sinensis
      Fulton, J.P., 1952
      Fulton, Robert W., 1950, 1952
      Price, W.C., 1938
      Price, W.C. and Ralph W.G. Wyckoff, 1939
  Vinca rosea
      Price, W.C., 1940
      Price, W.C., Frank P. McWhorter and Betty H.
      Steranka, 1950
  Viola cornuta
      Price, W.C., 1940
      Price, W.C., Frank P. McWhorter and Betty H.
      Steranka, 1950
  Zaluzianskya villosa
      Price, W.C., 1940
  Zea mays
      Fulton, J.P., 1952
      Fulton, Robert W., 1950
  Zinnia elegans
      Price, W.C., 1940

V. TOBACCO RING SPOT Fromme et al. 1927
  Acer ginnala
      Wilkinson, R.E., 1952
  Acer negundo
      Wilkinson, R.E., 1952
  Amaranthus caudatus
      Fulton, Robert W., 1941
      Price, W.C., 1940
  Amaranthus paniculatus
      Wingard, S.A., 1928
  Ambrosia trifida
      Wingard, S.A., 1928
  Anthriscus cerefolium
      Price, W.C., 1940
  Antirrhinum majus
      Berkeley, G.H., 1951, 1953
      Brierley, Philip, 1952
      Brierley, Philip and Floyd F. Smith, 1954
      Travis, R.V. and Philip Brierley, 1957
      Wingard, S.A., 1928
  Apium graveolens
      Anderson, C.W., 1954
  Apium graveolens var. dulce
      Severin, Henry H.P., 1950
  Aquilegia caerulea
      Price, W.C., 1940
  Aster amellus
      Pound, Glenn S., 1949
  Aster laevis
      Fulton, Robert W., 1941
      Wingard, S.A., 1928
  Aster spp.
      (K.M. Smith, 1957) R.E. Fitzpatrick, et al., 1958
  Barbarea barbarea
      Wingard, S.A., 1928
  Begonia semperflorens
      Price, W.C., 1940
  Beta vulgaris
      Cheo, Pen Ching and W.J. Zaumeyer, 1952
      Grogan, R.G. and W.C. Schnathorst, 1955
      Priode, C.N., 1928
      Wingard, S.A., 1928
  Beta vulgaris var. cicla
      Wingard, S.A., 1928
  Bidens discoidea
      Wingard, S.A., 1928

VIRUS
V. TOBACCO RING SPOT (cont.)

Calendula officinalis
Fulton, Robert W., 1941
Pound, Glenn S., 1949
Wingard, S.A., 1928

Callistephus chinensis
Anderson, C.W., 1954
Cheo, Pen Ching and W.J. Zaumeyer, 1952
Wingard, S.A., 1928

Campanula medium
Price, W.C., 1940

Canavalia ensiformis
Cheo, Pen Ching and W.J. Zaumeyer, 1952

Capsella bursa-pastoris
Pound, Glenn S., 1949

Capsicum frutescens (Capsicum annuum)
Anderson, C.W., 1954
Berkeley, G.H., 1951
Steere, Russell L., 1956

Cardiospermum halicacabum
Price, W.C., 1940

Centaurea moschata
Price, W.C., 1940

Chenopodium album
Wingard, S.A., 1928

Chenopodium amaranticolor
Hollings, M., 1956, 1957

Chenopodium spp.
(K.M. Smith, 1957) R.E. Fitzpatrick, et al., 1958
Travis, R.V. and Philip Brierley, 1957

Chrysanthemum spp.
Price, W.C., 1940

Cichorium endivia
Price, W.C., 1940

Citrullus vulgaris
Anderson, C.W., 1954
Bridgmon, G.H. and J.C. Walker, 1952
Grogan, R.G. and W.C. Schnathorst, 1955
McKeen, C.D., 1957
Pound, Glenn S., 1949
Rosberg, David W., 1953
Shepherd, Robert J. and F. Ben Struble, 1956
Steere, Russell L., 1956
Wingard, S.A., 1928

Citrullus vulgaris var. citroides
Anderson, C.W., 1954

Clarkia elegans
Price, W.C., 1940

Cleome spinosa
Price, W.C., 1940

Coleus blumei
Price, W.C., 1940

Convolvulus tricolor
Price, W.C., 1940

Crotalaria intermedia
LeBeau, F.J., 1947

Crotalaria spectabilis
Corbett, M.K., 1957
LeBeau, F.J., 1947

Cucumis melo
Bridgmon, G.H. and J.C. Walker, 1952
Cheo, Pen Ching and W.J. Zaumeyer, 1952
Henderson, R.G. and S.A. Wingard, 1931
Pound, Glenn S., 1949

Cucumis melo var. cantalupensis
Wingard, S.A., 1928

Cucumis melo var. reticulatus
McKeen, C.D., 1957

Cucumis sativus
Allington, William B., 1946
Anderson, C.W., 1954
Berkeley, G.H., 1951, 1953
Bridgmon, G.H. and J.C. Walker, 1952
Brierley, Philip and Floyd F. Smith, 1954
Cheo, Pen Ching and W.J. Zaumeyer, 1952
Fulton, Robert W., 1941
Ivanoff, S.S., 1942
Johnson, E.M., 1930
LeBeau, F.J., 1947
McKeen, C.D., 1957
McKinney, H.H. and E.E. Clayton, 1944
Pound, Glenn S., 1949
Rosberg, David W., 1953

VIRUS
V. TOBACCO RING SPOT (cont.)

Cucumis sativus
Shepherd, Robert J. and F. Ben Struble, 1956
Steere, Russell L., 1956
Wingard, S.A., 1928

Cucurbita maxima
McKeen, C.D., 1957
Pound, Glenn S., 1949

Cucurbita moschata
Bridgmon, G.H. and J.C. Walker, 1952
Wingard, S.A., 1928

Cucurbita pepo
Bridgmon, G.H. and J.C. Walker, 1952
Cheo, Pen Ching and W.J. Zaumeyer, 1952
Pound, Glenn S., 1949
Steere, Russell L., 1956
Wingard, S.A., 1928

Cucurbita pepo var. melopepo
Anderson, C.W., 1954
Henderson, R.G. and S.A. Wingard, 1931
Rosberg, David W., 1953
Wingard, S.A., 1928

Cucurbita pepo var. ovifera
Wingard, S.A., 1928

Cyamopsis psoraloides
Cooper, W.E., 1949
LeBeau, F.J., 1947
Starr, Chester K. and W.E. Cooper, 1944

Cyamopsis tetragonoloba
Cheo, Pen Ching and W.J. Zaumeyer, 1952

Cymbalaria muralis
Price, W.C., 1940

Cynoglossum amabile
Fulton, Robert W., 1941
Price, W.C., 1940

Datura metel
Price, W.C., 1940

Datura spp.
Smith, Kenneth M., 1929

Datura stramonium
Berkeley, G.H., 1951, 1953
Bridgmon, G.H. and J.C. Walker, 1952
Cheo, Pen Ching and W.J. Zaumeyer, 1952
Cooper, W.E., 1949
(K.M. Smith, 1957) R.E. Fitzpatrick, et al., 1958
Fulton, Robert W., 1941
Henderson, R.G. and S.A. Wingard, 1931
Johnson, E.M., 1930
Steere, Russell L., 1956
Thomas, H. Rex and W.J. Zaumeyer, 1950
Wingard, S.A., 1928

Delphinium hybrid
Severin, Henry H.P., 1942

Dianthus plumarius
Price, W.C., 1940

Dolichos lablab
Cheo, Pen Ching and W.J. Zaumeyer, 1952
Fulton, Robert W., 1941
Pierce, W.H., 1934
Wingard, S.A., 1928

Erigeron canadensis
Wingard, S.A., 1928

Eschscholtzia californica
Price, W.C., 1940

Fraxinus pennsylvanica
Wilkinson, R.E., 1952

Gilia capitata
Price, W.C., 1940

Gilia liniflora
Price, W.C., 1940

Gladiolus hortulanus
Berkeley, G.H., 1951, 1953
Bridgmon, G.H., 1951
Bridgmon, G.H. and J.C. Walker, 1952
Brierley, Philip, 1952
Smith, Floyd F. and Philip Brierley, 1955

Glycine max
Allington, William B., 1946
Bridgmon, G.H. and J.C. Walker, 1952
Cheo, Pen Ching and W.J. Zaumeyer, 1952
Cooper, W.E., 1949
Desjardins, P.R., R.L. Latterell and J.E. Mitchell, 1954

VIRUS
V. TOBACCO RING SPOT (cont.)
   Glycine max
      Dunleavy, John M., 1957
      Kahn, Robert P., 1956
      Kahn, Robert P. and Frances M. Latterell, 1955
      LeBeau, F.J., 1947
      Pierce, W.H., 1934
      Starr, Chester K. and W.E. Cooper, 1944
      Stubbs, M.W., 1937
   Godetia amoena
      Price, W.C., 1940
   Gomphrena globosa
      Berkeley, G.H., 1953
   Gomphrena spp.
      Travis, R.V. and Philip Brierley, 1957
   Heliotropium corymbosum
      Price, W.C., 1940
   Hesperis matronalis
      Pound, Glenn S., 1949
   Hibiscus esculentus
      Fulton, Robert W., 1941
      Wingard, S.A., 1928
   Hibiscus syriacus
      Wilkinson, R.E., 1952
   Hyoscyamus albus
      Price, W.C., 1940
   Hyoscyamus niger
      Price, W.C., 1940
   Impatiens balsamina
      Price, W.C., 1940
   Incarvillea delavayi
      Price, W.C., 1940
   Ipomoea purpurea
      Wingard, S.A., 1928
   Iris germanica
      Travis, R.V. and Philip Brierley, 1957
   Lactuca sativa
      Grogan, R.G., Roy Bardin and W.C. Schnathorst, 1954
      Grogan, R.G. and W.C. Schnathorst, 1955
   Lactuca sativa var. capitata
      Wingard, S.A., 1928
   Lactuca scariola
      Wingard, S.A., 1928
   Lactuca serriola
      Grogan, R.G. and W.C. Schnathorst, 1955
   Lagenaria siceraria (Lagenaria leucantha)
      Wingard, S.A., 1928
   Lathyrus odoratus
      Stubbs, M.W., 1937
   Lavatera trimestris
      Price, W.C., 1940
   Lilium longiflorum
      Travis, R.V. and Philip Brierley, 1957
   Linaria macedonica
      Price, W.C., 1940
   Lobelia tenuior
      Price, W.C., 1940
   Lobularia maritima
      Price, W.C., 1940
   Luffa aegyptiaca (Luffa cylindrica)
      Wingard, S.A., 1928
   Lupinus albus
      Cheo, Pen Ching and W.J. Zaumeyer, 1952
      LeBeau, F.J., 1947
      Pierce, W.H., 1934
      Stubbs, M.W., 1937
   Lychnis alba
      Price, W.C., 1940
   Lychnis chalcedonica
      Price, W.C., 1940
   Lycopersicon esculentum
      Anderson, C.W., 1954
      Henderson, R.G. and S.A. Wingard, 1931
      Steere, Russell L., 1956
   Medicago sativa
      (K.M. Smith, 1957) R.E. Fitzpatrick, et al., 1958
   Melilotus alba
      Fenne, S.B., 1931
      Henderson, R.G., 1934
      Pierce, W.H., 1934
      Pound, Glenn S., 1949
      Rich, Saul, 1940
      Stubbs, M.W., 1937

VIRUS
V. TOBACCO RING SPOT (cont.)
   Melilotus indica
      LeBeau, F.J., 1947
      Pound, Glenn S., 1949
   Melilotus officinalis
      Henderson, R.G., 1934
      Henderson, R.G. and S.A. Wingard, 1931
      Stubbs, M.W., 1937
      Wingard, S.A., 1928
   Mimulus moschatus
      Price, W.C., 1940
   Mirabilis jalapa
      Price, W.C., 1940
   Mucuna spp.
      Pierce, W.H., 1934
   Nemesia strumosa
      Price, W.C., 1940
   Nemophila menziesii subsp. insignis
      Price, W.C., 1940
   Nicandra physalodes
      Fulton, Robert W., 1941
      Johnson, E.M., 1930
      Wingard, S.A., 1928
   Nicotiana acuminata
      Wingard, S.A., 1928
   Nicotiana alata
      Steere, Russell L., 1956
   Nicotiana clevelandi
      Wingard, S.A., 1928
   Nicotiana digluta * x Nicotiana tabacum
      Tall, M.G., W.C. Price and Kenneth Wertman, 1949
   Nicotiana glauca
      Grogan, R.G. and W.C. Schnathorst, 1955
      Smith, Kenneth M., 1931
   Nicotiana glutinosa
      Anderson, C.W., 1954
      Benedict, W.G., 1955
      Berkeley, G.H., 1951, 1953
      Bridgmon, G.H. and J.C. Walker, 1952
      Cheo, Pen Ching and W.J. Zaumeyer, 1952
      Cooper, W.E., 1949
      (K.M. Smith, 1957) R.E. Fitzpatrick, et al., 1958
      Fromme, F.D., S.A. Wingard and C.N. Priode, 1927
      Fulton, Robert W., 1941
      Grogan, R.G., Roy Bardin and W.C. Schnathorst, 1954
      Grogan, R.G. and W.C. Schnathorst, 1955
      Pierce, W.H., 1934
      Pound, Glenn S., 1949
      Wingard, S.A., 1928
   Nicotiana langsdorffii
      Fromme, F.D., S.A. Wingard and C.N. Priode, 1927
      Wingard, S.A., 1928
   Nicotiana longiflora
      Cheo, Pen Ching and W.J. Zaumeyer, 1952
      Wingard, S.A., 1928
   Nicotiana multivalvis
      (K.M. Smith, 1957) R.E. Fitzpatrick, et al., 1958
      Wingard, S.A., 1928
   Nicotiana paniculata
      Fromme, F.D., S.A. Wingard and C.N. Priode, 1927
      Wingard, S.A., 1928
   Nicotiana plumbaginifolia
      Cheo, Pen Ching and W.J. Zaumeyer, 1952
      Wingard, S.A., 1928
   Nicotiana quadrivalvis
      Wingard, S.A., 1928
   Nicotiana repanda
      Wingard, S.A., 1928
   Nicotiana rustica
      Grogan, R.G., Roy Bardin and W.C. Schnathorst, 1954
      Grogan, R.G. and W.C. Schnathorst, 1955
      Johnson, E.M., 1930
      Pound, Glenn S., 1949
      Wingard, S.A., 1928
   Nicotiana rustica var. jamaicensis *
      Wingard, S.A., 1928

VIRUS
V. TOBACCO RING SPOT (cont.)
Nicotiana sanderae
Wingard, S.A., 1928
Nicotiana suaveolens
Wingard, S.A., 1928
Nicotiana sylvestris
Cheo, Pen Ching and W.J. Zaumeyer, 1952
Fromme, F.D., S.A. Wingard and C.N. Priode, 1927
Price, W.C., 1936
Wingard, S.A., 1928
Nicotiana tabacum
Allington, William B., 1946
Anderson, C.W., 1954
Benedict, W.G., 1955
Berkeley, G.H., 1951, 1953
Bridgmon, G.H. and J.C. Walker, 1952
Brierley, Philip, 1952
Cheo, Pen Ching and W.J. Zaumeyer, 1952
Cook, A.A., 1956
Cooper, W.E., 1949
Dunleavy, John M., 1957
Fenne, S.B., 1931
(K.M. Smith, 1957) R.E. Fitzpatrick, et al., 1958
Fromme, F.D., S.A. Wingard and C.N. Priode, 1927
Fulton, Robert W., 1941
Grogan, R.G., Roy Bardin and W.C. Schnathorst, 1954
Grogan, R.G. and W.C. Schnathorst, 1955
Harrison, B.D., 1957
Henderson, R.G. and S.A. Wingard, 1931
Hoggan, I.A., 1933
Johnson, E.M., 1930
Kahn, Robert P. and Frances M. Latterell, 1955
LeBeau, F.J., 1947
McKinney, H.H., 1943
McKinney, H.H. and E.E. Clayton, 1944
Nolla, J.A.B., 1934
Pierce, W.H., 1934
Pound, Glenn S., 1949
Price, W.C., 1936
Roberts, Daniel A., 1952
Rosberg, David W., 1953
Shepherd, Robert J. and F. Ben Struble, 1956
Smith, Kenneth M., 1929, 1935
Starr, Chester K. and W.E. Cooper, 1944
Steere, Russell L., 1956
Stubbs, M.W., 1937
Tall, M.G., W.C. Price and Kenneth Wertman, 1949
Travis, R.V. and Philip Brierley, 1957
Valleau, W.D., 1932, 1935, 1941
Walters, H.J., 1952
Wingard, S.A., 1928
Nicotiana tabacum var. atropurpurea *
Wingard, S.A., 1928
Nicotiana tabacum var. auriculata *
Wingard, S.A., 1928
Nicotiana tabacum var. brasiliensis
Wingard, S.A., 1928
Nicotiana tabacum var. calyciflora
Wingard, S.A., 1928
Nicotiana tabacum var. calycina *
Wingard, S.A., 1928
Nicotiana tabacum var. cavala *
Wingard, S.A., 1928
Nicotiana tabacum var. colossea *
Wingard, S.A., 1928
Nicotiana tabacum var. gigantea *
Wingard, S.A., 1928
Nicotiana tabacum var. lacerata *
Wingard, S.A., 1928
Nicotiana tabacum var. latissima
Wingard, S.A., 1928
Nicotiana tabacum var. macrophylla
Wingard, S.A., 1928
Nicotiana tabacum var. microphylla *
Wingard, S.A., 1928
Nicotiana tabacum var. purpurea *
Wingard, S.A., 1928
Nicotiana tabacum var. sanguinea *
Wingard, S.A., 1928

VIRUS
V. TOBACCO RING SPOT (cont.)
Nicotiana tomentosa
Wingard, S.A., 1928
Nicotiana trigonophylla
Wingard, S.A., 1928
Parthenium argentatum
Severin, Henry H.P., 1945
Penstemon spp.
Price, W.C., 1940
Petunia hybrida
Berkeley, G.H., 1953
Cheo, Pen Ching and W.J. Zaumeyer, 1952
Cooper, W.E., 1949
Dunleavy, John M., 1957
Grogan, R.G., Roy Bardin and W.C. Schnathorst, 1954
Grogan, R.G. and W.C. Schnathorst, 1955
Pound, Glenn S., 1949
Priode, C.N., 1928
Shepherd, Robert J. and F. Ben Struble, 1956
Smith, Kenneth M., 1929
Starr, Chester K. and W.E. Cooper, 1944
Steere, Russell L., 1956
Petunia violacea
Fulton, Robert W., 1941
Henderson, R.G., 1931
Henderson, R.G. and S.A. Wingard, 1931
Wingard, S.A., 1928
Phacelia campanularia
Price, W.C., 1940
Phaseolus aconitifolius
Cheo, Pen Ching and W.J. Zaumeyer, 1952
Phaseolus acutifolius var. latifolius
Cheo, Pen Ching and W.J. Zaumeyer, 1952
Phaseolus angularis
Cheo, Pen Ching and W.J. Zaumeyer, 1952
Pierce, W.H., 1934
Phaseolus aureus
Cheo, Pen Ching and W.J. Zaumeyer, 1952
Cooper, W.E., 1949
Pierce, W.H., 1934
Starr, Chester K. and W.E. Cooper, 1944
Phaseolus calcaratus
Pierce, W.H., 1934
Phaseolus coccineus
Cheo, Pen Ching and W.J. Zaumeyer, 1952
Phaseolus lathyroides
Cheo, Pen Ching and W.J. Zaumeyer, 1952
Phaseolus limensis
Pierce, W.H., 1934
Phaseolus lunatus
Cooper, W.E., 1949
LeBeau, F.J., 1947
Pierce, W.H., 1934
Wingard, S.A., 1928
Phaseolus multiflora
LeBeau, F.J., 1947
Phaseolus mungo
Cheo, Pen Ching and W.J. Zaumeyer, 1952
Phaseolus vulgaris
Allington, William B., 1946
Anderson, C.W., 1954
Berkeley, G.H., 1951, 1953
Bridgmon, G.H. and J.C. Walker, 1952
Brierley, Philip, 1952
Cheo, Pen Ching and W.J. Zaumeyer, 1952
Cooper, W.E., 1949
(K.M. Smith, 1957) R.E. Fitzpatrick, et al., 1958
Grogan, R.G., Roy Bardin and W.C. Schnathorst, 1954
Grogan, R.G. and W.C. Schnathorst, 1955
Kahn, Robert P. and Frances M. Latterell, 1955
LeBeau, F.J., 1947
McKinney, H.H. and E.E. Clayton, 1944
Pierce, W.H., 1944
Pound, Glenn S., 1949
Roberts, Daniel A., 1952
Rosberg, David W., 1953
Shepherd, Robert J. and F. Ben Struble, 1956
Stubbs, M.W., 1937
Tall, M.G., W.C. Price and Kenneth Wertman, 1949
Thomas, H. Rex and W.J. Zaumeyer, 1950
Travis, R.V. and Philip Brierley, 1957

VIRUS
V. TOBACCO RING SPOT (cont.)
  Phaseolus vulgaris
    Wingard, S.A., 1928
    Zaumeyer, W.J. and B.L. Wade, 1935
  Physalis angulata
    Wingard, S.A., 1928
  Physalis heterophylla var. nyctaginea
    Johnson, E.M., 1930
  Physalis peruviana
    Price, W.C., 1940
  Physalis pubescens
    Cooper, W.E., 1949
  Physostegia virginiana
    Price, W.C., 1940
  Phytolacca decandra
    Johnson, E.M., 1930
    Priode, C.N., 1928
    Wingard, S.A., 1928
  Pisum sativum
    Berkeley, G.H., 1951, 1953
    Bridgmon, G.H. and J.C. Walker, 1952
    Cheo, Pen Ching and W.J. Zaumeyer, 1952
    Cooper, W.E., 1949
    Grogan, R.G. and W.C. Schnathorst, 1955
    LeBeau, F.J., 1947
    Pound, Glenn S., 1949
    Rosberg, David W., 1953
    Stubbs, M.W., 1937
  Pisum sativum var. arvense
    LeBeau, F.J., 1947
  Plantago lanceolata
    Price, W.C., 1940
  Platycodon grandiflorum
    Price, W.C., 1940
  Polanisia trachysperma
    Price, W.C., 1940
  Polygonum hydropiper
    Wingard, S.A., 1928
  Portulaca grandiflora
    Price, W.C., 1940
  Primula obconica
    Price, W.C., 1940
  Proboscidea louisiana
    Price, W.C., 1940
  Prunus avium
    Wilkinson, R.E., 1952
  Rheum rhaponticum
    Price, W.C., 1940
  Ricinus communis
    Cook, A.A., 1956
    Wingard, S.A., 1928
  Rumex crispus
    Price, W.C., 1940
  Salpiglossis sinuata
    Price, W.C., 1940
  Salvia splendens
    Fulton, Robert W., 1941
    Wingard, S.A., 1928
  Sambucus canadensis
    Wilkinson, R.E., 1952
  Scabiosa atropurpurea
    Wingard, S.A., 1928
  Sesamum orientale
    Cooper, W.E., 1949
  Solanum carolinense
    Wingard, S.A., 1928
  Solanum melongena
    Fulton, Robert W., 1941
    Ivanoff, S.S., 1942
    Jones, S.E., 1942
    Valleau, W.D., 1951
  Solanum melongena var. esculentum
    Wingard, S.A., 1928
  Solanum nigrum
    Wingard, S.A., 1928
  Solanum nodiflorum
    Price, W.C., 1940
  Solanum pseudocapsicum
    Wingard, S.A., 1928
  Solanum triflorum
    Pound, Glenn S., 1949
  Solanum tuberosum
    Cheo, Pen Ching and W.J. Zaumeyer, 1952

VIRUS
V. TOBACCO RING SPOT (cont.)
  Solanum tuberosum
    Grogan, R.G. and W.C. Schnathorst, 1955
    Henderson, R.G. and S.A. Wingard, 1931
    Valleau, W.D., 1932
  Spinacia oleracea
    Bridgmon, G.H. and J.C. Walker, 1952
    Cheo, Pen Ching and W.J. Zaumeyer, 1952
    (K.M. Smith, 1957) R.E. Fitzpatrick, et al., 1958
    Fulton, Robert W., 1941
    Grogan, R.G. and W.C. Schnathorst, 1955
    Hoggan, I.A., 1933
  Tagetes erecta
    Grogan, R.G. and W.C. Schnathorst, 1955
    Wingard, S.A., 1928
  Tetragonia expansa
    Cheo, Pen Ching and W.J. Zaumeyer, 1952
    Priode, C.N., 1928
    Wingard, S.A., 1928
  Thlaspi arvense
    Pound, Glenn S., 1949
  Trachymene caerulea
    Price, W.C., 1940
  Trifolium hybridum
    Rich, Saul, 1940
  Trifolium incarnatum
    Cheo, Pen Ching and W.J. Zaumeyer, 1952
    Pierce, W.H., 1934
    Stubbs, M.W., 1937
  Trifolium pratense
    Benedict, W.G., 1955
    Cheo, Pen Ching and W.J. Zaumeyer, 1952
    Pound, Glenn S., 1949
  Trifolium repens
    (K.M. Smith, 1957) R.E. Fitzpatrick, et al., 1958
  Trigonella foenum-graecum
    Grogan, R.G. and W.C. Schnathorst, 1955
  Tropaeolum majus
    Anderson, C.W., 1954
    Price, W.C., 1940
  Tropaeolum peregrinum
    Price, W.C., 1940
  Ulmus americana
    Wilkinson, R.E., 1952
  Verbascum phoeniceum
    Price, W.C., 1940
  Verbena venosa
    Price, W.C., 1940
  Verbesina alternifolia
    Fenne, S.B., 1931
    Henderson, R.G. and S.A. Wingard, 1931
  Veronica longifolia
    Price, W.C., 1940
  Vicia faba
    Cheo, Pen Ching and W.J. Zaumeyer, 1952
    (K.M. Smith, 1957) R.E. Fitzpatrick, et al., 1958
    Pound, Glenn S., 1949
  Vicia faba var. minor *
    Pierce, W.H., 1934
    Stubbs, M.W., 1937
  Vicia sativa
    Cheo, Pen Ching and W.J. Zaumeyer, 1952
    LeBeau, F.J., 1947
    Pierce, W.H., 1934
  Vigna cylindrica (Vigna catjang)
    Cooper, W.E., 1949
  Vigna sesquipedalis
    Cooper, W.E., 1949
    Pierce, W.H., 1934
  Vigna sinensis
    Anderson, C.W., 1954
    Benedict, W.G., 1955
    Berkeley, G.H., 1953
    Bridgmon, G.H. and J.C. Walker, 1952
    Cheo, Pen Ching and W.J. Zaumeyer, 1952
    Cooper, W.E., 1949
    Desjardins, P.R., R.L. Latterell and J.E.
      Mitchell, 1954
    Dunleavy, John M., 1957
    Grogan, R.G., Roy Bardin and W.C. Schnathorst,
      1954
    Grogan, R.G. and W.C. Schnathorst, 1955
    Kahn, Robert P., 1956

VIRUS
V. TOBACCO RING SPOT (cont.)
  Vigna sinensis
    Kahn, Robert P. and Frances M. Latterell, 1955
    LeBeau, F.J., 1947
    Pierce, W.H., 1934
    Pound, Glenn S., 1949
    Price, W.C., 1936
    Rosberg, David W., 1953
    Shepherd, Robert J. and F. Ben Struble, 1956
    Starr, Chester K. and W.E. Cooper, 1944
    Steere, Russell L., 1956
    Walters, H.J., 1952
    Wingard, S.A., 1928
  Vinca rosea
    Price, W.C., 1940
  Viola cornuta
    Price, W.C., 1940
  Viola papilionacea
    Wingard, S.A., 1928
  Viola tricolor
    (K.M. Smith, 1957) R.E. Fitzpatrick, et al., 1958
    McKinney, H.H. and E.E. Clayton, 1944
    Wingard, S.A., 1928
  Zaluzianskya villosa
    Price, W.C., 1940
  Zea mays
    Bridgmon, G.H., 1951
    Bridgmon, G.H. and J.C. Walker, 1952
  Zinnia elegans
    Anderson, C.W., 1954
    Bridgmon, G.H. and J.C. Walker, 1952
    Cheo, Pen Ching and W.J. Zaumeyer, 1952
    Fulton, Robert W., 1941
    Grogan, R.G. and W.C. Schnathorst, 1955
    Pound, Glenn S., 1949
    Price, W.C., 1935
    Wingard, S.A., 1928

V. TOBACCO RING SPOT NO. 2 Price 1936
  Althaea rosea
    Wilkinson, R.E., 1952
  Amaranthus caudatus
    Hildebrand, E.M., 1942
    Price, W.C., 1940
  Anthriscus cerefolium
    Price, W.C., 1940
  Antirrhinum majus
    Brierley, Philip, 1954
  Arctium lappa
    Wilkinson, R.E., 1952
  Asperula odorata
    Price, W.C., 1940
  Begonia semperflorens
    Price, W.C., 1940
  Beta vulgaris
    Hildebrand, E.M., 1942
    Price, W.C., 1940
  Callistephus chinensis
    Brierley, Philip, 1954
    Hildebrand, E.M., 1942
    Price, W.C., 1940
  Campanula medium
    Price, W.C., 1940
  Clarkia elegans
    Price, W.C., 1940
  Cleome spinosa
    Price, W.C., 1940
  Coleus blumei
    Hildebrand, E.M., 1942
    Price, W.C., 1940
  Convolvulus tricolor
    Price, W.C., 1940
  Cucumis sativus
    Brierley, Philip, 1954
    Hildebrand, E.M., 1942
    Price, W.C., 1940
  Cucurbita maxima
    Steere, Russell L., 1956
    Wilkinson, R.E., 1952
  Cucurbita moschata
    Steere, Russell L., 1956
  Cymbalaria muralis
    Hildebrand, E.M., 1942

VIRUS
V. TOBACCO RING SPOT NO. 2 (cont.)
  Cymbalaria muralis
    Price, W.C., 1940
  Datura stramonium
    Brierley, Philip, 1954
  Eschscholtzia californica
    Brierley, Philip, 1954
  Gilia capitata
    Brierley, Philip, 1954
  Gilia liniflora
    Price, W.C., 1940
  Godetia amoena
    Price, W.C., 1940
  Helichrysum bracteatum
    Brierley, Philip, 1954
  Heliotropium carymbosum
    Price, W.C., 1940
  Hibiscus manihot
    Price, W.C., 1940
  Hydrangea macrophylla
    Brierley, Philip, 1954
  Impatiens balsamina
    Price, W.C., 1940
  Ipomoea setosa
    Price, W.C., 1940
  Linaria macedonica
    Price, W.C., 1940
  Lobularia maritima
    Hildebrand, E.M., 1942
    Price, W.C., 1940
  Lychnis chalcedonica
    Hildebrand, E.M., 1942
    Price, W.C., 1940
  Lycopersicon esculentum
    Brierley, Philip, 1954
    Hildebrand, E.M., 1942
    Price, W.C., 1936
    Thomas, H. Rex and W.J. Zaumeyer, 1950
  Mimulus moschatus
    Price, W.C., 1940
  Mirabilis jalapa
    Price, W.C., 1940
  Nemesia strumosa
    Price, W.C., 1940
  Nemophila menziesii subsp. insignis
    Hildebrand, E.M., 1942
    Price, W.C., 1940
  Nicotiana alata
    Wilkinson, R.E., 1952
  Nicotiana digluta * x Nicotiana tabacum
    Tall, M.G., W.C. Price and Kenneth Wertman, 1949
  Nicotiana glutinosa
    Hildebrand, E.M., 1942
    Price, W.C., 1936
  Nicotiana langsdorffii
    Hildebrand, E.M., 1942
    Price, W.C., 1936
  Nicotiana rustica
    Hildebrand, E.M., 1941, 1942
  Nicotiana sylvestris
    Hildebrand, E.M., 1942
    Price, W.C., 1936
  Nicotiana tabacum
    Brierley, Philip, 1954
    Hildebrand, E.M., 1941, 1942
    Price, W.C., 1936
    Tall, M.G.; W.C. Price and Kenneth Wertman, 1949
  Oenothera spp.
    Wilkinson, R.E., 1952
  Pastinaca sativa
    Wilkinson, R.E., 1952
  Pelargonium hortorum
    Hildebrand, E.M., 1942
    Price, W.C., 1940
  Penstemon spp.
    Price, W.C., 1940
  Petunia hybrida
    Brierley, Philip, 1954
  Phaseolus vulgaris
    Hildebrand, E.M., 1942
    Price, W.C., 1936

VIRUS
V. TOBACCO RING SPOT NO. 2 (cont.)
  Phaseolus vulgaris
    Tall, M.G., W.C. Price and Kenneth Wertman, 1949
    Thomas, H. Rex and W.J. Zaumeyer, 1950
  Phlox drummondii
    Brierley, Philip, 1954
    Hildebrand, E.M., 1942
    Price, W.C., 1940
  Phytolacca decandra
    Hildebrand, E.M., 1942
    Price, W.C., 1940
  Pisum sativum
    Wilkinson, R.E., 1952
  Platycodon grandiflorum
    Brierley, Philip, 1954
  Proboscidea louisiana
    Price, W.C., 1940
  Raphanus sativus
    Price, W.C., 1940
  Reseda odorata
    Hildebrand, E.M., 1942
    Price, W.C., 1940
  Rheum rhaponticum
    Price, W.C., 1940
  Ribes sativum
    Hildebrand, E.M., 1941, 1942
  Ricinus communis
    Hildebrand, E.M., 1942
    Price, W.C., 1940
  Rumex crispus
    Price, W.C., 1940
  Sanvitalia procumbens
    Holmes, Francis O., 1946
  Sedum acre
    Hildebrand, E.M., 1942
    Price, W.C., 1940
  Senecio cruentus
    Brierley, Philip, 1954
  Silene compacta
    Brierley, Philip, 1954
  Sinningia speciosa
    Brierley, Philip, 1954
    Hildebrand, E.M., 1942
    Price, W.C., 1940
  Solanum carolinense
    Wilkinson, R.E., 1952
  Solanum nodiflorum
    Hildebrand, E.M., 1942
  Spinacia oleracea
    Brierley, Philip, 1954
  Tetragonia expansa
    Brierley, Philip, 1954
    Price, W.C., 1940
  Tropaeolum majus
    Brierley, Philip, 1954
  Verbascum pheoniceum
    Price, W.C., 1940
  Verbena venosa
    Price, W.C., 1940
  Verbesina encelioides
    Brierley, Philip, 1954
  Veronica longifolia
    Price, W.C., 1940
  Vigna sinensis
    Hildebrand, E.M., 1942
    Price, W.C., 1936
  Vinca rosea
    Hildebrand, E.M., 1942
    Price, W.C., 1940
  Viola cornuta
    Price, W.C., 1940
  Zaluzianskya villosa
    Price, W.C., 1940
  Zinnia elegans
    Brierley, Philip, 1954
    Hildebrand, E.M., 1942
    Price, W.C., 1940

V. TOBACCO STREAK J. Johnson 1936
  Abutilon theophrasti
    Fulton, Robert W., 1948

VIRUS
V. TOBACCO STREAK (cont.)
  Aeschynomene indica
    Fulton, Robert W., 1948
  Althaea rosea
    Fulton, Robert W., 1948
  Ambrosia artemisiifolia
    Fulton, Robert W., 1948
  Ambrosia trifida
    Fulton, Robert W., 1948
  Antirrhinum spp.
    (K.M. Smith, 1957) R.E. Fitzpatrick, et al., 1958
  Apium graveolens
    Fulton, Robert W., 1948
  Arctium minus
    Fulton, Robert W., 1948
  Asclepias syriaca
    Fulton, Robert W., 1948
  Beta patellaris
    Costa, A.S., 1952
  Beta vulgaris
    Fulton, Robert W., 1948
  Brassica kaber (Brassica arvensis)
    Fulton, Robert W., 1948
  Callistephus chinensis
    Fulton, Robert W., 1948
  Capsicum frutescens (Capsicum annuum)
    Fulton, Robert W., 1948
  Cerastium vulgatum
    Fulton, Robert W., 1948
  Chenopodium album
    Fulton, Robert W., 1948
  Chenopodium spp.
    (K.M. Smith, 1957) R.E. Fitzpatrick, et al., 1958
  Cichorium endiva
    Fulton, Robert W., 1948
  Citrullus vulgaris
    Fulton, Robert W., 1948
  Convolvulus arvensis
    Fulton, Robert W., 1948
  Convolvulus spp.
    Fulton, Robert W., 1948
  Crotalaria intermedia
    Fulton, Robert W., 1948
  Crotalaria spectabilis
    Thomas, H. Rex and W.J. Zaumeyer, 1950
  Cucumis melo
    Fulton, Robert W., 1948
  Cucumis sativus
    Fulton, Robert W., 1948
    Thomas, H. Rex and W.J. Zaumeyer, 1950
  Cucurbita maxima
    Fulton, Robert W., 1948
  Cucurbita pepo
    Fulton, Robert W., 1948
  Cyamopsis tetragonoloba
    Fulton, Robert W., 1948
    Thomas, H. Rex and W.J. Zaumeyer, 1950
  Datura metel
    Fulton, Robert W., 1948
  Datura stramonium
    Fulton, Robert W., 1941, 1948
    Johnson, J., 1936
    Thomas, H. Rex and W.J. Zaumeyer, 1950
  Dolichos biflorus
    Fulton, Robert W., 1948
  Fagopyrum esculentum
    Fulton, Robert W., 1948
  Fragaria virginiana
    Fulton, Robert W., 1948
  Geum spp.
    Fulton, Robert W., 1948
  Glycine max
    Fulton, Robert W., 1948
    Thomas, H. Rex and W.J. Zaumeyer, 1950
  Gossypium hirsutum
    Fulton, Robert W., 1948
  Hedysarum coronarium
    Fulton, Robert W., 1948
  Hibiscus esculentus
    Fulton, Robert W., 1948
  Hibiscus spp.
    Fulton, Robert W., 1948

VIRUS
V. TOBACCO STREAK (cont.)
   Iodanthus pinnatifidus
      Fulton, Robert W., 1948
   Lactuca sativa
      Fulton, Robert W., 1948
   Lupinus albus
      Thomas, H. Rex and W.J. Zaumeyer, 1950
   Lupinus angustifolius
      Thomas, H. Rex and W.J. Zaumeyer, 1950
   Lychnis alba
      Fulton, Robert W., 1948
   Lycium halimifolium
      Fulton, Robert W., 1948
   Lycopersicon esculentum
      Fulton, Robert W., 1948
   Malva rotundifolia
      Fulton, Robert W., 1948
   Melilotus alba
      Fulton, Robert W., 1948
      Thomas, H. Rex and W.J. Zaumeyer, 1950
   Melilotus indica
      Diachun, Stephen and W.D. Valleau, 1950
   Melilotus officinalis
      Fulton, Robert W., 1948
   Melilotus spp.
      (K.M. Smith, 1957) R.E. Fitzpatrick, et al., 1958
   Mirabilis jalapa
      Fulton, Robert W., 1948
   Nepeta cataria
      Fulton, Robert W., 1948
   Nicandra physalodes
      Fulton, Robert W., 1948
      Johnson, J., 1936
   Nicotiana acuminata
      Diachun, Stephen and W.D. Valleau, 1954
   Nicotiana alata
      Diachun, Stephen and W.D. Valleau, 1954
   Nicotiana arentsii
      Diachun, Stephen and W.D. Valleau, 1954
   Nicotiana attenuata
      Diachun, Stephen and W.D. Valleau, 1954
   Nicotiana benavidesii
      Diachun, Stephen and W.D. Valleau, 1954
   Nicotiana benthamiana
      Diachun, Stephen and W.D. Valleau, 1947, 1954
   Nicotiana bigelovii
      Diachun, Stephen and W.D. Valleau, 1954
   Nicotiana bonariensis
      Diachun, Stephen and W.D. Valleau, 1954
   Nicotiana clevelandi
      Diachun, Stephen and W.D. Valleau, 1947, 1954
   Nicotiana cordifolia
      Diachun, Stephen and W.D. Valleau, 1954
   Nicotiana corymbosa
      Diachun, Stephen and W.D. Valleau, 1954
   Nicotiana debneyi
      Diachun, Stephen and W.D. Valleau, 1954
   Nicotiana exigua
      Diachun, Stephen and W.D. Valleau, 1954
   Nicotiana fragrans
      Diachun, Stephen and W.D. Valleau, 1954
   Nicotiana glauca
      Diachun, Stephen and W.D. Valleau, 1947, 1954
   Nicotiana glutinosa
      Diachun, Stephen and W.D. Valleau, 1954
      Fulton, Robert W., 1941
      Johnson, J., 1936
      Thomas, H. Rex and W.J. Zaumeyer, 1950
   Nicotiana goodspeedii
      Diachun, Stephen and W.D. Valleau, 1954
   Nicotiana gossei
      Diachun, Stephen and W.D. Valleau, 1947, 1954
   Nicotiana knightiana
      Diachun, Stephen and W.D. Valleau, 1954
   Nicotiana langsdorffii
      Diachun, Stephen and W.D. Valleau, 1954
   Nicotiana linearis
      Diachun, Stephen and W.D. Valleau, 1954
   Nicotiana longiflora
      Diachun, Stephen and W.D. Valleau, 1954
   Nicotiana maritima
      Diachun, Stephen and W.D. Valleau, 1954

VIRUS
V. TOBACCO STREAK (cont.)
   Nicotiana megalosiphon
      Diachun, Stephen and W.D. Valleau, 1947, 1954
   Nicotiana miersii
      Diachun, Stephen and W.D. Valleau, 1947, 1954
   Nicotiana nesophila
      Diachun, Stephen and W.D. Valleau, 1954
   Nicotiana nudicaulis
      Diachun, Stephen and W.D. Valleau, 1954
   Nicotiana occidentalis
      Diachun, Stephen and W.D. Valleau, 1954
   Nicotiana otophora
      Diachun, Stephen and W.D. Valleau, 1954
   Nicotiana palmeri
      Diachun, Stephen and W.D. Valleau, 1954
   Nicotiana paniculata
      Diachun, Stephen and W.D. Valleau, 1954
   Nicotiana pauciflora
      Diachun, Stephen and W.D. Valleau, 1954
   Nicotiana plumbaginifolia
      Diachun, Stephen and W.D. Valleau, 1954
   Nicotiana raimondii
      Diachun, Stephen and W.D. Valleau, 1954
   Nicotiana repanda
      Diachun, Stephen and W.D. Valleau, 1954
   Nicotiana rotundifolia
      Diachun, Stephen and W.D. Valleau, 1954
   Nicotiana rustica
      Diachun, Stephen, 1947
      Diachun, Stephen and W.D. Valleau, 1950, 1954
      Johnson, J., 1936
      Price, W.C. and L.M. Black, 1941
      Thomas, H. Rex and W.J. Zaumeyer, 1950
   Nicotiana setchellii
      Diachun, Stephen and W.D. Valleau, 1954
   Nicotiana spp.
      Fulton, Robert W., 1948
   Nicotiana stocktoni
      Diachun, Stephen and W.D. Valleau, 1954
   Nicotiana suaveolens
      Diachun, Stephen and W.D. Valleau, 1954
   Nicotiana sylvestris
      Diachun, Stephen and W.D. Valleau, 1954
   Nicotiana tabacum
      Costa, A.S., 1945, 1952
      Diachun, Stephen, 1947
      Diachun, Stephen and W.D. Valleau, 1950, 1954
      Fulton, Robert W., 1941, 1956
      Johnson, J., 1936
      Thomas, H. Rex and W.J. Zaumeyer, 1950
   Nicotiana tabacum x Nicotiana glutinosa
      Johnson, J., 1936
   Nicotiana tomentosa
      Diachun, Stephen and W.D. Valleau, 1954
   Nicotiana tomentosiformis
      Diachun, Stephen and W.D. Valleau, 1954
   Nicotiana trigonophylla
      Diachun, Stephen and W.D. Valleau, 1954
   Nicotiana undulata
      Diachun, Stephen and W.D. Valleau, 1954
   Nicotiana velutina
      Diachun, Stephen and W.D. Valleau, 1954
   Oenothera biennis
      Fulton, Robert W., 1948
   Petunia hybrida
      Fulton, Robert W., 1948
   Phaseolus aconitifolius
      Fulton, Robert W., 1948
      Thomas, H. Rex and W.J. Zaumeyer, 1950
   Phaseolus aureus
      Fulton, Robert W., 1948
      Thomas, H. Rex and W.J. Zaumeyer, 1950
   Phaseolus coccineus
      Thomas, H. Rex and W.J. Zaumeyer, 1950
   Phaseolus mungo
      Thomas, H. Rex and W.J. Zaumeyer, 1950
   Phaseolus vulgaris
      Fulton, Robert W., 1948
      Thomas, H. Rex and W.J. Zaumeyer, 1950
      Thomas, W.D., Jr., 1949
      Thomas, W.D., Jr. and R.W. Graham, 1951
   Physalis pubescens
      Fulton, Robert W., 1948

VIRUS
V. TOBACCO STREAK (cont.)
 Physalis pubescens
  Johnson, J., 1936
 Pisum sativum
  Fulton, Robert W., 1948
  Thomas, H. Rex and W.J. Zaumeyer, 1950
 Plantago major
  Fulton, Robert W., 1948
 Polygonum persicarae
  Fulton, Robert W., 1948
 Portulaca oleracea
  Fulton, Robert W., 1948
 Potentilla monspeliensis
  Fulton, Robert W., 1948
 Psoralea bituminosa
  Fulton, Robert W., 1948
 Robinia pseudoacacia
  Fulton, Robert W., 1948
 Rumex britannica
  Fulton, Robert W., 1948
 Rumex crispus
  Fulton, Robert W., 1948
 Schizanthus wisetonensis
  Fulton, Robert W., 1948
 Sicyos angulatus
  Fulton, Robert W., 1948
 Silene noctiflora
  Fulton, Robert W., 1948
 Sisymbrium officinale
  Fulton, Robert W., 1948
 Solanum aculeatissimum
  Fulton, Robert W., 1948
 Solanum dulcamara
  Fulton, Robert W., 1948
 Solanum integrifolium
  Fulton, Robert W., 1948
 Solanum melongena
  Fulton, Robert W., 1948
 Solanum nigrum
  Fulton, Robert W., 1948
 Solanum triflorum
  Fulton, Robert W., 1948
 Solanum tuberosum
  Fulton, Robert W., 1948
 Sonchus oleraceus
  Fulton, Robert W., 1948
 Spergula arvensis
  Fulton, Robert W., 1948
 Spinacia oleracea
  Fulton, Robert W., 1948
 Taraxacum officinale
  Fulton, Robert W., 1948
 Trifolium glomeratum
  Fulton, Robert W., 1948
 Trifolium incarnatum
  Fulton, Robert W., 1948
  Thomas, H. Rex and W.J. Zaumeyer, 1950
 Trifolium pratense
  Fulton, Robert W., 1948
  Thomas, H. Rex and W.J. Zaumeyer, 1950
 Trifolium repens
  Fulton, Robert W., 1948
 Trigonella spp.
  Fulton, Robert W., 1948
 Tropaeolum majus
  Fulton, Robert W., 1948
 Venidium fastuosum
  Fulton, Robert W., 1948
 Verbascum thapsus
  Fulton, Robert W., 1948
 Vicia faba
  Fulton, Robert W., 1948
  Thomas, H. Rex and W.J. Zaumeyer, 1950
 Vicia sativa
  Thomas, H. Rex and W.J. Zaumeyer, 1950
 Vigna sesquipedalis
  Thomas, H. Rex and W.J. Zaumeyer, 1950
 Vigna sinensis
  Thomas, H. Rex and W.J. Zaumeyer, 1950
 Vinca rosea
  Fulton, Robert W., 1948
 Zinnia elegans
  Fulton, Robert W., 1948

VIRUS
V. TOBACCO STUNT *
 Nicotiana tabacum
  Hidaka, Zyun, Tetsuo Uozumi and Chuji Hiruki, 1956

V. TOBACCO VEIN DISTORTING Smith 1945
 Datura stramonium
  (K.M. Smith, 1957) R.E. Fitzpatrick, et al., 1958
 Lycopersicon esculentum
  (K.M. Smith, 1957) R.E. Fitzpatrick, et al., 1958
 Nicotiana glutinosa
  (K.M. Smith, 1957) R.E. Fitzpatrick, et al., 1958
 Nicotiana sylvestris
  (K.M. Smith, 1957) R.E. Fitzpatrick, et al., 1958
 Nicotiana tabacum
  (K.M. Smith, 1957) R.E. Fitzpatrick, et al., 1958

V. TOBACCO YELLOW DWARF Hill 1937
 Brassica adpressa
  Helson, G.A.H., 1950
 Callistephus chinensis
  Helson, G.A.H., 1950
 Cryptostemma calendulaceum
  Helson, G.A.H., 1950
  Hill, A.V., 1950
 Datura stramonium
  Helson, G.A.H., 1950
  Hill, A.V., 1950
  Hill, A.V. and M. Mandryk, 1954
 Datura stramonium var. tatula
  Helson, G.A.H., 1950
 Erodium cicutarium
  Helson, G.A.H., 1950
  Hill, A.V., 1950
 Erodium cygnorum
  Helson, G.A.H., 1950
 Hypochoeris radicata
  Helson, G.A.H., 1950
 Lycopersicon esculentum
  Hill, A.V., 1950
  Hill, A.V. and M. Mandryk, 1954
 Malva parviflora
  Helson, G.A.H., 1950
 Medicago denticulata
  Helson, G.A.H., 1950
  Hill, A.V., 1950
 Medicago sativa
  Helson, G.A.H., 1950
 Modiola caroliniana
  Helson, G.A.H., 1950
 Nicotiana australasiae
  Hill, A.V. and M. Mandryk, 1954
 Nicotiana excelsior
  Hill, A.V. and M. Mandryk, 1954
 Nicotiana glauca
  Hill, A.V., 1950
  Hill, A.V. and M. Mandryk, 1954
 Nicotiana glutinosa
  Hill, A.V., 1950
  Hill, A.V. and M. Mandryk, 1954
 Nicotiana gossei
  Hill, A.V. and M. Mandryk, 1954
 Nicotiana maritima
  Hill, A.V. and M. Mandryk, 1954
 Nicotiana rustica
  Hill, A.V. and M. Mandryk, 1954
 Nicotiana suaveolens
  Hill, A.V. and M. Mandryk, 1954
 Nicotiana tabacum
  Hill, A.V., 1950
  Hill, A.V. and M. Mandryk, 1954
 Nicotiana tabacum var. atropurpurea *
  Hill, A.V. and M. Mandryk, 1954
 Silybum marianum
  Helson, G.A.H., 1950
 Solanum laciniatum
  Hill, A.V., 1950
 Solanum nigrum
  Hill, A.V., 1950
 Solanum opacum
  Hill, A.V. and M. Mandryk, 1954
 Sonchus oleraceus
  Helson, G.A.H., 1950
 Trifolium repens
  Helson, G.A.H., 1950

VIRUS
V. TOMATO ASPERMY Belncowe and Caldwell 1949
  Antirrhinum majus
    Brierley, Philip, Floyd F. Smith and S.P. Doolittle, 1955
    Hollings, M., 1955
  Beta vulgaris
    Brierley, Philip, Floyd F. Smith and S.P. Doolittle, 1955
    Hollings, M., 1955
  Calendula officinalis
    Brierley, Philip, Floyd F. Smith and S.P. Doolittle, 1955
    Hollings, M., 1955
  Callistephus chinensis
    Brierley, Philip, Floyd F. Smith and S.P. Doolittle, 1953, 1955
    Hollings, M., 1955
  Canna indica
    Ocfemia, G.O., 1956
  Capsicum frutescens (Capsicum annuum)
    Brierley, Philip, Floyd F. Smith and S.P. Doolittle, 1953, 1955
    Hollings, M., 1955
  Celosia argentea var. cristata
    Brierley, Philip, Floyd F. Smith and S.P. Doolittle, 1955
  Chenopodium amaranticolor
    Hollings, M., 1955, 1956
  Chrysanthemum carinatum
    Hollings, M., 1955
  Chrysanthemum coccineum
    Hollings, M., 1955
  Chrysanthemum frutescens
    Brierley, Philip, Floyd F. Smith and S.P. Doolittle, 1955
  Chrysanthemum hortorum
    Graham, D.C., 1957
  Chrysanthemum indicum
    (K.M. Smith, 1957) R.E. Fitzpatrick, et al., 1958
    Hollings, M., 1955
  Chrysanthemum leucanthemum
    Brierley, Philip, Floyd F. Smith and S.P. Doolittle, 1955
  Chrysanthemum morifolium
    Blencowe, J.W. and John Caldwell, 1949
    Brierley, Philip, 1955
    Brierley, Philip and Floyd F. Smith, 1953, 1957
    Brierley, Philip, Floyd F. Smith and S.P. Doolittle, 1953, 1955
    Hollings, M., 1955
    Holmes, Francis O., 1956
    Ocfemia, G.O., 1956
  Chrysanthemum parthenium f. flosculosum *
    Brierley, Philip, Floyd F. Smith and S.P. Doolittle, 1955
  Convolvulus tricolor
    Brierley, Philip, Floyd F. Smith and S.P. Doolittle, 1955
  Cucumis sativus
    Brierley, Philip, Floyd F. Smith and S.P. Doolittle, 1953, 1955
    Hollings, M., 1955
  Datura inoxia
    Brierley, Philip, Floyd F. Smith and S.P. Doolittle, 1955
  Datura stramonium
    Brierley, Philip, Floyd F. Smith and S.P. Doolittle, 1955
    Hollings, M., 1955
  Delphinium ajacis
    Brierley, Philip, Floyd F. Smith and S.P. Doolittle, 1955
  Emilia sagittata
    Brierley, Philip, Floyd F. Smith and S.P. Doolittle, 1955
  Gaillardia pulchella var. picta
    Brierley, Philip, Floyd F. Smith and S.P. Doolittle, 1955
  Galinsoga parviflora
    Brierley, Philip, Floyd F. Smith and S.P. Doolittle, 1955
  Glycine max
    (K.M. Smith, 1957) R.E. Fitzpatrick, et al., 1958

VIRUS
V. TOMATO ASPERMY (cont.)
  Gomphrena globosa
    Hollings, M., 1955
  Helichrysum bracteatum
    Brierley, Philip, Floyd F. Smith and S.P. Doolittle, 1955
    Hollings, M., 1955
  Hyoscyamus niger
    Hollings, M., 1955
  Impatiens balsamina
    Brierley, Philip, Floyd F. Smith and S.P. Doolittle, 1955
  Ipomoea purpurea
    Brierley, Philip, Floyd F. Smith and S.P. Doolittle, 1955
  Lactuca sativa
    Brierley, Philip, Floyd F. Smith and S.P. Doolittle, 1953, 1955
    Hollings, M., 1955
  Lilium longiflorum
    Brierley, Philip, Floyd F. Smith and S.P. Doolittle, 1955
  Lobelia erinus
    Hollings, M., 1955
  Lycopersicon esculentum
    Blencowe, J.W. and John Caldwell, 1949
    Brierley, Philip and Floyd F. Smith, 1953
    Brierley, Philip, Floyd F. Smith and S.P. Doolittle, 1953, 1955
    Hollings, M., 1955
  Nicotiana glutinosa
    Blencowe, J.W. and John Caldwell, 1949
    Brierley, Philip, Floyd F. Smith and S.P. Doolittle, 1955
    Hollings, M., 1955
    Ocfemia, G.O., 1956
    Wilkinson, John, 1952
  Nicotiana rustica
    Brierley, Philip, Floyd F. Smith and S.P. Doolittle, 1955
    Hollings, M., 1955
  Nicotiana sylvestris
    Brierley, Philip, Floyd F. Smith and S.P. Doolittle, 1955
  Nicotiana tabacum
    Blencowe, J.W. and John Caldwell, 1949
    Brierley, Philip, 1955
    Brierley, Philip and Floyd F. Smith, 1953
    Brierley, Philip, Floyd F. Smith and S.P. Doolittle, 1953, 1955
    Hollings, M., 1955
    Ocfemia, G.O., 1956
  Petunia hybrida
    Brierley, Philip and Floyd F. Smith, 1953
    Brierley, Philip, Floyd F. Smith and S.P. Doolittle, 1953, 1955
  Petunia hybrida var. erecta *
    Hollings, M., 1955
  Petunia hybrida var. nana compacta *
    Hollings, M., 1955
  Phaseolus vulgaris
    Hollings, M., 1955
  Phlox drummondii
    Brierley, Philip, Floyd F. Smith and S.P. Doolittle, 1955
    Hollings, M., 1955
  Physalis angulata
    Brierley, Philip and Floyd F. Smith, 1953
    Brierley, Philip, Floyd F. Smith and S.P. Doolittle, 1953, 1955
  Physalis floridana
    Brierley, Philip, Floyd F. Smith and S.P. Doolittle, 1955
  Primula sinensis
    Hollings, M., 1955
  Primula sinensis var. stellata
    (K.M. Smith, 1957) R.E. Fitzpatrick, et al., 1958
  Rheum rhaponticum
    (K.M. Smith, 1957) R.E. Fitzpatrick, et al., 1958
  Salpiglossis sinuata
    Hollings, M., 1955
  Senecio cruentus
    Brierley, Philip, Floyd F. Smith and S.P. Doolittle, 1955

VIRUS
V. TOMATO ASPERMY (cont.)
  Senecio cruentus
    Hollings, M., 1955
  Solanum melongena
    Brierley, Philip, Floyd F. Smith and S.P. Doolittle, 1955
  Spinacia oleracea
    Brierley, Philip, Floyd F. Smith and S.P. Doolittle, 1953, 1955
    Hollings, M., 1955
  Tetragonia expansa
    Brierley, Philip, Floyd F. Smith and S.P. Doolittle, 1955
  Tropaeolum majus
    Hollings, M., 1955
  Verbesina encelioides
    Brierley, Philip, Floyd F. Smith and S.P. Doolittle, 1955
  Vigna sinensis
    Hollings, M., 1955
  Zinnia elegans
    Brierley, Philip, Floyd F. Smith and S.P. Doolittle, 1955
    Hollings, M., 1955

V. TOMATO BIG BUD Samuel et al. 1933
  Apium graveolens
    Helms, Katie, 1957
  Beta vulgaris
    Helms, Katie, 1957
    Hill, A.V. and M. Mandryk, 1954
  Calendula officinalis
    Helms, Katie, 1957
  Crotalaria goreensis
    Helms, Katie, 1957
  Datura stramonium
    Helms, Katie, 1957
    Hill, A.V. and M. Mandryk, 1954
    Norris, D.O., 1954
  Datura stramonium var. tatula
    Helms, Katie, 1957
  Daucus carota
    Helms, Katie, 1957
  Daucus carota var. sativa
    Kunkel, L.O., 1951
  Lactuca sativa
    Helms, Katie, 1957
  Lycopersicon esculentum
    Alvarez-Garcia, L.A. and Jose Adsuar, 1950
    Dana, B.F., 1940
    Helms, Katie, 1957
    Hill, A.V. and M. Mandryk, 1954
    Hutton, E.M. and D.C. Work, 1947
    Menzies, J.D., 1950
    Norris, D.O., 1954
    Samuel, G., J.G. Bald and C.M. Eardley, 1933
    Vasudeva, R. Sahai and T.B. Lal, 1944
  Lycopersicon hirsutum
    Hutton, E.M. and D.C. Work, 1947
  Lycopersicon peruvianum
    Hutton, E.M. and D.C. Work, 1947
  Lycopersicon pimpinellifolium
    Hutton, E.M. and D.C. Work, 1947
  Lycopersicon spp.
    Dana, B.F., 1940
  Medicago sativa
    Helms, Katie, 1957
  Nicotiana glauca
    Hill, A.V. and M. Mandryk, 1954
  Nicotiana glutinosa
    Helms, Katie, 1957
    Hill, A.V. and M. Mandryk, 1954
  Nicotiana rustica
    Helms, Katie, 1957
  Nicotiana tabacum
    Helms, Katie, 1957
    Hill, A.V. and M. Mandryk, 1954
  Nicotiana tabacum var. atropurpurea *
    Helms, Katie, 1957
  Petunia spp.
    Helms, Katie, 1957
  Solanum melongena
    Hill, A.V. and M. Mandryk, 1954

VIRUS
V. TOMATO BIG BUD (cont.)
  Solanum opacum
    Hill, A.V. and M. Mandryk, 1954
  Solanum tuberosum
    Helms, Katie, 1957
    Hill, A.V. and M. Mandryk, 1954
    Norris, D.O., 1954
  Vinca rosea
    Hill, A.V. and M. Mandryk, 1954
  Vinca rosea var. alba
    Helms, Katie, 1957
  Vinca rosea var. oculata *
    Helms, Katie, 1957

V. TOMATO BLACK FLECK *
  Chenopodium amaranticolor
    Hollings, M., 1957

V. TOMATO BLACK RING Smith 1945
  Antirrhinum spp.
    (K.M. Smith, 1957) R.E. Fitzpatrick, et al., 1958
  Atropa belladonna
    (K.M. Smith, 1957) R.E. Fitzpatrick, et al., 1958
  Cheiranthus cheiri
    (K.M. Smith, 1957) R.E. Fitzpatrick, et al., 1958
  Chenopodium amaranticolor
    Harrison, B.D., 1958
    Hollings, M., 1956
  Cucumis sativus
    (K.M. Smith, 1957) R.E. Fitzpatrick, et al., 1958
  Cucurbita pepo
    (K.M. Smith, 1957) R.E. Fitzpatrick, et al., 1958
  Datura stramonium
    (K.M. Smith, 1957) R.E. Fitzpatrick, et al., 1958
  Dipsacus sylvestris
    (K.M. Smith, 1957) R.E. Fitzpatrick, et al., 1958
  Gloxinia spp.
    (K.M. Smith, 1957) R.E. Fitzpatrick, et al., 1958
  Lapsana communis
    (K.M. Smith, 1957) R.E. Fitzpatrick, et al., 1958
  Lycopersicon esculentum
    (K.M. Smith, 1957) R.E. Fitzpatrick, et al., 1958
  Nicotiana glutinosa
    (K.M. Smith, 1957) R.E. Fitzpatrick, et al., 1958
  Nicotiana langsdorffii
    (K.M. Smith, 1957) R.E. Fitzpatrick, et al., 1958
  Nicotiana paniculata
    (K.M. Smith, 1957) R.E. Fitzpatrick, et al., 1958
  Nicotiana rustica
    Harrison, B.D., 1958
  Nicotiana sylvestris
    (K.M. Smith, 1957) R.E. Fitzpatrick, et al., 1958
  Nicotiana tabacum
    Harrison, B.D., 1958
  Petunia hybrida
    Harrison, B.D., 1958
  Phaseolus vulgaris
    Harrison, B.D., 1958
  Rubus idaeus
    Harrison, B.D., 1958
  Schizanthus spp.
    (K.M. Smith, 1957) R.E. Fitzpatrick, et al., 1958
  Spinacia oleracea
    (K.M. Smith, 1957) R.E. Fitzpatrick, et al., 1958
  Tetragonia expansa
    (K.M. Smith, 1957) R.E. Fitzpatrick, et al., 1958
  Tropaeolum majus
    (K.M. Smith, 1957) R.E. Fitzpatrick, et al., 1958
  Viola spp.
    (K.M. Smith, 1957) R.E. Fitzpatrick, et al., 1958

V. TOMATO BUNCHY TOP McClean 1931, 1935
  Capsicum frutescens (Capsicum annuum)
    (K.M. Smith, 1957) R.E. Fitzpatrick, et al., 1958
  Nicandra physalodes
    (K.M. Smith, 1957) R.E. Fitzpatrick, et al., 1958
  Nicotiana glutinosa
    (K.M. Smith, 1957) R.E. Fitzpatrick, et al., 1958
  Nicotiana tabacum
    (K.M. Smith, 1957) R.E. Fitzpatrick, et al., 1958
  Physalis angulata
    (K.M. Smith, 1957) R.E. Fitzpatrick, et al., 1958

VIRUS

V. TOMATO BUNCHY TOP (cont.)
Physalis peruviana
(K.M. Smith, 1957) R.E. Fitzpatrick, et al., 1958
Physalis viscosa
(K.M. Smith, 1957) R.E. Fitzpatrick, et al., 1958
Solanum aculeastrum
(K.M. Smith, 1957) R.E. Fitzpatrick, et al., 1958
Solanum aculeatissimum
(K.M. Smith, 1957) R.E. Fitzpatrick, et al., 1958
Solanum giganteum
(K.M. Smith, 1957) R.E. Fitzpatrick, et al., 1958
Solanum incanum
(K.M. Smith, 1957) R.E. Fitzpatrick, et al., 1958
Solanum indicum
(K.M. Smith, 1957) R.E. Fitzpatrick, et al., 1958
Solanum nigrum
(K.M. Smith, 1957) R.E. Fitzpatrick, et al., 1958
Solanum sisymbrifolium
(K.M. Smith, 1957) R.E. Fitzpatrick, et al., 1958
Solanum sodomaeum
(K.M. Smith, 1957) R.E. Fitzpatrick, et al., 1958
Zinnia elegans
(K.M. Smith, 1957) R.E. Fitzpatrick, et al., 1958

V. TOMATO BUSHY STUNT Smith 1935
Amaranthus caudatus
(K.M. Smith, 1957) R.E. Fitzpatrick, et al., 1958
Aster spp.
(K.M. Smith, 1957) R.E. Fitzpatrick, et al., 1958
Callistephus chinensis
Smith, Kenneth M., 1935
Cucumis sativus
(K.M. Smith, 1957) R.E. Fitzpatrick, et al., 1958
Datura meteloides
Steere, Russell L., 1953
Datura stramonium
Steere, Russell L., 1953
Lycopersicon esculentum
Johnson, Folke, 1941
Smith, Kenneth M., 1935
Steere, Russell L., 1953
Mimulus guttatus
Smith, Kenneth M., 1935
Mimulus luteus
(K.M. Smith, 1957) R.E. Fitzpatrick, et al., 1958
Nicotiana glutinosa
Bawden, F.C. and F.M. Roberts, 1948
Smith, Kenneth M., 1935
Steere, Russell L., 1953
Nicotiana langsdorffii
(K.M. Smith, 1957) R.E. Fitzpatrick, et al., 1958
Smith, Kenneth M., 1935
Nicotiana tabacum
Smith, Kenneth M., 1935
Phaseolus vulgaris
(K.M. Smith, 1957) R.E. Fitzpatrick, et al., 1958
Solanum tuberosum
Smith, Kenneth M., 1935
Vigna sinensis
(K.M. Smith, 1957) R.E. Fitzpatrick, et al., 1958
Smith, Kenneth M., 1935
Zinnia elegans
(K.M. Smith, 1957) R.E. Fitzpatrick, et al., 1958
Smith, Kenneth M., 1935

V. TOMATO FILIFORM LEAF DISEASE *
Nicotiana tabacum
Schwarze, C.A., 1914

V. TOMATO RING SPOT Samson and Imle 1942 ((Distinct
from V. Tomato spotted wilt.))
Amaranthus retroflexus
Samson, R.W. and E.P. Imle, 1942
Amaranthus tricolor
Samson, R.W. and E.P. Imle, 1942
Androcera rostrata
Samson, R.W. and E.P. Imle, 1942
Capsicum frutescens (Capsicum annuum)
Samson, R.W. and E.P. Imle, 1942
Datura spp.
Samson, R.W. and E.P. Imle, 1942
Datura stramonium
Imle, E.P. and R.W. Samson, 1937

VIRUS

V. TOMATO RING SPOT (cont.)
Datura stramonium
Samson, R.W. and E.P. Imle, 1942
Datura stramonium var. tatula
Samson, R.W. and E.P. Imle, 1942
Glycine max
Kahn, Robert P., 1956
Kahn, Robert P. and Frances M. Latterell, 1955
Gomphrena globosa
Brierley, Philip, 1956
Brierley, Philip and Paul Lorentz, 1956, 1957
Hydrangea macrophylla
Brierley, Philip and Paul Lorentz, 1956
Brierley, Philip and Floyd F. Smith, 1953
Hyoscyamus niger
Samson, R.W. and E.P. Emle, 1942
Lycopersicon esculentum
Imle, E.P. and R.W. Samson, 1937
Samson, R.W. and E.P. Imle, 1942
Varney, E.H. and J. Duain Moore, 1952
Lycopersicon pimpinellifolium
Samson, R.W. and E.P. Imle, 1942
Martynia louisiana
Samson, R.W. and E.P. Imle, 1942
Nicandra physalodes
Samson, R.W. and E.P. Imle, 1942
Nicotiana affinis
Samson, R.W. and E.P. Imle, 1942
Nicotiana glutinosa
Bennett, C.W., 1944
Varney, E.H. and J. Duain Moore, 1952
Nicotiana tabacum
Bennett, C.W., 1944
Brierley, Philip and Paul Lorentz, 1957
Brierley, Philip and Floyd F. Smith, 1953
Imle, E.P. and R.W. Sanson, 1937
Kahn, Robert P. and Frances M. Latterell, 1955
Samson, R.W. and E.P. Imle, 1942
Varney, E.H. and J. Duain Moore, 1952
Petunia axillaris
Samson, R.W. and E.P. Imle, 1942
Petunia hybrida var. grandiflora *
Samson, R.W. and E.P. Imle, 1942
Phaseolus vulgaris
Kahn, Robert P. and Frances M. Latterell, 1955
Physalis alkekengi
Samson, R.W. and E.P. Imle, 1942
Solanum carolinense
Samson, R.W. and E.P. Imle, 1942
Solanum melongena
(K.M. Smith, 1957) R.E. Fitzpatrick, et al., 1958
Samson, R.W. and E.P. Imle, 1942
Solanum pseudocapsicum
Samson, R.W. and E.P. Imle, 1942
Solanum tuberosum
Samson, R.W. and E.P. Imle, 1942
Ulmus americana
Varney, E.H. and J. Duain Moore, 1952
Vigna sinensis
Kahn, Robert P., 1956
Kahn, Robert P. and Frances M. Latterell, 1955
Varney, E.H. and J. Duain Moore, 1952

V. TOMATO SHOESTRING *
Lycopersicon esculentum
Doering, G.R., W.C. Price and S.B. Fenne, 1957
Nicotiana glutinosa
Doering, G.R., W.C. Price and S.B. Fenne, 1957
Nicotiana rustica
Doering, G.R., W.C. Price and S.B. Fenne, 1957
Nicotiana sylvestris
Doering, G.R., W.C. Price and S.B. Fenne, 1957
Nicotiana tabacum
Doering, G.R., W.C. Price and S.B. Fenne, 1957

V. TOMATO SPOTTED WILT Samuel et al. 1930
Amaranthus retroflexus
Milbrath, J.A., 1939
Amaryllis hybrid
Gardner, M.W., C.M. Tompkins and O.C. Whipple, 1935
(Hippeastrum) spp.
(K.M. Smith, 1957) R.E. Fitzpatrick, et al., 1958

VIRUS
V. TOMATO SPOTTED WILT (cont.)
  Ananas comosus
    Carter, W., 1935
    Illingworth, J.F., 1931
    Linford, M.B., 1931, 1932, 1943
    Sakimura, K., 1940
  Anemone spp.
    (K.M. Smith, 1957) R.E. Fitzpatrick, et al., 1958
  Antirrhinum spp.
    (K.M. Smith, 1957) R.E. Fitzpatrick, et al., 1958
  Apium graveolens var. dulce
    Gardner, M.W., C.M. Tompkins and O.C. Whipple, 1935
    Sakimura, K., 1940
  Aquilegia vulgaris
    (K.M. Smith, 1957) R.E. Fitzpatrick, et al., 1958
  Arum palaestinum
    Tompkins, C.M. and Henry H.P. Severin, 1950
  Aster spp.
    (K.M. Smith, 1957) R.E. Fitzpatrick, et al., 1958
  Atropa belladonna
    Smith, Kenneth M., 1932
  Begonia semperflorens
    Gardner, M.W., C.M. Tompkins and O.C. Whipple, 1935
  Brassica oleracea var. botrytis
    Gardner, M.W., C.M. Tompkins and O.C. Whipple, 1935
  Browallia americana (Browallia demissa)
    Gardner, M.W., C.M. Tompkins and O.C. Whipple, 1935
  Browallia speciosa
    (K.M. Smith, 1957) R.E. Fitzpatrick, et al., 1958
  Calceolaria spp.
    (K.M. Smith, 1957) R.E. Fitzpatrick, et al., 1958
  Callistephus chinensis
    Black, L.M., M.K. Brakke and A.E. Vatter, 1952
    Gardner, M.W. and O.C. Whipple, 1934
    Smith, Kenneth M., 1932
    Tompkins, C.M. and M.W. Gardner, 1934
    Whipple, O.C., 1936
  Campanula americana
    Gardner, M.W., C.M. Tompkins and O.C. Whipple, 1935
  Campanula pyramidalis
    (K.M. Smith, 1957) R.E. Fitzpatrick, et al., 1958
  Capsicum frutescens (Capsicum annuum)
    Ferguson, I.A.C., 1951
    Gardner, M.W. and O.C. Whipple, 1934
    Kendrick, J.B., Jr., L.D. Anderson and R.C. Dickson, 1951
    Smith, Kenneth M., 1932
    Tompkins, C.M. and M.W. Gardner, 1934
    Yu, T.F., 1947
  Capsicum frutescens var. grossum
    Sakimura, K., 1940
  Capsicum spp.
    Smith, Kenneth M., 1931, 1932
  Cheiranthus cheiri
    Gardner, M.W., C.M. Tompkins and O.C. Whipple, 1935
  Cheiranthus spp.
    (K.M. Smith, 1957) R.E. Fitzpatrick, et al., 1958
  Chenopodium amaranticolor
    Hollings, M., 1956
  Chrysanthemum morifolium
    Gardner, M.W. and O.C. Whipple, 1934
  Chrysanthemum spp.
    (K.M. Smith, 1957) R.E. Fitzpatrick, et al., 1958
  Cichorium endivia
    Sakimura, K., 1940
  Cichorium intybus
    Sakimura, K., 1940
  Cinararia cruenta
    Jones, Leon K., 1944
  Convolvulus arvensis
    Sherf, A.F., 1948
  Coreopsis drummondii
    (K.M. Smith, 1957) R.E. Fitzpatrick, et al., 1958
  Cosmos bipinnatus
    (K.M. Smith, 1957) R.E. Fitzpatrick, et al., 1958
  Dahlia pinnata
    Holmes, Francis O., 1948, 1955

VIRUS
V. TOMATO SPOTTED WILT (cont.)
  Dahlia pinnata
    Smith, Kenneth M., 1932
  Dahlia variabilis
    Brierley, Philip, 1933
    (K.M. Smith, 1957) R.E. Fitzpatrick, et al., 1958
    Gardner, M.W. and O.C. Whipple, 1934
  Datura stramonium
    Ainsworth, G.C., 1933
    Ainsworth, G.C., G.H. Berkeley and J. Caldwell, 1934
    Gardner, M.W., C.M. Tompkins and O.C. Whipple, 1935
    Gardner, M.W. and O.C. Whipple, 1934
    Milbrath, J.A., 1939
    Norris, D.O., 1951
    Sakimura, K., 1940
    Shapovalov, M., 1934
    Smith, Kenneth M., 1931, 1932, 1935
    Snyder, W.C. and H. Rex Thomas, 1936
    Whipple, O.C., 1936
  Datura wrightii
    (K.M. Smith, 1957) R.E. Fitzpatrick, et al., 1958
  Delphinium cultorum
    Gardner, M.W., C.M. Tompkins and O.C. Whipple, 1935
  Delphinium hybrid
    Severin, Henry H.P., 1942
  Emilia sagittata
    Gardner, M.W., C.M. Tompkins and O.C. Whipple, 1935
    Linford, M.B., 1931, 1932
    Whipple, O.C., 1936
  Emilia sonchifolia
    Norris, D.O., 1951
    Parris, G.K., 1940
    Sakimura, K., 1940
  Gaillardia aristata
    Gardner, M.W., C.M. Tompkins and O.C. Whipple, 1935
  Gladiolus spp.
    (K.M. Smith, 1957) R.E. Fitzpatrick, et al., 1958
  Godetia grandiflora
    Gardner, M.W., C.M. Tompkins and O.C. Whipple, 1935
  Hoya carnosa
    Prentice, I.W., 1952
  Hyoscyamus niger
    Smith, Kenneth M., 1932
  Lactuca sativa
    Gardner, M.W. and O.C. Whipple, 1934
    Milbrath, J.A., 1939
    Sakimura, K., 1940
    Tompkins, C.M. and M.W. Gardner, 1934
  Lactuca sativa var. capitata
    Ainsworth, G.C., 1940
    Snyder, W.C. and H. Rex Thomas, 1936
  Lactuca sativa var. longifolia
    Snyder, W.C. and H. Rex Thomas, 1936
    Tompkins, C.M. and M.W. Gardner, 1934
  Lactuca scariola
    Milbrath, J.A., 1939
  Lathyrus odoratus
    Ainsworth, G.C., 1940
    Snyder, W.C. and H. Rex Thomas, 1936
  Layia elegans
    Gardner, M.W., C.M. Tompkins and O.C. Whipple, 1935
  Lobelia spp.
    (K.M. Smith, 1957) R.E. Fitzpatrick, et al., 1958
  Lupinus albus
    Gardner, M.W. and O.C. Whipple, 1934
  Lupinus angustifolius
    Smith, Kenneth M., 1932
  Lupinus leucophyllus
    (K.M. Smith, 1957) R.E. Fitzpatrick, et al., 1958
  Lycium ferocissimum
    (K.M. Smith, 1957) R.E. Fitzpatrick, et al., 1958
  Lycopersicon esculentum
    Ainsworth, G.C., 1933, 1940
    Ainsworth, G.C., G.H. Berkeley and J. Caldwell, 1934
    Bennett, C.W., 1944

VIRUS
V. TOMATO SPOTTED WILT (cont.)
  Lycopersicon esculentum
    Berkeley, G.H., 1935
    Best, Rupert J. and Geoffrey Samuel, 1936
    Black, L.M., M.K. Brakke and A.E. Vatter, 1952
    Doolittle, S.P. and C.B. Summer, 1931, 1934
    Ferguson, I.A.C., 1951
    Gardner, M.W., C.M. Tompkins and O.C. Whipple,
      1935
    Gardner, M.W. and O.C. Whipple, 1934
    Holmes, Francis O., 1948
    Hutton, E.M. and A.R. Peak, 1949, 1953
    Jones, Leon K., 1944
    MacNeill, Blair H., 1955
    McWhorter, F.P., 1935
    McWhorter, F.P. and J.A. Milbrath, 1935
    Milbrath, J.A., 1939
    Norris, D.O., 1951
    Parris, G.K., 1940
    Sakimura, K., 1940
    Shapovalov, M., 1934
    Sherf, A.F., 1948
    Smith, Kenneth M., 1931, 1932, 1935
    Smith, Paul G., 1944
    Smith, Paul G. and M.W. Gardner, 1948, 1951
    Snyder, W.C. and H. Rex Thomas, 1936
    Tompkins, C.M. and M.W. Gardner, 1934
    Whipple, O.C., 1936
    Yu, T.F., 1947
  Lycopersicon hirsutum
    Smith, Paul G., 1944
  Lycopersicon hybrids
    Hutton, E.M. and A.R. Peak, 1949
  Lycopersicon peruvianum
    Hutton, E.M. and A.R. Peak, 1949, 1953
  Lycopersicon pimpinellifolium
    Hutton, E.M. and A.R. Peak, 1949, 1953
    Sakimura, K., 1940
    Smith, Paul G., 1944
    Smith, Paul G. and M.W. Gardner, 1948, 1951
  Lycopersicon pimpinellifolium x Lycopersicon
  esculentum
    Smith, Paul G. and M.W. Gardner, 1948
  Malva rotundifolia
    Milbrath, J.A., 1939
  Martynia annua
    Gardner, M.W. and O.C. Whipple, 1934
  Nepeta cataria
    Milbrath, J.A., 1939
  Nicandra physalodes
    Gardner, M.W. and O.C. Whipple, 1934
  Nicotiana acuminata
    Gardner, M.W. and O.C. Whipple, 1934
  Nicotiana alata
    Gardner, M.W. and O.C. Whipple, 1934
  Nicotiana atropurpureum
    (K.M. Smith, 1957) R.E. Fitzpatrick, et al., 1958
  Nicotiana bigelovii
    (K.M. Smith, 1957) R.E. Fitzpatrick, et al., 1958
  Nicotiana calyciflora *
    (K.M. Smith, 1957) R.E. Fitzpatrick, et al., 1958
  Nicotiana chinensis
    (K.M. Smith, 1957) R.E. Fitzpatrick, et al., 1958
  Nicotiana glauca
    Gardner, M.W., C.M. Tompkins and O.C. Whipple,
      1935
    Smith, Kenneth M., 1932
  Nicotiana glutinosa
    Ainsworth, G.C., 1933
    Ainsworth, G.C., G.H. Berkeley and J. Caldwell,
      1934
    Berkeley, G.H., 1935
    Black, L.M., M.K. Brakke and A.E. Vatter, 1952
    Ferguson, I.A.C., 1951
    Gardner, M.W. and O.C. Whipple, 1934
    Holmes, Francis O., 1948
    Kendrick, J.B., Jr., L.D. Anderson and R.C.
    Dickson, 1951
    Milbrath, J.A., 1939
    Norris, D.O., 1951
    Sakimura, K., 1940
    Shapovalov, M., 1934
    Smith, Kenneth M., 1932

VIRUS
V. TOMATO SPOTTED WILT (cont.)
  Nicotiana glutinosa
    Snyder, W.C. and H. Rex Thomas, 1936
    Whipple, O.C., 1936
  Nicotiana langsdorffii
    Gardner, M.W. and O.C. Whipple, 1934
  Nicotiana longiflora
    (K.M. Smith, 1957) R.E. Fitzpatrick, et al., 1958
  Nicotiana paniculata
    (K.M. Smith, 1957) R.E. Fitzpatrick, et al., 1958
  Nicotiana rustica
    Black, L.M., M.K. Brakke and A.E. Vatter, 1952
    Gardner, M.W. and O.C. Whipple, 1934
    Smith, Kenneth M., 1932
    Tompkins, C.M. and M.W. Gardner, 1934
  Nicotiana sanderae
    Gardner, M.W. and O.C. Whipple, 1934
  Nicotiana suaveolens
    (K.M. Smith, 1957) R.E. Fitzpatrick, et al., 1958
  Nicotiana sylvestris
    (K.M. Smith, 1957) R.E. Fitzpatrick, et al., 1958
  Nicotiana tabacum
    Ainsworth, G.C., 1933
    Ainsworth, G.C., G.H. Berkeley and J. Caldwell,
      1934
    Bennett, C.W., 1944
    Berkeley, G.H., 1935
    Best, Rupert J. and Geoffrey Samuel, 1936
    Black, L.M., M.K. Brakke and A.E. Vatter, 1952
    Doolittle, S.P. and C.B. Summer, 1934
    Ferguson, I.A.C., 1951
    Gardner, M.W., C.M. Tompkins and O.C.
    Whipple, 1935
    Gardner, M.W. and O.C. Whipple, 1934
    Milbrath, J.A., 1939
    Price, W.C., 1936
    Sakimura, K., 1940
    Shapovalov, M., 1934
    Sherf, A.F., 1948
    Smith, Kenneth M., 1931, 1932
    Snyder, W.C. and H. Rex Thomas, 1936
    Whipple, O.C., 1936
    Yu, T.F., 1947
  Nicotiana tabacum var. angustifolia
    (K.M. Smith, 1957) R.E. Fitzpatrick, et al., 1958
  Nicotiana tabacum var. atropurpureum *
    Norris, D.O., 1951
  Paeonia spp.
    (K.M. Smith, 1957) R.E. Fitzpatrick, et al., 1958
  Papaver orientale
    Gardner, M.W., C.M. Tompkins and O.C.
    Whipple, 1935
  Papaver spp.
    (K.M. Smith, 1957) R.E. Fitzpatrick, et al., 1958
  Penstemon hirsutus
    Gardner, M.W., C.M. Tompkins and O.C.
    Whipple, 1935
  Petunia hybrida
    Gardner, M.W. and O.C. Whipple, 1934
    Milbrath, J.A., 1939
    Sakimura, K., 1940
  Petunia spp.
    Berkeley, G.H., 1935
    Norris, D.O., 1951
    Smith, Kenneth M., 1932
  Phaseolus vulgaris
    (K.M. Smith, 1957) R.E. Fitzpatrick, et al., 1958
  Physalis pubescens
    Gardner, M.W. and O.C. Whipple, 1934
    Tompkins, C.M. and M.W. Gardner, 1934
  Pisum sativum
    Ainsworth, G.C., 1940
    Jones, Leon K., 1944
    Milbrath, J.A., 1939
    Snyder, W.C. and H. Rex Thomas, 1936
    Whipple, O.C., 1936
  Plantago major
    Smith, Kenneth M., 1932
  Polygonum convolvulus
    (K.M. Smith, 1957) R.E. Fitzpatrick, et al., 1958
  Polygonum spp.
    (K.M. Smith, 1957) R.E. Fitzpatrick, et al., 1958

VIRUS
V. TOMATO SPOTTED WILT (cont.)
Primula malacoides
(K.M. Smith, 1957) R.E. Fitzpatrick, et al., 1958
Primula obconica
Gardner, M.W., C.M. Tompkins and O.C. Whipple, 1935
Severin, Henry H.P. and C.M. Tompkins, 1950
Primula sinensis
(K.M. Smith, 1957) R.E. Fitzpatrick, et al., 1958
Ranunculus spp.
(K.M. Smith, 1957) R.E. Fitzpatrick, et al., 1958
Salpiglossis sinuata
Gardner, M.W. and O.C. Whipple, 1934
Tompkins, C.M. and M.W. Gardner, 1934
Salvia splendens
Gardner, M.W., C.M. Tompkins and O.C. Whipple, 1935
Scabiosa spp.
(K.M. Smith, 1957) R.E. Fitzpatrick, et al., 1958
Schizanthus pinnatus
Gardner, M.W. and O.C. Whipple, 1934
Tompkins, C.M. and M.W. Gardner, 1934
Senecio cruentus
Gardner, M.W. and O.C. Whipple, 1934
Sinningia speciosa
Gardner, M.W., C.M. Tompkins and O.C. Whipple, 1935
Solanum aculeatissimum
Smith, Kenneth M., 1932
Solanum capsicastrum
Milbrath, J.A., 1939
Smith, Kenneth M., 1931, 1932
Solanum dulcamara
Smith, Kenneth M., 1932
Solanum laciniatum
Smith, Kenneth M., 1931, 1932
Solanum marginatum
Smith, Kenneth M., 1932
Solanum melongena
Ferguson, I.A.C., 1951
Gardner, M.W. and O.C. Whipple, 1934
Sakimura, K., 1940
Smith, Kenneth M., 1932
Tompkins, C.M. and M.W. Gardner, 1934
Solanum miniatum
(K.M. Smith, 1957) R.E. Fitzpatrick, et al., 1958
Solanum nigrum
Milbrath, J.A., 1939
Smith, Kenneth M., 1931, 1932
Solanum nodiflorum
Smith, Kenneth M., 1931, 1932
Solanum sanitwongsei
(K.M. Smith, 1957) R.E. Fitzpatrick, et al., 1958
Solanum seaforthianum
(K.M. Smith, 1957) R.E. Fitzpatrick, et al., 1958
Solanum sodomaeum
(K.M. Smith, 1957) R.E. Fitzpatrick, et al., 1958
Solanum tuberosum
Gardner, M.W. and O.C. Whipple, 1934
Hutton, E.M., 1947
Hutton, E.M. and A.R. Peak, 1952
Milbrath, J.A., 1939
Norris, D.O., 1951
Norris, D. and J.G. Bald, 1943
Parris, G.K., 1940
Sakimura, K., 1940
Smith, Kenneth M., 1931, 1932
Spinacia oleracea
Sakimura, K., 1940
Stellaria media
Holmes, Francis O., 1948
Streptosolen jamesonii
(K.M. Smith, 1957) R.E. Fitzpatrick, et al., 1958
Trachelium caeruleum
(K.M. Smith, 1957) R.E. Fitzpatrick, et al., 1958
Trachelium spp.
(K.M. Smith, 1957) R.E. Fitzpatrick, et al., 1958
Tropaeolum majus
Black, L.M., M.K. Brakke and A.E. Vatter, 1952
Gardner, M.W. and O.C. Whipple, 1934
Milbrath, J.A., 1939
Whipple, O.C., 1936

VIRUS
V. TOMATO SPOTTED WILT (cont.)
Urtica dioica
Gardner, M.W. and O.C. Whipple, 1934
Verbena hybrida
Gardner, M.W., C.M. Tompkins and O.C. Whipple, 1935
Vicia faba
Gardner, M.W. and O.C. Whipple, 1934
Sakimura, K., 1940
Yu, T.F., 1947
Vigna sinensis
Yu, T.F., 1947
Zantedeschia aethiopica
Gardner, M.W., C.M. Tompkins and O.C. Whipple, 1935
Tompkins, C.M. and Henry H.P. Severin, 1950
Whipple, O.C., 1936
Zantedeschia albo-maculata
Tompkins, C.M. and Henry H.P. Severin, 1950
Zantedeschia elliottiana
Tompkins, C.M. and Henry H.P. Severin, 1950
Zantedeschia melanoleuca
Tompkins, C.M. and Henry H.P. Severin, 1950
Zantedeschia rehmannii
Tompkins, C.M. and Henry H.P. Severin, 1950
Zinnia elegans
Gardner, M.W. and O.C. Whipple, 1934
Milbrath, J.A., 1939
Smith, Kenneth M., 1932
Yu, T.F., 1947

V. TOMATO TWISTED LEAF Ferguson 1951
Capsicum frutescens (Capsicum annuum)
Ferguson, I.A.C., 1951
Lycopersicon esculentum
Ferguson, I.A.C., 1951
Lycopersicon esculentum x Lycopersicon pimpinellifolium
Ferguson, I.A.C., 1951

V. TOMATO V-52-1 Miller 1953
Datura stramonium
Miller, Patrick M., 1953
Lycopersicon esculentum
Miller, Patrick M., 1953
Nicotiana glutinosa
Miller, Patrick M., 1953
Nicotiana tabacum
Miller, Patrick M., 1953
Phaseolus vulgaris
Miller, Patrick M., 1953
Solanum melongena
Miller, Patrick M., 1953
Vigna sinensis
Miller, Patrick M., 1953

V. TOMATO YELLOW NET Sylvester 1954
Lycopersicon esculentum
Sylvester, Edward S., 1954
Lycopersicon pimpinellifolium
Sylvester, Edward S., 1954

V. TOMATO YELLOW TOP Costa 1949; Sutton 1955
Lycopersicon esculentum
(K.M. Smith, 1957) R.E. Fitzpatrick, et al., 1958

V. TULIP BREAKING McKenny Hughes 1930
Calochortus spp.
Brierley, Philip and Floyd F. Smith, 1944
Fritillaria pudica
Brierley, Philip and Floyd F. Smith, 1944
Lilium amabile luteum *
Brierley, Philip, 1940
Lilium auratum
Brierley, Philip, 1940
Lilium brownii var. leucanthemum
Brierley, Philip, 1940
Brierley, Philip and Floyd F. Smith, 1944
Lilium canadense
Brierley, Philip, 1940
Lilium candidum
Brierley, Philip, 1940
Brierley, Philip and Floyd F. Smith, 1944

VIRUS
V. TULIP BREAKING (cont.)
  Lilium cernuum
    Brierley, Philip, 1940
  Lilium chalcedonicum
    Brierley, Philip, 1940
  Lilium croceum
    Brierley, Philip, 1940
  Lilium dauricum
    Brierley, Philip and Floyd F. Smith, 1944
  Lilium dauricum var. luteum
    Brierley, Philip, 1940
  Lilium davidi var. willmottiae *
    Brierley, Philip and Floyd F. Smith, 1944
  Lilium davmottiae *
    Brierley, Philip, 1940
  Lilium elegans
    Brierley, Philip, 1940
    Brierley, Philip and Floyd F. Smith, 1944
  Lilium formosanum *
    Brierley, Philip, 1939, 1940
    Brierley, Philip and S.P. Doolittle, 1940
    Brierley, Philip and Floyd F. Smith, 1944
    Smith, Floyd F. and Philip Brierley, 1948
  Lilium giganteum
    Brierley, Philip, 1940
  Lilium henryi
    Brierley, Philip, 1940
  Lilium longiflorum
    Brierley, Philip, 1939
    Brierley, Philip and S.P. Doolittle, 1940
    Brierley, Philip and Floyd F. Smith, 1944
    Smith, Floyd F. and Philip Brierley, 1948
  Lilium myriophyllus var. superbum *
    Brierley, Philip, 1940
  Lilium princeps
    Brierley, Philip, 1940
  Lilium pumilum
    Brierley, Philip, 1940
  Lilium regale
    Brierley, Philip, 1940
  Lilium sargentiae
    Brierley, Philip, 1940
  Lilium speciosum
    Brierley, Philip, 1940
  Lilium superbum
    Brierley, Philip, 1940
    Brierley, Philip and Floyd F. Smith, 1944
  Lilium testaceum
    Brierley, Philip, 1940
  Lilium tigrinum
    Brierley, Philip, 1940
    Brierley, Philip and Floyd F. Smith, 1944
  Lilium umbellatum
    Brierley, Philip, 1940
    Brierley, Philip and Floyd F. Smith, 1944
  Lilium wallacei
    Brierley, Philip, 1940
  Narcissus poeticus
    McWhorter, F.P., 1932
  Tulipa clusiana
    Cayley, Dorothy M., 1932
  Tulipa eichleri
    Cayley, Dorothy M., 1932
  Tulipa gesneriana
    Brierley, Philip, 1939, 1941
    Brierley, Philip and S.P. Doolittle, 1940
    Brierley, Philip and M.B. McKay, 1938
    Brierley, Philip and Floyd F. Smith, 1944
    Cayley, D.M., 1928, 1932
    Hughes, A.W. McKenny, 1930, 1931, 1934
    McWhorter, F.P., 1935, 1938
  Tulipa gesneriana var. spathulata
    Cayley, Dorothy M., 1932
  Tulipa greigii
    Cayley, Dorothy M., 1932
  Tulipa linifolia
    Cayley, Dorothy M., 1932
  Zygadenus fremontii
    Brierley, Philip and Floyd F. Smith, 1944

V. TULIP WHITE STREAK Smith 1950
  Nicotiana glutinosa
    (K.M. Smith, 1957) R.E. Fitzpatrick, et al., 1958

VIRUS
V. TULIP WHITE STREAK (cont.)
  Nicotiana tabacum
    (K.M. Smith, 1957) R.E. Fitzpatrick, et al., 1958
  Petunia spp.
    (K.M. Smith, 1957) R.E. Fitzpatrick, et al., 1958
  Phaseolus vulgaris
    (K.M. Smith, 1957) R.E. Fitzpatrick, et al., 1958
  Tulipa spp.
    (K.M. Smith, 1957) R.E. Fitzpatrick, et al., 1958

V. TURNIP CRINKLE Broadbent and Blencowe 1955
  Barbarea vulgaris
    Broadbent, L. and G.D. Heathcote, 1958
  Brassica hirta (Brassica alba)
    Broadbent, L. and G.D. Heathcote, 1958
  Brassica kaber (Brassica arvensis)
    Broadbent, L. and G.D. Heathcote, 1958
    (K.M. Smith, 1957) R.E. Fitzpatrick, et al., 1958
  Brassica napus
    Broadbent, L. and G.D. Heathcote, 1958
    Lister, R.M., 1958
  Brassica nigra
    Broadbent, L. and G.D. Heathcote, 1958
  Brassica oleracea var. botrytis
    Broadbent, L. and G.D. Heathcote, 1958
  Brassica oleracea var. capitata
    Broadbent, L. and G.D. Heathcote, 1958
  Brassica oleracea var. gemmifera
    Broadbent, L. and G.D. Heathcote, 1958
  Brassica pekinensis
    Broadbent, L. and G.D. Heathcote, 1958
  Brassica rapa
    Broadbent, L. and G.D. Heathcote
    Lister, R.M., 1958
  Camelina sativa
    Broadbent, L. and G.D. Heathcote, 1958
  Capsella bursa-pastoris
    Broadbent, L. and G.D. Heathcote, 1958
  Celosia argentea var. plumosa *
    Broadbent, L. and G.D. Heathcote, 1958
  Cheiranthus cheiri
    Broadbent, L. and G.D. Heathcote, 1958
  Chenopodium album
    Broadbent, L. and G.D. Heathcote, 1958
  Chenopodium amaranticolor
    Broadbent, L. and G.D. Heathcote, 1958
    Hollings, M., 1957
    Lister, R.M., 1958
  Cleome spinosa
    Broadbent, L. and G.D. Heathcote, 1958
  Cucumis sativus
    Broadbent, L. and G.D. Heathcote, 1958
    Lister, R.M., 1958
  Datura stramonium
    Broadbent, L. and G.D. Heathcote, 1958
  Erysimum cheiranthoides
    Broadbent, L. and G.D. Heathcote, 1958
  Gomphrena globosa
    Broadbent, L. and G.D. Heathcote, 1958
  Lactuca sativa var. capitata
    Broadbent, L. and G.D. Heathcote, 1958
  Lepidium campestre
    Broadbent, L. and G.D. Heathcote, 1958
  Lunaria annua
    Broadbent, L. and G.D. Heathcote, 1958
  Lycopersicon esculentum
    Broadbent, L. and G.D. Heathcote, 1958
  Neslia paniculata
    Broadbent, L. and G.D. Heathcote, 1958
  Nicotiana bigelovii var. multivalvis
    Broadbent, L. and G.D. Heathcote, 1958
  Nicotiana rustica
    Lister, R.M., 1958
  Nicotiana tabacum
    Broadbent, L. and G.D. Heathcote, 1958
    Lister, R.M., 1958
  Raphanus raphanistrum
    Broadbent, L. and G.D. Heathcote, 1958
  Raphanus sativus
    Broadbent, L. and G.D. Heathcote, 1958
  Reseda odorata
    Broadbent, L. and G.D. Heathcote, 1958

VIRUS
V. TURNIP CRINKLE (cont.)
   Sisymbrium officinale
      Broadbent, L. and G.D. Heathcote, 1958
   Tetragonia expansa
      Broadbent, L. and G.D. Heathcote, 1958
   Thlaspi arvense
      Broadbent, L. and G.D. Heathcote, 1958

V. TURNIP MOSAIC Gardner and Kendrick; Schultz 1921;
Chamberlain 1936; Tompkins 1938
   Abutilon theophrasti
      Walker, J.C., Francis J. LeBeau and Glenn S.
      Pound, 1945
   Alyssum maritimum
      Tompkins, C.M., 1939
   Amaranthus caudatus
      Pound, Glenn S., 1948
   Amaranthus tricolor
      Walker, J.C., Francis J. LeBeau and Glenn S.
      Pound, 1945
   Armoracia rusticana
      Dana, B.F. and F.P. McWhorter, 1932
      Hoggan, I.A. and J. Johnson, 1935
      Pound, Glenn S., 1948, 1949
   Barbarea vulgaris
      Pound, Glenn S., 1948
   Begonia semperflorens
      Tompkins, C.M., 1938
   Berteroa incana
      Walker, J.C., Francis J. LeBeau and Glenn S.
      Pound, 1945
   Beta vulgaris
      LeBeau, Francis J. and J.C. Walker, 1945
      Walker, J.C., Francis J. LeBeau and Glenn S.
      Pound, 1945
   Beta vulgaris var. cicla
      LeBeau, Francis J. and J.C. Walker, 1945
      Walker, J.C., Francis J. LeBeau and Glenn S.
      Pound, 1945
   Brassica adpressa
      Bennett, C.W., 1944
      Tompkins, C.M., 1938, 1939
   Brassica campestris
      LeBeau, Francis J. and J.C. Walker, 1945
      Sylvester, Edward S., 1953
      Tompkins, C.M., 1938
      Walker, J.C., Francis J. LeBeau and Glenn S.
      Pound, 1945
   Brassica campestris var. napobrassica
      Berkeley, G.H. and J.H. Tremaine, 1954
      Berkeley, G.H. and M. Weintraub, 1952
      Clayton, E.E., 1930
      LeBeau, Francis J. and J.C. Walker, 1945
      Sylvester, Edward S., 1953
      Tompkins, C.M., 1938
   Brassica carinata
      Takahashi, William N., 1949
   Brassica chinensis
      Clayton, E.E., 1930
      Dale, W.T., 1948
      Sylvester, Edward S., 1953
      Sylvester, Edward S. and John N. Simons, 1951
      Takahashi, William N., 1949
   Brassica hirta (Brassica alba)
      Berkeley, G.H. and M. Weintraub, 1952
      Clayton, E.E., 1930
      LeBeau, Francis J. and J.C. Walker, 1945
      Sylvester, Edward S., 1953
      Takahashi, William N., 1949
      Tompkins, C.M., 1939
      Walker, J.C., Francis J. LeBeau and Glenn S.
      Pound, 1945
   Brassica juncea (Brassica japonica)
      Dale, W.T., 1948
      LeBeau, Francis J. and J.C. Walker, 1945
      Pound, Glenn S., 1948
      Schultz, E.S., 1921
      Sylvester, Edward S., 1950, 1953, 1954
      Sylvester, Edward S. and John N. Simons, 1951
      Takahashi, William N., 1949
      Tompkins, C.M., 1938, 1939
      Walker, J.C., Francis J. LeBeau and Glenn S.
      Pound, 1945

VIRUS
V. TURNIP MOSAIC (cont.)
   Brassica kaber (Brassica arvensis)
      Takahashi, William N., 1949
      Tompkins, C.M., 1939
      Tompkins, C.M. and H. Rex Thomas, 1938
   Brassica kaber var. pinnatifida
      Walker, J.C., Francis J. LeBeau and Glenn S.
      Pound, 1945
   Brassica napus
      Berkeley, G.H. and J.H. Tremaine, 1954
      Berkeley, G.H. and M. Weintraub, 1952
      Clayton, E.E., 1930
      Dale, W.T., 1948
      LeBeau, Francis J. and J.C. Walker, 1945
      Pound, Glenn S., 1949
      Takahashi, William N., 1949
      Walker, J.C., Francis J. LeBeau and Glenn S.
      Pound, 1945
   Brassica napus var. biennis *
      Sylvester, Edward S., 1953
   Brassica nigra
      Berkeley, G.H. and M. Weintraub, 1952
      Clayton, E.E., 1930
      Dana, B.F. and F.P. McWhorter, 1932
      Hoggan, I.A. and J. Johnson, 1935
      LeBeau, Francis J. and J.C. Walker, 1945
      Sylvester, Edward S., 1953
      Takahashi, William N., 1949
      Tompkins, C.M., 1939
      Walker, J.C., Francis J. LeBeau and Glenn S.
      Pound, 1945
   Brassica oleracea
      Takahashi, William N., 1949
   Brassica oleracea var. botrytis
      Berkeley, G.H. and J.H. Tremaine, 1954
      Berkeley, G.H. and M. Weintraub, 1952
      Clayton, E.E., 1930
      LeBeau, Francis J. and J.C. Walker, 1945
      Pound, Glenn S., 1948
      Tompkins, C.M., 1938
      Tompkins, C.M. and H. Rex Thomas, 1938
      Walker, J.C., Francis J. LeBeau and Glenn S.
      Pound, 1945
   Brassica oleracea var. capitata
      Berkeley, G.H. and J.H. Tremaine, 1954
      Berkeley, G.H. and M. Weintraub, 1952
      Hoggan, I.A. and J. Johnson, 1935
      LeBeau, Francis J. and J.C. Walker, 1945
      Natti, J.J., 1956
      Pound, Glenn S., 1946, 1947, 1948
      Tompkins, C.M., 1938
      Tompkins, C.M. and H. Rex Thomas, 1938
      Walker, J.C., Francis J. LeBeau and Glenn S.
      Pound, 1945
   Brassica oleracea var. gemmifera
      Berkeley, G.H. and J.H. Tremaine, 1954
      Clayton, E.E., 1930
      LeBeau, Francis J. and J.C. Walker, 1945
      Pound, Glenn S., 1948
      Walker, J.C., Francis J. LeBeau and Glenn S.
      Pound, 1945
   Brassica oleracea var. gongylodes
      Berkeley, G.H. and J.H. Tremaine, 1954
      LeBeau, Francis J. and J.C. Walker, 1945
      Walker, J.C., Francis J. LeBeau and Glenn S.
      Pound, 1945
   Brassica oleracea var. italica *
      (K.M. Smith, 1957) R.E. Fitzpatrick, et al., 1958
   Brassica oleracea var. viridis
      Berkeley, G.H. and J.H. Tremaine, 1954
      LeBeau, Francis J. and J.C. Walker, 1945
      Walker, J.C., Francis J. LeBeau and Glenn S.
      Pound, 1945
   Brassica pekinensis
      Berkeley, G.H. and J.H. Tremaine, 1954
      Berkeley, G.H. and M. Weintraub, 1952
      LeBeau, Francis J. and J.C. Walker, 1945
      Schultz, E.S., 1921
      Sylvester, Edward S., 1953
      Takahashi, William N., 1949
      Tompkins, C.M., 1938, 1939
      Tompkins, C.M. and H. Rex Thomas, 1938
      Walker, J.C., Francis J. LeBeau and Glenn S.
      Pound, 1945

VIRUS
V. TURNIP MOSAIC (cont.)
    Brassica rapa
        Berkeley, G.H. and M. Weintraub, 1952
        Clayton, E.E., 1930
        Dale, W.T., 1948
        Dana, B.F. and F.P. McWhorter, 1932
        (K.M. Smith, 1957) R.E. Fitzpatrick, et al., 1958
        Gardner, Max W. and James B. Kendrick, 1921
        Hoggan, I.A. and J. Johnson, 1935
        LeBeau, Francis J. and J.C. Walker, 1945
        Schultz, E.S., 1921
        Sylvester, Edward S., 1953
        Tompkins, C.M., 1938, 1939
        Tompkins, C.M. and H. Rex Thomas, 1938
        Walker, J.C., Francis J. LeBeau and Glenn S.
            Pound, 1945
    Calendula officinalis
        Walker, J.C., Francis J. LeBeau and Glenn S.
            Pound, 1945
    Capsella bursa-pastoris
        Berkeley, G.H. and M. Weintraub, 1952
        Pound, Glenn S., 1948
        Tompkins, C.M., 1938, 1939
        Tompkins, C.M. and H. Rex Thomas, 1938
        Walker, J.C., Francis J. LeBeau and Glenn S.
            Pound, 1945
    Celosia argentea var. cristata
        Pound, Glenn S., 1948
        Walker, J.C., Francis J. LeBeau and Glenn S.
            Pound, 1945
    Centaurea moschata
        Walker, J.C., Francis J. LeBeau and Glenn S.
            Pound, 1945
    Cheiranthus allionii
        Pound, Glenn S., 1948
    Cheiranthus cheiri
        Berkeley, G.H. and J.H. Tremaine, 1954
        Berkeley, G.H. and M. Weintraub, 1952
        Pound, Glenn S., 1948
        Tompkins, C.M., 1939
        Walker, J.C., Francis J. LeBeau and Glenn S.
            Pound, 1945
    Chenopodium album
        Pound, Glenn S., 1948
        Tompkins, C.M., 1938, 1939
        Walker, J.C., Francis J. LeBeau and Glenn S.
            Pound, 1945
    Chenopodium murale
        Tompkins, C.M., 1939
    Datura metel
        Walker, J.C., Francis J. LeBeau and Glenn S.
            Pound, 1945
    Datura meteloides
        Walker, J.C., Francis J. LeBeau and Glenn S.
            Pound, 1945
    Delphinium ajacis
        Walker, J.C., Francis J. LeBeau and Glenn S.
            Pound, 1945
    Digitalis purpurea
        Walker, J.C., Francis J. LeBeau and Glenn S.
            Pound, 1945
    Dimorphotheca aurantiaca
        Walker, J.C., Francis J. LeBeau and Glenn S.
            Pound, 1945
    Godetia amoena
        Walker, J.C., Francis J. LeBeau and Glenn S.
            Pound, 1945
    Gomphrena globosa
        Berkeley, G.H. and J.H. Tremaine, 1954
    Hesperis matronalis
        Berkeley, G.H. and J.H. Tremaine, 1954
        LeBeau, Francis J. and J.C. Walker, 1945
        Tompkins, C.M., 1938, 1939
        Walker, J.C., Francis J. LeBeau and Glenn S.
            Pound, 1945
    Iberis amara
        Walker, J.C., Francis J. LeBeau and Glenn S.
            Pound, 1945
    Lepidium sativum
        Berkeley, G.H. and M. Weintraub, 1952
        Walker, J.C., Francis J. LeBeau and Glenn S.
            Pound, 1945

VIRUS
V. TURNIP MOSAIC (cont.)
    Lepidium virginicum
        Dale, W.T., 1948
        Pound, Glenn S., 1948
        Walker, J.C., Francis J. LeBeau and Glenn S.
            Pound, 1945
    Lobularia maritima
        Pound, Glenn S., 1948
    Lunaria annua
        Tompkins, C.M., 1938, 1939
        Tompkins, C.M. and H. Rex Thomas, 1938
    Lycium halimifolium
        Walker, J.C., Francis J. LeBeau and Glenn S.
            Pound, 1945
    Lycopersicon pimpinellifolium
        Hoggan, I.A. and J. Johnson, 1935
    Malcomia maritima
        Pound, Glenn S., 1948
        Tompkins, C.M., 1938, 1939
        Tompkins, C.M. and H. Rex Thomas, 1938
        Walker, J.C., Francis J. LeBeau and Glenn S.
            Pound, 1945
    Matthiola bicornis
        Tompkins, C.M., 1939
        Tompkins, C.M. and H. Rex Thomas, 1938
        Walker, J.C., Francis J. LeBeau and Glenn S.
            Pound, 1945
    Matthiola incana
        Berkeley, G.H. and J.H. Tremaine, 1954
        Berkeley, G.H. and M. Weintraub, 1952
    Matthiola incana var. annua
        LeBeau, Francis J. and J.C. Walker, 1945
        Pound, Glenn S., 1948
        Severin, Henry H.P. and C.M. Tompkins, 1950
        Tompkins, C.M., 1938, 1939
        Tompkins, C.M. and H. Rex Thomas, 1938
        Walker, J.C., Francis J. LeBeau and Glenn S.
            Pound, 1945
    Neslia paniculata
        Walker, J.C., Francis J. LeBeau and Glenn S.
            Pound, 1945
    Nicandra physalodes
        Walker, J.C., Francis J. LeBeau and Glenn S.
            Pound, 1945
    Nicotiana acuminata
        Walker, J.C., Francis J. LeBeau and Glenn S.
            Pound, 1945
    Nicotiana alata var. grandiflora
        Walker, J.C., Francis J. LeBeau and Glenn S.
            Pound, 1945
    Nicotiana glutinosa
        Bennett, C.W., 1944
        Berkeley, G.H. and J.H. Tremaine, 1954
        Berkeley, G.H. and M. Weintraub, 1952
        Hoggan, I.A. and J. Johnson, 1935
        LeBeau, Francis J. and J.C. Walker, 1945
        Pound, Glenn S., 1948
        Pound, Glenn S. and Lewis G. Weathers, 1953
        Tompkins, C.M., 1938, 1939
        Tompkins, C.M. and H. Rex Thomas, 1938
        Walker, J.C., Francis J. LeBeau and Glenn S.
            Pound, 1945
    Nicotiana langsdorffii
        Tompkins, C.M., 1939
    Nicotiana longiflora
        Walker, J.C., Francis J. LeBeau and Glenn S.
            Pound, 1945
    Nicotiana multivalvis
        LeBeau, Francis J. and J.C. Walker, 1945
        Pound, Glenn S. and Lewis G. Weathers, 1953
        Walker, J.C., Francis J. LeBeau and Glenn S.
            Pound, 1945
    Nicotiana nudicaulis
        Walker, J.C., Francis J. LeBeau and Glenn S.
            Pound, 1945
    Nicotiana paniculata
        Walker, J.C., Francis J. LeBeau and Glenn S.
            Pound, 1945
    Nicotiana quadrivalvis
        Walker, J.C., Francis J. LeBeau and Glenn S.
            Pound, 1945
    Nicotiana repanda
        LeBeau, Francis J. and J.C. Walker, 1945

VIRUS
V. TURNIP MOSAIC (cont.)
  Nicotiana rustica
    LeBeau, Francis J. and J.C. Walker, 1945
    Pound, Glenn S. and Lewis G. Weathers, 1953
    Walker, J.C., Francis J. LeBeau and Glenn S.
    Pound, 1945
  Nicotiana sanderae
    Walker, J.C., Francis J. LeBeau and Glenn S.
    Pound, 1945
  Nicotiana sylvestris
    LeBeau, Francis J. and J.C. Walker, 1945
    Walker, J.C., Francis J. LeBeau and Glenn S.
    Pound, 1945
  Nicotiana tabacum
    Bennett, C.W., 1944
    Berkeley, G.H. and J.H. Tremaine, 1954
    Berkeley, G.H. and M. Weintraub, 1952
    Dale, W.T., 1948
    Hoggan, Isme A., 1934
    Hoggan, I.A. and J. Johnson, 1935
    LeBeau, Francis J. and J.C. Walker, 1945
    Pound, Glenn S. and Lewis G. Weathers, 1953
    Tompkins, C.M., 1938, 1939
    Tompkins, C.M. and H. Rex Thomas, 1938
    Walker, J.C., Francis J. LeBeau and Glenn S.
    Pound, 1945
  Nicotiana tabacum var. macrophylla
    Dale, W.T., 1948
  Nicotiana tabacum x Nicotiana glutinosa
    Hoggan, I.A. and J. Johnson, 1935
    LeBeau, Francis J. and J.C. Walker, 1945
  Nicotiana trigonophylla
    Walker, J.C., Francis J. LeBeau and Glenn S.
    Pound, 1945
  Petunia hybrida
    Berkeley, G.H. and J.H. Tremaine, 1954
    Berkeley, G.H. and M. Weintraub, 1952
    LeBeau, Francis J. and J.C. Walker, 1945
    Tompkins, C.M., 1938, 1939
  Physalis pubescens
    Walker, J.C., Francis J. LeBeau and Glenn S.
    Pound, 1945
  Raphanus sativus
    Tompkins, C.M., 1939
    Walker, J.C., Francis J. LeBeau and Glenn S.
    Pound, 1945
  Raphanus sativus var. hortensis *
    Dale, W.T., 1948
  Raphanus sativus var. longipinnatus *
    Tompkins, C.M., 1938, 1939
  Reseda odorata
    Tompkins, C.M., 1938, 1939
    Walker, J.C., Francis J. LeBeau and Glenn S.
    Pound, 1945
  Salpiglossis sinuata
    Walker, J.C., Francis J. LeBeau and Glenn S.
    Pound, 1945
  Scabiosa atropurpurea
    Walker, J.C., Francis J. LeBeau and Glenn S.
    Pound, 1945
  Senecio cruentus
    Walker, J.C., Francis J. LeBeau and Glenn S.
    Pound, 1945
  Sisymbrium altissimum
    Walker, J.C., Francis J. LeBeau and Glenn S.
    Pound, 1945
  Sisymbrium officinale
    Pound, Glenn S., 1948
  Solanum integrifolium
    Pound, Glenn S., 1948
    Walker, J.C., Francis J. LeBeau and Glenn S.
    Pound, 1945
  Solanum rostratum
    Walker, J.C., Francis J. LeBeau and Glenn S.
    Pound, 1945
  Solanum triflorum
    Pound, Glenn S., 1948
  Spinacia oleracea
    Berkeley, G.H. and J.H. Tremaine, 1954
    Hoggan, I.A. and J. Johnson, 1935
    LeBeau, Francis J. and J.C. Walker, 1945
    Tompkins, C.M., 1939
    Walker, J.C., Francis J. LeBeau and Glenn S.
    Pound, 1945

VIRUS
V. TURNIP MOSAIC (cont.)
  Stellaria media
    Walker, J.C., Francis J. LeBeau and Glenn S.
    Pound, 1945
  Thlaspi arvense
    Pound, Glenn S., 1948
    Walker, J.C., Francis J. LeBeau and Glenn S.
    Pound, 1945
  Verbena hybrida
    Tompkins, C.M., 1938
    Walker, J.C., Francis J. LeBeau and Glenn S.
    Pound, 1945
  Vinca minor
    Walker, J.C., Francis J. LeBeau and Glenn S.
    Pound, 1945
  Zinnia elegans
    Berkeley, G.H. and J.H. Tremaine, 1954
    Dale, W.T., 1948
    LeBeau, Francis J. and J.C. Walker, 1945

V. TURNIP ROSETTE *
  Barbarea vulgaris
    Broadbent, L. and G.D. Heathcote, 1958
  Brassica kaber (Brassica arvensis)
    Broadbent, L. and G.D. Heathcote, 1958
  Brassica napus
    Broadbent, L. and G.D. Heathcote, 1958
    Lister, R.M., 1958
  Brassica oleracea var. botrytis
    Broadbent, L. and G.D. Heathcote, 1958
  Brassica oleracea var. capitata
    Broadbent, L. and G.D. Heathcote, 1958
  Brassica oleracea var. gemmifera
    Broadbent, L. and G.D. Heathcote, 1958
  Brassica pekinensis
    Broadbent, L. and G.D. Heathcote, 1958
    Lister, R.M., 1958
  Brassica rapa
    Broadbent, L. and G.D. Heathcote, 1958
    Lister, R.M., 1958
  Camelina sativa
    Broadbent, L. and G.D. Heathcote, 1958
  Cheiranthus cheiri
    Broadbent, L. and G.D. Heathcote, 1958
  Datura stramonium
    Broadbent, L. and G.D. Heathcote, 1958
  Erysimum cheiranthoides
    Broadbent, L. and G.D. Heathcote, 1958
  Lactuca sativa var. capitata
    Broadbent, L. and G.D. Heathcote, 1958
  Lepidium campestre
    Broadbent, L. and G.D. Heathcote, 1958
  Lunaria annua
    Broadbent, L. and G.D. Heathcote, 1958
  Nicotiana bigelovii var. multivalvis *
    Broadbent, L. and G.D. Heathcote, 1958
  Raphanus raphanistrum
    Broadbent, L. and G.D. Heathcote, 1958
  Raphanus sativus
    Broadbent, L. and G.D. Heathcote, 1958
  Reseda odorata
    Broadbent, L. and G.D. Heathcote, 1958
  Sisymbrium officinale
    Broadbent, L. and G.D. Heathcote, 1958
  Thlaspi arvense
    Broadbent, L. and G.D. Heathcote, 1958

V. TURNIP YELLOW MOSAIC Markham and Smith 1944
  Barbarea vulgaris
    Broadbent, L. and G.D. Heathcote, 1958
  Brassica carinata
    (K.M. Smith, 1957) R.E. Fitzpatrick, et al., 1958
  Brassica hirta (Brassica alba)
    Broadbent, L. and G.D. Heathcote, 1958
  Brassica juncea (Brassica japonica)
    Broadbent, L. and G.D. Heathcote, 1958
  Brassica kaber (Brassica arvensis)
    Broadbent, L. and G.D. Heathcote, 1958
    (K.M. Smith, 1957) R.E. Fitzpatrick, et al., 1958
  Brassica napus
    Broadbent, L. and G.D. Heathcote, 1958
    Lister, R.M., 1958

VIRUS

V. TURNIP YELLOW MOSAIC (cont.)

Brassica nigra
  Broadbent, L. and G.D. Heathcote, 1958
Brassica oleracea var. botrytis
  Broadbent, L. and G.D. Heathcote, 1958
  Croxall, H.E., D.C. Gwynne and L. Broadbent, 1953
Brassica oleracea var. capitata
  Broadbent, L. and G.D. Heathcote, 1958
Brassica oleracea var. caulorapa
  (K.M. Smith, 1957) R.E. Fitzpatrick, et al., 1958
Brassica oleracea var. gemmifera
  Broadbent, L. and G.D. Heathcote, 1958
  Croxall, H.E., D.C. Gwynne and L. Broadbent, 1953
Brassica pekinensis
  Broadbent, L. and G.D. Heathcote, 1958
  Lister, R.M., 1958
Brassica rapa
  Broadbent, L. and G.D. Heathcote, 1958
  Lister, R.M., 1958
Capsella bursa-pastoris
  Broadbent, L. and G.D. Heathcote, 1958
Cheiranthus cheiri
  Broadbent, L. and G.D. Heathcote, 1958
Conringia orientalis
  Broadbent, L. and G.D. Heathcote, 1958
Diplotaxis tenufolia
  Broadbent, L. and G.D. Heathcote, 1958
Erysimum cheiranthoides
  Broadbent, L. and G.D. Heathcote, 1958
Lepidium campestre
  Broadbent, L. and G.D. Heathcote, 1958
Lunaria annua
  Broadbent, L. and G.D. Heathcote, 1958
Nasturtium officinale (Rorippa nasturtium-aquaticum)
  (K.M. Smith, 1957) R.E. Fitzpatrick, et al., 1958
Neslia paniculata
  Broadbent, L. and G.D. Heathcote, 1958
Raphanus raphanistrum
  Broadbent, L. and G.D. Heathcote, 1958
Raphanus sativus
  Broadbent, L. and G.D. Heathcote, 1958
Reseda odorata
  Broadbent, L. and G.D. Heathcote, 1958
Sisymbrium officinale
  Broadbent, L. and G.D. Heathcote, 1958
Thlaspi arvense
  Broadbent, L. and G.D. Heathcote, 1958

V. VACCINIUM FALSE BLOSSOM

Apium graveolens
  Kunkel, L.O., 1945
Brachycome iberidifolia
  Kunkel, L.O., 1945
Calendula officinalis
  Kunkel, L.O., 1945
Callistephus chinensis
  (K.M. Smith, 1957) R.E. Fitzpatrick, et al., 1958
Centaurea imperialis
  Kunkel, L.O., 1945
Convolvulus arvensis
  (K.M. Smith, 1957) R.E. Fitzpatrick, et al., 1958
Cryptostemma calendulaceum
  (K.M. Smith, 1957) R.E. Fitzpatrick, et al., 1958
Cuscuta campestris
  Costa, A.S., 1944
Datura fastuosa
  (K.M. Smith, 1957) R.E. Fitzpatrick, et al., 1958
Daucus carota
  Kunkel, L.O., 1945
Dianthus spp.
  Kunkel, L.O., 1945
Dimorphotheca aurantiacum
  Kunkel, L.O., 1945
Erodium cicutarium
  (K.M. Smith, 1957) R.E. Fitzpatrick, et al., 1958
Erodium cygnorum
  (K.M. Smith, 1957) R.E. Fitzpatrick, et al., 1958
Eschscholtzia californica
  Kunkel, L.O., 1945
Gaillardia aristata
  Kunkel, L.O., 1945

VIRUS

V. VACCINIUM FALSE BLOSSOM (cont.)

Lycopersicon esculentum
  Costa, A.S., 1944
  Kunkel, L.O., 1943, 1945
Nicotiana chinensis
  (K.M. Smith, 1957) R.E. Fitzpatrick, et al., 1958
Nicotiana glutinosa
  Kunkel, L.O., 1945
Nicotiana langsdorffii
  Kunkel, L.O., 1945
Nicotiana purpurea *
  (K.M. Smith, 1957) R.E. Fitzpatrick, et al., 1958
Nicotiana rustica
  Kunkel, L.O., 1945
Nicotiana tabacum
  Kunkel, L.O., 1945
Nicotiana trigonophylla
  (K.M. Smith, 1957) R.E. Fitzpatrick, et al., 1958
Nierembergia frutescens
  Kunkel, L.O., 1945
Pastinaca sativa
  Kunkel, L.O., 1945
Petroselinum hortense
  Kunkel, L.O., 1945
Petunia hybrida
  Kunkel, L.O., 1945
Phlox drummondii
  Kunkel, L.O., 1945
Salpiglossis spp.
  Kunkel, L.O., 1945
Scabiosa atropurpurea
  Kunkel, L.O., 1945
Schizanthus spp.
  Kunkel, L.O., 1945
Solanum nigrum
  (K.M. Smith, 1957) R.E. Fitzpatrick, et al., 1958
Solanum seaforthianum
  (K.M. Smith, 1957) R.E. Fitzpatrick, et al., 1958
Solanum trilobatum
  (K.M. Smith, 1957) R.E. Fitzpatrick, et al., 1958
Solanum tuberosum
  Kunkel, L.O., 1945
Solanum xanthocarpum
  (K.M. Smith, 1957) R.E. Fitzpatrick, et al., 1958
Tagetes erecta
  Kunkel, L.O., 1945
Tragopogon porrifolius
  Kunkel, L.O., 1945
Vaccinium macrocarpon (Oxycoccus macrocarpon)
  Bergman, H.F. and W.E. Truran, 1933
  Kunkel, L.O., 1943, 1945
  Stevens, Neil E., 1944
  Wilcox, R.B., 1950, 1951
  Wilcox, R.B. and C.S. Beckwith, 1933
Veronica peregrina
  Kunkel, L.O., 1945
Vinca rosea
  Kunkel, L.O., 1945
Withania somnifera
  (K.M. Smith, 1957) R.E. Fitzpatrick, et al., 1958

V. VACCINIUM MOSAIC *

Vaccinium angustifolium
  Varney, E.H., 1957

V. VACCINIUM RING SPOT Hutchinson and Varney 1954

Datura stramonium
  Hilborn, M.T. and Reiner Bonde, 1956
Vaccinium angustifolium
  Hilborn, M.T. and Reiner Bonde, 1956
Vaccinium corymbosum
  Hutchinson, M.T. and E.H. Varney, 1954

V. VACCINIUM SHOESTRING *

Vaccinium angustifolium
  Varney, E.H., 1957

V. VACCINIUM STUNT Wilcox 1942

Vaccinium angustifolium
  Demaree, J.B., 1946
Vaccinium atrococcum
  Hutchinson, M.T., A.C. Goheen and E.H. Varney, 1955

VIRUS

V. VACCINIUM STUNT (cont.)
 Vaccinium australe
  (K.M. Smith, 1957) R.E. Fitzpatrick, et al., 1958
 Vaccinium corymbosum
  Hutchinson, M.T., A.C. Goheen and E.H. Varney, 1955
 Vaccinium stamineum
  Hutchinson, M.T., A.C. Goheen and E.H. Varney, 1955
 Vaccinium vacillans
  Hutchinson, M.T., A.C. Goheen and E.H. Varney, 1955
 Vinca rosea
  Hutchinson, M.T., A.C. Goheen and E.H. Varney, 1955

V. VIGNA 1 *
 Vigna sinensis
  Warid, W.A. and A.G. Plakidas, 1950, 1952

V. VIGNA 2 *
 Vigna sinensis
  Warid, W.A. and A.G. Plakidas, 1950, 1952

V. VIGNA 3 *
 Vigna sinensis
  Warid, W.A. and A.G. Plakidas, 1950, 1952

V. VIGNA 3A *
 Vigna sinensis
  Warid, W.A. and A.G. Plakidas, 1950, 1952

V. VINCA YELLOWS *
 Daucus carota
  Maramorosch, Karl, 1956
 Daucus carota var. sativa
  Maramorosch, Karl, 1957
 Vinca rosea
  Maramorosch, Karl, 1956

V. VINE INFECTIOUS DEGENERATION Branas 1948;
Doubals and Huglin 1950
 Vitis rupestris
  Hewitt, Wm. B., 1956
 Vitis vinifera
  (K.M. Smith, 1957) R.E. Fitzpatrick, et al., 1958
  Hewitt, Wm. B., 1945, 1956

V. VINE LEAF ROLL Scheu 1936
 Vitis vinifera
  Harmon, F.N. and J.H. Weinberger, 1956

V. VINE YELLOW MOSAIC Hewitt 1953
 Vitis vinifera
  Hewitt, Wm. B. and Charles J. Delp, 1953

V. (VINE) YELLOW VEIN *
 Vitis vinifera
  Hewitt, Wm. B., 1956

V. WALNUT BROOMING DISEASE *
 Juglans cinerea
  Hutchins, Lee M. and Horace V. Wester, 1947
 Juglans cordiformis var. ailantifolia
  Hutchins, Lee M. and Horace V. Wester, 1947
 Juglans nigra
  Hutchins, Lee M. and Horace V. Wester, 1947

V. WATERMELON MOSAIC Anderson 1954
 Citrullus vulgaris
  Anderson, C.W., 1952, 1954
  Lindberg, G.D., D.H. Hall and J.C. Walker, 1956
  Pound, Glenn S., 1949
  Walker, M.N., 1933
 Citrullus vulgaris var. citroides
  Anderson, C.W., 1954
 Cucumis melo
  Anderson, C.W., 1954
  Lindberg, G.D., D.H. Hall and J.C. Walker, 1956
  Pound, Glenn S., 1949
 Cucumis melo var. reticulatus
  Anderson, C.W., 1952

VIRUS

V. WATERMELON MOSAIC (cont.)
 Cucumis sativus
  Anderson, C.W., 1952, 1954
  Lindberg, G.D., D.H. Hall and J.C. Walker, 1956
 Cucurbita maxima
  Anderson, C.W., 1952, 1954
  Lindberg, G.D., D.H. Hall and J.C. Walker, 1956
 Cucurbita moschata
  Anderson, C.W., 1954
  Lindberg, G.D., D.H. Hall and J.C. Walker, 1956
 Cucurbita okeechobeensis
  Anderson, C.W., 1954
 Cucurbita pepo
  Lindberg, G.D., D.H. Hall and J.C. Walker, 1956
 Cucurbita pepo var. medullosa *
  Anderson, C.W., 1954
 Cyclanthera pedata
  Anderson, C.W., 1954
 Lagenaria siceria (Lagenaria leucantha)
  Anderson, C.W., 1954
 Luffa aegyptiaca (Luffa cylindrica)
  Anderson, C.W., 1954
 Melothria pendula
  Anderson, C.W., 1954
 Melothria spp.
  Anderson, C.W., 1952
 Nicotiana tabacum
  Pound, Glenn S., 1949
 Phaseolus vulgaris
  Pound, Glenn S., 1949
 Pisum sativum
  Pound, Glenn S., 1949

V. WATSONIA MOSAIC *
 Tritonia crocata
  Smith, Floyd F. and Philip Brierley, 1944
 Watsonia marginata
  Smith, Floyd F. and Philip Brierley, 1944

V. WESTERN WATERMELON MOSAIC Freitag 1952
 Citrullus vulgaris
  Freitag, J.H., 1952

V. WHEAT SPOT MOSAIC *
 Eragrostis cilianensis
  Slykhuis, John T., 1956
 Hordeum vulgare
  Slykhuis, John T., 1956
 Setaria italica
  Slykhuis, John T., 1956
 Setaria verticillata
  Slykhuis, John T., 1956
 Setaria virdis
  Slykhuis, John T., 1956
 Triticum aestivum
  Slykhuis, John T., 1956
 Triticum dicoccum
  Slykhuis, John T., 1956
 Triticum durum
  Slykhuis, John T., 1956
 Triticum timopheevi
  Slykhuis, John T., 1956
 Zea mays
  Slykhuis, John T., 1956

V. WHEAT STREAK MOSAIC McKinney 1944, 1953
 Aegilops crassa
  McKinney, H.H. and Hurley Fellows, 1951
 Aegilops cylindrica
  McKinney, H.H. and Hurley Fellows, 1951
 Aegilops ovata
  McKinney, H.H. and Hurley Fellows, 1951
 Aegilops triuncialis
  McKinney, H.H. and Hurley Fellows, 1951
 Aegilops ventricosa
  McKinney, H.H. and Hurley Fellows, 1951
 Agropyron elongatum
  McKinney, H.H. and W.J. Sando, 1951
 Agropyron hybrid
  Sill, W.H., Jr., 1956
 Agropyron intermedium
  McKinney, H.H. and W.J. Sando, 1951

VIRUS
V. WHEAT STREAK MOSAIC (cont.)

Agropyron lasianthum
McKinney, H.H. and W.J. Sando, 1951

Agropyron pungens
McKinney, H.H. and W.J. Sando, 1951

Agropyron trachycaulum
McKinney, H.H. and W.J. Sando, 1951

Agropyron ugamicum
McKinney, H.H. and W.J. Sando, 1951

Avena byzantina
McKinney, H.H., 1949

Avena fatua
Slykhuis, John T., 1955

Avena sativa
Finley, A.M., 1957
Houston, Byron R. and John W. Oswald, 1952
McKinney, H.H., 1949
Slykhuis, J.T., 1952, 1955

Avena sativa var. orientalis
McKinney, H.H., 1949

Avena spp.
Sill, W.H., Jr. and Patrick C. Agusiobo, 1955

Bouteloua hirsuta
McKinney, H.H. and Hurley Fellows, 1951

Bromus japonicus
McKinney, H.H. and Hurley Fellows, 1951
Slykhuis, J.T., 1952, 1955

Bromus secalinus
Slykhuis, J.T., 1952, 1955

Bromus tectorum
Slykhuis, J.T., 1952, 1955

Digitaria ischaemum
McKinney, H.H. and Hurley Fellows, 1951
Meiners, Jack P. and H.H. McKinney, 1954

Digitaria sanguinalis
Slykhuis, J.T., 1952, 1955

Echinochloa crus-galli
Sill, W.H., Jr. and Patrick C. Agusiobo, 1955
Slykhuis, J.T., 1952, 1955

Elymus canadensis
McKinney, H.H. and Hurley Fellows, 1951
Slykhuis, John T., 1955

Elymus condensatus
McKinney, H.H. and Hurley Fellows, 1951

Elymus giganteus
McKinney, H.H. and Hurley Fellows, 1951

Elymus virginicus
McKinney, H.H. and Hurley Fellows, 1951

Eragrostis cilianensis (Eragrostis major)
Slykhuis, J.T., 1952, 1955

Eragrostis trichodes
McKinney, H.H. and Hurley Fellows, 1951

Euchlaena mexicana
Sill, W.H., Jr. and Patrick C. Agusiobo, 1955

Haynaldia villosa *
McKinney, H.H. and Hurley Fellows, 1951

Hordeum gussoneanum
McKinney, H.H. and Hurley Fellows, 1951

Hordeum murinum
McKinney, H.H. and Hurley Fellows, 1951

Hordeum spp.
McKinney, H.H. and Hurley Fellows, 1951
Sill, W.H., Jr. and Patrick C. Agusiobo, 1955

Hordeum vulgare
Finley, A.M., 1957
McKinney, H.H., 1949, 1956
Slykhuis, J.T., 1952, 1954, 1955

Oryzopsis hymenoides
McKinney, H.H. and Hurley Fellows, 1951
Slykhuis, John T., 1954, 1955

Panicum capillare
Slykhuis, J.T., 1952, 1955

Panicum miliaceum
Sill, W.H., Jr. and Patrick C. Agusiobo, 1955
Slykhuis, John T., 1955

Panicum ramosum
Sill, W.H., Jr. and Patrick C. Agusiobo, 1955

Phalaris paradoxa
McKinney, H.H. and Hurley Fellows, 1951

Poa bulbosa
McKinney, H.H. and Hurley Fellows, 1951

Poa compressa
McKinney, H.H. and Hurley Fellows, 1951

VIRUS
V. WHEAT STREAK MOSAIC (cont.)

Poa compressa
Slykhuis, John T., 1954, 1955

Poa stenantha
McKinney, H.H. and Hurley Fellows, 1951

Saccharum officinarum
McKinney, H.H., 1949

Secale cereale
McKinney, H.H. and W.J. Sando, 1951
Slykhuis, John T., 1954, 1955

Secale cereale subsp. ancestrale *
McKinney, H.H. and W.J. Sando, 1951

Secale montanum
McKinney, H.H. and W.J. Sando, 1951

Secale spp.
Sill, W.H., Jr. and Patrick C. Agusiobo, 1955

Setaria italica
Sill, W.H., Jr. and Patrick C. Agusiobo, 1955
Slykhuis, John T., 1955

Setaria verticillata
Slykhuis, J.T., 1952, 1955

Setaria virdis
Finley, A.M., 1957
McKinney, H.H. and Hurley Fellows, 1951
Slykhuis, John T., 1951, 1952, 1955

Stipa robusta
McKinney, H.H. and Hurley Fellows, 1951

Triticum aegilopoides *
McKinney, H.H. and W.J. Sando, 1951

Triticum aestivum
Andrews, J.E. and J.T. Slykhuis, 1956
Atkinson, R.E., 1949
Bellingham, Roscoe C., Hurley Fellows and
Webster H. Sill, Jr., 1957
Fellows, Hurley and John W. Schmidt, 1953
Fellows, H., W.H. Sill, Jr. and H.H. McKinney,
1952
Finley, A.M., 1957
Lal, S.B. and W.H. Sill, Jr., 1957
Lal, S.B., W.H. Sill, Jr., Maria S. Del Rosario
and J.M. Kainski, 1957
McKinney, H.H., 1949, 1956
McKinney, H.H. and W.J. Sando, 1951
Meiners, Jack P. and H.H. McKinney, 1954
Sill, W.H., Jr., 1952, 1953
Sill, W.H., Jr. and H. Fellows, 1953
Slykhuis, J.T., 1953, 1954, 1955

Triticum dicoccoides
McKinney, H.H. and W.J. Sando, 1951

Triticum dicoccoides var. strausianum *
McKinney, H.H. and W.J. Sando, 1951

Triticum dicoccum
McKinney, H.H., 1949
McKinney, H.H. and W.J. Sando, 1951
Slykhuis, John T., 1955

Triticum durum
McKinney, H.H. and W.J. Sando, 1951
Slykhuis, John T., 1955

Triticum monococcum
McKinney, H.H. and W.J. Sando, 1951

Triticum monococcum var. flavescens *
McKinney, H.H. and W.J. Sando, 1951

Triticum monococcum var. laetissimum *
McKinney, H.H. and W.J. Sando, 1951

Triticum orientale
McKinney, H.H. and W.J. Sando, 1951

Triticum persicum var. stramineum *
McKinney, H.H. and W.J. Sando, 1951

Triticum polonicum
McKinney, H.H., 1949
McKinney, H.H. and W.J. Sando, 1951

Triticum spelta
McKinney, H.H., 1949
McKinney, H.H. and W.J. Sando, 1951

Triticum sphaerococcum
McKinney, H.H. and W.J. Sando, 1951

Triticum timopheevi
McKinney, H.H. and W.J. Sando, 1951
Slykhuis, John T., 1955

Triticum turgidum
McKinney, H.H., 1949
McKinney, H.H. and W.J. Sando, 1951

VIRUS
V. WHEAT STREAK MOSAIC (cont.)
   Triticum vulgare
      Slykhuis, J.T., 1952
   Zea mays
      Finley, A.M., 1957
      McKinney, H.H., 1949
      Meiners, Jack P. and H.H. McKinney, 1954
      Sill, W.H., Jr., 1956
      Sill, W.H., Jr. and Patrick C. Agusiobo, 1955
      Slykhuis, John T., 1955
   Zea mays var. saccharata
      McKinney, H.H., 1949

V. WHEAT STRIATE MOSAIC Slykhuis 1952
   Avena sativa
      Slykhuis, J.T., 1953
      Slykhuis, John T. and Marion A. Watson, 1958
   Eragrostis cilianensis (Eragrostis major)
      Slykhuis, J.T., 1952, 1953
   Hordeum vulgare
      Slykhuis, J.T., 1953
      Slykhuis, John T. and Marion A. Watson, 1958
   Lolium multiflorum
      Slykhuis, John T. and Marion A. Watson, 1958
   Lolium perenne
      Slykhuis, John T. and Marion A. Watson, 1958
   Panicum capillare
      Slykhuis, J.T., 1952, 1953
   Secale cereale
      Slykhuis, John T. and Marion A. Watson, 1958
   Triticum aestivum
      Slykhuis, John T. and Marion A. Watson, 1958
   Triticum dicoccum
      Slykhuis, J.T., 1953
   Triticum durum
      Slykhuis, J.T., 1953
   Triticum vulgare
      Slykhuis, J.T., 1952, 1953

V. WILD CUCUMBER MOSAIC *
   Cucurbita maxima
      Freitag, J.H., 1941
   Echinocystis lobata
      Fernow, Karl Hermann, 1925
   Nicandra physalodes
      Fernow, Karl Hermann, 1925
   Nicotiana glutinosa
      Fernow, Karl Hermann, 1925
   Sicyos angulatus
      Freitag, J.H., 1952

V. WISCONSIN PEA STREAK Hagedorn and Walker 1949
   Glycine max
      Hagedorn, D.J., 1952
      Hagedorn, D.J. and J.C. Walker, 1949, 1954
   Lathyrus hirsutus
      Hagedorn, D.J. and J.C. Walker, 1949, 1954
   Lathyrus odoratus
      Hagedorn, D.J. and J.C. Walker, 1949, 1954
   Medicago orbicularis
      Hagedorn, D.J. and J.C. Walker, 1949, 1954
   Melilotus alba
      Hagedorn, D.J. and J.C. Walker, 1949, 1954
   Melilotus officinalis
      Hagedorn, D.J. and J.C. Walker, 1949, 1954
      Skotland, C.B., 1953
      Skotland, C.B. and D.J. Hagedorn, 1954
   Pisum sativum
      Hagedorn, D.J., 1952
      Hagedorn, D.J. and J.C. Walker, 1949, 1954
      Skotland, C.B., 1953
      Skotland, C.B. and D.J. Hagedorn, 1954, 1955
   Pisum sativum var. arvense
      Hagedorn, D.J. and J.C. Walker, 1949, 1954
   Trifolium hybridum
      Hagedorn, D.J. and J.C. Walker, 1949, 1954
      Skotland, C.B., 1953
   Trifolium incarnatum
      Hagedorn, D.J., 1952
      Hagedorn, D.J. and J.C. Walker, 1949, 1954
   Trifolium pratense
      Hagedorn, D.J., 1952
      Hagedorn, D.J. and J.C. Walker, 1949, 1954

VIRUS
V. WISCONSIN PEA STREAK (cont.)
   Trifolium pratense
      Hanson, E.W. and D.J. Hagedorn, 1952
      Skotland, C.B., 1953
      Skotland, C.B. and D.J. Hagedorn, 1954
   Trifolium repens
      Hagedorn, D.J. and J.C. Walker, 1949, 1954
   Trigonella foenum-graecum
      Hagedorn, D.J., 1952
      Hagedorn, D.J. and J.C. Walker, 1949, 1954
   Vicia atropurpurea
      Hagedorn, D.J. and J.C. Walker, 1949, 1954
   Vicia faba var. major *
      Hagedorn, D.J. and J.C. Walker, 1954
   Vicia faba var. minor *
      Hagedorn, D.J. and J.C. Walker, 1954
      Skotland, C.B. and D.J. Hagedorn, 1954
   Vicia grandiflora
      Hagedorn, D.J. and J.C. Walker, 1949, 1954
   Vicia monantha
      Hagedorn, D.J. and J.C. Walker, 1949, 1954
   Vicia villosa
      Hagedorn, D.J. and J.C. Walker, 1949, 1954

V. WINTER WHEAT MOSAIC Zazhurilo and Sitnikova
   Triticum aestivum   1939
      Webb, Robert W., 1927, 1928

V. WISTERIA MOSAIC *
   Wisteria floribunda
      Brierley, Philip and Paul Lorentz, 1957
   Wisteria sinensis
      Brierley, Philip and Paul Lorentz, 1957
   Wisteria spp.
      Brierley, Philip and Paul Lorentz, 1957

V. YAM MOSAIC *
   Capsicum frutescens (Capsicum annuum)
      Adsuar, J., 1955
   Cucumis sativus
      Adsuar, J., 1955
   Dioscorea rotundata
      Adsuar, J., 1955
   Nicotiana tabacum
      Adsuar, J., 1955

VIRUS

V. ABACA BUNCHY TOP Ocfemia 1930
Musa balbisiana
  Bernardo, Fernando A. and Dioscoro L. Umali,
  1956
Musa cavendishii
  Ocfemia, G.O. and Gabino G. Buhay, 1934
Musa paradisiaca subsp. sapientum var. cineria
  Ocfemia, G.O. and Gabino G. Buhay, 1934
Musa paradisiaca subsp. sapientum var. lacatan
  Ocfemia, G.O. and Gabino G. Buhay, 1934
Musa paradisiaca subsp. sapientum var. suaveolens
  Ocfemia, G.O. and Gabino G. Buhay, 1934
Musa sapientum var. compressa *
  Ocfemia, G.O. and Gabino G. Buhay, 1934
Musa textilis x Musa balbisiana
  Umali, D.L., F.A. Bernardo and .G.O. Ocfemia,
  1956

V. ABUTILON INFECTIOUS VARIEGATION ((Morren 1869)) Brierley 1944
Abelmoschus esculentus
  Bird, Julio, 1958
Boehmeria nivea
  Silberschmidt, Karl M., 1948
Chamaesyce hypericifolia
  Bird, Julio, 1958
Crotalaria striata
  Bird, Julio, 1958
Datura stramonium
  Bird, Julio, 1958
Euphorbia prunifolia
  Bird, Julio, 1958
  Costa, A.S. and C.W. Bennett, 1950
Gossypium hirsutum
  Bird, Julio, 1958
Ipomoea batata
  Bird, Julio, 1958
Ipomoea quinquefolia
  Bird, Julio, 1958
Jatropha gossypifolia
  Bird, Julio, 1958
Malachra capitata
  Bird, Julio, 1958
Nicotiana tabacum
  Silberschmidt, K. and L.R. Tommasi, 1956
Phaseolus vulgaris
  Bird, Julio, 1958
Physalis angulata
  Bird, Julio, 1958
Sida rhombifolia
  Silberschmidt, Karl M., 1948
Triumfetta lappula
  Bird, Julio, 1958
Triumfetta semitriloba
  Bird, Julio, 1958
Zinnia elegans
  Bird, Julio, 1958

V. AGROPYRON MOSAIC McKinney 1944
Agropyron ciliare *
  Slykhuis, J.T., 1952
Agropyron cristatum
  Slykhuis, J.T., 1952
Agropyron dasystachyum
  Slykhuis, J.T., 1952
Agropyron desertorum
  Slykhuis, J.T., 1952
Agropyron trachycaulum
  Slykhuis, J.T., 1952
Agropyron trichophorum
  Slykhuis, J.T., 1952
Avena fatua
  Slykhuis, J.T., 1952
Avena sativa
  Slykhuis, J.T., 1952
Bromus inermis
  Slykhuis, J.T., 1952
Bromus japonicus
  Slykhuis, J.T., 1952
Bromus secalinus
  Slykhuis, J.T., 1952
Bromus tectorum
  Slykhuis, J.T., 1952

VIRUS

V. AGROPYRON MOSAIC (cont.)
Digitaria sanguinalis
  Slykhuis, J.T., 1952
Echinochloa crus-galli
  Slykhuis, J.T., 1952
Eragrostis cilianensis (Eragrostis major)
  Slykhuis, J.T., 1952
Hordeum jubatum
  Slykhuis, J.T., 1952
Hordeum vulgare
  Slykhuis, J.T., 1952
Panicum capillare
  Slykhuis, J.T., 1952
Panicum miliaceum
  Slykhuis, J.T., 1952
Phalaris arundinacea
  Slykhuis, J.T., 1952
Phleum pratense
  Slykhuis, J.T., 1952
Poa pratensis
  Slykhuis, J.T., 1952
Setaria italica
  Slykhuis, J.T., 1952
Setaria lutescens
  Slykhuis, J.T., 1952
Setaria verticillata
  Slykhuis, J.T., 1952
Setaria virdis
  Slykhuis, J.T., 1952
Sorghum vulgare
  Slykhuis, J.T., 1952
Zea mays
  Slykhuis, J.T., 1952

V. ALSIKE CLOVER MOSAIC Zaumeyer and Wade 1935
Crotalaria retusa
  Zaumeyer, W.J., 1940
Crotalaria spectabilis
  Zaumeyer, W.J., 1940
Datura stramonium
  Zaumeyer, W.J., 1940
Glycine max
  Zaumeyer, W.J., 1940
Nicotiana glauca
  Zaumeyer, W.J., 1940
Nicotiana glutinosa
  Zaumeyer, W.J., 1940
Nicotiana tabacum
  Zaumeyer, W.J., 1940
Petunia hybrida
  Zaumeyer, W.J., 1940
Phaseolus aureus
  Zaumeyer, W.J., 1940
Phaseolus lunatus
  Zaumeyer, W.J., 1940
Trifolium pratense
  Zaumeyer, W.J., 1940
Trifolium repens
  Zaumeyer, W.J., 1940
Vicia sativa
  Zaumeyer, W.J., 1940

V. ANEMONE BROWN RING *
Ageratum conyzoides
  Hollings, M., 1958
Alonsoa warscewiczii
  Hollings, M., 1958
Antirrhinum majus
  Hollings, M., 1958
Apium graveolens
  Hollings, M., 1958
Beta vulgaris
  Hollings, M., 1958
Brassica pekinensis
  Hollings, M., 1958
Brassica rapa
  Hollings, M., 1958
Callistephus chinensis
  Hollings, M., 1958
Celosia argentea
  Hollings, M., 1958
Chrysanthemum morifolium
  Hollings, M., 1958

VIRUS
V. ANEMONE BROWN RING * (cont.)
  Convolvulus tricolor
    Hollings, M., 1958
  Cucumis sativus
    Hollings, M., 1958
  Datura stramonium
    Hollings, M., 1958
  Dianthus barbatus
    Hollings, M., 1958
  Fagopyrum esculentum
    Hollings, M., 1958
  Fumaria officinalis
    Hollings, M., 1958
  Hyoscyamus niger
    Hollings, M., 1958
  Lactuca sativa
    Hollings, M., 1958
  Lythrum salicaria
    Hollings, M., 1958
  Nicotiana affinis
    Hollings, M., 1958
  Nicotiana clevelandi
    Hollings, M., 1958
  Nicotiana glutinosa
    Hollings, M., 1958
  Nicotiana rustica
    Hollings, M., 1958
  Nicotiana tabacum
    Hollings, M., 1958
  Papaver somniferum
    Hollings, M., 1958
  Passiflora caerulea
    Hollings, M., 1958
  Petunia hybrida
    Hollings, M., 1958
  Phaseolus coccineus
    Hollings, M., 1958
  Phaseolus vulgaris
    Hollings, M., 1958
  Phlox drummondii
    Hollings, M., 1958
  Physalis floridana
    Hollings, M., 1958
  Phytolacca americana
    Hollings, M., 1958
  Plantago lanceolata
    Hollings, M., 1958
  Primula malacoides
    Hollings, M., 1958
  Reseda odorata
    Hollings, M., 1958
  Senecio vulgaris
    Hollings, M., 1958
  Spinacia oleracea
    Hollings, M., 1958
  Stellaria media
    Hollings, M., 1958
  Trifolium repens
    Hollings, M., 1958
  Tropaeolum majus
    Hollings, M., 1958
  Verbena hybrida
    Hollings, M., 1958
  Vicia faba
    Hollings, M., 1958
  Vigna sinensis
    Hollings, M., 1958
  Zinnia elegans
    Hollings, M., 1958

V. ANEMONE MOSAIC *
  Anchusa azurea
    Hollings, M., 1957
  Antirrhinum majus
    Hollings, M., 1957
  Apium graveolens var. dulce
    Hollings, M., 1957
  Beta vulgaris
    Hollings, M., 1957
  Brassica oleracea var. acephala
    Hollings, M., 1957
  Brassica oleracea var. botrytis
    Hollings, M., 1957

VIRUS
V. ANEMONE MOSAIC * (cont.)
  Brassica oleracea var. caulorapa
    Hollings, M., 1957
  Brassica oleracea var. gemmifera
    Hollings, M., 1957
  Callistephus chinensis
    Hollings, M., 1957
  Canna indica
    Hollings, M., 1957
  Capsicum frutescens (Capsicum annuum)
    Hollings, M., 1957
  Cheiranthus cheiri
    Hollings, M., 1957
  Chrysanthemum morifolium
    Hollings, M., 1957
  Convolvulus sepium
    Hollings, M., 1957
  Cucumis sativus
    Hollings, M., 1957
  Dahlia pinnata
    Hollings, M., 1957
  Datura stramonium
    Hollings, M., 1957
  Dianthus barbatus
    Hollings, M., 1957
  Echium vulgare
    Hollings, M., 1957
  Epilobium montanum
    Hollings, M., 1957
  Euphorbia peplus
    Hollings, M., 1957
  Helichrysum bracteatum
    Hollings, M., 1957
  Ipomoea tricolor
    Hollings, M., 1957
  Lactuca sativa
    Hollings, M., 1957
  Lobularia maritima
    Hollings, M., 1957
  Lycopersicon esculentum
    Hollings, M., 1957
  Melilotus alba
    Hollings, M., 1957
  Myosotis sylvatica
    Hollings, M., 1957
  Nasturtium officinale
    Hollings, M., 1957
  Pelargonium domesticum
    Hollings, M., 1957
  Phaseolus vulgaris
    Hollings, M., 1957
  Phlox drummondii
    Hollings, M., 1957
  Pisum sativum
    Hollings, M., 1957
  Ranunculus acris
    Hollings, M., 1957
  Ranunculus ficaria
    Hollings, M., 1957
  Ranunculus repens
    Hollings, M., 1957
  Raphanus sativus
    Hollings, M., 1957
  Salvia splendens
    Hollings, M., 1957
  Solanum tuberosum
    Hollings, M., 1957
  Spinacia oleracea
    Hollings, M., 1957
  Trifolium repens
    Hollings, M., 1957
  Tropaeolum majus
    Hollings, M., 1957
  Vigna sinensis
    Hollings, M., 1957

V. APPLE MOSAIC Khristov 1934 ((May be identical
with V. Plum line pattern Gilmer 1956.))
  Cuscuta campestris
    Yarwood, C.E., 1955
  Cuscuta subinclusa
    Yarwood, C.E., 1955
    Yarwood, C.E. and H.E. Thomas, 1954

VIRUS
V. ASCLEPIAS YELLOWS *
  Cuscuta campestris
    Kunkel, L.O., 1950

V. ASTER YELLOWS Kunkel 1926, 1936
  Apium graveolens var. dulce
    Severin, Henry H.P., 1934
  Beta vulgaris
    Severin, Henry H.P., 1929
  Callistephus chinensis
    Brierley, Philip and Floyd F. Smith, 1957
  Centauria cyanus
    Kunkel, L.O., 1928
  Cuscuta campestris
    Brierley, Philip and Floyd F. Smith, 1957
    Fulton, J.P., 1957
    Johnson, Folke, 1941
  Cuscuta spp.
    Self, R.L. and H.M. Darling, 1949
  Dianthus caryophyllus
    Smith, Floyd F. and Philip Brierley, 1953
  Lactuca bourgaei
    Tompson, Ross C., 1944
  Lactuca marschallii *
    Tompson, Ross C., 1944
  Lactuca tatarica
    Tompson, Ross C., 1944
  Parthenium argentatum
    Severin, Henry H.P., 1945
  Plantago lanceolata
    Kunkel, L.O., 1928
  Prunus persica (Amygdalus persica)
    McClintock, J.A., 1931
  Rosa spp.
    Brierley, Philip and Floyd F. Smith, 1940
  Secale cereale
    Black, L.M., 1941
  Spinacia oleracea
    Severin, H.H.P., 1928

V. BARLEY STRIPE MOSAIC McKinney 1953; Hagborg 1954
  Agropyron ciliare *
    Slykhuis, J.T., 1952
  Agropyron cristatum
    Slykhuis, J.T., 1952
  Agropyron dasystachyum
    Slykhuis, J.T., 1952
  Agropyron desertorum
    Slykhuis, J.T., 1952
  Agropyron elongatum
    Slykhuis, J.T., 1952
  Agropyron inerme
    Slykhuis, J.T., 1952
  Agropyron intermedium
    Slykhuis, J.T., 1952
  Agropyron junceum
    Slykhuis, J.T., 1952
  Agropyron pertenue
    Slykhuis, J.T., 1952
  Agropyron repens
    Slykhuis, J.T., 1952
  Agropyron rigidum
    Slykhuis, J.T., 1952
  Agropyron trachycaulum
    Slykhuis, J.T., 1952
  Agropyron trichophorum
    Slykhuis, J.T., 1952
  Avena fatua
    Slykhuis, J.T., 1952
  Avena sativa
    Sill, W.H., Jr. and E.D. Hansing, 1955
    Slykhuis, J.T., 1952
  Beta vulgaris
    Sill, W.H., Jr. and E.D. Hansing, 1955
  Beta vulgaris var. cicla
    Sill, W.H., Jr. and E.D. Hansing, 1955
  Bromus inermis
    Slykhuis, J.T., 1952
  Cucumis sativus
    McKinney, H.H., 1953
    Sill, W.H., Jr. and E.D. Hansing, 1955
  Festuca rubra
    Slykhuis, J.T., 1952

VIRUS
V. BARLEY STRIPE MOSAIC (cont.)
  Glycine max
    Sill, W.H., Jr. and E.D. Hansing, 1955
  Lycopersicon esculentum
    Sill, W.H., Jr. and E.D. Hansing, 1955
  Medicago sativa
    Sill, W.H., Jr. and E.D. Hansing, 1955
  Phalaris arundinacea
    Slykhuis, J.T., 1952
  Phaseolus vulgaris
    McKinney, H.H., 1953
    Sill, W.H., Jr. and E.D. Hansing, 1955
  Phleum pratense
    Slykhuis, J.T., 1952
  Poa pratensis
    Slykhuis, J.T., 1952
  Setaria lutescens
    Slykhuis, J.T., 1952
  Sorghum vulgare
    Sill, W.H., Jr. and E.D. Hansing, 1955
    Slykhuis, J.T., 1952

V. BARLEY YELLOW DWARF Oswald and Houston 1951
  Agropyron amurense *
    Bruehl, G.W. and H.V. Toko, 1957
  Agropyron cristatum
    Bruehl, G.W. and H.V. Toko, 1957
    Oswald, John W. and Byron R. Houston, 1953
  Agropyron elongatum
    Bruehl, G.W. and H.V. Toko, 1957
  Agropyron inerme
    Bruehl, G.W. and H.V. Toko, 1957
  Agropyron intermedium
    Bruehl, G.W. and H.V. Toko, 1957
  Agropyron repens
    Bruehl, G.W. and H.V. Toko, 1957
  Agropyron sibiricum
    Bruehl, G.W. and H.V. Toko, 1957
  Agropyron smithii
    Bruehl, G.W. and H.V. Toko, 1957
  Agropyron trachycaulum
    Bruehl, G.W. and H.V. Toko, 1957
  Agropyron trichophorum
    Bruehl, G.W. and H.V. Toko, 1957
  Agrostis alba
    Bruehl, G.W. and H.V. Toko, 1957
    Oswald, John W. and Byron R. Houston, 1953
  Agrostis exarata
    Oswald, John W. and Byron R. Houston, 1953
  Agrostis palustris
    Bruehl, G.W. and H.V. Toko, 1957
  Alopecurus arundinaceus
    Bruehl, G.W. and H.V. Toko, 1957
  Alopecurus pratensis
    Bruehl, G.W. and H.V. Toko, 1957
    Oswald, John W. and Byron R. Houston, 1953
  Arrhenatherum elatius
    Bruehl, G.W. and H.V. Toko, 1957
    Oswald, John W. and Byron R. Houston, 1953
  Beckmannia syzigachne
    Bruehl, G.W. and H.V. Toko, 1957
  Bouteloua gracilis
    Oswald, John W. and Byron R. Houston, 1953
  Bromus inermis
    Bruehl, G.W. and H.V. Toko, 1957
  Deschampsia caespitosa
    Bruehl, G.W. and H.V. Toko, 1957
  Deschampsia danthonioides
    Oswald, John W. and Byron R. Houston, 1953
  Digitaria sanguinalis
    Oswald, John W. and Byron R. Houston, 1953
  Echinochloa crus-galli
    Bruehl, G.W. and H.V. Toko, 1957
    Oswald, John W. and Byron R. Houston, 1953
  Elymus canadensis
    Bruehl, G.W. and H.V. Toko, 1957
  Elymus condensatus
    Bruehl, G.W. and H.V. Toko, 1957
  Elymus giganteus
    Bruehl, G.W. and H.V. Toko, 1957
  Elymus glaucus
    Bruehl, G.W. and H.V. Toko, 1957
    Oswald, John W. and Byron R. Houston, 1953

VIRUS
V. BARLEY YELLOW DWARF (cont.)
  Elymus junceus
    Bruehl, G.W. and H.V. Toko, 1957
  Elymus triticoides
    Bruehl, G.W. and H.V. Toko, 1957
  Holcus lanatus
    Bruehl, G.W. and H.V. Toko, 1957
    Oswald, John W. and Byron R. Houston, 1953
  Lolium perenne
    Bruehl, G.W. and H.V. Toko, 1957
    Oswald, John W. and Byron R. Houston, 1953
  Oryzopsis hymenoides
    Bruehl, G.W. and H.V. Toko, 1957
    Oswald, John W. and Byron R. Houston, 1953
  Paspalum dilatatum
    Oswald, John W. and Byron R. Houston, 1953
  Phalaris tuberosa
    Bruehl, G.W. and H.V. Toko, 1957
  Phleum boehmeri
    Bruehl, G.W. and H.V. Toko, 1957
  Phleum phleoides
    Bruehl, G.W. and H.V. Toko, 1957
  Phleum pratense
    Oswald, John W. and Byron R. Houston, 1953
  Poa ampla
    Bruehl, G.W. and H.V. Toko, 1957
  Poa bulbosa
    Bruehl, G.W. and H.V. Toko, 1957
  Poa canbyi
    Bruehl, G.W. and H.V. Toko, 1957
  Poa compressa
    Bruehl, G.W. and H.V. Toko, 1957
  Poa pratensis
    Bruehl, G.W. and H.V. Toko, 1957
  Secale cereale
    Bruehl, G.W. and H.V. Toko, 1955
  Secale montanum
    Bruehl, G.W. and H.V. Toko, 1957
  Setaria virdis
    Bruehl, G.W. and H.V. Toko, 1957
    Oswald, John W. and Byron R. Houston, 1953
  Sorghum vulgare
    Oswald, John W. and Byron R. Houston, 1953
  Stipa cernua
    Oswald, John W. and Byron R. Houston, 1953
  Zea mays
    Oswald, John W. and Byron R. Houston, 1953

V. BAYBERRY YELLOWS Raychaudhuri 1953
  Calendula officinalis
    Raychaudhuri, S.P., 1953
  Callistephus chinensis
    Raychaudhuri, S.P., 1953
  Cuscuta campestris
    Raychaudhuri, S.P., 1952, 1953
  Cuscuta subinclusa
    Raychaudhuri, S.P., 1953
  Datura stramonium
    Raychaudhuri, S.P., 1953
  Gomphrena globosa
    Raychaudhuri, S.P., 1953
  Lycopersicon esculentum
    Raychaudhuri, S.P., 1953
  Medicago sativa
    Raychaudhuri, S.P., 1953
  Nicotiana glauca
    Raychaudhuri, S.P., 1953
  Nicotiana glutinosa
    Raychaudhuri, S.P., 1953
  Nicotiana rustica
    Raychaudhuri, S.P., 1953
  Nicotiana tabacum
    Raychaudhuri, S.P., 1953
  Phaseolus vulgaris
    Raychaudhuri, S.P., 1953
  Prunus persica (Amygdalus persica)
    Raychaudhuri, S.P., 1953
  Solanum melongena
    Raychaudhuri, S.P., 1953
  Solanum tuberosum
    Raychaudhuri, S.P., 1953
  Trifolium incarnatum
    Raychaudhuri, S.P., 1953

VIRUS
V. BAYBERRY YELLOWS (cont.)
  Vaccinium corymbosum
    Raychaudhuri, S.P., 1953
  Vaccinium macrocarpon (Oxycoccus macrocarpon)
    Raychaudhuri, S.P., 1953
  Vicia faba
    Raychaudhuri, S.P., 1953
  Zinnia multiflora
    Raychaudhuri, S.P., 1953

V. BEAN COMMON MOSAIC
  Cajanus indicus
    Zaumeyer, W.J. and B.L. Wade, 1935
  Canavalia ensiformis
    Reddick, D. and V.B. Stewart, 1919
  Canavalia gladiata
    Nelson, Ray, 1932
    Zaumeyer, W.J. and B.L. Wade, 1935
  Cicer arietinum
    Reddick, D. and V.B. Stewart, 1919
    Snyder, W.C., 1942
    Zaumeyer, W.J. and B.L. Wade, 1935
  Cucumis sativus
    Ainsworth, G.C., 1940
    Doolittle, S.P. and W.W. Gilbert, 1918
  Dolichos lablab
    Nelson, Ray, 1932
    Reddick, D. and V.B. Stewart, 1919
    Zaumeyer, W.J. and B.L. Wade, 1935
  Glycine max
    Snyder, W.C., 1942
    Zaumeyer, W.J. and B.L. Wade, 1935
  Lactuca sativa var. capitata
    Ainsworth, G.C., 1940
  Lathyrus odoratus
    Ainsworth, G.C., 1940
    Doolittle, S.P. and F.R. Jones, 1925
    Snyder, W.C., 1942
    Zaumeyer, W.J. and B.L. Wade, 1933, 1935
  Lens esculenta
    Zaumeyer, W.J. and B.L. Wade, 1935
  Lupinus albus
    Zaumeyer, W.J. and B.L. Wade, 1935
  Lycopersicon esculentum
    Ainsworth, G.C., 1940
  Medicago sativa
    Snyder, W.C., 1942
    Zaumeyer, W.J. and B.L. Wade, 1935
  Melilotus alba
    Snyder, W.C., 1942
    Zaumeyer, W.J. and B.L. Wade, 1935
  Melilotus indica
    Snyder, W.C., 1942
  Mucuna deeringianum
    Zaumeyer, W.J. and B.L. Wade, 1935
  Nicotiana glutinosa
    Grogan, Raymond G. and J.C. Walker, 1948
    Snyder, W.C., 1942
  Nicotiana tabacum
    Snyder, W.C., 1942
  Phaseolus aconitifolius
    Reddick, D. and V.B. Stewart, 1919
  Phaseolus acutifolius var. latifolius
    Zaumeyer, W.J. and B.L. Wade, 1935
  Phaseolus angularis
    Zaumeyer, W.J. and B.L. Wade, 1935
  Phaseolus aureus
    Nelson, Ray, 1932
    Reddick, D. and V.B. Stewart, 1919
    Zaumeyer, W.J. and B.L. Wade, 1935
  Phaseolus calcaratus
    Zaumeyer, W.J. and B.L. Wade, 1935
  Phaseolus lunatus
    Zaumeyer, W.J. and B.L. Wade, 1935
  Phaseolus lunatus f. macrocarpus
    Zaumeyer, W.J. and B.L. Wade, 1935
  Phaseolus mungo
    Zaumeyer, W.J. and B.L. Wade, 1935
  Pisum sativum
    Ainsworth, G.C., 1940
    Doolittle, S.P. and F.R. Jones, 1925
    Snyder, W.C., 1942
    Zaumeyer, W.J. and B.L. Wade, 1933, 1935

VIRUS

V. BEAN COMMON MOSAIC (cont.)
Pisum sativum var. saccharatum
Pierce, W.H., 1935
Trifolium pratense
Ainsworth, G.C., 1940
Snyder, W.C., 1942
Zaumeyer, W.J. and B.L. Wade, 1935
Trifolium repens
Ainsworth, G.C., 1940
Snow, Gordon F., 1955
Snyder, W.C., 1942
Zaumeyer, W.J. and B.L. Wade, 1935
Vicia americana
Zaumeyer, W.J. and B.L. Wade, 1935
Vicia faba
Zaumeyer, W.J. and B.L. Wade, 1935
Vigna cylindrica (Vigna catjang)
Snyder, W.C., 1942
Vigna sesquipedalis
Zaumeyer, W.J. and B.L. Wade, 1935
Vigna sinensis
Reddick, D. and V.B. Stewart, 1919
Zaumeyer, W.J. and B.L. Wade, 1935

V. BEAN MONTANA *
Medicago sativa
Afanasiev, M.M. and H.E. Morris, 1946
Trifolium hybridum
Afanasiev, M.M. and H.E. Morris, 1946
Trifolium pratense
Afanasiev, M.M. and H.E. Morris, 1946
Trifolium repens
Afanasiev, M.M. and H.E. Morris, 1946

V. BEAN MOSAIC 3 *
Lathyrus odoratus
Zaumeyer, W.J. and B.L. Wade, 1935
Pisum sativum
Zaumeyer, W.J. and B.L. Wade, 1935

V. BEAN POD MOTTLE Zaumeyer and Thomas 1948
Beta vulgaris
Zaumeyer, W.J. and H. Rex Thomas, 1948
Brassica oleracea var. botrytis
Zaumeyer, W.J. and H. Rex Thomas, 1948
Callistephus chinensis
Zaumeyer, W.J. and H. Rex Thomas, 1948
Capsicum frutescens (Capsicum annuum)
Zaumeyer, W.J. and H. Rex Thomas, 1948
Cucumis sativus
Zaumeyer, W.J. and H. Rex Thomas, 1948
Datura stramonium
Zaumeyer, W.J. and H. Rex Thomas, 1948
Dianthus superbus
Zaumeyer, W.J. and H. Rex Thomas, 1948
Lactuca sativa
Zaumeyer, W.J. and H. Rex Thomas, 1948
Lycopersicon esculentum
Zaumeyer, W.J. and H. Rex Thomas, 1948
Melilotus alba
Zaumeyer, W.J. and H. Rex Thomas, 1948
Nicotiana glutinosa
Zaumeyer, W.J. and H. Rex Thomas, 1948
Nicotiana tabacum
Zaumeyer, W.J. and H. Rex Thomas, 1948
Pelargonium hortorum
Zaumeyer, W.J. and H. Rex Thomas, 1948
Phaseolus angularis
Zaumeyer, W.J. and H. Rex Thomas, 1948
Phaseolus aureus
Zaumeyer, W.J. and H. Rex Thomas, 1948
Phaseolus coccineus
Zaumeyer, W.J. and H. Rex Thomas, 1948
Phaseolus lunatus f. macrocarpus
Zaumeyer, W.J. and H. Rex Thomas, 1948
Phaseolus mungo
Zaumeyer, W.J. and H. Rex Thomas, 1948
Pisum sativum
Zaumeyer, W.J. and H. Rex Thomas, 1948
Silene compacta
Zaumeyer, W.J. and H. Rex Thomas, 1948
Trifolium incarnatum
Zaumeyer, W.J. and H. Rex Thomas, 1948

VIRUS

V. BEAN POD MOTTLE (cont.)
Vicia faba
Zaumeyer, W.J. and H. Rex Thomas, 1948
Vigna sesquipedalis
Zaumeyer, W.J. and H. Rex Thomas, 1948
Vigna sinensis
Zaumeyer, W.J. and H. Rex Thomas, 1948
Vinca rosea
Zaumeyer, W.J. and H. Rex Thomas, 1948

V. BEAN SOUTHERN MOSAIC
Beta vulgaris
Zaumeyer, W.J. and L.L. Harter, 1943
Brassica rapa
Zaumeyer, W.J. and L.L. Harter, 1943
Capsicum frutescens (Capsicum annuum)
Zaumeyer, W.J. and L.L. Harter, 1943
Cicer arietinum
Zaumeyer, W.J. and L.L. Harter, 1943
Crotalaria spectabilis
Zaumeyer, W.J. and L.L. Harter, 1943
Cucumis sativus
Zaumeyer, W.J. and L.L. Harter, 1943
Datura stramonium
Zaumeyer, W.J. and L.L. Harter, 1943
Glycine max
Zaumeyer, W.J. and L.L. Harter, 1943
Lupinus albus
Zaumeyer, W.J. and L.L. Harter, 1943
Lupinus luteus
Zaumeyer, W.J. and L.L. Harter, 1943
Lycopersicon esculentum
Zaumeyer, W.J. and L.L. Harter, 1943
Medicago sativa
Zaumeyer, W.J. and L.L. Harter, 1943
Melilotus alba
Zaumeyer, W.J. and L.L. Harter, 1943
Mucuna deeringianum
Zaumeyer, W.J. and L.L. Harter, 1943
Nicotiana glutinosa
Zaumeyer, W.J. and L.L. Harter, 1943
Nicotiana tabacum
Zaumeyer, W.J. and L.L. Harter, 1943
Petunia hybrida
Zaumeyer, W.J. and L.L. Harter, 1943
Phaseolus angularis
Zaumeyer, W.J. and L.L. Harter, 1943
Phaseolus aureus
Zaumeyer, W.J. and L.L. Harter, 1943
Phaseolus coccineus
Zaumeyer, W.J. and L.L. Harter, 1943
Phaseolus lunatus f. macrocarpus
Zaumeyer, W.J. and L.L. Harter, 1943
Phaseolus mungo
Zaumeyer, W.J. and L.L. Harter, 1943
Pisum sativum
Zaumeyer, W.J. and L.L. Harter, 1943
Trifolium incarnatum
Zaumeyer, W.J. and L.L. Harter, 1943
Trifolium pratense
Zaumeyer, W.J. and L.L. Harter, 1943
Trifolium repens
Zaumeyer, W.J. and L.L. Harter, 1943
Vicia cylindrica *
Zaumeyer, W.J. and L.L. Harter, 1943
Vicia faba
Zaumeyer, W.J. and L.L. Harter, 1943
Vicia sativa
Zaumeyer, W.J. and L.L. Harter, 1943
Vicia villosa
Zaumeyer, W.J. and L.L. Harter, 1943
Vigna sesquipedalis
Zaumeyer, W.J. and L.L. Harter, 1943
Vigna sinensis
Zaumeyer, W.J. and L.L. Harter, 1943

V. BEAN YELLOW MOSAIC Pierce 1934
Antirrhinum majus
Thomas, H. Rex and W.J. Zaumeyer, 1953
Arachis hypogaea
Grogan, Raymond G. and J.C. Walker, 1948
Belamcanda chinensis
Brierley, Philip and Floyd F. Smith, 1948

VIRUS
V. BEAN YELLOW MOSAIC (cont.)
  Beta vulgaris
    Conover, Robert A., 1948
  Brassica oleracea var. capitata
    Thomas, H. Rex and W.J. Zaumeyer, 1953
  Cajanus indicus
    Zaumeyer, W.J. and B.L. Wade, 1935
  Canavalia gladiata
    Zaumeyer, W.J. and B.L. Wade, 1935
  Crotalaria retusa
    Zaumeyer, W.J., 1940
  Crotalaria spectabilis
    Conover, Robert A., 1948
  Cucumis sativus
    Ainsworth, G.C., 1940
    Grogan, Raymond G. and J.C. Walker, 1948
    Hagedorn, D.J. and J.C. Walker, 1950, 1954
    Thomas, H. Rex and W.J. Zaumeyer, 1953
    Zaumeyer, W.J. and H.H. Fisher, 1953
  Datura stramonium
    Hagedorn, D.J. and J.C. Walker, 1950, 1954
    Thomas, H. Rex and W.J. Zaumeyer, 1953
    Zaumeyer, W.J., 1940
  Dolichos lablab
    Zaumeyer, W.J. and H.H. Fisher, 1953
    Zaumeyer, W.J. and B.L. Wade, 1935
  Glycine max
    Baggett, James R., 1957
    Grogan, Raymond G. and J.C. Walker, 1948
    Johnson, James, 1942
    Zaumeyer, W.J., 1940, 1952
    Zaumeyer, W.J. and B.L. Wade, 1935
  Lactuca sativa var. capitata
    Ainsworth, G.C., 1940
  Lathyrus odoratus
    Doolittle, S.P. and F.R. Jones, 1925
  Lespedeza striata
    Conover, Robert A., 1948
  Lupinus albus
    Zaumeyer, W.J. and H.H. Fisher, 1953
    Zaumeyer, W.J. and B.L. Wade, 1935
  Lupinus angustifolius
    Conover, Robert A., 1948
  Lupinus luteus
    Conover, Robert A., 1948
  Lycopersicon esculentum
    Ainsworth, G.C., 1940
    Conover, Robert A., 1948
    Hagedorn, D.J. and J.C. Walker, 1950, 1954
    Thomas, H. Rex and W.J. Zaumeyer, 1953
  Medicago hispida
    Grogan, Raymond G. and J.C. Walker, 1948
  Medicago sativa
    Afanasiev, M.M. and H.E. Morris, 1952
    Conover, Robert A., 1948
    Elliott, J.A., 1921
    Hagedorn, D.J. and J.C. Walker, 1950, 1954
    Houston, Byron R. and John W. Oswald, 1953
    Pierce, W.H., 1935
    Thomas, H. Rex and W.J. Zaumeyer, 1953
    Zaumeyer, W.J., 1952
    Zaumeyer, W.J. and H.H. Fisher, 1953
    Zaumeyer, W.J. and B.L. Wade, 1935
  Melilotus alba
    Baggett, James R., 1957
    Grogan, Raymond G. and J.C. Walker, 1948
    Zaumeyer, W.J. and B.L. Wade, 1935
  Melilotus officinalis
    Grogan, Raymond G. and J.C. Walker, 1948
  Mucuna deeringianum
    Zaumeyer, W.J. and B.L. Wade, 1935
  Nicotiana glauca
    Zaumeyer, W.J., 1940
  Nicotiana glutinosa
    Thomas, H. Rex and W.J. Zaumeyer, 1953
    Zaumeyer, W.J., 1940
    Zaumeyer, W.J. and H.H. Fisher, 1953
  Nicotiana rustica
    Grogan, Raymond G. and J.C. Walker, 1948
    Hagedorn, D.J. and J.C. Walker, 1950, 1954
  Nicotiana tabacum
    Conover, Robert A., 1948
    Grogan, Raymond G. and J.C. Walker, 1948

VIRUS
V. BEAN YELLOW MOSAIC (cont.)
  Nicotiana tabacum
    Hagedorn, D.J. and J.C. Walker, 1950, 1954
    Pierce, W.H., 1935
    Zaumeyer, W.J., 1940
  Petunia hybrida
    Pierce, W.H., 1935
    Zaumeyer, W.J., 1940
  Phaseolus acutifolius var. latifolius
    Zaumeyer, W.J. and B.L. Wade, 1935
  Phaseolus angularis
    Zaumeyer, W.J. and H.H. Fisher, 1953
    Zaumeyer, W.J. and B.L. Wade, 1935
  Phaseolus aureus
    Conover, Robert A., 1948
    Zaumeyer, W.J., 1940
  Phaseolus calcaratus
    Pierce, W.H., 1934
    Zaumeyer, W.J. and H.H. Fisher, 1953
    Zaumeyer, W.J. and B.L. Wade, 1935
  Phaseolus coccineus
    Baggett, James R., 1956
    Conover, Robert A., 1948
    Thomas, H. Rex and W.J. Zaumeyer, 1953
    Zaumeyer, W.J. and H.H. Fisher, 1953
  Phaseolus limensis
    Pierce, W.H., 1934
  Phaseolus lunatus
    Conover, Robert A., 1948
    Grogan, Raymond G. and J.C. Walker, 1948
    Thomas, H. Rex and W.J. Zaumeyer, 1953
    Zaumeyer, W.J., 1940
    Zaumeyer, W.J. and B.L. Wade, 1935
  Phaseolus lunatus f. macrocarpus
    Pierce, W.H., 1934
    Zaumeyer, W.J. and B.L. Wade, 1935
  Phaseolus mungo
    Conover, Robert A., 1948
    Zaumeyer, W.J. and H.H. Fisher, 1953
    Zaumeyer, W.J. and B.L. Wade, 1935
  Pisum sativum
    Afanasiev, M.M. and H.E. Morris, 1952
    Doolittle, S.P. and F.R. Jones, 1925
    Zaumeyer, W.J., 1952
    Zaumeyer, W.J. and H.H. Fisher, 1953
  Spinacia oleracea
    Thomas, H. Rex and W.J. Zaumeyer, 1953
  Trifolium hybridum
    Afanasiev, M.M. and H.E. Morris, 1952
  Trifolium incarnatum
    Zaumeyer, W.J., 1952
    Zaumeyer, W.J. and H.H. Fisher, 1953
  Trifolium pratense
    Afanasiev, M.M. and H.E. Morris, 1952
    Ainsworth, G.C., 1940
    Baggett, James R., 1957
    Grogan, Raymond G. and J.C. Walker, 1948
    Thomas, H. Rex and W.J. Zaumeyer, 1953
    Zaumeyer, W.J., 1940, 1952
    Zaumeyer, W.J. and H.H. Fisher, 1953
  Trifolium repens
    Afanasiev, M.M. and H.E. Morris, 1952
    Baggett, James R., 1957
    Elliott, J.A., 1921
    Grogan, Raymond G. and J.C. Walker, 1948
    Hagedorn, D.J. and J.C. Walker, 1950, 1954
    Pierce, W.H., 1935
    Zaumeyer, W.J., 1940, 1952
    Zaumeyer, W.J. and H.H. Fisher, 1953
    Zaumeyer, W.J. and B.L. Wade, 1935
  Trifolium subterraneum
    Baggett, James R., 1957
  Vicia americana
    Zaumeyer, W.J. and B.L. Wade, 1935
  Vicia atropurpurea
    Grogan, Raymond G. and J.C. Walker, 1948
  Vicia faba
    Grogan, Raymond G. and J.C. Walker, 1948
  Vicia sativa
    Grogan, Raymond G. and J.C. Walker, 1948
    Zaumeyer, W.J., 1940
  Vicia villosa
    Baggett, James R., 1957

VIRUS
V. BEAN YELLOW MOSAIC (cont.)
   Vigna sesquipedalis
     Conover, Robert A., 1948
     Zaumeyer, W.J. and B.L. Wade, 1935
   Vigna sinensis
     Conover, Robert A., 1948
     Hagedorn, D.J. and J.C. Walker, 1950, 1954
     Zaumeyer, W.J., 1952
     Zaumeyer, W.J. and B.L. Wade, 1935
   Zinnia elegans
     Thomas, H. Rex and W.J. Zaumeyer, 1953

V. BEAN YELLOW STIPPLE Zaumeyer and Thomas 1950
   Apium graveolens
     Zaumeyer, W.J. and H. Rex Thomas, 1950
   Beta vulgaris
     Zaumeyer, W.J. and H. Rex Thomas, 1950
   Brassica oleracea
     Zaumeyer, W.J. and H. Rex Thomas, 1950
   Canavalia ensiformis
     Zaumeyer, W.J. and H. Rex Thomas, 1950
   Cucumis sativus
     Zaumeyer, W.J. and H. Rex Thomas, 1950
   Datura stramonium
     Zaumeyer, W.J. and H. Rex Thomas, 1950
   Lycopersicon esculentum
     Zaumeyer, W.J. and H. Rex Thomas, 1950
   Medicago sativa
     Zaumeyer, W.J. and H. Rex Thomas, 1950
   Melilotus alba
     Zaumeyer, W.J. and H. Rex Thomas, 1950
   Nicotiana tabacum
     Zaumeyer, W.J. and H. Rex Thomas, 1950
   Petunia hybrida
     Zaumeyer, W.J. and H. Rex Thomas, 1950
   Phaseolus aconitifolius
     Zaumeyer, W.J. and H. Rex Thomas, 1950
   Phaseolus angularis
     Zaumeyer, W.J. and H. Rex Thomas, 1950
   Phaseolus aureus
     Zaumeyer, W.J. and H. Rex Thomas, 1950
   Phaseolus coccineus
     Zaumeyer, W.J. and H. Rex Thomas, 1950
   Phaseolus lathyroides
     Zaumeyer, W.J. and H. Rex Thomas, 1950
   Phaseolus lunatus
     Zaumeyer, W.J. and H. Rex Thomas, 1950
   Phaseolus lunatus f. macrocarpus
     Zaumeyer, W.J. and H. Rex Thomas, 1950
   Sesbania exaltata
     Zaumeyer, W.J. and H. Rex Thomas, 1950
   Trifolium incarnatum
     Zaumeyer, W.J. and H. Rex Thomas, 1950
   Trifolium pratense
     Zaumeyer, W.J. and H. Rex Thomas, 1950
   Trifolium repens
     Zaumeyer, W.J. and H. Rex Thomas, 1950
   Tropaeolum majus
     Zaumeyer, W.J. and H. Rex Thomas, 1950
   Vicia faba
     Zaumeyer, W.J. and H. Rex Thomas, 1950
   Vigna vexillata
     Zaumeyer, W.J. and H. Rex Thomas, 1950

V. BEET CURLY TOP ((Ball 1909; Boucquet and Hartung 1915)) Carsner 1919; Severin 1919
   Amaranthus caudatus
     Bennett, C.W. and A.S. Costa, 1949
   Amaranthus retroflexus
     Bennett, C.W. and A.S. Costa, 1949
   Amaranthus spp.
     Bennett, C.W., Eubanks Carsner, F.H. Coons and E.W. Brandes, 1946
   Apium graveolens var. dulce
     Carsner, E., 1919
   Arachis hypogaea
     Bennett, C.W., Eubanks Carsner, F.H. Coons and E.W. Brandes, 1946
   Artemisia californica
     Severin, Henry H.P., 1939
   Asclepias mexicana
     Carsner, E., 1919

VIRUS
V. BEET CURLY TOP (cont.)
   Atriplex polycarpa
     Carsner, E., 1919
     Severin, Henry H.P. and Charles F. Henderson, 1928
   Atriplex semibaccata
     Bennett, C.W. and A.S. Costa, 1949
   Atriplex spinifera
     Severin, Henry H.P. and Charles F. Henderson, 1928
   Beta macrocarpa
     Costa, A.S., 1952
   Beta patellaris
     Bennett, C.W. and A.S. Costa, 1949
     Costa, A.S., 1952
   Beta patula
     Costa, A.S., 1952
   Beta vulgaris
     Costa, A.S., 1952
   Beta vulgaris var. cicla
     Costa, A.S., 1952
   Brassica adpressa
     Giddings, N.J., 1944
   Brassica oleracea
     Carsner, E., 1919
   Brassica pekinensis
     Costa, A.S., 1952
     Severin, Henry H.P., 1929
   Callistephus chinensis
     Bennett, C.W. and A.S. Costa, 1949
     Costa, A.S., 1952
     Severin, Henry H.P., 1929
   Capsicum frutescens (Capsicum annuum)
     Bennett, C.W., Eubanks Carsner, F.H. Coons and E.W. Brandes, 1946
     Costa, A.S., 1952
   Capsicum frutescens var. grossum
     Costa, A.S., 1952
   Capsicum spp.
     Carsner, E., 1919
   Ceanothus cuneatus
     Severin, Henry H.P., 1939
   Chenopodium album
     Bennett, C.W. and A.S. Costa, 1949
   Chenopodium leptophyllum
     Carsner, E., 1919
   Chenopodium murale
     Carsner, E., 1919
   Chrysopsis villosa
     Severin, Henry H.P., 1939
   Coffea arabica
     Bennett, C.W. and A.S. Costa, 1949
   Cucumis melo
     Carsner, E., 1919
   Cucumis sativus
     Carsner, E., 1919
   Cuscuta californica
     Bennett, C.W., 1944, 1951, 1955
     Lackey, C.F., 1941
     Lackey, C.F. and C.W. Bennett, 1949
   Cuscuta campestris
     Bennett, C.W., 1944
     Johnson, Folke, 1941
   Cuscuta subinclusa
     Bennett, C.W., 1940, 1944
     Fulton, Robert W., 1955
     Giddings, N.J., 1947
     Lackey, C.F. and C.W. Bennett, 1949
   Datura meteloides
     Bennett, C.W., Eubanks Carsner, F.H. Coons and E.W. Brandes, 1946
     Giddings, N.J., C.W. Bennett and A.L. Harrison, 1951
   Datura spp.
     Bennett, C.W. and A.S. Costa, 1949
   Datura stramonium
     Bennett, C.W., Eubanks Carsner, F.H. Coons and E.W. Brandes, 1946
   Delphinium hybrid
     Severin, Henry H.P., 1942
   Eremocarpus setigerus
     Carsner, E., 1919

VIRUS
V. BEET CURLY TOP (cont.)
Erigeron bonariensis
    Bennett, C.W. and A.S. Costa, 1949
Eschscholtzia californica
    Carsner, E., 1919
Euphorbia prunifolia
    Costa, A.S., 1952
Fagopyron esculentum
    Costa, A.S., 1952
Feijoa sellowiana
    Giddings, N.J., 1944
Frankenia grandifolia
    Severin, Henry H.P., 1939
Galinsoga parviflora
    Costa, A.S., 1952
Gossypium hirsutum
    Bennett, C.W. and A.S. Costa, 1949
    Costa, A.S., 1952
    Giddings, N.J., 1944
    Severin, Henry H.P., 1929
Gossypium spp.
    Carsner, E., 1919
Grindelia camporum
    Severin, Henry H.P., 1939
Gutierrezia californica
    Severin, Henry H.P., 1939
Haplopappus venetus subsp. verononioides *
    Severin, Henry H.P., 1939
Hemizonia virgata
    Severin, Henry H.P., 1939
Hibiscus esculentus
    Giddings, N.J., 1944
Hordeum vulgare
    Carsner, E., 1919
Isomeris arborea
    Severin, Henry H.P., 1939
Lactuca sativa
    Bennett, C.W. and A.S. Costa, 1949
    Carsner, E., 1919
    Severin, Henry H.P., 1929
Lavatera assurgentiflora
    Carsner, E., 1919
Lepidium nitidum
    Giddings, N.J., 1938
Lepidospartum squamatum
    Severin, Henry H.P., 1939
Lessingia glandulifera
    Severin, Henry H.P., 1939
Lupinus affinis
    Carsner, E., 1919
Lycopersicon chilense
    Virgin, Walter J., 1940
Lycopersicon esculentum
    Bennett, C.W., Eubanks Carsner, F.H. Coons and
      E.W. Brandes, 1946
    Giddings, N.J., 1938
Lycopersicon peruvianum
    Giddings, N.J., C.W. Bennett and A.L. Harrison,
      1951
Lycopersicon pimpinellifolium
    Giddings, N.J., C.W. Bennett and A.L. Harrison,
      1951
Malcomia africana
    Giddings, N.J., 1944
Malus spp.
    Giddings, N.J., 1944
Marrubium vulgare
    Carsner, E., 1919
    Severin, Henry H.P., 1939
Medicago sativa
    Giddings, N.J., 1944
Nicandra physalodes
    Costa, A.S., 1952
Nicotiana acuminata
    Giddings, N.J., C.W. Bennett and A.L. Harrison,
      1951
Nicotiana glauca
    Bennett, C.W. and A.S. Costa, 1949
    Costa, A.S., 1952
    Giddings, N.J., C.W. Bennett and A.L. Harrison,
      1951
Nicotiana glutinosa
    Bennett, C.W., Eubanks Carsner, F.H. Coons and
      E.W. Brandes, 1946

VIRUS
V. BEET CURLY TOP (cont.)
Nicotiana glutinosa
    Costa, A.S., 1952
Nicotiana tabacum
    Bennett, C.W., Eubanks Carsner, F.H. Coons and
      E.W. Brandes, 1946
    Costa, A.S., 1952
    Giddings, N.J., 1938, 1944
    Giddings, N.J., C.W. Bennett and A.L. Harrison,
      1951
Oxalis spp.
    Bennett, C.W. and A.S. Costa, 1949
Parthenium argentatum
    Severin, Henry H.P., 1945
Petunia hybrida
    Bennett, C.W. and A.S. Costa, 1949
    Costa, A.S., 1952
Phaseolus vulgaris
    Bennett, C.W., Eubanks Carsner, F.H. Coons and
      E.W. Brandes, 1946
    Bennett, C.W. and A.S. Costa, 1949
    Carsner, E., 1919
    Giddings, N.J., 1938
    Murphy, Donald M. and W.H. Pierce, 1938
Physalis spp.
    Costa, A.S., 1952
Phytolacca americana
    Bennett, C.W. and A.S. Costa, 1949
    Giddings, N.J., C.W. Bennett and A.L. Harrison,
      1951
Plantago erecta
    Giddings, N.J., 1938
Pluchea sericea
    Severin, Henry H.P., 1939
Portulaca oleracea
    Bennett, C.W. and A.S. Costa, 1949
    Carsner, E., 1919
Punica granatum
    Giddings, N.J., 1944
Raphanus sativus
    Carsner, E., 1919
Ricinus communis
    Giddings, N.J., C.W. Bennett and A.L. Harrison,
      1951
Rosa chinensis
    Giddings, N.J., 1944
Rumex crispus
    Carsner, E., 1919
Samolus floribundus
    Costa, A.S., 1952
Senecio douglassii
    Severin, Henry H.P., 1939
Sida hederacea
    Severin, Henry H.P., 1939
Sida rhombifolia
    Bennett, C.W. and A.S. Costa, 1949
Solanum melongena
    Costa, A.S., 1952
Solanum nigrum
    Bennett, C.W. and A.S. Costa, 1949
    Carsner, E., 1919
    Costa, A.S., 1952
Solanum tuberosum
    Bennett, C.W. and A.S. Costa, 1949
Spinacia oleracea
    Costa, A.S., 1952
Stellaria media
    Costa, A.S., 1952
Trifolium pratense
    Giddings, N.J., 1944
Trifolium repens
    Giddings, N.J., 1944
Tropaeolum majus
    Carsner, E., 1919
Verbena prostrata
    Carsner, E., 1919
Vinca rosea
    Bennett, C.W. and A.S. Costa, 1949
Zinnia elegans
    Costa, A.S., 1952

V. BEET MOSAIC Robbins 1921; Hoggan 1933
Apium graveolens var. dulce
    Severin, Henry H.P. and Roger M. Drake, 1948

VIRUS
V. BEET MOSAIC (cont.)
  Atropa belladonna
    Pound, Glenn S., 1947
  Brassica campestris
    Severin, Henry H.P. and Roger M. Drake, 1947
  Brassica juncea (Brassica japonica)
    Pound, Glenn S., 1947
  Brassica nigra
    Bennett, C.W., 1949
  Brassica oleracea var. botrytis
    Severin, Henry H.P. and Roger M. Drake, 1948
  Brassica oleracea var. capitata
    Pound, Glenn S., 1947
    Severin, Henry H.P. and Roger M. Drake, 1948
  Brassica oleracea var. gemmifera
    Pound, Glenn S., 1947
  Brassica oleracea var. gongylodes
    Pound, Glenn S., 1947
  Brassica pekinensis
    Pound, Glenn S., 1947
  Calendula officinalis
    Pound, Glenn S., 1947
  Campanula medium
    Pound, Glenn S., 1947
  Capsicum frutescens var. cerasiforme
    Pound, Glenn S., 1947
  Capsicum frutescens var. grossum
    Severin, Henry H.P. and Roger M. Drake, 1948
  Centaurea nigra
    Pound, Glenn S., 1947
  Centaurea repens
    Pound, Glenn S., 1947
  Cheiranthus cheiri
    Pound, Glenn S., 1947
  Chrysanthemum morifolium
    Pound, Glenn S., 1947
  Cirsium arvense
    Pound, Glenn S., 1947
  Cucumis sativus
    Bennett, C.W., 1949
    Pound, Glenn S., 1947
    Severin, Henry H.P. and Roger M. Drake, 1948
  Cucurbita pepo
    Pound, Glenn S., 1947
  Cuscuta californica
    Bennett, C.W., 1944
  Cuscuta campestris
    Bennett, C.W., 1944
  Cuscuta subinclusa
    Bennett, C.W., 1940, 1944
  Dahlia pinnata
    Pound, Glenn S., 1947
  Datura metel
    Pound, Glenn S., 1947
  Datura meteloides
    Bennett, C.W., 1949
  Datura stramonium
    Bennett, C.W., 1949
    Severin, Henry H.P. and Roger M. Drake, 1947
  Daucus carota
    Pound, Glenn S., 1947
  Delphinium ajacis
    Pound, Glenn S., 1947
  Dianthus barbatus
    Pound, Glenn S., 1947
  Digitalis purpurea
    Pound, Glenn S., 1947
  Hesperis matronalis
    Pound, Glenn S., 1947
  Lactuca sativa
    Bennett, C.W., 1949
    Pound, Glenn S., 1947
  Lathyrus odoratus
    Pound, Glenn S., 1947
  Lepidium virginicum
    Pound, Glenn S., 1947
  Lobularia maritima
    Pound, Glenn S., 1947
  Lupinus pubescens
    Pound, Glenn S., 1947
  Lycopersicon esculentum
    Bennett, C.W., 1949
    Pound, Glenn S., 1947

VIRUS
V. BEET MOSAIC (cont.)
  Lycopersicon esculentum
    Severin, Henry H.P. and Roger M. Drake, 1948
  Malva rotundifolia
    Severin, Henry H.P. and Roger M. Drake, 1947
  Matthiola incana var. annua
    Pound, Glenn S., 1947
    Severin, Henry H.P. and Roger M. Drake, 1948
  Medicago sativa
    Bennett, C.W., 1949
  Melilotus alba
    Bennett, C.W., 1949
  Neslia paniculata
    Pound, Glenn S., 1947
  Nicandra physalodes
    Pound, Glenn S., 1947
  Nicotiana acuminata
    Bennett, C.W., 1949
  Nicotiana glauca
    Bennett, C.W., 1949
  Nicotiana glutinosa
    Bennett, C.W., 1949
    Severin, Henry H.P. and Roger M. Drake, 1948
  Nicotiana langsdorffii
    Bennett, C.W., 1949
  Nicotiana longiflora
    Bennett, C.W., 1949
  Nicotiana palmeri
    Bennett, C.W., 1949
  Nicotiana paniculata
    Bennett, C.W., 1949
  Nicotiana rustica
    Bennett, C.W., 1949
    Pound, Glenn S., 1947
  Nicotiana sylvestris
    Bennett, C.W., 1949
  Nicotiana tabacum
    Bennett, C.W., 1949
    Hoggan, I.A., 1933
    Pound, Glenn S., 1947
  Parthenium argentatum
    Severin, Henry H.P., 1945
  Petunia hybrida
    Bennett, C.W., 1949
  Phaseolus coccineus
    Pound, Glenn S., 1947
  Phaseolus vulgaris
    Bennett, C.W., 1949
    Pound, Glenn S., 1947
    Severin, Henry H.P. and Roger M. Drake, 1948
  Phlox drummondii
    Pound, Glenn S., 1947
  Physalis pubescens
    Pound, Glenn S., 1947
  Phytolacca americana
    Bennett, C.W., 1949
    Pound, Glenn S., 1947
  Plantago lanceolata
    Bennett, C.W., 1949
  Plantago major
    Severin, Henry H.P. and Roger M. Drake, 1947
  Polygonum hydropiper
    Pound, Glenn S., 1947
  Polygonum scandens
    Pound, Glenn S., 1947
  Raphanus sativus
    Pound, Glenn S., 1947
  Reseda odorata
    Pound, Glenn S., 1947
  Rumex acetosella
    Bennett, C.W., 1949
    Severin, Henry H.P. and Roger M. Drake, 1947
  Rumex crispus
    Severin, Henry H.P. and Roger M. Drake, 1947
  Rumex occidentalis
    Pound, Glenn S., 1947
  Rumex pulcher
    Severin, Henry H.P. and Roger M. Drake, 1947
  Salvia splendens
    Pound, Glenn S., 1947
  Scabiosa atropurpurea
    Pound, Glenn S., 1947

VIRUS
V. BEET MOSAIC (cont.)
  Sisymbrium irio
    Bennett, C.W., 1949
  Solanum integrifolium
    Pound, Glenn S., 1947
  Solanum melongena
    Pound, Glenn S., 1947
  Solanum nigrum
    Severin, Henry H.P. and Roger M. Drake, 1947
  Solanum tuberosum
    Pound, Glenn S., 1947
  Sonchus asper
    Bennett, C.W., 1949
    Severin, Henry H.P. and Roger M. Drake, 1947
  Sonchus oleraceus
    Severin, Henry H.P. and Roger M. Drake, 1947
  Tagetes patula
    Pound, Glenn S., 1947
  Thlaspi arvense
    Pound, Glenn S., 1947
  Trifolium pratense
    Bennett, C.W., 1949
  Trifolium repens
    Bennett, C.W., 1949
  Vicia faba
    Severin, Henry H.P. and Roger M. Drake, 1948
  Vigna sinensis
    Pound, Glenn S., 1947
  Zinnia elegans
    Bennett, C.W., 1949

V. BEET RING SPOT *
  Agropyron repens
    Harrison, B.D., 1957
  Equisetum arvense
    Harrison, B.D., 1957
  Pteris aquilina
    Harrison, B.D., 1957

V. BEET ROSETTE *
  Chenopodium album
    Bennett, C.W. and James E. Duffus, 1957
  Chenopodium amaranticolor
    Bennett, C.W. and James E. Duffus, 1957
  Chenopodium capitatum
    Bennett, C.W. and James E. Duffus, 1957
  Cuscuta californica
    Bennett, C.W. and James E. Duffus, 1957
  Cuscuta campestris
    Bennett, C.W. and James E. Duffus, 1957
  Cuscuta subinclusa
    Bennett, C.W. and James E. Duffus, 1957
  Nicotiana tabacum
    Bennett, C.W. and James E. Duffus, 1957
  Spinacia oleracea
    Bennett, C.W. and James E. Duffus, 1957

V. BEET YELLOW NET Sylvester 1948
  Atriplex patula
    Sylvester, Edward S., 1948
  Atriplex rosea
    Sylvester, Edward S., 1948
  Brassica campestris
    Sylvester, Edward S., 1948
  Brassica chinensis
    Sylvester, Edward S., 1948
  Calendula officinalis
    Sylvester, Edward S., 1948
  Callistephus chinensis
    Sylvester, Edward S., 1948
  Capsella bursa-pastoris
    Sylvester, Edward S., 1948
  Chenopodium murale
    Sylvester, Edward S., 1948
  Cucumis sativus
    Sylvester, Edward S., 1948
  Dahlia pinnata
    McLean, D.M., 1952
  Datura stramonium
    Sylvester, Edward S., 1948
  Erodium moschatum
    Sylvester, Edward S., 1948

VIRUS
V. BEET YELLOW NET (cont.)
  Fragaria vesca
    McLean, D.M., 1952
  Gladiolus spp.
    McLean, D.M., 1952
  Ipomoea purpurea
    Sylvester, Edward S., 1948
  Lactuca sativa var. romana
    Sylvester, Edward S., 1948
  Lycopersicon esculentum
    Sylvester, Edward S., 1948
  Nicotiana tabacum
    Sylvester, Edward S., 1948
  Plantago major
    Sylvester, Edward S., 1948
  Polygonum coccineum
    Sylvester, Edward S., 1948
  Polygonum persicaria
    Sylvester, Edward S., 1948
  Rumex crispus
    Sylvester, Edward S., 1948
  Sonchus arvensis
    Sylvester, Edward S., 1948
  Spinacia oleracea
    McLean, D.M., 1952
    Sylvester, Edward S., 1948
  Stellaria media
    McLean, D.M., 1952
  Verbesina encelioides
    McLean, D.M., 1952
  Zinnia elegans
    McLean, D.M., 1952

V. BEET YELLOW VEIN DISEASE *
  Cuscuta californica
    Bennett, C.W., 1944, 1956
  Cuscuta campestris
    Bennett, C.W., 1944, 1956
  Cuscuta subinclusa
    Bennett, C.W., 1944, 1956

V. BEET YELLOW WILT Bennett and Munck 1946
  Cucumis sativus
    Bennett, C.W. and Carlos Munck, 1946
  Cuscuta campestris
    Bennett, C.W. and Carlos Munck, 1946
  Cuscuta subinclusa
    Bennett, C.W. and Carlos Munck, 1946
  Nicotiana tabacum
    Bennett, C.W. and Carlos Munck, 1946
  Petunia hybrida
    Bennett, C.W. and Carlos Munck, 1946
  Phaseolus vulgaris
    Bennett, C.W. and Carlos Munck, 1946

V. BEET YELLOWS Watson 1942; Petherbridge and
Achillea millefolium   Stirrup 1935
    Roland, G. and J. Tahon, 1961
  Aegopodium podagraria
    Roland, G. and J. Tahon, 1961
  Agropyron repens
    Roland, G. and J. Tahon, 1961
  Allium cepa
    Roland, G. and J. Tahon, 1961
  Ambrosia psilostachya
    Roland, G. and J. Tahon, 1961
  Ambrosia trifida
    Roland, G. and J. Tahon, 1961
  Ammannia coccinea
    Roland, G. and J. Tahon, 1961
  Anagallis arvensis
    Roland, G. and J. Tahon, 1961
  Anemopsis californica
    Roland, G. and J. Tahon, 1961
  Apium graveolens
    Roland, G. and J. Tahon, 1961
  Arachis hypogaea
    Roland, G. and J. Tahon, 1961
  Arctium tomentosum
    Roland, G. and J. Tahon, 1961
  Artemisia vulgaris
    Roland, G. and J. Tahon, 1961

VIRUS
V. BEET YELLOWS (cont.)

Atriplex lentiformis
    Roland, G. and J. Tahon, 1961
Atriplex polycarpa
    Roland, G. and J. Tahon, 1961
Avena sativa
    Roland, G. and J. Tahon, 1961
Borago officinalis
    Roland, G. and J. Tahon, 1961
Brassica campestris
    Roland, G. and J. Tahon, 1961
Brassica kaber (Brassica arvensis)
    Roland, G. and J. Tahon, 1961
Brassica napus
    Roland, G. and J. Tahon, 1961
Brassica nigra
    Roland, G. and J. Tahon, 1961
Brassica oleracea
    Roland, G. and J. Tahon, 1961
Brassica rapa
    Roland, G. and J. Tahon, 1961
Calendula officinalis
    Roland, G. and J. Tahon, 1961
Capsicum frutescens (Capsicum annuum)
    Roland, G. and J. Tahon, 1961
Carthamus tinctorius
    Roland, G. and J. Tahon, 1961
Centaurea cyanus
    Roland, G. and J. Tahon, 1961
Cerastium caespitosum
    Roland, G. and J. Tahon, 1961
Chaerefolium silvestre
    Roland, G. and J. Tahon, 1961
Cheiranthus cheiri
    Roland, G. and J. Tahon, 1961
Chorisia spp.
    Roland, G. and J. Tahon, 1961
Cichorium intybus
    Roland, G. and J. Tahon, 1961
Cirsium arvense
    Roland, G. and J. Tahon, 1961
Cirsium vulgare
    Roland, G. and J. Tahon, 1961
Citrullus vulgaris
    Roland, G. and J. Tahon, 1961
Citrus sinensis
    Roland, G. and J. Tahon, 1961
Cochlearia armoracia
    Roland, G. and J. Tahon, 1961
Conium maculatum
    Roland, G. and J. Tahon, 1961
Convolvulus arvensis
    Roland, G. and J. Tahon, 1961
Cucumis sativus
    Roland, G. and J. Tahon, 1961
Cuscuta americana
    Roland, G. and J. Tahon, 1961
Cuscuta epithymum
    Roland, G. and J. Tahon, 1961
Cyamopsis tetragonoloba
    Roland, G. and J. Tahon, 1961
Cyclamen persicum (Cyclamen indicum)
    Roland, G. and J. Tahon, 1961
Dahlia spp.
    Roland, G. and J. Tahon, 1961
Datura meteloides
    Roland, G. and J. Tahon, 1961
Datura stramonium
    Roland, G. and J. Tahon, 1961
Datura stramonium var. tatula
    Roland, G. and J. Tahon, 1961
Daucus carota
    Roland, G. and J. Tahon, 1961
Dianthus barbatus
    Roland, G. and J. Tahon, 1961
Dianthus caryophyllus
    Roland, G. and J. Tahon, 1961
Dianthus chinensis
    Roland, G. and J. Tahon, 1961
Dithyrea wislizenii
    Roland, G. and J. Tahon, 1961
Eclipta alba
    Roland, G. and J. Tahon, 1961

VIRUS
V. BEET YELLOWS (cont.)

Epilobium angustifolium
    Roland, G. and J. Tahon, 1961
Epilobium paniculatum
    Roland, G. and J. Tahon, 1961
Equisetum arvense
    Roland, G. and J. Tahon, 1961
Eremocarpus setigerus
    Roland, G. and J. Tahon, 1961
Erigeron canadensis
    Roland, G. and J. Tahon, 1961
Eriogonum fasciculatum
    Roland, G. and J. Tahon, 1961
Erodium cicutarium
    Roland, G. and J. Tahon, 1961
Eschscholtzia californica
    Roland, G. and J. Tahon, 1961
Euphorbia helioscopia
    Roland, G. and J. Tahon, 1961
Euphorbia maculata
    Roland, G. and J. Tahon, 1961
Euphorbia peplus
    Roland, G. and J. Tahon, 1961
Euphorbia serphyllifolia
    Roland, G. and J. Tahon, 1961
Galeopsis speciosa
    Roland, G. and J. Tahon, 1961
Galeopsis tetrahit
    Roland, G. and J. Tahon, 1961
Galinsoga parviflora
    Roland, G. and J. Tahon, 1961
Geranium dissectum
    Roland, G. and J. Tahon, 1961
Geranium maculatum
    Roland, G. and J. Tahon, 1961
Gnaphalium beneolens
    Roland, G. and J. Tahon, 1961
Gossypium hirsutum
    Roland, G. and J. Tahon, 1961
Helianthus annuus
    Roland, G. and J. Tahon, 1961
Helianthus tuberosus
    Roland, G. and J. Tahon, 1961
Helichrysum brackatum *
    Roland, G. and J. Tahon, 1961
Heliotropium curassavicum
    Roland, G. and J. Tahon, 1961
Hibiscus esculentus
    Roland, G. and J. Tahon, 1961
Hibiscus rosa-sinensis
    Roland, G. and J. Tahon, 1961
Hordeum vulgare
    Roland, G. and J. Tahon, 1961
Hyoscyamus niger
    Roland, G. and J. Tahon, 1961
Hypochoeris radicata
    Roland, G. and J. Tahon, 1961
Impatiens spp.
    Roland, G. and J. Tahon, 1961
Ipomoea purpurea
    Roland, G. and J. Tahon, 1961
Lactuca sativa
    Roland, G. and J. Tahon, 1961
Lactuca serriola
    Roland, G. and J. Tahon, 1961
Lamium album
    Roland, G. and J. Tahon, 1961
Lamium purpureum
    Roland, G. and J. Tahon, 1961
Lathyrus odoratus
    Roland, G. and J. Tahon, 1961
Lepidium lasiocarpum
    Roland, G. and J. Tahon, 1961
Linaria vulgaris
    Roland, G. and J. Tahon, 1961
Linum lewisii
    Roland, G. and J. Tahon, 1961
Linum usitatissimum
    Roland, G. and J. Tahon, 1961
Lupinus albus
    Roland, G. and J. Tahon, 1961
Lycopersicon esculentum
    Roland, G. and J. Tahon, 1961

VIRUS
V. BEET YELLOWS (cont.)
Malva parviflora
Roland, G. and J. Tahon, 1961
Malva rotundifolia
Roland, G. and J. Tahon, 1961
Malva sylvestris
Roland, G. and J. Tahon, 1961
Marrubium vulgare
Roland, G. and J. Tahon, 1961
Matricaria chamomilla
Roland, G. and J. Tahon, 1961
Matricaria discoidea
Roland, G. and J. Tahon, 1961
Matricaria inodora
Roland, G. and J. Tahon, 1961
Matthiola incana
Roland, G. and J. Tahon, 1961
Medicago lupulina
Roland, G. and J. Tahon, 1961
Medicago sativa
Roland, G. and J. Tahon, 1961
Melandryum album
Roland, G. and J. Tahon, 1961
Melandryum rubrum
Roland, G. and J. Tahon, 1961
Melilotus alba
Roland, G. and J. Tahon, 1961
Melilotus dentata
Roland, G. and J. Tahon, 1961
Mentzelia pumila
Roland, G. and J. Tahon, 1961
Mesembryanthemum aequilaterale
Roland, G. and J. Tahon, 1961
Mimulus spp.
Roland, G. and J. Tahon, 1961
Mirabilis jalapa
Roland, G. and J. Tahon, 1961
Myosotis arvensis
Roland, G. and J. Tahon, 1961
Nemesia spp.
Roland, G. and J. Tahon, 1961
Nicandra physalodes
Roland, G. and J. Tahon, 1961
Nicotiana glauca
Roland, G. and J. Tahon, 1961
Nicotiana glutinosa
Bennett, C.W. and Carlos Munck, 1946
Roland, G. and J. Tahon, 1961
Nicotiana paniculata
Roland, G. and J. Tahon, 1961
Nicotiana plumbaginifolia
Roland, G. and J. Tahon, 1961
Nicotiana rustica
Roland, G. and J. Tahon, 1961
Nicotiana stocktonii
Roland, G. and J. Tahon, 1961
Nicotiana sylvestris
Roland, G. and J. Tahon, 1961
Nicotiana tabacum
Roland, G. and J. Tahon, 1961
Oxalis corniculata
Roland, G. and J. Tahon, 1961
Papaver somniferum
Roland, G. and J. Tahon, 1961
Parthenium argentatum
Roland, G. and J. Tahon, 1961
Petroselinum crispum
Roland, G. and J. Tahon, 1961
Petunia hybrida
Roland, G. and J. Tahon, 1961
Phacelia campanularia
Roland, G. and J. Tahon, 1961
Phaseolus lunatus
Roland, G. and J. Tahon, 1961
Phaseolus vulgaris
Roland, G. and J. Tahon, 1961
Physalis wrightii
Roland, G. and J. Tahon, 1961
Phytolacca decandra
Roland, G. and J. Tahon, 1961
Pisum sativum
Roland, G. and J. Tahon, 1961

VIRUS
V. BEET YELLOWS (cont.)
Plantago coronopus
Roland, G. and J. Tahon, 1961
Poa pratensis
Roland, G. and J. Tahon, 1961
Polygonum acre
Roland, G. and J. Tahon, 1961
Polygonum argyrocoleon
Roland, G. and J. Tahon, 1961
Polygonum heterophyllum
Roland, G. and J. Tahon, 1961
Polygonum lapathifolium
Roland, G. and J. Tahon, 1961
Polygonum nodosum
Roland, G. and J. Tahon, 1961
Portulaca marginata
Roland, G. and J. Tahon, 1961
Portulaca oleracea
Roland, G. and J. Tahon, 1961
Portulaca retusa
Roland, G. and J. Tahon, 1961
Primula kewensis
Roland, G. and J. Tahon, 1961
Prunus persica (Amygdalus persica)
Roland, G. and J. Tahon, 1961
Pueraria lobata
Roland, G. and J. Tahon, 1961
Raphanus sativus
Roland, G. and J. Tahon, 1961
Rumex acetosa
Roland, G. and J. Tahon, 1961
Rumex acetosella
Roland, G. and J. Tahon, 1961
Rumex aquaticus
Roland, G. and J. Tahon, 1961
Rumex conglomeratus
Roland, G. and J. Tahon, 1961
Rumex crispus
Roland, G. and J. Tahon, 1961
Rumex domesticus
Roland, G. and J. Tahon, 1961
Rumex obtusifolius
Roland, G. and J. Tahon, 1961
Rumex persicarioides
Roland, G. and J. Tahon, 1961
Rumex pulcher
Roland, G. and J. Tahon, 1961
Saintpaulia spp.
Roland, G. and J. Tahon, 1961
Salvia splendens
Roland, G. and J. Tahon, 1961
Samolus parviflorus
Roland, G. and J. Tahon, 1961
Sanguisorba minor
Roland, G. and J. Tahon, 1961
Senecio cruentus
Roland, G. and J. Tahon, 1961
Senecio macrophyllus
Roland, G. and J. Tahon, 1961
Silene dichotoma
Roland, G. and J. Tahon, 1961
Silene nutans
Roland, G. and J. Tahon, 1961
Silene verecunda
Roland, G. and J. Tahon, 1961
Silene vulgaris
Roland, G. and J. Tahon, 1961
Sisymbrium altissimum
Roland, G. and J. Tahon, 1961
Sisymbrium irio
Roland, G. and J. Tahon, 1961
Sisymbrium officinale
Roland, G. and J. Tahon, 1961
Solanum dulcamara
Roland, G. and J. Tahon, 1961
Solanum elaeagnifolium
Roland, G. and J. Tahon, 1961
Solanum nigrum
Roland, G. and J. Tahon, 1961
Solanum tuberosum
Roland, G. and J. Tahon, 1961
Solidago virgaurea
Roland, G. and J. Tahon, 1961

VIRUS
V. BEET YELLOWS (cont.)
Sonchus arvensis
Roland, G. and J. Tahon, 1961
Sonchus asper
Roland, G. and J. Tahon, 1961
Sonchus oleraceus
Roland, G. and J. Tahon, 1961
Sorghum halepense
Roland, G. and J. Tahon, 1961
Sorghum vulgare
Roland, G. and J. Tahon, 1961
Stachys arvensis
Roland, G. and J. Tahon, 1961
Tanacetum vulgare
Roland, G. and J. Tahon, 1961
Taraxacum megalorrhizon
Roland, G. and J. Tahon, 1961
Taraxacum officinale
Roland, G. and J. Tahon, 1961
Tigridia spp.
Roland, G. and J. Tahon, 1961
Tribulus terrestris
Roland, G. and J. Tahon, 1961
Trifolium incarnatum
Roland, G. and J. Tahon, 1961
Trifolium pratense
Roland, G. and J. Tahon, 1961
Tropaeolum peregrinum
Roland, G. and J. Tahon, 1961
Tulipa silvestris
Roland, G. and J. Tahon, 1961
Tussilago farfara
Roland, G. and J. Tahon, 1961
Urtica californica
Roland, G. and J. Tahon, 1961
Urtica dioica
Roland, G. and J. Tahon, 1961
Urtica urens
Roland, G. and J. Tahon, 1961
Veronica agrestis
Roland, G. and J. Tahon, 1961
Veronica arvensis
Roland, G. and J. Tahon, 1961
Veronica hederaefolia
Roland, G. and J. Tahon, 1961
Veronica peregrina
Roland, G. and J. Tahon, 1961
Vicia faba
Roland, G. and J. Tahon, 1961
Vicia sativa
Roland, G. and J. Tahon, 1961
Vigna sinensis
Roland, G. and J. Tahon, 1961
Vinca rosea
Roland, G. and J. Tahon, 1961
Viola arvensis
Roland, G. and J. Tahon, 1961
Viola tricolor
Roland, G. and J. Tahon, 1961
Vitis spp.
Roland, G. and J. Tahon, 1961
Zea mays
Roland, G. and J. Tahon, 1961
Zinnia elegans
Roland, G. and J. Tahon, 1961
Zygocactus truncatus
Roland, G. and J. Tahon, 1961

V. BLACK RASPBERRY NECROSIS
Rosa spp.
Brierley, Philip and Floyd F. Smith, 1940

V. BROAD BEAN MOTTLE Bawden et al. 1951
Cucumis sativus
Yu, T.F., 1939
Datura stramonium
Bawden, F.C., R.P. Chaudhuri and B. Kassanis,
1951
Dolichos lablab
Yu, T.F., 1939
Glycine max
Yu, T.F., 1939

VIRUS
V. BROAD BEAN MOTTLE (cont.)
Lycopersicon esculentum
Bawden, F.C., R.P. Chaudhuri and B. Kassanis,
1951
Yu, T.F., 1939
Medicago sativa
Bawden, F.C., R.P. Chaudhuri and B. Kassanis,
1951
Nicotiana glutinosa
Bawden, F.C., R.P. Chaudhuri and B. Kassanis,
1951
Nicotiana tabacum
Bawden, F.C., R.P. Chaudhuri and B. Kassanis,
1951
Yu, T.F., 1939
Phaseolus aureus
Yu, T.F., 1939
Phaseolus vulgaris
Yu, T.F., 1939
Vicia sativa
Bawden, F.C., R.P. Chaudhuri and B. Kassanis,
1951
Vigna sinensis
Yu, T.F., 1939

V. CABBAGE BLACK RING SPOT Smith 1935 ((? A
strain of V. Turnip mosaic (q.v.).))
Ajuga reptans var. rubra
Tompkins, C.M., M.W. Gardner and H. Rex
Thomas, 1938
Althaea rosea
Tompkins, C.M., M.W. Gardner and H. Rex
Thomas, 1938
Alyssum saxatile
Tompkins, C.M., M.W. Gardner and H. Rex
Thomas, 1938
Anchusa officinalis
Tompkins, C.M., M.W. Gardner and H. Rex
Thomas, 1938
Anemone coronaria
Hollings, M., 1957
Antirrhinum majus
Tompkins, C.M., M.W. Gardner and H. Rex
Thomas, 1938
Apium graveolens
Tompkins, C.M., M.W. Gardner and H. Rex
Thomas, 1938
Arabis albida
Tompkins, C.M., M.W. Gardner and H. Rex
Thomas, 1938
Avena sativa
Tompkins, C.M., M.W. Gardner and H. Rex
Thomas, 1938
Bellis perennis
Tompkins, C.M., M.W. Gardner and H. Rex
Thomas, 1938
Beta vulgaris
Tompkins, C.M., M.W. Gardner and H. Rex
Thomas, 1938
Beta vulgaris var. cicla
Tompkins, C.M., M.W. Gardner and H. Rex
Thomas, 1938
Brassica integrifolia var. chevalieri *
Tompkins, C.M., M.W. Gardner and H. Rex
Thomas, 1938
Callistephus chinensis
Tompkins, C.M., M.W. Gardner and H. Rex
Thomas, 1938
Campanula medium
Tompkins, C.M., M.W. Gardner and H. Rex
Thomas, 1938
Chrysanthemum maximum
Tompkins, C.M., M.W. Gardner and H. Rex
Thomas, 1938
Clarkia elegans
Tompkins, C.M., M.W. Gardner and H. Rex
Thomas, 1938
Cucumis sativus
Tompkins, C.M., M.W. Gardner and H. Rex
Thomas, 1938
Datura stramonium
Tompkins, C.M., M.W. Gardner and H. Rex
Thomas, 1938

VIRUS
V. CABBAGE BLACK RING SPOT (cont.)
  Delphinium ajacis
    Tompkins, C.M., M.W. Gardner and H. Rex
    Thomas, 1938
  Delphinium cultorum
    Tompkins, C.M., M.W. Gardner and H. Rex
    Thomas, 1938
  Dianthus barbatus
    Tompkins, C.M., M.W. Gardner and H. Rex
    Thomas, 1938
  Gaillardia pulchella var. picta
    Tompkins, C.M., M.W. Gardner and H. Rex
    Thomas, 1938
  Gerbera jamesonii var. transvaalensis
    Tompkins, C.M., M.W. Gardner and H. Rex
    Thomas, 1938
  Geum chiloense
    Tompkins, C.M., M.W. Gardner and H. Rex
    Thomas, 1938
  Godetia grandiflora
    Tompkins, C.M., M.W. Gardner and H. Rex
    Thomas, 1938
  Gypsophila paniculata
    Tompkins, C.M., M.W. Gardner and H. Rex
    Thomas, 1938
  Heliotropium peruvianum
    Tompkins, C.M., M.W. Gardner and H. Rex
    Thomas, 1938
  Ipomoea purpurea
    Tompkins, C.M., M.W. Gardner and H. Rex
    Thomas, 1938
  Lactuca sativa var. capitata
    Tompkins, C.M., M.W. Gardner and H. Rex
    Thomas, 1938
  Limonium latifolium
    Tompkins, C.M., M.W. Gardner and H. Rex
    Thomas, 1938
  Lobelia hybrida
    Tompkins, C.M., M.W. Gardner and H. Rex
    Thomas, 1938
  Lycopersicon esculentum var. vulgare
    Tompkins, C.M., M.W. Gardner and H. Rex
    Thomas, 1938
  Lycopersicon pimpinellifolium
    Tompkins, C.M., M.W. Gardner and H. Rex
    Thomas, 1938
  Malva parviflora
    Tompkins, C.M., M.W. Gardner and H. Rex
    Thomas, 1938
  Medicago sativa
    Tompkins, C.M., M.W. Gardner and H. Rex
    Thomas, 1938
  Nicotiana rustica var. humulis *
    Tompkins, C.M., M.W. Gardner and H. Rex
    Thomas, 1938
  Papaver orientale
    Tompkins, C.M., M.W. Gardner and H. Rex
    Thomas, 1938
  Pelargonium hortorum
    Tompkins, C.M., M.W. Gardner and H. Rex
    Thomas, 1938
  Penstemon barbatus
    Tompkins, C.M., M.W. Gardner and H. Rex
    Thomas, 1938
  Pisum sativum
    Tompkins, C.M., M.W. Gardner and H. Rex
    Thomas, 1938
  Raphanus sativus
    Tompkins, C.M., M.W. Gardner and H. Rex
    Thomas, 1938
  Ricinus communis
    Tompkins, C.M., M.W. Gardner and H. Rex
    Thomas, 1938
  Salvia farinacea
    Tompkins, C.M., M.W. Gardner and H. Rex
    Thomas, 1938
  Solanum aviculare
    Tompkins, C.M., M.W. Gardner and H. Rex
    Thomas, 1938
  Solanum melongena var. esculentum
    Tompkins, C.M., M.W. Gardner and H. Rex
    Thomas, 1938

VIRUS
V. CABBAGE BLACK RING SPOT (cont.)
  Solanum tuberosum
    Tompkins, C.M., M.W. Gardner and H. Rex
    Thomas, 1938
  Tagetes patula
    Tompkins, C.M., M.W. Gardner and H. Rex
    Thomas, 1938
  Taraxacum officinale
    Tompkins, C.M., M.W. Gardner and H. Rex
    Thomas, 1938
  Tropaeolum majus
    Tompkins, C.M., M.W. Gardner and H. Rex
    Thomas, 1938
  Valeriana officinalis
    Tompkins, C.M., M.W. Gardner and H. Rex
    Thomas, 1938
  Vicia faba
    Tompkins, C.M., M.W. Gardner and H. Rex
    Thomas, 1938
  Viola tricolor
    Tompkins, C.M., M.W. Gardner and H. Rex
    Thomas, 1938
  Zea mays
    Tompkins, C.M., M.W. Gardner and H. Rex
    Thomas, 1938

V. CABBAGE RING NECROSIS Larson and Walker 1941
  Antirrhinum majus
    Larson, R.H. and J.C. Walker, 1941
  Apium graveolens
    Larson, R.H. and J.C. Walker, 1941
  Callistephus chinensis
    Larson, R.H. and J.C. Walker, 1941
  Chenopodium album
    Larson, R.H. and J.C. Walker, 1941
  Citrullus vulgaris
    Larson, R.H. and J.C. Walker, 1941
  Cucumis melo
    Larson, R.H. and J.C. Walker, 1941
  Datura stramonium
    Larson, R.H. and J.C. Walker, 1941
  Lycopersicon esculentum
    Larson, R.H. and J.C. Walker, 1941
  Lycopersicon pimpinellifolium
    Larson, R.H. and J.C. Walker, 1941
  Nicotiana longiflora
    Larson, R.H. and J.C. Walker, 1941
  Nicotiana nudicaulis
    Larson, R.H. and J.C. Walker, 1941
  Nicotiana sanderae
    Larson, R.H. and J.C. Walker, 1941
  Senecio cruentus
    Larson, R.H. and J.C. Walker, 1941
  Solanum melongena
    Larson, R.H. and J.C. Walker, 1941
  Solanum nigrum
    Larson, R.H. and J.C. Walker, 1941
  Solanum tuberosum
    Larson, R.H. and J.C. Walker, 1941
  Tagetes patula
    Larson, R.H. and J.C. Walker, 1941
  Taraxacum officinale
    Larson, R.H. and J.C. Walker, 1941
  Tropaeolum majus
    Larson, R.H. and J.C. Walker, 1941
  Vicia faba
    Larson, R.H. and J.C. Walker, 1941
  Viola tricolor
    Larson, R.H. and J.C. Walker, 1941

V. CACAO SWOLLEN SHOOT (((W.F. Stevens) 1937))
  Abutilon asiaticum   Posnette 1940
    Tinsley, T.W. and A.L. Wharton, 1958
  Alstonia congensis
    Posnette, A.F., N.F. Robertson and J. McA.
    Todd, 1950
  Ananas sativus
    Tinsley, T.W. and A.L. Wharton, 1958
  Apeiba tibourbou var. membranacea *
    Tinsley, T.W. and A.L. Wharton, 1958
  Arachis hypogaea
    Tinsley, T.W. and A.L. Wharton, 1958

VIRUS
V. CACAO SWOLLEN SHOOT (cont.)

Artocarpus incisa
Posnette, A.F., N.F. Robertson and J. McA.
Todd, 1950

Baphia nitida
Tinsley, T.W. and A.L. Wharton, 1958

Berrya ammonilla
Tinsley, T.W. and A.L. Wharton, 1958

Bixa orellana
Tinsley, T.W. and A.L. Wharton, 1958

Bombax buonopozense
Posnette, A.F., N.F. Robertson and J. McA.
Todd, 1950
Tinsley, T.W. and A.L. Wharton, 1958

Buettneria catalpifolia
Tinsley, T.W. and A.L. Wharton, 1958

Caesalpinia pulcherrima
Tinsley, T.W. and A.L. Wharton, 1958

Canthium glabriflorum
Posnette, A.F., N.F. Robertson and J. McA.
Todd, 1950

Capsicum frutescens (Capsicum annuum)
Tinsley, T.W. and A.L. Wharton, 1958

Carica papaya
Posnette, A.F., N.F. Robertson and J. McA.
Todd, 1950

Cassia occidentalis
Tinsley, T.W. and A.L. Wharton, 1958

Ceiba pentandra
Tinsley, T.W. and A.L. Wharton, 1958

Christiana africana
Tinsley, T.W. and A.L. Wharton, 1958

Cistanthera papaverifera
Posnette, A.F., N.F. Robertson and J. McA.
Todd, 1950

Citrus aurantifolia
Tinsley, T.W. and A.L. Wharton, 1958

Citrus sinensis
Tinsley, T.W. and A.L. Wharton, 1958

Clappertonia ficifolia
Tinsley, T.W. and A.L. Wharton, 1958

Cochlospermum vitifolia
Tinsley, T.W. and A.L. Wharton, 1958

Cola caricaefolia *
Tinsley, T.W. and A.L. Wharton, 1958

Cola chlamydantha
Posnette, A.F., N.F. Robertson and J. McA.
Todd, 1950
Tinsley, T.W. and A.L. Wharton, 1958

Cola gigantea var. glabrescens *
Tinsley, T.W. and A.L. Wharton, 1958

Cola heterophylla
Tinsley, T.W. and A.L. Wharton, 1958

Cola lateritia var. maclaudi *
Tinsley, T.W. and A.L. Wharton, 1958

Cola millenii (Cola togoensis)
Tinsley, T.W. and A.L. Wharton, 1958

Cola nitida
Posnette, A.F., N.F. Robertson and J.McA.
Todd, 1950
Tinsley, T.W. and A.L. Wharton, 1958

Cola togoensis
Posnette, A.F., N.F. Robertson and J. McA.
Todd, 1950

Cola umbratilis *
Tinsley, T.W. and A.L. Wharton, 1958

Cola verticillata
Posnette, A.F., N.F. Robertson and J. McA.
Todd, 1950
Tinsley, T.W. and A.L. Wharton, 1958

Cucumis sativus
Tinsley, T.W. and A.L. Wharton, 1958

Datura stramonium
Tinsley, T.W. and A.L. Wharton, 1958

Desplatsia dewevrei *
Tinsley, T.W. and A.L. Wharton, 1958

Desplatzia lutea
Posnette, A.F., N.F. Robertson and J. McA.
Todd, 1950

Dombeya buettneri
Tinsley, T.W. and A.L. Wharton, 1958

Elaeis guineensis
Tinsley, T.W. and A.L. Wharton, 1958

VIRUS
V. CACAO SWOLLEN SHOOT (cont.)

Elaeophorbia drupifera
Tinsley, T.W. and A.L. Wharton, 1958

Erythropsis barteri
Posnette, A.F., N.F. Robertson and J. McA.
Todd, 1950

Ficus exasperata
Posnette, A.F., N.F. Robertson and J. McA.
Todd, 1950

Funtumia elastica
Posnette, A.F., N.F. Robertson and J. McA.
Todd, 1950

Glycine soya
Tinsley, T.W. and A.L. Wharton, 1958

Glyphaea brevis
Tinsley, T.W. and A.L. Wharton, 1958

Gossypium hirsutum
Posnette, A.F., N.F. Robertson and J. McA.
Todd, 1950

Grewia similis
Tinsley, T.W. and A.L. Wharton, 1958

Gauzuma ulmifolia
Tinsley, T.W. and A.L. Wharton, 1958

Harpullia pendula
Tinsley, T.W. and A.L. Wharton, 1958

Hermannia candicans var. discolor *
Tinsley, T.W. and A.L. Wharton, 1958

Herrania balaensis
Tinsley, T.W. and A.L. Wharton, 1958

Herrania spp.
Tinsley, T.W. and A.L. Wharton, 1958

Hevea brasilensis (Siphonia ridleyana)
Tinsley, T.W. and A.L. Wharton, 1958

Hibiscus esculentus
Tinsley, T.W. and A.L. Wharton, 1958

Kleinhovia hospita
Tinsley, T.W. and A.L. Wharton, 1958

Leptonychia pubescens
Tinsley, T.W. and A.L. Wharton, 1958

Manihot esculenta (Manihot utilissima)
Tinsley, T.W. and A.L. Wharton, 1958

Manihot glaziovii
Tinsley, T.W. and A.L. Wharton, 1958

Mansonia altissima
Tinsley, T.W. and A.L. Wharton, 1958

Melochia melissaefolia
Tinsley, T.W. and A.L. Wharton, 1958

Melochia pyramidata
Tinsley, T.W. and A.L. Wharton, 1958

Millettia thonningii
Tinsley, T.W. and A.L. Wharton, 1958

Nesogordonia papaverifera
Tinsley, T.W. and A.L. Wharton, 1958

Nicotiana glutinosa
Tinsley, T.W. and A.L. Wharton, 1958

Nicotiana tabacum
Tinsley, T.W. and A.L. Wharton, 1958

Ochroma lagopus (Ochroma pyramidale)
Tinsley, T.W. and A.L. Wharton, 1958

Octolobus angustatus
Tinsley, T.W. and A.L. Wharton, 1958

Omphalocarpum procerum
Tinsley, T.W. and A.L. Wharton, 1958

Pachira oleagina
Tinsley, T.W. and A.L. Wharton, 1958

Pelargonium domesticum
Tinsley, T.W. and A.L. Wharton, 1953

Persea americana
Tinsley, T.W. and A.L. Wharton, 1958

Phaseolus lunatus
Tinsley, T.W. and A.L. Wharton, 1958

Phaseolus vulgaris
Tinsley, T.W. and A.L. Wharton, 1958

Pterygota macrocarpa
Posnette, A.F., N.F. Robertson and J. McA.
Todd, 1950
Tinsley, T.W. and A.L. Wharton, 1958

Pycnanthus kombo
Posnette, A.F., N.F. Robertson and J. McA.
Todd, 1950

Ricinodendron africanus
Posnette, A.F., N.F. Robertson and J. McA.
Todd, 1950

VIRUS

V. CACAO SWOLLEN SHOOT (cont.)
Ricinodendron heudelotii
Tinsley, T.W. and A.L. Wharton, 1958
Scaphopetalum amoenum
Tinsley, T.W. and A.L. Wharton, 1958
Scytopetalum tieghemii
Tinsley, T.W. and A.L. Wharton, 1958
Sterculia foetida
Tinsley, T.W. and A.L. Wharton, 1958
Sterculia oblonga
Tinsley, T.W. and A.L. Wharton, 1958
Sterculia rhinopetala
Posnette, A.F., N.F. Robertson and J.McA.
Todd, 1950
Tinsley, T.W. and A.L. Wharton, 1958
Sterculia tragacantha
Posnette, A.F., N.F. Robertson and J. McA.
Todd, 1950
Tinsley, T.W. and A.L. Wharton, 1958
Tarrietia utilis *
Tinsley, T.W. and A.L. Wharton, 1958
Theobroma angustifolia
Tinsley, T.W. and A.L. Wharton, 1958
Theobroma balaoense *
Posnette, A.F. and J.McA. Todd, 1951
Theobroma bicolor
Tinsley, T.W. and A.L. Wharton, 1958
Theobroma grandiflorum
Tinsley, T.W. and A.L. Wharton, 1958
Theobroma mariae
Posnette, A.F. and J. McA. Todd, 1951
Theobroma obovata
Tinsley, T.W. and A.L. Wharton, 1958
Theobroma speciosa
Tinsley, T.W. and A.L. Wharton, 1958
Thespesia lampas *
Posnette, A.F., N.F. Robertson and J. McA.
Todd, 1950
Thespesia populnea *
Tinsley, T.W. and A.L. Wharton, 1958
Tilia platyphyllos
Tinsley, T.W. and A.L. Wharton, 1958
Trema guineensis
Tinsley, T.W. and A.L. Wharton, 1958
Triplochiton scleroxylon *
Posnette, A.F., N.F. Robertson and J. McA.
Todd, 1950
Tinsley, T.W. and A.L. Wharton, 1958
Urena lobata
Tinsley, T.W. and A.L. Wharton, 1958
Vigna sinensis
Tinsley, T.W. and A.L. Wharton, 1958
Waltheria indica
Tinsley, T.W. and A.L. Wharton, 1958
Waltheria lanceolata
Tinsley, T.W. and A.L. Wharton, 1958
Xanthosoma sagittaefolium
Posnette, A.F., N.F. Robertson and J. McA.
Todd, 1950

V. CANNA MOSAIC Fukushi 1932
Cucumis melo
Castillo, B.S., C.E. Yarwood and A.H. Gold, 1956
Cucumis sativus
Brierley, Philip and Floyd F. Smith, 1948
Castillo, B.S., C.E. Yarwood and A.H. Gold, 1956
Celino, M.S. and G.O. Ocfemia, 1941
Gossypium hirsutum
Castillo, B.S., C.E. Yarwood and A.H. Gold, 1956
Gossypium spp.
Celino, M.S. and G.O. Ocfemia, 1941
Hedychium coronarium
Brierley, Philip and Floyd F. Smith, 1948
Lycopersicon esculentum
Castillo, B.S., C.E. Yarwood and A.H. Gold, 1956
Maranta arundinaceae
Castillo, B.S., C.E. Yarwood and A.H. Gold, 1956
Musa cavendishii
Brierley, Philip and Floyd F. Smith, 1948
Musa ensete
Castillo, B.S., C.E. Yarwood and A.H. Gold, 1956
Musa textilis
Brierley, Philip and Floyd F. Smith, 1948

VIRUS

V. CANNA MOSAIC (cont.)
Nicotiana tabacum
Castillo, B.S., C.E. Yarwood and A.H. Gold, 1956
Phaseolus limensis
Castillo, B.S., C.E. Yarwood and A.H. Gold, 1956
Vicia faba
Brierley, Philip and Floyd F. Smith, 1948
Castillo, B.S., C.E. Yarwood and A.H. Gold, 1956
Vigna sinensis
Castillo, B.S., C.E. Yarwood and A.H. Gold, 1956

V. CARNATION MOSAIC Creager 1943
Callistephus chinensis
Brierley, Philip and Floyd F. Smith, 1955, 1957
Cucumis sativus
Brierley, Philip and Floyd F. Smith, 1955, 1957
Gomphrena globosa
Brierley, Philip and Floyd F. Smith, 1955
Nicotiana tabacum
Brierley, Philip and Floyd F. Smith, 1955, 1957
Phaseolus vulgaris
Brierley, Philip and Floyd F. Smith, 1955, 1957

V. CARNATION MOTTLE Kassanis 1955
Beta vulgaris
Brierley, Philip and Floyd F. Smith, 1957
Callistephus chinensis
Brierley, Philip and Floyd F. Smith, 1957
Nicotiana tabacum
Brierley, Philip and Floyd F. Smith, 1957
Kassanis, B., 1955
Phaseolus vulgaris
Brierley, Philip and Floyd F. Smith, 1957
Kassanis, B., 1955

V. CARNATION VEIN MOTTLE Kassanis 1955
Gomphrena globosa
Kassanis, B., 1955
Nicotiana tabacum
Kassanis, B., 1955
Phaseolus vulgaris
Kassanis, B., 1955

V. CAULIFLOWER MOSAIC Tompkins 1934
Abutilon theophrasti
Walker, J.C., Francis J. LeBeau and Glenn S.
Pound, 1945
Alyssum maritimum
Caldwell, John and Ian W. Prentice, 1942
Tompkins, C.M., 1937
Alyssum saxatile
Tompkins, C.M., 1937
Alyssum saxatile var. compactum
Caldwell, John and Ian W. Prentice, 1942
Amaranthus tricolor
Walker, J.C., Francis J. LeBeau and Glenn S.
Pound, 1945
Apium graveolens
Alvarez-Garcia, L.A., 1951
Tompkins, C.M., 1937
Arabis albida
Tompkins, C.M., 1937
Athysanus pusillus
Tompkins, C.M., 1937
Atropa belladonna
Walker, J.C., Francis J. LeBeau and Glenn S.
Pound, 1945
Barbarea vulgaris
Walker, J.C., Francis J. LeBeau and Glenn S.
Pound, 1945
Berteroa incana
Walker, J.C., Francis J. LeBeau and Glenn S.
Pound, 1945
Beta vulgaris
Alvarez-Garcia, L.A., 1951
Berkeley, G.H. and J.H. Tremaine, 1954
Walker, J.C., Francis J. LeBeau and Glenn S.
Pound, 1945
Beta vulgaris var. cicla
Alvarez-Garcia, L.A., 1951
Berkeley, G.H. and J.H. Tremaine, 1954
Walker, J.C., Francis J. LeBeau and Glenn S.
Pound, 1945

VIRUS
V. CAULIFLOWER MOSAIC (cont.)

Brassica juncea (Brassica japonica)
   Tompkins, C.M., 1937

Brassica oleracea var. botrytis
   Berkeley, G.H. and J.H. Tremaine, 1954

Brassica rapa
   Caldwell, John and Ian W. Prentice, 1942

Calendula officinalis
   Walker, J.C., Francis J. LeBeau and Glenn S.
   Pound, 1945

Capsella bursa-pastoris
   Caldwell, John and Ian W. Prentice, 1942

Capsicum frutescens (Capsicum annuum)
   Alvarez-Garcia, L.A., 1951

Capsicum frutescens var. cerasiforme
   Walker, J.C., Francis J. LeBeau and Glenn S.
   Pound, 1945

Capsicum frutescens var. grossum
   Tompkins, C.M., 1937

Cardamine hirsuta
   Caldwell, John and Ian W. Prentice, 1942

Cardamine pratensis
   Caldwell, John and Ian W. Prentice, 1942

Celosia argentea var. cristata
   Walker, J.C., Francis J. LeBeau and Glenn S.
   Pound, 1945

Centaurea moschata
   Walker, J.C., Francis J. LeBeau and Glenn S.
   Pound, 1945

Centaurea nigra
   Walker, J.C., Francis J. LeBeau and Glenn S.
   Pound, 1945

Cheiranthus allionii
   Caldwell, John and Ian W. Prentice, 1942

Cheiranthus cheiri
   Caldwell, John and Ian W. Prentice, 1942
   Tompkins, C.M., 1937

Chenopodium album
   Walker, J.C., Francis J. LeBeau and Glenn S.
   Pound, 1945

Cucumis sativus
   Alvarez-Garcia, L.A., 1951

Datura metel
   Walker, J.C., Francis J. LeBeau and Glenn S.
   Pound, 1945

Datura meteloides
   Walker, J.C., Francis J. LeBeau and Glenn S.
   Pound, 1945

Datura stramonium
   Alvarez-Garcia, L.A., 1951
   Walker, J.C., Francis J. LeBeau and Glenn S.
   Pound, 1945

Delphinium ajacis
   Walker, J.C., Francis J. LeBeau and Glenn S.
   Pound, 1945

Digitalis purpurea
   Walker, J.C., Francis J. LeBeau and Glenn S.
   Pound, 1945

Dimorphotheca aurantiaca
   Walker, J.C., Francis J. LeBeau and Glenn S.
   Pound, 1945

Dolichos lablab
   Walker, J.C., Francis J. LeBeau and Glenn S.
   Pound, 1945

Erysimum perofskianum
   Tompkins, C.M., 1937

Erysimum spp.
   Caldwell, John and Ian W. Prentice, 1942

Glycine max
   Walker, J.C., Francis J. LeBeau and Glenn S.
   Pound, 1945

Godetia amoena
   Walker, J.C., Francis J. LeBeau and Glenn S.
   Pound, 1945

Gomphrena globosa
   Alvarez-Garcia, L.A., 1951
   Berkeley, G.H. and J.H. Tremaine, 1954

Hesperis matronalis
   Berkeley, G.H. and J.H. Tremaine, 1954
   Tompkins, C.M., 1937
   Walker, J.C., Francis J. LeBeau and Glenn S.
   Pound, 1945

VIRUS
V. CAULIFLOWER MOSAIC (cont.)

Hesperis spp.
   Caldwell, John and Ian W. Prentice, 1942

Hibiscus esculentus
   Walker, J.C., Francis J. LeBeau and Glenn S.
   Pound, 1945

Iberis amara
   Caldwell, John and Ian W. Prentice, 1942

Ipomoea purpurea
   Walker, J.C., Francis J. LeBeau and Glenn S.
   Pound, 1945

Isatis glauca
   Caldwell, John and Ian W. Prentice, 1942

Lactuca sativa
   Alvarez-Garcia, L.A., 1951

Lactuca sativa var. capitata
   Tompkins, C.M., 1937

Lactuca sativa var. romana
   Tompkins, C.M., 1937

Lycium halimifolium
   Walker, J.C., Francis J. LeBeau and Glenn S.
   Pound, 1945

Lycopersicon esculentum
   Alvarez-Garcia, L.A., 1951
   Caldwell, John and Ian W. Prentice, 1942

Lycopersicon esculentum var. vulgare
   Tompkins, C.M., 1937

Lycopersicon pimpinellifolium
   Tompkins, C.M., 1937

Malcomia maritima
   Caldwell, John and Ian W. Prentice, 1942
   Tompkins, C.M., 1937
   Walker, J.C., Francis J. LeBeau and Glenn S.
   Pound, 1945

Matthiola incana var. annua
   Caldwell, John and Ian W. Prentice, 1942

Medicago sativa
   Alvarez-Garcia, L.A., 1951

Mirabilis jalapa
   Walker, J.C., Francis J. LeBeau and Glenn S.
   Pound, 1945

Nasturtium officinale
   Caldwell, John and Ian W. Prentice, 1942

Nasturtium palustre
   Caldwell, John and Ian W. Prentice, 1942

Nicandra physalodes
   Walker, J.C., Francis J. LeBeau and Glenn S.
   Pound, 1945

Nicotiana acuminata
   Walker, J.C., Francis J. LeBeau and Glenn S.
   Pound, 1945

Nicotiana affinis
   Caldwell, John and Ian W. Prentice, 1942

Nicotiana alata var. grandiflora
   Walker, J.C., Francis J. LeBeau and Glenn S.
   Pound, 1945

Nicotiana glutinosa
   Alvarez-Garcia, L.A., 1951
   Berkeley, G.H. and J.H. Tremaine, 1954
   Caldwell, John and Ian W. Prentice, 1942
   Smith, Kenneth M., 1935
   Tompkins, C.M., 1937
   Walker, J.C., Francis J. LeBeau and Glenn S.
   Pound, 1945

Nicotiana langsdorffii
   Alvarez-Garcia, L.A., 1951
   Tompkins, C.M., 1937

Nicotiana longiflora
   Walker, J.C., Francis J. LeBeau and Glenn S.
   Pound, 1945

Nicotiana multivalvis
   Walker, J.C., Francis J. LeBeau and Glenn S.
   Pound, 1945

Nicotiana nudicaulis
   Walker, J.C., Francis J. LeBeau and Glenn S.
   Pound, 1945

Nicotiana paniculata
   Walker, J.C., Francis J. LeBeau and Glenn S.
   Pound, 1945

Nicotiana quadrivalvis
   Walker, J.C., Francis J. LeBeau and Glenn S.
   Pound, 1945

VIRUS

V. CAULIFLOWER MOSAIC (cont.)

Nicotiana rustica
  Alvarez-Garcia, L.A., 1951
  Walker, J.C., Francis J. LeBeau and Glenn S.
  Pound, 1945
Nicotiana rustica var. jamaicensis *
  Caldwell, John and Ian W. Prentice, 1942
Nicotiana sanderae
  Walker, J.C., Francis J. LeBeau and Glenn S.
  Pound, 1945
Nicotiana sylvestris
  Walker, J.C., Francis J. LeBeau and Glenn S.
  Pound, 1945
Nicotiana tabacum
  Alvarez-Garcia, L.A., 1951
  Berkeley, G.H. and J.H. Tremaine, 1954
  Caldwell, John and Ian W. Prentice, 1942
  Tompkins, C.M., 1937
  Walker, J.C., Francis J. LeBeau and Glenn S.
  Pound, 1945
Nicotiana trigonophylla
  Walker, J.C., Francis J. LeBeau and Glenn S.
  Pound, 1945
Petunia hybrida
  Berkeley, G.H. and J.H. Tremaine, 1954
Phaseolus coccineus
  Walker, J.C., Francis J. LeBeau and Glenn S.
  Pound, 1945
Phaseolus vulgaris
  Alvarez-Garcia, L.A., 1951
Physalis pubescens
  Walker, J.C., Francis J. LeBeau and Glenn S.
  Pound, 1945
Physalis spp.
  Alvarez-Garcia, L.A., 1951
Pisum sativum
  Alvarez-Garcia, L.A., 1951
Portulaca spp.
  Alvarez-Garcia, L.A., 1951
Reseda odorata
  Walker, J.C., Francis J. LeBeau and Glenn S.
  Pound, 1945
Rorippa nasturtium
  Tompkins, C.M., 1937
Salpiglossis sinuata
  Walker, J.C., Francis J. LeBeau and Glenn S.
  Pound, 1945
Scabiosa atropurpurea
  Walker, J.C., Francis J. LeBeau and Glenn S.
  Pound, 1945
Senecio cruentus
  Walker, J.C., Francis J. LeBeau and Glenn S.
  Pound, 1945
Sisymbrium alliaria
  Caldwell, John and Ian W. Prentice, 1942
Solanum dulcamara
  Walker, J.C., Francis J. LeBeau and Glenn S.
  Pound, 1945
Solanum integrifolium
  Alvarez-Garcia, L.A., 1951
  Walker, J.C., Francis J. LeBeau and Glenn S.
  Pound, 1945
Solanum melongena
  Alvarez-Garcia, L.A., 1951
Solanum nigrum
  Alvarez-Garcia, L.A., 1951
Solanum pseudocapsicum
  Walker, J.C., Francis J. LeBeau and Glenn S.
  Pound, 1945
Solanum rostratum
  Walker, J.C., Francis J. LeBeau and Glenn S.
  Pound, 1945
Spinacia oleracea
  Alvarez-Garcia, L.A., 1951
  Berkeley, G.H. and J.H. Tremaine, 1954
  Tompkins, C.M., 1937
  Walker, J.C., Francis J. LeBeau and Glenn S.
  Pound, 1945
Stanleya pinnata
  Tompkins, C.M., 1937
Stellaria media
  Walker, J.C., Francis J. LeBeau and Glenn S.
  Pound, 1945

VIRUS

V. CAULIFLOWER MOSAIC (cont.)

Tagetes patula
  Walker, J.C., Francis J. LeBeau and Glenn S.
  Pound, 1945
Thlaspi arvense
  Caldwell, John and Ian W. Prentice, 1942
Thysanocarpus radians
  Tompkins, C.M., 1937
Tropaeolum majus
  Tompkins, C.M., 1937
Verbena hybrida
  Walker, J.C., Francis J. LeBeau and Glenn S.
  Pound, 1945
Vicia faba
  Tompkins, C.M., 1937
Vigna sinensis
  Alvarez-Garcia, L.A., 1951
  Walker, J.C., Francis J. LeBeau and Glenn S.
  Pound, 1945
Vinca minor
  Walker, J.C., Francis J. LeBeau and Glenn S.
  Pound, 1945
Zinnia elegans
  Alvarez-Garcia, L.A., 1951
  Berkeley, G.H. and J.H. Tremaine, 1954

V. CELERY MOSAIC   Holmes   1939

Beta vulgaris
  Freitag, Julius H. and Henry H.P. Severin, 1945
Bidens leucantha
  Doolittle, S.P. and F.L. Wellman, 1934
Brassica oleracea var. botrytis
  Freitag, Julius H. and Henry H.P. Severin, 1945
Calendula officinalis
  Freitag, Julius H. and Henry H.P. Severin, 1945
Capsicum frutescens var. grossum
  Freitag, Julius H. and Henry H.P. Severin, 1945
Cichorium intybus
  Freitag, Julius H. and Henry H.P. Severin, 1945
Conium maculatum
  Freitag, Julius H. and Henry H.P. Severin, 1945
Cucumis sativus
  Freitag, Julius H. and Henry H.P. Severin, 1945
  Severin, Henry H.P. and Julius H. Freitag, 1938
Cucurbita pepo
  Freitag, Julius H. and Henry H.P. Severin, 1945
Datura stramonium
  Freitag, Julius H. and Henry H.P. Severin, 1945
Dimorphotheca aurantiaca
  Freitag, Julius H. and Henry H.P. Severin, 1945
Heracleum maximum (Heracleum lanatum)
  Freitag, Julius H. and Henry H.P. Severin, 1945
Lactuca sativa var. capitata
  Freitag, Julius H. and Henry H.P. Severin, 1945
Lycopersicon esculentum var. commune *
  Freitag, Julius H. and Henry H.P. Severin, 1945
Nicotiana glutinosa
  Freitag, Julius H. and Henry H.P. Severin, 1945
Nicotiana tabacum
  Freitag, Julius H. and Henry H.P. Severin, 1945
Parthenium argentatum
  Severin, Henry H.P., 1945
Solanum melongena var. esculentum
  Freitag, Julius H. and Henry H.P. Severin, 1945
Solanum tuberosum
  Freitag, Julius H. and Henry H.P. Severin, 1945
Spinacia oleracea var. inermis *
  Freitag, Julius H. and Henry H.P. Severin, 1945
Zinnia elegans
  Freitag, Julius H. and Henry H.P. Severin, 1945

V. CHERRY FRECKLE FRUIT DISEASE *

Prunus armeniaca
  Williams, H.E. and J.A. Milbrath, 1955
Prunus persica (Amygdalus persica)
  Williams, H.E. and J.A. Milbrath, 1955

V. CHERRY LITTLE CHERRY   Foster and Lott   1947

Prunus demissa
  Wilks, Jack M. and J.A. Milbrath, 1956
Prunus persica (Amygdalus persica)
  Milbrath, J.A. and H.E. Williams, 1956

VIRUS
V. CHERRY RUGOSE MOSAIC Thomas and Rawlins 1951
  Prunus domestica
    Berkeley, G.H. , 1950

V. CHILLI (PEPPER) MOSAIC Ferguson 1951
  Apium graveolens
    Dale, W.T. , 1954
  Beta vulgaris
    Jha, Ashrafi and S.P. Raychaudhuri, 1956
  Brassica campestris var. toria *
    Jha, Ashrafi and S.P. Raychaudhuri, 1956
  Brassica oleracea var. botrytis
    Jha, Ashrafi and S.P. Raychaudhuri, 1956
  Brassica oleracea var. capitata
    Jha, Ashrafi and S.P. Raychaudhuri, 1956
  Brassica oleracea var. caulorapa
    Jha, Ashrafi and S.P. Raychaudhuri, 1956
  Brassica rapa
    Jha, Ashrafi and S.P. Raychaudhuri, 1956
  Cajanus cajan
    Jha, Ashrafi and S.P. Raychaudhuri, 1956
  Calendula officinalis
    Jha, Ashrafi and S.P. Raychaudhuri, 1956
  Callistephus chinensis
    Jha, Ashrafi and S.P. Raychaudhuri, 1956
  Chenopodium hybridum
    Dale, W.T. , 1954
  Chrysanthemum morifolium
    Jha, Ashrafi and S.P. Raychaudhuri, 1956
  Cicer arientinum
    Jha, Ashrafi and S.P. Raychaudhuri, 1956
  Citrullus vulgaris
    Jha, Ashrafi and S.P. Raychaudhuri, 1956
  Citrullus vulgaris var. fistulosus *
    Jha, Ashrafi and S.P. Raychaudhuri, 1956
  Citrus limon
    Jha, Ashrafi and S.P. Raychaudhuri, 1956
  Crotalaria juncea
    Jha, Ashrafi and S.P. Raychaudhuri, 1956
  Crotalaria mucronata
    Jha, Ashrafi and S.P. Raychaudhuri, 1956
  Cucumis melo
    Jha, Ashrafi and S.P. Raychaudhuri, 1956
  Cucumis sativus
    Dale, W.T. , 1954
  Cucurbita pepo
    Dale, W.T. , 1954
  Cyamopsis tetragonoloba
    Jha, Ashrafi and S.P. Raychaudhuri, 1956
  Daucus carota
    Jha, Ashrafi and S.P. Raychaudhuri, 1956
  Dolichos lablab
    Jha, Ashrafi and S.P. Raychaudhuri, 1956
  Gossypium arboreum
    Jha, Ashrafi and S.P. Raychaudhuri, 1956
  Hibiscus rosa-sinensis
    Jha, Ashrafi and S.P. Raychaudhuri, 1956
  Lagenaria siceraria (Lagenaria leucantha)
    Jha, Ashrafi and S.P. Raychaudhuri, 1956
  Lycopersicon esculentum
    Dale, W.T. , 1954
    Ferguson, I.A.C. , 1951
    Jha, Ashrafi and S.P. Raychaudhuri, 1956
  Medicago sativa
    Jha, Ashrafi and S.P. Raychaudhuri, 1956
  Momordica charantia
    Jha, Ashrafi and S.P. Raychaudhuri, 1956
  Nicotiana glauca
    Adsuar, J. and L. Lopez Matos, 1955
  Nicotiana glutinosa
    Ferguson, I.A.C. , 1951
  Nicotiana rustica
    Ferguson, I.A.C. , 1951
  Nicotiana sylvestris
    Ferguson, I.A.C. , 1951
  Phaseolus vulgaris
    Dale, W.T. , 1954
  Pisum sativum
    Jha, Ashrafi and S.P. Raychaudhuri, 1956
  Psidium guajava
    Jha, Ashrafi and S.P. Raychaudhuri, 1956
  Raphanus sativus
    Jha, Ashrafi and S.P. Raychaudhuri, 1956

VIRUS
V. CHILLI (PEPPER MOSAIC (cont.)
  Solanum melongena
    Dale, W.T. , 1954
    Ferguson, I.A.C. , 1951
    Jha, Ashrafi and S.P. Raychaudhuri, 1956
  Solanum nodiflorum
    Jha, Ashrafi and S.P. Raychaudhuri, 1956
  Solanum tuberosum
    Jha, Ashrafi and S.P. Raychaudhuri, 1956
  Tagetes erecta
    Jha, Ashrafi and S.P. Raychaudhuri, 1956
  Trifolium alexandrium
    Jha, Ashrafi and S.P. Raychaudhuri, 1956
  Vicia faba
    Jha, Ashrafi and S.P. Raychaudhuri, 1956
  Vigna unguiculata
    Dale, W.T. , 1954
    Ferguson, I.A.C. , 1951
  Vinca rosea
    Jha, Ashrafi and S.P. Raychaudhuri, 1956
  Zinnia elegans
    Dale, W.T. , 1954
    Jha, Ashrafi and S.P. Raychaudhuri, 1956

V. CHILLI VEINBANDING Simon 1956
  Amaranthus spinosus
    Simons, John N. , 1956
  Apium graveolens var. dulce
    Simons, John N. , 1956
  Beta vulgaris var. cicla
    Simons, John N. , 1956
  Brassica oleracea
    Simons, John N. , 1956
  Commelina spp.
    Simons, John N. , 1956
  Cucumis sativus
    Simons, John N. , 1956
  Cucurbita pepo var. melopepo
    Simons, John N. , 1956
  Datura stramonium
    Simons, John N. , 1956
  Medicago sativa
    Simons, John N. , 1956
  Vigna sinensis
    Simons, John N. , 1956

V. CHRYSANTHEMUM B (MILD MOSAIC) *
  Ageratum conyzioides
    Hollings, M. , 1957
  Alonsoa warscewiczii
    Hollings, M. , 1957
  Amaranthus caudatus
    Hollings, M. , 1957
  Anchusa azurea
    Hollings, M. , 1957
  Antirrhinum majus
    Hollings, M. , 1957
  Apium graveolens
    Hollings, M. , 1957
  Aquilegia caerulea
    Hollings, M. , 1957
  Beta vulgaris
    Hollings, M. , 1957
  Brassica oleracea var. botrytis
    Hollings, M. , 1957
  Brassica oleracea var. capitata
    Hollings, M. , 1957
  Brassica oleracea var. gemmifera
    Hollings, M. , 1957
  Brassica oleracea var. italica *
    Hollings, M. , 1957
  Brassica pekinensis
    Hollings, M. , 1957
  Brassica rapa
    Hollings, M. , 1957
  Calendula chrysantha
    Hollings, M. , 1957
  Callistephus chinensis
    Hollings, M. , 1957
  Calystegia sepium
    Hollings, M. , 1957
  Capsicum frutescens (Capsicum annuum)
    Hollings, M. , 1957

VIRUS

V. CHRYSANTHEMUM B (MILD MOSAIC) * (cont.)

Celosia argentea
  Hollings, M., 1957
Cheiranthus cheiri
  Hollings, M., 1957
Chenopodium album
  Hollings, M., 1957
Chenopodium amaranticolor
  Hollings, M., 1957
Convolvulus tricolor
  Hollings, M., 1957
Cucumis sativus
  Hollings, M., 1957
Cucurbita pepo
  Hollings, M., 1957
Dahlia pinnata
  Hollings, M., 1957
Datura stramonium
  Hollings, M., 1957
Delphinium grandiflorum
  Hollings, M., 1957
Dianthus barbatus
  Hollings, M., 1957
Epilobium montanum
  Hollings, M., 1957
Fagopyrum esculentum
  Hollings, M., 1957
Geum chiloensis
  Hollings, M., 1957
Gomphrena globosa
  Hollings, M., 1957
Helichrysum bracteatum
  Hollings, M., 1957
Lactuca muralis
  Hollings, M., 1957
Lactuca sativa
  Hollings, M., 1957
Lavatera trimestris
  Hollings, M., 1957
Lobularia maritima
  Hollings, M., 1957
Lupinus polyphyllus
  Hollings, M., 1957
Lycopersicon esculentum
  Hollings, M., 1957
Lythrum salicaria
  Hollings, M., 1957
Matthiola incana var. annua
  Hollings, M., 1957
Medicago sativa
  Hollings, M., 1957
Melilotus alba
  Hollings, M., 1957
Mimulus luteus
  Hollings, M., 1957
Myosotis sylvatica
  Hollings, M., 1957
Nicandra physalodes
  Hollings, M., 1957
Nicotiana tabacum
  Hollings, M., 1957
Papaver rhoeas
  Hollings, M., 1957
Papaver somniferum
  Hollings, M., 1957
Pelargonium domesticum
  Hollings, M., 1957
Phaseolus vulgaris
  Hollings, M., 1957
Phlox drummondii
  Hollings, M., 1957
Physalis floridana
  Hollings, M., 1957
Phytolacca americana
  Hollings, M., 1957
Pisum sativum
  Hollings, M., 1957
Plantago lanceolata
  Hollings, M., 1957
Portulaca oleracea
  Hollings, M., 1957
Primula malacoides
  Hollings, M., 1957

VIRUS

V. CHRYSANTHEMUM B (MILD MOSAIC) * (cont.)

Primula sinensis
  Hollings, M., 1957
Ranunculus ficaria
  Hollings, M., 1957
Ranunculus repens
  Hollings, M., 1957
Raphanus sativus
  Hollings, M., 1957
Saintpaulia ionantha
  Hollings, M., 1957
Salpiglossis sinuata
  Hollings, M., 1957
Salvia splendens
  Hollings, M., 1957
Schizanthus pinnatus
  . Hollings, M., 1957
Solanum tuberosum
  Hollings, M., 1957
Spinacia oleracea
  Hollings, M., 1957
Stellaria media
  Hollings, M., 1957
Tagetes erecta
  Hollings, M., 1957
Taraxacum officinale
  Hollings, M., 1957
Trifolium repens
  Hollings, M., 1957
Tropaeolum majus
  Hollings, M., 1957
Verbena hybrida
  Hollings, M., 1957
Vigna sinensis
  Hollings, M., 1957
Zinnia elegans
  Hollings, M., 1957

V. CHRYSANTHEMUM LATENT *

Beta vulgaris
  Hollings, M., 1957
Brassica pekinensis
  Hollings, M., 1957
Cucumis sativus
  Hollings, M., 1957
Dianthus barbatus
  Hollings, M., 1957
Lycopersicon esculentum
  Hollings, M., 1957
Lythrum salicaria
  Hollings, M., 1957
Passiflora caerulea
  Hollings, M., 1957
Phaseolus vulgaris
  Hollings, M., 1957
Phytolacca americana
  Hollings, M., 1957
Plantago lanceolata
  Hollings, M., 1957
Portulaca oleracea
  Hollings, M., 1957
Primula malacoides
  Hollings, M., 1957
Spinacia oleracea
  Hollings, M., 1957
Stellaria media
  Hollings, M., 1957

V. CHRYSANTHEMUM Q Keller 1950

Lycopersicon esculentum
  Brierley, Philip and Floyd F. Smith, 1953
Nicotiana tabacum
  Brierley, Philip and Floyd F. Smith, 1953

V. CHRYSANTHEMUM RING SPOT Brierley and Smith 1955

Antirrhinum majus
  Brierley, Philip and Floyd F. Smith, 1955
Callistephus chinensis
  Brierley, Philip and Floyd F. Smith, 1955
Datura stramonium
  Brierley, Philip and Floyd F. Smith, 1955
Gomphrena globosa
  Brierley, Philip and Floyd F. Smith, 1955

VIRUS
V. CHRYSANTHEMUM RING SPOT (cont.)
Nicotiana glutinosa
    Brierley, Philip and Floyd F. Smith, 1955
Nicotiana tabacum
    Brierley, Philip and Floyd F. Smith, 1955
Petunia hybrida
    Brierley, Philip and Floyd F. Smith, 1955
Phaseolus vulgaris
    Brierley, Philip and Floyd F. Smith, 1955
Physalis angulata
    Brierley, Philip and Floyd F. Smith, 1955
Senecio cruentus
    Brierley, Philip and Floyd F. Smith, 1955
Zinnia elegans
    Brierley, Philip and Floyd F. Smith, 1955

V. CHRYSANTHEMUM STUNT Brierley and Smith 1949
Achillea filipendulina
    Brierley, Philip, 1953
Ageratum houstonianum
    Brierley, Philip, 1953
Ambrosia artemesiifolia
    Brierley, Philip, 1953
Arctotis stoechadifolia var. grandis
    Brierley, Philip, 1953
Artemisia vulgaris
    Brierley, Philip, 1953
Boltonia latisquama
    Brierley, Philip, 1953
Brickellia laciniata
    Brierley, Philip, 1953
Calendula officinalis
    Brierley, Philip, 1953
Callistephus chinensis
    Brierley, Philip, 1953
Catananche caerulea
    Brierley, Philip, 1953
Centaurea imperialis
    Brierley, Philip, 1953
Cichorium intybus
    Brierley, Philip, 1953
Coreopsis douglasii
    Brierley, Philip, 1953
Coreopsis drummondii
    Brierley, Philip, 1953
Coreopsis lanceolata
    Brierley, Philip, 1953
Cosmos bipinnatus
    Brierley, Philip, 1953
Cucumis sativus
    Keller, John R., 1953
Cuscuta gronovii
    Keller, John R., 1953
Cynara cardunculus
    Brierley, Philip, 1953
Doronicum cordatum
    Brierley, Philip, 1953
Echinops ritro
    Brierley, Philip, 1953
Gaillardia pulchella var. picta
    Brierley, Philip, 1953
Galinsoga parviflora
    Brierley, Philip, 1953
Gazania spp.
    Brierley, Philip, 1953
Gerbera jamesonii
    Brierley, Philip, 1953
Helianthus cucumerifolius
    Brierley, Philip, 1953
Helichrysum bracteatum
    Brierley, Philip, 1953
Lactuca sativa
    Brierley, Philip, 1953
Ligularia clivorum
    Brierley, Philip, 1953
Nicotiana glutinosa
    Brierley, Philip, 1953
Nicotiana tabacum
    Brierley, Philip, 1953
Phaseolus vulgaris
    Brierley, Philip, 1953
Rudbeckia serotina
    Brierley, Philip, 1953

VIRUS
V. CHRYSANTHEMUM STUNT (cont.)
Senecio elegans
    Brierley, Philip, 1953
Stokesia laevis
    Brierley, Philip, 1953
Tagetes erecta
    Brierley, Philip, 1953
Tragopogon porrifolius
    Brierley, Philip, 1953
Tropaeolum majus var. nanum
    Keller, John R., 1953
Xeranthemum annuum
    Brierley, Philip, 1953

V. CINERARIA MOSAIC Jones 1942
Cucumis sativus
    Jones, Leon K., 1944
Lactuca sativa
    Jones, Leon K., 1944
Lycopersicon esculentum
    Jones, Leon K., 1944
Nicotiana tabacum
    Jones, Leon K., 1944
Pisum sativum
    Jones, Leon K., 1944

V. CITRUS EXOCORTIS Moreira 1955
Citrus aurantifolia
    Olson, E.O. and A.V. Shull, 1956

V. CITRUS PSOROSIS ((Swingle and Weber 1896))
Cuscuta californica   Fawcett 1936
    Bennett, C.W., 1944
Cuscuta campestris
    Bennett, C.W., 1944
Cuscuta subinclusa
    Bennett, C.W., 1944

V. CITRUS TRISTEZA Meneghini 1946
Acanthospermum hispidum
    Bennett, C.W. and A.S. Costa, 1949
Aegle marmelos
    Knorr, L.C., 1956
Aeglopsis chevalieri
    Knorr, L.C., 1956
Amaranthus caudatus
    Bennett, C.W. and A.S. Costa, 1949
Atalantia ceylanica
    Knorr, L.C., 1956
Atalantia citroides
    Knorr, L.C., 1956
Beta vulgaris
    Knorr, L.C., 1956
Brassica oleracea
    Knorr, L.C., 1956
Brassica pekinensis
    Bennett, C.W. and A.S. Costa, 1949
Calendula spp.
    Knorr, L.C., 1956
Callistephus chinensis
    Bennett, C.W. and A.S. Costa, 1949
Canavalia ensiformis
    Bennett, C.W. and A.S. Costa, 1949
Capsicum spp.
    Knorr, L.C., 1956
Casimiroa edulis
    Knorr, L.C., 1956
Celosia spp.
    Knorr, L.C., 1956
Citrus grandis
    Knorr, L.C., 1956
Citrus limon
    Knorr, L.C., 1956
Citrus nobilis var. unshiu on Citrus sinensis x
Poncirus trifoliata
    Olson, Edward O. and James R. McDonald, 1954
Citrus nobilis var. unshiu on Poncirus trifoliata
    Olson, Edward O. and James R. McDonald, 1954
Citrus paradisi on Citrus paradisi x Poncirus
trifoliata
    Olson, Edward O. and James R. McDonald, 1954

VIRUS
V. CITRUS TRISTEZA (cont.)
  Citrus paradisi x Citrus reticulata on Citrus sinensis x
  Poncirus trifoliata
    Olson, Edward O. and James R. McDonald, 1954
  Citrus paradisi on Citrus sinensis x Poncirus trifoliata
    Olson, Edward O. and James R. McDonald, 1954
  Citrus reticulata
    Knorr, L.C., 1956
  Citrus sinensis
    Olson, Edward O. and James R. McDonald, 1954
  Citrus sinensis on Citrus paradisi x Poncirus trifoliata
    Olson, Edward O. and James R. McDonald, 1954
  Citrus sinensis on Poncirus trifoliata
    Olson, Edward O. and James R. McDonald, 1954
  Cucumis sativus
    Knorr, L.C., 1956
  Cuscuta americana
    Bennett, C.W. and A.S. Costa, 1949
  Cuscuta campestris
    Bennett, C.W. and A.S. Costa, 1949
  Cuscuta indecora
    Bennett, C.W. and A.S. Costa, 1949
  Cuscuta subinclusa
    Bennett, C.W. and A.S. Costa, 1949
  Datura spp.
    Bennett, C.W. and A.S. Costa, 1949
    Knorr, L.C., 1956
  Datura stramonium
    Bennett, C.W. and A.S. Costa, 1949
  Dianthus caryophyllus
    Knorr, L.C., 1956
  Erigeron bonariensis
    Bennett, C.W. and A.S. Costa, 1949
  Euphorbia pilulifera
    Bennett, C.W. and A.S. Costa, 1949
  Euphorbia prunifolia
    Bennett, C.W. and A.S. Costa, 1949
  Evodia spp.
    Knorr, L.C., 1956
  Fortunella margarita on Poncirus trifoliata
    Olson, Edward O. and James R. McDonald, 1954
  Gossypium hirsutum
    Bennett, C.W. and A.S. Costa, 1949
  Gycosmis citrifolia *
    Knorr, L.C., 1956
  Iberis spp.
    Knorr, L.C., 1956
  Lactuca sativa
    Knorr, L.C., 1956
  Luffa spp.
    Knorr, L.C., 1956
  Lycopersicon esculentum
    Bennett, C.W. and A.S. Costa, 1949
  Murraya koenigii
    Knorr, L.C., 1956
  Nicotiana glauca
    Bennett, C.W. and A.S. Costa, 1949
  Nicotiana tabacum
    Bennett, C.W. and A.S. Costa, 1949
    Knorr, L.C., 1956
  Ocimum basilicum
    Knorr, L.C., 1956
  Oxalis spp.
    Bennett, C.W. and A.S. Costa, 1949
  Phaseolus vulgaris
    Bennett, C.W. and A.S. Costa, 1949
  Phyllanthus corcovadensis
    Bennett, C.W. and A.S. Costa, 1949
  Ptelea trifoliata
    Knorr, L.C., 1956
  Ruta chalepensis
    Knorr, L.C., 1956
  Ruta graveolens
    Knorr, L.C., 1956
  Ruta spp.
    Bennett, C.W. and A.S. Costa, 1949
  Severinia buxifolia
    Knorr, L.C., 1956
  Severinia disticha
    Knorr, L.C., 1956
  Solanum tuberosum
    Bennett, C.W. and A.S. Costa, 1949

VIRUS
V. CITRUS TRISTEZA (cont.)
  Spinacia oleracea
    Bennett, C.W. and A.S. Costa, 1949
  Stellaria media
    Bennett, C.W. and A.S. Costa, 1949
  Swinglea gultinosa
    Knorr, L.C., 1956
  Triphasia trifolia
    Knorr, L.C., 1956
  Vigna sinensis
    Bennett, C.W. and A.S. Costa, 1949
  Zinnia spp.
    Knorr, L.C., 1956

V. CITRUS XYLOPOROSIS Reichert and Perlberger 1934
  Citrus aurantifolia
    Olson, E.O. and A.V. Shull, 1956
  Citrus paradisi x Citrus reticulata
    Olson, E.O. and A.V. Shull, 1956

V. CLOVER BIG VEIN Black 1944
  Medicago sativa
    Black, L.M. and M.K. Brakke, 1952

V. CLOVER WITCHES' BROOM *
  Cuscuta campestris
    Frazier, N.W. and A.F. Posnette, 1957
  Cuscuta europaea
    Frazier, N.W. and A.F. Posnette, 1957
  Cuscuta subinclusa
    Frazier, N.W. and A.F. Posnette, 1957

V. CORN NEW MOSAIC *
  Avena sativa
    Finley, A.M., 1954

V. COWPEA MOSAIC
  Ambrosia artemisiifolia
    Anderson, C.W., 1955
  Apium graveolens
    Anderson, C.W., 1955
    Yu, T.F., 1946
  Arachis hypogaea
    Yu, T.F., 1946
  Beta vulgaris
    Yu, T.F., 1946
  Bidens pilosa
    Anderson, C.W., 1955
  Cajanus cajan
    Capoor, S.P. and P.M. Varma, 1956
  Canavalia ensiformis
    Yu, T.F., 1946
  Capsicum frutescens (Capsicum annuum)
    Anderson, C.W., 1955
    Capoor, S.P. and P.M. Varma, 1956
    McLean, D.M., 1941
    Yu, T.F., 1946
  Commelina nudiflora
    Anderson, C.W., 1955
  Crotalaria retusa
    Capoor, S.P. and P.M. Varma, 1956
  Cucumis sativus
    Anderson, C.W., 1955
    Capoor, S.P. and P.M. Varma, 1956
    Dale, W.T., 1949
    McLean, D.M., 1941
    Yu, T.F., 1946
  Cucurbita pepo
    Capoor, S.P. and P.M. Varma, 1956
  Datura inoxia
    Capoor, S.P. and P.M. Varma, 1956
  Datura stramonium
    McLean, D.M., 1941
    Yu, T.F., 1946
  Dolichos biflorus
    Capoor, S.P. and P.M. Varma, 1956
  Dolichos lablab
    Capoor, S.P. and P.M. Varma, 1956
    Yu, T.F., 1946
  Glycine max
    Yu, T.F., 1946
  Lagenaria siceraria (Lagenaria leucantha)
    Capoor, S.P. and P.M. Varma, 1956

VIRUS
V. COWPEA MOSAIC (cont.)
  Lathyrus odoratus
    McLean, D.M., 1941
    Yu, T.F., 1946
  Lathyrus sativus
    Capoor, S.P. and P.M. Varma, 1956
  Lens esculenta
    Yu, T.F., 1946
  Lespedeza bicolor
    Yu, T.F., 1946
  Lupinus albus
    Yu, T.F., 1946
  Lycopersicon esculentum
    Anderson, C.W., 1955
    Capoor, S.P. and P.M. Varma, 1956
    Dale, W.T., 1949
    McLean, D.M., 1941
    Yu, T.F., 1946
  Lycopersicon pimpinellifolium
    Yu, T.F., 1946
  Medicago sativa
    Capoor, S.P. and P.M. Varma, 1956
    Yu, T.F., 1946·
  Melilotus alba
    Yu, T.F., 1946
  Mucuna deeringianum
    Capoor, S.P. and P.M. Varma, 1956
  Nicotiana glutinosa
    Anderson, C.W., 1955
    Capoor, S.P. and P.M. Varma, 1956
    Dale, W.T., 1949
    McLean, D.M., 1941
  Nicotiana rustica
    Capoor, S.P. and P.M. Varma, 1956
  Nicotiana tabacum
    Anderson, C.W., 1955
    Capoor, S.P. and P.M. Varma, 1956
    Dale, W.T., 1949
    McLean, D.M., 1941
    Yu, T.F., 1946
  Pachyrhizus tuberosus
    Yu, T.F., 1946
  Petunia hybrida
    Capoor, S.P. and P.M. Varma, 1956
    McLean, D.M., 1941
    Yu, T.F., 1946
  Phaseolus aconitifolius
    Capoor, S.P. and P.M. Varma, 1956
  Phaseolus aureus
    Capoor, S.P. and P.M. Varma, 1956
    McLean, D.M., 1941
  Phaseolus lunatus
    McLean, D.M., 1941
  Phaseolus mungo
    Capoor, S.P. and P.M. Varma, 1956
  Phaseolus trilobus
    Capoor, S.P. and P.M. Varma, 1956
  Phaseolus vulgaris
    Anderson, C.W., 1955
    Capoor, S.P. and P.M. Varma, 1956
    Dale, W.T., 1949
    McLean, D.M., 1941
    Yu, T.F., 1946
  Physalis peruviana
    Capoor, S.P. and P.M. Varma, 1956
  Phytolacca rigida
    Anderson, C.W., 1955
  Pisum sativum
    Anderson, C.W., 1955
    McLean, D.M., 1941
    Yu, T.F., 1946
  Pisum sativum var. arvense
    McLean, D.M., 1941
    Yu, T.F., 1946
  Sesbania speciosa
    Capoor, S.P. and P.M. Varma, 1956
  Sida spp.
    Anderson, C.W., 1955
  Solanum melongena
    Capoor, S.P. and P.M. Varma, 1956
    Yu, T.F., 1946
  Solanum nigrum
    Capoor, S.P. and P.M. Varma, 1956

VIRUS
V. COWPEA MOSAIC (cont.)
  Solanum tuberosum
    McLean, D.M., 1941
    Yu, T.F., 1946
  Spinacia oleracea
    Capoor, S.P. and P.M. Varma, 1956
  Trifolium pratense
    Yu, T.F., 1946
  Trifolium repens
    Yu, T.F., 1946
  Tropaeolum majus
    Capoor, S.P. and P.M. Varma, 1956
  Vicia faba
    Capoor, S.P. and P.M. Varma, 1956
    McLean, D.M., 1941
    Yu, T.F., 1946
  Vicia sativa
    Yu, T.F., 1946
  Vicia villosa
    Yu, T.F., 1946
  Zinnia elegans
    Capoor, S.P. and P.M. Varma, 1956
    McLean, D.M., 1941
    Yu, T.F., 1946

V. CROTALARIA MOSAIC Johnson and Lefebvre 1938
  Carica papaya
    Jensen, D.D., 1949

V. CUCUMBER GREEN MOTTLE MOSAIC Ainsworth
1935 ((This virus is serologically related to V. Tobacco
mosaic and is generally regarded as a strain of it, but
see Knight 1955.))
  Brassica chinensis
    Vasudeva, R.S., S.P. Raychaudhuri and Jagannath
    Singh, 1949
  Brassica oleracea
    Vasudeva, R.S., S.P. Raychaudhuri and Jagannath
    Singh, 1949
  Brassica oleracea var. gongylodes
    Vasudeva, R.S., S.P. Raychaudhuri and Jagannath
    Singh, 1949
  Bryonia dioica
    Ainsworth, G.C., 1935
  Cajanus cajan
    Vasudeva, R.S., S.P. Raychaudhuri and Jagannath
    Singh, 1949
  Capsicum frutescens (Capsicum annuum)
    Vasudeva, R.S. and T.K. Nariani, 1952
  Cicer arietinum
    Vasudeva, R.S., S.P. Raychaudhuri and Jagannath
    Singh, 1949
  Citrullus vulgaris
    Ainsworth, G.C., 1935
  Cucurbita pepo
    Ainsworth, G.C., 1935
  Cuscuta campestris
    Johnson, Folke, 1941
  Datura stramonium
    Ainsworth, G.C., 1935
  Hibiscus esculentus
    Vasudeva, R.S., S.P. Raychaudhuri and Jagannath
    Singh, 1949
  Lycopersicon esculentum
    Ainsworth, G.C., 1935
    Vasudeva, R.S. and T.K. Nariani, 1952
    Vasudeva, R.S., S.P. Raychaudhuri and Jagannath
    Singh, 1949
  Nicotiana glutinosa
    Ainsworth, G.C., 1935
    Vasudeva, R.S., S.P. Raychaudhuri and Jagannath
    Singh, 1949
  Nicotiana tabacum
    Ainsworth, G.C., 1935
    Vasudeva, R.S., S.P. Raychaudhuri and Jagannath
    Singh, 1949
  Nicotiana tabacum x Nicotiana glutinosa
    Fulton, Robert W., 1950
  Petunia hybrida
    Vasudeva, R.S., S.P. Raychaudhuri and Jagannath
    Singh, 1949
  Pisum sativum
    Vasudeva, R.S., S.P. Raychaudhuri and Jagannath
    Singh, 1949

VIRUS

V. CUCUMBER GREEN MOTTLE MOSAIC (cont.)

Solanum nigrum
  Ainsworth, G.C., 1935
Vigna sinensis
  Vasudeva, R.S., S.P. Raychaudhuri and Jagannath
  Singh, 1949

V. CUCUMBER MOSAIC Doolittle 1916, 1920

Abelmoschus esculentus
  Adsuar, Jose and A. Cruz Miret, 1950
Achillea millefolium
  Wellman, F.L., 1935
Adenoropium gossypifolium
  Adsuar, Jose and A. Cruz Miret, 1950
Adiantum capillus-veneris
  Wellman, F.L., 1935
Agapanthus africanus
  Brierley, Philip and Floyd F. Smith, 1944
Ageratum houstonianum
  Wellman, F.L., 1935
Allium cepa
  Brierley, Philip and Floyd F. Smith, 1944
Allium cernuum
  Brierley, Philip and Floyd F. Smith, 1944
Allium odorum
  Brierley, Philip and Floyd F. Smith, 1944
Allium speciosum
  Brierley, Philip and Floyd F. Smith, 1944
Aloe spp.
  Brierley, Philip and Floyd F. Smith, 1944
Alsine media
  Wellman, F.L., 1935
Althaea rosea
  Burnett, G., 1934
Amaranthus cruentus
  Adsuar, Jose and A. Cruz Miret, 1950
Amaranthus dubius
  Adsuar, Jose and A. Cruz Miret, 1950
Amaranthus hybridus
  Wellman, F.L., 1935
Amaranthus retroflexus
  Burnett, G., 1934
Amaranthus spinosus
  Wellman, F.L., 1935
Amaryllis (Hippeastrum) vittatum
  Wellman, F.L., 1935
Ambrosia artemisiifolia
  Anderson, C.W., 1955
Ananas sativus
  Wellman, F.L., 1935
Anchusa officinalis
  Wellman, F.L., 1935
Antirrhinum majus
  Govier, D.A., 1957
Apium graveolens
  Bhargava, K.S., 1951
Apium graveolens var. dulce
  Simons, John N., 1957
Arachis hypogaea
  Wellman, F.L., 1935
Asparagus asparagoides
  Brierley, Philip and Floyd F. Smith, 1944
Asparagus officinalis
  Wellman, F.L., 1935
Asparagus plumosus
  Wellman, F.L., 1935
Asparagus sprengeri
  Brierley, Philip and Floyd F. Smith, 1944
Asphodeline lutea
  Brierley, Philip and Floyd F. Smith, 1944
Aster novae-angliae
  Wellman, F.L., 1935
Aster spp.
  Burnett, G., 1934
Avena sativa
  McWhorter, F.P. and H.H. Millsap, 1954
  Wellman, F.L., 1935
Belamcanda chinensis
  Brierley, Philip and Floyd F. Smith, 1944
Beta vulgaris
  Adsuar, Jose and A. Cruz Miret, 1950
  Govier, D.A., 1957
  Nienow, Inez, 1948

VIRUS

V. CUCUMBER MOSAIC (cont.)

Beta vulgaris var. cicla
  Govier, D.A., 1957
Bidens cynapiifolia
  Adsuar, Jose and A. Cruz Miret, 1950
Bidens leucantha *
  Wellman, F.L., 1935
Bidens pilosa
  Anderson, C.W., 1955
Brassica campestris var. napobrassica
  Wellman, F.L., 1935
Brassica hirta (Brassica alba)
  Johnson, E.M., 1930
  Wellman, F.L., 1935
Brassica napus
  Wellman, F.L., 1935
Brassica nigra
  Wellman, F.L., 1935
Brassica oleracea
  Doolittle, S.P. and W.J. Zaumeyer, 1953
  Johnson, E.M., 1930
  Simons, John N., 1957
Brassica oleracea var. acephala
  Wellman, F.L., 1935
Brassica oleracea var. botrytis
  Berkeley, G.H. and J.H. Tremaine, 1954
  Wellman, F.L., 1935
Brassica oleracea var. capitata
  Berkeley, G.H. and J.H. Tremaine, 1954
  Bridgmon, G.H. and J.C. Walker, 1952
  Wellman, F.L., 1935
Brassica oleracea var. caulorapa
  Nienow, Inez, 1948
  Wellman, F.L., 1935
Brassica oleracea var. gemmifera
  Berkeley, G.H. and J.H. Tremaine, 1954
  Wellman, F.L., 1935
Brassica oleracea var. gongylodes
  Berkeley, G.H. and J.H. Tremaine, 1954
Brassica oleracea var. viridis
  Berkeley, G.H. and J.H. Tremaine, 1954
Brassica pekinensis
  Berkeley, G.H. and J.H. Tremaine, 1954
  Wellman, F.L., 1935
Brassica rapa
  Brierley, Philip and Floyd F. Smith, 1944
  Nienow, Inez, 1948
  Wellman, F.L., 1935
Brassica rapa var. depressa *
  Johnson, E.M., 1930
Brodiaea uniflora
  Brierley, Philip and Floyd F. Smith, 1944
Calendula officinalis
  Wellman, F.L., 1935
Callistephus chinensis
  Doolittle, S.P. and W.J. Zaumeyer, 1953
  Simons, John N., 1957
  Wellman, F.L., 1935
Camassia leichtlinii
  Brierley, Philip and Floyd F. Smith, 1944
Campanula medium
  Wellman, F.L., 1935
Canavalia ensiformis
  Anderson, C.W., 1955
Canavalia gladiata
  Anderson, C.W., 1955
Canna edulis ·
  Celino, Martin S., 1940
Canna glauca
  Wellman, F.L., 1935
Capsicum frutescens (Capsicum annuum)
  Adsuar, Jose and A. Cruz Miret, 1950
  Anderson, C.W. and M.K. Corbett, 1957
  Burnett, G., 1934
  Govier, D.A., 1957
  Vasudeva, R. Sahai and T.B. Lal, 1943
Capsicum frutescens var. cerasiforme
  Pound, Glenn S. and J.C. Walker, 1948
Carica papaya
  Adsuar, Jose and A. Cruz Miret, 1950
  Wellman, F.L., 1935
Cassia tora
  Anderson, C.W., 1954, 1955

VIRUS
V. CUCUMBER MOSAIC (cont.)

Catharanthus roseus
Adsuar, Jose and A. Cruz Miret, 1950
Celeri graveolens
Adsuar, Jose and A. Cruz Miret, 1950
Celosia argentia
Wellman, F.L., 1935
Centaurea cyanus
Wellman, F.L., 1935
Chapmannia floridana
Wellman, F.L., 1935
Cheiranthus cheiri
Govier, D.A., 1957
Chenopodium album
Burnett, G., 1934
Chenopodium botrys
Wellman, F.L., 1935
Chrysanthemum carinatum
Wellman, F.L., 1935
Chrysanthemum coccineum
Govier, D.A., 1957
Chrysanthemum leucanthemum
Wellman, F.L., 1935
Chrysanthemum morifolium
Wellman, F.L., 1935
Chrysanthemum parthenium
Govier, D.A., 1957
Wellman, F.L., 1935
Cicer arietinum
Wellman, F.L., 1935
Cichorium endivia
Wellman, F.L., 1935
Cichorium intybus
Pound, Glenn S. and J.C. Walker, 1948
Wellman, F.L., 1935
Citrullus citrullus
Adsuar, Jose and A. Cruz Miret, 1950
Citrullus vulgaris
Nariani, T.K. and Nirmaljit Singh, 1952
Citrullus vulgaris var. fistulosus *
Nariani, T.K. and Nirmaljit Singh, 1952
Citrus aurantium
Wellman, F.L., 1935
Citrus grandis
Wellman, F.L., 1935
Citrus nobilis
Wellman, F.L., 1935
Citrus sinensis
Wellman, F.L., 1935
Citrus spp.
Bennett, C.W., 1944
Clarkia elegans
Wellman, F.L., 1935
Cleome spinosa
Adsuar, Jose and A. Cruz Miret, 1950
Clerodendron fragans
Adsuar, Jose and A. Cruz Miret, 1950
Clitoria ternatea
Wellman, F.L., 1935
Codiaeum variegatum
Wellman, F.L., 1935
Coleus lanuginosus
Adsuar, Jose and A. Cruz Miret, 1950
Commelina coelestis
Brierley, Philip and Floyd F. Smith, 1944
Commelina nudiflora
Anderson, C.W., 1955
Brierley, Philip and Floyd F. Smith, 1944
Commelina spp.
Simons, John N., 1957
Convallaria majalis
Brierley, Philip and Floyd F. Smith, 1944
Coreopsis drummondii
Wellman, F.L., 1935
Coreopsis tinctoria
Wellman, F.L., 1935
Cosmos bipinnatus
Wellman, F.L., 1935
Crassina elegans
Adsuar, Jose and A. Cruz Miret, 1950
Crotalaria spectabilis
Anderson, C.W., 1955
Wellman, F.L., 1935

VIRUS
V. CUCUMBER MOSAIC (cont.)

Crotalaria spp.
Wellman, F.L., 1935
Cucumis melo
Govier, D.A., 1957
Cucumis sativus
McWhorter, F.P. and H.H. Millsap, 1954
Peterson, Paul D. and H.H. McKinney, 1938
Cucurbita lagenaria
Adsuar, Jose and A. Cruz Miret, 1950
Cuscuta californica
Bennett, C.W., 1940
Cuscuta campestris
Bennett, C.W., 1944
Costa, A.S., 1944
Cuscuta sandwichiana
Sakimura, K., 1947
Cuscuta subinclusa
Bennett, C.W., 1940
Cynodon dactylon
Wellman, F.L., 1935
Cyperus compressus
Wellman, F.L., 1935
Cyperus esculentus
Wellman, F.L., 1935
Dahlia pinnata
Wellman, F.L., 1935
Dahlia variabilis
Brierley, Philip and Floyd F. Smith, 1950
Daphne cneorum
Milbrath, J.A. and Roy A. Young, 1956
Datura spp.
Adsuar, Jose and A. Cruz Miret, 1950
Datura stramonium
Burnett, G., 1934
Harter, L.L., 1938
Lindberg, G.D., D.H. Hall and J.C. Walker, 1956
McKnight, T., 1953
Vasudeva, R. Sahai and T.B. Lal, 1943
Dendropogon usneoides
Wellman, F.L., 1935
Desmodium incanum
Anderson, C.W., 1955
Dianthus caryophyllus
Wellman, F.L., 1935
Dianthus plumarius
Wellman, F.L., 1935
Digitalis purpurea
Wellman, F.L., 1935
Dioscorea alata
Brierley, Philip and Floyd F. Smith, 1944
Dioscorea bulbifera
Wellman, F.L., 1935
Dolichos lablab
Wellman, F.L., 1935
Dracaena sanderiana
Brierley, Philip and Floyd F. Smith, 1944
Ecballium elaterium
Jagger, I.C., 1918
Emilia sonchifolia
Adsuar, Jose and A. Cruz Miret, 1950
Erigeron spp.
Wellman, F.L., 1935
Eriogonum fasciculatum
Bennett, C.W., 1944
Erythronium spp.
Brierley, Philip and Floyd F. Smith, 1944
Euphorbia marginata
Wellman, F.L., 1935
Euphorbia pulcherrima
Wellman, F.L., 1935
Ferula communis
Wellman, F.L., 1935
Freesia hybrida
Brierley, Philip and Floyd F. Smith, 1944
Gaillardia pulchella
Wellman, F.L., 1935
Galtonia candicans
Brierley, Philip and Floyd F. Smith, 1944
Gerardia divaricata
Wellman, F.L., 1935
Gladiolus lemoinei
Wellman, F.L., 1935

VIRUS
V. CUCUMBER MOSAIC (cont.)

Glycine hispida
Vasudeva, R. Sahai and T.B. Lal, 1943

Glycine max
Anderson, C.W., 1955
Bridgmon, G.H. and J.C. Walker, 1952
Costa, A.S., 1944
Harter, L.L., 1938
Johnson, E.M., 1930
Wellman, F.L., 1935
Whipple, O.C. and J.C. Walker, 1941

Gomphrena globosa
Wellman, F.L., 1935

Gossypium hirsutum
Wellman, F.L., 1935

Gossypium spp.
Celino, Martin S., 1940

Gypsophila paniculata
Wellman, F.L., 1935

Haworthia altilinea
Brierley, Philip and Floyd F. Smith, 1944

Hedychium coronarium
Brierley, Philip and Floyd F. Smith, 1944
Celino, Martin S., 1940

Helichrysum bracteatum
Wellman, F.L., 1935

Heliotropium peruvianum
Wellman, F.L., 1935

Hemerocallis flava
Wellman, F.L., 1935

Hibiscus esculentus
Wellman, F.L., 1935

Hibiscus rosa-sinensis
Wellman, F.L., 1935

Holcus sorghum
Adsuar, Jose and A. Cruz Miret, 1950

Hordeum vulgare
McWhorter, F.P. and H.H. Millsap, 1954
Wellman, F.L., 1935

Hosta plantaginea
Brierley, Philip and Floyd F. Smith, 1944

Hymenocallis spp.
Wellman, F.L., 1935

Iberis umbellata
Wellman, F.L., 1935

Impatiens balsamina
Doolittle, S.P. and W.J. Zaumeyer, 1953
Wellman, F.L., 1935

Ionoxalis violacea
Wellman, F.L., 1935

Ipomoea batata
Doolittle, S.P. and L.L. Harter, 1945

Ipomoea quinquefolia
Adsuar, Jose and A. Cruz Miret, 1950

Iris filifolia
Brierley, Philip and Floyd F. Smith, 1944

Iris germanica
Brierley, Philip and Frank P. McWhorter, 1936

Iris pallida
Brierley, Philip and Floyd F. Smith, 1944

Iris versicolor
Brierley, Philip and Floyd F. Smith, 1944

Isotoma longiflora
Adsuar, Jose and A. Cruz Miret, 1950

Jussiaea angustifolia
Adsuar, Jose and A. Cruz Miret, 1950

Kniphofia tucki
Brierley, Philip and Floyd F. Smith, 1944

Kochia scoparia
Wellman, F.L., 1935

Lactuca sativa
Burnett, G., 1934
Govier, D.A., 1957
Nienow, Inez, 1948

Lactuca sativa var. capitata
Ainsworth, G.C., 1940
Wellman, F.L., 1935

Lactuca sativa var. crispa
Wellman, F.L., 1935

Lactuca sativa var. longifolia
Wellman, F.L., 1935

Lagenaria siceraria (Lagenaria leucantha)
Nariani, T.K. and Nirmaljit Singh, 1952

VIRUS
V. CUCUMBER MOSAIC (cont.)

Lamium amplexicaule
Burnett, G., 1934

Lantana sellowiana
Wellman, F.L., 1935

Lathyrus odoratus
Bhargava, K.S., 1951
Harter, L.L., 1938
Wellman, F.L., 1935

Lens esculenta
Harter, L.L., 1938

Leonotis nepetaefolia
Adsuar, Jose and A. Cruz Miret, 1950

Lepidium virginicum
Wellman, F.L., 1935

Lilium davidi
Brierley, Philip, 1940

Lilium hansonii
Brierley, Philip, 1940
Brierley, Philip and Floyd F. Smith, 1944

Lilium henryi
Brierley, Philip and Floyd F. Smith, 1944

Lilium humboldtii
Brierley, Philip and Floyd F. Smith, 1944

Lilium martagon var. album x Lilium hansonii
Brierley, Philip, 1940

Lilium nepalense
Brierley, Philip, 1940

Lilium pardalinum
Brierley, Philip and Floyd F. Smith, 1944

Lilium pardalinum var. giganteum *
Brierley, Philip, 1940

Lilium parryi
Brierley, Philip and Floyd F. Smith, 1944

Lilium parvum
Brierley, Philip and Floyd F. Smith, 1944

Lilium sargentiae
Brierley, Philip and Floyd F. Smith, 1944

Lilium superbum
Brierley, Philip and Floyd F. Smith, 1944

Limonium latifolium
Wellman, F.L., 1935

Linaria canadensis
Wellman, F.L., 1935

Linaria floridana
Wellman, F.L., 1935

Lobelia erinus
Wellman, F.L., 1935

Lobularia maritima
Wellman, F.L., 1935

Luffa aegyptiaca (Luffa cylindrica)
Nariani, T.K. and Nirmaljit Singh, 1952

Lupinus albus
Harter, L.L., 1938

Lupinus hirsutus
Wellman, F.L., 1935

Lupinus mutabilis
McKnight, T., 1953

Lupinus polyphyllus
Govier, D.A., 1957

Lycopersicon esculentum
Doolittle, S.P. and W.W. Gilbert, 1918
McKnight, T., 1953
Vasudeva, R. Sahai and T.B. Lal, 1943

Lycopersicon lycopersicon *
Adsuar, Jose and A. Cruz Miret, 1950

Malva rotundifolia
Burnett, G., 1934

Manihot esculenta (Manihot ultissima)
Wellman, F.L., 1935

Matthiola incana
Govier, D.A., 1957
Wellman, F.L., 1935

Medeola virginica
Brierley, Philip and Floyd F. Smith, 1944

Medicago sativa
Doolittle, S.P. and W.J. Zaumeyer, 1953
Hagedorn, D.J. and J.C. Walker, 1954
Simons, John N., 1957

Melilotus alba
Bridgmon, G.H. and J.C. Walker, 1952

Melilotus officinalis
Whipple, O.C. and J.C. Walker, 1941

VIRUS
V. CUCUMBER MOSAIC (cont.)

Mentha spicata
Wellman, F.L., 1935

Mirabilis jalapa
Adsuar, Jose and A. Cruz Miret, 1950
Wellman, F.L., 1935

Momordica charantia
Adsuar, Jose and A. Cruz Miret, 1950

Moraea iridioides
Brierley, Philip and Floyd F. Smith, 1944

Musa balbisiana
Bernardo, Fernando A. and Dioscoro L. Umali, 1956

Musa banksii
Bernardo, Fernando A. and Dioscoro L. Umali, 1956

Musa cavendishii
Brierley, Philip and Floyd F. Smith, 1944
Celino, M.S. and Aureo L. Martinez, 1956

Musa ornatus
Bernardo, Fernando A. and Dioscoro L. Umali, 1956

Musa paradisiaca
Adsuar, Jose and A. Cruz Miret, 1950

Musa paradisiaca subsp. sapientum
Adsuar, Jose and A. Cruz Miret, 1950

Musa paradisiaca subsp. sapientum var. cinerea
Celino, Martin S., 1940

Musa paradisiaca subsp. sapientum var. lacatan
Celino, Martin S., 1940

Musa paradisiaca subsp. sapientum var. suaveolens
Celino, Martin S., 1940

Musa sapientum var. compressa *
Celino, Martin S., 1940

Musa textilis
Brierley, Philip and Floyd F. Smith, 1944

Musa textilis x Musa balbisiana
Umali, D.L., F.A. Bernardo and G.O. Ocfemia, 1956

Muscari polyanthum
Brierley, Philip and Floyd F. Smith, 1944

Myosotis scorpioides
Wellman, F.L., 1935

Narcissus tazetta
Wellman, F.L., 1935

Nicotiana glauca
Johnson, J., 1926, 1927

Nicotiana glutinosa
Adsuar, Jose and A. Cruz Miret, 1950
Lindberg, G.D., D.H. Hall and J.C. Walker, 1956

Nicotiana rustica
Lindberg, G.D., D.H. Hall and J.C. Walker, 1956

Nicotiana tabacum
Adsuar, Jose and A. Cruz Miret, 1950
Doolittle, S.P. and W.W. Gilbert, 1918
Lindberg, G.D., D.H. Hall and J.C. Walker, 1956
McKnight, T., 1953
McWhorter, F.P. and H.H. Millsap, 1954
Vasudeva, R. Sahai and T.B. Lal, 1943

Nigella damascena
Wellman, F.L., 1935

Nothoscordum fragrans
Brierley, Philip and Floyd F. Smith, 1944

Ophiopogon jaburan
Brierley, Philip and Floyd F. Smith, 1944

Ornithogalum thyrsoides
Brierley, Philip and Floyd F. Smith, 1944
Smith, Floyd F. and Philip Brierley, 1944

Oryza sativa
Adsuar, Jose and A. Cruz Miret, 1950
McWhorter, F.P. and H.H. Millsap, 1954
Wellman, F.L., 1935

Panicum barbinode
Wellman, F.L., 1935

Papaver orientale
Wellman, F.L., 1935

Papaver rhoeas
Wellman, F.L., 1935

Papaver somniferum
Wellman, F.L., 1935

Parthenium argentatum
Severin, Henry H.P., 1945

VIRUS
V. CUCUMBER MOSAIC (cont.)

Pelargonium zonale
Govier, D.A., 1957

Petunia hybrida
Vasudeva, R. Sahai and T.B. Lal, 1943

Petunia violacea
Johnson, J., 1926

Phaseolus calcaratus
Harter, L.L., 1938

Phaseolus limensis
Simons, John N., 1957
Wellman, F.L., 1935

Phaseolus lunatus
Adsuar, Jose and A. Cruz Miret, 1950

Phaseolus vulgaris
Adsuar, Jose and A. Cruz Miret, 1950
Anderson, C.W., 1951
Berkeley, G.H., 1953
Bridgmon, G.H. and J.C. Walker, 1952
Brierley, Philip, 1952
Doolittle, S.P. and W.W. Gilbert, 1918
Govier, D.A., 1957
Harter, L.L., 1936, 1938
Johnson, E.M., 1930
Milbrath, J.A. and Roy A. Young, 1956
Nienow, Inez, 1948
Pound, Glenn S. and J.C. Walker, 1948
Simons, John N., 1957
Wellman, F.L., 1934, 1935
Whipple, O.C. and J.C. Walker, 1941

Philodendron spp.
Brierley, Philip and Floyd F. Smith, 1944

Physalis angulata
Adsuar, Jose and A. Cruz Miret, 1950

Phytolacca decandra
Govier, D.A., 1957
Johnson, J., 1926, 1927

Piaropus crassipes
Wellman, F.L., 1935

Pisum sativum
Berkeley, G.H., 1953
Bridgmon, G.H. and J.C. Walker, 1952
Burnett, G., 1934
Govier, D.A., 1957
Harter, L.L., 1938
Johnson, E.M., 1930
Wellman, F.L., 1935

Plantago major
Adsuar, Jose and A. Cruz Miret, 1950

Plantago spp.
Wellman, F.L., 1935

Poa pratensis
Wellman, F.L., 1935

Polygonum aviculare
Harter, L.L., 1938

Polypodium vulgare
Wellman, F.L., 1935

Pontederia cordata
Wellman, F.L., 1935

Portulaca grandiflora
Wellman, F.L., 1935

Primula vulgaris
Govier, D.A., 1957

Psidium guajava
Wellman, F.L., 1935

Raphanus sativus
Burnett, G., 1934
Johnson, E.M., 1930
Wellman, F.L., 1935

Reseda odorata
Wellman, F.L., 1935

Ricinus communis
Bennett, C.W., 1944
Wellman, F.L., 1935

Rivina humilis aurantica *
Adsuar, Jose and A. Cruz Miret, 1950

Rosa dilecta
Wellman, F.L., 1935

Rosa laevigata
Wellman, F.L., 1935

Ruellia tuberosa
Adsuar, Jose and A. Cruz Miret, 1950

VIRUS
V. CUCUMBER MOSAIC (cont.)
Rumex occidentalis
　Nienow, Inez, 1948
Saccharum officinarum
　Wellman, F.L., 1935
Salpiglossis sinuata
　Wellman, F.L., 1935
Salvia splendens
　Wellman, F.L., 1935
Sansevieria thrysiflora
　Wellman, F.L., 1935
Sansevieria zeylanica
　Brierley, Philip and Floyd F. Smith, 1944
Schizanthus pinnatus
　Wellman, F.L., 1935
Sechium edule
　Adsuar, Jose and A. Cruz Miret, 1950
Senecio cruentus
　Govier, D.A., 1957
　Wellman, F.L., 1935
Sida carpinifolia
　Adsuar, Jose and A. Cruz Miret, 1950
Smilacina racemosa
　Brierley, Philip and Floyd F. Smith, 1944
Smilax spp.
　Brierley, Philip and Floyd F. Smith, 1944
Solanum caribaeum
　Adsuar, Jose and A. Cruz Miret, 1950
Solanum dulcamara
　Govier, D.A., 1957
Solanum melongena
　Adsuar, Jose and A. Cruz Miret, 1950
　Burnett, G., 1934
　Johnson, J., 1926
Solanum pseudocapsicum
　Burnett, G., 1934
　Wellman, F.L., 1935
Solanum tuberosum
　Bhargava, K.S., 1951
　Burnett, G., 1934
　Dykstra, T.P., 1939
　Nariani, T.K. and Nirmaljit Singh, 1952
　Wellman, F.L., 1935
Sonchus oleraceus
　Wellman, F.L., 1935
Sorghum vulgare
　McWhorter, F.P. and H.H. Millsap, 1954
Spinacia oleracea
　Burnett, G., 1934
Stenotaphrum secundatum
　Wellman, F.L., 1935
Tigridia pavonia
　Brierley, Philip and Floyd F. Smith, 1944
Tillandsia fasciculata
　Wellman, F.L., 1935
Trachymene caerulea
　Wellman, F.L., 1935
Tragopogon porrifolius
　Wellman, F.L., 1935
Tricholaena-repens (Tricholaena rosea)
　Wellman, F.L., 1935
Tricyrtis hirta
　Brierley, Philip and Floyd F. Smith, 1944
Trifolium hybridum
　Harter, L.L., 1938
Trifolium incarnatum
　Bridgmon, G.H. and J.C. Walker, 1952
Trifolium pratense
　Bridgmon, G.H. and J.C. Walker, 1952
　Costa, A.S., 1944
　Doolittle, S.P. and W.J. Zaumeyer, 1953
Trifolium repens
　Doolittle, S.P. and W.J. Zaumeyer, 1953
　Wellman, F.L., 1935
　Whipple, O.C. and J.C. Walker, 1941
Trillium spp.
　Brierley, Philip and Floyd F. Smith, 1944
Triticum aestivum
　McWhorter, F.P. and H.H. Millsap, 1954
Tritonia crocata
　Brierley, Philip and Floyd F. Smith, 1944
Tulipa gesneriana
　Wellman, F.L., 1935

VIRUS
V. CUCUMBER MOSAIC (cont.)
Typha angustifolia
　Wellman, F.L., 1935
Uvularia sessilifolia
　Brierley, Philip and Floyd F. Smith, 1944
Valerianoides jamaicensis
　Adsuar, Jose and A. Cruz Miret, 1950
Vallota purpurea
　Brierley, Philip and Floyd F. Smith, 1944
Verbena hybrida
　Wellman, F.L., 1935
Vicia faba
　Adsuar, Jose and A. Cruz Miret, 1950
　Anderson, C.W., 1951
　Harter, L.L., 1936
　Whipple, O.C. and J.C. Walker, 1941
Vicia sativa
　Harter, L.L., 1938
Vicia villosa
　Harter, L.L., 1938
Vigna sinensis
　Anderson, C.W., 1951
　Govier, D.A., 1957
　Lindberg, G.D., D.H. Hall and J.C. Walker, 1956
　Simons, John N., 1957
　Wellman, F.L., 1934, 1935
Vigna unguiculata
　Adsuar, Jose and A. Cruz Miret, 1950
　Vasudeva, R. Sahai and T.B. Lal, 1943
Viola floridana
　Wellman, F.L., 1935
Viola odorata
　Wellman, F.L., 1935
Viola primulifolia
　Wellman, F.L., 1935
Viola tricolor
　Burnett, G., 1934
　Govier, D.A., 1957
　Wellman, F.L., 1935
Xanthosoma spp.
　Wellman, F.L., 1935
Xanthoxalis corniculata
　Wellman, F.L., 1935
Yucca baccata
　Brierley, Philip and Floyd F. Smith, 1944
Yucca flaccida
　Brierley, Philip and Floyd F. Smith, 1944
Yucca gloriosa
　Wellman, F.L., 1935
Zea mays
　Adsuar, Jose and A. Cruz Miret, 1950
　Harter, L.L., 1938
Zinnia elegans
　Lindberg, G.D., D.H. Hall and J.C. Walker, 1956

V. (CUCUMBER) O.S.C. ISOLATE 606 *
Beta vulgaris
　Porter, Clark A. and Frank P. McWhorter, 1951
Capsicum frutescens (Capsicum annuum)
　Porter, Clark A. and Frank P. McWhorter, 1951
Citrullus vulgaris
　Porter, Clark A. and Frank P. McWhorter, 1951
Cucumis melo
　Porter, Clark A. and Frank P. McWhorter, 1951
Cucurbita moschata
　Porter, Clark A. and Frank P. McWhorter, 1951
Nicotiana tabacum
　Porter, Clark A. and Frank P. McWhorter, 1951
Phaseolus vulgaris
　Porter, Clark A. and Frank P. McWhorter, 1951
Trifolium subterraneum
　Porter, Clark A. and Frank P. McWhorter, 1951
Vicia faba
　Porter, Clark A. and Frank P. McWhorter, 1951
Zinnia elegans
　Porter, Clark A. and Frank P. McWhorter, 1951

V. CUCUMBER WESTERN MOSAIC *
Parthenium argentatum
　Severin, Henry H.P., 1945

VIRUS
V. CUCURBIT MOSAIC *
 Citrullus vulgaris
  Doolittle, S.P. and M.N. Walker, 1925
 Cuscuta campestris
  Johnson, Folke, 1941

V. DAHLIA MOSAIC Brierley 1933
 Cichorium endivia
  Brierley, Philip and Floyd F. Smith, 1950
 Coreopsis lanceolata
  Brierley, Philip and Floyd F. Smith, 1950
 Cosmos bipinnatus
  Brierley, Philip and Floyd F. Smith, 1950
 Cucumis sativus
  Brierley, Philip and Floyd F. Smith, 1950
 Cynara cardunculus
  Brierley, Philip and Floyd F. Smith, 1950
 Doronicum caucasicum
  Brierley, Philip and Floyd F. Smith, 1950
 Lactuca sativa
  Brierley, Philip and Floyd F. Smith, 1950
 Rudbeckia serotina
  Brierley, Philip and Floyd F. Smith, 1950
 Rudbeckia serotina f. pulcherrima *
  Brierley, Philip and Floyd F. Smith, 1950
 Tithonia rotundifolia
  Brierley, Philip and Floyd F. Smith, 1950

V. DANDELION YELLOW MOSAIC Kassanis 1944
 Apium graveolens
  Kassanis, B., 1947
 Calendula officinalis
  Kassanis, B., 1947
 Cichorium intybus
  Kassanis, B., 1947
 Nicotiana glutinosa
  Kassanis, B., 1947
 Nicotiana tabacum
  Kassanis, B., 1947
 Pastinaca sativa
  Kassanis, B., 1947
 Petroselinum sativum
  Kassanis, B., 1947
 Sonchus oleraceus
  Kassanis, B., 1947

V. DATURA DISTORTION MOSAIC Capoor and Varma
 Beta vulgaris   1952
  Capoor, S.P. and P.M. Varma, 1952
 Cassia sophera
  Capoor, S.P. and P.M. Varma, 1952
 Crotalaria juncea
  Capoor, S.P. and P.M. Varma, 1952
 Cucumis sativus
  Capoor, S.P. and P.M. Varma, 1952
 Dahlia pinnata
  Capoor, S.P. and P.M. Varma, 1952
 Dolichos lablab
  Capoor, S.P. and P.M. Varma, 1952
 Glycine max
  Capoor, S.P. and P.M. Varma, 1952
 Hibiscus esculentus
  Capoor, S.P. and P.M. Varma, 1952
 Lagenaria vulgaris
  Capoor, S.P. and P.M. Varma, 1952
 Luffa acutangula
  Capoor, S.P. and P.M. Varma, 1952
 Nicotiana atropurpureum *
  Capoor, S.P. and P.M. Varma, 1952
 Phaseolus limensis
  Capoor, S.P. and P.M. Varma, 1952
 Phaseolus lunatus f. macrocarpus
  Capoor, S.P. and P.M. Varma, 1952
 Phaseolus vulgaris
  Capoor, S.P. and P.M. Varma, 1952
 Physalis alkekengi
  Capoor, S.P. and P.M. Varma, 1952
 Physalis peruviana
  Capoor, S.P. and P.M. Varma, 1952
 Solanum melongena
  Capoor, S.P. and P.M. Varma, 1952
 Solanum nigrum
  Capoor, S.P. and P.M. Varma, 1952

VIRUS
V. DATURA DISTORTION MOSAIC (cont.)
 Solanum nodiflorum
  Capoor, S.P. and P.M. Varma, 1952
 Spinacia oleracea
  Capoor, S.P. and P.M. Varma, 1952
 Tagetes erecta
  Capoor, S.P. and P.M. Varma, 1952
 Vicia faba
  Capoor, S.P. and P.M. Varma, 1952
 Vigna sinensis
  Capoor, S.P. and P.M. Varma, 1952
 Viola odorata
  Capoor, S.P. and P.M. Varma, 1952
 Zinnia elegans
  Capoor, S.P. and P.M. Varma, 1952

V. DOCK MOSAIC Grainger and Cockerham 1930
 Lactuca sativa
  Newhall, A.G., 1923

V. DODDER LATENT MOSAIC Bennett 1944
 Amaranthus graecizans
  Bennett, C.W., 1944
 Amaranthus retroflexus
  Bennett, C.W., 1944
 Atropa belladonna
  Bennett, C.W., 1944
 Brassica oleracea
  Bennett, C.W., 1944
 Cucurbita maxima
  Bennett, C.W., 1944
 Cucurbita pepo
  Bennett, C.W., 1944
 Cuscuta californica
  Bennett, C.W., 1944
 Cuscuta campestris
  Bennett, C.W., 1944
 Cuscuta subinclusa
  Bennett, C.W., 1944
 Datura meteloides
  Bennett, C.W., 1944
 Datura stramonium
  Bennett, C.W., 1944
 Daucus carota
  Bennett, C.W., 1944
 Eriogonum fasciculatum
  Bennett, C.W., 1944
 Hieracium argutum
  Bennett, C.W., 1944
 Lactuca sativa
  Bennett, C.W., 1944
 Matthiola incana
  Bennett, C.W., 1944
 Melilotus indica
  Bennett, C.W., 1944
 Nicotiana sylvestris
  Bennett, C.W., 1944
 Pastinaca sativa
  Bennett, C.W., 1944
 Phaseolus vulgaris
  Bennett, C.W., 1944
 Pisum sativum
  Bennett, C.W., 1944
 Sisymbrium irio
  Bennett, C.W., 1944
 Solanum gilo
  Bennett, C.W., 1944
 Solanum integrifolium
  Bennett, C.W., 1944
 Stellaria media
  Bennett, C.W., 1944
 Verbascum thapsus
  Bennett, C.W., 1944

V. EGGPLANT MOSAIC Ferguson 1951
 Apium graveolens
  Dale, W.T., 1954
 Cucumis sativus
  Ferguson, I.A.C., 1951
 Cucurbita pepo
  Dale, W.T., 1954
  Ferguson, I.A.C., 1951

VIRUS
V. EGGPLANT MOSAIC (cont.)
  Nicotiana alata var. grandiflora
    Ferguson, I.A.C., 1951
  Nicotiana chinensis
    Ferguson, I.A.C., 1951
  Nicotiana rustica
    Ferguson, I.A.C., 1951
  Nicotiana sanderae
    Ferguson, I.A.C., 1951
  Nicotiana sylvestris
    Ferguson, I.A.C., 1951
  Nicotiana tabacum
    Ferguson, I.A.C., 1951
  Zinnia elegans
    Dale, W.T., 1954

V. ELM MOSAIC Swingle et al. 1941
  Prunus serrulata
    Callahan, Kemper L. and J. Duain Moore, 1957

V. ERYNGIUM YELLOW MOSAIC *
  Lycopersicon esculentum
    Johnson, James and Edith M. Hein, 1948

V. EUPHORBIA MOSAIC Costa and Bennett 1950
  Acanthospermum hispidum
    Costa, A.S. and C.W. Bennett, 1950
  Amaranthus caudatus
    Costa, A.S. and C.W. Bennett, 1950
  Antirrhinum majus
    Costa, A.S. and C.W. Bennett, 1950
  Brassica pekinensis
    Costa, A.S. and C.W. Bennett, 1950
  Calendula officinalis
    Costa, A.S. and C.W. Bennett, 1950
  Callistephus chinensis
    Costa, A.S. and C.W. Bennett, 1950
  Canavalia ensiformis
    Costa, A.S. and C.W. Bennett, 1950
  Celosia argentea
    Costa, A.S. and C.W. Bennett, 1950
  Centaurea cyanus
    Costa, A.S. and C.W. Bennett, 1950
  Chrysanthemum cinerariifolium
    Costa, A.S. and C.W. Bennett, 1950
  Delphinium spp.
    Costa, A.S. and C.W. Bennett, 1950
  Erigeron bonariensis
    Costa, A.S. and C.W. Bennett, 1950
  Euphorbia pilulifera
    Costa, A.S. and C.W. Bennett, 1950
  Gossypium hirsutum
    Costa, A.S. and C.W. Bennett, 1950
  Impatiens balsamina
    Costa, A.S. and C.W. Bennett, 1950
  Ipomoea spp.
    Costa, A.S. and C.W. Bennett, 1950
  Lycopersicon esculentum
    Costa, A.S. and C.W. Bennett, 1950
  Manihot esculenta (Manihot utilissima)
    Costa, A.S. and C.W. Bennett, 1950
  Papaver spp.
    Costa, A.S. and C.W. Bennett, 1950
  Physalis spp.
    Costa, A.S. and C.W. Bennett, 1950
  Raphanus sativus
    Costa, A.S. and C.W. Bennett, 1950
  Ricinus communis
    Costa, A.S. and C.W. Bennett, 1950
  Sida rhombifolia
    Costa, A.S. and C.W. Bennett, 1950
  Silene pendula
    Costa, A.S. and C.W. Bennett, 1950
  Solanum tuberosum
    Costa, A.S. and C.W. Bennett, 1950
  Tagetes spp.
    Costa, A.S. and C.W. Bennett, 1950
  Tropaeolum majus
    Costa, A.S. and C.W. Bennett, 1950
  Vinca rosea
    Costa, A.S. and C.W. Bennett, 1950
  Viola tricolor
    Costa, A.S. and C.W. Bennett, 1950

VIRUS
V. EUPHORBIA MOSAIC (cont.)
  Zinnia elegans
    Costa, A.S. and C.W. Bennett, 1950

V. FIG MOSAIC Condit and Horne 1933
  Ficus palmata
    Condit, I.J. and W.T. Horne, 1933

V. FILAREE RED LEAF Frazier 1951
  Apium graveolens var. dulce
    Frazier, Norman W., 1951
  Beta vulgaris
    Frazier, Norman W., 1951
  Brassica oleracea var. botrytis
    Frazier, Norman W., 1951
  Callistephus chinensis
    Frazier, Norman W., 1951
  Cicer arietinum
    Frazier, Norman W., 1951
  Cucumis sativus
    Frazier, Norman W., 1951
  Cucurbita pepo
    Frazier, Norman W., 1951
  Fragaria chiloensis var. ananassa
    Frazier, Norman W., 1951
  Glycine max
    Frazier, Norman W., 1951
  Lathyrus odoratus
    Frazier, Norman W., 1951
  Lycopersicon esculentum
    Frazier, Norman W., 1951
  Matthiola incana
    Frazier, Norman W., 1951
  Medicago sativa
    Frazier, Norman W., 1951
  Nicotiana glutinosa
    Frazier, Norman W., 1951
  Nicotiana tabacum
    Frazier, Norman W., 1951
  Pelargonium hortorum
    Frazier, Norman W., 1951
  Phaseolus vulgaris
    Frazier, Norman W., 1951
  Pisum sativum
    Frazier, Norman W., 1951
  Plantago major
    Frazier, Norman W., 1951
  Spinacia oleracea
    Frazier, Norman W., 1951
  Trifolium pratense
    Frazier, Norman W., 1951
  Trifolium repens
    Frazier, Norman W., 1951
  Vicia faba
    Frazier, Norman W., 1951
  Vicia villosa
    Frazier, Norman W., 1951
  Vigna sinensis
    Frazier, Norman W., 1951
  Vitis californica
    Frazier, Norman W., 1951

V. GLADIOLUS *
  Antirrhinum majus
    Snow, Gordon F., 1955
  Cucumis sativus
    Snow, Gordon F., 1955
  Melilotus alba
    Snow, Gordon F., 1955
  Nicotiana tabacum
    Snow, Gordon F., 1955
  Trifolium pratense
    Snow, Gordon F., 1955
  Vicia faba
    Snow, Gordon F., 1955
  Zinnia elegans
    Snow, Gordon F., 1955

V. HENBANE MOSAIC K.M. Smith 1957
  Ageratum officinalis *
    Hamilton, Marion A., 1932
  Atropa belladonna
    Hamilton, Marion A., 1932

VIRUS

V. HENBANE MOSAIC (cont.)
   Brassica oleracea
      Hamilton, Marion A., 1932
   Brassica rapa
      Hamilton, Marion A., 1932
   Myosotis sylvaticum
      Hamilton, Marion A., 1932
   Raphanus raphanstrum
      Hamilton, Marion A., 1932
   Reseda odorata
      Hamilton, Marion A., 1932
   Solanum dulcamara
      Hamilton, Marion A., 1932
   Solanum melongena
      Hamilton, Marion A., 1932
   Solanum nodiflorum
      Hamilton, Marion A., 1932
   Solanum tuberosum
      Hamilton, Marion A., 1932

V. HIBISCUS YELLOW VEIN MOSAIC Capoor and Varma
   Abutilon indicum   1950
      Capoor, S.P. and P.M. Varma, 1950
   Ageratum conyzoides
      Capoor, S.P. and P.M. Varma, 1950
   Capsicum frutescens (Capsicum annuum)
      Capoor, S.P. and P.M. Varma, 1950
   Cassia tora
      Capoor, S.P. and P.M. Varma, 1950
   Corchorus trilocularis
      Capoor, S.P. and P.M. Varma, 1950
   Cuscuta reflexa
      Capoor, S.P. and P.M. Varma, 1950
   Datura alba
      Capoor, S.P. and P.M. Varma, 1950
   Dolichos lablab
      Capoor, S.P. and P.M. Varma, 1950
   Eclipta alba
      Capoor, S.P. and P.M. Varma, 1950
   Euphorbia geniculata
      Capoor, S.P. and P.M. Varma, 1950
   Gossypium peruvianum x Gossypium barbadense
      Capoor, S.P. and P.M. Varma, 1950
   Hibiscus furcatus
      Capoor, S.P. and P.M. Varma, 1950
   Hibiscus manihot
      Capoor, S.P. and P.M. Varma, 1950
   Lycopersicon esculentum
      Capoor, S.P. and P.M. Varma, 1950
   Medicago sativa
      Capoor, S.P. and P.M. Varma, 1950
   Nicotiana gultinosa
      Capoor, S.P. and P.M. Varma, 1950
   Nicotiana tabacum
      Capoor, S.P. and P.M. Varma, 1950
   Petunia hybrida
      Capoor, S.P. and P.M. Varma, 1950
   Phaseolus vulgaris
      Capoor, S.P. and P.M. Varma, 1950
   Sida rhombifolia
      Capoor, S.P. and P.M. Varma, 1950
   Solanum melongena
      Capoor, S.P. and P.M. Varma, 1950
   Solanum nigrum
      Capoor, S.P. and P.M. Varma, 1950
   Sonchus spp.
      Capoor, S.P. and P.M. Varma, 1950
   Trifolium pratense
      Capoor, S.P. and P.M. Varma, 1950
   Vernonia anthelmintica
      Capoor, S.P. and P.M. Varma, 1950
   Vigna sinensis
      Capoor, S.P. and P.M. Varma, 1950
   Zinnia elegans
      Capoor, S.P. and P.M. Varma, 1950

V. HIBISCUS YELLOWS *
   Gossypium barbadense
      Hendrix, J. Walter, 1950
   Gossypium hirsutum
      Hendrix, J. Walter, 1950
   Hibiscus esculentus
      Hendrix, J. Walter, 1950

VIRUS

V. HIBISCUS YELLOWS * (cont.)
   Hibiscus sabdariffa
      Hendrix, J. Walter, 1950
   Hibiscus tiliaceus (Pariti tiliaceum)
      Hendrix, J. Walter, 1950
   Hibiscus youngianus
      Hendrix, J. Walter, 1950
   Sida fallax
      Hendrix, J. Walter, 1950
   Thespesia populnea *
      Hendrix, J. Walter, 1950

V. HYDRANGEA *
   Nicotiana tabacum
      Brierley, Philip, 1954

V. HYDRANGEA RING SPOT Brierley and Smith 1952
   Antirrhinum majus
      Brierley, Philip and Floyd F. Smith, 1952
   Callistephus chinensis
      Brierley, Philip and Paul Lorentz, 1956, 1957
   Capsicum frutescens (Capsicum annuum)
      Brierley, Philip and Paul Lorentz, 1957
   Chrysanthemum morifolium
      Brierley, Philip and Paul Lorentz, 1957
   Cyamopsis tetragonoloba
      Brierley, Philip and Paul Lorentz, 1956, 1957
   Datura stramonium
      Brierley, Philip and Paul Lorentz, 1957
   Lycopersicon esculentum
      Brierley, Philip and Paul Lorentz, 1957
   Nicotiana glutinosa
      Brierley, Philip and Paul Lorentz, 1957
   Nicotiana tabacum
      Brierley, Philip and Paul Lorentz, 1956, 1957
   Petunia hybrida
      Brierley, Philip and Paul Lorentz, 1957
   Phaseolus vulgaris
      Brierley, Philip and Paul Lorentz, 1956, 1957
   Silene compacta
      Brierley, Philip and Paul Lorentz, 1957
   Zinnia elegans
      Brierley, Philip and Paul Lorentz, 1957

V. IRIS MOSAIC Brierley and McWhorter 1936
   Belamcanda chinensis
      Brierley, Philip and Floyd F. Smith, 1948
      Travis, R.V., 1957
   Lycopersicon esculentum
      Brierley, Philip and Frank P. McWhorter, 1936
   Nicotiana tabacum
      Brierley, Philip and Frank P. McWhorter, 1936
   Ornithogalum thyrsoides
      Smith, Floyd F. and Philip Brierley, 1944
   Petunia hybrida
      Brierley, Philip and Frank P. McWhorter, 1936
   Tulipa gesneriana
      Brierley, Philip and Frank P. McWhorter, 1936

V. IRIS RING SPOT *
   Belamcanda chinensis
      Travis, R.V., 1957

V. IRIS SPURIA MOSAIC *
   Gladiolus hortulanus
      Brierley, Philip and Floyd F. Smith, 1948

V. KAIMI CLOVER DISEASE *
   Lathyrus odoratus
      Murakishi, Harry H., 1952
   Medicago sativa
      Murakishi, Harry H., 1952
   Melilotus alba
      Murakishi, Harry H., 1952
   Melilotus officinalis
      Murakishi, Harry H., 1952
   Pisum sativum
      Murakishi, Harry H., 1952
   Trifolium pratense
      Murakishi, Harry H., 1952

VIRUS

V. LETTUCE MOSAIC Jagger 1921; Ainsworth and
    Brassica oleracea var. botrytis cymosa * Ogilvie 1939
        Ainsworth, G.C. and L. Ogilvie, 1939
    Carduus arvensis
        Ainsworth, G.C. and L. Ogilvie, 1939
    Cineraria cruenta
        Jones, Leon K., 1944
    Cucumis sativus
        Ainsworth, G.C., 1940
        Ainsworth, G.C. and L. Ogilvie, 1939
    Datura stramonium
        Ainsworth, G.C. and L. Ogilvie, 1939
    Lycopersicon esculentum
        Ainsworth, G.C., 1940
        Ainsworth, G.C. and L. Ogilvie, 1939
    Nicotiana glutinosa
        Ainsworth, G.C. and L. Ogilvie, 1939
    Nicotiana tabacum
        Ainsworth, G.C. and L. Ogilvie, 1939
    Phaseolus vulgaris
        Ainsworth, G.C., 1940
    Sonchus arvensis
        Ainsworth, G.C. and L. Ogilvie, 1939
    Sonchus oleraceus
        Ainsworth, G.C. and L. Ogilvie, 1939
    Taraxacum officinale
        Ainsworth, G.C. and L. Ogilvie, 1939
    Trifolium pratense
        Ainsworth, G.C., 1940
    Trifolium repens
        Ainsworth, G.C., 1940

V. LILAC WITCHES' BROOM Lorentz and Brierley 1953
    Callistephus chinensis
        Brierley, Philip, 1955
    Cuscuta campestris
        Brierley, Philip, 1955
    Cuscuta subinclusa
        Brierley, Philip, 1955
    Forsythia suspensa
        Brierley, Philip, 1955
    Fraxinus pennsylvanica
        Brierley, Philip, 1955
    Ligustrum lucidum
        Brierley, Philip, 1955
        Lorentz, Paul and Philip Brierley, 1953
    Ligustrum obtusifolium var. regelianum
        Brierley, Philip, 1955
    Ligustrum ovalifolium
        Lorentz, Paul and Philip Brierley, 1953
    Nicotiana rustica
        Brierley, Philip, 1955

V. LILY SYMPTOMLESS Brierley and Smith 1944
    Agapanthus africanus
        Brierley, Philip and Floyd F. Smith, 1944
    Allium cepa
        Brierley, Philip and Floyd F. Smith, 1944
    Allium cernuum
        Brierley, Philip and Floyd F. Smith, 1944
    Allium odorum
        Brierley, Philip and Floyd F. Smith, 1944
    Allium speciosum
        Brierley, Philip and Floyd F. Smith, 1944
    Aloe spp.
        Brierley, Philip and Floyd F. Smith, 1944
    Asparagus asparagoides
        Brierley, Philip and Floyd F. Smith, 1944
    Asparagus sprengeri
        Brierley, Philip and Floyd F. Smith, 1944
    Asphodeline lutea
        Brierley, Philip and Floyd F. Smith, 1944
    Belamcanda chinensis
        Brierley, Philip and Floyd F. Smith, 1944
    Brassica rapa
        Brierley, Philip and Floyd F. Smith, 1944
    Brodiaea uniflora
        Brierley, Philip and Floyd F. Smith, 1944
    Camassia leichtlinii
        Brierley, Philip and Floyd F. Smith, 1944
    Commelina coelestis
        Brierley, Philip and Floyd F. Smith, 1944

VIRUS

V. LILY SYMPTOMLESS (cont.)
    Commelina nudiflora
        Brierley, Philip and Floyd F. Smith, 1944
    Convallaria majalis
        Brierley, Philip and Floyd F. Smith, 1944
    Dioscorea alata
        Brierley, Philip and Floyd F. Smith, 1944
    Dracaena sanderiana
        Brierley, Philip and Floyd F. Smith, 1944
    Erythronium spp.
        Brierley, Philip and Floyd F. Smith, 1944
    Freesia hybrida
        Brierley, Philip and Floyd F. Smith, 1944
    Galtonia candicans
        Brierley, Philip and Floyd F. Smith, 1944
    Haworthia altilinea
        Brierley, Philip and Floyd F. Smith, 1944
    Hedychium coronarium
        Brierley, Philip and Floyd F. Smith, 1944
    Hosta plantaginea
        Brierley, Philip and Floyd F. Smith, 1944
    Iris filifolia
        Brierley, Philip and Floyd F. Smith, 1944
    Iris pallida
        Brierley, Philip and Floyd F. Smith, 1944
    Iris versicolor
        Brierley, Philip and Floyd F. Smith, 1944
    Kniphofia tucki
        Brierley, Philip and Floyd F. Smith, 1944
    Lilium hansonii
        Brierley, Philip and Floyd F. Smith, 1944
    Lilium henryi
        Brierley, Philip and Floyd F. Smith, 1944
    Lilium humboldtii
        Brierley, Philip and Floyd F. Smith, 1944
    Lilium pardalinum
        Brierley, Philip and Floyd F. Smith, 1944
    Lilium parryi
        Brierley, Philip and Floyd F. Smith, 1944
    Lilium sargentiae
        Brierley, Philip and Floyd F. Smith, 1944
    Lilium superbum
        Brierley, Philip and Floyd F. Smith, 1944
    Medeola virginica
        Brierley, Philip and Floyd F. Smith, 1944
    Moraea iridioides
        Brierley, Philip and Floyd F. Smith, 1944
    Musa cavendishii
        Brierley, Philip and Floyd F. Smith, 1944
    Musa textilis
        Brierley, Philip and Floyd F. Smith, 1944
    Muscari polyanthum
        Brierley, Philip and Floyd F. Smith, 1944
    Nothoscordum fragrans
        Brierley, Philip and Floyd F. Smith, 1944
    Ophiopogon jaburan
        Brierley, Philip and Floyd F. Smith, 1944
    Ornithogalum thyrsoides
        Brierley, Philip and Floyd F. Smith, 1944
        Smith, Floyd F. and Philip Brierley, 1944
    Philodendron spp.
        Brierley, Philip and Floyd F. Smith, 1944
    Sansevieria zeylanica
        Brierley, Philip and Floyd F. Smith, 1944
    Smilacina racemosa
        Brierley, Philip and Floyd F. Smith, 1944
    Smilax spp.
        Brierley, Philip and Floyd F. Smith, 1944
    Tigridia pavonia
        Brierley, Philip and Floyd F. Smith, 1944
    Tricyrtis hirta
        Brierley, Philip and Floyd F. Smith, 1944
    Trillium spp.
        Brierley, Philip and Floyd F. Smith, 1944
    Tritonia crocata
        Brierley, Philip and Floyd F. Smith, 1944
    Uvularia sessilifolia
        Brierley, Philip and Floyd F. Smith, 1944
    Vallota purpurea
        Brierley, Philip and Floyd F. Smith, 1944
    Yucca baccata
        Brierley, Philip and Floyd F. Smith, 1944
    Yucca flaccida
        Brierley, Philip and Floyd F. Smith, 1944

VIRUS
V. LOVAGE MOSAIC Smith and Markham 1944
   Apium graveolens
      Smith, Kenneth M. and Roy Markham, 1944
   Daucus carota
      Smith, Kenneth M. and Roy Markham, 1944
   Solanum tuberosum
      Smith, Kenneth M. and Roy Markham, 1944

V. LUCERNE DWARF
   Aesculus californica
      Freitag, J.H., 1951
   Amaranthus graecizans
      Porter, D.R., 1935
   Ambrosia psilostachya
      Porter, D.R., 1935
   Beta vulgaris
      Freitag, J.H., 1951
   Bidens pilosa
      Freitag, J.H., 1951
   Brassica campestris
      Freitag, J.H., 1951
   Calycanthus occidentalis
      Freitag, J.H., 1951
   Citrus limon
      Freitag, J.H., 1951
   Citrus reticulata
      Freitag, J.H., 1951
   Cotoneaster franchetii
      Freitag, J.H., 1951
   Diplacus aurantiacus
      Freitag, J.H., 1951
   Distichlis spicata
      Freitag, J.H., 1951
   Helianthus spp.
      Freitag, J.H., 1951
   Malus sylvestris
      Freitag, J.H., 1951
   Malva parviflora
      Freitag, J.H., 1951
   Matricaria suaveolens
      Freitag, J.H., 1951
   Philadelphus lewisii var. californicus *
      Freitag, J.H., 1951
   Plantago lanceolata
      Freitag, J.H., 1951
   Poa pratensis
      Freitag, J.H., 1951
   Polypogon monspeliensis
      Freitag, J.H., 1951
   Populus spp.
      Freitag, J.H., 1951
   Portulaca oleracea
      Freitag, J.H., 1951
   Prunus demissa
      Freitag, J.H., 1951
   Prunus mume
      Freitag, J.H., 1951
   Pseudotsuga taxifolia
      Freitag, J.H., 1951
   Pyracantha angustifolia
      Freitag, J.H., 1951
   Tetragonia expansa
      Freitag, J.H., 1951

V. LUCERNE MOSAIC
   Beta vulgaris
      Kreitlow, K.W. and W.C. Price, 1949
      Thomas, H. Rex, 1951
   Brassica oleracea var. capitata
      Thomas, H. Rex, 1951
   Cajanus indicus
      Zaumeyer, W.J., 1938
      Zaumeyer, W.J. and B.L. Wade, 1935
   Callistephus chinensis
      Kreitlow, K.W. and W.C. Price, 1949
   Canavalia gladiata
      Zaumeyer, W.J. and B.L. Wade, 1935
   Capsicum frutescens (Capsicum annuum)
      Johnson, E.M., 1946
      Thomas, H. Rex, 1951
      Zaumeyer, W.J., 1953
   Cassia tora
      Anderson, C.W., 1954

VIRUS
V. LUCERNE MOSAIC (cont.)
   Cicer arietinum
      Zaumeyer, W.J. and B.L. Wade, 1935
   Cucumis sativus
      Berkeley, G.H., 1947
      Johnson, E.M. 1946
      Kreitlow, K.W. and W.C. Price, 1949
      Zaumeyer, W.J., 1938, 1953
   Cuscuta campestris
      Kreitlow, K.W. and W.C. Price, 1949
   Dolichos lablab
      Zaumeyer, W.J. and B.L. Wade, 1935
   Glycine max
      Zaumeyer, W.J. and B.L. Wade, 1935
   Lactuca sativa
      Kreitlow, K.W. and W.C. Price, 1949
   Lathyrus odoratus
      Zaumeyer, W.J., 1938
      Zaumeyer, W.J. and B.L. Wade, 1933
   Lespedeza striata
      Zaumeyer, W.J., 1938
   Lotus corniculatus
      Kreitlow, K.W. and W.C. Price, 1949
   Lupinus albus
      Zaumeyer, W.J. and B.L. Wade, 1935
   Lupinus spp.
      Kreitlow, K.W. and W.C. Price, 1949
   Lycopersicon esculentum
      Berkeley, G.H., 1947
      Johnson, E.M., 1946
      Kreitlow, K.W. and W.C. Price, 1949
      Oswald, John W., 1950
      Thomas, H. Rex, 1951
      Zaumeyer, W.J., 1938, 1953
   Medicago lupulina
      Kreitlow, K.W. and W.C. Price, 1949
   Medicago sativa
      Johnson, E.M., 1946
      Kreitlow, K.W. and W.C. Price, 1949
      Porter, D.R., 1935
   Mucuna deeringianum
      Zaumeyer, W.J., 1938
      Zaumeyer, W.J. and B.L. Wade, 1935
   Nicotiana tabacum
      Porter, D.R., 1935
   Parthenium argentatum
      Severin, Henry H.P., 1945
   Petunia hybrida
      Zaumeyer, W.J., 1953
   Phaseolus acutifolius var. latifolius
      Zaumeyer, W.J., 1938
      Zaumeyer, W.J. and B.L. Wade, 1935
   Phaseolus calcaratus
      Zaumeyer, W.J., 1938
   Phaseolus lunatus
      Zaumeyer, W.J. and B.L. Wade, 1935
   Phaseolus lunatus f. macrocarpus
      Zaumeyer, W.J., 1938
      Zaumeyer, W.J. and B.L. Wade, 1935
   Phaseolus vulgaris
      Harrison, Arthus L., 1935
   Phytolacca americana
      Johnson, E.M., 1946
   Pisum sativum
      Pierce, W.H., 1937
      Zaumeyer, W.J. and B.L. Wade, 1933, 1935
   Solanum melongena
      Zaumeyer, W.J., 1938
   Solanum tuberosum
      Thomas, H. Rex, 1951
   Spinacia oleracea
      Kreitlow, K.W. and W.C. Price, 1949
      Thomas, H.R., 1953
   Trifolium pratense
      Zaumeyer, W.J., 1953
   Trifolium procumbens
      Kreitlow, K.W. and W.C. Price, 1949
   Trifolium repens
      Zaumeyer, W.J. and B.L. Wade, 1935
   Vigna sesquipedalis
      Zaumeyer, W.J. and B.L. Wade, 1935
   Vigna sinensis
      Zaumeyer, W.J. and B.L. Wade, 1935

VIRUS
V. LUCERNE MOSAIC (cont.)
Zinnia elegans
Johnson, E.M., 1946
Zaumeyer, W.J., 1938

V. LUCERNE WITCHES' BROOM Edwards 1936
Astragalus canadensis
Klostermeyer, E.C. and J.D. Menzies, 1951
Astragalus cicer
Klostermeyer, E.C. and J.D. Menzies, 1951
Cuscuta campestris
Helms, Katie, 1957
Kunkel, L.O., 1952
Lathyrus pratensis
Klostermeyer, E.C. and J.D. Menzies, 1951
Lotus corniculatus
Menzies, J.D., 1946
Medicago arabica
Menzies, J.D., 1946
Medicago lacinata
Klostermeyer, E.C. and J.D. Menzies, 1951
Melilotus spp.
Menzies, J.D., 1944
Onobrychis spp.
Menzies, J.D., 1946
Onobrychis transcaucasica
Klostermeyer, E.C. and J.D. Menzies, 1951
Onobrychis viciaefolia
Klostermeyer, E.C. and J.D. Menzies, 1951
Phaseolus vulgaris
Menzies, J.D., 1946
Robinia pseudoacacia
Menzies, J.D., 1946
Swainsona salsula
Klostermeyer, E.C. and J.D. Menzies, 1951
Trifolium fragiferum
Menzies, J.D., 1946
Trifolium hybridum
Menzies, J.D., 1946
Trifolium incarnatum
Menzies, J.D., 1946
Trifolium spp.
Menzies, J.D., 1944
Vicia variabilis
Klostermeyer, E.C. and J.D. Menzies, 1951

V. LUPINE DISEASE *
Glycine max
Weimer, J.L., 1950
Lupinus albus
Weimer, J.L., 1950
Lycopersicon esculentum
Weimer, J.L., 1950

V. MAIZE LEAF FLECK Stoner 1952
Allium cepa
Stoner, Warren N., 1952
Apium graveolens
Stoner, Warren N., 1952
Avena sativa
Stoner, Warren N., 1952
Beta vulgaris
Stoner, Warren N., 1952
Cucurbita pepo
Stoner, Warren N., 1952
Freesia refracta
Stoner, Warren N., 1952
Hordeum vulgare
Stoner, Warren N., 1952
Nicotiana tabacum
Stoner, Warren N., 1952
Saccharum officinarum
Stoner, Warren N., 1952
Sorghum vulgare
Stoner, Warren N., 1952
Sorghum vulgare var. sudanense
Stoner, Warren N., 1952
Triticum vulgare
Stoner, Warren N., 1952
Zantedeschia aethiopica
Stoner, Warren N., 1952

VIRUS
V. MAIZE STREAK Storey 1925
Dactylis glomerata
Finley, A.M., 1954
Eleusine indica
Storey, H.H. and A.P.D. McClean, 1930
Nicotiana tabacum
Finley, A.M., 1954

V. MALVA YELLOW VEIN MOSAIC *
Althaea rosea
Costa, A.S. and James E. Duffus, 1957
Beta vulgaris
Costa, A.S. and James E. Duffus, 1957
Gossypium hirsutum
Costa, A.S. and James E. Duffus, 1957
Hibiscus esculentus
Costa, A.S. and James E. Duffus, 1957
Lycopersicon esculentum
Costa, A.S. and James E. Duffus, 1957
Nicotiana tabacum
Costa, A.S. and James E. Duffus, 1957
Spinacia oleracea
Costa, A.S. and James E. Duffus, 1957

V. MILKWEED MOSAIC *
Lactuca sativa
Newhall, A.G., 1923

V. MUSKMELON MOSAIC Rader et al. 1947
Allium cepa
Rader, Wm. E., Hugh F. Fitzpatrick and E.M. Hildebrand, 1947
Anthemis cotula
Rader, Wm. E., Hugh F. Fitzpatrick and E.M. Hildebrand, 1947
Apium graveolens
Rader, Wm. E., Hugh F. Fitzpatrick and E.M. Hildebrand, 1947
Aster spp.
Rader, Wm. E., Hugh F. Fitzpatrick and E.M. Hildebrand, 1947
Astragalus spp.
Rader, Wm. E., Hugh F. Fitzpatrick and E.M. Hildebrand, 1947
Baptisia spp.
Rader, Wm. E., Hugh F. Fitzpatrick and E.M. Hildebrand, 1947
Barbarea vulgaris
Rader, Wm. E., Hugh F. Fitzpatrick and E.M. Hildebrand, 1947
Beta vulgaris
Rader, Wm. E., Hugh F. Fitzpatrick and E.M. Hildebrand, 1947
Brassica kaber (Brassica arvensis)
Rader, Wm. E., Hugh F. Fitzpatrick and E.M. Hildebrand, 1947
Brassica rapa
Rader, Wm. E., Hugh F. Fitzpatrick and E.M. Hildebrand, 1947
Browallia elata
Rader, Wm. E., Hugh F. Fitzpatrick and E.M. Hildebrand, 1947
Calendula officinalis
Rader, Wm. E., Hugh F. Fitzpatrick and E.M. Hildebrand, 1947
Capsicum frutescens (Capsicum annuum)
Anderson, C.W., 1954
Rader, Wm. E., Hugh F. Fitzpatrick and E.M. Hildebrand, 1947
Chrysanthemum carinatum
Rader, Wm. E., Hugh F. Fitzpatrick and E.M. Hildebrand, 1947
Chrysanthemum segetum
Rader, Wm. E., Hugh F. Fitzpatrick and E.M. Hildebrand, 1947
Citrullus vulgaris
Rader, Wm. E., Hugh F. Fitzpatrick and E.M. Hildebrand, 1947
Coleus blumei
Rader, Wm. E., Hugh F. Fitzpatrick and E.M. Hildebrand, 1947
Datura stramonium
Lindberg, G.D., D.H. Hall and J.C. Walker, 1956

VIRUS
V. MUSKMELON MOSAIC (cont.)

Erysimum cheiranthoides
  Rader, Wm. E., Hugh F. Fitzpatrick and E.M. Hildebrand, 1947
Eschscholtzia californica
  Rader, Wm. E., Hugh F. Fitzpatrick and E.M. Hildebrand, 1947
Fagopyrum esculentum
  Rader, Wm. E., Hugh F. Fitzpatrick and E.M. Hildebrand, 1947
Glycine max
  Rader, Wm. E., Hugh F. Fitzpatrick and E.M. Hildebrand, 1947
Hyocyamus albus
  Rader, Wm. E., Hugh F. Fitzpatrick and E.M. Hildebrand, 1947
Hyocyamus niger
  Rader, Wm. E., Hugh F. Fitzpatrick and E.M. Hildebrand, 1947
Lactuca sativa
  Rader, Wm. E., Hugh F. Fitzpatrick and E.M. Hildebrand, 1947
Malva moschata
  Rader, Wm. E., Hugh F. Fitzpatrick and E.M. Hildebrand, 1947
Mentha spicata
  Rader, Wm. E., Hugh F. Fitzpatrick and E.M. Hildebrand, 1947
Nicotiana glutinosa
  Lindberg, G.D., D.H. Hall and J.C. Walker, 1956
Nicotiana rustica
  Lindberg, G.D., D.H. Hall and J.C. Walker, 1956
  Rader, Wm. E., Hugh F. Fitzpatrick and E.M. Hildebrand, 1947
Nicotiana tabacum
  Anderson, C.W., 1954
  Lindberg, G.D., D.H. Hall and J.C. Walker, 1956
  Rader, Wm. E., Hugh F. Fitzpatrick and E.M. Hildebrand, 1947
Petunia hybrida
  Rader, Wm. E., Hugh F. Fitzpatrick and E.M. Hildebrand, 1947
Phaseolus lunatus
  Rader, Wm. E., Hugh F. Fitzpatrick and E.M. Hildebrand, 1947
Phaseolus vulgaris
  Rader, Wm. E., Hugh F. Fitzpatrick and E.M. Hildebrand, 1947
Portulaca oleracea
  Rader, Wm. E., Hugh F. Fitzpatrick and E.M. Hildebrand, 1947
Raphanus sativus
  Rader, Wm. E., Hugh F. Fitzpatrick and E.M. Hildebrand, 1947
Rorippa palustris
  Rader, Wm. E., Hugh F. Fitzpatrick and E.M. Hildebrand, 1947
Rudbeckia hirta
  Rader, Wm. E., Hugh F. Fitzpatrick and E.M. Hildebrand, 1947
Secale cereale
  Rader, Wm. E., Hugh F. Fitzpatrick and E.M. Hildebrand, 1947
Solanum melongena
  Rader, Wm. E., Hugh F. Fitzpatrick and E.M. Hildebrand, 1947
Solanum tuberosum
  Rader, Wm. E., Hugh F. Fitzpatrick and E.M. Hildebrand, 1947
Spinacia oleracea
  Rader, Wm. E., Hugh F. Fitzpatrick and E.M. Hildebrand, 1947
Trifolium pratense
  Rader, Wm. E., Hugh F. Fitzpatrick and E.M. Hildebrand, 1947
Triticum aestivum
  Rader, Wm. E., Hugh F. Fitzpatrick and E.M. Hildebrand, 1947
Tropaeolum majus
  Rader, Wm. E., Hugh F. Fitzpatrick and E.M. Hildebrand, 1947
Verbascum blattaria
  Rader, Wm. E., Hugh F. Fitzpatrick and E.M. Hildebrand, 1947

VIRUS
V. MUSKMELON MOSAIC (cont.)

Verbascum thapsus
  Rader, Wm. E., Hugh F. Fitzpatrick and E.M. Hildebrand, 1947
Vigna sinensis
  Lindberg, G.D., D.H. Hall and J.C. Walker, 1956
  Rader, Wm. E., Hugh F. Fitzpatrick and E.M. Hildebrand, 1947
Vinca rosea
  Rader, Wm. E., Hugh F. Fitzpatrick and E.M. Hildebrand, 1947
Zea mays
  Rader, Wm. E., Hugh F. Fitzpatrick and E.M. Hildebrand, 1947
Zebrina pendula
  Rader, Wm. E., Hugh F. Fitzpatrick and E.M. Hildebrand, 1947
Zinnia elegans
  Anderson, C.W., 1954
  Lindberg, G.D., D.H. Hall and J.C. Walker, 1956
  Rader, Wm. E., Hugh F. Fitzpatrick and E.M. Hildebrand, 1947

V. NARCISSUS MOSAIC McWhorter and Weiss 1932; Haasis 1939
Allium cepa
  Haasis, Frank A., 1939
Amaryllis spp.
  Haasis, Frank A., 1939
Cooperia spp.
  Haasis, Frank A., 1939
Hypoxis spp.
  Haasis, Frank A., 1939
Lilium longiflorum var. gigantium
  Haasis, Frank A., 1939
Pancratium maritimum
  Haasis, Frank A., 1939
Sprekelia formosissima
  Haasis, Frank A., 1939
Tulipa gesneriana
  Haasis, Frank A., 1939
Zephyranthes candida
  Haasis, Frank A., 1939
Zephyranthes carinata
  Haasis, Frank A., 1939

V. NARCISSUS WHITE STREAK *
Ornithogalum thyrsoides
  Smith, Floyd F. and Philip Brierley, 1944

V. NICOTIANA GLUTINOSA MOSAIC *
Atropa belladonna
  Allard, H.A., 1916
Capsicum cerasiforme
  Allard, H.A., 1916
Lathyrus odoratus
  Allard, H.A., 1916
Lycopersicon esculentum
  Allard, H.A., 1916
Nicotiana rustica
  Allard, H.A., 1916
Nicotiana tabacum
  Allard, H.A., 1916
Phytolacca decandra
  Allard, H.A., 1916
Solanum tuberosum
  Allard, H.A., 1916

V. NICOTIANA GLUTINOSA ROOT NECROSIS *
Capsicum frutescens (Capsicum annuum)
  Cetas, Robert C. and A. Frank Ross, 1952
Cucumis sativus
  Cetas, Robert C. and A. Frank Ross, 1952
Datura stramonium
  Cetas, Robert C. and A. Frank Ross, 1952
Gomphrena globosa
  Cetas, Robert C. and A. Frank Ross, 1952
Phaseolus vulgaris
  Cetas, Robert C. and A. Frank Ross, 1952
Solanum tuberosum
  Cetas, Robert C. and A. Frank Ross, 1952
Vigna sinensis
  Cetas, Robert C. and A. Frank Ross, 1952
Zinnia elegans
  Cetas, Robert C. and A. Frank Ross, 1952

VIRUS

V. NOTHOSCORDUM MOSAIC McKinney 1950

Allium cepa
    McKinney, H.H., 1950
Allium vineale
    McKinney, H.H., 1950
Avena sativa
    McKinney, H.H., 1950
Beta vulgaris
    McKinney, H.H., 1950
Cucumis sativus
    McKinney, H.H., 1950
Datura stramonium
    McKinney, H.H., 1950
Lilium formosanum *
    McKinney, H.H., 1950
Lycopersicon esculentum
    McKinney, H.H., 1950
Nicotiana tabacum
    McKinney, H.H., 1950
Ornithogalum thyrsoides
    McKinney, H.H., 1950
Phaseolus vulgaris
    McKinney, H.H., 1950
Sesamum indicum
    McKinney, H.H., 1950
Sparaxis tricolor
    McKinney, H.H., 1950
Triticum aestivum
    McKinney, H.H., 1950
Zea mays
    McKinney, H.H., 1950

V. ONION YELLOW DWARF Melhus et al. 1929; Drake, Harris and Tate 1932

Allium canadense
    Henderson, W.J., 1935
Allium fistulosum
    Brierley, Philip and Floyd F. Smith, 1946
Allium fistulosum x Allium cepa
    Brierley, Philip and Floyd F. Smith, 1946
Allium porrum
    Henderson, W.J., 1935
Allium sativum
    Henderson, W.J., 1935
Allium schoenoprasum
    Henderson, W.J., 1935
Amaranthus retroflexus
    Henderson, W.J., 1935
Asclepias syriaca
    Henderson, W.J., 1935
Beta vulgaris
    Henderson, W.J., 1935
Canna generalis
    Henderson, W.J., 1935
Chenopodium album
    Henderson, W.J., 1935
Cucumis sativus
    Henderson, D.M., 1953
    Henderson, W.J., 1935
Cucurbita moschata
    Henderson, W.J., 1935
Datura stramonium
    Henderson, D.M., 1953
Gladiolus spp.
    Henderson, W.J., 1935
Hyacinthus orientalis
    Henderson, W.J., 1935
Iris persica
    Henderson, W.J., 1935
Lilium auratum
    Henderson, W.J., 1935
Lilium candidum
    Henderson, W.J., 1935
Lilium longiflorum
    Henderson, W.J., 1935
Lilium regale
    Henderson, W.J., 1935
Lilium speciosum
    Henderson, W.J., 1935
Lilium tigrinum
    Henderson, W.J., 1935
Medicago sativa
    Henderson, W.J., 1935

VIRUS

V. ONION YELLOW DWARF (cont.)

Melilotus alba
    Henderson, W.J., 1935
Muhlenbergia mexicana
    Henderson, W.J., 1935
Narcissus poeticus
    Henderson, W.J., 1935
Nicotiana glutinosa
    Henderson, D.M., 1953
Nicotiana tabacum
    Henderson, D.M., 1953
Ornithogalum thyrsoides
    Smith, Floyd F. and Philip Brierley, 1944
Phaseolus vulgaris
    Henderson, W.J., 1935
Plantago major
    Henderson, W.J., 1935
Setaria lutescens
    Henderson, W.J., 1935
Trifolium pratense
    Henderson, W.J., 1935
Tulipa gesneriana
    Henderson, W.J., 1935
Zea indentata
    Henderson, W.J., 1935

V. ORCHID (CATTLEYA) MOSAIC Jensen 1949

Tropaeolum majus
    Jensen, D.D., 1949

V. ORCHID (CYMBIDIUM) MOSAIC Jensen 1950

Apium graveolens
    Jensen, D.D., 1951
Beta vulgaris
    Jensen, D.D., 1951
Brassica chinensis
    Jensen, D.D., 1951
Brassica oleracea var. botrytis
    Jensen, D.D., 1951
Callistephus chinensis
    Jensen, D.D., 1951
Cattleya trianaei
    Jensen, D.D., 1951
Cucurbita maxima
    Jensen, D.D., 1951
Cyclamen persicum (Cyclamen indicum)
    Jensen, D.D., 1951
Datura meteloides
    Jensen, D.D. and A.H. Gold, 1955
Erodium moschatum
    Jensen, D.D., 1951
Fragaria bracteata
    Jensen, D.D., 1951
Freesia refracta
    Jensen, D.D., 1951
Glycine max
    Jensen, D.D., 1951
Lycopersicon esculentum
    Jensen, D.D., 1951
Nicotiana glutinosa
    Jensen, D.D., 1951
Nicotiana tabacum
    Jensen, D.D., 1951
Phaseolus vulgaris
    Jensen, D.D., 1951
Plantago major
    Jensen, D.D., 1951
Primula obconica
    Jensen, D.D., 1951
Raphanus sativus
    Jensen, D.D., 1951
Rubus loganobaccus
    Jensen, D.D., 1951
Trifolium incarnatum
    Jensen, D.D., 1951
Trifolium procumbens
    Jensen, D.D., 1951
Tropaeolum majus
    Jensen, D.D., 1951
Viola spp.
    Jensen, D.D., 1951
Zea mays
    Jensen, D.D., 1951

VIRUS

V. ORCHID (VANDA) MOSAIC Murakishi 1950

Allium tuberosum
 Murakishi, Harry H., 1952
Anthurium andraeanum
 Murahishi, Harry H., 1952
Beta vulgaris
 Murakishi, Harry H., 1952
Brassica napus var. chinensis *
 Murakishi, Harry H., 1952
Callistephus chinensis
 Murakishi, Harry H., 1952
Capsicum frutescens (Capsicum annuum)
 Murakishi, Harry H., 1952
Carica papaya
 Murakishi, Harry H., 1952
Cattleya gaskelliana
 Murakishi, Harry H., 1952
Cattleya spp.
 Murakishi, Harry H., 1952
Cattleya trianaei
 Murakishi, Harry H., 1952
Cucumis sativus
 Murakishi, Harry H., 1952
Cucurbita pepo
 Murakishi, Harry H., 1952
Dianthus caryophyllus
 Murakishi, Harry H., 1952
Glycine max
 Murakishi, Harry H., 1952
Hemerocallis flava
 Murakishi, Harry H., 1952
Hibiscus rosa-sinensis
 Murakishi, Harry H., 1952
Impatiens sultanii (or sometimes Impatiens holstii)
 Murakishi, Harry H., 1952
Laeliocattleya spp.
 Murakishi, Harry H., 1952
Lilium longiflorum
 Murakishi, Harry H., 1952
Lycopersicon esculentum
 Murakishi, Harry H., 1952
Matthiola incana
 Murakishi, Harry H., 1952
Neomarica caerulea
 Murakishi, Harry H., 1952
Nicotiana glutinosa
 Murakishi, Harry H., 1952
Nicotiana rustica
 Murakishi, Harry H., 1952
Nicotiana tabacum
 Murakishi, Harry H., 1952
Phaseolus vulgaris
 Murakishi, Harry H., 1952
Pisum sativum
 Murakishi, Harry H., 1952
Tropaeolum majus
 Murakishi, Harry H., 1952
Vigna sinensis
 Murakishi, Harry H., 1952
Zea mays
 Murakishi, Harry H., 1952
Zinnia elegans
 Murakishi, Harry H., 1952

V. ORCHID (ODONTOGLOSSUM) RING SPOT Jensen and
Apium graveolens   Gold 1951
 Jensen, D.D. and A. Herbert Gold, 1951
Beta vulgaris
 Jensen, D.D. and A. Herbert Gold, 1951
Brassica chinensis
 Jensen, D.D. and A. Herbert Gold, 1951
Callistephus chinensis
 Jensen, D.D. and A. Herbert Gold, 1951
Cucumis sativus
 Jensen, D.D. and A. Herbert Gold, 1951
Cucurbita maxima
 Jensen, D.D. and A. Herbert Gold, 1951
Cymbidium spp.
 Jensen, D.D. and A. Herbert Gold, 1951
Cynara scolymus
 Jensen, D.D. and A. Herbert Gold, 1951
Datura stramonium
 Jensen, D.D. and A. Herbert Gold, 1951

VIRUS

V. ORCHID (ODONTOGLOSSUM) RING SPOT (cont.)

Lactuca sativa
 Jensen, D.D. and A. Herbert Gold, 1951
Lycopersicon esculentum
 Jensen, D.D. and A. Herbert Gold, 1951
Matthiola incana var. annua
 Jensen, D.D. and A. Herbert Gold, 1951
Nicotiana glutinosa
 Jensen, D.D. and A. Herbert Gold, 1951
Nicotiana tabacum
 Jensen, D.D. and A. Herbert Gold, 1951
Plantago major
 Jensen, D.D. and A. Herbert Gold, 1951
Trifolium incarnatum
 Jensen, D.D. and A. Herbert Gold, 1951
Tropaeolum majus
 Jensen, D.D. and A. Herbert Gold, 1951
Vigna sinensis
 Jensen, D.D. and A. Herbert Gold, 1951
Zea mays
 Jensen, D.D. and A. Herbert Gold, 1951
Zinnia spp.
 Jensen, D.D. and A. Herbert Gold, 1951

V. ORNITHOGALUM MOSAIC Smith and Brierley 1944

Agapanthus africanus
 Smith, Floyd F. and Philip Brierley, 1944
Allium cepa
 Smith, Floyd F. and Philip Brierley, 1944
Allium cernuum
 Smith, Floyd F. and Philip Brierley, 1944
Allium fistulosum
 Smith, Floyd F. and Philip Brierley, 1944
Allium porrum
 Smith, Floyd F. and Philip Brierley, 1944
Camassia leichtlinii
 Smith, Floyd F. and Philip Brierley, 1944
Gloriosa rothschildiana
 Smith, Floyd F. and Philip Brierley, 1944
Hyacinthus azureus
 Smith, Floyd F. and Philip Brierley, 1944
Lilium formosanum *
 Smith, Floyd F. and Philip Brierley, 1944
Lilium longiflorum
 Smith, Floyd F. and Philip Brierley, 1944
Muscari botryoides
 Smith, Floyd F. and Philip Brierley, 1944
Nicotiana tabacum
 Smith, Floyd F. and Philip Brierley, 1944
Pancratium maritimum
 Smith, Floyd F. and Philip Brierley, 1944
Scilla peruviana
 Smith, Floyd F. and Philip Brierley, 1944
Tritonia crocata
 Smith, Floyd F. and Philip Brierley, 1944
Tulipa gesneriana
 Smith, Floyd F. and Philip Brierley, 1944
Zephyranthes spp.
 Smith, Floyd F. and Philip Brierley, 1944

V. PANAX RING SPOT Aragaki et al. 1953

Lycopersicon esculentum
 Aragaki, M., H. Murakishi and J.W. Hendrix,
 1953
Nicotiana glutinosa
 Aragaki, M., H. Murakishi and J.W. Hendrix,
 1953
Tropaeolum majus
 Aragaki, M., H. Murakishi and J.W. Hendrix,
 1953

V. PANICUM MOSAIC *

Agropyron elongatum
 Sill, W.H., Jr. and R.C. Pickett, 1957
Agropyron repens
 Sill, W.H., Jr. and R.C. Pickett, 1957
Aster spp.
 Sill, W.H., Jr. and R.C. Pickett, 1957
Avena sativa
 Sill, W.H., Jr. and R.C. Pickett, 1957
Bromus inermis
 Sill, W.H., Jr. and R.C. Pickett, 1957

VIRUS
V. PANICUM MOSAIC * (cont.)
   Cyperus esculentus
      Sill, W.H., Jr. and R.C. Pickett, 1957
   Dactylis glomerata
      Sill, W.H., Jr. and R.C. Pickett, 1957
   Eleusine indica
      Sill, W.H., Jr. and R.C. Pickett, 1957
   Gomphrena globosa
      Sill, W.H., Jr. and R.C. Pickett, 1957
   Hordeum vulgare
      Sill, W.H., Jr. and R.C. Pickett, 1957
   Lolium spp.
      Sill, W.H., Jr. and R.C. Pickett, 1957
   Nicotiana glutinosa
      Sill, W.H., Jr. and R.C. Pickett, 1957
   Nicotiana tabacum
      Sill, W.H., Jr. and R.C. Pickett, 1957
   Panicum depauperatum
      Sill, W.H., Jr. and R.C. Pickett, 1957
   Panicum maximum
      Sill, W.H., Jr. and R.C. Pickett, 1957
   Paspalum spp.
      Sill, W.H., Jr. and R.C. Pickett, 1957
   Pennisetum glaucum
      Sill, W.H., Jr. and R.C. Pickett, 1957
   Phalaris arundinacea
      Sill, W.H., Jr. and R.C. Pickett, 1957
   Secale cereale
      Sill, W.H., Jr. and R.C. Pickett, 1957
   Sorghum vulgare
      Sill, W.H., Jr. and R.C. Pickett, 1957
   Triticum aestivum
      Sill, W.H., Jr. and R.C. Pickett, 1957
   Vinca rosea
      Sill, W.H., Jr. and R.C. Pickett, 1957
   Zea mays
      Sill, W.H., Jr. and R.C. Pickett, 1957

V. PAPAW MOSAIC Capoor and Varma 1948
   Abelmoschus esculentus
      Adsuar, Jose, 1950
   Adenoropium gossypifolium
      Adsuar, Jose, 1950
   Amaranthus cruentus
      Adsuar, Jose, 1950
   Amaranthus dubius
      Adsuar, Jose, 1950
   Beta vulgaris
      Adsuar, Jose, 1950
   Bidens cynapiifolia
      Adsuar, Jose, 1950
   Capsicum frutescens (Capsicum annuum)
      Adsuar, Jose, 1950
   Catharanthus roseus
      Adsuar, Jose, 1950
   Citrullus citrullus
      Adsuar, Jose, 1950
   Cleome spinosa
      Adsuar, Jose, 1950
   Coleus lanuginosus
      Adsuar, Jose, 1950
   Crassina elegans
      Adsuar, Jose, 1950
   Cucumis sativus
      Adsuar, Jose, 1950
   Cucurbita lagenaria
      Adsuar, Jose, 1950
   Cucurbita moschata
      Adsuar, Jose, 1950
   Cucurbita pepo
      Adsuar, Jose, 1950
   Datura stramonium
      Adsuar, Jose, 1950
   Emilia sonchifolia
      Adsuar, Jose, 1950
   Ipomoea crassicaulis
      Adsuar, Jose, 1950
   Ipomoea pes-caprae
      Adsuar, Jose, 1950
   Ipomoea quinquefolia
      Adsuar, Jose, 1950
   Ipomoea rubra
      Adsuar, Jose, 1950

VIRUS
V. PAPAW MOSAIC (cont.)
   Isotoma longiflora
      Adsuar, Jose, 1950
   Jussiaea angustifolia
      Adsuar, Jose, 1950
   Leonotis nepetaefolia
      Adsuar, Jose, 1950
   Luffa aegyptiaca (Luffa cylindrica)
      Adsuar, Jose, 1950
   Lycopersicon esculentum
      Adsuar, Jose, 1950
   Mirabilis jalapa
      Adsuar, Jose, 1950
   Momordica charantia
      Adsuar, Jose, 1950
   Nicotiana glutinosa
      Adsuar, Jose, 1950
   Nicotiana tabacum
      Adsuar, Jose, 1950
   Passiflora edulis
      Adsuar, Jose, 1950
   Passiflora foetida
      Adsuar, Jose, 1950
   Phaseolus lunatus
      Adsuar, Jose, 1950
   Phaseolus vulgaris
      Adsuar, Jose, 1950
   Physalis angulata
      Adsuar, Jose, 1950
   Plantago major
      Adsuar, Jose, 1950
   Rivina humilis aurantica *
      Adsuar, Jose, 1950
   Ruellia tuberosa
      Adsuar, Jose, 1950
   Sechium edule
      Adsuar, Jose, 1950
   Sicana odorifera
      Adsuar, Jose, 1950
   Sida carpinifolia
      Adsuar, Jose, 1950
   Solanum caribaeum
      Adsuar, Jose, 1950
   Solanum melongena
      Adsuar, Jose, 1950
   Solanum torvum
      Adsuar, Jose, 1950
   Valerianoides jamaicensis
      Adsuar, Jose, 1950
   Vigna unguiculata
      Adsuar, Jose, 1950
   Zea mays
      Adsuar, Jose, 1950

V. PAPAW RING SPOT Jensen 1947
   Beta vulgaris
      Jensen, D.D., 1949
   Brassica chinensis
      Jensen, D.D., 1949
   Capsicum frutescens (Capsicum annuum)
      Jensen, D.D., 1949
   Commelina diffusa
      Jensen, D.D., 1949
   Crotalaria incana
      Jensen, D.D., 1949
   Cucumis sativus
      Jensen, D.D., 1949
   Kalanchoe (Bryophyllum) calycinum)
      Jensen, D.D., 1949
   Lactuca sativa
      Jensen, D.D., 1949
   Lycopersicon esculentum
      Jensen, D.D., 1949
   Malvastrum coromandelianum
      Jensen, D.D., 1949
   Mirabilis jalapa
      Jensen, D.D., 1949
   Nicotiana tabacum
      Jensen, D.D., 1949
   Passiflora foetida
      Jensen, D.D., 1949
   Passiflora pfordtii
      Jensen, D.D., 1949

VIRUS

V. PAPAW RING SPOT (cont.)
  Portulaca oleracea
    Jensen, D.D., 1949
  Solanum tuberosum
    Jensen, D.D., 1949

V. PEA DIE BACK *
  Phaseolus vulgaris
    Zaumeyer, W.J., 1939

V. PEA ENATION MOSAIC Pierce 1935
  Apium graveolens var. dulce
    Simons, John N., 1954
  Arachis hypogaea
    Osborn, H.T., 1938
  Beta vulgaris
    Simons, John N., 1954
  Brassica juncea (Brassica japonica)
    Simons, John N., 1954
  Cicer arietinum
    Johnson, Folke and Leon K. Jones, 1937
  Cucumis sativus
    Ainsworth, G.C., 1940
    Simons, John N., 1954
  Lactuca sativa var. capitata
    Ainsworth, G.C., 1940
  Lens esculenta
    Johnson, Folke and Leon K. Jones, 1937
  Lotus corniculatus
    McEwen, F.L. and W.T. Schroeder, 1956
  Lotus uliginosus
    McEwen, F.L. and W.T. Schroeder, 1956
  Lupinus albus
    Hagedorn, D.J. and J.C. Walker, 1954
    Stubbs, M.W., 1937
  Lycopersicon esculentum
    Ainsworth, G.C., 1940
    Hagedorn, D.J. and J.C. Walker, 1954
    Osborn, H.T., 1938
    Simons, John N., 1954
    Stubbs, M.W., 1937
  Medicago lupulina
    Johnson, Folke and Leon K. Jones, 1937
    McEwen, F.L. and W.T. Schroeder, 1956
  Medicago sativa
    Hagedorn, D.J. and J.C. Walker, 1954
    Osborn, H.T., 1938
    Pierce, W.H., 1935
    Simons, John N., 1954
    Stubbs, M.W., 1937
  Melilotus alba
    Hagedorn, D.J. and J.C. Walker, 1954
    Osborn, H.T., 1938
    Stubbs, M.W., 1937
  Melilotus officinalis
    Johnson, Folke and Leon K. Jones, 1937
    Pierce, W.H., 1935
  Nicotiana glutinosa
    Ainsworth, G.C., 1940
    Chaudhuri, R.P., 1950
    Hagedorn, D.J. and J.C. Walker, 1954
    Osborn, H.T., 1938
    Stubbs, M.W., 1937
  Nicotiana langsdorffii
    Osborn, H.T., 1938
  Nicotiana sylvestris
    Osborn, H.T., 1938
  Nicotiana tabacum
    Ainsworth, G.C., 1940
    Chaudhuri, R.P., 1950
    Hagedorn, D.J. and J.C. Walker, 1954
    Johnson, Folke and Leon K. Jones, 1937
    Osborn, H.T., 1938
    Pierce, W.H., 1935
    Simons, John N., 1954
    Stubbs, M.W., 1937
  Petunia hybrida
    Pierce, W.H., 1935
  Phaseolus aureus
    Osborn, H.T., 1938
  Phaseolus vulgaris
    Ainsworth, G.C., 1940
    Chaudhuri, R.P., 1950

VIRUS

V. PEA ENATION MOSAIC (cont.)
  Phaseolus vulgaris
    Hagedorn, D.J. and J.C. Walker, 1954
    McEwen, F.L. and W.T. Schroeder, 1956
    Osborn, H.T., 1938
    Pierce, W.H., 1935, 1937
    Simons, John N., 1954
    Stubbs, M.W., 1936, 1937
  Solanum tuberosum
    Osborn, H.T., 1938
  Trifolium hybridum
    Hagedorn, D.J. and J.C. Walker, 1954
    McEwen, F.L. and W.T. Schroeder, 1956
    Osborn, H.T., 1938
    Simons, John N., 1954
    Stubbs, M.W., 1937
  Trifolium pratense
    Ainsworth, G.C., 1940
    Chaudhuri, R.P., 1950
    Hagedorn, D.J. and J.C. Walker, 1954
    Johnson, Folke and Leon K. Jones, 1937
    McEwen, F.L. and W.T. Schroeder, 1956
    Osborn, H.T., 1938
    Pierce, W.H., 1935
    Simons, John N., 1954
    Stubbs, M.W., 1936, 1937
  Trifolium repens
    Ainsworth, G.C., 1940
    Chaudhuri, R.P., 1950
    Hagedorn, D.J. and J.C. Walker, 1954
    Johnson, Folke and Leon K. Jones, 1937
    Osborn, H.T., 1938
    Pierce, W.H., 1935
    Simons, John N., 1954
    Stubbs, M.W., 1937
  Trifolium subterranean
    Chaudhuri, R.P., 1950
  Vicia faba
    Chaudhuri, R.P., 1950
    Johnson, Folke and Leon K. Jones, 1937
    Simons, John N., 1954
  Vicia sativa
    Chaudhuri, R.P., 1950
    Johnson, Folke and Leon K. Jones, 1937
  Vicia villosa
    Simons, John N., 1954
  Vigna sinensis
    Hagedorn, D.J. and J.C. Walker, 1954
    Stubbs, M.W., 1937

V. PEA MOSAIC Doolittle and Jones 1925; Chamberlain
  Allium cepa   1936, 1937
    Murphy, D.M. and W.H. Pierce, 1937
  Apios americana (Apios tuberosa)
    Murphy, D.M. and W.H. Pierce, 1937
  Armeria formosa
    Murphy, D.M. and W.H. Pierce, 1937
  Aster spp.
    Murphy, D.M. and W.H. Pierce, 1937
  Baptisia australis
    Murphy, D.M. and W.H. Pierce, 1937
  Brassica oleracea var. capitata
    Murphy, D.M. and W.H. Pierce, 1937
  Bromus brizaeformis
    Murphy, D.M. and W.H. Pierce, 1937
  Calendula officinalis
    Murphy, D.M. and W.H. Pierce, 1937
  Calonyction aculeatum
    Murphy, D.M. and W.H. Pierce, 1937
  Campanula medium
    Murphy, D.M. and W.H. Pierce, 1937
  Campanula pyramidalis
    Murphy, D.M. and W.H. Pierce, 1937
  Cassia medsgeri
    Murphy, D.M. and W.H. Pierce, 1937
  Crotalaria retusa
    Murphy, D.M. and W.H. Pierce, 1937
  Cucumis sativus
    Ainsworth, G.C., 1940
    Murphy, D.M. and W.H. Pierce, 1937
  Cucurbita maxima
    Murphy, D.M. and W.H. Pierce, 1937

VIRUS
V. PEA MOSAIC (cont.)
  Delphinium grandiflorum
    Murphy, D.M. and W.H. Pierce, 1937
  Dianthus barbatus
    Murphy, D.M. and W.H. Pierce, 1937
  Dianthus deltoides
    Murphy, D.M. and W.H. Pierce, 1937
  Digitalis purpurea
    Murphy, D.M. and W.H. Pierce, 1937
  Dolichos lablab
    Murphy, D.M. and W.H. Pierce, 1937
  Dolichos lignosus
    Murphy, D.M. and W.H. Pierce, 1937
  Geranium sanguineum
    Murphy, D.M. and W.H. Pierce, 1937
  Glycine max
    Chaudhuri, R.P., 1950
    Hagedorn, D.J. and J.C. Walker, 1954
    Murphy, D.M. and W.H. Pierce, 1937
    Pierce, W.H., 1935
    Stubbs, M.W., 1937
  Impatiens balsamina
    Murphy, D.M. and W.H. Pierce, 1937
  Lactuca sativa var. capitata
    Ainsworth, G.C., 1940
  Lathyrus latifolius
    Murphy, D.M. and W.H. Pierce, 1937
  Lathyrus tuberosus
    Murphy, D.M. and W.H. Pierce, 1937
  Lavatera trimestris
    Murphy, D.M. and W.H. Pierce, 1937
  Linum grandiflorum
    Murphy, D.M. and W.H. Pierce, 1937
  Lobelia spp.
    Murphy, D.M. and W.H. Pierce, 1937
  Lotus ornithopodioides
    Murphy, D.M. and W.H. Pierce, 1937
  Lupinus polyphyllus
    Chaudhuri, R.P., 1950
  Lycopersicon esculentum
    Ainsworth, G.C., 1940
    Chaudhuri, R.P., 1950
    Hagedorn, D.J. and J.C. Walker, 1954
    Osborn, H.T., 1937
    Stubbs, M.W., 1937
  Lycopersicon esculentum var. commune *
    Murphy, D.M. and W.H. Pierce, 1937
  Matthiola incana
    Murphy, D.M. and W.H. Pierce, 1937
  Medicago lupulina
    Murphy, D.M. and W.H. Pierce, 1937
  Medicago sativa
    Chaudhuri, R.P., 1950
    Hagedorn, D.J. and J.C. Walker, 1954
    Murphy, D.M. and W.H. Pierce, 1937
    Pierce, W.H., 1935
    Stubbs, M.W., 1937
  Melilotus alba
    Hagedorn, D.J. and J.C. Walker, 1954
    Stubbs, M.W., 1937
  Melilotus officinalis
    Osborn, H.T., 1938
  Mesembryanthemum crystallinum
    Murphy, D.M. and W.H. Pierce, 1937
  Mirabilis jalapa
    Murphy, D.M. and W.H. Pierce, 1937
  Myosotis sylvatica
    Murphy, D.M. and W.H. Pierce, 1937
  Nicotiana glutinosa
    Chaudhuri, R.P., 1950
    Hagedorn, D.J. and J.C. Walker, 1954
    Osborn, H.T., 1937
    Stubbs, M.W., 1937
  Nicotiana tabacum
    Chaudhuri, R.P., 1950
    Hagedorn, D.J. and J.C. Walker, 1954
    Murphy, D.M. and W.H. Pierce, 1937
    Osborn, H.T., 1937
    Pierce, W.H., 1935
    Stubbs, M.W., 1937
  Oenothera missouriensis
    Murphy, D.M. and W.H. Pierce, 1937

VIRUS
V. PEA MOSAIC (cont.)
  Pastinaca sativa
    Murphy, D.M. and W.H. Pierce, 1937
  Petunia hybrida
    Murphy, D.M. and W.H. Pierce, 1937
    Pierce, W.H., 1935
  Phacelia campanularia
    Murphy, D.M. and W.H. Pierce, 1937
  Phaseolus aconitifolius
    Murphy, D.M. and W.H. Pierce, 1937
  Phaseolus aureus
    Murphy, D.M. and W.H. Pierce, 1937
    Osborn, H.T., 1937
  Phaseolus coccineus
    Murphy, D.M. and W.H. Pierce, 1937
  Phaseolus limensis
    Murphy, D.M. and W.H. Pierce, 1937
  Phaseolus vulgaris
    Ainsworth, G.C., 1940
    Chaudhuri, R.P., 1950
    Hagedorn, D.J. and J.C. Walker, 1954
    Harrison, Arthur L., 1935
    Murphy, D.M. and W.H. Pierce, 1937
    Pierce, W.H., 1935, 1937
    Stubbs, M.W., 1936, 1937
    Zaumeyer, W.J. and B.L. Wade, 1936
  Phlox drummondii
    Murphy, D.M. and W.H. Pierce, 1937
  Physalis pubescens
    Murphy, D.M. and W.H. Pierce, 1937
  Pueraria hirsuta
    Murphy, D.M. and W.H. Pierce, 1937
  Raphanus sativus
    Murphy, D.M. and W.H. Pierce, 1937
  Ricinus communis
    Murphy, D.M. and W.H. Pierce, 1937
  Rumex acetosa
    Murphy, D.M. and W.H. Pierce, 1937
  Saponaria vaccaria
    Murphy, D.M. and W.H. Pierce, 1937
  Scabiosa atropurpurea
    Murphy, D.M. and W.H. Pierce, 1937
  Setaria lutescens
    Murphy, D.M. and W.H. Pierce, 1937
  Solanum nigrum
    Murphy, D.M. and W.H. Pierce, 1937
  Thunbergia alata
    Murphy, D.M. and W.H. Pierce, 1937
  Trifolium hybridum
    Hagedorn, D.J. and J.C. Walker, 1954
    Stubbs, M.W., 1937
  Trifolium medium
    Murphy, D.M. and W.H. Pierce, 1937
  Trifolium pratense
    Ainsworth, G.C., 1940
    Chaudhuri, R.P., 1950
    Hagedorn, D.J. and J.C. Walker, 1954
    Stubbs, M.W., 1936, 1937
    Zaumeyer, W.J. and B.L. Wade, 1935
  Trifolium repens
    Ainsworth, G.C., 1940
    Chaudhuri, R.P., 1950
    Hagedorn, D.J. and J.C. Walker, 1954
    Murphy, D.M. and W.H. Pierce, 1937
    Osborn, H.T., 1937
    Pierce, W.H., 1935
    Stubbs, M.W., 1937
  Tropaeolum majus
    Murphy, D.M. and W.H. Pierce, 1937
  Valerianella olitoria
    Murphy, D.M. and W.H. Pierce, 1937
  Verbascum thapsus
    Murphy, D.M. and W.H. Pierce, 1937
  Vicia villosa
    Murphy, D.M. and W.H. Pierce, 1937
  Vigna sinensis
    Hagedorn, D.J. and J.C. Walker, 1954
    Murphy, D.M. and W.H. Pierce, 1937
    Stubbs, M.W., 1937, 1937
  Viola tricolor var. hortensis
    Murphy, D.M. and W.H. Pierce, 1937

VIRUS
V. PEA MOTTLE F. Johnson 1942
  Barbarea vulgaris
    Johnson, Folke, 1942
  Beta vulgaris
    Johnson, Folke, 1942
  Brassica oleracea var. capitata
    Johnson, Folke, 1942
  Callistephus chinensis
    Johnson, Folke, 1942
  Cicer arietinum
    Johnson, F. and L.K. Jones, 1936, 1937
  Cuscuta campestris
    Johnson, Folke, 1942
  Datura stramonium
    Johnson, Folke, 1942
  Glycine max
    Johnson, Folke, 1942
  Lactuca sativa
    Johnson, Folke, 1942
  Lilium formosanum *
    Johnson, Folke, 1942
  Lycopersicon esculentum
    Johnson, Folke, 1942
  Nicotiana glutinosa
    Johnson, Folke, 1942
  Nicotiana rustica
    Johnson, Folke, 1942
  Nicotiana sylvestris
    Johnson, Folke, 1942
  Nicotiana tabacum
    Johnson, Folke, 1942
    Johnson, Folke and Leon K. Jones, 1937
  Plantago lanceolata
    Johnson, Folke, 1942
  Plantago major
    Johnson, Folke, 1942
  Raphanus sativus
    Johnson, Folke, 1942
  Rumex acetosella
    Johnson, Folke, 1942
  Solanum nigrum
    Johnson, Folke, 1942
  Taraxacum officinale
    Johnson, Folke, 1942
  Vigna sinensis
    Johnson, Folke, 1942
  Zea mays
    Johnson, Folke, 1942
  Zinnia elegans
    Johnson, Folke, 1942

V. PEA STEM STREAK *
  Phaseolus vulgaris
    Zaumeyer, W.J., 1939

V. PEA STREAK Zaumeyer and Wade 1938
  Cajanus indicus
    Zaumeyer, W.J., 1938
  Capsicum frutescens (Capsicum annuum)
    Zaumeyer, W.J., 1938
  Cucumis sativus
    Zaumeyer, W.J., 1938
  Datura stramonium
    Zaumeyer, W.J., 1938
  Lathyrus odoratus
    Zaumeyer, W.J., 1938
  Lespedeza striata
    Zaumeyer, W.J., 1938
  Lupinus albus
    Zaumeyer, W.J., 1938
  Lupinus luteus
    Zaumeyer, W.J., 1938
  Lycopersicon esculentum
    Zaumeyer, W.J., 1938
  Mucuna deeringianum
    Zaumeyer, W.J., 1938
  Nicotiana tabacum
    Zaumeyer, W.J., 1938
  Petunia hybrida
    Zaumeyer, W.J., 1938
  Phaseolus acutifolius var. latifolius
    Zaumeyer, W.J., 1938

VIRUS
V. PEA STREAK (cont.)
  Phaseolus angularis
    Zaumeyer, W.J., 1938
  Phaseolus aureus
    Zaumeyer, W.J., 1938
  Phaseolus calcaratus
    Zaumeyer, W.J., 1938
  Phaseolus lunatus
    Zaumeyer, W.J., 1938
  Phaseolus lunatus f. macrocarpus
    Zaumeyer, W.J., 1938
  Phaseolus mungo
    Zaumeyer, W.J., 1938
  Phaseolus vulgaris
    Zaumeyer, W.J., 1938
  Solanum melongena
    Zaumeyer, W.J., 1938
  Solanum tuberosum
    Zaumeyer, W.J., 1938
  Vicia villosa
    Zaumeyer, W.J., 1938
  Vigna sesquipedalis
    Zaumeyer, W.J., 1938
  Vigna sinensis
    Zaumeyer, W.J., 1938
  Zinnia elegans
    Zaumeyer, W.J., 1938

V. PEA WILT F. Johnson 1942
  Antirrhinum majus
    Johnson, Folke, 1942
  Barbarea vulgaris
    Johnson, Folke, 1942
  Beta vulgaris
    Johnson, Folke, 1942
  Brassica oleracea var. capitata
    Johnson, Folke, 1942
  Callistephus chinensis
    Johnson, Folke, 1942
  Cucumis sativus
    Johnson, Folke, 1942
  Cuscuta campestris
    Johnson, Folke, 1942
  Datura stramonium
    Johnson, Folke, 1942
  Glycine max
    Johnson, Folke, 1942
  Lactuca sativa
    Johnson, Folke, 1942
  Lilium formosanum *
    Johnson, Folke, 1942
  Lupinus hirsutus
    Johnson, Folke, 1942
  Lycopersicon esculentum
    Johnson, Folke, 1942
  Medicago sativa
    Johnson, Folke, 1942
  Nicotiana glutinosa
    Johnson, Folke, 1942
  Nicotiana rustica
    Johnson, Folke, 1942
  Nicotiana sylvestris
    Johnson, Folke, 1942
  Nicotiana tabacum
    Johnson, Folke, 1942
  Phaseolus vulgaris
    Pierce, W.H., 1935
  Plantago lanceolata
    Johnson, Folke, 1942
  Plantago major
    Johnson, Folke, 1942
  Raphanus sativus
    Johnson, Folke, 1942
  Rumex acetosella
    Johnson, Folke, 1942
  Solanum nigrum
    Johnson, Folke, 1942
  Spinacia oleracea
    Johnson, Folke, 1942
  Stellaria media
    Johnson, Folke, 1942
  Taraxacum officinale
    Johnson, Folke, 1942

VIRUS

V. PEA WILT (cont.)
  Zea mays
    Johnson, Folke, 1942
  Zinnia elegans
    Johnson, Folke, 1942

V. PEA YELLOW MOSAIC *
  Cucumis sativus
    Ainsworth, G.C., 1940
  Lactuca sativa var. capitata
    Ainsworth, G.C., 1940
  Lycopersicon esculentum
    Ainsworth, G.C., 1940
  Phaseolus vulgaris
    Ainsworth, G.C., 1940
  Trifolium repens
    Ainsworth, G.C., 1940

V. PEACH BLOTCH Willison 1946
  Prunus armeniaca
    Willison, R.S., 1946
  Prunus avium
    Willison, R.S., 1946
  Prunus cerasifera
    Willison, R.S., 1946
  Prunus cerasus
    Willison, R.S., 1946
  Prunus domestica
    Willison, R.S., 1946
  Prunus mahaleb
    Willison, R.S., 1946
  Prunus salicina
    Willison, R.S., 1946

V. PEACH MOSAIC Hutchins 1932
  Cuscuta californica
    Bennett, C.W., 1944
  Cuscuta campestris
    Bennett, C.W., 1944
  Cuscuta subinclusa
    Bennett, C.W., 1944
  Prunus cerasus
    Richards, B.L. and L.C. Cochran, 1956
  Prunus fasciculata
    Richards, B.L. and L.C. Cochran, 1956
  Prunus fremontii
    Richards, B.L. and L.C. Cochran, 1956
  Prunus persica (Amygdalus persica)
    Bodine, E.W. and L.W. Durrell, 1941
  Prunus virginiana var. demissa
    Richards, B.L. and L.C. Cochran, 1956

V. PEACH NECROTIC LEAF SPOT Cation 1942
  Prunus cerasus
    Fridlund, Paul R., 1954
  Prunus persica (Amygdalus persica)
    Fridlund, Paul R., 1954
  Prunus tomentosa
    Fridlund, Paul R., 1954

V. PEACH RING SPOT Cochran and Hutchins 1941
  Citrullus vulgaris
    Hobbs, Gordon A., 1951
  Cucurbita maxima
    Hobbs, Gordon A., 1951
  Prunus besseyi
    Fink, Harry C., 1950, 1955
  Prunus domestica
    Moore, J. Duain and G.W. Keitt, 1944
  Prunus salicina x Prunus americana
    Fink, Harry C., 1950
  Prunus salicina x Prunus munsoniana
    Fink, Harry C., 1955

V. PEACH ROSETTE ((E.F. Smith 1891)) McClintock
  Erigeron canadensis   1923
    McClintock, J.A., 1931

V. PEACH WESTERN X DISEASE Reeves and Hutchins
  Cuscuta campestris   1941
    Weathers, Lewis G. and George W. Cochran, 1950
  Cuscuta subinclusa
    Weathers, Lewis G. and George W. Cochran, 1950

VIRUS

V. PEACH WESTERN X DISEASE (cont.)
  Prunus andersoni
    Rawlins, T.E. and H. Earl Thomas, 1941
  Prunus cerasifera
    Rawlins, T.E. and H. Earl Thomas, 1941
  Prunus domestica
    Rawlins, T.E. and H. Earl Thomas, 1941
  Prunus emarginata
    Rawlins, T.E. and H. Earl Thomas, 1941
  Prunus fremontii
    Rawlins, T.E. and H. Earl Thomas, 1941
  Prunus ilicifolia
    Rawlins, T.E. and H. Earl Thomas, 1941
  Prunus mahaleb
    Rawlins, T.E. and K.G. Parker, 1934
  Prunus marianna *
    Rawlins, T.E. and H. Earl Thomas, 1941
  Prunus subcordata
    Rawlins, T.E. and H. Earl Thomas, 1941
  Rosa californica
    Rawlins, T.E. and H. Earl Thomas, 1941

V. PEACH X DISEASE Stoddard 1938
  Cuscuta campestris
    Hildebrand, E.M., 1953
    Kunkel, L.O., 1944
  Cuscuta subinclusa
    Slack, Derald A., 1952
  Prunus serotina
    Gilmer, R.M., 1951
    Gilmer, R.M., J. Duain Moore and G.W. Keitt, 1954

V. PEACH YELLOW BUD MOSAIC Thomas et al. 1944
  Prunus avium
    Schlocker, Archie, H. Keith Wagnon and James R. Breece, 1957
  Prunus cerasifera
    Schlocker, Archie, H. Keith Wagnon and James R. Breece, 1957
  Prunus salicina
    Schlocker, Archie, H. Keith Wagnon and James R. Breece, 1957

V. PELARGONIUM LEAF CURL Pape 1927
  Lycopersicon esculentum
    Jones, Leon K., 1940

V. PELARGONIUM RING SPOT *
  Alonsoa warscewiczii
    Hollings, M., 1957
  Amaranthus caudatus
    Hollings, M., 1957
  Antirrhinum majus
    Hollings, M., 1957
  Brassica pekinensis
    Hollings, M., 1957
  Chenopodium amaranticolor
    Hollings, M., 1957
  Cucumis sativus
    Hollings, M., 1957
  Gomphrena globosa
    Hollings, M., 1957
  Lactuca sativa
    Hollings, M., 1957
  Lavatera trimestris
    Hollings, M., 1967
  Nicandra physalodes
    Hollings, M., 1957
  Nicotiana clevelandi
    Hollings, M., 1957
  Nicotiana glutinosa
    Hollings, M., 1957
  Nicotiana rustica
    Hollings, M., 1957
  Nicotiana tabacum
    Hollings, M., 1957
  Phaseolus vulgaris
    Hollings, M., 1957
  Physalis floridana
    Hollings, M., 1957
  Tetragonia expansa
    Hollings, M., 1957

VIRUS
V. PELARGONIUM RING SPOT * (cont.)
  Vicia faba
    Hollings, M., 1957
  Vigna sinensis
    Hollings, M., 1957
  Zinnia elegans
    Hollings, M., 1957

V. PEONY LEAF CURL *
  Antirrhinum majus
    Brierley, Philip and Paul Lorentz, 1957
  Dianthus barbatus
    Brierley, Philip and Paul Lorentz, 1957
  Gomphrena spp.
    Brierley, Philip and Paul Lorentz, 1957
  Nicotiana tabacum
    Brierley, Philip and Paul Lorentz, 1957
  Petunia hybrida
    Brierley, Philip and Paul Lorentz, 1957
  Silene compacta
    Brierley, Philip and Paul Lorentz, 1957
  Verbesina encelioides
    Brierley, Philip and Paul Lorentz, 1957

V. PETUNIA MOSAIC Johnson 1926
  Capsicum frutescens (Capsicum annuum)
    Johnson, J., 1926, 1927
  Solanum melongena
    Johnson, J., 1926

V. PHYSALIS FLORIDANA YELLOW NET Webb 1955
  Beta vulgaris
    Webb, R.E., 1955
  Brassica campestris var. napobrassica
    Webb, R.E., 1955
  Brassica oleracea var. acephala
    Webb, R.E., 1955
  Brassica oleracea var. botrytis
    Webb, R.E., 1955
  Brassica rapa
    Webb, R.E., 1955
  Lycopersicon esculentum
    Webb, R.E., 1955
  Nicotiana glutinosa
    Webb, R.E., 1955
  Nicotiana rustica
    Webb, R.E., 1955
  Nicotiana tabacum
    Webb, R.E., 1955
  Solanum tuberosum
    Webb, R.E., 1955

V. PIGEON PEA STERILITY MOSAIC Capoor 1952
  Cyamopsis psoraloides
    Capoor, S.P., 1952
  Datura inoxia
    Capoor, S.P., 1952
  Nicotiana tabacum
    Capoor, S.P., 1952
  Phaseolus vulgaris
    Capoor, S.P., 1952
  Physalis peruviana
    Capoor, S.P., 1952

V. POKEWEED MOSAIC *
  Cucumis sativus
    Doolittle, S.P. and W.W. Gilbert, 1918
  Datura stramonium
    Allard, H.A., 1918
  Lycopersicon esculentum
    Allard, H.A., 1918
  Nicotiana tabacum
    Allard, H.A., 1918
  Petunia hybrida
    Allard, H.A., 1918
  Physalis pubescens
    Allard, H.A., 1918
  Solanum nigrum
    Allard, H.A., 1918

VIRUS
V. POTATO A Murphy and McKay 1932
  Callistephus chinensis
    MacLachlan, D.S., R.H. Larson and J.C. Walker, 1953
  Capsicum frutescens (Capsicum annuum)
    MacLachlan, D.S., R.H. Larson and J.C. Walker, 1953
  Cucumis sativus
    MacLachlan, D.S., R.H. Larson and J.C. Walker, 1953
  Datura aegyptiaca
    MacLachlan, D.S., R.H. Larson and J.C. Walker, 1953
  Datura bernhardii
    MacLachlan, D.S., R.H. Larson and J.C. Walker, 1953
  Datura chorantha
    MacLachlan, D.S., R.H. Larson and J.C. Walker, 1953
  Datura fastuosa
    MacLachlan, D.S., R.H. Larson and J.C. Walker, 1953
  Datura ferox
    MacLachlan, D.S., R.H. Larson and J.C. Walker, 1953
  Datura metel
    MacLachlan, D.S., R.H. Larson and J.C. Walker, 1953
  Datura meteloides
    MacLachlan, D.S., R.H. Larson and J.C. Walker, 1953
  Lycopersicon esculentum
    MacLachlan, D.S., R.H. Larson and J.C. Walker, 1953
  Nicotiana glutinosa
    MacLachlan, D.S., R.H. Larson and J.C. Walker, 1953
  Nicotiana rustica
    MacLachlan, D.S., R.H. Larson and J.C. Walker, 1953
    Vasudeva, R. Sahai and C.S. Ramamoorthy, 1946
  Nicotiana tabacum
    Koch, Karl and James Johnson, 1935
    Schultz, E.S. and Donald Folsom, 1923
  Petunia hybrida
    Vasudeva, R. Sahai and C.S. Ramamoorthy, 1946
  Physalis angulata
    MacLachlan, D.S., R.H. Larson and J.C. Walker, 1953
  Physalis floridana
    MacLachlan, D.S., R.H. Larson and J.C. Walker, 1953
  Physalis peruviana
    MacLachlan, D.S., R.H. Larson and J.C. Walker, 1953
  Physalis pubescens
    MacLachlan, D.S., R.H. Larson and J.C. Walker, 1953
  Physalis virginiana
    MacLachlan, D.S., R.H. Larson and J.C. Walker, 1953
  Solanum andigenum *
    MacLachlan, D.S., R.H. Larson and J.C. Walker, 1953
  Solanum carolinense
    MacLachlan, D.S., R.H. Larson and J.C. Walker, 1953
  Solanum chacoense
    MacLachlan, D.S., R.H. Larson and J.C. Walker, 1953
  Solanum commersonii
    MacLachlan, D.S., R.H. Larson and J.C. Walker, 1953
  Solanum dulcamara
    MacLachlan, D.S., R.H. Larson and J.C. Walker, 1953
  Solanum integrifolium
    MacLachlan, D.S., R.H. Larson and J.C. Walker, 1953
  Solanum longipedicellatum
    MacLachlan, D.S., R.H. Larson and J.C. Walker, 1953

VIRUS

V. POTATO A (cont.)

Solanum nigrum
MacLachlan, D.S., R.H. Larson and J.C. Walker, 1953
Vasudeva, R. Sahai and C.S. Ramamoorthy, 1946

Solanum nodiflorum
Vasudeva, R. Sahai and C.S. Ramamoorthy, 1946

Solanum polyadenium
MacLachlan, D.S., R.H. Larson and J.C. Walker, 1953

Solanum pseudocapsicum
MacLachlan, D.S., R.H. Larson and J.C. Walker, 1953

Solanum saltense
MacLachlan, D.S., R.H. Larson and J.C. Walker, 1953

Solanum schickii
MacLachlan, D.S., R.H. Larson and J.C. Walker, 1953

Solanum verrucosum
MacLachlan, D.S., R.H. Larson and J.C. Walker, 1953

Trifolium hybridum
MacLachlan, D.S., R.H. Larson and J.C. Walker, 1953

Trifolium incarnatum
MacLachlan, D.S., R.H. Larson and J.C. Walker, 1953

Trifolium pratense
MacLachlan, D.S., R.H. Larson and J.C. Walker, 1953

Trifolium repens
MacLachlan, D.S., R.H. Larson and J.C. Walker, 1953

Vigna sinensis
MacLachlan, D.S., R.H. Larson and J.C. Walker, 1953

Zinnia linearis
MacLachlan, D.S., R.H. Larson and J.C. Walker, 1953

V. POTATO LEAF ROLL Appel 1907

Brassica campestris
MacCarthy, H.R., 1954

Brassica campestris var. napobrassica
MacCarthy, H.R., 1954

Brassica juncea (Brassica japonica)
MacCarthy, H.R., 1954

Brassica napus
MacCarthy, H.R., 1954

Brassica nigra
MacCarthy, H.R., 1954

Brassica oleracea var. botrytis
MacCarthy, H.R., 1954

Brassica oleracea var. capitata
MacCarthy, H.R., 1954

Brassica pekinensis
MacCarthy, H.R., 1954

Capsicum frutescens (Capsicum annuum)
Dykstra, T.P., 1933

Malva spp.
MacCarthy, H.R., 1954

Nicotiana tabacum
Koch, Karl and James Johnson, 1935
Quanjer, H.M., 1920

Physalis francheti
MacCarthy, H.R., 1954

Physalis heterophylla
MacCarthy, H.R., 1954

Physalis ixocarpa
MacCarthy, H.R., 1954

Physalis peruviana
Webb, R.E., R.H. Larson and J.C. Walker, 1952

Physalis pubescens
MacCarthy, H.R., 1954
Webb, R.E., R.H. Larson and J.C. Walker, 1952

Physalis spp.
Dykstra, T.P., 1933

Solanum melongena
Webb, R.E., R.H. Larson and J.C. Walker, 1952

VIRUS

V. POTATO LEAF ROLLING MOSAIC ((Schultz and Folsom 1923)) Folsom 1926; J. Johnson 1929

Nicotiana tabacum
Dykstra, T.P., 1939

V. POTATO M *

Capsicum frutescens (Capsicum annuum)
Bagnall, R.H. and R.H. Larson, 1957
Bagnall, R.H., R.H. Larson and J.C. Walker, 1956

Nicandra physalodes
Bagnall, R.H., R.H. Larson and J.C. Walker, 1956

Nicotiana glutinosa
Bagnall, R.H. and R.H. Larson, 1957

Nicotiana sylvestris
Bagnall, R.H., R.H. Larson and J.C. Walker, 1956

Nicotiana tabacum
Bagnall, R.H. and R.H. Larson, 1957
Bagnall, R.H., R.H. Larson and J.C. Walker, 1956

Physalis floridana
Bagnall, R.H. and R.H. Larson, 1957
Bagnall, R.H., R.H. Larson and J.C. Walker, 1956

Physalis philadelphica
Bagnall, R.H., R.H. Larson and J.C. Walker, 1956

V. POTATO PARACRINKLE Salaman and LePelley 1930

Capsicum frutescens (Capsicum annuum)
Bagnall, R.H. and R.H. Larson, 1957
Bagnall, R.H., R.H. Larson and J.C. Walker, 1956

Lycopersicon esculentum
Bagnall, R.H. and R.H. Larson, 1957
Bagnall, R.H., R.H. Larson and J.C. Walker, 1956
Kassanis, B., 1955

Nicandra physalodes
Bagnall, R.H., R.H. Larson and J.C. Walker, 1956

Nicotiana glutinosa
Bagnall, R.H. and R.H. Larson, 1957
Kassanis, B., 1955

Nicotiana sylvestris
Bagnall, R.H., R.H. Larson and J.C. Walker, 1956

Nicotiana tabacum
Bagnall, R.H. and R.H. Larson, 1957
Bagnall, R.H., R.H. Larson and J.C. Walker, 1956
Kassanis, B., 1955

Physalis floridana
Bagnall, R.H. and R.H. Larson, 1957
Bagnall, R.H., R.H. Larson and J.C. Walker, 1956

Solanum melongena
Bagnall, R.H. and R.H. Larson, 1957
Bagnall, R.H., R.H. Larson and J.C. Walker, 1956

V. POTATO SPINDLE TUBER K.M. Smith 1957

Datura stramonium
Goss, R.W., 1931

Nicandra physalodes
Goss, R.W., 1931

Physalis heterophylla
Goss, R.W., 1931

Solanum lycopersicum
Goss, R.W., 1931

V. POTATO STEM MOTTLE Rozendaal 1947

Cuscuta campestris
Van der Want, J.P.H., 1955

Cuscuta subinclusa
Van der Want, J.P.H., 1955

V. POTATO YELLOW DWARF Barrus and Chupp 1922

Cucumis sativus
Hougas, R.W., 1951

VIRUS
V. POTATO YELLOW DWARF (cont.)
  Medicago sativa
    Black, L.M., 1943
  Phaseolus lunatus
    Hougas, R.W., 1951
  Vigna sinensis
    Hougas, R.W., 1951

V. POTATO X K.M. Smith 1931
  Atropa belladonna
    Cockerham, George, 1943
    Dennis, R.W.G., 1939
  Brassica hirta (Brassica alba)
    Johnson, E.M., 1930
  Brassica oleracea
    Johnson, E.M., 1930
  Brassica rapa var. depressa *
    Johnson, E.M., 1930
  Capsicum frutescens (Capsicum annuum)
    Dykstra, T.P., 1933
  Glycine max
    Johnson, E.M., 1930
  Lagenaria vulgaris
    Vasudeva, R. Sahai and T.B. Lal, 1944
  Lycium barbarum
    Cockerham, George, 1943
  Nicotiana glauca
    Johnson, James, 1927
  Petunia hybrida
    Vasudeva, R. Sahai and T.B. Lal, 1944
  Phaseolus vulgaris
    Folsom, Donald and Reiner Bonde, 1937
    Johnson, E.M., 1930
  Physalis francheti
    Smith, J. Henderson, 1928
  Phytolacca decandra
    Johnson, James, 1927
  Pisum sativum
    Johnson, E.M., 1930
  Raphanus sativus
    Johnson, E.M., 1930
  Solanum dulcamara
    Dykstra, T.P., 1933
  Solanum melongena var. esculentum
    Smith, J. Henderson, 1928
  Solanum tuberosum
    Hamilton, Marion A., 1932
    Johnson, James, 1927

V. POTATO Y Smith 1931
  Ananas comosus
    Sakimura, K., 1953
  Atropa belladonna
    Cockerham, George, 1943
  Beta vulgaris
    Johnson, E.M., 1930
  Brassica hirta (Brassica alba)
    Johnson, E.M., 1930
  Brassica oleracea
    Johnson, E.M., 1930
  Brassica oleracea var. capitata
    Bawden, F.C. and F.M.L. Sheffield, 1944
  Brassica oleracea var. gemmifera
    Bawden, F.C. and F.M.L. Sheffield, 1944
  Brassica rapa var. depressa *
    Johnson, E.M., 1930
  Capsicum frutescens (Capsicum annuum)
    Cockerham, George, 1943
    Dykstra, T.P., 1933
  Cassia tora
    Anderson, C.W., 1954
  Cucumis sativus
    Alvarez-Garcia, L.A. and Jose Adsuar, 1943
    Bald, J.G. and D.O. Norris, 1945
    Johnson, E.M., 1930
    Roque, Arturo and Jose Adsuar, 1941
  Datura aegyptiaca
    Darby, J.F., R.H. Larson and J.C. Walker, 1951
  Datura fastuosa
    Darby, J.F., R.H. Larson and J.C. Walker, 1951
  Datura meteloides
    Darby, J.F., R.H. Larson and J.C. Walker, 1951

VIRUS
V. POTATO Y (cont.)
  Datura stramonium
    Anderson, C.W. and M.K. Corbett, 1957
    Bagnall, R.H., R.H. Larson and J.C. Walker, 1956
    Bald, J.G. and D.O. Norris, 1945
    Bawden, F.C. and B. Kassanis, 1951
    Bawden, F.C. and F.M.L. Sheffield, 1944
    Cockerham, George, 1943
    Conover, Robert A. and Robert W. Fulton, 1953
    Dennis, R.W.G., 1939
    Dykstra, T.P., 1933
    Johnson, E.M., 1930
    Jones, Leon K. and C.L. Vincent, 1937
    Koch, K.L., 1933
    Roque, Arturo and Jose Adsuar, 1941
    Smith, Kenneth M. and R.W.G. Dennis, 1940
    Vasudeva, R. Sahai and T.B. Lal, 1945
  Datura stramonium var. chalybea *
    Sakimura, K., 1953
  Datura stramonium var. tatula
    Darby, J.F., R.H. Larson and J.C. Walker, 1951
    Dykstra, T.P., 1933
  Emilia sonchifolia
    Sakimura, K., 1953
  Glycine max
    Johnson, E.M., 1930
  Gomphrena globosa
    Ross, A. Frank, 1950
  Lycopersicon esculentum
    Hamilton, Marion A., 1932
  Nicandra physalodes
    Johnson, E.M., 1930
  Nicotiana repanda
    Roque, Arturo and Jose Adsuar, 1941
  Nicotiana sylvestris
    Roque, Arturo and Jose Adsuar, 1941
  Nicotiana tabacum
    Dennis, R.W.G., 1939
  Phaseolus lunatus
    Roque, Arturo and Jose Adsuar, 1941
  Phaseolus vulgaris
    Bald, J.G. and D.O. Norris, 1945
    Johnson, E.M., 1930
    Peterson, Paul D. and H.H. McKinney, 1938
    Roque, Arturo and Jose Adsuar, 1941
  Physalis longifolia
    Koch, K.L., 1933
  Phytolacca decandra
    Johnson, E.M., 1930
    Johnson, James, 1927
  Pisum sativum
    Bald, J.G. and D.O. Norris, 1945
    Johnson, E.M., 1930
  Raphanus sativus
    Johnson, E.M., 1930
  Schizanthus retusus
    Smith, Kenneth M. and R.W.G. Dennis, 1940
  Solanum antipoviczii
    Easton, G.D., R.H. Larson and R.W. Hougas, 1958
  Solanum carolinense
    Johnson, E.M., 1930
    Koch, K.L., 1933
  (Solanum demissum x Solanum goniocalyx) x (Solanum stoloniferum)
    Easton, G.D., R.H. Larson and R.W. Hougas, 1958
  (Solanum demissum x Solanum rybinii) x (Solanum stoloniferum)
    Easton, G.D., R.H. Larson and R.W. Hougas, 1958
  (Solanum demissum x Solanum soukupii) x (Solanum stoloniferum)
    Easton, G.D., R.H. Larson and R.W. Hougas, 1958
  Solanum dulcamara
    Dykstra, T.P., 1933
  Solanum melongena
    Koch, K.L., 1933
  Solanum nigrum
    Easton, G.D., R.H. Larson and R.W. Hougas, 1958

VIRUS
V. POTATO Y (cont.)
Solanum nodiflorum
Roque, Arturo and Jose Adsuar, 1941
Smith, Kenneth M. and R.W.G. Dennis, 1940
Solanum tuberosum
Hamilton, Marion A., 1932
Roque, Arturo and Jose Adsuar, 1941
Vicia faba
Bald, J.G. and D.O. Norris, 1945
Vigna sinensis
Alvarez-Garcia, L.A. and Jose Adsuar, 1943
Bald, J.G. and D.O. Norris, 1945
Zinnia elegans
Bald, J.G. and D.O. Norris, 1945

V. PRIMULA MOSAIC
Anagallis arvensis
Tompkins, C.M. and John T. Middleton, 1941
Anemone coronaria
Tompkins, C.M. and John T. Middleton, 1941
Antirrhinum majus
Tompkins, C.M. and John T. Middleton, 1941
Apium graveolens
Tompkins, C.M. and John T. Middleton, 1941
Apium graveolens var. dulce
Severin, Henry H.P. and C.M. Tompkins, 1950
Begonia semperflorens
Tompkins, C.M. and John T. Middleton, 1941
Bellis perennis
Tompkins, C.M. and John T. Middleton, 1941
Beta vulgaris
Severin, Henry H.P. and C.M. Tompkins, 1950
Brassica oleracea var. botrytis
Tompkins, C.M. and John T. Middleton, 1941
Brassica oleracea var. capitata
Tompkins, C.M. and John T. Middleton, 1941
Brassica pekinensis
Tompkins, C.M. and John T. Middleton, 1941
Brassica rapa
Tompkins, C.M. and John T. Middleton, 1941
Callistephus chinensis
Tompkins, C.M. and John T. Middleton, 1941
Campanula medium
Tompkins, C.M. and John T. Middleton, 1941
Capsicum frutescens var. grossum
Tompkins, C.M. and John T. Middleton, 1941
Cucumis sativus
Severin, Henry H.P. and C.M. Tompkins, 1950
Tompkins, C.M. and John T. Middleton, 1941
Cucurbita pepo
Severin, Henry H.P. and C.M. Tompkins, 1950
Cucurbita pepo var. melopepo
Tompkins, C.M. and John T. Middleton, 1941
Cyclamen persicum (Cyclamen indicum)
Tompkins, C.M. and John T. Middleton, 1941
Datura stramonium
Tompkins, C.M. and John T. Middleton, 1941
Delphinium cultorum
Tompkins, C.M. and John T. Middleton, 1941
Dianthus barbatus
Tompkins, C.M. and John T. Middleton, 1941
Gerbera jamesonii
Tompkins, C.M. and John T. Middleton, 1941
Geum chiloense
Tompkins, C.M. and John T. Middleton, 1941
Lactuca sativa var. longifolia
Tompkins, C.M. and John T. Middleton, 1941
Lobelia hybrida
Tompkins, C.M. and John T. Middleton, 1941
Lycopersicon esculentum
Severin, Henry H.P. and C.M. Tompkins, 1950
Lycopersicon esculentum var. vulgare
Tompkins, C.M. and John T. Middleton, 1941
Matthiola incana var. annua
Tompkins, C.M. and John T. Middleton, 1941
Myosotis alpestris
Tompkins, C.M. and John T. Middleton, 1941
Nicotiana glutinosa
Severin, Henry H.P. and C.M. Tompkins, 1950
Tompkins, C.M. and John T. Middleton, 1941
Nicotiana tabacum
Severin, Henry H.P. and C.M. Tompkins, 1950
Tompkins, C.M. and John T. Middleton, 1941

VIRUS
V. PRIMULA MOSAIC (cont.)
Papaver orientale
Tompkins, C.M. and John T. Middleton, 1941
Penstemon barbatus
Tompkins, C.M. and John T. Middleton, 1941
Pisum sativum
Tompkins, C.M. and John T. Middleton, 1941
Primula auricula
Tompkins, C.M. and John T. Middleton, 1941
Primula veris
Tompkins, C.M. and John T. Middleton, 1941
Ranunculus asiaticus
Tompkins, C.M. and John T. Middleton, 1941
Raphanus sativus
Tompkins, C.M. and John T. Middleton, 1941
Reseda odorata
Tompkins, C.M. and John T. Middleton, 1941
Ricinus communis
Tompkins, C.M. and John T. Middleton, 1941
Senecio cruentus
Tompkins, C.M. and John T. Middleton, 1941
Solanum tuberosum
Tompkins, C.M. and John T. Middleton, 1941
Spinacia oleracea
Tompkins, C.M. and John T. Middleton, 1941
Tagetes patula
Tompkins, C.M. and John T. Middleton, 1941
Tropaeolum majus
Tompkins, C.M. and John T. Middleton, 1941
Verbena hybrida
Tompkins, C.M. and John T. Middleton, 1941
Vicia faba
Tompkins, C.M. and John T. Middleton, 1941
Vigna sinensis
Tompkins, C.M. and John T. Middleton, 1941
Viola tricolor
Tompkins, C.M. and John T. Middleton, 1941
Zea mays
Tompkins, C.M. and John T. Middleton, 1941

V. PRUNE DWARF Thomas and Hildebrand 1936
Prunus avium
Hildebrand, E.M., 1942
Prunus cerasus
Hildebrand, E.M., 1942
Thomas, H.E. and E.M. Hildebrand, 1936
Prunus domestica
Moore, J. Duain and H.R. Cameron, 1956
Prunus persica (Amygdalus persica)
Thomas, H.E. and E.M. Hildebrand, 1936
Prunus salicina
Cochran, L.C., 1956

V. PRUNUS A *
Benincasa hispida
Fulton, Robert W., 1957
Boltonia latisquama
Fulton, Robert W., 1957
Browallia elata
Fulton, Robert W., 1957
Callistephus chinensis
Fulton, Robert W., 1957
Cassia marilandica
Fulton, Robert W., 1957
Chenopodium album
Fulton, Robert W., 1957
Coleus blumei
Fulton, Robert W., 1957
Crotalaria capensis
Fulton, Robert W., 1957
Crotalaria mucronata
Fulton, Robert W., 1957
Crotalaria spectabilis
Fulton, Robert W., 1957
Datura stramonium
Fulton, Robert W., 1957
Gleditsia triacanthos
Fulton, Robert W., 1957
Lagenaria siceraria (Lagenaria leucantha)
Fulton, Robert W., 1957
Luffa aegyptiaca (Luffa cylindrica)
Fulton, Robert W., 1957

VIRUS
V. PRUNUS A * (cont.)
    Melilotus officinalis
        Fulton, Robert W., 1957
    Melothria guadalupensis
        Fulton, Robert W., 1957
    Momordica charantia
        Fulton, Robert W., 1957
    Nepeta cataria
        Fulton, Robert W., 1957
    Nicotiana spp.
        Fulton, Robert W., 1957
    Phlox drummondii
        Fulton, Robert W., 1957
    Physalis aequata
        Fulton, Robert W., 1957
    Plantago virginica
        Fulton, Robert W., 1957
    Prunus persica (Amygdalus persica)
        Fulton, Robert W., 1957
    Rheum rhaponticum
        Fulton, Robert W., 1957
    Salpiglossis sinuata
        Fulton, Robert W., 1957
    Solidago spp.
        Fulton, Robert W., 1957
    Thunbergia alata
        Fulton, Robert W., 1957
    Tithonia speciosa
        Fulton, Robert W., 1957
    Verbascum thapsus
        Fulton, Robert W., 1957
    Zinnia elegans
        Fulton, Robert W., 1957

V. PRUNUS B *
    Asclepias syriaca
        Fulton, Robert W., 1957
    Cassia marilandica
        Fulton, Robert W., 1957
    Cassia tora
        Fulton, Robert W., 1957
    Chenopodium album
        Fulton, Robert W., 1957
    Crotalaria intermedia
        Fulton, Robert W., 1957
    Crotalaria mucronata
        Fulton, Robert W., 1957
    Cucumis prophetarum
        Fulton, Robert W., 1957
    Cyamopsis tetragonoloba
        Fulton, Robert W., 1957
    Gomphrena globosa
        Fulton, Robert W., 1957
    Hedysarum coronarium
        Fulton, Robert W., 1957
    Indigofera hirsuta
        Fulton, Robert W., 1957
    Luffa aegyptiaca (Luffa cylindrica)
        Fulton, Robert W., 1957
    Pisum sativum
        Fulton, Robert W., 1957
    Potentilla palustris
        Fulton, Robert W., 1957
    Prunus persica (Amygdalus persica)
        Fulton, Robert W., 1957
    Rheum rhaponticum
        Fulton, Robert W., 1957

V. PRUNUS E *
    Asclepias syriaca
        Fulton, Robert W., 1957
    Astragalus rubyi
        Fulton, Robert W., 1957
    Benincasa hispida
        Fulton, Robert W., 1957
    Boltonia latisquama
        Fulton, Robert W., 1957
    Callistephus chinensis
        Fulton, Robert W., 1957
    Chenopodium album
        Fulton, Robert W., 1957
    Citrullus colocynthis
        Fulton, Robert W., 1957

VIRUS
V. PRUNUS E * (cont.)
    Citrullus vulgaris
        Fulton, Robert W., 1957
    Citrullus vulgaris var. citroides *
        Fulton, Robert W., 1957
    Crotalaria capensis
        Fulton, Robert W., 1957
    Crotalaria spectabilis
        Fulton, Robert W., 1957
    Cynoglossum amabile
        Fulton, Robert W., 1957
    Gleditsia triacanthos
        Fulton, Robert W., 1957
    Gomphrena globosa
        Fulton, Robert W., 1957
    Hedysarum coronarium
        Fulton, Robert W., 1957
    Lactuca sativa
        Fulton, Robert W., 1957
    Lagenaria siceraria (Lagenaria leucantha)
        Fulton, Robert W., 1957
    Luffa aegyptiaca (Luffa cylindrica)
        Fulton, Robert W., 1957
    Melilotus alba
        Fulton, Robert W., 1957
    Melilotus indica
        Fulton, Robert W., 1957
    Melilotus officinalis
        Fulton, Robert W., 1957
    Momordica charantia
        Fulton, Robert W., 1957
    Nepeta cataria
        Fulton, Robert W., 1957
    Nicotiana spp.
        Fulton, Robert W., 1957
    Nicotiana tabacum
        Fulton, Robert W., 1957
    Phlox drummondii
        Fulton, Robert W., 1957
    Pisum sativum
        Fulton, Robert W., 1957
    Plantago virginica
        Fulton, Robert W., 1957
    Potentilla palustris
        Fulton, Robert W., 1957
    Prunus persica (Amygdalus persica)
        Fulton, Robert W., 1957
    Rheum rhaponticum
        Fulton, Robert W., 1957
    Solidago spp.
        Fulton, Robert W., 1957
    Thunbergia alata
        Fulton, Robert W., 1957
    Tithonia speciosa
        Fulton, Robert W., 1957
    Trifolium repens
        Fulton, Robert W., 1957
    Verbascum thapsus
        Fulton, Robert W., 1957
    Vinca rosea
        Fulton, Robert W., 1957
    Zinnia elegans
        Fulton, Robert W., 1957

V. PRUNUS G *
    Astragalus rubyi
        Fulton, Robert W., 1957
    Boltonia latisquama
        Fulton, Robert W., 1957
    Cassia marilandica
        Fulton, Robert W., 1957
    Chenopodium album
        Fulton, Robert W., 1957
    Citrullus colocynthis
        Fulton, Robert W., 1957
    Citrullus vulgaris
        Fulton, Robert W., 1957
    Citrullus vulgaris var. citroides *
        Fulton, Robert W., 1957
    Coleus blumei
        Fulton, Robert W., 1957
    Crotalaria spectabilis
        Fulton, Robert W., 1957

VIRUS
V. PRUNUS G * (cont.)
  Cucurbita pepo
    Fulton, Robert W., 1957
  Cynoglossum amabile
    Fulton, Robert W., 1957
  Datura stramonium
    Fulton, Robert W., 1957
  Gleditsia triacanthos
    Fulton, Robert W., 1957
  Gossypium hirsutum
    Fulton, Robert W., 1957
  Lactuca sativa
    Fulton, Robert W., 1957
  Lagenaria siceraria (Lagenaria leucantha)
    Fulton, Robert W., 1957
  Luffa aegyptiaca (Luffa cylindrica)
    Fulton, Robert W., 1957
  Melilotus officinalis
    Fulton, Robert W., 1957
  Melothria pendula
    Fulton, Robert W., 1957
  Momordica charantia
    Fulton, Robert W., 1957
  Nepeta cataria
    Fulton, Robert W., 1957
  Nicotiana benthamiana
    Fulton, Robert W., 1957
  Nicotiana spp.
    Fulton, Robert W., 1957
  Phlox drummondii
    Fulton, Robert W., 1957
  Plantago virginica
    Fulton, Robert W., 1957
  Prunus persica (Amygdalus persica)
    Fulton, Robert W., 1957
  Salpiglossis sinuata
    Fulton, Robert W., 1957
  Sesbania sesban
    Fulton, Robert W., 1957
  Solidago spp.
    Fulton, Robert W., 1957
  Tithonia speciosa
    Fulton, Robert W., 1957
  Trifolium repens
    Fulton, Robert W., 1957

V. RADISH MOSAIC Tompkins 1939
  Antirrhinum majus
    Tompkins, C.M., 1939
  Apium graveolens
    Tompkins, C.M., 1939
  Begonia semperflorens
    Tompkins, C.M., 1939
  Bellis perennis
    Tompkins, C.M., 1939
  Brassica campestris var. napobrassica
    Tompkins, C.M., 1939
  Brassica integrifolia var. chevalieri *
    Tompkins, C.M., 1939
  Brassica napus
    Tompkins, C.M., 1939
  Callistephus chinensis
    Tompkins, C.M., 1939
  Campanula medium
    Tompkins, C.M., 1939
  Chrysanthemum coronarium
    Tompkins, C.M., 1939
  Chrysanthemum maximum
    Tompkins, C.M., 1939
  Clarkia elegans
    Tompkins, C.M., 1939
  Cucumis sativus
    Tompkins, C.M., 1939
  Datura stramonium
    Tompkins, C.M., 1939
  Dianthus barbatus
    Tompkins, C.M., 1939
  Dimorphotheca aurantiaca
    Tompkins, C.M., 1939
  Gaillardia pulchella var. picta
    Tompkins, C.M., 1939
  Geum chiloense
    Tompkins, C.M., 1939

VIRUS
V. RADISH MOSAIC (cont.)
  Godetia grandiflora
    Tompkins, C.M., 1939
  Gypsophila paniculata
    Tompkins, C.M., 1939
  Heliotropium peruvianum
    Tompkins, C.M., 1939
  Hesperis matronalis
    Tompkins, C.M., 1939
  Lactuca sativa var. capitata
    Tompkins, C.M., 1939
  Lobelia hybrida
    Tompkins, C.M., 1939
  Lunaria annua
    Tompkins, C.M., 1939
  Lycopersicon esculentum var. vulgare
    Tompkins, C.M., 1939
  Lycopersicon pimpinellifolium
    Tompkins, C.M., 1939
  Matthiola incana var. annua
    Tompkins, C.M., 1939
  Myosotis alpestris
    Tompkins, C.M., 1939
  Papaver nudicaule
    Tompkins, C.M., 1939
  Papaver orientale
    Tompkins, C.M., 1939
  Pelargonium zonale
    Tompkins, C.M., 1939
  Penstemon barbatus
    Tompkins, C.M., 1939
  Petunia hybrida
    Tompkins, C.M., 1939
  Pisum sativum
    Tompkins, C.M., 1939
  Reseda odorata
    Tompkins, C.M., 1939
  Rheum rhaponticum
    Tompkins, C.M., 1939
  Ricinus communis
    Tompkins, C.M., 1939
  Salvia farinacea
    Tompkins, C.M., 1939
  Scabiosa atropurpurea
    Tompkins, C.M., 1939
  Senecio cruentus
    Tompkins, C.M., 1939
  Solanum aviculare
    Tompkins, C.M., 1939
  Solanum tuberosum
    Tompkins, C.M., 1939
  Tagetes erecta
    Tompkins, C.M., 1939
  Tagetes patula
    Tompkins, C.M., 1939
  Taraxacum officinale
    Tompkins, C.M., 1939
  Tropaeolum majus
    Tompkins, C.M., 1939
  Verbena hybrida
    Tompkins, C.M., 1939
  Vicia faba
    Tompkins, C.M., 1939
  Viola tricolor
    Tompkins, C.M., 1939
  Zea mays
    Tompkins, C.M., 1939

V. RAPE SAVOY Holmes 1939
  Brassica oleracea var. botrytis
    Ling, Lee and Juhwa Y. Yang, 1940
  Brassica oleracea var. capitata
    Ling, Lee and Juhwa Y. Yang, 1940
  Brassica oleracea var. caulorapa
    Ling, Lee and Juhwa Y. Yang, 1940
  Raphanus sativus
    Ling, Lee and Juhwa Y. Yang, 1940

V. RASPBERRY ALPHA LEAF CURL
  Rubus occidentalis
    Bennett, C.W., 1930
    Rankin, W. Howard, 1931

VIRUS

V. RASPBERRY NECROTIC FERN LEAF MOSAIC
 Nicotiana tabacum   Chamberlain 1941
     Chamberlain, G.C., 1941

V. RASPBERRY STREAK   Zeller 1923
 Cuscuta spp.
     Horn, Norman L., 1948
 Cuscuta subinclusa
     Horn, N.L. and M.W. Woods, 1949

V. RED CLOVER MOSAIC *
 Cajanus indicus
     Zaumeyer, W.J. and B.L. Wade, 1935
 Canavalia gladiata
     Zaumeyer, W.J. and B.L. Wade, 1935
 Dolichos lablab
     Zaumeyer, W.J. and B.L. Wade, 1935
 Glycine max
     Zaumeyer, W.J. and B.L. Wade, 1935
 Lathyrus odoratus
     Zaumeyer, W.J. and B.L. Wade, 1935
 Lupinus albus
     Zaumeyer, W.J. and B.L. Wade, 1935
 Medicago sativa
     Elliott, J.A., 1921
     Zaumeyer, W.J. and B.L. Wade, 1935
 Melilotus alba
     Dickson, B.T., 1922
     Zaumeyer, W.J. and B.L. Wade, 1935
 Melilotus officinalis
     Dickson, B.T., 1922
 Mucuna deeringianum
     Zaumeyer, W.J. and B.L. Wade, 1935
 Phaseolus acutifolius var. latifolius
     Zaumeyer, W.J. and B.L. Wade, 1935
 Phaseolus angularis
     Zaumeyer, W.J. and B.L. Wade, 1935
 Phaseolus calcaratus
     Zaumeyer, W.J. and B.L. Wade, 1935
 Phaseolus lunatus
     Zaumeyer, W.J. and B.L. Wade, 1935
 Phaseolus lunatus f. macrocarpus
     Zaumeyer, W.J. and B.L. Wade, 1935
 Phaseolus mungo
     Zaumeyer, W.J. and B.L. Wade, 1935
 Phaseolus vulgaris
     Zaumeyer, W.J., 1933
     Zaumeyer, W.J. and B.L. Wade, 1933, 1935
 Trifolium repens
     Elliott, J.A., 1921
     Zaumeyer, W.J. and B.L. Wade, 1935
 Vigna sesquipedalis
     Zaumeyer, W.J. and B.L. Wade, 1935
 Vigna sinensis
     Zaumeyer, W.J. and B.L. Wade, 1935

V. RED CLOVER VEIN MOSAIC   Osborn 1937
 Cucumis sativus
     Hagedorn, D.J. and E.W. Hanson, 1951
     Hagedorn, D.J. and J.C. Walker, 1949, 1954
     Roberts, D.A., 1957
 Datura stramonium
     Hagedorn, D.J. and J.C. Walker, 1949, 1954
 Glycine max
     Hagedorn, D.J. and E.W. Hanson, 1951
     Hagedorn, D.J. and J.C. Walker, 1949, 1954
 Lycopersicon esculentum
     Hagedorn, D.J. and E.W. Hanson, 1951
     Hagedorn, D.J. and J.C. Walker, 1949, 1954
     Osborn, H.T., 1937
 Medicago orbicularis
     Hagedorn, D.J. and J.C. Walker, 1949, 1954
 Medicago sativa
     Graves, Clinton H., Jr. and D.J. Hagedorn, 1956
     Hagedorn, D.J. and E.W. Hanson, 1951
     Hagedorn, D.J. and J.C. Walker, 1949, 1954
     Osborn, H.T., 1937
 Nicotiana glutinosa
     Osborn, H.T., 1937
 Nicotiana langsdorffii
     Osborn, H.T., 1937
 Nicotiana rustica
     Osborn, H.T., 1937

VIRUS

V. RED CLOVER VEIN MOSAIC (cont.)
 Nicotiana sylvestris
     Osborn, H.T., 1937
 Nicotiana tabacum
     Hagedorn, D.J. and E.W. Hanson, 1951
     Hagedorn, D.J. and J.C. Walker, 1949, 1954
     Osborn, H.T., 1937
     Roberts, D.A., 1957
 Phaseolus aureus
     Osborn, H.T., 1937
 Phaseolus vulgaris
     Hagedorn, D.J. and E.W. Hanson, 1951
     Hagedorn, D.J. and J.C. Walker, 1949, 1954
     Osborn, H.T., 1937
     Roberts, D.A., 1957
 Solanum tuberosum
     Hagedorn, D.J. and J.C. Walker, 1949
     Osborn, H.T., 1937
 Trifolium repens
     Graves, Clinton H., Jr. and D.J. Hagedorn, 1956
     Hagedorn, D.J. and J.C. Walker, 1949
 Vicia angustifolia
     Graves, Clinton H., Jr. and D.J. Hagedorn, 1956
 Vicia faba var. major *
     Hagedorn, D.J. and J.C. Walker, 1949
 Vicia faba var. minor *
     Hagedorn, D.J. and J.C. Walker, 1949
 Vicia villosa
     Hagedorn, D.J. and J.C. Walker, 1949, 1954
 Vigna sinensis
     Hagedorn, D.J. and E.W. Hanson, 1951
     Hagedorn, D.J. and J.C. Walker, 1949, 1954
     Roberts, D.A., 1957

V. RED CURRANT RING SPOT   Klesser 1951
 Beta vulgaris
     Klesser, P.J., 1951
 Brassica oleracea var. capitata
     Klesser, P.J., 1951
 Brassica sinensis *
     Klesser, P.J., 1951
 Calendula officinalis
     Klesser, P.J., 1951
 Cucurbits pepo
     Klesser, P.J., 1951
 Dahlia variabilis
     Klesser, P.J., 1951
 Hyoscyamus niger
     Klesser, P.J., 1951
 Lycium barbarum
     Klesser, P.J., 1951
 Medicago lupulina
     Klesser, P.J., 1951
 Melilotus officinalis
     Klesser, P.J., 1951
 Mimulus luteus
     Klesser, P.J., 1951
 Phaseolus vulgaris
     Klesser, P.J., 1951
 Phlox drummondii
     Klesser, P.J., 1951
 Pisum sativum
     Klesser, P.J., 1951
 Silybum marianum
     Klesser, P.J., 1951
 Solanum capsicastrum
     Klesser, P.J., 1951
 Solanum capsicum *
     Klesser, P.J., 1951
 Tropaeolum majus
     Klesser, P.J., 1951
 Vicia faba
     Klesser, P.J., 1951

V. RICE AND CORN LEAF-GALL *
 Chloris barbata
     Agati, Julian A. and Carlos A. Calica, 1950
 Digitaria macrobachne
     Agati, Julian A. and Carlos A. Calica, 1950
 Digitaria sanguinalis
     Agati, Julian A. and Carlos A. Calica, 1950
 Echinochloa spp.
     Agati, Julian A. and Carlos A. Calica, 1950

VIRUS
V. RICE AND CORN LEAF-GALL * (cont.)
    Eragrostis amabilis
        Agati, Julian A. and Carlos A. Calica, 1950
    Panicum colonum
        Agati, Julian A. and Carlos A. Calica, 1950
    Triticum vulgare
        Agati, Julian A. and Carlos A. Calica, 1950

V. ROSE MOSAIC Weiss and McWhorter 1928
    Cuscuta campestris
        Fulton, Robert W., 1952
    Cuscuta gronovii
        Fulton, Robert W., 1952
    Cuscuta subinclusa
        Fulton, Robert W., 1952
    (Rosa chinensis x Rosa moschata) x Rosa foetida
        White, R.P., 1930
    Rosa odorata
        White, R.P., 1930
    Rosa polyantha
        White, R.P., 1930

V. ROSE STREAK Brierley 1935
    Rosa chinensis var. manetti
        Brierley, Philip and Floyd F. Smith, 1940
    Rosa hugonis
        Brierley, Philip and Floyd F. Smith, 1940

V. SOIL-BORNE OAT MOSAIC McKinney 1946, 1953
    Zea mays
        McKinney, H.H., 1946

V. SOIL-BORNE WHEAT MOSAIC McKinney 1925, 1953
    Avena sativa
        McKinney, H.H., 1930
    Hordeum vulgare
        McKinney, H.H., 1947

V. (SOUR)CHERRY YELLOWS Keitt and Clayton 1939,
    Prunus avium   1943
        Keitt, G.W. and C.N. Clayton, 1943
    Prunus cistena *
        Young, H.C., Jr., 1951
    Prunus domestica
        Moore, J. Duain and H.R. Cameron, 1956
        Moore, J. Duain and G.W. Keitt, 1944

V. SOYBEAN MOSAIC Gardner and Kendrick 1921
    Beta vulgaris
        Conover, Robert A., 1948
    Crotalaria spectabilis
        Conover, Robert A., 1948
    Lespedeza striata
        Conover, Robert A., 1948
    Lupinus angustifolius
        Conover, Robert A., 1948
    Lupinus luteus
        Conover, Robert A., 1948
    Lycopersicon esculentum
        Conover, Robert A., 1948
    Medicago sativa
        Conover, Robert A., 1948
        Pierce, W.H., 1935
    Melilotus alba
        Conover, Robert A., 1948
    Melilotus officinalis
        Conover, Robert A., 1948
        Pierce, W.H., 1935
    Nicotiana tabacum
        Conover, Robert A., 1948
        Pierce, W.H., 1935
    Petunia hybrida
        Pierce, W.H., 1935
    Phaseolus aureus
        Conover, Robert A., 1948
    Phaseolus coccineus
        Conover, Robert A., 1948
    Phaseolus lunatus
        Conover, Robert A., 1948
    Phaseolus mungo
        Conover, Robert A., 1948
    Phaseolus vulgaris
        Conover, Robert A., 1948

VIRUS
V. SOYBEAN MOSAIC (cont.)
    Phaseolus vulgaris
        Harrison, Arthur L., 1935
        Kendrick, James B. and Max W. Gardner, 1924
        Pierce, W.H., 1935
    Pisum sativum
        Pierce, W.H., 1935
    Pisum sativum var. arvense
        Kendrick, James B. and Max W. Gardner, 1924
    Pisum sativum var. saccharatum
        Pierce, W.H., 1935
    Trifolium incarnatum
        Conover, Robert A., 1948
    Trifolium pratense
        Kendrick, James B. and Max W. Gardner, 1924
        Pierce, W.H., 1935
    Trifolium repens
        Pierce, W.H., 1935
    Vicia faba
        Conover, Robert A., 1948
    Vicia faba var. minor *
        Pierce, W.H., 1935
    Vigna sesquipedalis
        Conover, Robert A., 1948
    Vigna sinensis
        Conover, Robert A., 1948
        Kendrick, James B. and Max W. Gardner, 1924

V. SPINACH YELLOW DWARF Severin and Little 1947
    Apium graveolens var. dulce
        Severin, Henry H.P. and Donald H. Little, 1947
    Beta vulgaris
        Severin, Henry H.P. and Donald H. Little, 1947
    Beta vulgaris var. cicla
        Severin, Henry H.P. and Donald H. Little, 1947
    Brassica campestris
        Seveirn, Henry H.P. and Donald H. Little, 1947
    Brassica oleracea var. capitata
        Severin, Henry H.P. and Donald H. Little, 1947
    Callistephus chinensis
        Severin, Henry H.P. and Donald H. Little, 1947
    Campanula medium
        Severin, Henry H.P. and Donald H. Little, 1947
    Capsicum frutescens (Capsicum annuum)
        Severin, Henry H.P. and Donald H. Little, 1947
    Citrullus vulgaris
        Severin, Henry H.P. and Donald H. Little, 1947
    Cucumis sativus
        Severin, Henry H.P. and Donald H. Little, 1947
    Cucurbita pepo
        Severin, Henry H.P. and Donald H. Little, 1947
    Datura stramonium
        Severin, Henry H.P. and Donald H. Little, 1947
    Foeniculum vulgare var. dulce
        Severin, Henry H.P. and Donald H. Little, 1947
    Gossypium hirsutum
        Severin, Henry H.P. and Donald H. Little, 1947
    Lactuca sativa
        Severin, Henry H.P. and Donald H. Little, 1947
    Lupinus hartwegii
        Severin, Henry H.P. and Donald H. Little, 1947
    Lycopersicon esculentum
        Severin, Henry H.P. and Donald H. Little, 1947
    Matthiola incana var. annua
        Severin, Henry H.P. and Donald H. Little, 1947
    Mirabilis jalapa
        Severin, Henry H.P. and Donald H. Little, 1947
    Nicotiana alata var. grandiflora
        Severin, Henry H.P. and Donald H. Little, 1947
    Nicotiana glutinosa
        Severin, Henry H.P. and Donald H. Little, 1947
    Nicotiana tabacum
        Severin, Henry H.P. and Donald H. Little, 1947
    Pelargonium zonale
        Severin, Henry H.P. and Donald H. Little, 1947
    Petunia hybrida
        Severin, Henry H.P. and Donald H. Little, 1947
    Primula veris
        Severin, Henry H.P. and Donald H. Little, 1947
    Solanum tuberosum
        Severin, Henry H.P. and Donald H. Little, 1947
    Tetragonia expansa
        Severin, Henry H.P. and Donald H. Little, 1947

VIRUS
V. SQUASH MOSAIC Middleton 1949
  Alyssum saxatile
    Freitag, J.H., 1956
  Amaranthus retroflexus
    Freitag, J.H., 1956
  Antirrhinum majus
    Freitag, J.H., 1956
  Apium graveolens var. dulce
    Freitag, J.H., 1956
  Aquilegia spp.
    Freitag, J.H., 1956
  Arachis hypogaea
    Freitag, J.H., 1956
  Asclepias tuberosa
    Freitag, J.H., 1956
  Atriplex bracteosa
    Freitag, J.H., 1956
  Atriplex expansa
    Freitag, J.H., 1956
  Beta vulgaris
    Freitag, J.H., 1956
  Brassica oleracea var. botrytis
    Freitag, J.H., 1956
  Brassica oleracea var. capitata
    Freitag, J.H., 1956
  Brassica rapa
    Freitag, J.H., 1956
  Calendula officinalis
    Freitag, J.H., 1956
  Callistephus chinensis
    Freitag, J.H., 1956
  Campanula carpatica
    Freitag, J.H., 1956
  Campanula medium
    Freitag, J.H., 1956
  Capsicum frutescens var. grossum
    Freitag, J.H., 1956
  Carum carvi
    Freitag, J.H., 1956
  Celosia argentea
    Freitag, J.H., 1956
  Cheiranthus cheiri
    Freitag, J.H., 1956
  Chrysanthemum parthenium
    Freitag, J.H., 1956
  Citrullus vulgaris
    Freitag, J.H., 1956
    Lindberg, G.D., D.H. Hall and J.C. Walker, 1956
  Cosmos bipinnatus
    Freitag, J.H., 1956
  Cynoglossum amabile
    Freitag, J.H., 1956
  Datura stramonium
    Freitag, J.H., 1956
    Lindberg, G.D., D.H. Hall and J.C. Walker, 1956
  Daucus carota var. sativa
    Freitag, J.H., 1956
  Delphinium spp.
    Freitag, J.H., 1956
  Dianthus caryophyllus
    Freitag, J.H., 1956
  Digitalis purpurea
    Freitag, J.H., 1956
  Dimorphotheca sinuata
    Freitag, J.H., 1956
  Eschscholtzia californica
    Freitag, J.H., 1956
  Euphorbia marginata
    Freitag, J.H., 1956
  Glycine max
    Freitag, J.H., 1956
  Gossypium hirsutum
    Freitag, J.H., 1956
  Hesperis matronalis
    Freitag, J.H., 1956
  Hibiscus esculentus
    Freitag, J.H., 1956
  Iberis umbellata
    Freitag, J.H., 1956
  Ipomoea nil
    Freitag, J.H., 1956
  Kochia scoparia
    Freitag, J.H., 1956

VIRUS
V. SQUASH MOSAIC (cont.)
  Lactuca sativa
    Freitag, J.H., 1956
  Lactuca sativa var. longifolia
    Freitag, J.H., 1956
  Limonium sinuatum
    Freitag, J.H., 1956
  Lupinus hartwegii
    Freitag, J.H., 1956
  Lupinus polyphyllus
    Freitag, J.H., 1956
  Lycopersicon esculentum
    Freitag, J.H., 1956
  Matthiola incana var. annua
    Freitag, J.H., 1956
  Medicago hispida
    Freitag, J.H., 1956
  Medicago sativa
    Freitag, J.H., 1956
  Melilotus alba
    Freitag, J.H., 1956
  Melilotus indica
    Freitag, J.H., 1956
  Melilotus officinalis
    Freitag, J.H., 1956
  Mirabilis jalapa
    Freitag, J.H., 1956
  Nasturtium officinale
    Freitag, J.H., 1956
  Nemophila menziessii
    Freitag, J.H., 1956
  Nicotiana alata var. grandiflora
    Freitag, J.H., 1956
  Nicotiana glauca
    Freitag, J.H., 1956
  Nicotiana glutinosa
    Freitag, J.H., 1956
    Lindberg, G.D., D.H. Hall and J.C. Walker, 1956
  Nicotiana langsdorffii
    Freitag, J.H., 1956
  Nicotiana rustica
    Lindberg, G.D., D.H. Hall and J.C. Walker, 1956
  Nicotiana rustica var. humulus *
    Freitag, J.H., 1956
  Nicotiana tabacum
    Freitag, J.H., 1956
    Lindberg, G.D., D.H. Hall and J.C. Walker, 1956
  Pastinaca sativa
    Freitag, J.H., 1956
  Pelargonium zonale
    Freitag, J.H., 1956
  Petroselinum crispum
    Freitag, J.H., 1956
  Petunia hybrida
    Freitag, J.H., 1956
  Phaseolus limensis var. limenanus *
    Freitag, J.H., 1956
  Phaseolus vulgaris
    Freitag, J.H., 1956
  Phlox drummondii
    Freitag, J.H., 1956
  Pisum sativum
    Freitag, J.H., 1956
  Primula veris
    Freitag, J.H., 1956
  Raphanus sativus
    Freitag, J.H., 1956
  Reseda odorata
    Freitag, J.H., 1956
  Ricinus communis
    Freitag, J.H., 1956
  Rumex acetosa
    Freitag, J.H., 1956
  Salpiglossis sinuata
    Freitag, J.H., 1956
  Solanum tuberosum
    Freitag, J.H., 1956
  Spinacia oleracea
    Freitag, J.H., 1956
  Tagetes erecta
    Freitag, J.H., 1956
  Tagetes patula
    Freitag, J.H., 1956

VIRUS
V. SQUASH MOSAIC (cont.)
  Trachymene caerulea
    Freitag, J.H., 1956
  Trifolium incarnatum
    Freitag, J.H., 1956
  Trifolium pratense
    Freitag, J.H., 1956
  Trifolium repens
    Freitag, J.H., 1956
  Trifolium repens var. latum *
    Freitag, J.H., 1956
  Tropaeolum majus
    Freitag, J.H., 1956
  Vicia faba
    Freitag, J.H., 1956
  Vigna sesquipedalis
    Freitag, J.H., 1956
  Vigna sinensis
    Freitag, J.H., 1956
    Lindberg, G.D., D.H. Hall and J.C. Walker, 1956
  Vinca rosea
    Freitag, J.H., 1956
  Zea mays
    Freitag, J.H., 1956
  Zinnia elegans
    Freitag, J.H., 1956
    Lindberg, G.D., D.H. Hall and J.C. Walker, 1956

V. SQUASH MOSAIC (SOUTHERN) Anderson 1951
  Apium graveolens var. dulce
    Anderson, C.W., 1951
  Beta vulgaris
    Anderson, C.W., 1951
  Capsicum frutescens (Capsicum annuum)
    Anderson, C.W., 1951
  Lycopersicon esculentum
    Anderson, C.W., 1951
  Nicotiana glutinosa
    Anderson, C.W., 1951
  Nicotiana tabacum
    Anderson, C.W., 1951
  Phaseolus vulgaris
    Anderson, C.W., 1951
  Vicia faba
    Anderson, C.W., 1951
  Vigna sinensis
    Anderson, C.W., 1951
  Zinnia elegans
    Anderson, C.W., 1951

V. STONE FRUIT *
  Abutilon theophrasti
    Boyle, J.S., J. Duain Moore and G.W. Keitt, 1954
  Amaranthus graecizans
    Boyle, J.S., J. Duain Moore and G.W. Keitt, 1954
  Anthemis cotula
    Boyle, J.S., J. Duain Moore and G.W. Keitt, 1954
  Arctium minus
    Boyle, J.S., J. Duain Moore and G.W. Keitt, 1954
  Asclepias syriaca
    Boyle, J.S., J. Duain Moore and G.W. Keitt, 1954
  Brassica kaber (Brassica arvensis)
    Boyle, J.S., J. Duain Moore and G.W. Keitt, 1954
  Capsella bursa-pastoris
    Boyle, J.S., J. Duain Moore and G.W. Keitt, 1954
  Centaurea spp.
    Boyle, J.S., J. Duain Moore and G.W. Keitt, 1954
  Cerastium vulgatum
    Boyle, J.S., J. Duain Moore and G.W. Keitt, 1954
  Chelone glabra
    Boyle, J.S., J. Duain Moore and G.W. Keitt, 1954
  Chenopodium album
    Boyle, J.S., J. Duain Moore and G.W. Keitt, 1954
  Cichorium intybus
    Boyle, J.S., J. Duain Moore and G.W. Keitt, 1954
  Cirsium arvense
    Boyle, J.S., J. Duain Moore and G.W. Keitt, 1954
  Citrullus vulgaris
    Boyle, J.S., J. Duain Moore and G.W. Keitt, 1954
  Cucumis melo
    Boyle, J.S., J. Duain Moore and G.W. Keitt, 1954
  Cucurbita maxima
    Boyle, J.S., J. Duain Moore and G.W. Keitt, 1954

VIRUS
V. STONE FRUIT * (cont.)
  Cucurbita pepo
    Boyle, J.S., J. Duain Moore and G.W. Keitt, 1954
  Cuscuta campestris
    Boyle, J.S., J. Duain Moore and G.W. Keitt, 1954
  Datura stramonium
    Boyle, J.S., J. Duain Moore and G.W. Keitt, 1954
  Echinocystis lobata (Micrampelis lobata)
    Boyle, J.S., J. Duain Moore and G.W. Keitt, 1954
  Erysimum cheiranthoides
    Boyle, J.S., J. Duain Moore and G.W. Keitt, 1954
  Euphorbia esula
    Boyle, J.S., J. Duain Moore and G.W. Keitt, 1954
  Fagopyrum esculentum
    Boyle, J.S., J. Duain Moore and G.W. Keitt, 1954
  Gossypium hirsutum
    Boyle, J.S., J. Duain Moore and G.W. Keitt, 1954
  Hesperis matronalis
    Boyle, J.S., J. Duain Moore and G.W. Keitt, 1954
  Hypericum perforatum
    Boyle, J.S., J. Duain Moore and G.W. Keitt, 1954
  Iodanthus pinnatifidus
    Boyle, J.S., J. Duain Moore and G.W. Keitt, 1954
  Leonurus cardiaca
    Boyle, J.S., J. Duain Moore and G.W. Keitt, 1954
  Lychnis alba
    Boyle, J.S., J. Duain Moore and G.W. Keitt, 1954
  Lycium halimifolium
    Boyle, J.S., J. Duain Moore and G.W. Keitt, 1954
  Lycopersicon esculentum
    Boyle, J.S., J. Duain Moore and G.W. Keitt, 1954
  Malva rotundifolia
    Boyle, J.S., J. Duain Moore and G.W. Keitt, 1954
  Melilotus alba
    Boyle, J.S., J. Duain Moore and G.W. Keitt, 1954
  Melilotus officinalis
    Boyle, J.S., J. Duain Moore and G.W. Keitt, 1954
  Mollugo verticillata
    Boyle, J.S., J. Duain Moore and G.W. Keitt, 1954
  Nepeta cataria
    Boyle, J.S., J. Duain Moore and G.W. Keitt, 1954
  Nicandra physalodes
    Boyle, J.S., J. Duain Moore and G.W. Keitt, 1954
  Nicotiana glutinosa
    Boyle, J.S., J. Duain Moore and G.W. Keitt, 1954
  Nicotiana rustica
    Boyle, J.S., J. Duain Moore and G.W. Keitt, 1954
  Nicotiana tabacum
    Boyle, J.S., J. Duain Moore and G.W. Keitt, 1954
  Phaseolus vulgaris
    Boyle, J.S., J. Duain Moore and G.W. Keitt, 1954
  Physalis pubescens
    Boyle, J.S., J. Duain Moore and G.W. Keitt, 1954
  Pisum sativum
    Boyle, J.S., J. Duain Moore and G.W. Keitt, 1954
  Portulaca oleracea
    Boyle, J.S., J. Duain Moore and G.W. Keitt, 1954
  Potentilla monspeliensis
    Boyle, J.S., J. Duain Moore and G.W. Keitt, 1954
  Rumex britannica
    Boyle, J.S., J. Duain Moore and G.W. Keitt, 1954
  Rumex crispus
    Boyle, J.S., J. Duain Moore and G.W. Keitt, 1954
  Sisymbrium officinale
    Boyle, J.S., J. Duain Moore and G.W. Keitt, 1954
  Solanum nigrum
    Boyle, J.S., J. Duain Moore and G.W. Keitt, 1954
  Sonchus oleraceus
    Boyle, J.S., J. Duain Moore and G.W. Keitt, 1954
  Spinacia oleracea
    Boyle, J.S., J. Duain Moore and G.W. Keitt, 1954
  Taraxacum officinale
    Boyle, J.S., J. Duain Moore and G.W. Keitt, 1954
  Thlaspi arvense
    Boyle, J.S., J. Duain Moore and G.W. Keitt, 1954
  Trifolium incarnatum
    Boyle, J.S., J. Duain Moore and G.W. Keitt, 1954
  Verbascum thapsus
    Boyle, J.S., J. Duain Moore and G.W. Keitt, 1954
  Vigna sinensis
    Boyle, J.S., J. Duain Moore and G.W. Keitt, 1954
  Xanthium echinatum
    Boyle, J.S., J. Duain Moore and G.W. Keitt, 1954

VIRUS

V. STONE FRUIT * (cont.)
Zinnia elegans
Boyle, J.S., J. Duain Moore and G.W. Keitt, 1954

V. STONE FRUIT NECROTIC RING SPOT *
Prunus domestica
Moore, J. Duain and H.R. Cameron, 1956

V. STRAWBERRY CRINKLE Zeller and Vaughan 1932
Cuscuta subinclusa
Smith, Harlan E. and J. Duain Moore, 1952
Rosa spp.
Brierley, Philip and Floyd F. Smith, 1940

V. STRAWBERRY GREEN PETAL Posnette 1953 ((May be a strain of V. Aster yellows Frazier and Posnette 1956))
Cuscuta campestris
Frazier, N.W. and A.F. Posnette, 1957
Cuscuta europaea
Frazier, N.W. and A.F. Posnette, 1957
Cuscuta subinclusa
Frazier, N.W. and A.F. Posnette, 1957

V. STRAWBERRY MOTTLE Prentice 1952
Cuscuta campestris
Demaree, J.B. and C.P. Marcus, 1951
Cuscuta gronovii
Smith, Harlan E. and J. Duain Moore, 1952
Cuscuta subinclusa
Smith, Harlan E. and J. Duain Moore, 1952

V. STRAWBERRY, TYPE 2 *
Cuscuta subinclusa
Smith, Harlan E. and J. Duain Moore, 1952

V. SUGARCANE MOSAIC Brandes 1920
Agrostis palustris
Brandes, E.W. and Peter J. Klaphaak, 1923
Andropogon elliottii
Brandes, E.W. and Peter J. Klaphaak, 1923
Andropogon scoparius
Brandes, E.W. and Peter J. Klaphaak, 1923
Andropogon virginicus
Brandes, E.W. and Peter J. Klaphaak, 1923
Avena sativa
Brandes, E.W. and Peter J. Klaphaak, 1923
Coix lachryma-jobi
Brandes, E.W. and Peter J. Klaphaak, 1923
Eleusine coracana
Brandes, E.W. and Peter J. Klaphaak, 1923
Eriochloa subglabra
Chardon, C.E. and R.A. Veve, 1923
Euchlaena mexicana
Brandes, E.W. and Peter J. Klaphaak, 1923
Holcus halepensis
Brandes, E.W. and Peter J. Klaphaak, 1923
Hordeum vulgare
Brandes, E.W. and Peter J. Klaphaak, 1923
Leptochloa filiformis
Brandes, E.W. and Peter J. Klaphaak, 1923
Miscanthus sinensis var. variegatus
Brandes, E.W. and Peter J. Klaphaak, 1923
Miscanthus sinensis var. zebrinus
Brandes, E.W. and Peter J. Klaphaak, 1923
Oryza sativa
Brandes, E.W. and Peter J. Klaphaak, 1923
Panicum barbinode
Brandes, E.W. and Peter J. Klaphaak, 1923
Pennisetum purpureum
Brandes, E.W. and Peter J. Klaphaak, 1923
Phleum pratense
Brandes, E.W. and Peter J. Klaphaak, 1923
Phyllostachys pubescens *
Brandes, E.W. and Peter J. Klaphaak, 1923
Phyllostachys quilioi
Brandes, E.W. and Peter J. Klaphaak, 1923
Poa pratensis
Brandes, E.W. and Peter J. Klaphaak, 1923
Saccharum officinarum
Storey, H.H., 1929
Secale cereale
Brandes, E.W. and Peter J. Klaphaak, 1923
Setaria virdis
Brandes, E.W. and Peter J. Klaphaak, 1923

VIRUS

V. SUGARCANE MOSAIC (cont.)
Sorghastrum nutans
Brandes, E.W. and Peter J. Klaphaak, 1923
Tripsacum dactyloides
Brandes, E.W. and Peter J. Klaphaak, 1923
Triticum aestivum
Brandes, E.W. and Peter J. Klaphaak, 1923

V. SUGARCANE STREAK Storey 1925
Digitaria horizontalis
Storey, H.H. and A.P.D. McClean, 1930
Eleusine indica
Storey, H.H. and A.P.D. McClean, 1930

V. SWEET POTATO FEATHERY MOTTLE Doolittle and Harter 1945
Cucumis sativus
Doolittle, S.P. and L.L. Harter, 1945
Webb, Raymon E., 1954
Datura stramonium
Doolittle, S.P. and L.L. Harter, 1945
Datura stramonium var. tatula
Webb, Raymon E., 1954
Ipomoea batata
Doolittle, S.P. and L.L. Harter, 1945
Ipomoea cairica
Webb, Raymon E., 1954
Ipomoea nil
Webb, Raymon E., 1954
Ipomoea purpurea
Doolittle, S.P. and L.L. Harter, 1945
Ipomoea rubra
Webb, Raymon E., 1954
Ipomoea sinuata
Webb, Raymon E., 1954
Ipomoea spp.
Webb, Raymon E., 1954
Ipomoea tricolor
Webb, Raymon E., 1954
Nicandra physalodes
Webb, Raymon E., 1954
Nicotiana glutinosa
Doolittle, S.P. and L.L. Harter, 1945
Webb, Raymon E., 1954
Nicotiana rustica
Webb, Raymon E., 1954
Nicotiana sylvestris
Webb, Raymon E., 1954
Nicotiana tabacum
Doolittle, S.P. and L.L. Harter, 1945
Webb, Raymon E., 1954
Physalis floridana
Webb, Raymon E., 1954
Quamoclit coccinea
Webb, Raymon E., 1954
Quamoclit sloteri
Webb, Raymon E., 1954
Vigna sinensis
Webb, Raymon E., 1954

V. SWEET POTATO MOSAIC Sheffield 1953
Amaryllis spp.
Borders, H.I. and T.J. Ratcliff, 1954
Brassica oleracea
Borders, H.I. and T.J. Ratcliff, 1954
Capsicum frutescens (Capsicum annuum)
Borders, H.I. and T.J. Ratcliff, 1954
Cucumis sativus
Borders, H.I. and T.J. Ratcliff, 1954
Cucurbita pepo
Borders, H.I. and T.J. Ratcliff, 1954
Euphorbia pulcherrima
Borders, H.I. and T.J. Ratcliff, 1954
Ipomoea purpurea
Borders, H.I. and T.J. Ratcliff, 1954
Ipomoea spp.
Borders, H.I. and T.J. Ratcliff, 1954
Ipomoea tricolor
Borders, H.I. and T.J. Ratcliff, 1954
Lycopersicon esculentum
Borders, H.I. and T.J. Ratcliff, 1954
Nicotiana tabacum
Borders, H.I. and T.J. Ratcliff, 1954
Phaseolus vulgaris
Borders, H.I. and T.J. Ratcliff, 1954

VIRUS

V. TEASEL MOSAIC Stoner 1951
    Apium graveolens
        Stoner, Warren N., 1951
    Beta vulgaris
        Stoner, Warren N., 1951
    Cucumis sativus
        Stoner, Warren N., 1951
    Cucurbita pepo
        Stoner, Warren N., 1951
    Nicotiana tabacum
        Stoner, Warren N., 1951

V. TITHONIA ROTUNDIFOLIA MOSAIC *
    Nicotiana tabacum
        Cook, M.T., 1936

V. TOBACCO BROAD RING SPOT J. Johnson and Fulton
    Beta vulgaris   1940
        Johnson, James and Robert W. Fulton, 1942
    Citrullus vulgaris
        Johnson, James and Robert W. Fulton, 1942
    Medicago sativa
        Johnson, James and Robert W. Fulton, 1942
    Melilotus alba
        Johnson, James and Robert W. Fulton, 1942

V. TOBACCO COARSE ETCH E.M. Johnson 1930
    Beta vulgaris
        Johnson, E.M., 1930
    Brassica hirta (Brassica alba)
        Johnson, E.M., 1930
    Brassica oleracea
        Johnson, E.M., 1930
    Brassica rapa var. depressa *
        Johnson, E.M., 1930
    Capsicum frutescens (Capsicum annuum)
        Johnson, E.M., 1930
    Cucumis sativus
        Johnson, E.M., 1930
    Glycine max
        Johnson, E.M., 1930
    Lycopersicon esculentum
        Johnson, E.M., 1930
    Phaseolus vulgaris
        Johnson, E.M., 1930
    Pisum sativum
        Johnson, E.M., 1930
    Raphanus sativus
        Johnson, E.M., 1930
    Solanum carolinense
        Johnson, E.M., 1930

V. TOBACCO ETCH E.M. Johnson 1930
    Acalypha virginica
        Holmes, Francis O., 1946
    Adlumia fungosa
        Holmes, Francis O., 1946
    Ageratum conyzoides
        Holmes, Francis O., 1946
    Allium cepa
        Holmes, Francis O., 1946
    Althaea rosea
        Holmes, Francis O., 1946
    Amaranthus tricolor
        Holmes, Francis O., 1946
    Amaryllis (Hippeastrum) puniceum
        Holmes, Francis O., 1946
    Ambrosia trifida
        Holmes, Francis O., 1946
    Anagallis arvensis
        Holmes, Francis O., 1946
    Anchusa azurea
        Holmes, Francis O., 1946
    Anchusa capensis
        Holmes, Francis O., 1946
    Antirrhinum majus
        Holmes, Francis O., 1946
    Apium graveolens
        Anderson, C.W., 1954
        Holmes, Francis O., 1946
    Aquilegia caerulea
        Holmes, Francis O., 1946

VIRUS

V. TOBACCO ETCH (cont.)
    Arctium lappa
        Holmes, Francis O., 1946
    Asclepias curassavica
        Holmes, Francis O., 1946
    Asclepias syriaca
        Holmes, Francis O., 1946
    Avena sativa
        Holmes, Francis O., 1946
    Barbarea vulgaris
        Holmes, Francis O., 1946
    Begonia semperflorens
        Holmes, Francis O., 1946
    Bellis perennis
        Holmes, Francis O., 1946
    Beta vulgaris
        Bennett, C.W., 1944
        Holmes, Francis O., 1946
        Johnson, E.M., 1930
    Bidens frondosa
        Holmes, Francis O., 1946
    Brassica campestris var. napobrassica
        Holmes, Francis O., 1946
    Brassica hirta (Brassica alba)
        Johnson, E.M., 1930
    Brassica oleracea
        Holmes, Francis O., 1946
        Johnson, E.M., 1930
    Brassica oleracea var. gemmifera
        Bennett, C.W., 1944
    Brassica pekinensis
        Holmes, Francis O., 1946
    Brassica rapa var. depressa *
        Johnson, E.M., 1930
    Browallia americana (Browallia demissa)
        Holmes, Francis O., 1946
    Calendula officinalis
        Holmes, Francis O., 1946
    Calonyction aculeatum
        Holmes, Francis O., 1946
    Campanula carpatica
        Holmes, Francis O., 1946
    Campanula lactiflora
        Holmes, Francis O., 1946
    Campanula medium
        Holmes, Francis O., 1946
    Campanula petiolata (Campanula rotundifolia of Amer.
        Holmes, Francis O., 1946   auths.)
    Campanula pyramidalis
        Holmes, Francis O., 1946
    Capsella bursa-pastoris
        Holmes, Francis O., 1946
    Capsicum frutescens (Capsicum annuum)
        McKinney, H.H., 1952
    Carica papaya
        Holmes, Francis O., 1946
    Centaurea americana
        Holmes, Francis O., 1946
    Centaurea montana
        Holmes, Francis O., 1946
    Centaurea moschata
        Holmes, Francis O., 1946
    Cheiranthus allionii
        Holmes, Francis O., 1946
    Cheiranthus cheiri
        Holmes, Francis O., 1946
    Chelidonium majus
        Holmes, Francis O., 1946
    Chenopodium album
        Holmes, Francis O., 1946
    Chenopodium ambrosioides
        Holmes, Francis O., 1946
    Chenopodium glaucum
        Holmes, Francis O., 1946
    Chenopodium rubrum
        Holmes, Francis O., 1946
    Chrysanthemum leucanthemum
        Holmes, Francis O., 1946
    Cichorium endivia
        Holmes, Francis O., 1946
    Citrullus vulgaris
        Holmes, Francis O., 1946

VIRUS
V. TOBACCO ETCH (cont.)

Clarkia elegans
    Holmes, Francis O., 1946
Cleome spinosa
    Holmes, Francis O., 1946
Cobaea scandens
    Holmes, Francis O., 1946
Coleus blumei
    Holmes, Francis O., 1946
Coreopsis grandiflora
    Holmes, Francis O., 1946
Cucumis melo
    Holmes, Francis O., 1946
Cucumis sativus
    Anderson, C.W., 1954
    Bennett, C.W., 1944
    Holmes, Francis O., 1946
    Johnson, E.M., 1930
Cucurbita maxima
    Holmes, Francis O., 1946
Cucurbita pepo
    Holmes, Francis O., 1946
Cuscuta californica
    Bennett, C.W., 1944
Cuscuta campestris
    Bennett, C.W., 1944
Cuscuta subinclusa
    Bennett, C.W., 1944
Cynoglossum amabile
    Holmes, Francis O., 1946
Cyphomandra betacea
    Holmes, Francis O., 1946
Dahlia pinnata
    Holmes, Francis O., 1946
Daucus carota
    Holmes, Francis O., 1946
Delphinium cultorum
    Holmes, Francis O., 1946
Dianthus barbatus
    Holmes, Francis O., 1946
Dianthus chinensis
    Holmes, Francis O., 1946
Digitalis purpurea
    Holmes, Francis O., 1946
Dolichos lablab
    Holmes, Francis O., 1946
Echium vulgare
    Holmes, Francis O., 1946
Emilia flammea
    Holmes, Francis O., 1946
Erigeron annuus
    Holmes, Francis O., 1946
Erigeron speciosus
    Holmes, Francis O., 1946
Euphorbia heterophylla
    Holmes, Francis O., 1946
Euphorbia marginata
    Holmes, Francis O., 1946
Euphorbia preslii
    Holmes, Francis O., 1946
Fagopyrum esculentum
    Holmes, Francis O., 1946
Gaillardia aristata
    Holmes, Francis O., 1946
Galinsoga parviflora
    Holmes, Francis O., 1946
Geranium carolinianum
    Holmes, Francis O., 1946
Geum canadense
    Holmes, Francis O., 1946
Geum chiloense
    Holmes, Francis O., 1946
Gilia capitata
    Holmes, Francis O., 1946
Gilia liniflora
    Holmes, Francis O., 1946
Glycine max
    Holmes, Francis O., 1946
    Johnson, E.M., 1930
Gomphrena haageana
    Holmes, Francis O., 1946
Gossypium hirsutum
    Holmes, Francis O., 1946

VIRUS
V. TOBACCO ETCH (cont.)

Helianthus tuberosus
    Holmes, Francis O., 1946
Helichrysum bracteatum
    Holmes, Francis O., 1946
Heliopsis scabra
    Holmes, Francis O., 1946
Heliotropium corymbosum
    Holmes, Francis O., 1946
Hibiscus esculentus
    Holmes, Francis O., 1946
Hibiscus manihot
    Holmes, Francis O., 1946
Holcus sudanensis
    Holmes, Francis O., 1946
Hordeum vulgare
    Holmes, Francis O., 1946
Hunnemannia fumariaefolia
    Holmes, Francis O., 1946
Hypericum boreale
    Holmes, Francis O., 1946
Iberis gibraltarica
    Holmes, Francis O., 1946
Iberis sempervirens
    Holmes, Francis O., 1946
Iberis umbellata
    Holmes, Francis O., 1946
Impatiens balsamina
    Holmes, Francis O., 1946
Impatiens sultanii (or sometimes Impatiens holstii)
    Holmes, Francis O., 1946
Incarvillea variabilis
    Holmes, Francis O., 1946
Ipomoea batata
    Holmes, Francis O., 1946
Ipomoea nil
    Holmes, Francis O., 1946
Ipomoea setosa
    Holmes, Francis O., 1946
Ipomoea tricolor
    Holmes, Francis O., 1946
Kalanchoe daigremontiana
    Holmes, Francis O., 1946
Kochia scoparia
    Holmes, Francis O., 1946
Lantana camara
    Holmes, Francis O., 1946
Lavatera trimestris
    Holmes, Francis O., 1946
Lens esculenta
    Holmes, Francis O., 1946
Leptosyne maritima
    Holmes, Francis O., 1946
Lilium philippinense
    Holmes, Francis O., 1946
Limonium bonduelli
    Holmes, Francis O., 1946
Limonium sinuatum
    Holmes, Francis O., 1946
Linaria vulgaris
    Holmes, Francis O., 1946
Linum flavum
    Holmes, Francis O., 1946
Linum grandiflorum
    Holmes, Francis O., 1946
Linum perenne
    Holmes, Francis O., 1946
Lobelia erinus
    Holmes, Francis O., 1946
Lobularia maritima
    Holmes, Francis O., 1946
Luffa acutangula
    Holmes, Francis O., 1946
Lunaria annua
    Holmes, Francis O., 1946
Lupinus hartwegii
    Holmes, Francis O., 1946
Lychnis coeli-rosa
    Holmes, Francis O., 1946
Lycopersicon chilense
    Holmes, Francis O., 1946
Lycopus rubellus
    Holmes, Francis O., 1946

VIRUS
V. TOBACCO ETCH (cont.)
Malope trifida
    Holmes, Francis O., 1946
Malva rotundifolia
    Holmes, Francis O., 1946
Marrubium vulgare
    Holmes, Francis O., 1946
Matthiola bicornis
    Holmes, Francis O., 1946
Matthiola incana
    Holmes, Francis O., 1946
Medicago sativa
    Holmes, Francis O., 1946
Melissa officinalis
    Holmes, Francis O., 1946
Mentha spicata
    Holmes, Francis O., 1946
Mesembryanthemum crystallinum
    Holmes, Francis O., 1946
Mesembryanthemum lineare
    Holmes, Francis O., 1946
Mimulus luteus
    Holmes, Francis O., 1946
Mimulus moschatus
    Holmes, Francis O., 1946
Mirabilis jalapa
    Holmes, Francis O., 1946
Momordica charantia
    Holmes, Francis O., 1946
Myosotis scorpioides
    Holmes, Francis O., 1946
Myosotis sylvatica
    Holmes, Francis O., 1946
Nemesia strumosa
    Holmes, Francis O., 1946
Nepeta cataria
    Holmes, Francis O., 1946
Nepeta hederacea
    Holmes, Francis O., 1946
Nepeta mussini
    Holmes, Francis O., 1946
Nicotiana glauca
    Bennett, C.W., 1944
Nicotiana otophora
    Holmes, Francis O., 1946
Nicotiana palmeri
    Holmes, Francis O., 1946
Nicotiana raimondii
    Holmes, Francis O., 1946
Nicotiana tomentosiformis
    Holmes, Francis O., 1946
Nicotiana wigandioides
    Holmes, Francis O., 1946
Oenothera lamarckiana
    Holmes, Francis O., 1946
Oxalis corniculata
    Holmes, Francis O., 1946
Oxalis stricta
    Holmes, Francis O., 1946
Papaver nudicaule
    Holmes, Francis O., 1946
Papaver orientale
    Holmes, Francis O., 1946
Pastinaca sativa
    Holmes, Francis O., 1946
Pelargonium hortorum
    Holmes, Francis O., 1946
Pelargonium odoratissimum
    Holmes, Francis O., 1946
Petroselinum hortense
    Holmes, Francis O., 1946
Phaseolus aureus
    Holmes, Francis O., 1946
Phaseolus coccineus
    Holmes, Francis O., 1946
Phaseolus limensis
    Holmes, Francis O., 1946
Phaseolus vulgaris
    Anderson, C.W., 1954
    Holmes, Francis O., 1946
    Johnson, E.M., 1930
Phlox drummondii
    Holmes, Francis O., 1946

VIRUS
V. TOBACCO ETCH (cont.)
Phytolacca decandra
    Holmes, Francis O., 1946
    Johnson, E.M., 1930
Pisum sativum
    Anderson, C.W., 1954
    Holmes, Francis O., 1946
    Johnson, E.M., 1930
Plantago lanceolata
    Holmes, Francis O., 1946
Plantago major
    Holmes, Francis O., 1946
Plantago rugelii
    Holmes, Francis O., 1946
Polanisia trachysperma
    Holmes, Francis O., 1946
Polygonum hydropiper
    Holmes, Francis O., 1946
Potentilla arguta
    Holmes, Francis O., 1946
Potentilla monspeliensis
    Holmes, Francis O., 1946
Primula obconica
    Holmes, Francis O., 1946
Prunella vulgaris
    Holmes, Francis O., 1946
Ranunculus asiaticus
    Holmes, Francis O., 1946
Raphanus raphanistrum
    Holmes, Francis O., 1946
Raphanus sativus
    Holmes, Francis O., 1946
    Johnson, E.M., 1930
Reseda odorata
    Holmes, Francis O., 1946
Ricinus communis
    Holmes, Francis O., 1946
Rosa odorata
    Holmes, Francis O., 1946
Rudbeckia hirta
    Holmes, Francis O., 1946
Rumex crispus
    Holmes, Francis O., 1946
Rumex obtusifolius
    Holmes, Francis O., 1946
Saintpaulia ionantha
    Holmes, Francis O., 1946
Salvia azurea
    Holmes, Francis O., 1946
Salvia farinacea
    Holmes, Francis O., 1946
Salvia patens
    Holmes, Francis O., 1946
Salvia splendens
    Holmes, Francis O., 1946
Sanvitalia procumbens
    Holmes, Francis O., 1946
Scabiosa atropurpurea
    Holmes, Francis O., 1946
Scabiosa caucasica
    Holmes, Francis O., 1946
Secale cereale
    Holmes, Francis O., 1946
Silene pendula
    Holmes, Francis O., 1946
Sinningia speciosa
    Holmes, Francis O., 1946
Solanum dulcamara
    Holmes, Francis O., 1946
Solanum melongena
    Bawden, F.C. and B. Kassanis, 1941
Solanum melongena var. esculentum
    Johnson, E.M., 1930
Solanum nodiflorum
    Bawden, F.C. and B. Kassanis, 1941
Solanum sanitwongsei
    Holmes, Francis O., 1946
Solidago rugosa
    Holmes, Francis O., 1946
Spinacia oleracea
    Holmes, Francis O., 1946
Stellaria media
    Holmes, Francis O., 1946

VIRUS

V. TOBACCO ETCH (cont.)

Symplocarpus foetidus
    Holmes, Francis O., 1946
Tagetes erecta
    Holmes, Francis O., 1946
Tagetes patula
    Holmes, Francis O., 1946
Tagetes signata
    Holmes, Francis O., 1946
Taraxacum officinale
    Holmes, Francis O., 1946
Thelesperma hybridum
    Holmes, Francis O., 1946
Thunbergia alata
    Holmes, Francis O., 1946
Trachymene caerulea
    Holmes, Francis O., 1946
Trifolium incarnatum
    Holmes, Francis O., 1946
Trifolium pratense
    Holmes, Francis O., 1946
Trifolium repens
    Holmes, Francis O., 1946
Triticum aestivum
    Holmes, Francis O., 1946
Tropaeolum majus
    Holmes, Francis O., 1946
Verbascum phoeniceum
    Holmes, Francis O., 1946
Verbena canadensis
    Holmes, Francis O., 1946
Verbena venosa
    Holmes, Francis O., 1946
Veronica longifolia
    Holmes, Francis O., 1946
Veronica officinalis
    Holmes, Francis O., 1946
Veronica peregrina
    Holmes, Francis O., 1946
Vicia faba
    Holmes, Francis O., 1946
Vicia sativa
    Holmes, Francis O., 1946
Vigna sinensis
    Anderson, C.W., 1954
    Holmes, Francis O., 1946
Vinca rosea
    Holmes, Francis O., 1946
Viola arvensis
    Holmes, Francis O., 1946
Zea mays
    Holmes, Francis O., 1946
Zinnia haageana
    Holmes, Francis O., 1946

V. TOBACCO GREEN MOSAIC McKinney 1929 ((Synonym of V. Tobacco mosaic K.M. Smith 1957.))

Cucumis sativus
    Peterson, Paul D. and H.H. McKinney, 1938
Lycopersicon esculentum
    McKinney, H.H., 1929
    Peterson, Paul D. and H.H. McKinney, 1938
Phaseolus vulgaris
    Peterson, Paul D. and H.H. McKinney, 1938

V. TOBACCO LEAF CURL Storey 1932

Capsicum frutescens (Capsicum annuum)
    Bird, Julio, 1957
Datura stramonium
    Bird, Julio, 1957
Gossypium hirsutum
    Nariani, T.K., 1956
Hibiscus esculentus
    Nariani, T.K., 1956
Hibiscus rosa-sinensis
    Nariani, T.K., 1956
Physalis peruviana
    Bird, Julio, 1957
Solanum melongena
    Bird, Julio, 1957

VIRUS

V. TOBACCO MOSAIC Allard 1914

Abelmoschus esculentus
    Das, C.R. and S.P. Raychaudhuri, 1953
Acalypha virginica
    Holmes, Francis O., 1938, 1946
Ageratum conyzoides
    Holmes, Francis O., 1946
Allium cepa
    Holmes, Francis O., 1946
Althaea rosea
    Holmes, Francis O., 1946
Amaryllis (Hippeastrum) puniceum
    Holmes, Francis O., 1946
Apium graveolens
    Doolittle, S.P. and F.S. Beecher, 1942
Aquilegia caerulea
    Holmes, Francis O., 1946
Arachis hypogaea
    Das, C.R. and S.P. Raychaudhuri, 1953
Arctium minus
    Stover, W.G. and M.T. Vermillion, 1933
Asclepias curassavica
    Holmes, Francis O., 1946
Asclepias syriaca
    Holmes, Francis O., 1946
Aster ericoides
    Holmes, Francis O., 1938
Aster lateriflorus
    Holmes, Francis O., 1938
Aster multiflorus
    Holmes, Francis O., 1938
Atropa belladonna
    Allard, H.A., 1916
Avena sativa
    Holmes, Francis O., 1946
Barbarea vulgaris
    Holmes, Francis O., 1946
Begonia semperflorens
    Holmes, Francis O., 1946
Beta vulgaris
    Doolittle, S.P. and F.S. Beecher, 1942
    Johnson, E.M., 1930
Brassica hirta (Brassica alba)
    Johnson, E.M., 1930
Brassica oleracea
    Holmes, Francis O., 1946
    Johnson, E.M., 1930
Brassica pekinensis
    Holmes, Francis O., 1946
Brassica rapa var. depressa *
    Johnson, E.M., 1930
Callistephus chinensis
    Stover, W.G. and M.T. Vermillion, 1933
Campanula carpatica
    Holmes, Francis O., 1946
Campanula lactiflora
    Holmes, Francis O., 1946
Campanula medium
    Holmes, Francis O., 1946
Campanula petiolata (Campanula rotundifolia of Amer.
    Holmes, Francis O., 1946   auths.)
Campanula pyramidalis
    Holmes, Francis O., 1946
Capsicum frutescens (Capsicum annuum)
    Das, C.R. and S.P. Raychaudhuri, 1953
    Johnson, J., 1926, 1927
Cassia tora
    Anderson, C.W., 1954
Centaurea moschata
    Holmes, Francis O., 1946
Chrysanthemum leucanthemum
    Holmes, Francis O., 1946
Circaea lutetiana
    Holmes, Francis O., 1938
Cirsium arvense
    Holmes, Francis O., 1938
Citrullus vulgaris
    Doolittle, S.P. and F.S. Beecher, 1942
    Holmes, Francis O., 1946
Clarkia elegans
    Holmes, Francis O., 1946
Cobaea scandens
    Holmes, Francis O., 1946

VIRUS
V. TOBACCO MOSAIC (cont.)
  Crotalaria mucronata
    Das, C.R. and S.P. Raychaudhuri, 1953
  Cucumis melo
    Doolittle, S.P. and F.S. Beecher, 1942
    Holmes, Francis O., 1946
  Cucumis sativus
    Ainsworth, G.C., 1933, 1937
    Doolittle, S.P. and F.S. Beecher, 1942
    Doolittle, S.P. and W.W. Gilbert, 1918
    Holmes, Francis O., 1941, 1946
    Jarrett, Phyllis H., 1930
    Johnson, E.M., 1930
    Peterson, Paul D. and H.H. McKinney, 1938
    Stover, W.G. and M.T. Vermillion, 1933
  Cucurbita maxima
    Holmes, Francis O., 1946
  Cucurbita pepo
    Holmes, Francis O., 1946
  Cuscuta californica
    Bennett, C.W., 1944
  Cuscuta campestris
    Bennett, C.W., 1944
    Cochran, G.W., 1946
    Costa, A.S., 1944
    Johnson, Folke, 1941
  Cuscuta subinclusa
    Bennett, C.W., 1940, 1944
  Cyphomandra betacea
    Holmes, Francis O., 1946
  Dahlia pinnata
    Holmes, Francis O., 1946
  Datura fastuosa
    Allard, H.A., 1916
  Daucus carota
    Holmes, Francis O., 1938
  Delphinium cultorum
    Holmes, Francis O., 1946
  Dianthus barbatus
    Holmes, Francis O., 1946
  Dianthus chinensis
    Holmes, Francis O., 1946
  Dolichos lablab
    Holmes, Francis O., 1946
  Erigeron canadensis
    Holmes, Francis O., 1938
  Erigeron speciosus
    Holmes, Francis O., 1946
  Euphorbia heterophylla
    Holmes, Francis O., 1946
  Euphorbia maculata
    Holmes, Francis O., 1938
  Euphorbia marginata
    Holmes, Francis O., 1946
  Euphorbia preslii
    Holmes, Francis O., 1946
  Gaillardia aristata
    Holmes, Francis O., 1946
  Galium triflorum
    Holmes, Francis O., 1938
  Geum canadense
    Holmes, Francis O., 1938, 1946
  Geum chiloense
    Holmes, Francis O., 1946
  Glycine max
    Holmes, Francis O., 1946
    Johnson, E.M., 1930
  Gomphrena haageana
    Holmes, Francis O., 1946
  Gossypium hirsutum
    Das, C.R. and S.P. Raychaudhuri, 1953
    Holmes, Francis O., 1946
  Helianthus tuberosus
    Holmes, Francis O., 1938, 1946
  Heliopsis scabra
    Holmes, Francis O., 1946
  Hibiscus esculentus
    Holmes, Francis O., 1946
  Hibiscus manihot
    Holmes, Francis O., 1946
  Hieracium scabrum
    Holmes, Francis O., 1938

VIRUS
V. TOBACCO MOSAIC (cont.)
  Holcus sudanensis
    Holmes, Francis O., 1946
  Hordeum vulgare
    Holmes, Francis O., 1946
  Hunnemannia fumariaefolia
    Holmes, Francis O., 1946
  Hypericum boreale
    Holmes, Francis O., 1938, 1946
  Iberis sempervirens
    Holmes, Francis O., 1946
  Impatiens balsamina
    Holmes, Francis O., 1946
  Impatiens biflora
    Holmes, Francis O., 1938
  Ipomoea batata
    Doolittle, S.P. and L.L. Harter, 1945
    Holmes, Francis O., 1946
  Ipomoea setosa
    Holmes, Francis O., 1946
  Lactuca sativa
    Doolittle, S.P. and F.S. Beecher, 1942
  Lagenaria siceraria (Lagenaria leucantha)
    Das, C.R. and S.P. Raychaudhuri, 1953
  Lantana camara
    Holmes, Francis O., 1946
  Lathyrus odoratus
    Allard, H.A., 1916
  Lavatera trimestris
    Holmes, Francis O., 1946
  Lens esculenta
    Holmes, Francis O., 1946
  Lilium philippinense
    Holmes, Francis O., 1946
  Linum flavum
    Holmes, Francis O., 1946
  Linum grandiflorum
    Holmes, Francis O., 1946
  Linum perenne
    Holmes, Francis O., 1946
  Lobelia inflata
    Holmes, Francis O., 1938
  Luffa acutangula
    Holmes, Francis O., 1946
  Lupinus hartwegii
    Holmes, Francis O., 1946
  Lychnis alba
    Holmes, Francis O., 1938
  Lycopersicon chilense
    Holmes, Francis O., 1943
  Lycopersicon esculentum
    McKinney, H.H., 1935
  Lycopus rubellus
    Holmes, Francis O., 1938
  Lycopus virginicus
    Holmes, Francis O., 1938
  Malope trifida
    Holmes, Francis O., 1946
  Malva rotundifolia
    Holmes, Francis O., 1938, 1946
  Matthiola incana
    Holmes, Francis O., 1946
  Medicago sativa
    Costa, A.S., 1944
    Holmes, Francis O., 1938, 1946
    Johnson, Folke, 1941
  Mirabilis jalapa
    Holmes, Francis O., 1946
  Momordica charantia
    Holmes, Francis O., 1946
  Nepeta cataria
    Stover, W.G. and M.T. Vermillion, 1933
  Nepeta hederacea
    Holmes, Francis O., 1946
  Nicandra physalodes
    Fernow, K.H., 1923
  Nicotiana glauca
    Adsuar, J. and L. Lopez Matos, 1955
    Johnson, James, 1927
  Nicotiana glutinosa
    Allard, H.A., 1916, 1917
    Johnson, J., 1926, 1927

VIRUS
V. TOBACCO MOSAIC (cont.)
Nicotiana glutinosa x Nicotiana tabacum
    Allard, H.A., 1916
Nicotiana tabacum
    Valleau, W.D., 1935
Oenothera lamarckiana
    Holmes, Francis O., 1946
Oxalis corniculata
    Holmes, Francis O., 1938, 1946
Oxalis stricta
    Holmes, Francis O., 1938, 1946
Papaver orientale
    Holmes, Francis O., 1946
Pastinaca sativa
    Holmes, Francis O., 1946
Pelargonium hortorum
    Holmes, Francis O., 1946
Pelargonium odoratissimum
    Holmes, Francis O., 1946
Phaseolus aureus
    Holmes, Francis O., 1946
Phaseolus coccineus
    Holmes, Francis O., 1946
Phaseolus limensis
    Holmes, Francis O., 1946
Phaseolus vulgaris
    Holmes, Francis O., 1941
    Johnson, E.M., 1930
    McKinney, H.H., 1952
    Price, W.C. and S.B. Fenne, 1951
Phytolacca decandra
    Allard, H.A., 1916, 1918
    Doolittle, S.P. and F.S. Beecher, 1942
    Johnson, E.M., 1930
    Johnson, J., 1926, 1927
Pisum sativum
    Das, C.R. and S.P. Raychaudhuri, 1953
    Holmes, Francis O., 1946
    Johnson, E.M., 1930
Polygonum hydropiper
    Holmes, Francis O., 1938
Polygonum persicaria
    Holmes, Francis O., 1938
Portulaca oleracea
    Holmes, Francis O., 1938
Potentilla arguta
    Holmes, Francis O., 1938, 1946
Potentilla monspeliensis
    Holmes, Francis O., 1938, 1946
Radicula palustris
    Holmes, Francis O., 1938
Ranunculus asiaticus
    Holmes, Francis O., 1946
Raphanus raphanistrum
    Holmes, Francis O., 1946
Raphanus sativus
    Holmes, Francis O., 1946
    Johnson, E.M., 1930
Reseda odorata
    Holmes, Francis O., 1946
Ricinus communis
    Holmes, Francis O., 1946
Rosa odorata
    Holmes, Francis O., 1946
Rudbeckia hirta
    Holmes, Francis O., 1938
Rumex acetosella
    Holmes, Francis O., 1938
Rumex crispus
    Stover, W.G. and M.T. Vermillion, 1933
Saintpaulia ionantha
    Holmes, Francis O., 1946
Sanicula conadensis
    Holmes, Francis O., 1938
Scabiosa atropurpurea
    Holmes, Francis O., 1946
Scabiosa caucasica
    Holmes, Francis O., 1946
Secale cereale
    Holmes, Francis O., 1946
Solanum melongena
    Johnson, J., 1926

VIRUS
V. TOBACCO MOSAIC (cont.)
Solanum tuberosum
    Allard, H.A., 1916
    Quanjer, H.M., 1920
    Schultz, E.S. and Donald Folsom, 1923
Solidago graminifolia
    Holmes, Francis O., 1938
Solidago rugosa
    Holmes, Francis O., 1938, 1946
Stellaria media
    Holmes, Francis O., 1938
Symplocarpus foetidus
    Holmes, Francis O., 1946
Taraxacum officinale
    Holmes, Francis O., 1938, 1946
Thelesperma hybridum
    Holmes, Francis O., 1946
Thunbergia alata
    Holmes, Francis O., 1946
Tithonia rotundifolia
    Cook, M.T., 1936
Trachymene caerulea
    Holmes, Francis O., 1946
Trifolium alexandrinum
    Das, C.R. and S.P. Raychaudhuri, 1953
Trifolium incarnatum
    Costa, A.S., 1944
    Holmes, Francis O., 1946
Trifolium pratense
    Holmes, Francis O., 1946
Trifolium repens
    Holmes, Francis O., 1938, 1946
Triticum aestivum
    Holmes, Francis O., 1946
Verbena urticifolia
    Holmes, Francis O., 1938
Verbena venosa
    Holmes, Francis O., 1946
Veronica officinalis
    Holmes, Francis O., 1938
Veronica peregrina
    Holmes, Francis O., 1938
Vicia faba
    Holmes, Francis O., 1946
Vicia sativa
    Holmes, Francis O., 1946
Vigna sinensis
    Holmes, Francis O., 1946
    Smith, Kenneth M., 1935
Vinca rosea
    Holmes, Francis O., 1946
Viola arvensis
    Holmes, Francis O., 1946
Viola papilionacea
    Holmes, Francis O., 1938
Viola sagittata
    Holmes, Francis O., 1938
Zea mays
    Holmes, Francis O., 1946
Zinnia elegans
    Das, C.R. and S.P. Raychaudhuri, 1953

V. TOBACCO NECROSIS K.M. Smith and Bald 1935;
Begonia semperflorens   Price 1938
    Price, W.C., Frank P. McWhorter and Betty H.
    Steranka, 1950
Dianthus barbatus
    Kassanis, B., 1955
Dianthus caryophyllus
    Kassanis, B., 1955
Impatiens balsamina
    Price, W.C., Frank P. McWhorter and Betty H.
    Steranka, 1950
Lychnis alba
    Fulton, Robert W., 1950
Raphanus sativus
    Fulton, Robert W., 1950
Tropaeolum majus
    Fulton, Robert W., 1950

VIRUS
V. TOBACCO RING SPOT Fromme et al. 1927
  Althaea rosea
    Wingard, S.A., 1928
  Amaranthus retroflexus
    Henderson, R.G. and S.A. Wingard, 1931
  Arachis hypogaea
    Cooper, W.E., 1949
  Arctium lappa
    Fenne, S.B., 1931
  Asclepias spp.
    Fenne, S.B., 1931
  Berberis vulgaris
    Wingard, S.A., 1928
  Beta vulgaris
    Johnson, E.M., 1930
  Brassica campestris var. napobrassica
    Wingard, S.A., 1928
  Brassica hirta (Brassica alba)
    Johnson, E.M., 1930
    Wingard, S.A., 1928
  Brassica napus
    Pound, Glenn S., 1949
  Brassica oleracea
    Johnson, E.M., 1930
  Brassica oleracea var. acephala
    Stubbs, M.W., 1928
  Brassica oleracea var. botrytis
    Pound, Glenn S., 1949
  Brassica oleracea var. capitata
    Bridgmon, G.H. and J.C. Walker, 1952
    Smith, Kenneth M., 1929
    Wingard, S.A., 1928
  Brassica oleracea var. gemmifera
    Pound, Glenn S., 1949
  Brassica rapa
    Wingard, S.A., 1928
  Brassica rapa var. depressa *
    Johnson, E.M., 1930
  Capsicum frutescens (Capsicum annuum)
    Berkeley, G.H., 1953
    Cheo, Pen Ching and W.J. Zaumeyer, 1952
    Cooper, W.E., 1949
    Johnson, E.M., 1930
  Capsicum frutescens var. grossum
    Pound, Glenn S., 1949
    Wingard, S.A., 1928
  Centranthus ruber
    Wingard, S.A., 1928
  Chenopodium album
    Fenne, S.B., 1931
    Henderson, R.G. and S.A. Wingard, 1931
  Chrysanthemum carinatum
    Wingard, S.A., 1928
  Chrysopsis spp.
    Henderson, R.G. and S.A. Wingard, 1931
  Cirsium arvense
    Wingard, S.A., 1928
  Coleus blumei var. verschaffeltii
    Wingard, S.A., 1928
  Cosmos diversifolius
    Wingard, S.A., 1928
  Crotalaria intermedia
    Cooper, W.E., 1949
  Cuscuta campestris
    Johnson, Folke, 1941
  Dactylis glomerata
    Wingard, S.A., 1928
  Dahlia merckii
    Wingard, S.A., 1928
  Datura meteloides
    Cooper, W.E., 1949
  Datura stramonium
    Fenne, S.B., 1931
  Daucus carota var. sativa
    Wingard, S.A., 1928
  Dianthus barbatus
    Wingard, S.A., 1928
  Glycine hispida
    Wingard, S.A., 1928
  Glycine max
    Johnson, E.M., 1930
  Gomphrena globosa
    Cooper, W.E., 1949

VIRUS
V. TOBACCO RING SPOT (cont.)
  Ipomoea batata
    Cheo, Pen Ching and W.J. Zaumeyer, 1952
  Kalanchoe (Bryophyllum) pinnatum
    Wingard, S.A., 1928
  Lactuca virosa
    Fenne, S.B., 1931
  Lycopersicon esculentum
    Berkeley, G.H., 1953
    Bridgmon, G.H. and J.C. Walker, 1952
    Cooper, W.E., 1949
    Grogan, R.G. and W.C. Schnathorst, 1955
    Johnson, E.M., 1930
    Pound, Glenn S., 1949
    Stubbs, M.W., 1937
    Wingard, S.A., 1928
  Malcomia maritima
    Wingard, S.A., 1928
  Malus sylvestris
    Wingard, S.A., 1928
  Malva rotundifolia
    Fenne, S.B., 1931
  Medicago sativa
    Benedict, W.G., 1955
    Grogan, R.G. and W.C. Schnathorst, 1955
    Stubbs, M.W., 1937
  Melilotus alba
    Bridgmon, G.H. and J.C. Walker, 1952
    Cheo, Pen Ching and W.J. Zaumeyer, 1952
  Melilotus hybridum *
    Benedict, W.G., 1955
  Melilotus officinalis
    Benedict, W.G., 1955
  Mentha piperita
    Wingard, S.A., 1928
  Nicotiana glauca
    Grogan, R.G. and W.C. Schnathorst, 1955
  Nicotiana glutinosa
    Starr, Chester K. and W.E. Cooper, 1944
    Stubbs, M.W., 1937
  Oxalis repens
    Wingard, S.A., 1928
  Pastinaca sativa
    Wingard, S.A., 1928
  Pelargonium domesticum
    Wingard, S.A., 1928
  Petunia hybrida
    Rosberg, David W., 1953
  Phaseolus angularis
    Cooper, W.E., 1949
  Phaseolus vulgaris
    Johnson, E.M., 1930
  Phleum pratense
    Wingard, S.A., 1928
  Physalis pubescens
    Johnson, E.M., 1930
  Phytolacca americana
    Henderson, R.G. and S.A. Wingard, 1931
  Phytolacca decandra
    Fenne, S.B., 1931
  Pisum sativum
    Benedict, W.G., 1955
    Johnson, E.M., 1930
    Wingard, S.A., 1928
  Plantago major
    Fenne, S.B., 1931
    Henderson, R.G. and S.A. Wingard, 1931
    Wingard, S.A., 1928
  Polygonum hydropiper
    Henderson, R.G. and S.A. Wingard, 1931
  Polygonum spp.
    Fenne, S.B., 1931
  Raphanus sativus
    Johnson, E.M., 1930
    Wingard, S.A., 1928
  Rosa spp.
    Wingard, S.A., 1928
  Rumex abyssinicus
    Wingard, S.A., 1928
  Rumex obtusifolius
    Fenne, S.B., 1931
  Rumex patientia
    Wingard, S.A., 1928

VIRUS
V. TOBACCO RING SPOT (cont.)
Sesbania macrocarpa
Cooper, W.E., 1949
Solanum carolinense
Henderson, R.G. and S.A. Wingard, 1931
Johnson, E.M., 1930
Solanum dulcamara
Fenne, S.B., 1931
Wingard, S.A., 1928
Solanum melongena var. esculentum
Johnson, E.M., 1930
Solanum nigrum
Henderson, R.G. and S.A. Wingard, 1931
Smith, Kenneth M., 1929
Solanum tuberosum
Cheo, Pen Ching and W.J. Zaumeyer, 1952
Grogan, R.G. and W.C. Schnathorst, 1955
Wingard, S.A., 1928
Spinacia oleracea
Smith, Kenneth M., 1929
Wingard, S.A., 1928
Stellaria media
Wingard, S.A., 1928
Tradescantia fluminensis
Wingard, S.A., 1928
Tragopogon porrifolius
Wingard, S.A., 1928
Trifolium hybridum
Fenne, S.B., 1931
Stubbs, M.W., 1937
Trifolium incarnatum
Bridgmon, G.H. and J.C. Walker, 1952
Trifolium medium
Fenne, S.B., 1931
Trifolium pratense
Bridgmon, G.H. and J.C. Walker, 1952
Cheo, Pen Ching and W.J. Zaumeyer, 1952
Fenne, S.B., 1931
Stubbs, M.W., 1937
Trifolium repens
Fenne, S.B., 1931
Grogan, R.G. and W.C. Schnathorst, 1955
Stubbs, M.W., 1937
Triticum vulgare
Wingard, S.A., 1928
Tropaeolum majus
Wingard, S.A., 1928
Vicia villosa
Cooper, W.E., 1949
Vigna sinensis
Stubbs, M.W., 1937
Xanthium americanum
Henderson, R.G. and S.A. Wingard, 1931
Zea mays
Cheo, Pen Ching and W.J. Zaumeyer, 1952
Zebrina pendula
Wingard, S.A., 1928
Zinnia elegans
Cooper, W.E., 1949

V. TOBACCO RING SPOT NO. 2 Price 1936
Cheiranthus cheiri
Brierley, Philip, 1954
Dianthus plumarius
Brierley, Philip, 1954
Pelargonium hortorum
Brierley, Philip, 1954
Philadelphus coronarius
Brierley, Philip, 1954
Physalis angulata
Brierley, Philip, 1954
Physostegia virginiana
Brierley, Philip, 1954
Portulaca grandiflora
Brierley, Philip, 1954
Reseda odorata
Brierley, Philip, 1954

V. TOBACCO STREAK J. Johnson 1936
Apium graveolens
Thomas, H. Rex and W.J. Zaumeyer, 1950
Aquilegia canadensis
Thomas, H. Rex and W.J. Zaumeyer, 1950

VIRUS
V. TOBACCO STREAK (cont.)
Beta vulgaris
Thomas, H. Rex and W.J. Zaumeyer, 1950
Brassica oleracea var. botrytis
Thomas, H. Rex and W.J. Zaumeyer, 1950
Canavalia ensiformis
Thomas, H. Rex and W.J. Zaumeyer, 1950
Capsicum frutescens (Capsicum annuum)
Johnson, J., 1936
Lycopersicon esculentum
Johnson, J., 1936
Thomas, H. Rex and W.J. Zaumeyer, 1950
Malus sylvestris
Fulton, Robert W., 1956
Medicago sativa
Thomas, H. Rex and W.J. Zaumeyer, 1950
Nicotiana glutinosa
Thomas, H. Rex and W.J. Zaumeyer, 1950
Petunia hybrida
Thomas, H. Rex and W.J. Zaumeyer, 1950
Phaseolus angularis
Thomas, H. Rex and W.J. Zaumeyer, 1950
Phaseolus calcaratus
Thomas, H. Rex and W.J. Zaumeyer, 1950
Phaseolus lathyroides
Thomas, H. Rex and W.J. Zaumeyer, 1950
Phaseolus mungo
Cooper, W.E., 1949
Phytolacca americana
Thomas, H. Rex and W.J. Zaumeyer, 1950
Portulaca oleracea
Thomas, H. Rex and W.J. Zaumeyer, 1950
Sesbania exaltata
Thomas, H. Rex and W.J. Zaumeyer, 1950
Solanum melongena
Johnson, J., 1936
Solanum tuberosum
Johnson, J., 1936
Spinacia oleracea
Thomas, H. Rex and W.J. Zaumeyer, 1950
Trifolium repens
Thomas, H. Rex and W.J. Zaumeyer, 1950
Tropaeolum majus
Thomas, H. Rex and W.J. Zaumeyer, 1950
Zinnia elegans
Thomas, H. Rex and W.J. Zaumeyer, 1950

V. TOBACCO STUNT *
Lycopersicon esculentum
Hidaka, Zyun, Tetsuo Uozumi and Chuji Hiruki,
1956
Nicotiana alata
Hidaka, Zyun, Tetsuo Uozumi and Chuji Hiruki,
1956
Nicotiana glauca
Hidaka, Zyun, Tetsuo Uozumi and Chuji Hiruki,
1956
Nicotiana glutinosa
Hidaka, Zyun, Tetsuo Uozumi and Chuji Hiruki,
1956
Nicotiana gossei
Hidaka, Zyun, Tetsuo Uozumi and Chuji Hiruki,
1956
Nicotiana longiflora
Hidaka, Zyun, Tetsuo Uozumi and Chuji Hiruki,
1956
Nicotiana paniculata
Hidaka, Zyun, Tetsuo Uozumi and Chuji Hiruki,
1956
Nicotiana repanda
Hidaka, Zyun, Tetsuo Uozumi and Chuji Hiruki,
1956
Nicotiana rustica
Hidaka, Zyun, Tetsuo Uozumi and Chuji Hiruki,
1956
Nicotiana sanderae
Hidaka, Zyun, Tetsuo Uozumi and Chuji Hiruki,
1956
Nicotiana suaveolens
Hidaka, Zyun, Tetsuo Uozumi and Chuji Hiruki,
1956
Nicotiana sylvestris
Hidaka, Zyun, Tetsuo Uozumi and Chuji Hiruki,
1956

VIRUS

V. TOBACCO STUNT * (cont.)
  Nicotiana trigonophylla
    Hidaka, Zyun, Tetsuo Uozumi and Chuji Hiruki,
    1956
  Petunia hybrida
    Hidaka, Zyun, Tetsuo Uozumi and Chuji Hiruki,
    1956
  Solanum melongena
    Hidaka, Zyun, Tetsuo Uozumi and Chuji Hiruki,
    1956

V. TOBACCO YELLOW DWARF Hill 1937
  Nicotiana debneyi
    Hill, A. V. and M. Mandryk, 1954
  Nicotiana exigua
    Hill, A. V. and M. Mandryk, 1954
  Nicotiana rotundifolia
    Hill, A. V. and M. Mandryk, 1954
  Nicotiana velutina
    Hill, A. V. and M. Mandryk, 1954
  Solanum tuberosum
    Hill, A. V. and M. Mandryk, 1954

V. TOMATO ASPERMY Blencowe and Caldwell 1949
  Ambrosia artemisiifolia
    Brierley, Philip, Floyd F. Smith and S.P. Doolittle,
    1955
  Apium graveolens
    Brierley, Philip, Floyd F. Smith and S.P. Doolittle,
    1955
    Hollings, M., 1955
  Belamcanda chinensis
    Brierley, Philip, Floyd F. Smith and S.P. Doolittle,
    1955
  Bellis perennis
    Hollings, M., 1955
  Brassica chinensis
    Hollings, M., 1955
  Brassica oleracea var. botrytis
    Brierley, Philip, Floyd F. Smith and S.P. Doolittle,
    1955
    Hollings, M., 1955
  Brassica oleracea var. capitata
    Brierley, Philip, Floyd F. Smith and S.P. Doolittle,
    1955
    Hollings, M., 1955
  Cheiranthus cheiri
    Brierley, Philip, Floyd F. Smith and S.P. Doolittle,
    1955
    Hollings, M., 1955
  Coleus blumei
    Brierley, Philip, Floyd F. Smith and S.P. Doolittle,
    1955
  Convolvulus sepium
    Brierley, Philip, Floyd F. Smith and S.P. Doolittle,
    1955
  Coreopsis douglasii
    Brierley, Philip, Floyd F. Smith and S.P. Doolittle,
    1955
  Cosmos sulphureus
    Brierley, Philip, Floyd F. Smith and S.P. Doolittle,
    1955
  Cucumis sativus
    Blencowe, J. W. and John Caldwell, 1949
  Cucurbita pepo
    Hollings, M., 1955
  Cuscuta campestris
    Brierley, Philip and Floyd F. Smith, 1957
  Dahlia pinnata
    Brierley, Philip, Floyd F. Smith and S.P. Doolittle,
    1955
    Hollings, M., 1955
  Datura stramonium
    Blencowe, J. W. and John Caldwell, 1949
  Delphinium hybridum
    Brierley, Philip, Floyd F. Smith and S.P. Doolittle,
    1955
  Dianthus barbatus
    Hollings, M., 1955
  Dianthus caryophyllus
    Brierley, Philip, Floyd F. Smith and S.P. Doolittle,
    1955
    Hollings, M., 1955

VIRUS

V. TOMATO ASPERMY (cont.)
  Dianthus chinensis
    Brierley, Philip, Floyd F. Smith and S.P.
    Doolittle, 1955
  Erigeron annuus
    Brierley, Philip, Floyd F. Smith and S.P.
    Doolittle, 1955
  Erigeron canadensis
    Brierley, Philip, Floyd F. Smith and S.P.
    Doolittle, 1955
  Fuchsia magellanica
    Brierley, Philip, Floyd F. Smith and S.P.
    Doolittle, 1955
  Gladiolus spp.
    Brierley, Philip, Floyd F. Smith and S.P.
    Doolittle, 1955
  Gossypium hirsutum
    Brierley, Philip, Floyd F. Smith and S.P.
    Doolittle, 1955
  Helenium autumnale
    Hollings, M., 1955
  Hemerocallis fulva
    Brierley, Philip, Floyd F. Smith and S.P.
    Doolittle, 1955
  Hyoscyamus niger
    Blencowe, J.W. and John Caldwell, 1949
  Lactuca sativa
    Hollings, M., 1955
  Lilium formosanum *
    Brierley, Philip, Floyd F. Smith and S.P.
    Doolittle, 1955
  Lupinus polyphyllus
    Hollings, M., 1955
  Lychnis viscaria
    Brierley, Philip, Floyd F. Smith and S.P.
    Doolittle, 1955
  Matthiola incana
    Brierley, Philip, Floyd F. Smith and S.P.
    Doolittle, 1955
  Nicotiana sylvestris
    Blencowe, J.W. and John Caldwell, 1949
  Pelargonium hortorum
    Hollings, M., 1955
  Phaseolus vulgaris
    Brierley, Philip, Floyd F. Smith and S.P.
    Doolittle, 1955
  Plantago media
    Hollings, M., 1955
  Primula polyantha
    Brierley, Philip, Floyd F. Smith and S.P.
    Doolittle, 1955
  Quamoclit sloteri
    Brierley, Philip, Floyd F. Smith and S.P.
    Doolittle, 1955
  Saintpaulia ionantha
    Brierley, Philip, Floyd F. Smith and S.P.
    Doolittle, 1955
  Salvia splendens
    Brierley, Philip, Floyd F. Smith and S.P.
    Doolittle, 1955
  Sanvitalia procumbens
    Brierley, Philip, Floyd F. Smith and S.P.
    Doolittle, 1955
  Scabiosa atropurpurea
    Hollings, M., 1955
  Senecio mikanioides
    Brierley, Philip, Floyd F. Smith and S.P.
    Doolittle, 1955
  Silene compacta
    Brierley, Philip, Floyd F. Smith and S.P.
    Doolittle, 1955
  Solanum dulcamara
    Hollings, M., 1955
  Solanum nigrum
    Blencowe, J. W. and John Caldwell, 1949
  Solanum nodiflorum
    Blencowe, J. W. and John Caldwell, 1949
  Solanum tuberosum
    Brierley, Philip, Floyd F. Smith and S.P.
    Doolittle, 1955
    Hollings, M., 1955
  Sparaxis tricolor
    Brierley, Philip, Floyd F. Smith and S.P.
    Doolittle, 1955

VIRUS
V. TOMATO ASPERMY (cont.)
    Tagetes erecta
        Brierley, Philip, Floyd F. Smith and S. P. Doolittle,
        1955
    Tithonia rotundifolia
        Brierley, Philip, Floyd F. Smith and S. P. Doolittle,
        1955
    Tropaeolum majus
        Brierley, Philip, Floyd F. Smith and S. P. Doolittle,
        1955
        Hollings, M., 1955
    Vinca rosea
        Brierley, Philip, Floyd F. Smith and S. P. Doolittle,
        1955
    Viola tricolor
        Brierley, Philip, Floyd F. Smith and S. P. Doolittle,
        1955
    Zea mays
        Brierley, Philip, Floyd F. Smith and S. P. Doolittle,
        1955

V. TOMATO BIG BUD Samuel et al. 1933
    Cuscuta campestris
        Helms, Katie, 1957
        Hill, A. V. and M. Mandryk, 1954
        Kunkel, L. O., 1951
        Nicotiana glutinosa
        Samuel, G., J. G. Bald and C. M. Eardley, 1933
    Nicotiana tabacum
        Samuel, G., J. G. Bald and C. M. Eardley, 1933

V. TOMATO BUSHY STUNT Smith 1935
    Cuscuta campestris
        Johnson, Folke, 1941

V. TOMATO RING SPOT Samuel and Imle 1942 ((Distinct
from V. Tomato spotted wilt.))
    Abutilon theophrasti
        Samson, R. W. and E. P. Imle, 1942
    Ambrosia artemisiifolia
        Samson, R. W. and E. P. Imle, 1942
    Antirrhinum majus
        Samson, R. W. and E. P. Imle, 1942
    Asclepias tuberosa
        Samson, R. W. and E. P. Imle, 1942
    Begonia semperflorens
        Samson, R. W. and E. P. Imle, 1942
    Beta vulgaris
        Samson, R. W. and E. P. Imle, 1942
    Beta vulgaris var. cicla
        Samson, R. W. and E. P. Imle, 1942
    Bidens bipinnata
        Samson, R. W. and E. P. Imle, 1942
    Bidens discoidea
        Samson, R. W. and E. P. Imle, 1942
    Brassica hirta (Brassica alba)
        Samson, R. W. and E. P. Imle, 1942
    Brassica oleracea
        Samson, R. W. and E. P. Imle, 1942
    Brassica rapa
        Samson, R. W. and E. P. Imle, 1942
    Calendula officinalis
        Samson, R. W. and E. P. Imle, 1942
    Callistephus chinensis
        Samson, R. W. and E. P. Imle, 1942
    Chenopodium album
        Samson, R. W. and E. P. Imle, 1942
    Citrullus vulgaris
        Samson, R. W. and E. P. Imle, 1942
    Cucumis anguria
        Samson, R. W. and E. P. Imle, 1942
    Cucumis melo
        Samson, R. W. and E. P. Imle, 1942
    Cucumis sativus
        Samson, R. W. and E. P. Imle, 1942
    Cucurbita maxima
        Samson, R. W. and E. P. Imle, 1942
    Cucurbita moschata
        Samson, R. W. and E. P. Imle, 1942
    Cucurbita pepo
        Samson, R. W. and E. P. Imle, 1942
    Cuscuta californica
        Bennett, C. W., 1944

VIRUS
V. TOMATO RING SPOT (cont.)
    Cuscuta campestris
        Bennett, C. W., 1944
    Cuscuta subinclusa
        Bennett, C. W., 1944
    Daucus carota
        Samson, R. W. and E. P. Imle, 1942
    Delphinium ajacis
        Samson, R. W. and E. P. Imle, 1942
    Emilia sonchifolia
        Samson, R. W. and E. P. Imle, 1942
    Erigeron speciosus
        Samson, R. W. and E. P. Imle, 1942
    Euphorbia heterophylla
        Samson, R. W. and E. P. Imle, 1942
    Glycine max
        Samson, R. W. and E. P. Imle, 1942
    Hibiscus esculentus
        Samson, R. W. and E. P. Imle, 1942
    Ipomoea batata
        Samson, R. W. and E. P. Imle, 1942
    Ipomoea purpurea
        Samson, R. W. and E. P. Imle, 1942
    Lagenaria siceraria (Lagenaria leucantha)
        Samson, R. W. and E. P. Imle, 1942
    Luffa aegyptiaca (Luffa cylindrica)
        Samson, R. W. and E. P. Imle, 1942
    Lupinus hartwegii
        Samson, R. W. and E. P. Imle, 1942
    Lycopersicon peruvianum
        Samson, R. W. and E. P. Imle, 1942
    Nicotiana glutinosa
        Samson, R. W. and E. P. Imle, 1942
    Nicotiana sylvestris
        Samson, R. W. and E. P. Imle, 1942
    Pelargonium hortorum
        Samson, R. W. and E. P. Imle, 1942
    Pelargonium odoratissimum
        Samson, R. W. and E. P. Imle, 1942
    Persicaria hydropiperoides *
        Samson, R. W. and E. P. Imle, 1942
    Phaseolus limensis
        Samson, R. W. and E. P. Imle, 1942
    Phaseolus vulgaris
        Samson, R. W. and E. P. Imle, 1942
    Phlox drummondii
        Samson, R. W. and E. P. Imle, 1942
    Phytolacca decandra
        Samson, R. W. and E. P. Imle, 1942
    Plantago lanceolata
        Samson, R. W. and E. P. Imle, 1942
    Plantago major
        Samson, R. W. and E. P. Imle, 1942
    Quamoclit pennata
        Samson, R. W. and E. P. Imle, 1942
    Rumex acetosella
        Samson, R. W. and E. P. Imle, 1942
    Salpiglossis sinuata
        Samson, R. W. and E. P. Imle, 1942
    Scabiosa atropurpurea
        Samson, R. W. and E. P. Imle, 1942
    Tagetes erecta
        Samson, R. W. and E. P. Imle, 1942
    Tagetes signata
        Samson, R. W. and E. P. Imle, 1942
    Tetragonia expansa
        Samson, R. W. and E. P. Imle, 1942
    Tropaeolum majus
        Samson, R. W. and E. P. Imle, 1942
    Verbascum thaspus
        Samson, R. W. and E. P. Imle, 1942
    Vinca rosea
        Samson, R. W. and E. P. Imle, 1942
    Viola tricolor
        Samson, R. W. and E. P. Imle, 1942
    Zinnia elegans
        Samson, R. W. and E. P. Imle, 1942

V. TOMATO SPOTTED WILT Samuel et al. 1930
    Antirrhinum spp.
        Smith, Kenneth M., 1931, 1932
    Beta vulgaris
        Sakimura, K., 1940

VIRUS

V. TOMATO SPOTTED WILT (cont.)

Beta vulgaris
  Smith, Kenneth M., 1931
Beta vulgaris var. cicla
  Sakimura, K., 1940
Brassica oleracea var. botrytis
  Sakimura, K., 1940
Brassica oleracea var. capitata
  Sakimura, K., 1940
Calendula spp.
  Smith, Kenneth M., 1932
Callistephus chinensis
  Smith, Kenneth M., 1931
Capsicum frutescens (Capsicum annuum)
  Parris, G.K., 1940
Chrysanthemum coronarium
  Sakimura, K., 1940
Commelina nudiflora
  Sakimura, K., 1940
Commelina venghalensis *
  Sakimura, K., 1940
Cucumis sativus
  Ainsworth, G.C., 1940
Cuscuta californica
  Bennett, C.W., 1944
Cuscuta campestris
  Bennett, C.W., 1944
Cuscuta subinclusa
  Bennett, C.W., 1944
Gossypium hirsutum
  Smith, Kenneth M., 1931
Lactuca sativa
  Parris, G.K., 1940
Lycopersicon peruvianum
  Smith, Paul G., 1944
Nicotiana glauca
  Shapovalov, M., 1934
Phaseolus vulgaris
  Parris, G.K., 1940
  Smith, Kenneth M., 1931, 1932
Phytolacca decandra
  Smith, Kenneth M., 1931
Pisum sativum
  Parris, G.K., 1940
Spinacia oleracea
  Smith, Kenneth M., 1931
Tetragonia expansa
  Sakimura, K., 1940
  Smith, Kenneth M., 1931

V. TOMATO TWISTED LEAF Ferguson 1951

Nicotiana glutinosa
  Ferguson, I.A.C., 1951
Nicotiana tabacum
  Ferguson, I.A.C., 1951
Solanum melongena
  Ferguson, I.A.C., 1951

V. TOMATO YELLOW NET Sylvester 1954

Beta vulgaris
  Sylvester, Edward S., 1954
Geum chiloense
  Sylvester, Edward S., 1954
Nicotiana glutinosa
  Sylvester, Edward S., 1954
Solanum tuberosum
  Sylvester, Edward S., 1954

V. TROPAEOLUM MOSAIC Jensen 1950

Capsicum frutescens (Capsicum annuum)
  Silberschmidt, Karl, 1953
Lactuca sativa
  Silberschmidt, Karl, 1953
Lycopersicon esculentum
  Silberschmidt, Karl, 1953
Nicotiana rustica
  Silberschmidt, Karl, 1953
Oxalis spp.
  Silberschmidt, Karl, 1953
Pelargonium hortorum
  Silberschmidt, Karl, 1953
Petunia hybrida
  Silberschmidt, Karl, 1953

VIRUS

V. TULIP BREAKING McKenny Hughes 1931

Agapanthus africanus
  Brierley, Philip and Floyd F. Smith, 1944
Allium cepa
  Brierley, Philip and Floyd F. Smith, 1944
  McWhorter, F.P., 1935
Allium cernuum
  Brierley, Philip and Floyd F. Smith, 1944
Allium odorum
  Brierley, Philip and Floyd F. Smith, 1944
Allium speciosum
  Brierley, Philip and Floyd F. Smith, 1944
Aloe spp.
  Brierley, Philip and Floyd F. Smith, 1944
Amaryllis spp.
  Brierley, Philip and Floyd F. Smith, 1944
Asparagus asparagoides
  Brierley, Philip and Floyd F. Smith, 1944
Asparagus sprengeri
  Brierley, Philip and Floyd F. Smith, 1944
Asphodeline lutea
  Brierley, Philip and Floyd F. Smith, 1944
Avena sativa
  Brierley, Philip and Floyd F. Smith, 1944
Belamcanda chinensis
  Brierley, Philip and Floyd F. Smith, 1944
Brassica rapa
  Brierley, Philip and Floyd F. Smith, 1944
Brodiaea capitata
  McWhorter, F.P., 1935
Brodiaea uniflora
  Brierley, Philip and Floyd F. Smith, 1944
Camassia leichtlinii
  Brierley, Philip and Floyd F. Smith, 1944
Camassia quamash
  McWhorter, F.P., 1935
Canna generalis
  Brierley, Philip and Floyd F. Smith, 1944
Commelina coelestis
  Brierley, Philip and Floyd F. Smith, 1944
Commelina communis
  Brierley, Philip and Floyd F. Smith, 1944
Commelina nudiflora
  Brierley, Philip and Floyd F. Smith, 1944
Convallaria majalis
  Brierley, Philip and Floyd F. Smith, 1944
Dioscorea alata
  Brierley, Philip and Floyd F. Smith, 1944
Dracaena fragrans
  Brierley, Philip and Floyd F. Smith, 1944
Dracaena sanderiana
  Brierley, Philip and Floyd F. Smith, 1944
Erythronium spp.
  Brierley, Philip and Floyd F. Smith, 1944
Freesia hybrida
  Brierley, Philip and Floyd F. Smith, 1944
Galtonia candicans
  Brierley, Philip and Floyd F. Smith, 1944
Gloriosa rothschildiana
  Brierley, Philip and Floyd F. Smith, 1944
Gloriosa superba
  Brierley, Philip and Floyd F. Smith, 1944
Haworthia altilinea
  Brierley, Philip and Floyd F. Smith, 1944
Hedychium coronarium
  Brierley, Philip and Floyd F. Smith, 1944
Hosta plantaginea
  Brierley, Philip and Floyd F. Smith, 1944
Hyacinthus orientalis
  Brierley, Philip and Floyd F. Smith, 1944
Iris filifolia
  Brierley, Philip and Floyd F. Smith, 1944
Iris germanica
  Brierley, Philip and Frank P. McWhorter, 1936
  McWhorter, F.P., 1935
Iris pallida
  Brierley, Philip and Floyd F. Smith, 1944
Iris versicolor
  Brierley, Philip and Floyd F. Smith, 1944
Kniphofia tucki
  Brierley, Philip and Floyd F. Smith, 1944
Lilium davidi
  Brierley, Philip, 1940

VIRUS
V. TULIP BREAKING
  Lilium hansonii
    Brierley, Philip, 1940
    Brierley, Philip and Floyd F. Smith, 1944
  Lilium henryi
    Brierley, Philip and Floyd F. Smith, 1944
  Lilium humboldtii
    Brierley, Philip and Floyd F. Smith, 1944
  Lilium martagon var. album x Lilium hansonii
    Brierley, Philip, 1940
  Lilium nepalense
    Brierley, Philip, 1940
  Lilium pardalinum
    Brierley, Philip and Floyd F. Smith, 1944
  Lilium pardalinum var. giganteum *
    Brierley, Philip, 1940
  Lilium parryi
    Brierley, Philip and Floyd F. Smith, 1944
  Lilium parvum
    Brierley, Philip and Floyd F. Smith, 1944
  Lilium sargentiae
    Brierley, Philip and Floyd F. Smith, 1944
  Lilium superbum
    Brierley, Philip and Floyd F. Smith, 1944
  Lycopersicon esculentum
    McWhorter, F.P., 1935
  Maranta bicolor
    Brierley, Philip and Floyd F. Smith, 1944
  Medeola virginica
    Brierley, Philip and Floyd F. Smith, 1944
  Moraea iridioides
    Brierley, Philip and Floyd F. Smith, 1944
  Musa cavendishii
    Brierley, Philip and Floyd F. Smith, 1944
  Musa textilis
    Brierley, Philip and Floyd F. Smith, 1944
  Muscari polyanthum
    Brierley, Philip and Floyd F. Smith, 1944
  Narcissus poeticus
    McWhorter, F.P., 1935
  Narcissus pseudo-narcissus
    Brierley, Philip and Floyd F. Smith, 1944
  Nicotiana tabacum
    Brierley, Philip and S.P. Doolittle, 1940
  Nothoscordum fragrans
    Brierley, Philip and Floyd F. Smith, 1944
  Ophiopogon jaburan
    Brierley, Philip and Floyd F. Smith, 1944
  Ornithogalum thyrsoides
    Brierley, Philip and Floyd F. Smith, 1944
    Smith, Floyd F. and Philip Brierley, 1944
  Petunia hybrida
    McWhorter, F.P., 1935
    Tompkins, C.M., 1939
  Philodendron spp.
    Brierley, Philip and Floyd F. Smith, 1944
  Rhoeo discolor
    Brierley, Philip and Floyd F. Smith, 1944
  Saccharum officinarum
    Brierley, Philip and Floyd F. Smith, 1944
  Sansevieria zeylanica
    Brierley, Philip and Floyd F. Smith, 1944
  Scilla hispanica (Scilla campanulata)
    Brierley, Philip and Floyd F. Smith, 1944
  Secale cereale
    Brierley, Philip and Floyd F. Smith, 1944
  Smilacina racemosa
    Brierley, Philip and Floyd F. Smith, 1944
  Smilax spp.
    Brierley, Philip and Floyd F. Smith, 1944
  Tigridia pavonia
    Brierley, Philip and Floyd F. Smith, 1944
  Tricyrtis hirta
    Brierley, Philip and Floyd F. Smith, 1944
  Trillium spp.
    Brierley, Philip and Floyd F. Smith, 1944
  Tritonia crocata
    Brierley, Philip and Floyd F. Smith, 1944
  Tropaeolum majus
    McWhorter, F.P., 1935
  Uvularia sessilifolia
    Brierley, Philip and Floyd F. Smith, 1944

VIRUS
V. TULIP BREAKING
  Vallota purpurea
    Brierley, Philip and Floyd F. Smith, 1944
  Yucca baccata
    Brierley, Philip and Floyd F. Smith, 1944
  Yucca flaccida
    Brierley, Philip and Floyd F. Smith, 1944
  Zantedeschia aethiopica
    Brierley, Philip and Floyd F. Smith, 1944
  Zea mays
    Brierley, Philip and Floyd F. Smith, 1944
  Zephyranthes spp.
    Brierley, Philip and Floyd F. Smith, 1944

V. TURNIP CRINKLE Broadbent and Blencowe 1955
  Amaranthus caudatus
    Broadbent, L. and G.D. Heathcote, 1958
  Beta vulgaris
    Broadbent, L. and G.D. Heathcote, 1958
  Corydalis lutea
    Broadbent, L. and G.D. Heathcote, 1958
  Nicotiana clevelandi
    Broadbent, L. and G.D. Heathcote, 1958
  Nicotiana glutinosa
    Broadbent, L. and G.D. Heathcote, 1958
  Papaver rhoeas
    Broadbent, L. and G.D. Heathcote, 1958
  Phaseolus vulgaris
    Broadbent, L. and G.D. Heathcote, 1958
  Vicia faba
    Broadbent, L. and G.D. Heathcote, 1958
  Viola tricolor var. hortensis
    Broadbent, L. and G.D. Heathcote, 1958

V. TURNIP MOSAIC Gardner and Kendrick 1921;
Schultz 1921; Chamberlain 1936; Tompkins 1938
  Alyssum maritimum
    Tompkins, C.M., 1938, 1939
    Walker, J.C., Francis J. LeBeau and Glenn S.
    Pound, 1945
  Alyssum saxatile
    Tompkins, C.M., 1939
  Antirrhinum majus
    Tompkins, C.M., 1938, 1939
    Tompkins, C.M. and H. Rex Thomas, 1938
  Apium graveolens
    Tompkins, C.M., 1938, 1939
    Tompkins, C.M. and H. Rex Thomas, 1938
  Arabis albida
    LeBeau, Francis J. and J.C. Walker, 1945
    Tompkins, C.M., 1939
  Atropa belladonna
    Walker, J.C., Francis J. LeBeau and Glenn S.
    Pound, 1945
  Avena sativa
    Tompkins, C.M. and H. Rex Thomas, 1938
  Barbarea vulgaris
    Pound, Glenn S., 1948
    Walker, J.C., Francis J. LeBeau and Glenn S.
    Pound, 1945
  Begonia semperflorens
    Tompkins, C.M., 1939
    Tompkins, C.M. and H. Rex Thomas, 1938
  Bellis perennis
    Tompkins, C.M., 1938, 1939
    Tompkins, C.M. and H. Rex Thomas, 1938
  Beta vulgaris
    Berkeley, G.H. and J.H. Tremaine, 1954
    Dale, W.T., 1948
  Beta vulgaris var. cicla
    Berkeley, G.H. and J.H. Tremaine, 1954
    Dale, W.T., 1948
  Brassica adpressa
    Tompkins, C.M., 1939
  Brassica campestris var. napobrassica
    Tompkins, C.M., 1939
  Brassica hirta (Brassica alba)
    Tompkins, C.M., 1938
    Tompkins, C.M. and H. Rex Thomas, 1938
  Brassica integrifolia var. chevalieri *
    Tompkins, C.M., 1938
    Tompkins, C.M. and H. Rex Thomas, 1938

VIRUS
V. TURNIP MOSAIC (cont.)
Brassica juncea (Brassica japonica)
Tompkins, C.M. , 1939
Tompkins, C.M. and H. Rex Thomas, 1938
Brassica kaber (Brassica arvensis)
Tompkins, C.M. , 1938
Brassica napus
Tompkins, C.M. , 1938, 1939
Brassica nigra
Tompkins, C.M. , 1938
Brassica oleracea var. acephala
Sylvester, Edward S. , 1953
Takahashi, William N. , 1949
Tompkins, C.M. , 1938, 1939
Brassica oleracea var. botrytis
Dale, W.T. , 1948
LeBeau, Francis J. and J.C. Walker, 1945
Pound, Glenn S. , 1948
Severin, Henry H.P. and C.M. Tompkins, 1950
Sylvester, Edward S. , 1953
Takahashi, William N. , 1949
Tompkins, C.M. , 1938, 1939
Brassica oleracea var. capitata
Clayton, E.E. , 1930
Dale, W.T. , 1948
LeBeau, Francis J. and J.C. Walker, 1945
Sylvester, Edward S. , 1953
Takahashi, William N. , 1949
Tompkins, C.M. , 1939
Brassica oleracea var. caulorapa
Dale, W.T. , 1948
Sylvester, Edward S. , 1953
Takahashi, William N. , 1949
Tompkins, C.M. , 1938, 1939
Brassica oleracea var. gemmifera
LeBeau, Francis J. and J.C. Walker, 1945
Sylvester, Edward S. , 1953
Takahashi, William N. , 1949
Tompkins, C.M. , 1938, 1939
Brassica oleracea var. gongylodes
LeBeau, Francis J. and J.C. Walker, 1945
Brassica oleracea var. viridis
LeBeau, Francis J. and J.C. Walker, 1945
Callistephus chinensis
Tompkins, C.M. , 1939
Tompkins, C.M. and H. Rex Thomas, 1938
Campanula medium
Tompkins, C.M. , 1938, 1939
Tompkins, C.M. and H. Rex Thomas, 1938
Capsicum frutescens var. cerasiforme
Walker, J.C. , Francis J. LeBeau and Glenn S.
Pound, 1945
Centaurea nigra
Walker, J.C. , Francis J. LeBeau and Glenn S.
Pound, 1945
Cheiranthus allionii
LeBeau, Francis J. and J.C. Walker, 1945
Cheiranthus cheiri
Tompkins, C.M. , 1938, 1939
Chenopodium album
Tompkins, C.M. , 1939
Tompkins, C.M. and H. Rex Thomas, 1938
Chenopodium murale
Tompkins, C.M. , 1938, 1939
Tompkins, C.M. and H. Rex Thomas, 1938
Chrysanthemum coronarium
Tompkins, C.M. , 1938, 1939
Tompkins, C.M. and H. Rex Thomas, 1938
Chrysanthemum maximum
Tompkins, C.M. , 1939
Clarkia elegans
Tompkins, C.M. , 1938, 1939
Tompkins, C.M. and H. Rex Thomas, 1938
Cucumis sativus
Tompkins, C.M. , 1938, 1939
Tompkins, C.M. and H. Rex Thomas, 1938
Cuscuta californica
Bennett, C.W. , 1944
Cuscuta campestris
Bennett, C.W. , 1944
Cuscuta subinclusa
Bennett, C.W. , 1944

VIRUS
V. TURNIP MOSAIC (cont.)
Datura stramonium
Tompkins, C.M. , 1938, 1939
Tompkins, C.M. and H. Rex Thomas, 1938
Walker, J.C. , Francis J. LeBeau and Glenn S.
Pound, 1945
Delphinium ajacis
Tompkins, C.M. , 1938, 1939
Tompkins, C.M. and H. Rex Thomas, 1938
Delphinium cultorum
Tompkins, C.M. , 1939
Tompkins, C.M. and H. Rex Thomas, 1938
Dianthus barbatus
Tompkins, C.M. , 1938, 1939
Tompkins, C.M. and H. Rex Thomas, 1938
Dianthus caryophyllus
Tompkins, C.M. , 1939
Dimorphotheca aurantiaca
Tompkins, C.M. , 1938, 1939
Tompkins, C.M. and H. Rex Thomas, 1938
Dolichos lablab
Walker, J.C. , Francis J. LeBeau and Glenn S.
Pound, 1945
Gaillardia pulchella var. picta
Tompkins, C.M. , 1938, 1939
Tompkins, C.M. and H. Rex Thomas, 1938
Gerbera jamesonii var. transvaalensis
Tompkins, C.M. , 1939
Geum chiloense
Tompkins, C.M. , 1938, 1939
Tompkins, C.M. and H. Rex Thomas, 1938
Glycine max
Walker, J.C. , Francis J. LeBeau and Glenn S.
Pound, 1945
Godetia grandiflora
Tompkins, C.M. , 1938, 1939
Tompkins, C.M. and H. Rex Thomas, 1938
Gypsophila paniculata
Tompkins, C.M. , 1938, 1939
Tompkins, C.M. and H. Rex Thomas, 1938
Heliotropium peruvianum
Tompkins, C.M. , 1938, 1939
Tompkins, C.M. and H. Rex Thomas, 1938
Hesperis matronalis
LeBeau, Francis J. and J.C. Walker, 1945
Hibiscus esculentus
Walker, J.C. , Francis J. LeBeau and Glenn S.
Pound, 1945
Ipomoea purpurea
Tompkins, C.M. , 1939
Walker, J.C. , Francis J. LeBeau and Glenn S.
Pound, 1945
Lactuca sativa var. capitata
Tompkins, C.M. , 1938, 1939
Tompkins, C.M. and H. Rex Thomas, 1938
Limonium latifolium
Tompkins, C.M. , 1938
Lobelia hybrida
Tompkins, C.M. , 1938, 1939
Tompkins, C.M. and H. Rex Thomas, 1938
Lunaria annua
Tompkins, C.M. , 1939
Lycopersicon esculentum var. vulgare
Tompkins, C.M. , 1938, 1939
Tompkins, C.M. and H. Rex Thomas, 1938
Lycopersicon pimpinellifolium
Tompkins, C.M. , 1938, 1939
Tompkins, C.M. and H. Rex Thomas, 1938
Malcomia maritima
Tompkins, C.M. , 1939
Matthiola bicornis
Tompkins, C.M. , 1938
Matthiola incana
Tompkins, C.M. , 1939
Matthiola incana var. annua
LeBeau, Francis J. and J.C. Walker, 1945
Mirabilis jalapa
Walker, J.C. , Francis J. LeBeau and Glenn S.
Pound, 1945
Myosotis alpestris
Tompkins, C.M. , 1938, 1939
Tompkins, C.M. and H. Rex Thomas, 1938

VIRUS
V. TURNIP MOSAIC (cont.)
  Nicotiana alata var. grandiflora
    Dale, W.T., 1948
  Nicotiana chinensis
    Dale, W.T., 1948
  Nicotiana glauca
    Bennett, C.W., 1944
  Nicotiana glutinosa
    Dale, W.T., 1948
    Sylvester, Edward S., 1953
    Takahashi, William N., 1949
    Tompkins, C.M., 1939
  Nicotiana langsdorffii
    Tompkins, C.M., 1938, 1939
    Tompkins, C.M. and H. Rex Thomas, 1938
  Nicotiana repanda
    LeBeau, Francis J. and J.C. Walker, 1945
  Nicotiana rustica
    Dale, W.T., 1948
    LeBeau, Francis J. and J.C. Walker, 1945
  Nicotiana rustica var. humulis *
    Tompkins, C.M., 1938, 1939
  Nicotiana sanderae
    Dale, W.T., 1948
  Nicotiana sylvestris
    Dale, W.T., 1948
    LeBeau, Francis J. and J.C. Walker, 1945
  Nicotiana tabacum
    LeBeau, Francis J. and J.C. Walker, 1945
    Sylvester, Edward S., 1953
    Takahashi, William N., 1949
    Tompkins, C.M., 1938
  Nicotiana tabacum x Nicotiana glutinosa
    LeBeau, Francis J. and J.C. Walker, 1945
  Papaver Nudicaule
    Tompkins, C.M. and H. Rex Thomas, 1938
  Papaver orientale
    Tompkins, C.M., 1939
    Tompkins, C.M. and H. Rex Thomas, 1938
  Pelargonium zonale
    Tompkins, C.M., 1939
    Tompkins, C.M. and H. Rex Thomas, 1938
  Penstemon barbatus
    Tompkins, C.M., 1938, 1939
    Tompkins, C.M. and H. Rex Thomas, 1938
  Petunia hybrida
    Tompkins, C.M. and H. Rex Thomas, 1938
  Phaseolus coccineus
    Walker, J.C., Francis J. LeBeau and Glenn S.
    Pound, 1945
  Pisum sativum
    Tompkins, C.M., 1938, 1939
    Tompkins, C.M. and H. Rex Thomas, 1938
  Raphanus sativus
    Berkeley, G.H. and J.H. Tremaine, 1954
    Berkeley, G.H. and M. Weintraub, 1952
    Gardner, Max W. and James B. Kendrick, 1921
    Tompkins, C.M., 1938, 1939
  Raphanus sativus var. longipinnatus *
    Tompkins, C.M., 1939
  Raphanus sativus var. radicula
    Dale, W.T., 1948
  Reseda odorata
    Tompkins, C.M. and H. Rex Thomas, 1938
  Rheum rhaponticum
    Tompkins, C.M., 1938, 1939
    Tompkins, C.M. and H. Rex Thomas, 1938
  Ricinus communis
    Tompkins, C.M., 1938, 1939
    Tompkins, C.M. and H. Rex Thomas, 1938
  Salvia farinacea
    Tompkins, C.M., 1938, 1939
    Tompkins, C.M. and H. Rex Thomas, 1938
  Scabiosa atropurpurea
    Tompkins, C.M., 1938, 1939
    Tompkins, C.M. and H. Rex Thomas, 1938
  Senecio cruentus
    Tompkins, C.M., 1938, 1939
    Tompkins, C.M. and H. Rex Thomas, 1938
  Solanum aviculare
    Tompkins, C.M., 1938, 1939
    Tompkins, C.M. and H. Rex Thomas, 1938

VIRUS
V. TURNIP MOSAIC (cont.)
  Solanum dulcamara
    Walker, J.C., Francis J. LeBeau and Glenn S.
    Pound, 1945
  Solanum integrifolium
    Pound, Glenn S., 1948
    Walker, J.C., Francis J. LeBeau and Glenn S.
    Pound, 1945
  Solanum pseudocapsicum
    Walker, J.C., Francis J. LeBeau and Glenn S.
    Pound, 1945
  Solanum tuberosum
    Schultz, E.S., 1921
    Tompkins, C.M., 1938, 1939
    Tompkins, C.M. and H. Rex Thomas, 1938
  Spinacia oleracea
    LeBeau, Francis J. and J.C. Walker, 1945
    Tompkins, C.M., 1938, 1939
    Tompkins, C.M. and H. Rex Thomas, 1938
  Tagetes erecta
    Tompkins, C.M., 1938, 1939
    Tompkins, C.M. and H. Rex Thomas, 1938
  Tagetes patula
    Tompkins, C.M., 1938, 1939
    Tompkins, C.M. and H. Rex Thomas, 1938
    Walker, J.C., Francis J. LeBeau and Glenn S.
    Pound, 1945
  Taraxacum officinale
    Tompkins, C.M., 1938, 1939
    Tompkins, C.M. and H. Rex Thomas, 1938
  Tropaeolum majus
    Tompkins, C.M., 1938, 1939
    Tompkins, C.M. and H. Rex Thomas, 1938
  Verbena hybrida
    Tompkins, C.M., 1939
    Tompkins, C.M. and H. Rex Thomas, 1938
  Vicia faba
    Tompkins, C.M., 1938, 1939
    Tompkins, C.M. and H. Rex Thomas, 1938
  Vigna sinensis
    Walker, J.C., Francis J. LeBeau and Glenn S.
    Pound, 1945
  Vigna unguiculata
    Dale, W.T., 1948
  Viola cornuta
    Tompkins, C.M., 1939
  Viola tricolor
    Tompkins, C.M., 1938, 1939
    Tompkins, C.M. and H. Rex Thomas, 1938
  Zea mays
    Tompkins, C.M., 1938, 1939
    Tompkins, C.M. and H. Rex Thomas, 1938

V. TURNIP ROSETTE *
  Amaranthus caudatus
    Broadbent, L. and G.D. Heathcote, 1958
  Beta vulgaris
    Broadbent, L. and G.D. Heathcote, 1958
  Brassica hirta (Brassica alba)
    Broadbent, L. and G.D. Heathcote, 1958
  Brassica nigra
    Broadbent, L. and G.D. Heathcote, 1958
  Capsella bursa-pastoris
    Broadbent, L. and G.D. Heathcote, 1958
  Celosia argentea var. plumosa *
    Broadbent, L. and G.D. Heathcote, 1958
  Chenopodium album
    Broadbent, L. and G.D. Heathcote, 1958
  Chenopodium amaranticolor
    Broadbent, L. and G.D. Heathcote, 1958
  Cucumis sativus
    Broadbent, L. and G.D. Heathcote, 1958
  Gomphrena globosa
    Broadbent, L. and G.D. Heathcote, 1958
  Lycopersicon esculentum
    Broadbent, L. and G.D. Heathcote, 1958
  Nicotiana glutinosa
    Broadbent, L. and G.D. Heathcote, 1958
  Nicotiana tabacum
    Broadbent, L. and G.D. Heathcote, 1958
  Phaseolus vulgaris
    Broadbent, L. and G.D. Heathcote, 1958
  Vicia faba
    Broadbent, L. and G.D. Heathcote, 1958

VIRUS

V. TURNIP YELLOW MOSAIC Markham and Smith 1946
  Chenopodium album
    Broadbent, L. and G.D. Heathcote, 1958
  Chenopodium amaranticolor
    Broadbent, L. and G.D. Heathcote, 1958
  Cucumis sativus
    Broadbent, L. and G.D. Heathcote, 1958
  Datura stramonium
    Broadbent, L. and G.D. Heathcote, 1958
  Gomphrena globosa
    Broadbent, L. and G.D. Heathcote, 1958
  Nicotiana bigelovii var. multivalvis *
    Broadbent, L. and G.D. Heathcote, 1958
  Nicotiana clevelandi
    Broadbent, L. and G.D. Heathcote, 1958
  Nicotiana glutinosa
    Broadbent, L. and G.D. Heathcote, 1958
  Nicotiana tabacum
    Broadbent, L. and G.D. Heathcote, 1958
  Papaver rhoeas
    Broadbent, L. and G.D. Heathcote, 1958
  Phaseolus vulgaris
    Broadbent, L. and G.D. Heathcote, 1958
  Tetragonia expansa
    Broadbent, L. and G.D. Heathcote, 1958
  Vicia faba
    Broadbent, L. and G.D. Heathcote, 1958
  Viola tricolor var. hortensis
    Broadbent, L. and G.D. Heathcote, 1958

V. VACCINIUM FALSE BLOSSOM
  Begonia spp.
    Kunkel, L.O., 1945
  Callistephus chinensis
    Kunkel, L.O., 1945
  Cuscuta campestris
    Costa, A.S., 1944
    Kunkel, L.O., 1943, 1945
  Medicago sativa
    Costa, A.S., 1944
    Kunkel, L.O., 1945
  Prunus persica (Amygdalus persica)
    Kunkel, L.O., 1945

V. VACCINIUM RING SPOT Hutchinson and Varney 1954
  Cuscuta spp.
    Hilborn, M.T. and Reiner Bonde, 1956

V. VACCINIUM STUNT Wilcox 1942
  Cuscuta subinclusa
    Hutchinson, M.T., A.C. Goheen and E.H. Varney, 1955

V. VINCA YELLOWS *
  Cuscuta spp.
    Maramorosch, Karl, 1957
  Cuscuta subinclusa
    Maramorosch, Karl, 1956

V. WATERMELON MOSAIC Anderson 1954
  Capsicum frutescens (Capsicum annuum)
    Anderson, C.W., 1954
  Datura stramonium
    Lindberg, G.D., D.H. Hall and J.C. Walker, 1956
  Momordica charantia
    Anderson, C.W., 1954
  Nicotiana glutinosa
    Lindberg, G.D., D.H. Hall and J.C. Walker, 1956
  Nicotiana rustica
    Lindberg, G.D., D.H. Hall and J.C. Walker, 1956
  Nicotiana tabacum
    Anderson, C.W., 1954
    Lindberg, G.D., D.H. Hall and J.C. Walker, 1956
  Vigna sinensis
    Lindberg, G.D., D.H. Hall and J.C. Walker, 1956
  Zinnia elegans
    Anderson, C.W., 1954
    Lindberg, G.D., D.H. Hall and J.C. Walker, 1956

V. WHEAT SPOT MOSAIC *
  Avena fatua
    Slykhuis, John T., 1956

VIRUS

V. WHEAT SPOT MOSAIC * (cont.)
  Avena sativa
    Slykhuis, John T., 1956
  Bromus japonicus
    Slykhuis, John T., 1956
  Bromus secalinus
    Slykhuis, John T., 1956
  Bromus tectorum
    Slykhuis, John T., 1956
  Digitaria sanguinalis
    Slykhuis, John T., 1956
  Echinochloa crus-galli
    Slykhuis, John T., 1956
  Panicum capillare
    Slykhuis, John T., 1956
  Panicum miliaceum
    Slykhuis, John T., 1956
  Secale cereale
    Slykhuis, John T., 1956

V. WHEAT STREAK MOSAIC McKinney 1944, 1953
  Agropyron amurense
    McKinney, H.H. and W.J. Sando, 1951
  Agropyron ciliare *
    Slykhuis, J.T., 1952
  Agropyron cristatum
    McKinney, H.H. and W.J. Sando, 1951
    Slykhuis, J.T., 1952, 1955
  Agropyron dasysatchyum
    McKinney, H.H. and W.J. Sando, 1951
    Slykhuis, J.T., 1952
  Agropyron desertorum
    Slykhuis, J.T., 1952
  Agropyron divaricatum
    McKinney, H.H. and W.J. Sando, 1951
  Agropyron elongatum
    Fellows, Hurley and John W. Schmidt, 1953
    Slykhuis, J.T., 1952, 1955
  Agropyron inerme
    Slykhuis, J.T., 1952
  Agropyron intermedium
    Fellows, Hurley and John W. Schmidt, 1953
    Slykhuis, J.T., 1952, 1955
  Agropyron junceum
    Slykhuis, J.T., 1952
  Agropyron pertenue
    Slykhuis, J.T., 1952
  Agropyron repens
    McKinney, H.H. and W.J. Sando, 1951
    Slykhuis, J.T., 1952, 1955
  Agropyron rigidum
    Slykhuis, J.T., 1952
  Agropyron semicostatum
    McKinney, H.H. and W.J. Sando, 1951
  Agropyron sibiricum
    McKinney, H.H. and W.J. Sando, 1951
  Agropyron smithii
    Sill, W.H., Jr. and Patrick C. Agusiobo, 1955
    Slykhuis, John T., 1955
  Agropyron spicatum
    McKinney, H.H. and W.J. Sando, 1951
  Agropyron trachycaulum
    Slykhuis, J.T., 1952, 1955
  Agropyron trichophorum
    Slykhuis, J.T., 1952
  Agrostis alba
    Slykhuis, John T., 1955
  Allium cepa
    Sill, W.H., Jr. and Patrick C. Agusiobo, 1955
  Alopecurus pratensis
    Sill, W.H., Jr. and Patrick C. Agusiobo, 1955
  Amaryllis spp.
    Sill, W.H., Jr. and Patrick C. Agusiobo, 1955
  Andropogon hallii
    Sill, W.H., Jr. and Patrick C. Agusiobo, 1955
  Andropogon ischaemum
    Sill, W.H., Jr. and Patrick C. Agusiobo, 1955
  Andropogon sibiricus
    Sill, W.H., Jr. and Patrick C. Agusiobo, 1955
  Arrhenatherum elatius
    Sill, W.H., Jr. and Patrick C. Agusiobo, 1955
  Avena fatua
    Slykhuis, J.T., 1952

VIRUS
V. WHEAT STREAK MOSAIC (cont.)
  Belamcanda chinensis
    Sill, W.H., Jr. and Patrick C. Agusiobo, 1955
  Bromus carinatus
    McKinney, H.H., 1949
  Bromus inermis
    Sill, W.H., Jr. and Patrick C. Agusiobo, 1955
    Slykhuis, J.T., 1952, 1955
  Buchloe dactyloides
    Sill, W.H., Jr. and Patrick C. Agusiobo, 1955
  Canna spp.
    Sill, W.H., Jr. and Patrick C. Agusiobo, 1955
  Chenopodium album
    Meiners, Jack P. and H.H. McKinney, 1954
  Codiaeum variegatum
    Sill, W.H., Jr. and Patrick C. Agusiobo, 1955
  Coix lacryma-jobi
    Sill, W.H., Jr. and Patrick C. Agusiobo, 1955
  Convallaria majalis
    Sill, W.H., Jr. and Patrick C. Agusiobo, 1955
  Cortaderia selloana
    Sill, W.H., Jr. and Patrick C. Agusiobo, 1955
  Crocus spp.
    Sill, W.H., Jr. and Patrick C. Agusiobo, 1955
  Cyperus alternifolius
    Sill, W.H., Jr. and Patrick C. Agusiobo, 1955
  Cyperus esculentus
    Sill, W.H., Jr. and Patrick C. Agusiobo, 1955
  Cypripedium spp.
    Sill, W.H., Jr. and Patrick C. Agusiobo, 1955
  Dactylis glomerata
    Finley, A.M., 1957
    Sill, W.H., Jr. and Patrick C. Agusiobo, 1955
  Echinochloa crus-galli
    Sill, W.H., Jr. and Patrick C. Agusiobo, 1955
  Festuca elatior
    Slykhuis, John T., 1955
  Festuca rubra
    Slykhuis, J.T., 1952, 1955
  Ficus elastica
    Sill, W.H., Jr. and Patrick C. Agusiobo, 1955
  Gladiolus spp.
    Sill, W.H., Jr. and Patrick C. Agusiobo, 1955
  Hordeum jubatum
    Slykhuis, J.T., 1952, 1955
  Iris spp.
    Sill, W.H., Jr. and Patrick C. Agusiobo, 1955
  Kalanchoe spp.
    Sill, W.H., Jr. and Patrick C. Agusiobo, 1955
  Lilium candidum
    Sill, W.H., Jr. and Patrick C. Agusiobo, 1955
  Maranta bicolor
    Sill, W.H., Jr. and Patrick C. Agusiobo, 1955
  Musa spp.
    Sill, W.H., Jr. and Patrick C. Agusiobo, 1955
  Muscari armeniacum
    Sill, W.H., Jr. and Patrick C. Agusiobo, 1955
  Orchis spp.
    Sill, W.H., Jr. and Patrick C. Agusiobo, 1955
  Ornithogalum spp.
    Sill, W.H., Jr. and Patrick C. Agusiobo, 1955
  Oryza sativa
    Kahn, Robert P. and Ottie J. Dickerson, 1957
  Panicum maximum
    Sill, W.H., Jr. and Patrick C. Agusiobo, 1955
  Panicum miliaceum
    Sill, W.H., Jr. and Patrick C. Agusiobo, 1955
    Slykhuis, J.T., 1952
  Panicum virgatum
    Sill, W.H., Jr. and Patrick C. Agusiobo, 1955
  Pedilanthus tithymaloides
    Sill, W.H., Jr. and Patrick C. Agusiobo, 1955
  Pennisetum glaucum
    Sill, W.H., Jr. and Patrick C. Agusiobo, 1955
  Peperomia spp.
    Sill, W.H., Jr. and Patrick C. Agusiobo, 1955
  Phalaris arundinacea
    Sill, W.H., Jr. and Patrick C. Agusiobo, 1955
    Slykhuis, J.T., 1952
  Phalaris arundinacea x Phalaris tuberosa
    Sill, W.H., Jr. and Patrick C. Agusiobo, 1955
  Philodendron spp.
    Sill, W.H., Jr. and Patrick C. Agusiobo, 1955

VIRUS
V. WHEAT STREAK MOSAIC (cont.)
  Phleum pratense
    Slykhuis, J.T., 1952, 1955
  Poa pratensis
    Slykhuis, J.T., 1952, 1955
  Polygonatum spp.
    Sill, W.H., Jr. and Patrick C. Agusiobo, 1955
  Rhoeo discolor
    Sill, W.H., Jr. and Patrick C. Agusiobo, 1955
  Saccharum officinarum
    Sill, W.H., Jr. and Patrick C. Agusiobo, 1955
  Sagittaria montevidensis
    Sill, W.H., Jr. and Patrick C. Agusiobo, 1955
  Sansevieria thyrsiflora
    Sill, W.H., Jr. and Patrick C. Agusiobo, 1955
  Secale cereale
    Slykhuis, J.T., 1952
  Setaria lutescens
    Slykhuis, J.T., 1952, 1955
  Smilacina spp.
    Sill, W.H., Jr. and Patrick C. Agusiobo, 1955
  Sorghastrum nutans
    Sill, W.H., Jr. and Patrick C. Agusiobo, 1955
  Sorghum almum
    Sill, W.H., Jr. and Patrick C. Agusiobo, 1955
  Sorghum halepense
    Sill, W.H., Jr. and Patrick C. Agusiobo, 1955
  Sorghum versicolor
    Sill, W.H., Jr. and Patrick C. Agusiobo, 1955
  Sorghum vulgare
    Sill, W.H., Jr. and Patrick C. Agusiobo, 1955
    Slykhuis, J.T., 1952
  Sorghum vulgare var. saccharatum
    Finley, A.M., 1957
  Sorghum vulgare var. sudanense
    Sill, W.H., Jr. and Patrick C. Agusiobo, 1955
  Tulipa spp.
    Sill, W.H., Jr. and Patrick C. Agusiobo, 1955
  Typha latifolia
    Sill, W.H., Jr. and Patrick C. Agusiobo, 1955
  Yucca glauca
    Sill, W.H., Jr. and Patrick C. Agusiobo, 1955
  Zea mays
    Sill, W.H., Jr. and Patrick C. Agusiobo, 1955
    Slykhuis, J.T., 1952
  Zebrina pendula
    Sill, W.H., Jr. and Patrick C. Agusiobo, 1955

V. WISCONSIN PEA STREAK Hagedorn and Walker 1949
  Cucumis sativus
    Hagedorn, D.J. and J.C. Walker, 1949, 1954
  Datura stramonium
    Hagedorn, D.J. and J.C. Walker, 1949, 1954
  Lupinus angustifolius
    Hagedorn, D.J. and J.C. Walker, 1949, 1954
  Lycopersicon esculentum
    Hagedorn, D.J. and J.C. Walker, 1949, 1954
  Medicago sativa
    Hagedorn, D.J. and J.C. Walker, 1949, 1954
    Skotland, C.B. and D.J. Hagedorn, 1954
  Nicotiana glutinosa
    Hagedorn, D.J. and J.C. Walker, 1949, 1954
  Nicotiana rustica
    Hagedorn, D.J. and J.C. Walker, 1949, 1954
  Nicotiana tabacum
    Hagedorn, D.J. and J.C. Walker, 1949, 1954
  Phaseolus vulgaris
    Hagedorn, D.J. and J.C. Walker, 1949, 1954
  Trifolium repens
    Hagedorn, D.J. and J.C. Walker, 1949, 1954
  Vicia faba var. major *
    Hagedorn, D.J. and J.C. Walker, 1949
  Vicia faba var. minor
    Hagedorn, D.J. and J.C. Walker, 1949
  Vicia sativa
    Hagedorn, D.J. and J.C. Walker, 1949, 1954
  Vigna sinensis
    Hagedorn, D.J. and J.C. Walker, 1949, 1954

ABUTILONVIRUS

Abutilonvirus variegans, Roland 1959, 127.
  (Sp. Vir.) (Not Val. Pub.: Rule 12a2)
  Marmor abutilon, Holmes 1939b, 50, q.v.

ACARINOPHILUS, Ryzhkov 1952, 466.
  (Gen. Vir.) (Val. Pub., Leg.)
  Dacavirus, Hansen 1956, 130.
  Type sp. (Subs. des. Barkley 1960, 68):
  Acarinophilus antholysatus, Ryzhkov 1952, 466.

Acarinophilus antholysatus, Ryzhkov 1952, 466.
  (Sp. Vir.) (Val. Pub., Illeg.: Rule 24b)
  Acrogenus ribis, Holmes 1939b, 122, q.v.
  Comment: Type species of genus Acarinophilus,
                       Ryzhkov 1952, 466.
ACAVIRACEAE, Hansen 1956, 130.
  (Fam. Vir.) (Val. Pub., Illeg.: Rule 3)
  Comment: Includes one collective genus:
  Dacavirus, Hansen 1956, 130.

ACROGENUS, Holmes 1939, 110.
  (Gen. Vir.) (Val. Pub., Leg.)
  Type sp. (orig. des.): Acrogenus solani, Holmes
                       1939, 111.
ACROGENUS, Holmes 1939a, 435.
  (Gen. Vir.) (Not Val. Pub.: Rule 12a2)
  Acrogenus, Holmes 1939b, 110, q.v.
  Type sp. (orig. des.): Acrogenus solani, Holmes
                       1939a, 435.
ACROGENUS, Holmes 1939b, 110: McKinney 1944a, 152.
  (Gen. Vir.) (Val. Pub., Leg.)
  Acrogenus, Holmes 1939a, 435.
  Aerogenodes, Bitancourt 1953, 453.
  Mexevirus, Hansen 1956, 128.
  Type sp. (orig. des.): Acrogenus solani, Holmes
                       1939b, 111.
Acrogenus ribis, Holmes 1939b, 112.
  (Sp. Vir.) (Val. Pub., Leg.)
  Acarinophilus antholysatus, Ryzhkov 1952, 466.
  Type species of genus Acarinophilus, Ryzhkov 1952, 466.
  Dacavirus ribis, (Holmes) Hansen 1956, 130.
  Type species of genus Dacavirus, Hansen 1956, 130.
  Ribesvirus senticosum, Roland 1959, 128.

Acrogenus rosettae, "Holmes" in Smith 1957, 24.
  in syn. (Sp. Vir.) (Not Val. Pub., Rule 12d)
  Acrogenus rosettae, van Katwijk 1953, 235.

Acrogenus rosettae, van Katwijk 1953, 235.
  (Sp. Vir.) (Val. Pub., Leg.)
  Pyrusvirus rosettans, Roland 1959, 127.

Acrogenus solani, Holmes 1939a, 435.
  (Sp. Vir.) (Not Val. Pub.: Rule 12a2)
  Acrogenus solani, Holmes 1939b, 111, q.v.
  Type species of genus Acrogenus, Holmes 1939b, 110.
  Comment: Type species of genus Acrogenus, Holmes
                       1939a, 435.
Acrogenus solani, Holmes 1939b, 111.
  (Sp. Vir.) (Val. Pub., Leg.)
  Mexevirus solani, (Holmes) Hansen 1956, 128,
  type species of genus Mexevirus, Hansen 1956, 128.
  Solanumvirus coleopterotranslatum, Roland 1952b, 53.
  Solanumvirus fusifaciens, Kohler 1952, 51.
  Solanumvirus fusiformis, (sic) Roland 1959, 129.
  Comment: Type species of genus Acrogenus, Holmes
                       1939b, 110.
Acrogenus solani var. severus, Holmes 1939b, 112.
  (Var. Vir.) (Val. Pub., Leg.)

Acrogenus solani var. vulgaris, Holmes 1939b, 111.
  (Var. Vir.) (Val. Pub., Illeg.: Rule 7)
  Comment: Type variety of Acrogenus solani, Holmes
                       1939b, 111.
ADELANODES, Bitancourt 1953, 453.
  (Gen. Vir.) (Not Val. Pub.: Rule 12c2)
  Adelonosus, Brierley and Smith 1944, 551, q.v.

ADELONOSUS, Brierley and Smith 1944, 551.
  (Gen. Vir.) (Val. Pub., Leg.)
  Adelanodes, Bitancourt 1953, 453.
  Type sp. (orig. des.): Adelonosus lilii, Brierley and
                         Smith 1944, 551.
Adelonosus lilii, Brierley and Smith 1944, 551.
  (Sp. Vir.) (Val. Pub.: Leg.)
  Liliumvirus occultum, Roland 1959, 129.
  Comment: Type species of genus Adelonosus, Brierley
  and Smith 1944, 551.

AGALLIOPHILUS, Ryzhkov 1952, 466.
  (Gen. Vir.) (Val. Pub., Illeg.: Rule 24a)
  Aureogenus, Black 1944, 141, q.v.
  Type sp. (monotype): Agalliphilus tuberosi, Ryzhkov
                         1952, 466.
Agalliophilus tuberosi, Ryzhkov 1952, 466.
  (Sp. Vir.) (Not Val. Pub., : Rule 14a2)
  Marmor vastans, Holmes 1939b, 94, q.v.
  Aureogenus vastans, (Holmes) Black 1944, 141, q.v.,
  type species of genus Aureogenus, Black 1944, 141.

AGROPYRUMVIRUS

Agropyrumvirus maculans, Roland 1959, 127.
  (Sp. Vir.) (Not Val. Pub.: Rule 12a2)
  Marmor agropyri, McKinney 1944b, 326, q.v.

ALEVIRACEAE, Hansen 1956, 129.
  (Fam. Vir.) (Val. Pub., Illeg., Rule 3)
  Comment: Includes collective genera
  Malevirus, Hansen 1956, 129 and
  Dalevirus, Hansen 1956, 129.

ALLIUMVIRUS

Alliumvirus flavorugans, Roland 1959, 129.
  (Sp. Vir.) (Not Val. Pub.: Rule 12a2)
  Marmor cepae, Holmes 1939b, 66, q.v.

ANNULACEAE, Holmes 1939b, 97.
  (Fam. Vir.) (Val. Pub., Leg.)
  Type genus: Annulus, Holmes 1939b, 97.

ANEMONEVIRUS

Anemonevirus deformans, Roland 1959, 127.
  (Sp. Vir.) (Not Val. Pub.: Rule 12a2)
  Galla anemones, Holmes 1939b, 108, q.v.

ANNULUS, Holmes 1939a, 435.
  (Gen. Vir.) (Not Val. Pub.: Rule 12a2)
  Annulus, Holmes 1939b, 97, q.v.
  Type sp. (orig. des.): Annulus tabaci, Holmes 1939a,
                         435.
ANNULUS, Holmes 1939b, 97.
  (Gen. Vir.) (Val. Pub., Leg.)
  Annulus, Holmes 1939a, 435.
  Minglobus, Hansen 1956, 127.
  Type sp. (orig. des.): Annulus tabaci, Holmes 1939b,
                         98.
Annulus apertus, Holmes 1948, 1214.
  (Sp. Vir.) (Val. Pub.: Leg.)

Annulus behrensianus, Schmelzer 1957, 311.
  (Sp. Vir.) (Val. Pub., Leg.)

Annulus bergerac, Holmes 1939, 102.
  Source: Bergerac-ring spot of tobacco (Nicotiana
  tabacum).
  (B. '48, 1216)

Annulus cerasi, Hildebrand 1944, 1003.
  (Sp. Vir.) (Val. Pub., Leg.)
  Prunivir circummaculatum, Cochran et al. 1951, 71.
  Prunivir circummaculatum, "Fawcett" in Smith 1957,
  342.
  Persicavirus anulosum, Roland 1959, 193.

Annulus delphinii, Holmes 1948, 1216.
  (Sp. Vir.) (Val. Pub., Leg.)

Annulus dubius, (Holmes) Holmes 1948, 1214.
(Sp. Vir.) (Val. Pub., Leg.)
Marmor dubium, Holmes 1939a, 434.
Marmor dubium, Holmes 1939b, 42, q.v.
Solanophilus tuberosi, Ryzhkov 1952, 465,
type species of genus Solanophilus, Ryzhkov 1952, 465.
Solanum-virus deformans, Kohler 1952a, 294, type
species of genus Solanum-virus, Kohler 1952a, 465.
Minflexus solani, Hansen 1956, 127,
type species of genus Minflexus, Hansen 1956, 127.
Minvirus solani, Hansen 1958, 222.
Type var. (orig. des.): Annulus dubius var. vulgaris,
Holmes 1948, 1215.

Annulus dubius var. annulus, (Holmes) Holmes 1948, 1215.
(Va. Vir.) (Val. Pub., Leg.)
Marmor dubium var. annulus, Holmes 1939a, 435.
Marmor dubium var. annulus, Holmes 1939b, 44, q.v.
Solanumvirus anulosum, Kohler 1952b, 51.
Solanum virus contactutranslatum, Roland 1952, 55.
Solanumvirus X-nominatum, Roland 1959, 129.

Annulus dubius var. flavus, (Holmes) Holmes 1948, 1216.
(Var. Vir.) (Val. Pub., Leg.)
Marmor dubium var. flavum, Holmes 1939b, 46, q.v.

Annulus dubius var. obscurus, (Holmes) Holmes 1948,
(Var. Vir.) (Val. Pub., Leg.)   1216.
Marmor dubium var. obscurum, Holmes 1939b, 46, q.v.

Annulus dubius var. vulgaris, (Holmes) Holmes 1948,
(Var. Vir.) (Va. Pub., Illeg.: Rule 7)   1215.
Marmor dubium var. vulgaris, Holmes 1939b, 42, q.v.
Comment: Type variety of species Annulus dubius,
(Holmes) Holmes 1948, 1214.

Annulus lamii, Lovisolo 1957, 131.
(Sp. Vir.) (Val. Pub., Leg.)

Annulus orae, Holmes 1939b, 103.
(Sp. Vir.) (Val. Pub., Leg.)
Tractus orae, (Holmes) Valleau 1940, 826, q.v.,
type species of genus Tractus, Valleau 1940, 826.
Nicotianavirus vulnerans, Roland 1959, 130.

Annulus orae var. phaseoli, Thomas and Zaumeyer 1950
(Var. Vir.) (Val. Pub., Leg.)   845.

Annulus pruni, Christoff 1958, 383.
(Sp. Vir.) (Val. Pub., Illeg.: Rule 24a)
Marmor persicae, Holmes 1939b, 81, q.v.
Flavimacula persicae, (Holmes) McKinney 1944a, 149,
q.v.,
type species of genus Flavimacula, McKinney 1944a,
149.

Annulus pyri, Christoff 1958, 424.
(Sp. Vir.) (Val. Pub., Leg.)
Marmor dilucidum, van Katwijk according to Baumann
1958, 126, 132.

Annulus tabaci, Holmes 1939a, 435.
(Sp. Vir.) (Not Val. Pub.: Rule 12a2)
Annulus tabaci, Holmes 1939b, 98, q.v.

Annulus tabaci, Holmes 1939b, 98.
(Sp. Vir.) (Val. Pub., Leg.)
Annulus tabaci, Holmes 1939a, 435.
Marmor anularium, McKinney 1944b, 327.
Minvirus nico-orbis, Hansen 1948, 222.
Minglobus nico-orbis, Hansen 1956, 127.
Nicotianavirus anulosum, Roland 1959, 130.
Type sp. of genus Annulus, Holmes 1939b, 97.
Source: Ring spot of tobacco (Nicotiana tabacum)

Annulus tabaci var. auratus, Holmes 1939a, 435.
(Var. Vir.) (Not Val. Pub.: Rule 12a2)
Annulus tabaci var. auratus, Holmes 1939a, 100.

Annulus tabaci var. cyamopsis, Cooper 1949, 356.
(Var. Vir.) (Val. Pub., Leg.)

Annulus tabaci var. kentuckiensis, Holmes 1939a, 435.
(Var. Vir.) (Not Val. Pub.: Rule 12a2)
Annulus tabaci var. kentuckiensis, Holmes 1939b, 99.

Annulus tabaci var. kentuckiensis, Holmes 1939b, 99.
(Var. Vir.) (Val. Pub., Leg.)
Annulus tabaci var. kentuckiensis, Holmes 1939a, 435.
Source: Green ring spot of tobacco (Nicotiana tabacum)

Annulus tabaci var. pennsylvanicus, Tall, Price and
Wertman 1949, 288.
(Var. Vir.) (Val. Pub., Leg.)

Annulus tabaci var. virginiensis, Holmes 1939a, 435.
(Var. Vir.) (Not Val. Pub.: Rule 12a2)
Annulus tabaci var. virginiensis, Holmes 1939b, 98,
q.v.

Annulus tabaci var. virginiensis, Holmes 1939b, 98.
(Var. Vir.) (Val. Pub., Leg.)
Annulus tabaci var. virginiensis, Holmes 1939a, 435.
Marmor anularium, McKinney 1944, 327.
Type var. of sp. Annulus tabaci, Holmes 1939b, 98.

Annulus wellmanii, Anderson 1954a, 91.
(Sp. Vir.) (Val. Pub., Leg.)

Annulus zonatus, Holmes 1939a, 435.
(Sp. Vir.) (Not Val. Pub.: Rule 12a2)
Annulus zonatus, Holmes 1939b, 101, q.v.

Annulus zonatus, Holmes 1939b, 101.
(Sp. Vir.) (Val. Pub., Leg.)
Annulus zonatus, Holmes 1939a, 435.

APHICHORDOIDEAE, Hansen 1956, 123.
(Sub fam. Vir.) (Val. Pub., Illeg., Rule 3)
Comment: Includes Maphichorda, Hansen 1956, 123.

APHIDOLPHILUS, Ryzhkov 1952, 465.
(Gen. Vir.) (Val. Pub., Illeg.: Rule 24a)
Murialba, Valleau 1940, 823, q.v.
Type sp. (subs. des. : Barkley 1958, 124):
Aphidolphilus cucumeris, (Holmes) Ryzhkov 1952, 465.

Aphidophilus betae, Ryzhkov 1952, 465.
(Sp. Vir.) (Not Val. Pub.: Rule 14a2)
Marmor betae, Holmes 1939b, 72, q.v.

Aphidophilus cruciferae, Ryzhkov 1952, 465.
(Sp. Vir.) (Not Val. Pub.: Rule 14a2)
Marmor brassicae, Holmes 1939b, 70, q.v.

Aphidophilus cruciferae, Ryzhkov in Klinkowski and
Uschdraweit 1958, 84.
(Sp. Vir.) (Val Pub., Illeg.: Rule 24a)
Marmor brassicae, Holmes 1939b, 70, q.v.

Aphidophilus cucurbitae, Kohler and Klinkowski 1954, 677.
(Sp. Vir.) (Val. Pub., Illeg.: Rule 24a)
Marmor cucumeris, Holmes 1939b, 31, q.v.
Murialba cucumeris, (Holmes) Valleau 1940, 823, q.v.

Aphidophilus phaseoli, Ryzhkov 1952, 465.
(Sp. Vir.) (Not Val. Pub.: Rule 14a2)
Marmor phaseoli, Holmes 1938b, 87, q.v.

Aphidophilus tuberosi, Ryzhkov 1952, 465.
(Sp. Vir.) (Not Val. Pub.: Rule 14a2)
Marmor upsilon, (Holmes) Holmes 1948, 1172, q.v.

Aphidophilus tulipae, Ryzhkov 1952, 465.
(Sp. Vir.) (Not Val. Pub.: Rule 14a2)
Marmor tulipae, Holmes 1939b, 52, q.v.

APHIDOPHILACEAE, Ryzhkov 1952, 466.
(Fam. Vir.) (Val. Pub., Leg.)
Type genus: Aphidophilus, Ryzhkov (Aphidaephilaceae,
Sukhov, p. 264.)

APHIGLOBOIDEAE, Hansen 1956, 123, 124.
(Subfam. Vir.) (Val. Pub., Illeg., Rule 3)
Comment: Includes Maphiglobus, Hansen 1956, 123,
124.

APHIVIRACEAE, Hansen 1956, 122.
(Fam. Vir.) (Val. Pub., Illeg., Rule 3)
Comment: Includes 3 subfamilies:
Aphiflexoideae, Hansen 1956, 123,
Aphichordoideae, Hansen 1956, 123,
Aphigloboideae, Hansen 1956, 124,
and 2 collective genera: Maphivirus, Hansen 1956, 122
and Daphivirus, Hansen 1956, 123.

APHIVIRALES, Hansen 1956, 122.
(Ord. Vir.) (Val. Pub., Leg.)
Comment: Includes the family Aphiviraceae, Hansen
1956, 122.

APIUMVIRUS

Apiumvirus maculans, Roland 1959, 128.
(Sp. Vir.) (Not Val. Pub.: Rule 12a2)
Marmor umbelliferarum, Holmes 1939b, 67, q.v.

ARACHISVIRUS

Arachisvirus rosettans, Roland 1959, 128.
(Sp. Vir.) (Not Val. Pub.: Rule 12a2)
Marmor arachidis, Holmes 1939b, 67, q.v.

ARCANA, Thomas and Rawlins 1951d, 189.
(Gen. Vir.) (Val. Pub., Illeg.: Rule 12, Principle 1
((2)))
Comment: See Editorial Board 1953, 114.

Arcana caelestia, Thomas and Rawlins 1951d, 189.
(Sp. Vir.) (Val. Pub., Illeg.: Rule 12, Principle 1
((2)))
Comment: Dr. Thomas in correspondence states that
"my binomials are not intended as usable names for
the corresponding viruses." See Editorial Board 1953,
114.

ARTHROPODOPHAGA, Krieg 1961, 42.
(Class Vir.) (Val. Pub., Leg.)

ARTHROPODOPHAGI, Holmes 1939a, 436.
(Class, Vir.) (Val. Pub., Leg.)
Crystallobiotae, Ryzhkov 1950, 14.
Thymonucleoproteinales, Zukhov 1956, 264.
Pseudocrystallinae, Ryzhkov 1952, 465.

AUREOGENUS, Black 1944, 141.
(Gen. Vir.) (Val. Pub., Leg.)
Solanivir, Fawcett 1940, 560.
Agalliophilus, Ryzhkov 1952, 466.
Mecicavirus, Hansen 1956, 124.
Aureogenusvirus, Krieg and Huger 1960, 404.
Aureogenusvirus, Krieg 1961, 145.
Type sp. (orig. des.): Aureogenus vastans, Black
1944, 141.
Aureogenus clavifolium, Black 1944, 141.
(Sp. Vir.) (Val. Pub., Leg.)
Trifoliumvirus clavifoliatum, Roland 1959, 128.
Aureogenusvirus clavifolium, (Black) Krieg 1961, 146.

Aureogenus magnivena, Black 1944, 144.
(Sp. Vir.) (Val. Pub., Leg.)
Dacicavirus tumefaciens, Hansen 1956, 125.
Trifoliumvirus nervicrassans, Roland 1959, 128.
Aureogenusvirus magnivena, (Black) Krieg and Huger
1960, 404.
Aureogenusvirus magnivena, (Black) Krieg 1961, 145.

Aureogenus vastans, Black 1944, 141.
(Sp. Vir.) (Val Pub., Leg.)
Marmor vastans, Holmes 1939b, 94, q.v.
Solanivir vestans, Fawcett 1940, 560, type
species of genus Solanivir, Fawcett 1940, 560.
Agalliophilus tuberose, Ryzhkov 1952, 466, type
species of genus Agalliophilus, Ryzhkov 1952, 466.
Solanumvirus vastans, (Holmes) Kohler 1952, 51.
Solanumvirus aceratogalliatranslatum, (sic) Roland
1952, 53.
Mecicavirus solani, Hansen 1956, 124, type
species of genus Mecicavirus, Hansen 1956, 124.
Aureogenusvirus vestans, (sic) Krieg 1961, 146, type
species of genus Aureogenusvirus, Krieg 1961, 146.
Type var. (subs. des. Holmes 1948, 1156):
Aureogenus vastans var. vulgare, Black 1944, 141.
Comment: Type species of genus Aureogenus, Black
1944, 141.
Aureogenus vastans var. agalliae, (Black) Black 1944, 141.
(Var. Vir.) (Val. Pub., Leg.)
Marmor vastans var. agalliae, Black 1941, 233.

Aureogenus vastans var. lethale, (Black) Holmes 1948,
(Var. Vir.) (Val. Pub., Leg.)   1156.
Marmor vastans var. lethale, Black 1940, 391.

Aureogenus vastans var. vulgare, (Black) Black 1944,
(Var. Vir.) (Val. Pub., Illeg.: Rule 7)   141.
Marmor vastans var. vulgare, Black 1940, 391.
Comment: Type variety of species Aureogenus vastans,
(Holmes) Black 1944, 141.

AUREOGENUSVIRUS, Krieg 1961, 145.
(Gen. Vir.) (Val. Pub., Illeg.: Rules 23, 24a)
Aureogenus, Black 1944, 141, q.v.
Type sp. (implied): Aureogenusvirus vestans, (sic)
(Holmes) Krieg 1961, 146.

AUREOGENUSVIRUS, Krieg and Huger 1960a, 404.
(Gen. Vir.) (Not Val. Pub.: Rule 12a3)
Aureogenus, Black 1944, 141, q.v.

Aureogenusvirus clavifolium, (Black) Krieg 1961, 146.
(Ap. Vir.) (Val. Pub., Illeg.: Rule 24a)
Aureogenus clavifolium, Black 1944, 141, q.v.

Aureogenusvirus magnivena, (Black) Krieg 1961, 145.
(Sp. Vir.) (Val. Pub., Illeg.: Rule 24a)
Aureogenus magnivena, Black 1944, 144, q.v.

Aureogenusvirus magnivena, (Black) Krieg and Huger
1960, 404.
(Sp. Vir.) (Not Val. Pub.: Rule 12a2)
Aureogenus magnivena, Black 1944, 144, q.v.

Aureogenusvirus vestans, (sic) Krieg 1961, 146.
(Ap. Vir.) (Val. Pub., Illeg.: Rules 23, 23a)
Marmor vastans, Holmes 1939b, 94, q.v.
Aureogenus vastans, (Holmes) Black 1944, 141, q.v.
Type species of genus Aureogenus, Black 1944, 141.
Comment: Type species of genus Aureogenusvirus,
Krieg 1961, 146.

AVENAVIRUS

Avenavirus maculans, Roland 1959, 129.
(Sp. Vir.) (Not Val. Pub.: Rule 12a2)

Avenavirus rosettae, Klinkowski and Kreutzberg 1958, 4.
(Sp. Vir.) (Not Val. Pub.: Rule 12c3)
Fractilinea avenae, McKinney 1944, 327, q.v.
Graminevirus avenae, (McKinney) Ryzhkov 1952, 466,
q.v.
Avenavirus rosettans, Roland 1959, 129.
(Sp. Vir.) (Not Val. Pub.: Rule 12a2)
Fractilinea avenae, McKinney 1944b, 327, q.v.
Graminevirus avenae, (McKinney) Ryzhkov 1952, 466,
q.v.
BACULUS, Limasset 1954, 94.
(Gen. Vir.) (Not Val. Pub.: Rule 13e)
Marmor, Holmes 1939b, 16, q.v.

BETAVIR, Fawcett 1940, 560.
(Gen. Vir.) (Not Val. Pub.: Rule 12a2)
Rugavirus, Krieg 1961, 151, q.v.
Type sp. (monotype): Betavir eutetticola, Fawcett
1940, 560.
Betavir eutetticola, (sic) Fawcett 1940, 560.
(Sp. Vir.) (Not Val. Pub.: Rule 12a2)
Chlorogenus eutettigicola, Holmes 1939b, 11, q.v.
Comment: Type species of genus Betavir, Fawcett
1940, 560.
Betavir verrucans, Roland 1959, 128.
(Sp. Vir.) (Not Val. Pub.: Rule 12a2)
Chlorogenus eutettigicola, Holmes 1939b, 11, q.v.

Beta virus innocens, "Smith" in Klinkowski 1958, 38.
(Sp. Vir.) (Not Val. Pub.: Rule 5a)
Comment: Reference to proposal by Smith not found.

Betavirus maculans, Roland 1959, 128.
(Sp. Vir.) (Not Val. Pub.: Rule 12a2)
Marmor betae, Holmes 1939b, 72, q.v.

Betavirus reticulosum, Roland 1959, 128.
(Sp. Vir.) (Not Val. Pub.: Rule 12a2)

BIRETEXVIRUS, Hansen 1958, 222.
  (Gen. Vir.) (Val. Pub., Illeg.: Rule 24a)
  Tarpeia, Holmes 1948, 1268, q.v.
  Type sp. (monotype): Biretexvirus suis, Hansen 1958,
                                                    222.

BLASTOGENUS, McKinney 1944a, 151.
  (Gen. Vir.) (Val. Pub., Leg.)
  Type sp. (orig. des.): Blastogenus fragariae,
  McKinney 1944a, 151.

Blastogenus fragariae, (Holmes) McKinney 1944a, 151.
  (Sp. Vir., Leg.)
  Nanus fragariae, Holmes 1939b, 128, q.v.
  Fragariavirus everriculosum, Roland 1959, 130.
  Comment: Type species of genus Blastogenus,
  McKinney 1944a, 151.

BRASSICAVIRUS

Brassicavirus anulolaedens, Roland 1959, 128.
  (Sp. Vir.) (Not Val. Pub.: Rule 12a2)

Brassicavirus crispans, Roland 1959, 130.
  (Sp. Vir.) (Not. Val. Pub.: Rule 12a2)
  Savoia napi, Holmes 1939b, 133, q.v.

Brassicavirus nerviclarens, Roland 1959, 128.
  (Sp. Vir.) (Not Val. Pub.: Rule 12a2)
  Marmor cruciferarum, Holmes 1939b, 69, q.v.

Brassicavirus nigromaculans, Roland 1959, 128.
  (Sp. Vir.) (Not Val. Pub.: Rule 12a2)
  Marmor brassicae, Holmes 1939b, 70, q.v.

BROMVIRUS

Bromvirus maculans, Roland 1959, 128.
  (Sp. Vir.) (Not Val. Pub.: Rule 12a2)
  Marmor graminis, McKinney 1944b, 325, q.v.

BRYOVIRUS, Thornberry 1941, 25.
  (Gen. Vir.) (Not Val. Pub.: Rules 12a2, 12c2, 13a)

CALCEOLARIVIR, Fawcett 1940, 560.
  (Gen. Vir.) (Not Val. Pub.: Rules 12a2, 13e)

CALLISTEPHUSVIRUS

Callistephusvirus flavescens, Roland 1959, 128.
  (Sp. Vir.) (Not Val. Pub.: Rule 12a2)
  Chlorogenus callistephi, Holmes 1939b, 2, q.v.

CAMELLIAVIRUS

Camelliavirus librinecans, Roland 1959, 130.
  (Sp. Vir.) (Not Val. Pub.: Rule 12a2)

CANNAVIRUS

Cannavirus maculans, Roland 1959, 128.
  (Sp. Vir.) (Not Val. Pub.: Rule 12a2)

Cannavirus maculans, Roland 1959, 129.
  (Sp. Vir.) (Not Val. Pub.: Rule 12a2)

CARPOPHTHORA, McKinney 1944a, 152; Holmes 1948,
  (Gen. Vir.) (Val. Pub., Leg.)   1151.
  Daxevirus, Hansen 1956, 128.
  Carpophtoravirus, (sic) Krieg 1961, 150.
  Type sp. (orig. des.): Carpophthora lacerans,
  (Holmes) McKinney 1944a, 152.

Carpophthora lacerans, (Holmes) McKinney 1944a, 152.
  (Sp. Vir.) (Val. Pub., Leg.)
  Marmor lacerans, Holmes 1939b, 82, q.v.
  Daxevirus pruni, Hansen 1956, 128, type
  species of genus Daxevirus, Hansen 1956, 128.
  Persicavirus lacerans, Roland 1959, 129.
  Carpophthoravirus lacerans, (Holmes) Krieg 1961, 150,
  type species of genus Carpophthoravirus, (sic) Krieg
  1961, 150.
  Comment: Type species of genus Carpophthora,
  McKinney 1944a, 152.

Carpophthora rosettae, (Holmes) Holmes 1948, 1152.
  (Sp. Vir.) (Val. Pub., Leg.)
  Chlorogenus rosettae, Holmes 1939a, 434.
  Nanus rosettae, Holmes 1939b, 125, q.v.
  Prunivir rosettae, Fawcett 1940, 560,
  type species of genus Prunivir, Fawcett 1940, 560.
  Persicavirus rosettans, Roland 1959, 129.

CARPOPHTORAVIRUS, (sic) Krieg 1951, 150.
  (Gen. Vir.) (Val. Pub., Illeg.: Rules 23, 24a)
  Carpophthora, McKinney 1944a, 152; Holmes 1948,
  1141, q.v.
  Type sp. (monotype): Carpophthoravirus lacerans,
  (McKinney) Krieg 1961, 150.

Carpophthoravirus lacerans, (Holmes) Krieg 1961, 150.
  (Sp. Vir.) (Val. Pub., Illeg.: Rules 23, 24a)
  Marmor lacerans, Holmes 1939b, 82, q.v.
  Carpophthora lacerans, (Holmes) McKinney 1944a,
  152, q.v., type species of genus Carpophthora,
  McKinney 1944a, 152.

CATTLEYAVIRUS

Cattleyavirus maculans, Roland 1959, 129.
  (Sp. Vir.) (Not Val. Pub.: Rule 12a2)

CERASUSVIRUS

Cerasusvirus asperans, Roland 1959, 128.
  (Sp. Vir.) (Not Val. Pub.: Rule 12a2)
  Rimocortius kwanzani, Milbrath and Zeller 1942, 430,
                                                    q.v.
Cerasusvirus flavescens, Roland 1959, 128.
  (Sp. Vir.) (Not Val. Pub.: Rule 12a2)
  Chlorogenus cerasi, Hildebrand 1944, 1003, q.v.

Cerasusvirus maculans, Roland 1959, 128.
  (Sp. Vir.) (Not Val. Pub.: Rule 12a2)
  Marmor cerasi, Zeller and Evans 1941, 467, q.v.

Cerasusvirus rubiginosum, Roland 1959, 128.
  (Sp. Vir.) (Not Val. Pub.: Rule 12a2)
  Marmor rubiginosum, Reeves 1940, 789, q.v.

Cerasusvirus verrucans, Roland 1959, 128.
  (Sp. Vir.) (Not Val. Pub.: Rule 12a2)

CHLOROGENACEAE, Holmes 1939, 1.
  (Fam. Vir.) (Val. Pub., Leg.)

CHLOROGENUS, Holmes 1939a, 434.
  (Gen. Vir.) (Not Val. Pub.: Rule 12a2)
  Chlorogenus, Holmes 1939b, 1, q.v.
  Type sp. (orig. des.): Chlorogenus callistephi,
  Holmes 1939a, 434.

CHLOROGENUS, Holmes 1939b, 1.
  (Gen. Vir.) (Val. Pub., Leg.)
  Chlorogenus, Holmes 1939a, 434.
  Dacicavirus, Hansen 1956, 125.
  Chlorogenusvirus, Krieg and Huger 1960a, 404.
  Chlorogenusvirus, Krieg 1951, 143.
  Type sp. (orig. des.): Chlorogenus callistephi,
  Holmes 1939b, 2.

Chlorogenus australiensis, (Holmes) Holmes 1948, 1147.
  (Sp. Vir.) (Val. Pub., Leg.)
  Galla australiensis, Holmes 1939b, 107, q.v.
  Leptomotropus lycopersici, Ryzhkov 1952, 466.
  Leptomotropus lycopersici, Kohler and Klinkowski
  1954, 601.
  Hyalesthesophilus solenacii, Sukhov 1956, 264.
  Lycopersicumvirus australiense, Roland 1959, 130.
  Comment: Klinkowski and Uschdraweit 1958, 103,
  Consider this synonymous with Chlorogenus vaccinii,
  Holmes 1939b, 10.

Chlorogenus australiensis var. stolbur, Kovachevski 1954,
  (Var. Vir.) (Val. Pub., Leg.)   164, 165.
  Leptomotropus korozevscianus, Ryzhkov 1952, 466.
  Leptomotropus korozevscianus, "Ryzhkov" in Kohler
  and Klinkowski 1954, 601.

Chlorogenus callistephi, Holmes 1939a, 434.
(Sp. Vir.) (Not Val. Pub.: Rule 12a3)
Chlorogenus callistephi, Holmes 1939b, 2, q.v.,
type species of genus Chlorogenus, Holmes 1939b, 1.
Comment: Type species of genus Chlorogenus,
Holmes 1939a, 434.

Chlorogenus callistephi, Holmes 1939b, 2.
(Sp. Vir.) (Val. Pub., Leg.)
Chlorogenus callistephi, Holmes 1939a, 434, type
species of genus Chlorogenus, Holmes 1939a, 434.
Dacicavirus callistephi, (Holmes) Hansen 1956, 125,
type species of genus Dacicavirus, Hansen 1956, 125.
Callistephusvirus flavescens, Roland 1959, 128.
Chlorogenusvirus callistephi, (Holmes) Krieg and
Huger 1960, 404.
Chlorogenusvirus callistephi, Krieg 1961, 143, type
species of genus Chlorogenusvirus, Krieg 1961, 143.
Calligenus (sic) callistephi, "Harris" in Beirne 1952,
228.
Type var. (orig. des.): Chlorogenus callistephi var.
vulgaris, Holmes 1939b, 3.
Comment: Type species of genus Chlorogenus, Holmes
1939b, 1.

Chlorogenus callistephi var. albifrons, Heinze 1959, 140.
(Var. Vir.) (Val. Pub., Leg.)

Chlorogenus callistephi var. attenuatus, Holmes 1939a,
(Var. Vir.) (Not Val. Pub.: Rule 12a3)   434.
Chlorogenus callistephi var. attenuatus, Holmes 1939b,
4, q.v.

Chlorogenus callistephi var. attenuatus, Holmes 1939b, 4.
(Var. Vir.) (Val. Pub., Leg.)
Chlorogenus callistephi var. attenuatus, Holmes 1939a,
434.

Chlorogenus callistephi var. californicus, Holmes 1939a,
(Var. Vir.) (Not Val. Pub.: Rule 12a2)   434.
Chlorogenus callistephi var. californicus, Holmes
1939a, 3, q.v.

Chlorogenus callistephi var. californicus, Holmes 1939b,
(Var. Vir.) (Val. Pub., Leg.)   3.
Chlorogenus callistephi var. californicus, Holmes
1939b, 434.

Chlorogenus callistephi var. vulgaris, Holmes 1939a,
(Var. Vir.) (Not Val. Pub.: Rule 12a2)   434.
Chlorogenus callistephi var. vulgaris, Holmes 1939b,
q.v., type variety of species Chlorogenus callistephi,
Holmes 1939b, 2.

Chlorogenus cerasae, Hildebrand 1944, 1003.
Chlorogenus cerasi, Hildebrand 1944, 1003, q.v.

Chlorogenus cerasi, Hildebrand 1944, 1003.
(Sp. Vir.) (Val. Pub., Leg.) as Chlorogenus cerasae.
Cerasusvirus flavescens, Roland 1959, 128.

Chlorogenus eutetticola, (sic) Holmes 1939b, 11,
name corrected to Chlorogenus eutettigicola by Holmes
1948, 1219.

Chlorogenus eutettigicola, Holmes 1939b, 11 as
Chlorogenus euttigicola
(Sp. Vir.) (Val. Pub., Leg.)
Betavir eutetticola, (sic) Fawcett 1940, 560, type
species of genus Betavir, Fawcett 1940, 560.
Dacicavirus beta, Hansen 1956, 125.
Ruga verrucosans, Carnser and Bennett 1943, 386;
Holmes 1948, 1219.
Betavirus verrucans, Roland 1959, 128.
Rugavirus verrucosans, (Carsner and Bennett) Krieg
1961, 151, type
species of genus Rugavirus, Krieg 1961, 151.
Comment: Spelling corrected, Holmes, 1948, 1219.

Chlorogenus fragariae, Holmes 1939a, 434.
(Sp. Vir.) (Not Val. Pub.: Rule 12a2)

Chlorogenus humuli, Holmes 1939b, 15.
(Sp. Vir.) (Val. Pub., Leg.)
Humulusvirus urticans, Roland 1959, 128.

Chlorogenus medicaginis, Holmes 1939b, 14.
(Sp. Vir.) (Val. Pub., Leg.)
Medicagovirus everriculosum, Roland 1959, 129.

Chlorogenus myricae, Raychaudhuri 1953, 19.
(Sp. Vir.) (Val. Pub., Leg.)

Chlorogenus patagoniensis, Bennett and Munck 1946, 60.
(Sp. Vir.) (Val. Pub., Leg.)

Chlorogenus persicae, Holmes 1939a, 434.
(Sp. Vir.) (Not Val. Pub.: Rule 12a2)
Chlorogenus persicae, Holmes 1939b, 5. q.v.
Type var. (orig. des.): Chlorogenus persicae var.
vulgaris, Holmes 1939a, 434.

Chlorogenus persicae, Holmes 1939b, 5.
(Sp. Vir.) (Val. Pub., Leg.)
Chlorogenus persicae, Holmes 1939a, 434.
Persicavirus flavescens, Roland 1959, 129.
Type var. (orig. des.): Chlorogenus persicae var.
vulgaris, Holmes 1939b, 5.

Chlorogenus persicae var. micropersica, Holmes 1939a,
(Var. Vir.) (Not Val. Pub.: Rule 12a2)   434.
Chlorogenus persicae var. micropersica, Holmes
1939b, 6, q.v.

Chlorogenus persicae var. micropersica, Holmes 1939b,
(Var. Vir.) (Val. Pub., Leg.)   6.
Chlorogenus persicae var. micropersica, Holmes
1939a, 434.

Chlorogenus persicae var. vulgaris, Holmes 1939a, 434.
(Var. Vir.) (Not Val. Pub.: Rule 12a2)
Chlorogenus persicae var. vulgaris, Holmes 1939b,
4, q.v.
Comment: Type variety of species Chlorogenus
persicae, Holmes 1939a, 434.

Chlorogenus persicae var. vulgaris, Holmes 1939b, 5.
(Var. Vir.) (Val. Pub., Illeg.: Rule 7)
Chlorogenus persicae var. vulgaris, Holmes 1939a,
Persicavirus nudans, Roland 1959, 129.   434.
Comment: Type variety of species Chlorogenus
persicae, Holmes 1939b, 5.

Chlorogenus robiniae, Holmes 1939a, 434.
(Sp. Vir.) (Not Val. Pub.: Rule 12a2)
Chlorogenus robiniae, Holmes 1939b, 13, q.v.
Polycladus robiniae, (Holmes) McKinney 1944a, 131,
type species of genus Polycladus,   q.v.
McKinney 1944a, 151.

Chlorogenus robiniae, Holmes 1939b, 13.
(Sp. Vir.) (Val. Pub., Leg.)
Polycladus robiniae, (Holmes) McKinney 1944a, 151,
q.v., type species of genus Polycladus, McKinney
1944a, 151.
Robiniavirus everriculosum, Roland 1959, 130.
Chlorogenus robiniae, Holmes 1939a, 434.

Chlorogenus rosettae, Holmes 1939a, 434.
(Sp. Vir.) (Not Val. Pub.: Rule 12a2)
Nanus rosettae, Holmes 1939b, 125, q.v.
Carpophthora rosettae, (Holmes) Holmes 1948, 1152,
        q.v.
Chlorogenus santali, Holmes 1939a, 434.
(Sp. Vir.) (Not Val. Pub.: Rule 12a2)
Chlorogenus santali, Holmes 1939b, 8, q.v.

Chlorogenus santali, Holmes 1939b, 8.
(Sp. Vir.) (Val. Pub., Leg.)
Chlorogenus santali, Holmes 1939a, 434.
Santalumvirus spicans, Roland 1959, 130.

Chlorogenus sesami, Kohler and Klinkowski 1954, 665.
(Sp. Vir.) (Val. Pub., Leg.)

Chlorogenus solani, Holmes 1939a, 434.
(Sp. Vir.) (Not Val. Pub.: Rule 12a2)
Chlorogenus solani, Holmes 1939b, 7, q.v.
Chlorophthora solani, (Holmes) McKinney 1944a, 151,
q.v., type species of genus Chlorophthora, McKinney
1944a, 151.

Chlorogenus solani, Holmes 1939b, 7.
   (Sp. Vir.) (Va. Pub., Leg.)
   Chlorogenus solani, Holmes 1939a, 434.
   Chlorophthora solani, (Holmes) McKinney 1944a, 151,
   q.v., type species of genus Chlorophthora, McKinney
   1944a, 151.
   Solanum virus cuscutotranslatum, Roland 1952, 53.
   Solanumvirus everriculosum, Roland 1959, 129.

Chlorogenus vaccinii, Holmes 1939a, 434.
   (Sp. Vir.) (Not Val. Pub.: Rule 12a2)
   Chlorogenus vaccinii, Holmes 1939b, 10, q.v.

Chlorogenus vaccinii, Holmes 1939b, 10.
   (Sp. Vir.) (Val. Pub., Leg.)
   Chlorogenus vaccinii, Holmes 1939a, 434.
   Leptomotropus vaccinii, Ryzhkov 1952, 466,
   type species of genus Leptomotropus, Ryzhkov 1952,
   466.
   Vacciniavirus sterilefaciens, Roland 1959, 130.

Chlorogenus zeae var. mexicanus, Maramorosch 1958,
   (Var. Vir.) (Val. Pub., Leg.)   450.
   Chlorogenusvirus zeae var. mexicanus, (Maramorosch)
   Krieg 1961, 144.

Chlorogenus zeae var. riograndensis, Maramorosch 1958,
   (Var. Vir.) (Val. Pub., Leg.)   450.
   Chlorogenusvirus var. riograndensis, (Maramorosch)
   Krieg 1961, 144.

CHLOROGENUSVIRUS, Krieg 1961, 143.
   (Gen. Vir.) (Val. Pub., Illeg.: Rules 23, 24a)
   Chlorogenus, Holmes 1939b, 1, q.v.
   Type sp. (implied): Chlorogenusvirus callistephi,
   (Holmes) Krieg 1961, 143.

CHLOROGENUSVIRUS, Krieg and Huger 1960, 404.
   (Gen. Vir.) (Not Val. Pub.: Rule 12a2)
   Chlorogenus, Holmes 1939b, 1, q.v.

Chlorogenusvirus callistephi, (Holmes) Krieg 1961, 143.
   (Sp. Vir.) (Val. Pub., Illeg.: Rule 24a)
   Chlorogenus callistephi, Holmes 1939a, 2, q.v.
   type species of genus Chlorogenus, Holmes 1939a, 1.
   Comment: Type species of genus Chlorogenusvirus,
   Krieg 1961, 143.

Chlorogenusvirus callistephi, Krieg and Huger 1960, 404.
   (Sp. Vir.) (Not Val. Pub.: Rule 12a2)
   Chlorogenus callistephi, Holmes 1939b, 2, q.v.
   type species of genus Chlorogenus, Holmes 1939b, 1.

Chlorogenusvirus zeae, (Maramorosch) Krieg 1961, 144.
   (Sp. Vir.) (Val. Pub., Illeg.: Rule 24a)
   Chlorogenus zeae, Maramorosch 1958, 450, q.v.

Chlorogenusvirus zeae var. mexicanus, (Maramorosch)
   Krieg 1961, 144.
   (Var. Vir.) (Not Val. Pub., Rule 12a)
   Chlorogenus zeae var. mexicanus, Maramorosch 1958,
                                       450, q.v.
Chlorogenusvirus zeae var. riograndensis, (Maramorosch)
   Krieg 1961, 144.
   (Var. Vir.) (Not Val. Pub.: Rule 12a)
   Chlorogenus zeae var. riograndensis, Maramorosch
   1958, 450, q.v.

CHLOROPHTHORA, McKinney 1944a, 151.
   (Gen. Vir.) (Val. Pub., Leg.)
   Type sp. (orig. des.): Chlorophthora solani, (Holmes)
   McKinney 1944a, 151.

Chlorophthora solani, (Holmes) McKinney 1944a, 151.
   (Sp. Vir.) (Val. Pub., Leg.)
   Chlorogenus solani, Holmes 1939a, 434.
   Chlorogenus solani, Holmes 1939b, 7, q.v.
   Solanum virus cuscutotranslatum, Roland 1952, 53.
   Leptomotropus solanacearum, Ryzhkov 1952, 466.
   Leptomotropus solanacearum, Kohler and Klinkowski
   1954, 661.
   Solanumvirus everriculosum, Roland 1959, 129.
   Comment: Type species of genus Chlorophthora,
   McKinney 1944a, 151.

CICAVIRACEAE, Hansen 1956, 124.
   (Fam. Vir.) (Val. Pub., Illeg., Rule 3)
   Comment: Includes 2 collective genera
   Mecicavirus, Hansen 1956, 124 and
   Dacicavirus, Hansen 1956, 125.

CICAVIRALES, Hansen 1956, 124.
   (Ord. Vir.) (Val. Pub., Leg.)
   Comment: Includes Family: Cicaviraceae.

CITRIVIR, Fawcett 1940, 561; 1941, 357.
   (Gen. Vir.) (Not Val. Pub.: Rule 12c)
   Dinvirus, Hansen 1956, 125, q.v.
   Type sp. (Subs. des.) Holmes 1948, 1209):
   Citrivir psorosis, Fawcett 1941, 561.

Citrivir italicum, Fawcett 1940, 561; 1941, 357.
   (Sp. Vir.) (Val. Pub., Illeg.: Rule 24b)
   Marmor italicum, (Fawcett) Holmes 1948, 1202, q.v.

Citrivir pertinaciae, (sic) Fawcett 1946a, 676.
   (Sp. Vir.) (Val. Pub., Illeg.: Rule 24b)
   Citrusvirus pertinax, Roland 1959, 128.

Citrivir psorosis, Fawcett 1940, 561; 1941, 357.
   (Sp. Vir.) (Val. Pub., Illeg.: Rule 24b)
   Rimocortius psorosis, (Fawcett) Holmes 1948, 1210,
   q.v.
   Type var. (orig. des.): Citrivir psorosis var.
   vulgare, Fawcett 1940, 561.
   Comment: Type species of genus Citrivir, Fawcett
                                       1940, 561.
Citrivir psorosis, Fawcett 1941, 357.
   Rimocortius psorosis, Fawcett 1948, 1210.
   Source: Rutaceae-Citrus sinensis, Osbeck, orange;
   Citrus limonis, Osbeck, lemon; Citrus maxima, Merr.,
                                       grapefruit.
Citrivir psorosis var. alveatum, Fawcett and Bitancourt
   1943, 854.
   (Var. Vir.) (Val. Pub., Illeg.: Rule 24b)
   Rimocortius psorosis var. alveatum, (Fawcett and
   Bitancourt) Holmes 1948, 1211, q.v.

Citrivir psorosis var. anulatum, Fawcett 1940, 561;
   1941, 357.
   (Var. Vir.) (Val. Pub., Illeg.: Rule 24b)
   Rimocortius psorosis var. anulatum, (Fawcett)
   Holmes 1948, 1210, q.v.

Citrivir psorosis var. concavum, Fawcett and Bitancourt
   1943, 850.
   (Var. Vir.) (Val. Pub., Illeg.: Rule 24b)
   Rimocortius psorosis var. concavum, (Fawcett and
   Bitancourt) Holmes 1948, 1210, q.v.

Citrivir psorosis var. vulgare, Fawcett 1940, 561; 1941,
   (Var. Vir.) (Val. Pub., Illeg.: Rule 7)   357.
   Rimocortius psorosis var. vulgare, (Fawcett) Holmes
   1949, 1210, q.v.
   Comment: Type variety of species Citrivir psorosis,
   Fawcett 1940, 561.

Citrusvirus maculans, Roland 1959, 128.
   (Sp. Vir.) (Not Val. Pub.: Rule 12a2)
   Marmor italicum, (Fawcett) Holmes 1948, 1202, q.v.

Citrusvirus pertinax, Roland 1959, 128.
   (Sp. Vir.) (Not Val. Pub.: Rule 12a2)
   Citrivir pertinaciae, (sic) Fawcett 1946a, 676, q.v.

Citrusvirus scabiosum, Roland 1959, 128.
   (Sp. Vir.) (Not Val. Pub.: Rule 12a2)
   Rimocortius psorosis, Holmes 1948, 1219, q.v.

Citrusvirus vastans, Roland 1959, 128.
   (Sp. Vir.) (Not Val. Pub., Rule 12a2)

CORIODES, Bitancourt, 1953, 453.
   (Gen. Vir.) (Not Val. Pub.: Rule 12c2)
   Corium, Holmes 1939b, 119, q.v.

CORIUM, Holmes 1939b, 119.
(Gen. Vir.) (Val. Pub., Leg.)
Coriodes, Bitancourt 1953, 453.
Quanjeria, Ryzhkov 1952, 466.
Corium virus, Krieg 1961, 151.
Type sp. (orig. des.): Corium solani, Holmes 1939b, 120.

Corium betae, Holmes 1948, 1204.
(Sp. Vir.) (Val. Pub., Leg.)
Daphivirus betae, (Holmes) Hansen 1956, 123, q.v.
type species of genus Daphivirus, Hansen 1956, 123.
Daphiflexus betae, (Holmes) Hansen 1958, 222,
type species of genus Daphiflexus, Hansen 1958, 222.
Betavirus flavescens, Roland 1959, 128.

Corium rubi, Holmes 1939b, 121.
(Sp. Vir.) (Val. Pub., Leg.)
Rubusvirus crispans, Roland 1959, 130.
Type var. (orig. des.): Corium rubi var. alpha, Holmes 1939b, 121.

Corium rubi var. alpha, Holmes 1939b, 121.
(Var. Vir.) (Val. Pub., Illeg.: Rule 7)
Comment: Type variety of species Corium rubi, Holmes 1939b, 121.

Corium rubi var. beta, Holmes 1939b, 122.
(Var. Vir.) (Val. Pub., Leg.)

Corium ruborum, (Zeller and Braun) Holmes 1948, 1205.
(Sp. Vir.) (Val. Pub., Leg.) ·
Minuor ruborum, Zeller and Braun 1943, 161, q.v.
type species of genus Minuor, Zeller and Braun 1943, 161.

Corium solani, Holmes 1939b, 120.
(Sp. Vir.) (Val. Pub., Leg.)
Quanjeria tuberosi, Ryzhkov 1952, 466,
type species of genus Quanjeria, Ryzhkov 1952, 466.
Solanum virus altathermus, Roland 1952, 53.
Solanum virus librimortiferum, Roland 1952, 53.
Solanumvirus varians, Kohler 1952b, 51.
Solanumvirus rigidiformis, Kohler 1952b, 51.
Daphivirus solani, (Holmes) Hansen 1956, 128.
Solanumvirus perniciosum, Roland 1959, 129.
Coriumvirus solani, (Holmes) Krieg 1961, 151.
type species of genus Coriumvirus, Krieg 1961, 151.
Comment: Type species of genus Corium, Holmes 1939b, 119.

Corium viatoris, Heinze 1959, 170, 176, 181, 182.
(Sp. Vir.) (Val. Pub., Leg.)

Corium zeae, Stoner 1952, 688.
(Sp. Vir.) (Val. Pub., Leg.)
Zeavirus variegans, Roland 1959, 129.

CORIUMVIRUS, Krieg 1961, 151.
(Gen. Vir.) (Val. Pub., Illeg.: Rule 24a)
Corium, Holmes 1939b, 119, q.v.
Type sp. (monotype): Coriumvirus solani, (Holmes) Krieg 1961, 151.

Coriumvirus solani, (Holmes) Krieg 1961, 151.
(Sp. Vir.) (Val. Pub., Illeg.: Rule 24a)
Corium solani, Holmes 1939b, 120, q.v.,
type species of Corium, Holmes 1939b, 119.
Comment: Type species of genus Coriumvirus, Krieg 1961, 151.

CROTALARIAVIRUS

Crotalariavirus maculans, Roland 1959, 128.
(Sp. Vir.) (Not Val. Pub.: Rule 12a2)

CRYSTALLOCOCCUS, Ryzhkov 1952, 465.
(Gen. Vir.) (Val. Pub., Leg.)
Type sp. (Subs. des.: Barkley 1960, 68):
Crystallococcus lycopersici, Ryzhkov 1952, 465.

Crystallococcus cruciferae, Ryzhkov 1952, 465.
(Sp. Vir.) (Not Val. Pub.: Rule 14a2)

Crystallococcus lycopersici, Ryzhkov 1952, 465.
(Sp. Vir.) (Val. Pub., Illeg.: Rule 24a)
Marmor dodecahedron, Holmes 1939b, 20, q.v.
Type sp. of Genus Crystallococcus, Ryzhkov 1952, 465.

Crystallococcus medicaginis, Ryzhkov 1952, 465.
(Sp. Vir.) (Not Val. Pub.: Rule 14a2)
Marmor medicaginis, Holmes 1939b, 91, q.v.

Crystallococcus tabaci, Ryzhkov 1952, 465.
(Sp. Vir.) (Not Val. Pub., Rule 14a2)
Marmor lethale, Holmes 1939b, 86, q.v.

CUCUMISVIRUS

Cucumisvirus maculans, Roland 1959, 128.
(Sp. Vir.) (Not Val. Pub.: Rule 12a2)
Marmor cucumeris, Holmes 1939b, 31, q.v.
Murialba cucumeris, (Holmes) Valleau 1940, 823, q.v.

Cucumisvirus vastans, Roland 1959, 129.
(Sp. Vir.) (Not Val. Pub.: Rule 12a2)
Marmor melonis, Rader et al. 1947, 815, q.v.

Cucumisvirus viridimaculans, Roland 1959, 128.
(Sp. Vir.) (Not Val. Pub.: Rule 12a2)
Marmor astrictum var. chlorogenum, Holmes 1939b, 27, q.v.

CUCURBITAVIRUS

Cucurbitavirus maculans, Roland 1959, 130.
(Sp. Vir.) (Not Val. Pub.: Rule 12a2)
Marmor cucumeris, Holmes 1939b, 31, q.v.
Murialba cucumeris, (Holmes) Valleau 1940, 823, q.v.

CUSCUTAVIR, Bennett 1944a, 89.
(Gen. Vir.) (Val. Pub., Illeg.: Rule 12d)
Type sp. (monotype): Cuscutavir secretum, Bennett 1944a, 89.
Cuscutavir secretum, Bennett 1944a, 89 in syn.
(Sp. Vir.) (Val. Pub., Illeg.: Rule 12d)
Marmor secretum, Bennett 1944a, 88, 89, q.v.
Comment: Type species of genus Cuscutavir, Bennett 1944a, 89.

CUSCUTAVIRUS

CUSCUTAVIRUS OCCULTUM, Roland 1959, 128.
(Sp. Vir.) (Not Val. Pub.: Rule 12a2)
Marmor secretum, Bennett 1944a, 88, 89, q.v.

CYMBIDIUMVIRUS

Cymbidiumvirus maculans, Roland 1959, 129.
(Sp. Vir.) (Not Val. Pub.: Rule 12a2)

CYTISSUSVIRUS

Cytissusvirus variegans, Roland 1959, 129.
(Sp. Vir.) (Not Val. Pub.: Rule 12a2)

DACAVIRUS, Hansen 1956, 130.
(Gen. Vir.) (Val. Pub., Illeg.: Rule 24a)
Acarinophilus, Ryzhkov 1952, 466, q.v.
Type sp. (orig. des.): Dacavirus ribis, Hansen 1956, 130.
Dacavirus ribis, (Holmes) Hansen 1956, 130.
(Sp. Vir.) (Val. Pub., Illeg.: Rule 24b)
Acrogenus ribis, Holmes 1939b, 112, q.v.
Comment: Type species of Dacavirus, Hansen 1956, 130.

DACICAVIRUS, Hansen 1956, 125.
(Gen. Vir.) (Val. Pub., Illeg.: Rules 23, 24a)
Chlorogenus, Holmes 1939b, 1, q.v.
Type sp. (orig des.): Dacicavirus callistephi, (Holmes) Hansen 1956, 125.

Dacicavirus betae, Hansen 1956, 125.
(Sp. Vir.) (Val. Pub., Illeg.: Rule 24a)
Chlorogenus eutettigicola, Holmes 1939b, 11, q.v.

Dacicavirus callistephi, (Holmes) Hansen 1956, 125.
(Sp. Vir.) (Val. Pub., Illeg.: Rule 24a)
Chlorogenus callistephi, Holmes 1939b, 2, q.v.,
type species of genus Chlorogenus, Holmes 1939b, 1.
Comment: Type species of genus Dacicavirus, Hansen 1956, 125.

Dacicavirus medi-vitis, Hansen 1956, 125.
  (Sp. Vir.) (Val. Pub., Illeg.: Rule 24a)
  Morsus suffodiens, Holmes 1948, 1153, q.v.,
  type species of genus Morsus, Holmes 1948, 1153.

Dacicavirus sacchari-galli, Hansen 1956, 125.
  (Sp. Vir.) (Val. Pub., Illeg.: Rule 24a)
  Aureogenus magnivena, Black 1944, 144, q.v.

Dacicavirus zeae, Hansen 1956, 125.
  (Sp. Vir.) (Val. Pub., Illeg.: Rule 24a)
  Marmor maidis, Holmes 1939b, 56, q.v.
  Fractilinea maidis, (Holmes) McKinney 1944a, 149,
  q.v., type species of genus Fractilinea, McKinney
  1944a, 148.

DACOCVIRUS, Hansen 1956, 129.
  (Gen. Vir.) (Val. Pub., Leg.)
  Type sp. (monotype): Dacocvirus theobromae,
  (Posnette) Hansen 1956, 129.

Dacocvirus theobromae, (Posnette) Hansen 1956, 129.
  (Sp. Vir.) (Val. Pub., Leg.)
  Marmor theobromae, Posnette 1947, 309, q.v.
  Theobromavirus inflans, Roland 1959, 128.
  Comment: Type species of genus Dacocvirus, Hansen
                                          1956, 129.

DAHETVIRUS, Hansen 1956, 130.
  (Gen. Vir.) (Val. Pub., Illeg.: Rules 23, 24a)
  Savioa, Holmes 1939b, 131, q.v.
  Type sp. (orig. des.): Dahetvirus betae, (Holmes)
  Hansen 1956, 130.

Dahetvirus betae, (Holmes) Hansen 1956, 130.
  (Sp. Vir.) (Val. Pub., Illeg.: Rule 24a)
  Savoia betae, Holmes 1939b, 132, q.v.,
  type species of genus Savoia, Holmes 1939b, 131.
  Comment: Type species of genus Dahetvirus, Hansen
                                          1956, 130.

DAHLIAVIRUS

Dahliavirus maculans, Roland 1959, 128.
  (Sp. Vir.) (Not Val. Pub.: Rules 12a2)
  Marmor dahliae, Holmes 1939b, 85, q.v.
  Nervillustrans dahliae, (Holmes) Limasset 1948, 293,
  q.v., type species of genus Nervillustrans, Limasset
                                          1948, 293.

DALEVIRUS, Hansen 1956, 129.
  (Gen. Vir.) (Val. Pub., Illeg.: Rules 23, 24a)
  Ruga, Holmes 1939b, 114, q.v.
  Type sp. (orig. des.): Dalevirus nicotianae, Hansen
                                          1956, 130.

Dalevirus abutiloni, Hansen 1956, 130.
  (Sp. Vir.) (Val. Pub., Illeg.: Rules 23, 24a)
  Marmor abutilon, Holmes 1939b, 50, q.v.

Dalevirus mani-caulis, Hansen 1956, 130.
  (Sp. Vir.) (Val. Pub., Illeg.: Rule 24b)

Dalevirus manihot, Hansen 1956, 130.
  (Sp. Vir.) (Val. Pub., Illeg.: Rules 23, 24a)
  Ruga bemisiae, Holmes 1939b, 117, q.v.
  Ochrosticta bemisiae, (Holmes) McKinney 1944a, 149,
  q.v., type species of genus Ochrosticta, McKinney
                                          1944a, 149.

DAPHIFLEXUS, Hansen 1958, 222.
  (Gen. Vir.) (Val. Pub., Illeg.: Rule 24a)
  Daphivirus, Hansen 1956, 123, q.v.
  Type sp. (orig. des.): Daphiflexus betae, Hansen
                                          1958, 222.

Daphiflexus betae, (Holmes) Hansen 1958, 222.
  (Sp. Vir.) (Val. Pub., Illeg.: Rule 24a)
  Corium betae, Holmes 1948, 1204, q.v.
  Daphivirus betae, (Holmes) Hansen 1956, 123, q.v.,
  type species of genus Daphivirus, Hansen 1956, 123.

DAPHIVIRUS, Hansen 1956, 123.
  (Gen. Vir.) (Val. Pub., Leg.)
  Daphiflexus, Hansen 1958, 222.
  Type sp. (orig. des.): Daphivirus betae, (Holmes)
  Hansen 1956, 123.

Daphivirus betae, (Holmes) Hansen 1956, 123.
  (Sp. Vir.) (Val. Pub., Leg.)
  Corium betae, Holmes 1948, 1204, q.v.
  Daphiflexus betae, (Holmes) Hansen 1958, 222,
  type species of genus Daphiflexus, Hansen 1958, 222.
  Comment: Type species of genus Daphivirus, Hansen
                                          1956, 123.

Daphivirus citri, Hansen 1956, 123.
  (Sp. Vir.) (Val. Pub., Leg.)

Daphivirus solani, (Holmes) Hansen 1956, 123.
  (Sp. Vir.) (Val. Pub., Illeg.: Rules 23, 24a)
  Corium solani, Holmes 1939b, 120, q.v.,
  type species of genus Corium, Holmes 1939b, 119.

DAXEVIRUS, Hansen 1956, 128.
  (Gen. Vir.) (Val. Pub., Illeg.: Rules 23, 24a)
  Carpophthora, McKinney 1944a, 152, q.v.
  Type sp. (orig. des.): Daxevirus pruni, Hansen 1956,
                                          128.

Daxevirus pruni, Hansen 1956, 128.
  (Sp. Vir.) (Val. Pub., Illeg.: Rules 23, 24a)
  Marmor lacerans, Holmes 1939b, 82, q.v.
  Carpophthora lacerans, McKinney 1944a, 152, q.v.,
  type species of genus Carpophthora, McKinney 1944a,
  152.
  Comment: Type species of genus Daxevirus, Hansen
                                          1956, 128.

DIANTHUSVIRUS

Dianthusvirus maculans, Roland 1959, 128.
  (Sp. Vir.) (Not Val. Pub.: Rule 12a2)

DINCHORDA, Hansen 1956, 127.
  (Gen. Vir.) (Not Val. Pub.: Rules 12a2, 13e)

DINGLOBUS, Hansen 1956, 127.
  (Gen. Vir.) (Not Val. Pub.: Rules 12a2, 13e)

DINVIRUS, Hansen 1956, 125.
  (Gen. Vir.) (Val. Pub., Leg.)
  Citrivir, Fawcett 1940, 561; 1941, 357.
  Type sp. (orig. des.): Dinvirus citri, Hansen 1956,
                                          126.

Dinvirus citri, Hansen 1956, 126.
  (Sp. Vir.) (Val. Pub., Illeg.: Rule 24a)
  Rimocortius psorosis, Holmes 1948, 1210, q.v.
  Comment: Type species of genus Dinvirus, Hansen
                                          1956, 125.

Dinvirus pruni, Hansen 1956, 126.
  (Sp. Vir.) (Val. Pub., Illeg.: Rule 24a)
  Rimocortius kwanzani, Milbrath and Zeller 1942, 430,
                                          q.v.

Dinvirus pyri, (Holmes) Hansen 1956, 126.
  (Sp. Vir.) (Val. Pub., Leg.)
  Rimocortius pyri, (Holmes) Holmes 1948, 1211, q.v.
  Marmor pyri, Holmes 1939b, 76, q.v.
  Pyrusvirus lignifaciens, Roland 1959, 129.

EPIPHYLLUMVIRUS

Epiphyllumvirus maculans, Roland 1959, 128.
  (Sp. Vir.) (Not Val. Pub.: Rule 12a2)

EVONYMUSVIRUS

Evonymusvirus variegans, Roland 1959, 128.
  (Sp. Vir.) (Not Val. Pub.: Rule 12a2)

FESTINA, Thomas in Thomas and Rawlins 1951c, 139.
  (Gen. Vir.) (Val. Pub. Illeg. principle 1 ((2)))
  Type sp. (monotype): Festina lente, Thomas in
  Thomas and Rawlins 1951, 139.
  Comment: Authors have stated intent to ridicule
  nomenclature as currently applied to the viruses.

Festina lente, Thomas in Thomas and Rawlins 1951c, 139.
  (Sp. Vir.) (Val. Pub. Illeg. Principle 1 ((2)))
  Comment: Type species of genus Festina, Thomas in
  Thomas and Rawlins 1951, 139.

FICIVIR, Condit and Horne 1941, 563.
(Gen. Vir.) (Val. Pub., Leg.)
Type sp. (monotype): Ficivir caricae, Condit and Horne
1941, 563.
Ficivir caricae, Condit and Horne 1941, 563.
(Sp. Vir.) (Val. Pub., Leg.)
Marmor caricae, (Condit and Horne) Holmes 1948,
1201, q.v.
Ficusvirus maculans, Roland 1959, 128.
Comment: Type species of genus Ficivir, Condit and
Horne 1941, 563.

FICUSVIRUS

Ficusvirus maculans, Roland 1959, 128.
(Sp. Vir.) (Not Val. Pub.: Rule 12a2)
Ficivir caricae, Condit and Horne 1941, 563, q.v.,
type species of genus Ficivir, Condit and Horne 1941,
563.
Marmor caricae, (Condit and Horne) Holmes 1948, 1201,
q.v.

FLAVIMACULA, McKinney 1944a, 149.
(Gen. Vir.) (Val. Pub., Leg.)
Type sp. (orig. des.): Flavimacula persicae, (Holmes)
McKinney 1944a, 149.

Flavimacula ipomeae, Doolittle and Harter 1945, 703.
(Sp. Vir.) (Val. Pub., Leg.)
Comment: Nomenclaturally legitimate, but according
to Hildebrand 1960, 751 this is an indeterminable
mixture of three viruses.

Flavimacula persicae, (Holmes) McKinney 1944a, 149.
(Sp. Vir.) (Val. Pub., Leg.)
Marmor persicae, Holmes 1939b, 81, q.v.
Annulus pruni, Christoff 1958, 383.
Persicavirus maculans, Roland 1959, 129.
Comment: Type species of genus Flavimacula,
McKinney 1944a, 149.

Flavimacula persicae, (Holmes) McKinney 1944a, 149.
(Sp. Vir.) (Val. Pub., Leg.)
Marmor persicae, Holmes 1939b, 81, q.v.
Prunivir flavimacula, Hutchins et al. 1951, 26.
Annulus pruni, Christoff 1958, 383.
Persicavirus maculans, Roland 1959, 129.
Comment: Type species of genus Flavimacula,
McKinney 1944a, 149.

FOLIOPELLIS, Valleau 1940, 825.
(Gen. Vir.) (Val. Pub., Leg.)
Type sp. (monotype): Foliopellis erodens, (Holmes)
Valleau 1940, 825.

Foliopellis erodens, (Holmes) Valleau 1940, 825.
(Sp. Vir.) (Val. Pub., Leg.)
Marmor erodens, Holmes 1939a, 435.
Marmor erodens, Holmes 1939b, 42, q.v.
Maphiflexus nico-erodens, Hansen 1956, 123.
Nicotianavirus erodens, Roland 1959, 130.
Comment: Type species of genus Foliopellis, Valleau
1940, 825.

FRACTILINEA, McKinney 1944a, 148.
(Gen. Vir.) (Val. Pub., Leg.)
Fractilineavirus, Krieg 1961, 147.
Type sp. (orig. des.): Fractilinea maidis, McKinney
1944a, 149.
Fractilinea avenae, McKinney 1944b, 327.
(Sp. Vir.) (Val. Pub., Leg.)
Graminevorus avenae, (McKinney) Ryzhkov 1952, 466,
q.v.
Liburnaefilus gramini, Sukhov 1956, 264,
type species of genus Liburnaefilus, Sukhov 1956, 264.
Avenavirus rosettae, Klinkowski and Kreutzbert 1958, 4.
Avenavirus rosettana, Roland 1959, 129.
Fractilineavirus avenae, (McKinney) Krieg 1961, 149.

Fractilinea maidis, (Holmes) McKinney 1944a, 149.
(Sp. Vir.) (Val. Pub., Leg.)
Marmor maidis, Holmes 1939b, 56, q.v.
Marmor maidis, Holmes 1939a, 435.
Dacicavirus zeae, Hansen 1956, 125.
Zeavirus virgatum, Roland 1959, 129.
Comment: Type species of genus Fractilinea, McKinney
1944a, 148.

Fractilinea maidis var. nitis, (Holmes) Holmes 1948,
(Var. Vir.) (Val. Pub., Leg.) 1160.
Marmor maidis var. mite, Holmes 1939b, 58, q.v.

Fractilinea maidis var. sacchari, (Holmes) Holmes 1948,
(Var. Vir.) (Val. Pub., Leg.) 1159.
Marmor maidis var. sacchari, Holmes 1939b, 57, q.v.

Fractilinea maidis var. typicum, (Holmes) Holmes 1948,
(Var. Vir.) (Val. Pub., Illeg.: Rule 7) 1159.
Marmor maidis var. typicum, (Holmes) Holmes
1939b, 56, q.v.,
type variety of species Marmor maidis, Holmes
1939b, 56.
Zeavirus virgatum, Roland 1959, 129.
Comment: Type variety of species Fractilinea maidis,
(Holmes) Holmes 1948, 1159.

Fractilinea oryzae, (Holmes) Holmes 1948, 1160.
(Sp. Vir.) (Val. Pub., Leg.)
Marmor oryzae, Holmes 1939b, 64, q.v.
Oryzavirus nanescens, Roland 1959, 130.
Fractilineavirus oryzae, (Holmes) Krieg 1961, 147.

Fractilinea quarta, (Holmes) Holmes 1948, 1161.
(Sp. Vir.) (Val. Pub., Leg.)
Marmor quartum, Holmes 1939b, 65, q.v.

Fractilinea tritici, McKinney 1944b, 327.
(Sp. Vir.) (Val. Pub., Leg.)
Graminevorus tritici, (McKinney) Ryzhkov 1952, 466,
q.v., type species of genus Graminivorus, Ryzhkov
1952, 466.
Triticumvirus retardans, Klinkowski and Kreutzberg
1958, 2, type species of genus Triticumvirus,
Klinkowski and Kruetzberg 1958, 2.
Fractiliniavirus tritici, (McKinney) Krieg 1961, 148.

Fractilinea zeae, (Holmes) Holmes 1948, 1161.
(Sp. Vir.) (Val. Pub., Leg.)
Marmor zeae, Holmes 1939b, 59, q.v.
Zeavirus maculans, Roland 1959, 129.

FRACTILINEAVIRUS, Krieg 1961, 147.
(Gen. Vir.) (Val. Pub., Illeg.: Rule 24a)
Fractilinea, McKinney 1944a, 148.
Type sp.: Fractilinea maidis, McKinney 1944a, 149.

Fractilineavirus avenae, (McKinney) Krieg 1961, 149.
(Sp. Vir.) (Val. Pub., Illeg.: Rule 24a)
Fractilinea avenae, McKinney 1944b, 327, q.v.
Graminevorus avenae, (McKinney) Ryzhkov 1952, 466,
q.v.

Fractilineavirus oryzae, (Holmes) Krieg 1961, 147.
(Sp. Vir.) (Val. Pub., Illeg.: Rules 24a, 24b)
Marmor oryzae, Holmes 1939b, 64, q.v.
Fractilinea oryzae, (Holmes) Holmes 1948, 1160, q.v.

Fractilineavirus tritici, (McKinney) Krieg 1961, 148.
(Sp. Vir.) (Val. Pub., Illeg.: Rule 24a)
Fractilinea tritici, McKinney 1944a, 327, q.v.

Fractilineavirus zeae, (Holmes) Krieg 1961, 149.
(Sp. Vir.) (Val. Pub., Illeg.: Rule 24a)
Marmor zeae, Holmes 1939b, 59, q.v.
Fractilinea zeae, (Holmes) Holmes 1948, 1161, q.v.

FRAGARIAVIRUS

Fragariavirus crispans, Roland 1959, 130.
(Sp. Vir.) (Not Val. Pub.: Rule 12a2)
Marmor fragariae, Holmes 1939b, 78, q.v.

Fragariavirus cupuliformans, Roland 1959, 130.
(Sp. Vir.) (Not Val. Pub.: Rule 12a2)
Nanus cupuliformans, Zeller and Weaver 1941, 851,
q.v.

Fragariavirus everriculosum, Roland 1959, 130.
(Sp. Vir.) (Not Val. Pub.: Rule 12a2)
Nanus fragariae, Holmes 1939b, 128, q.v.
Blastogenus fragariae, (Holmes) McKinney 1944a,
151, q.v., type species of genus Blastogenus,
McKinney 1944a, 151.

Fragariavirus marginans, Roland 1959, 130.
(Sp. Vir.) (Not Val. Pub.: Rule 12a2)
Marmor marginans, Holmes 1939b, 79, q.v.

GALLA, Holmes 1939a, 435.
(Gen. Vir.) (Not Val. Pub.: Rule 12a2)
Galla, Holmes 1939b, 105.
Type sp. (orig. des.): Galla fijiensis, Holmes 1939a,
435.

Galla anemones, Holmes 1939b, 108.
(Sp. Vir.) (Val. Pub., Leg.)
Anemonevirus deformans, Roland 1959, 127.

Galla australiensis, Holmes 1939b, 107.
(Sp. Vir.) (Val. Pub., Leg.)
Chlorogenus australiensis, (Holmes) Holmes 1948,
1147, q.v.
Leptomotropus lycopersici, Ryzhkov 1952, 466.
Leptomotropus lycopersici, Kohler and Klinkowski
1954, 601.
Hyalesthesophilus solenacii, Sukhov 1956, 264.
Lycopersicumvirus australiense, Roland 1959, 130.
Comment: Klinkowski and Uschdraweit 1958, 103,
consider this synonymous with Chlorogenus vaccinii,
Holmes 1939b, 10.

Galla fijiensis, Holmes 1939a, 435.
(Sp. Vir.) (Not Val. Pub.: Rule 12a2)
Galla fijiensis, Holmes 1939b, 106, q.v., type
species of genus Galla, Holmes 1939b, 105.

Galla fijiensis, Holmes 1939b, 106.
(Sp. Vir.) (Val. Pub., Leg.)
Galla fijiensis, Holmes 1939a, 435, type
species of genus Galla, Holmes 1939a, 435.
Dacicavirus facchari-galli, Hansen 1956, 125.
Saccharumvirus fijense, Roland 1959, 130.
Comment: Type species of genus Galla, Holmes 1939b,
105.

Galla queenslandiensis, Holmes 1939b, 109.
(Sp. Vir.) (Val. Pub., Leg.)
Saccharumvirus nanescens, Roland 1959, 130.

Galla verrucae, Blodgett 1943, 30.
(Sp. Vir.) (Val. Pub., Leg.)
Galla verrucae, "Holmes" in Smith 1957, 346.
Prunivir verruca, Blodgett et al. 1951, 56.
Prunivir verruca, "Fawcett" in Smith 1957, 346.
Persicavirus verrucans, Roland 1959, 129.

Galla zeae, McKinney 1944b, 328.
(Sp. Vir.) (Val. Pub., Leg.)
Zeavirus verrucans, Roland 1959, 129.

GAPHIVIRUS, Hansen 1958, 222.
(Gen. Vir.) (Not Val. Pub.: Rule 12a)
Hordeumvirus, Klinkowski and Kreutzberg 1958, 9, q.v.
Type sp. (orig. des.): Gaphivirus avenae, Hansen
1958, 222.

Gaphivirus avenae, Hansen 1958, 222.
(Sp. Vir.) (Not Val. Pub.: Rule 12a)
Minchorda hordei, Hansen 1956, 126, q.v.
Comment: Type species of genus Gaphivirus, Hansen
1958, 222.

GECICAVIRUS, Hansen 1958, 222
(Gen. Vir.) (Not Val. Pub.: Rule 13a)

GINCHORDA, Hansen 1956, 127.
(Gen. Vir.) (Val. Pub., Leg.)
Type sp. (orig. des.): Ginchorda nico-caulis, Hansen
1956, 127.

Ginchorda nico-caulis, Hansen 1956, 127.
(Sp. Vir.) (Val. Pub., Leg.)
Solanumvirus maculans, Roland 1959, 129.
Solanumvirus singulare, Kohler 1952, 51.
Nicotiana virus humetranslatum, Roland 1952, 53.
Comment: Type species of genus Ginchorda, Hansen
1956, 127.

GINGLOBUS, Hansen 1956, 127.
(Gen. Vir.) (Val. Pub., Leg.)
Ginvirus, Hansen 1956, 126.
Type sp. (orig. des.): Ginglobus nico-gamma, Hansen
1956, 127.

Ginglobus nico-alpha, Hansen 1956, 127.
(Sp. Vir.) (Val. Pub., Leg.)

Ginglobus nico-beta, Hansen 1956, 127.
(Sp. Vir.) (Val. Pub., Leg.)

Ginglobus nico-gamma, Hansen 1956, 127.
(Sp. Vir.) (Val. Pub., Illeg.: Rule 24a)
Marmor lethale, Holmes 1939b, 86, q.v.
Comment: Type species of genus Ginglobus, Hansen
1956, 127.

GINVIRUS, Hansen 1956, 126.
(Gen. Vir.) (Val. Pub., Illeg.: Rule 24a)
Ginglobus, Hansen 1956, 127, q.v.
Type sp. (orig. des.): Ginvirus nico-gamma, Hansen
1956, 126.

Ginvirus nicogamma, Hansen 1956, 126 in syn.
(Sp. Vir.) (Val. Pub., Illeg.: Rule 24a)
Marmor lethale, Holmes 1939b, 86, q.v.
Ginglobus nico-gamma, Hansen 1956, 127,
type species of genus Ginglobus, Hansen 1956, 127.
Comment: Type species of genus Ginvirus, Hansen
1956, 126.

Ginvirus tritici, Hansen 1956, 126.
(Sp. Vir.) (Val. Pub., Illeg.: Rule 24b)
Marmor tritici, Holmes 1939b, 61; McKinney 1944b,
323, q.v.

GOSSYPIUMVIRUS

Gossypiumvirus crispans, Roland 1959, 128.
(Sp. Vir.) (Not Val. Pub.: Rule 12a2)
Ruga gossypii, Holmes 1939b, 116, q.v.

GRAMINEVORUS, Ryzhkov 1952, 466.
(Gen. Vir.) (Val. Pub., Leg.)
Triticumvirus, Klinkowski and Kreutzberg 1958, 2.
Type sp. (subs. des. Barkley 1958, 125):
Graminevorus tritici, (McKinney) Ryzhkov 1952, 466.

Graminevorus avenae, (McKinney) Ryzhkov 1952, 466.
(Sp. Vir.) (Val. Pub., Leg.)
Fractilinea avenae, McKinney 1944b, 327.
Liburnaefilus gramini, Sukhov 1956, 264.
Avenavirus rosettae, Klinkowski and Kreutzberg 1958,
4.
Avenavirus rosettans, Roland 1959, 129.
Fractilineavirus avenae, (McKinney) Krieg 1961, 149.

Graminevorus tritici, (McKinney) Ryzhkov 1952, 466.
(Sp. Vir.) (Not Val. Pub.: Rule 12a2)
Fractilinea tritici, McKinney 1944a, 327.
Triticumvirus retardans, Klinkowski and Kreutzberg
1958, 2, type species of genus Triticumvirus,
Klinkowski and Kreutzberg 1958, 2.
Fractilineavirus tritici, (McKinney) Krieg 1961, 148.
Comment: Type species of genus Graminevorus,
Ryzhkov 1952, 466.

HETVIRACEAE, Hansen 1956, 130.
(Fam. Vir.) (Val. Pub., Illeg.: Rule 3)
Comment: Includes the collective genera:
Mehetvirus, Hansen 1956, 130 and
Dahetvirus, Hansen 1956, 130.

HIBISCUSVIRUS

Hibiscusvirus nervimaculans, Roland 1959, 128.
(Sp. Vir.) (Not Val. Pub.: Rule 12a2)
Ochrovena hibiscae, Capoor and Varma 1950, 229,
q.v., type species of genus Ochrovena, Capoor and
Varma 1950, 229.

HOLODISCUSVIRUS

Holodiscusvirus everriculosum, Roland 1959, 128.
(Sp. Vir.) (Not Val. Pub.: Rule 12a2)

HORDEUMVIRUS, Klinkowski and Kreutzberg 1958, 9.
(Gen. Vir.) (Val. Pub., Leg.)
Gaphivirus, Hansen 1958, 222.
Type sp. (monotype): Hordeumvirus nanescens,
Klinkowski and Kreutzberg 1958, 9.

Hordeumvirus nanescens, Klinkowski and Kreutzberg
1958, 9.
(Sp. Vir.) (Val. Pub., Illeg.: Rule 24a)
Minchorda hordei, Hansen 1956, 126, q.v.
Comment: Type species of genus Hordeumvirus,
Klinkowski and Kreutzberg 1958, 9.

HUMULUSVIRUS

Humulusvirus flavopingens, Roland 1959, 128.
(Sp. Vir.) (Not Val. Pub.: Rule 12a2)

Humulusvirus urticans, Roland 1959, 128.
(Sp. Vir.) (Not Val. Pub.: Rule 12a2)
Chlorogenus humuli, Holmes 1939b, 15, q.v.

HYALESTHESOPHILUS, Sukhov 1956, 264.
(Gen. Vir.) (Not Val. Pub.: Rule 13d)
Type sp. (monotype, subs. des. Barkley 1958, 125 as
Hyalesthesophilus soleneai):
Hyalesthesophilus solenacii, Sukhov 1956, 264.

Hyalesthesophilus solenacii, Sukhov 1956, 264.
(Sp. Vir.) (Not Val. Pub.: Rule 13d)
Chlorogenus australiensis, (Holmes) Holmes 1948,
1147, q.v.
Galla australiensis, Holmes 1939b, 107, q.v.
Comment: Type species of genus Hyalesthesophilus,
Sukhov 1956, 264.

HYOSCYAMUSVIRUS

Hyoscyamusvirus maculans, Roland 1959, 128.
(Sp. Vir.) (Not Val. Pub.: Rule 12a2)
Marmor hyoscyami, Holmes 1948, 1171, q.v.
Maphiflexus hyoscyami, (Holmes) Hansen 1956, 123,
q.v.

INCHORDOIDEAE, Hansen 1956, 126.
(Subfam. Vir.) (Val. Pub., Illeg., Rule 3)
Comment: Includes Minchorda, Hansen 1956, 126,
Dinchorda, 1956, 127, and
Ginchorda, 1956, 127.

INFLEXOIDEAE, Hansen 1956, 127.
(Sub. Fam. Vir.) (Val. Pub., Illeg., Rule 3)
Comment: Includes genus: Miniflexus, 1956, 127.

INGLOBOIDEAE, Hansen 1956, 127.
(Subfam. Vir.) (Val. Pub., Illeg., Rule 3)
Comment: Includes 3 genera: Minglobus, Hansen 1945,
Dinglobus, Hansen 1956, 127, and   127,
Ginglobus, Hansen 1956, 127.

INVIRACEAE, Hansen 1956, 125.
(Fam. Vir.) (Val. Pub., Illeg.: Rule 3)
Comment: Includes 3 subfamilies:
Inchordioeae, Hansen 1956, 126,
Inflexoideae, Hansen 1956, 127,
Ingloboideae, Hansen 1956, 127,
and 3 collective genera: Minvirus, Hansen 1956, 125,
Dinvirus, Hansen 1956, 125, and
Ginvirus, Hansen 1956, 126.

INVIRALES, Hansen 1956, 125.
(Ord. Vir.) (Val. Pub., Leg.)
Comment: Includes the family Inviraceae, Hansen 1956,
125.

IRIDIVIR, Fawcett 1940, 560.
(Gen. Vir.) (Not Val. Pub.: Rules 12a2, 13e)

IRISVIRUS

Irisvirus maculans, Roland 1959, 128.
(Sp. Vir.) (Not Val. Pub.: Rule 12a2)
Marmor iridis, Holmes 1939b, 55, q.v.

JATROPHAVIRUS

Jatrophavirus flavescens, Roland 1959, 128.
(Sp. Vir.) (Not Val. Pub.: Rule 12a2)

Jatrophavirus maculans, Roland 1959, 128.
(Sp. Vir.) (Not Val. Pub.: Rule 12a2)
Ruga bemisiae, Holmes 1939b, 117, q.v.
Ochrosticta bemisiae, (Holmes) McKinney 1944a,
149, q.v., type species of genus Ochrosticta,
McKinney 1944a, 149.

KREIZBERGIA, Ryzhkov 1952, 466.
(Gen. Vir.) (Not Val. Pub.: Rule 13a)
Type sp. (monotype): Kreizbergia pistasiae, Ryzhkov
1952, 466.
Kreizbergia pistaciae, Ryzhkov 1952, 466.
(Sp. Vir.) (Not Val. Pub.: Rule 14a2)

LACTUCAVIRUS

Lactucavirus maculans, Roland 1959, 129.
(Sp. Vir.) (Not Val. Pub.: Rule 12a2)
Marmor lactucae, Holmes 1939b, 84, q.v.

LETHACEAE, Holmes 1939b, 135.
(Fam. Vir.) (Val. Pub., Leg.)
Type genus Lethum, Holmes 1939, 135.

LETHUM, Holmes 1939b, 135.
(Gen. Vir.) (Val. Pub., Leg.)
Thripsophilus, Ryzhkov 1952, 466.
Methyvirus, Hansen 1956, 129.
Type sp. (orig. des.): Lethum australiense, Holmes
1939b, 136.
Lethum australiense, Holmes 1939b, 136.
(Sp. Vir.) (Val. Pub., Leg.)
Thripsophilus lycopersici, Ryzhkov 1952, 466,
type species of genus Thripsophilus, Ryzhkov 1952,
466.
Methyvirus lethum, Hansen 1956, 129,
type species of genus Methyvirus, Hansen 1956, 129.
Lycopersicumvirus zonatum, Roland 1959, 130.
Type var. (orig. des.): Lethum australiense var.
typicum, Holmes 1939b, 136.
Comment: Type species of genus Lethum, Holmes
1939b, 135.
Lethum australiense var. lethale, Holmes 1939b, 138.
(Var. Vir.) (Val. Pub., Leg.)

Lethum australiense var. typicum, Holmes 1939b, 136.
(Var. Vir.) (Val. Pub., Illeg.: Rule 7)

Lethum rhizospilum, Hildebrand 1960, 756.
(Sp. Vir.) (Val. Pub., Leg.)

LEVISTICUMVIRUS

Levisticumvirus maculans, Roland 1959, 129.
(Sp. Vir.) (Not Val. Pub.: Rule 12a2)

LIBURNIAFILUS, (sic) Sukhov 1956, 264.
(Gen. Vir.) (Not Val. Pub.: Rule 13a)
Type sp. (monotype): Liburniafilus gramini, Sukhov
1956, 264.
Liburniafilus gramini, Sukhov 1956, 264.
(Sp. Vir.) (Not Val. Pub.: Rule 14a2)
Fractilinea avenae, McKinney 194b, 327, q.v.
Graminevorus avenae, (McKinney) Ryzhkov 1952,
466, q.v.
Comment: Type species of genus Liburniafilus,
Sukhov 1956, 264.

LILIUMVIRUS

Liliumvirus occultum, Roland 1959, 129.
(Sp. Vir.) (Not Val. Pub.: Rule 12a2)
Adelonosus lilii, Brierley and Smith 1944, 551, q.v.,
type species of genus Adelonosus, Brierley and Smith
1944, 551.
Liliumvirus rosettans, Roland 1959, 129.
(Sp. Vir.) (Not Val. Pub.: Rule 12a2)
Marmor lilii, Heinze 1959, 91, 179, 245, q.v.

LYCOPERSICUMVIRUS

Lycopersicumvirus australiense, Roland 1959, 130.
(Sp. Vir.) (Not Val. Pub.: Rule 12a2)
Galla australiense, Holmes 1939b, 107, q.v.
Chlorogenus australiensis, (Holmes) Holmes 1948,
1147, q.v.

Lycopersicumvirus fructudecolorans, Roland 1959, 130.
(Sp. Vir.) (Not Val. Pub.: Rule 12a2)

Lycopersicumvirus reticulosum, Roland 1959, 130.
(Sp. Vir.)(Not Val. Pub.: Rule 12a2)

Lycopersicumvirus sterilefaciens, Roland 1959, 130.
(Sp. Vir.) (Not Val. Pub.: Rule 12a2)

Lycopersicumvirus zonatum, Roland 1959, 130.
(Sp. Vir.) (Not Val. Pub.: Rule 12a2)
Lethum australiense, Holmes 1939b, 136, q.v.

LYSOGENUS, Ryzhkov 1952, 466.
(Gen. Vir.) (Val. Pub., Illeg.: Rule 13a)
Type sp. (monotype): Lysogenus typhi, Ryzhkov 1952,
466.

MACAVIRUS, Hansen 1958, 223.
(Gen. Vir.) (Val. Pub., Leg.)
Type sp. (monotype): Macavirus tritici, Hansen 1958,
223.

Macavirus tritici, Hansen 1958, 223.
(Sp. Vir.) (Val. Pub., Illeg.: Rule 24a)
Marmor virgatum, McKinney 1944b, 324, q.v.
Comment: Type species of genus Macavirus, Hansen
1958, 223.

MALEVIRUS

Malevirus euphorbiae, Hansen 1956, 129.
(Sp. Vir.) (Val. Pub., Illeg.: Rule 24a)
Marmor conspicuum, Costa and Bennett 1950, 282,
q.v.
Comment: Type species of genus Malevirus, Hansen
1956, 129.

MAPHICHORDA, Hansen 1956, 123.
(Gen. Vir.) (Val. Pub., Leg.)
Type sp. (orig. des.): Maphichorda raphani, (Holmes)
Hansen 1956, 123.

Maphichorda dianthi-latens, Hansen 1956, 123.
(Sp. Vir.) (Val. Pub., Leg.)

Maphichorda raphani, Hansen 1956, 123.
(Sp. Vir.) (Val. Pub., Leg.)
Marmor raphani, Holmes 1948, 1200, q.v.
Maphivirus raphani, Hansen 1958, 222.
Raphanusvirus maculans, Roland 1959, 130.
Comment: Type species of genus Maphichorda,
Hansen 1956, 123.

MAPHIFLEXUS, Hansen 1956, 123.
(Gen. Vir.) (Val. Pub., Leg.)
Maphivirus, Hansen 1956, 222.
Vectomarmor, Limasset 1948, 293.
Type sp. (orig. des.): Maphiflexus solani, Hansen
1956, 123.
Maphiflexus hyoscyami, (Holmes) Hansen 1956, 123.
(Sp. Vir.) (Val. Pub., Leg.)
Marmor hyoscyami, Holmes 1948, 1171, q.v.
Hyoscyamusvirus maculans, Roland 1959, 128.

Maphiflexus nico-erodens, Hansen 1956, 123.
(Sp. Vir.) (Val. Pub., Illeg.: Rules 23, 24a)
Marmor erodens, Holmes 1939b, 40, q.v.
Foliopellis erodens, (Holmes) Valleau 1940, 825, q.v.,
type species of genus Foliopellis, Valleau 1940, 825.

Maphiflexus solani, Hansen 1956, 123.
(Sp. Vir.) (Val. Pub., Illeg.: Rules 23, 24a)
Marmor upsilon, (Holmes) Holmes 1948, 1172, q.v.
Comment: Type species of genus Maphiflexus,
Hansen 1956, 123.

MAPHIGLOBUS, Hansen 1956, 124.
(Gen. Vir.) (Val. Pub., Illeg.: Rule 24a)
Murialba, Valleau 1940, 823, q.v.
Type sp. (orig. des.): Maphiglobus cucumeris,
(Holmes) Hansen 1956, 124.

Maphiglobus cucumeris, (Holmes) Hansen 1956, 124,
(Sp. Vir.) (Val. Pub., Illeg.: Rule 24a)   126.
Marmor cucumeris, Holmes 1939b, 31, q.v.
Murialba cucumeris, (Holmes) Valleau 1940, 823, q.v.
Type species of genus Maphiglobus, Hansen 1956, 124.

MAPHIVIRUS, Hansen 1956, 122.
(Gen. Vir.) (Val. Pub., Illeg.: Rules 24a, 25e)
Maphiflexus, Hansen 1956, q.v.
Type sp. (orig. des.): Maphivirus solani, Hansen
1956, 123.
Maphivirus raphani, (Holmes) Hansen 1958, 222.
(Sp. Vir.) (Val. Pub., Illeg.: Rule 24b)
Maphichorda raphani, (Holmes) Hansen 1956, 123, q.v.,
type species of genus Maphichorda, Hansen 1956, 123.
Marmor raphani, Holmes 1948, 1200, q.v.

Maphivirus solani, Hansen 1956, 123.
(Sp. Vir.) (Val. Pub., Illeg.: Rules 23, 24a)
Marmor upsilon, (Holmes) Holmes 1948, 1172, q.v.
Comment: Type species of genus Maphivirus, Hansen
1956, 122.

MARMOR, Holmes 1939a, 434.
(Gen. Vir.) (Not Val. Pub.: Rule 12a2)
Type sp. (orig. des.): Marmor tabaci, (d'Herelle)
Holmes 1939a, 434.

MARMOR, Holmes 1939b, 16.
(Gen. Vir.) (Val. Pub., Leg.)
Musivum, Valleau 1940, 822.
Phytovirus, Thornberry 1941, 23.
Virothrix, Ryzhkov 1952, 465.
not Virothrix, Ryzhkov 1950, 16.
Crystallobiotus, Ryzhkov 1952, 472.
Phytovirus, Bawden 1953, 543.
Minchorda, Hansen 1956, 126.
Minvirus, Hansen 1956, 126.
Type sp. (orig. des.): Marmor tabaci, Holmes 1939b,
30.

Marmor abaca, Holmes 1939b, 63.
(Sp. Vir.) (Val. Pub., Leg.)
Musavirus rosettans, Roland 1959, 127.

Marmor abutilon, Holmes 1939a, 435.
(Sp. Vir.) (Not Val. Pub.: Rule 12a2)
Marmor abutilon, Holmes 1939b, 50, q.v.

Marmor abutilon, Holmes 1939b, 50.
(Sp. Vir.) (Val. Pub., Leg.)
Marmor abutilon, Holmes 1939a, 435.
Photophilus elegans, Ryzhkov 1952, 467.
Dalevirus abutiloni, Hansen 1956, 130.
Abutilonvirus variegans, Roland 1959, 127.

Marmor aevi, Holmes 1948, 1200.
(Sp. Vir.) (Val. Pub., Leg.)
Celery-calico virus
Source: CUCURBITACEAE - Cucumis sativus, L.
Cucumber: C. melo, L., Cajteloupe; Cucurbita pepo,
L., Summer crook neck squash; RANUNCULACEAE -
Delphinium chinensis; D. formosum, hardy larkspur;
D. grandiflorum; D. parryi; D. zalil; SOLANACEAE -
Lycopersicon esculentum, Mill., tomato;
UMBELLIFERAE - Apium graveolens, L., celery.

Marmor angeliae, (sic) Holmes 1948, xii,
see Marmor angliae, Holmes 1939b, 48.

Marmor angliae, Holmes 1939b, 48: 1948, xii
(see Marmor angeliae) (Sp. Vir.) (Val. Pub., Leg.)
Pseudomarmor angliae, Limasset 1948, 293.
Solanumvirus mirum, Kohler 1952b, 51.
Solanum virus experimentotranslatum, Roland 1952,
53.

Marmor agropyri, McKinney 1944b, 326.
(Sp. Vir.) (Val. Pub., Leg.)
Agropyrumvirus maculans, Roland 1959, 127.
Type var. (orig. des.): Marmor agropyri var.
typicum, McKinney 1944b, 326.

Marmor agropyri var. flavum, McKinney 1944b, 326.
(Var. Vir.) (Val. Pub., Illeg.: Rule 7)
non Marmor dubium var. flavum, Holmes 1939b, 46.

Marmor agropyri var. typicum, McKinney 1944b, 326.
(Var. Vir.) (Val. Pub., Illeg.: Rule 7)
Comment: Type variety of species Marmor agropyri,
McKinney 1944b, 326.

Marmor angustum, McKinney 1950, 705.
(Sp. Vir.) (Val. Pub., Leg.)
Nothoscordumvirus maculans, Roland 1959, 129.

Marmor anularium, McKinney 1944b, 327.
(Sp. Vir.) (Val. Pub., Illeg.: Rule 24b)
Annulus tabaci var. virginiensis, Holmes 1939b, 98.

Marmor arachidis, Holmes 1939b, 67.
(Sp. Vir.) (Val. Pub., Leg.)
Peanut-rosette virus
Source: Leguminosae - Arachis hypogaea, L., peanut.

Marmor arachidis, Holmes 1939b, 67.
(Sp. Vir.) (Val. Pub., Leg.)
Arachisvirus rosettans, Roland 1959, 128.

Marmor astri, Holmes 1939b, 83.
(Sp. Vir.) (Val. Pub., Leg.)
Peach asteroid-spot virus
Source: ROSACEAE - Prunus persica, (L.) Batsch,
                                              peach.
Marmor astri, Holmes 1939b, 83.
(Sp. Vir.) (Val. Pub., Leg.)
Persicavirus astrosignans, Roland 1959, 129.

Marmor astrictum, Holmes 1939b, 27; 1948, 1167.
(Sp. Vir.) (Val. Pub., Leg.)
Cucurbit-mosaic virus
Described as Marmor astrictum var. chlorogenum,
Holmes 1939b, 27.
Source: CUCURBITACEAE - Cucumis sativus, L.,
cucumber; C. anguria, L., gherkin; C. melo, L.,
melon; Citrullus vulgaris, Schrad., watermelon.
Type var. (orig. des.): Marmor astrictum var.
chlorogenum, Holmes 1939b, 27.

Marmor astrictum var. aucuba, Holmes 1939b, 29.
(Var. Vir.) (Val. Pub., Illeg.: Rule 7)
non Marmor aucuba, Holmes 1939b, 49.

Marmor astrictum var. chlorogenum, Holmes 1939b, 27.
(Var. Vir.) (Val. Pub., Illeg.: Rule 7)
Cucumisvirus viridimaculans, Roland 1959, 128.
Musivum astrictum, Valleau 1940, 823.
Minchorda cucumeris, Hansen 1956, 126.
Comment: Type variety of species Marmor astrictum,
Holmes 1939b, 27.

Marmor astrictum var. lagenari, (sic) Capoor and Varma
1948, 275,
see Marmor astrictum var. lagenariae.

Marmor astrictum var. lagenariae, Capoor and Varma
1948, 275.
(Var. Vir.) (Val. Pub., Leg.)
As Marmor astrictum lagenari.

Marmor astrictum var. subobscurum, Vasudeva,
Raychaudhuri and Singh 1949, 185.
(Var. Vir.) (Val. Pub., Leg.)

Marmor aucuba, Holmes 1939a, 435.
(Sp. Vir.) (Not Val. Pub.: Rule 12a2)
Marmor aucuba, Holmes 1939b, 49, q.v.

Marmor aucuba, Holmes 1939b, 49.
(Sp. Vir.) (Val. Pub., Leg.)
non Marmor astrictum var. aucuba, Holmes 1939b, 20.
Marmor aucuba, Holmes 1939a, 435.
Solanumvirus aucuboides, Kohler 1952b, 51.
Solanum virus aucubamarmor, Roland 1952, 53.
Phytovirus paracrystalis var. aucuba, Bawden 1953,
543.
Potato aucuba-mosaic virus
Source: SOLANACEAE - Solanum tuberosum, L.,
                                              potato.

Marmor aucuba var. canadense, Black and Price 1940,
(Var. Vir.) (Val. Pub., Illeg.: Rule 7)   444.
non Marmor tabaci var. canadense, Holmes 1939b, 23.
Canada-streak strain of potato aucuba-mosaic virus.

Marmor betae, Holmes 1939b, 72.
(Sp. Vir.) (Val. Pub., Leg.)
Aphidophilus betae, Ryzhkov 1952, 465.
Betavirus maculans, Roland 1959, 128.
Sugarbeet mosaic virus
Source: CHENOPODIACEAE - Beta vulgaris, L.,
beet; Spinacia oleracea, L., spinach.

Marmor brassicae, Holmes 1939b, 70.
(Sp. Vir.) (Val. Pub., Illeg.)
Marmor matthiolae, Holmes 1939b, 71.
Aphidophilus curciferae, Ryzhkov 1952, 465.
Aphidophilus cruciferae, Klinkowski and Unschdraweit
1958, 84.
Brassicavirus flavescens, Roland 1959, 139.
Brassicavirus nigromaculans, Roland 1959, 128.
Brassicavirus octahedron, Roland 1959, 130.
Matthiolavirus maculans, Roland 1959, 130.
Turnip mosaic virus
Source: CRUCIFERAE - Brassica rapa, L., turnip;
B. napobrassica, Mill., swede or rutabaga; B. napus,
L., rape; B. nigra, (L.) Koch, black mustard; B.
oleracea, L., cabbage; Armoracia rusticana, Gaertn.,
horseradish; Cheiranthus cheiri, L., wallflower;
Matthiola incana, R. Br., stock; Sinapis alba, L.,
white mustard.

Marmor campestre, McKinney 1944b, 324.
(Sp. Vir.) (Val. Pub., Leg.)
Type var. (orig. des.): Marmor campestre var.
typicum, McKinney 1944b, 324.

Marmor campestre var. galbinum, McKinney 1944b, 324.
(Var. Vir.) (Val. Pub., Leg.)

Marmor campestre var. typicum, McKinney 1944b, 324.
(Var. Vir.) (Val. Pub., Illeg.: Rule 7)
Comment: Type variety of species Marmor campestre,
McKinney 1944b, 324.

Marmor caricae, (Condit and Horne) Holmes 1948, 1201.
(Sp. Vir.) (Val. Pub., Leg.)
Ficivir caricae, Condit and Horne 1941, 563, q.v.
Ficusvirus maculans, Roland 1959, 128.
Source: MORACEAE - Ficus caria, L., fig; F.
altissima, Blume; F. krishna; and F. tsiela, Roxb.

Marmor cepae, Holmes 1939b, 66.
(Sp. Vir.) (Val. Pub., Leg.)
Alliumvirus flavorugans, Roland 1959, 129.
Onion yellow-dwarf virus.
Source: LILIACEAE - Allium cepa, L., onion.

Marmor cerasi, Zeller and Evans 1941, 467.
(Sp. Vir.) (Val. Pub., Leg.) as Marmor cerassae.
Prunivir cerasi, McLarty et al. 1951, 106.
Cerasusvirus maculans, Roland 1959, 128.
Cherry mottle-leaf virus
Source: ROSACEAE - Prunus avium, L., sweet
cherry; P. emarginata, (Dougl.) Walp., wild cherry.

Marmor cerassae, Zeller and Evans 1941, 467.
Marmor cerasi, q.v.

Marmor chrysanthemi, Keller 1953a, 35; 1953b, 406.
(Sp. Vir.) (Val. Pub., Leg.)
Marmor chrysanthemi, "Holmes" in Klinkowski 1958b,
                                                    194.
Marmor cichorii, Kvicala 1956, 624.
(Sp. Vir.) (Val. Pub., Leg.)

Marmor citrulii, Anderson 1954b, 201.
(Sp. Vir.) (Val. Pub., Leg.)

Marmor citrulii var. flavidanum, Anderson 1954, 201.
(Var. Vir.) (Val. Pub., Leg.)

Marmor colei, Klinkowski 1954, 559.
(Sp. Vir.) (Val. Pub., Leg.)

Marmor conspicuum, Costa and Bennett 1950, 282.
(Sp. Vir.) (Val. Pub., Leg.)
Malevirus euphorbiae, Hansen 1956, 129,
type species of genus Malevirus, Hansen 1956, 129.

Marmor constans, McKinney 1944, 326.
(Sp. Vir.) (Val. Pub., Leg.)
Tobacco mild dark-green mosaic virus.
Source: SOLANACEAE - Nicotiana glauca, R. Grah.,
tree tobacco.

Marmor cruciferarum, Holmes 1939b, 69.
(Sp. Vir.) (Val. Pub., Leg.)
Cauliflower-mosaic virus.
Source: CRUCIFERAE - Brassica oleracea, L.,
cauliflower, kale, Brussel sprouts, cabbage and
broccoli; B. campestris, L., wild yellow mustard;
Matthiola incana, R. Br., annual stock.

Marmor cruciferarum, Holmes 1939b, 69.
(Sp. Vir.) (Val. Pub., Leg.)
Brassicavirus nerviclarens, Roland 1959, 128.

Marmor cucumeris, Holmes 1939a, 434.
(Sp. Vir.) (Not Val. Pub., Rule 12a2)
Marmor cucumeris, Holmes 1949b, 31, q.v.
Murialba cucumeris, (Holmes) Valleau 1940, 823, q.v.

Marmor cucumeris, Holmes 1939b, 31.
Sp. Vir.) (Val. Pub., Leg.)
Marmor cucumeris, Holmes 1939a, 434.
Murialba cucumeris, (Holmes) Valleau 1940, 823, q.v.,
type species of genus Murialba, Valleau 1940, 823.
Aphidophilus cucumeris, (Holmes) Ryzhkov 1952, 465,
type species of genus Aphidophilus, Ryzhkov 1952, 465.
Virococcus cucurbitae, Ryzhkov 1952, 465, type
species of genus Virococcus, Ryzhkov 1952, 465.
Phytovirus paracrystalis var. cucumis, Bawden 1953,
543.
Aphidophilus cucurbitae, Kohler and Klinkowski 1954,
677.
Maphiglobus cucumeris, (Holmes) Hansen 1956, 124,
type species of Maphiglobus, Hansen 1956, 124.
Mexevirus cucurbitae, Hansen 1956, 128.
Mexeglobus cucurbitae, Hansen 1958, 222, type
species of genus Mexeglobus, Hansen 1958, 222.
Maphivirus cucumeris, Hansen 1958, 222.
Cucurbitavirus maculans, Roland 1959, 130.
Cucumisvirus maculans, Roland 1959, 128.
Type var. (orig. des.): Marmor cucumeris var.
vulgare, Holmes 1939b, 31.

Marmor cucumeris, Holmes 1948, 1173.
(Sp. Vir.) (Val. Pub., Leg.)
Murialba cucumeris, Valleau 1940, 823.
Cucumber-mosaic virus.
Described as Marmor cucumeris var. vulgare, Holmes
1939b, 31.
Source: Dicotyledonous and monocotyledonous plants;
cucumber; celery; spinach, tobacco and pepper.

Marmor cucumeris var. commelinae, Holmes 1939a, 434.
(Var. Vir.) (Not Val. Pub.: Rule 12a2)
Marmor cucumeris var. commelinae, Holmes 1939b,
35, q.v.

Marmor cucumeris var. commelinae, Holmes 1939b, 35.
(Var. Vir.) (Val. Pub., Leg.)
Marmor cucumeris var. commelinae, Holmes 1939a,
434.
Southern celery-mosaic strain of cucumber-mosaic
virus.
Source: Celery and other plants.

Marmor cucumeris var. judicis, Holmes 1939b, 38.
(Var. Vir.) (Val. Pub., Leg.)
Indicator strain of cucumber-mosaic virus.
Source: Zinnia.

Marmor cucumeris var. lilii, Holmes 1939a, 434.
(Var. Vir.) (Not Val. Pub.: Rule 12a2)
Marmor cucumeris var. lilii, Holmes 1939b, 37, q.v.

Marmor cucumeris var. lilii, Holmes 1949b, 37.
(Var. Vir.) (Val. Pub., Leg.)
Marmor cucumeris var. lilii, Holmes 1939a, 434.
Lily-mosaic strain of cucumber-mosaic strain.
Source: Lilies.

Marmor cucumeris var. phaseoli, Holmes 1939b, 36.
(Var. Vir.) (Val. Pub., Illeg.: Rule 7)
not Marmor phaseoli, 1939b, 87.
Lima-bean strain of cucumber-mosaic virus.
Source: Lima bean.

Marmor cucumeris var. upsilon, Holmes 1939a, 434.
(Var. Vir.) (Not Val. Pub.: Rule 12a2)
Marmor cucumeris var. upsilon, Holmes 1939b, 33,
q.v.
Marmor cucumeris var. upsilon, Holmes 1939b, 33.
(Var. Pub., Leg.)
Marmor upsilon, (Holmes) Holmes 1948, 1172, q.v.

Marmor cucumeris var. vignae, Holmes 1939b, 39.
(Var. Vir.) (Val. Pub., Leg.)
not Marmor vignae, Holmes 1948, 1188.
Cowpea-mottling strain of cucumber-mosaic virus.
Source: Black cowpea.

Marmor cucumeris var. vulgare, Holmes 1939a, 434;
1939b, 31.
(Var. Vir.) (Val. Pub., Illeg.: Rule 7)
Marmor cucumeris var. vulgare, Holmes 1939a, 434;
1939b, 31, q.v.

Marmor cucumeris var. zinae, Prasad and Raychaudhuri
1962, 125.
(Var. Vir.) (Val. Pub., Leg.)

Marmor cynarae, Costa, Duffus, Morton, Yarwood and
Bardin 1959, 52.
(Sp. Vir.) (Val. Pub., Leg.)

Marmor dahliae, Holmes 1939b, 85.
(Sp. Vir.) (Val. Pub., Leg.)
Mexevirus helianthi, Hansen 1956, 128.
Dahliavirus maculans, Roland 1959, 128.
Nervillustrans dahliae, (Holmes) Limasset 1948, 293,
q.v., type species of genus Nervillustrans, Limasset
1948, 293.

Marmor daturae, Capoor and Varma 1952, 312.
(Sp. Vir.) (Val. Pub., Leg.)

Marmor decipiens, Gilmer 1958, 434.
(Sp. Vir.) (Val. Pub., Leg.)

Marmor dilucidum, van Katwijk according to Baumann
1958, 126, 132.
(Sp. Vir.) (Val. Pub., Illeg.: Rule 24a)
Annulus pyri, Christoff 1958, 424, q.v.

Marmor dipsaci, Stoner 1951, 193.
(Sp. Vir.) (Val. Pub., Leg.)
as Marmor dipsacum.

Marmor dipsacum, Stoner 1951, 193,
see Marmor dipsaci.

Marmor dodecahedron, Holmes 1939b, 30.
(Sp. Vir.) (Val. Pub., Leg.)
Crystallococcus lycopersici, Ryzhkov 1952, 465.
Lycopersicumvirus dodecahedron, Roland 1959, 130.

Marmor dubium, Holmes 1939b, 42.
(Sp. Vir.) (Val. Pub., Leg.)
Marmor dubium, Holmes 1939a, 434.
Annulus dubius, (Holmes) Holmes 1948, 1214, q.v.
Solanophilus tuberosi, Ryzhkov 1952, 465, type species
of genus Solanophilus, Ryzhkov 1952, 465.
Solanum-virus deforms, Kohler 1952a, 294, type
species of genus Solanum-virus, Kohler 1952a, 294.
Minflexus solani, Hansen 1956, 127, type species of
genus Minflexus, Hansen 1956, 127.
Minvirus solani, Hansen 1958, 222.
Type var. (orig. des.): Marmor dubium var. vulgare,
Holmes 1939a, 434.

Marmor dubium var. annulus, Holmes 1939a, 435.
(Val. Vir.) (Not Val. Pub.: Rule 12a2)
Marmor dubium var. annulus, Holmes 1939b, 44, q.v.
Annulus dubius var. annulus, (Holmes) Holmes 1948,
1215, q.v.

Marmor dubium var. annulus, Holmes 1939b, 44.
(Var. Vir.) (Val. Pub., Leg.)
Annulus dubius var. annulus (Holmes) Holmes 1948,
1915, q.v.
Marmor dubium var. annulus, Holmes 1939a, 435.
Solanumvirus anulosum, Kohler 1952b, 51.
Solanum virus contactutranslatum, Roland 1952, 55.
Solanumvirus X-nominatum, Roland 1959, 129.

Marmor dubium var. flavum, Holmes 1939b, 46.
(Var. Vir.) (Val. Pub., Leg.)
Annulus dubius var. flavus, (Holmes) Holmes 1948,
1216, q.v.

Marmor dubium var. obscurum, Holmes 1939a, 435.
(Var. Vir.) (Not Val. Pub.: Rule 12a2)
Marmor dubium var. obscurum, Holmes 1939b, 46,
q.v.
Annulus dubius var. obscurus, (Holmes) Holmes 1948,
1216, q.v.

Marmor dubium var. obscurum, Holmes 1939b, 46.
(Var. Vir.) (Val. Pub., Leg.)
Annulus dubius var. obscurus, (Holmes) Holmes 1948,
1216, q.v.

Marmor dubium var. vulgare, Holmes 1939a, 435.
(Var. Vir.) (Not Val. Pub.: Rule 12a2)
Annulus dubius var. vulgaris, (Holmes) Holmes 1948,
1215, q.v.
Marmor dubium var. vulgaris, Holmes 1939b, 42, q.v.
Comment: Type variety of species Marmor dubium,
Holmes 1939a, 435.

Marmor dubium var. vulgaris, Holmes 1939b, 42.
(Var. Vir.) (Val. Pub., Illeg.: Rule 7)
Annulus dubius var. vulgaris, (Holmes) Holmes 1948,
1215, q.v.
Comment: Type variety of species Marmor dubium,
Holmes 1939b, 42.

Marmor efficiens, Johnson 1942, 114-115.
(Sp. Vir.) (Val. Pub., Leg.)
Pisumvirus maculosum, Roland 1959, 129.
Source: LEGUMINOSAE - Trifolium repens, L.,
white clover; Pisum sativum, L., pea.

Marmor erodens, Holmes 1939a, 435.
(Sp. Vir.) (Not Val. Pub.: Rule 12a2)
Marmor erodens, Holmes 1939b, 40, q.v.
Type var. (orig. des.): Marmor erodens var. vulgare,
Holmes 1939a, 435.

Marmor erodens, Holmes 1939b, 40; 1948, 1171.
(Sp. Vir.) (Val. Pub., Leg.)
Marmor erodens, Holmes 1939a, 435.
Foliopellis erodens, (Holmes) Valleau 1940, 825, q.v.,
type species of genus Foliopellis, Valleau, 1940, 825.
Maphiflexus nico-erodens, Hansen 1956, 123.
Nicotianavirus erodens, Roland 1959, 130.
Type var. (orig. des.): Marmor erodens var. vulgare,
Holmes 1939b, 40.

Marmor erodens var. severum, Holmes 1939a, 435.
(Var. Vir.) (Not Val. Pub.: Rule 12a2)
Marmor erodens var. severum, Holmes 1939b, 41,
q.v.
Marmor erodens var. severum, Holmes 1939b, 41.
(Var. Vir.) (Val. Pub., Leg.)
Marmor erodens var. severum, Holmes 1939a, 435.

Marmor erodens var. vulgare, Holmes 1939a, 435.
(Var. Vir.) (Not Val. Pub.: Rule 12a2)
Marmor erodens var. vulgare, Holmes 1939b, 40,
q.v., type variety of species Marmor erodens, Holmes
1939b, 40.
Comment: Type variety of species Marmor erodens,
Holmes 1939a, 435.

Marmor erodens var. vulgare, Holmes 1939b, 40.
(Var. Vir.) (Val. Pub., Illeg.: Rule 7)
Marmor erodens var. vulgare, Holmes 1939a, 435,
type variety of species Marmor erodens, Holmes
1939a, 435.
Comment: Type variety of species of Marmor erodens,
Holmes 1939b, 40.

Marmor euonymi, Holmes 1939b, 51.
(Sp. Vir.) (Val. Pub., Leg.)
Source: CELASTRACEAE - Euonymus japonica, L. f.
(sometimes written Evonymus japonicus). Probably
also E. radicans, Sieb.

Marmor fastidiens, Holmes 1948, 1189.
(Sp. Vir.) (Val. Pub., Leg.)
Type var. (orig. des.): Marmor fastidiens var.
fastidiens, Holmes 1948, 1190.
Source: LEGUMINOSAE - Trifolium hybridum, L.,
alsike clover; Pisum sativum, L., pea (except the
varieties Horal, Perfection and Surprise.)

Marmor fastidiens var. denudans, Holmes 1948, 1190.
(Var. Vir.) (Val. Pub., Leg.)

Marmor fastidiens var. fastidiens, Holmes 1948, 1190.
(Var. Vir.) (Val. Pub., Leg.)
Comment: Type variety of species Marmor fastidiens,
Holmes 1948, 1189.

Marmor fastidiens var. mite, Holmes 1948, 1190.
(Var. Vir.) (Val. Pub., Illeg.: Rule 7)
non Marmor mite, Holmes 1939b, 53.

Marmor fastidiens var. reprimens, Holmes 1948, 1190.
(Var. Vir.) (Val. Pub., Leg.)

Marmor flaccumfaciens, Holmes 1939b, 73.
(Sp. Vir.) (Val. Pub., Leg.)
Rosavirus flaccofaciens, Roland 1959, 130.

Marmor flavopunctum, Zaumeyer and Thomas 1950, 858.
(Sp. Vir.) (Val. Pub., Leg.)

Marmor fragariae, Holmes 1939b, 78.
(Sp. Vir.) (Val. Pub., Leg.)
Fragariavirus crispans, Roland 1959, 130.

Marmor graminis, McKinney 1944b, 325.
(Sp. Vir.) (Val. Pub., Leg.)
Bromusvirus maculans, Roland 1959, 128.
Source: GRAMINEAE - Bromus inermis, Leyss.,
awnless brome-grass.

Marmor hyoscyami, Holmes 1948, 1171.
(Sp. Vir.) (Val. Pub., Leg.)
Maphiflexus hyoscyami, (Holmes) Hansen 1956, 123,
q.v.
Hyoscyamusvirus maculans, Roland 1959, 128.
Source: SOLANACEAE - Hyoscyamus niger, L.,
henbane.

Marmor iners, Holmes 1948, 1190.
(Sp. Vir.) (Val. Pub., Leg.)
Source: LEGUMINOSAE - Pisum sativum, L., pea.

Marmor iridis, Holmes 1939b, 55.
(Sp. Vir.) (Val. Pub., Leg.)
Irisvirus maculans, Roland 1959, 128.
Source: IRIDACEAE - Iris filifolia, Boiss., I.
tingitana, Boiss. and Reut., and I. xiphium, L.,
bulbous irises; Iris ricardi, Hort., I. unguicularis,
Poir.; bearded iris, variety William Mohr.

Marmor italicum, Bitancourt 1953, 454.
(Sp. Vir.) (Not Val. Pub.: Rule 12c2, 14a2)
Marmor italicum, (Fawcett) Holmes 1948, 1202, q.v.
Comment: Type species of genus Marmorodes,
Bitancourt 1953, 453.

Marmor italicum, (Fawcett) Holmes 1948, 1202.
  (Sp. Vir.) (Val. Pub., Leg.)
  Citrivir italicum, Fawcett 1940, 561; 1941, 357.
  Marmorodes italicum, Bitancourt 1953, 454,
  type species of genus Marmorodes, Bitancourt 1953,
  453.
  Citrusvirus maculans, Roland 1959, 128.
  Source: RUTACEAE - Citrus aurantium, L., sour
  orange.

Marmor laburni, Holmes 1939b, 51.
  (Sp. Vir.) (Val. Pub., Leg.)
  Source: LEGUMINOSAE - Laburnum vulgare, Griseb.
  (L. anagyroides, Medic.), bean tree.

Marmor lacerans, Holmes 1939b, 82.
  (Sp. Vir.) (Val. Pub., Leg.)
  Carpophthora lacerans, (Holmes) McKinney 1944a,
  152, type species of genus Carpophthora, McKinney
  1944a, 152, q.v.
  Daxevirus pruni, Hansen 1956, 128,
  type species of genus Daxevirus, Hansen 1956, 128.
  Persicavirus lacerans, Roland 1959, 129.
  Carpophthoravirus lacerans, (Holmes) Krieg 1961,
  150, type species of genus Carpophthoravirus, (sic)
  Krieg 1961, 150.

Marmor lactucae, Holmes 1939b, 84.
  (Sp. Vir.) (Val. Pub., Leg.)
  Source: COMPOSITAE - Lactuca sativa, L., lettuce;
  Senecio vulgaris, L., groundsel.

Marmor laesiofaciens, Zaumeyer and Harter 1943b, 305.
  (Sp. Vir.) (Val. Pub., Leg.)
  Minglobus phaseoli, Hansen 1956, 127.
  Phaseolusvirus laedens, Roland 1959, 128.
  Source: LEGUMINOSAE - Phaseolus vulgaris, L.,
                                          bean.
Marmor laesiofaciens var. minus, Zaumeyer and Harter
  1943, 305.
  (Var. Vir.) (Val. Pub., Leg.)
  Marmor laesiofaciens var. minor, Smith 1957, 63.

Marmor leguminosarum, Holmes 1939b, 89.
  (Sp. Vir.) (Val. Pub., Leg.)
  Aphidophilus pisi, Ryzhkov 1952, 465.

Marmor lethale, Holmes 1939b, 86.
  (Sp. Vir.) (Val. Pub., Leg.)
  Crystallococcus tabaci, Ryzhkov 1952, 465.
  Ginvirus nico-gamma, Hansen 1956, 126,
  type species of genus Ginvirus, Hansen 1956, 126.
  Ginglobus nico-gamma, Hansen 1956, 127,
  type species of genus Ginglobus, Hansen 1956, 127.
  Nicotianavirus letale, (sic) Roland 1959, 130.
  Source: SOLANACEAE - Nicotiana tabacum, L.,
  tobacco; N. glutinosa, L.; N. langsdorffii, Weinm.;
  Lycopersicon esculentum, Mill., tomato; Solanum
  nigrum, L. COMPOSITAE - Aster. GERANIACEA -
  Pelargonium hortorum, Bailey. LEGUMINOSAE -
  Phaseolus vulgaris, L., bean.

Marmor ligustri, Holmes 1939b, 52.
  (Sp. Vir.) (Val. Pub., Leg.)
  Source: OLERACEA - Ligustrum vulgare, L., common
                                          privet.
Marmor lilii, Heinze 1959, 91, 179, 245.
  (Sp. Vir.) (Val. Pub., Illeg.: Rule 7)
  not Marmor cucumeris var. lilii, Holmes 1939b, 37.
  Liliumvirus rosettans, Roland 1959, 129.

Marmor lineopictum, Cation 1941, 1009.
  (Sp. Vir.) (Val. Pub., Leg.)
  Marmor pallidolimbatus, Zeller and Milbrath 1942,
  635.
  Annulus pruni var. artum, Christoff 1958, 390.
  Source: ROSACEAE - Prunus salicina, Lindl.,
  Japanese plum; P. mahaleb, L., mahaleb cherry;
  P. persica, (L.) Batsch, peach (Amygdalus persica,
                                          L.)

Marmor maidis, Holmes 1939a, 435.
  (Sp. Vir.) (Not Val. Pub.: Rule 12a2)
  Marmor maidis, Holmes 1939b, 56, q.v.
  Fractilinea maidis, (Holmes) McKinney 1944a, 149,
  q.v., type species of genus Fractilinea, McKinney
                                          1944a, 148.
Marmor maidis, Holmes 1939b, 56.
  (Sp. Vir.) (Val. Pub., Leg.)
  Marmor maidis, Holmes 1939a, 435.
  Fractilinea maidis, (Holmes) McKinney 1944a, 149,
  q.v., type species of genus Fractilinea, McKinney
  1944a, 148.
  Dacicavirus zeae, Hansen 1956, 125.
  Zeavirus virgatum, Roland 1959, 129.
  Described as Marmor maidis var. typicum, Holmes
  Source: Maize.   1939b, 56.

Marmor maidis var. mite, Holmes 1939b, 56.
  (Var. Vir.) (Val. Pub., Illeg.: Rule 7)
  not Marmor mite, Holmes 1939b, 53.
  Fractilinea maidis var. mitis, (Holmes) Holmes
  1948, 1160, q.v.

Marmor maidis var. sacchari, Holmes 1939b, 57.
  (Var. Vir.) (Val. Pub., Illeg.: Rule 7)
  not Marmor sacchari, Holmes 1939b, 60.
  Fractilinea maidis var. sacchari, (Holmes) Holmes
                                          1948, 1159.
Marmor maidis var. typicum, Holmes 1939b, 56.
  (Var. Vir.) (Val. Pub., Illeg.: Rule 7)
  Fractilinea maidis var. typicum, (Holmes) Holmes
  1948, 1159, q.v., type variety of species Fractilinea
  maidis, (Holmes) Holmes 1948, 1159.
  Zeavirus virgatum, Roland 1959, 129.
  Comment: Type variety of species Marmor maidis,
  Holmes 1939b, 56.

Marmor mali, Holmes 1939b, 75.
  (Sp. Vir.) (Val. Pub., Leg.)
  Pyrusvirus maculans, Roland 1959, 127.
  Source: ROSACEAE - Pyrus malus, L., apple.

Marmor malvae var. chlorogenus, Hein 1956, 233.
  (Var. Vir.) (Val. Pub., Leg.)

Marmor malvae var. vulgare, Hein, 1956, 233.
  (Var. Vir.) (Val. Pub., Illeg.: Rule 7)
  Comment: Type variety of species Marmor malvae,
  Hein 1956, 233.

Marmor manifestum, Frandsen 1952, 415.
  (Sp. Vir.) (Val. Pub., Leg.)

Marmor marginans, Holmes 1939b, 79.
  (Sp. Vir.) (Val. Pub., Leg.)
  Fragariavirus marginans, Roland 1959, 130.
  Source: ROSACEAE - Fragaria hybrids, strawberries;
  F. californica, C. and S.; F. chiloensis, Duch.
  (symptomless).

Marmor matthiolae, Holmes 1939b, 71.
  (Sp. Vir.) (Val. Pub., Illeg.: Rule 24a)
  Marmor brassicae, Holmes 1939b, 70, q.v.

Marmor medicaginis, Holmes 1939b, 91.
  (Sp. Vir.) (Val. Pub., Leg.)
  Crystallococcus medicaginis, Ryzhkov 1952, 465.
  Medicagovirus maculans, Roland 1959, 129.
  Type var. (subs. des.): Marmor medicaginis var.
  typicum, Black and Price 1940, 446.
  Source: LEGUMINOSAE - Medicago sativa, L.,
  alfalfa (lucerne). SOLANACEAE - Solanum tuberosum,
  L., potato.

Marmor medicaginis var. capsici, Berkeley 1947, 789.
  (Var. Vir.) (Val. Pub., Leg.)

Marmor medicaginis var. flavovarians, Zaumeyer 1953,
  (Var. Vir.) (Val. Pub., Leg.)   42.

Marmor medicaginis var. ladino, Kreitlow and Price
  1949, 526.
  (Var. Vir.) (Val. Pub., Leg.)

Marmor medicaginis var. phaseoli, Thomas 1951, 973.
(Var. Vir.) (Val. Pub., Illeg.: Rule 7)
non Marmor phaseoli, Holmes 1939b, 87.

Marmor medicaginis var. solani, Black and Price 1940,
(Var. Vir.) (Val. Pub., Illeg.: Rule 7)   446.
non Marmor solani, Holmes 1939b, 47.

Marmor medicaginis var. solani, Black and Price 1940,
(Var. Vir.) (Val. Pub., Illeg.: Rule 7)   446.
Medicago virus parvum, Roland 1952, 53.

Marmor medicaginis var. typicum, Black and Price 1940,
(Var. Vir.) (Val. Pub., Illeg.: Rule 7)   446.
Comment: Type variety of species Marmor medicaginis,
Holmes 1939b, 91.

Marmor melonis, Rader, Fitzpatrick and Hildebrand
1947, 815.
(Sp. Vir.) (Val. Pub., Leg.)
Cucumisvirus vastans, Roland 1959, 129.

Marmor melonis var. obscurum, Anderson 1954c, 373.
(Var. Vir.) (Val. Pub., Illeg.: Rule 7)
non Marmor tabaci var. obscurum, Holmes 1939b, 26.

Marmor mexicanum, Yerkes and Patino 1960, 338.
(Sp. Vir.) (Val. Pub., Leg.)

Marmor mite, Holmes 1939b, 53.
(Sp. Vir.) (Val. Pub., Leg.)
Source: LILIACEAE - Lilium amabile; L. auratum,
Lindl.; L. canadense, L.; L. candidum, L.; L.
cernuum; L. chalcedonicum; L. croceum, Chaix.; L.
davmottiae; L. elegans, Thunb.; L. formosanum,
Stapf.; L. giganteum; L. henryi, Baker; L.
leucanthemum; L. longiflorum, Thunb.; L.
myriophyllum; L. pumilum; L. regale, Wils.; L.
sargentiae, Wils.; L. speciosum, Thunb.; L.
superbum, L.; L. testaceum, Lindl.; L. tigrinum,
Ker.; L. umbellatum, Hort.; L. wallacei; Tulipa
gesneriana, L., garden tulip; T. clusiana, Vent.;
T. linifolia, Regel.

Marmor nerviclarens, Zeller and Evans 1941, 467.
(Sp. Vir.) (Val. Pub., Leg.)
Source: ROSACEAE - Prunus avium, L., sweet
cherry. Perhaps also P. serrulata, Lindl. and P.
domestica, L., on which symptoms similar to those
induced by this virus have been observed.

Marmor oryzae, Holmes 1939b, 64.
(Sp. Vir.) (Val. Pub., Leg.)
Fractilinea oryzae, (Holmes) Holmes 1948, 1160, q.v.
Oryzavirus nanescens, Roland 1959, 130.
Fractilineavirus oryzae, (Holmes) Krieg 1961, 147.

Marmor pachyrhizi, Holmes 1948, 1188.
(Sp. Vir.) (Val. Pub., Leg.)
Source: LEGUMINOSAE - Pachyrhizus erosus, (L.)
Urb. sincamas (yam bean)

Marmor pallidolimbatus, Zeller and Milbrath 1942, 50,
(Sp. Vir.) (Val. Pub., Illeg.: Rule 24a)   635.
Marmor lineopictum, Cation 1941, 1009, q.v.
Source: ROSACEAE - Prunus serrulata, Lindl.,
flowering cherry; P. avium, L., Mazzard cherry.

Marmor papavae, Capoor and Varma 1958, 231.
(Sp. Vir.) (Val. Pub., Leg.)

Marmor passiflorae, Holmes 1939b, 77.
(Sp. Vir.) (Val. Pub., Leg.)
Source: PASSIFLORACEAE - Passiflora edulis, Sims,
passion fruit; P. caerulea, L.

Marmor pelargonii, Holmes 1948, 1199.
(Sp. Vir.) (Val. Pub., Leg.)
Pelargoniumvirus crispans, Roland 1959, 129.
Source: GERANIACEAE - Pelargonium hortorum,
Bailey, geranium.

Marmor persicae, Holmes 1939b, 81.
(Sp. Vir.) (Val. Pub., Leg.)
Flavimacula persicae, (Holmes) McKinney 1944a, 149,
q.v., type species of genus Flavimacula, McKinney
1944a, 149.
Annulus pruni, Christhoff 1958, 383.
Persicavirus maculans, Roland 1957, 129.
Source: ROSACEAE - Prunus persica, (L.) Batsch,
peach and nectarine, all tested varieties.

Marmor phaseoli, Holmes 1939a, 435.
(Sp. Vir.) (Not Val. Pub.: Rule 12a2)
Marmor phaseoli, Holmes 1939b, 87, q.v.

Marmor phaseoli, Holmes 1939b, 87.
(Sp. Vir.) (Val. Pub., Leg.)
non Marmor cucumeris var. phaseoli, Holmes 1939b,
Marmor phaseoli, Holmes 1939a, 435.   36.
Aphidophilus phaseoli, Ryzhkov 1952, 465.
Phaseolusvirus maculans, Roland 1959, 128.
Source: LEGUMINOSAE - Phaseolus vulgaris, L.,
bean.

Marmor pintofolium, Kienholz 1947, 66.
(Sp. Vir.) (Val. Pub., Leg.)

Marmor pisi, Holmes 1939a, 435.
(Sp. Vir.) (Not Val. Pub.: Rule 12a2)
Marmor pisi, Holmes 1939b, 90, q.v.

Marmor pisi, Holmes 1939b, 90.
(Sp. Vir.) (Val. Pub., Leg.)
Marmor pisi, Holmes 1939a, 435.
Pisumvirus verrucans, Roland 1959, 129.
Source: LEGUMINOSAE - Pisum sativum, L., pea;
Vicia faba, L., broad bean.

Marmor primulae, Holmes 1948, 1201.
(Sp. Vir.) (Val. Pub., Leg.)
Primulavirus maculans, Roland 1959, 129.
Source: PRIMULACEAE - Primula obconica, Hance.

Marmor pyri, Holmes 1939b, 76.
(Sp. Vir.) (Val. Pub., Leg.)
Rimocortius pyri, (Holmes) Holmes 1948, 1211, q.v.
Pinvirus pyri, (Holmes) Hansen 1956, 126, q.v.
Pyrusvirus lignifaciens, Roland 1959, 129.

Marmor quartum, Holmes 1939b, 65.
(Sp. Vir.) (Val. Pub., Leg.)
Fractilinea quarta, (Holmes) Holmes 1948, 1161, q.v.

Marmor raphani, Holmes 1948, 1200.
(Sp. Vir.) (Val. Pub., Leg.)
Maphichorda raphani, (Holmes) Hansen 1956, 123, q.v.,
type species of genus Maphichorda, Hansen 1956, 123.
Maphivirus raphani, (Holmes) Hansen 1958, 222.
Raphanusvirus maculans, Roland 1959, 130.
Source: CRUCIFERAE - Raphanus sativus, L., radish.

Marmor repens, Johnson 1942, 114.
(Sp. Vir.) (Val. Pub., Leg.)
Source: LEGUMINOSAE - Trifolium repens, L.,
white clover.

Marmor rhei, Klinkowski 1958a, 278.
(Sp. Vir.) (Val. Pub., Leg.)

Marmor rosae, Holmes 1939b, 74; 1948, 1194.
(Sp. Vir.) (Val. Pub., Leg.)
Rosavirus maculans, Roland 1959, 130.
Source: ROSACEAE - Rosa rugosa, Thunb.; R.
chinensis, Jacq., var. nanetti, Dipp.; R. multiflora,
Thunb.; R. odorata, Sweet, tea rose; R. gymnocarpa;
Rubus parviflorus, Nutt.

Marmor rubi, Holmes 1939b, 80.
(Sp. Vir.) (Val. Pub., Leg.)
Poecile rubi, (Holmes) McKinney 1944a, 148, q.v.,
type species of genus Poecile, McKinney 1944a, 148.

Marmor rubi, Holmes 1939b, 80.
(Sp. Vir.) (Val. Pub., Leg.)
Poecile rubi, McKinney 1944, 148.
Source: ROSACEAE - Rubus idaeus, L., red raspberry;
R. occidentalis, L., black raspberry.

Marmor rubiginosum, Fawcett 1940, 789.
(Sp. Vir.) (Val. Pub., Leg.)
Prunivir rubiginosum, Fawcett 1940, 560.
Cerasusvirus rubiginosum, Roland 1959, 128.

Marmor sacchari, Holmes 1939a, 435.
(Sp. Vir.) (Not Val. Pub.: Rule 12a2)
Phytamoeba sacchari, McWhorter 1922, 110, q.v.,
type species of genus Phytamoeba, McWhorter 1922,
109.

Marmor sacchari, Holmes 1939b, 60.
(Sp. Vir.) (Val. Pub., Illeg.: Rule 24a)
Phytamoeba sacchari, McWhorter 1922, 110, q.v.,
type species of genus Phytamoeba, McWhorter 1922,
Sugarcane mosaic virus. 109.
Source: GRAMINEAE - Saccharum officinarum, L.,
sugarcane; Holcus sorghum, L., sorghum; H.
sudanensis, Bailey, Sudan grass; Brachiaria
plataphylla, Nash; Chaetochloa magna, Scribn.; C.
verticillata, Scribn.; Paspalum boscianum, Flugge;
Syntherisma sanguinale, Dulac.

Marmor santali, Holmes 1939b, 84.
(Sp. Vir.) (Val. Pub., Leg.)
Santalumvirus crispans, Roland 1959, 130.
Sandal leaf-curl virus
Source: SANTALACEAE - Santalum album, L.,
sandal.

Marmor scillearum, Smith and Brierley 1944, 503.
(Sp. Vir.) (Val. Pub., Leg.)
Ornithogalumvirus maculans, Roland 1959, 129.
Ornithogalum mosaic virus.
Source: LILIACEAE (of the tribe Scillaea) -
Ornithogalum thyrsoides, Jacq.; probably also
Galtonia candicans, Decne.; Hyacinthus orientalis, L.,
hyacinth; Lachenalia spp.

Marmor secretum, Bennett 1944a, 88, 89.
(Sp. Vir.) (Val. Pub., Leg.)
Cuscutavir secretum, (Bennett) Bennett 1944a, 89.
Cuscutavirus occultum, Roland 1959, 128.
Dodder latent-mosaic virus.
Source: CONVOLVULACEAE - Cuscuta californica,
Choisy, dodder.

Marmor senecionis, Klinkowski 1954, 698.
(Sp. Vir.) (Val. Pub., Leg.)
Seneciovirus maculans, Roland 1959, 128.

Marmor sohjae, Heinze 1959, 57, 162, 167, 175.
(Sp. Vir.) (Val. Pub., Leg.)

Marmor solani, Holmes 1939a, 435.
(Sp. Vir.) (Not Val. Pub.: Rule 12a2)
Marmor solani, Holmes 1939b, 47, q.v.

Marmor solani, Holmes 1939b, 547.
(Sp. Vir.) (Val. Pub., Leg.)
Marmor solani, Holmes 1939a, 435.
Solanumvirus alphaicum, Kohler 1952b, 52.
Solanum virus parvathermis, Roland 1952, 53.
Solanumvirus A-nominatum, Roland 1959, 129.

Marmor tabaci, Holmes 1939a, 434.
(Sp. Vir.) (Not Val. Publ.: Rule 12a2)
Protobios mosaicus, d'Herelle 1924, 343, q.v.
Type sp. of genus Marmor, Holmes 1939a, 434.

Marmor tabaci, (d'Herelle) Holmes 1939b, 17.
(Sp. Vir.) (Val. Pub., Illeg.: Rule 24a)
Protobios mosaicus, d'Herelle 1924, 343, q.v.
Type sp. of genus Marmor, Holmes 1939b, 16.
Described as Marmor tabaci var. vulgare, Holmes
1939b, 17.

Marmor tabaci, Holmes 1948, 1164.
(Sp. Vir.) (Val. Pub., Leg.)
Musivum tabaci, Valleau 1940, 822.
Phytovirus nicomosaicum, Thornberry 1941, 23.
Tobacco mosaic virus, tomato mosaic virus.
Source: SOLANACEAE - Nicotiana tabacum, L.,
tobacco; Lycopersicon esculentum, Mill., tomato; and
Capsicum frutescens, L., garden pepper.
PLANTAGINACEAE - Plantago lanceolata, L., ribgrass,
P. major, L. and P. rugelii, Decne., common broad-
leaved plantains.
Described as Marmor tabaci var. vulgare, Holmes
1939b, 17.

Marmor tabaci subsp. dahlemense, Melchers 1942, 48.
(Subsp. Vir.) (Val. Pub., Illeg.: Rule 24b)

Marmor tabaci subsp. dahlemense var. luridum,
Melchers 1942, 48.
(Var. Vir.) (Val. Pub., Illeg.: Principle 7)

Marmor tabaci var. artum, Holmes 1939b, 27.
(Var. Vir.) (Val. Pub., Illeg.: Rule 24b)

Marmor tabaci var. aucuba, Holmes 1939a, 434.
(Var. Vir.) (Not Val. Pub.: Rule 12a2)
Marmor tabaci var. aucuba, Holmes 1939b, 20, q.v.

Marmor tabaci var. canadense, Holmes 1939b, 23.
(Varl Vir.) (Val. Pub., Illeg.: Rule 24b)

Marmor tabaci, var. deformans, Holmes 1939a, 434.
(Var. Vir.) (Not Val. Pub.: Rule 12a2)
Marmor tabaci var. deformans, Holmes 1939b, 22,
q.v.

Marmor tabaci var. deformans, Holmes 1939b, 22.
(Var. Vir.) (Val. Pub., Illeg.: Rule 24b)
Marmor tabaci var. deformans, Holmes 1939a, 434.

Marmor tabaci var. immobile, Holmes 1939b, 26.
(Var. Vir.) (Val. Pub., Leg.)

Marmor tabaci var. lethale, Holmes 1939b, 24.
(Var. Vir.) (Val. Pub., Illeg.: Rules 7 and 24b)
not Marmor lethale, Holmes 1939b, 86.

Marmor tabaci var. luridum, Melchers 1942, 48.
(Var. Vir.) (Val. Pub., Illeg.: Rule 24b)

Marmor tabaci var. obscurum, Holmes 1939a, 434.
(Var. Vir.) (Not Val. Pub.: Rule 12a2)
Marmor tabaci var. obscurum, Holmes 1939b, 25,
q.v.

Marmor tabaci var. obscurum, Holmes 1939b, 25.
(Var. Vir.) (Val. Pub., Leg.)
Marmor tabaci var. obscurum, Holmes 1939a, 434.

Marmor tabaci var. plantaginis, Holmes 1941, 1097.
(Var. Vir.) (Val. Pub., Leg.)
Musivum tabaci var. plantaginis, (Holmes) Valleau
and Johnson 1943, 219.

Marmor tabaci var. rosettae, Price and Fenne 1951,
(Var. Vir.) (Val. Pub., Illeg.: Rule 24b) 1096.

Marmor tabaci var. siccans, Doolittle and Beecher 1942,
(Var. Vir.) (Val. Pub., Illeg.: Rule 24b) 994.

Marmor tabaci var. vulgare, Holmes 1939a, 434.
(Var. Vir.) (Not Val. Pub.: Rule 12a2)
Portobios mosaicus var. tabaci, d'Herelle 1924, 343,
q.v.

Marmor tabaci var. vulgare, Holmes 1939b, 17.
(Var. Vir.) (Val. Pub., Illeg.: Rules 7 and 24b)
Protobios mosaicus var. tabaci, d'Herelle 1924, 343,
q.v.

Marmor tabacum, (sic) Melchers 1942, 48.
Marmor tabaci, Holmes 1939b, 17, q.v.

Marmor tabacum (sic) var. flavum, Melchers 1942, 48.
(Var. Vir.) (Val. Pub., Illeg.: Rule 24b)

Marmor tabacum (sic) var. tenue, Melchers 1942, 48.
(Var. Vir.) (Val. Pub., Illeg.: Rule 24b)

Marmor taraxaci, Klinkowski 1954, 702.
(Sp. Vir.) (Val. Pub., Leg.)
Leptomotropus taraxaci, Ryzhkov 1952, 466.
Taraxacumvirus flavescens, Roland 1959, 128.

Marmor terrestre, McKinney 1946, 366.
(Sp. Vir.) (Val. Pub., Leg.)
Type var. (orig. des.): Marmor terrestre var.
typicum, McKinney 1946, 366.

Marmor terrestre var. oculatum, McKinney 1946, 368.
(Var. Vir.) (Val. Pub., Leg.)

Marmor terrestre var. typicum, McKinney 1946, 368.
(Var. Vir.) (Val. Pub., Illeg.: Rule 7)
Comment: Type variety of species Marmor teresstre,
McKinney 1946, 366.

Marmor theobromae, Posnette 1947, 390.
(Sp. Vir.) (Val. Pub., Leg.)
Dacovirus theobromae, (Posnette) Hansen 1956, 129,
q.v., type species of genus, Dacocvirus, Hansen 1956,
129.
Theobromavirus inflans, Roland 1959, 128.
Type var. (monotype): Marmor theobromae var. A,
Posnette 1947, 391.

Marmor theobromae var. A, Posnette 1947, 391.
(Var. Vir.) (Val. Pub., Illeg.: Rule 7)
Comment: Type variety of Marmor theobromae,
Posnette 1947, 390.

Marmor theo-bromae (sic) var. A, Heinze 1959, 104.
(Var. Vir.) (Not Val. Pub.: Rule 12a2)

Marmor trifolii, Holmes 1939b, 93.
(Sp. Vir.) (Val. Pub., Leg.)
Trifoliumvirus nervimaculans, Roland 1959, 128.

Marmor tritici, Holmes 1939a, 435.
(Sp. Vir.) (Not Val. Pub.: Rule 12a2)
Marmor tritici, Holmes 1939b, 61; McKinney 1944b,
323, q.v.
Marmor tritici, Holmes 1939b, 61; McKinney 1944b, 323.
(Sp. Vir.) (Val. Pub., Leg.)
Marmor tritici, Holmes 1939a, 435.
Ginvirus tritici, Hansen 1956, 126.
Triticumvirus maculans, Roland 1959, 130.
Type var. (subs. des.): Marmor tritici var. typicum,
McKinney 1944b, 323.

Marmor tritici var. fulvum, McKinney 1944b, 324.
(Var. Vir.) (Val. Pub., Leg.)

Marmor tritici var. typicum, McKinney 1944b, 323.
(Var. Vir.) (Val. Pub., Illeg.: Rule 7)
Comment: Type variety of species Marmor tritici,
Holmes 1939b, 61.

Marmor tulipae, Holmes 1939b, 52.
(Sp. Vir.) (Val. Pub., Leg.)
Aphidophilus tulipae, Ryzhkov 1952, 465.
Tulipavirus vulgare, Roland 1959, 130.
Source: LILIACEAE - Tulipa gesneriana, L., garden
tulip; T. eichleri, Regel; T. greigi, Regel.

Marmor umbelliferarum, Holmes 1939b, 67.
(Sp. Vir.) (Val. Pub., Leg.)
Apiumvirus maculans, Roland 1959, 128.

Marmor upsilon, (Holmes) Holmes 1948, 1172.
(Sp. Vir.) (Val. Pub., Leg.)
Marmor cucumeris var. upsilon, Holmes 1939a, 434.
Marmor cucumeris var. upsilon, Holmes 1939b, 33.
Murialba venataenia, Valleau 1940, 824.
Vectomarmor upsilon, Limasset 1948, 293,
type species of genus Vectomarmor, Limasset 1948,
Aphidophilus tuberosi, Ryzhkov 1952, 465.   293.
Solanum virus inpermanens, Roland 1952, 53.
Solanumvirus ypsilonicum, Kohler 1952, 51.
Maphiflexus solani, Hansen 1956, 123, type
species of genus Maphiflexus, Hansen 1956, 123.
Solanumvirus Y-nominatum, Roland 1959, 129.

Marmor valvolarum, Zaumeyer and Thomas 1948, 95.
(Sp. Vir.) (Val. Pub., Leg.)

Marmor vastans, Holmes 1939b, 94.
(Sp. Vir.) (Val. Pub., Leg.)
Aureogenus vastans, (Holmes) Black 1944, 141, q.v.,
type species of genus Aureogenus, Black 1944, 141.
Solanumvirus vastans, (Holmes) Kohler 1952, 51.
Solanum virus aceratagalliatranslatum, (sic) Roland
1952, 53.
Agalliophilus tuberosi, Ryzhkov 1952, 466,
type species of genus Agalliophilus, Ryzhkov 1952,
Mecicavirus solani, Hansen 1956, 124,   466.
type species of genus Mecicavirus, Hansen 1956, 124.
Aureogenusvirus vastans, (sic) Krieg 1961, 146,
type species of genus Aureogenusvirus, Krieg 1961,
146.

Marmor vastans var. agalliae, Black 1941, 233.
(Var. Vir.) (Val. Pub., Leg.)
Aureogenus vastans var. agalliae, (Black) Black 1944,
141.

Marmor vastans var. lethale, Black 1940, 391.
(Var. Vir.) (Val. Pub., Illeg.: Rule 7)
not Marmor lethale, Holmes 1939, 86.
Aureogenus vastans var. lethale, (Black) Holmes
1948, 1156.

Marmor vastans var. vulgare, Black 1940, 391.
(Var. Vir.) (Val. Pub., Illeg.: Rule &)
Aureogenus vastans var. vulgare, (Black) Black
1944, 141, type variety of Aureogenus vastans,
(Holmes) Black 1944, 141.

Marmor veneniferum, Holmes 1939b, 75.
(Sp. Vir.) (Val. Pub., Leg.)
Rosavirus caulomaculans, Roland 1959, 130.

Marmor vignae, Holmes 1948, 1188.
(Sp. Vir.) (Val. Pub., Illeg.: Rule 7)
non Marmor cucumeris var. vignae, Holmes 1939b,
39.
Vignavirus maculans, Roland 1959, 128.

Marmor vignae var. catjang, Capoor and Varma 1956,
101.
(Var. Vir.) (Val. Pub., Illeg.: Rule 24b)

Marmor virgatum, McKinney 1944b, 324.
(Sp. Vir.) (Val. Pub., Leg.)
Macavirus tritici, Hansen 1958, 223,
type species of genus Macavirus, Hansen 1958, 223.
Type var. (orig. des.): Marmor virgatum var.
typicum, McKinney 1944b, 325.

Marmor virgatum var. typicum, McKinney 1944b, 325.
(Var. Vir.) (Val. Pub., Illeg.: Rule 7)
Comment: Type variety of species Marmor virgatum,
McKinney 1944b, 325.

Marmor virgatum var. viride, McKinney 1944b, 325.
(Var. Vir.) (Val. Pub., Leg.)

Marmor viticola, Holmes 1939b, 83.
(Sp. Vir.) (Val. Pub., Leg.)

Marmor zeae, Holmes 1939b, 59.
(Sp. Vir.) (Val. Pub., Leg.)
Fractilinea zeae, (Holmes) Holmes 1948, 1161, q.v.
Zeavirus maculans, Roland 1959, 129.
Fractilineavirus zeae, (Holmes) Krieg 1961, 149.

MARMORACEAE, Holmes Emend. 1949, 16. (Family)
(B. '48, 1163)

Marmorodes, Bitancourt 1953, 453.
(Gen. Vir.) (Not Val. Pub.: Rule 12c2)
Type sp. (monotype): Marmorodes italicum,
Bitancourt 1953, 454.

MATTHIOLAVIRUS

Matthiolavirus maculans, Roland 1959, 130.
(Sp. Vir.) (Not Val. Pub.: Rule 12a2)
Marmor brassicae, Holmes 1939b, 70, q.v.

MECICAVIRUS, Hansen 1956, 124.
(Gen. Vir.) (Val. Pub., Illeg.: Rule 24a)
Aureogenus, Black 1944, 141, q.v.
Type sp. (orig. des.): Mecicavirus solani, Hansen
1956, 124.

Mecicavirus solani, Hansen 1956, 124.
(Sp. Vir.) (Val. Pub., Illeg.: Rule 24a)
Marmor vastans, Holmes 1939b, 94, q.v.
Aureogenus vastans, (Holmes) Black 1944, 141, q.v.,
type species of genus Aureogenus, Black 1944, 141.
Comment: Type species of genus Mecicavirus,
Hansen 1956, 124.

MEDICAGINIVIR, Fawcett 1940, 560.
(Gen. Vir.) (Not Val. Pub.: Rules 12a2, 13e)
Morsus, Holmes 1948, 1153, q.v.

MEDICAGOVIRUS

Medicagovirus everriculosum, Roland 1959, 129.
(Sp. Vir.) (Not Val. Pub.: Rule 12a2)
Chlorogenus medicaginis, Holmes 1939b, 14, q.v.

Medicagovirus maculans, Roland 1959, 129.
(Sp. Vir.) (Not Val. Pub.: Rule 12a2)
Marmor medicaginis, Holmes 1939b, 91, q.v.

Medicagovirus nanescens, Roland 1959, 129.
(Sp. Vir.) (Not Val. Pub.: Rule 12a2)
Morsus suffodiens, Holmes 1948, 1153, q.v., type
species of genus Morsus, Holmes 1948, 1153.

Medicagovirus parvum, Roland 1952, 53.
(Sp. Vir.) (Not Val. Pub.: Rule 12a2)
Marmor medicaginis var. solani, Black and Price
1940, 446, q.v.

MEHETVIRUS, Hansen 1956, 130.
(Gen. Vir.) (Val. Pub., Leg.)
Type sp. (orig. des.): Mehetvirus brassicae, Hansen
1956, 130.

Mehetvirus brassicae, Hansen 1956, 130.
(Sp. Vir.) (Val. Pub., Illeg.: Rules 23, 24a)
Savoia napi, Holmes 1939, 133, q.v.

METHYVIRUS, Hansen 1956, 129.
(Gen. Vir.) (Val. Pub., Illeg.: Rules 23, 24a)
Lethum, Holmes 1939b, 135, q.v.
Type sp. (orig. des.): Methyvirus lethum, Hansen
1956, 129.

Methyvirus lethum, Hansen 1956, 129.
(Sp. Vir.) (Val. Pub., Illeg.: Rules 23, 24a)
Lethum australiense, Holmes 1939b, 136, q.v.
Comment: Type species of genus Methyvirus, Hansen
1956, 129.

MEXEGLOBUS, Hansen 1958, 222.
(Gen. Vir.) (Val. Pub., Illeg.: Rule 24a)
Murialba, Valleau 1940, 823, q.v.
Type sp.: Mexeglobus cucurbitae, Hansen 1958, 222.

Mexeglobus cucurbitae, Hansen 1958, 222.
(Sp. Vir.) (Val. Pub., Illeg.: Rule 24a)
Marmor cucumeris, Holmes 1939b, 31, q.v.
Murialba cucumeris, (Holmes) Valleau 1940, 823, q.v.
Type sp. of genus Mexeglobus, Hansen 1958, 222.

MEXEVIRUS, Hansen 1956, 128.
(Gen. Vir.) (Val. Pub., Illeg.: Rules 23, 24a)
Acrogenus, Holmes 1939b, 110, q.v.
Type sp. (orig. des.): Mexevirus solani, (Holmes)
Hansen 1956, 128.

Mexevirus cucurbitae, Hansen 1956, 128.
(Sp. Vir.) (Val. Pub., Illeg.: Rule 24a)
Marmor cucumeris, Holmes 1939b, 31, q.v.
Murialba cucumeris, (Holmes) Valleau 1940, 823, q.v.

Mexevirus helianthi, Hansen 1956, 128.
(Sp. Vir.) (Val. Pub., Illeg.: Rule 24a)
Marmor dahliae, Holmes 1939b, 85, q.v.
Nervillustrans dahliae, (Holmes) Limasset 1948, 293,
q.v., type species of genus Nervillustrans, Limasset
1948, 293.

Mexevirus solani, (Holmes) Hansen 1956, 128.
(Sp. Vir.) (Val. Pub., Illeg.: Rule 24a)
Acrogenus solani, Holmes 1939b, 111, q.v.,
type species of genus Acrogenus, Holmes 1939b, 110.
Comment: Type species of genus Mexevirus, Hansen
1956, 128.

MINCHORDA, Hansen 1956, 126.
(Gen. Vir.) (Val. Pub., Illeg.: Rule 24a)
Marmor, Holmes 1939a, 16, q.v.
Type sp. (orig. des.): Minchorda nicotianae, Hansen
1956, 126.

Minchorda cucumeris, Hansen 1956, 126.
(Sp. Vir.) (Val. Pub., Illeg.: Rule 24a)
Marmor astrictum var. chlorogenum, Holmes 1939b,
27, q.v.

Minchorda hordei, Hansen 1956, 126.
(Sp. Vir.) (Val. Pub., Illeg.: Rule 24b)
Gaphivirus avenae, Hansen 1958, 222.
Hordeumvirus nanescens, Klinkowski and Kreutzberg
1958, 9.
Comment: Although this binomial is illegitimate, the
species was validly described so that the specific
epithet is available.

Minchorda nicotianae, Hansen 1956, 125, 126.
(Sp. Vir.) (Val. Pub., Illeg.: Rules 23 and 24a)
Protobios mosaicus, d'Herelle 1924, 343, q.v.
Type sp. of genus Minchorda, Hansen 1956, 126.

MINFLEXUS, Hansen 1956, 127.
(Gen. Vir.) (Val. Pub., Illeg.: Rule 24a)
Solanophilus, Ryzhkov 1952, 465, q.v.
Type sp. (orig. des.): Minflexus solani, Hansen 1956,
127.

Minflexus solani, Hansen 1956, 127.
(Sp. Vir.) (Val. Pub., Illeg.: Rule 24a)
Marmor dubium, Holmes 1939b, 42, q.v.
Annulus dubius, (Holmes) Holmes 1948, 1214, q.v.

MINGLOBUS, Hansen 1956, 127.
(Gen. Vir.) (Val. Pub., Illeg.: Rule 24a)
Annulus, Holmes 1939b, 97, q.v.
Type sp. (orig. des.): Minglobus nico-orbis, Hansen
1956, 127.

Minglobus dianthi-orbis, Hansen 1956, 127.
(Sp. Vir.) (Val. Pub., Illeg.: Rule 24b)

Minglobus nico-orbis, Hansen 1956, 127.
(Sp. Vir.) (Val. Pub., Illeg.: Rule 24a)
Annulus tabaci, Holmes 1939b, 98, q.v.
Type sp. of genus Minglobus, Hansen 1956, 127.

Minglobus phaseoli, Hansen 1956, 127.
(Sp. Vir.) (Val. Pub., Illeg.: Rule 24a)
Marmor laesiofaciens, Zaumeyer and Harter 1943b,
305, q.v.

MINUOR, Zeller and Braun 1943, 161.
(Gen. Vir.) (Val. Pub., Leg.)
Type sp. (orig. des.): Minuor ruborum, Zeller and
Braun 1943, 161.

Minuor ruborum, Zeller and Braun 1943, 161.
(Sp. Vir.) (Val. Pub., Leg.)
Corium ruborum, (Zeller and Braun) Holmes 1948,
1205, q.v.
Comment: Type species of genus Minuor, Zeller and
Braun 1943, 161.

MINVIRUS, Hansen 1956, 125.
(Gen. Vir.) (Val. Pub., Illeg.: Rule 24a)
Marmor, Holmes 1939a, 16.
Type sp. (orig. des.): Minvirus nicotianae, Hansen
1956, 125.

Minvirus nico-orbis, Hansen 1958, 222.
(Sp. Vir.) (Val. Pub., Illeg.: Rule 24a)
Annulus tabaci, Holmes 1939b, 98, q.v.

Minvirus nicotianae, Hansen 1956, 126.
(Sp. Vir.) (Val. Pub., Illeg.: Rule 24a)
Protobios mosaicus, d'Herelle 1924, 343, q.v.
Type sp. of genus Minvirus, Hansen 1956, 125.

Minvirus solani, Hansen 1958, 222.
(Sp. Vir.) (Val. Pub., Illeg.: Rule 24a)
Marmor dubium, Holmes 1939b, 42, q.v.
Annulus dubius, (Holmes) Holmes 1948, 1214, q.v.

MORSUS, Holmes 1948, 1153.
(Gen. Vir.) (Val. Pub., Leg.)
Medicaginivir, Fawcett 1940, 560.
Type sp. (orig. des.): Morsus suffodiens, Holmes
1948, 1153.

Morsus reprimens, Holmes 1948, 1154.
(Sp. Vir.) (Val. Pub., Leg.)
Nicotianavirus nanescens, Roland 1959, 130.

Morsus suffodiens, Holmes 1948, 1153.
(Sp. Vir.) (Val. Pub., Leg.)
Dacicavirus medi-vitis, Hansen 1956, 125.
Medicagovirus nanescens, Roland 1956, 1152.
Comment: Type species of genus Morsus, Holmes
1948, 1153.

Morsus ulmi, Holmes 1948, 1154.
(Sp. Vir.) (Val. Pub., Leg.)
Ulmusvirus librinescans, Roland 1959, 128.

MORSUSVIRUS

Morsusvirus maculans, Roland 1959, 129.
(Sp. Vir.) (Not Val. Pub.: Rule 12a2)

MURIALBA, Valleau 1940, 823.
(Gen. Vir.) (Val. Pub., Leg.)
Virococcus, Ryzhkov 1952, 465.
Aphidophilus, Ryzhkov 1952, 465.
Maphiglobus, Hansen 1956, 124.
Mexeglobus, Hansen 1958, 222.
Type sp. (Implied): Murialba cucumeris, (Holmes)
Valleau 1940, 823.

Murialba cucumeris, (Holmes) Valleau 1940, 823.
(Sp. Vir.) (Val. Pub., Leg.)
Marmor cucumeris, Holmes 1939a, 434.
Marmor cucumeris, Holmes 1939b, 31, q.v.
Aphidophilus cucumeris, (Holmes) Ryzhkov 1952, 465,
type species of genus Aphidophilus, Ryzhkov 1952, 465.
Virococcus cucurbitae, Ryzhkov 1952, 465, type
species of genus Virococcus, Ryzhkov 1952, 465.
Phytovirus paracrystalis var. cucumis, Bawden 1953
543.
Aphidophilus cucurbitae, Kohler and Klinkowski 1954,
677.
Maphiglobus cucumeris, (Holmes) Hansen 1956, 124,
type species of genus Maphiglobus, Hansen 1956, 124.
Mexevirus cucurbitae, Hansen 1956, 128.
Mexeglobus cucurbitae, Hansen 1958, 222, type
species of the genus Mexeglobus, Hansen 1956, 124.
Maphivirus cucumeris, Hansen 1958, 222.
Cucurbitavirus maculans, Roland 1959, 130.
Cucumisvirus maculans, Roland 1959, 128.
Comment: Type species of genus Murialba, Valleau
1940, 823.

Murialba venataenia, Valleau 1940, 824.
(Sp. Vir.) (Val. Pub., Leg.)
Marmor upsilon, Holmes 1948, 1172.
Described as Marmor cucumeris var. upsilon, Holmes
1939b, 33.
Source: SOLANACEAE - Solanum tuberosum, L.,
potato; Nicotiana tabacum, L., tobacco.

MUSAVIRUS

Musavirus deformans, Roland 1959, 128.
(Sp. Vir.) (Not Val. Pub.: Rule 12a2)

Musavirus rosettans, Roland 1959, 127.
(Sp. Vir.) Not Val. Pub.: Rule 12a2)
Marmor abaca, Holmes 1939b, 63, q.v.

MUSIVUM, Valleau 1940, 822.
(Gen. Vir.) (Val. Pub., Illeg.: Rules 23 and 24a)
Marmor, Holmes 1939a, 16.
Type sp. (orig. des.): Musivum tabaci, (Holmes)
Valleau 1940, 822.

Musivum astrictum, Valleau 1940, 823.
(Sp. Vir.) (Val. Pub., Illeg.: Rule 24b)
Marmor astrictum var. chlorogenum, Holmes 1939b,
27, q.v.

Musivum tabaci, (d'Herelle) Valleau 1940, 822.
(Sp. Vir.) (Val. Pub., Illeg.: Rule 24b)
Protobios mosaicus, d'Herelle 1924, 343.
Type sp. of genus Musivum, Valleau 1940, 822.

Musivum tabaci var. plantaginis, (Holmes) Valleau and
Johnson 1943, 219.
(Var. Vir.) (Val. Pub., Illeg.: Rule 24b)
Marmor tabaci var. plantaginis, Holmes 1941, 1097,
q.v.

NANUS, Holmes 1939b, 123.
(Gen. Vir.) (Val. Pub., Leg.)
Type species: Nanus loganobacci, Holmes 1939b, 124.

Nanus cupuliformans, Zeller and Weaver 1941, 851.
(Sp. Vir.) (Val. Pub., Leg.)
Source: ROSACEAE - Fragaria chiloensis, Duch., var.
ananassa, Bailey, cultivated strawberry.

Nanus fragariae, Holmes 1939b, 128.
(Sp. Vir.) (Val. Pub., Leg.)
Blastogenus fragariae, McKinney 1944, 151.
Source: ROSACEAE - Fragaria chiloensis, Duch., var.
ananassa, Bailey, cultivated strawberry.

Nanus holodisci, Holmes 1939b, 127.
(Sp. Vir.) (Val. Pub., Leg.)
Source: ROSACEAE - Holodiscus discolor, Max.,
ocean spray.

Nanus loganobacci, Holmes 1939b, 124.
(Sp. Vir.) (Val. Pub., Leg.)
Type species of genus Nanus, Holmes 1939b, 124.
Source: ROSACEAE - Rubus loganobaccus, Bailey,
loganberry and phenomenal berry.

Nanus mirabilis, Holmes 1939b, 126.
(Sp. Vir.) (Val. Pub., Leg.)
Source: ROSACEAE - Prunus persica, (L.) Batsch,
peach.

Nanus orientalis, Holmes 1939b, 124.
(Sp. Vir.) (Val. Pub., Leg.)
Source: ROSACEAE - Rubus occidentalis, L., black
raspberry.

Nanus pruni, Holmes 1939b, 128.
(Sp. Vir.) (Val. Pub., Leg.)
Source: ROSACEAE - Prunus domestica, L., var.
insititia, Bailey, the Damson plum, remains
symptomless.

Nanus rosettae, Holmes 1939b, 125.
(Sp. Vir.) (Val. Pub., Leg.)
Carpophthora rosettae, (Holmes) 1948, 1152.

Nanus sacchari, Holmes 1939b, 129.
(Sp. Vir.) (Val. Pub., Leg.)
Source: GRAMINEAE - Saccharum officinarum, L.,
sugarcane.

NORTHIELLA, Likhite 1929, 15.
(Gen. Vir.) (Not Val. Pub.: Rule 12a2)
Phytamoeba, McWhorter 1922, 110, q.v.
Type sp. (monotype): Northiella sacchari, Likhite
1929, 15.
Comment: Likhite ascribes the generic name
Northiella to Lyon. McWhorter (1922, 103) states that
Lyon in an unpublished manuscript, . . . proposed the
name Northiella sacchari, for the organism, i.e., the
foreign bodies found in the cell protoplasm of sugar
cane attacked by "Fiji disease".

Northiella sacchari, "Lyon" in Likhite 1929, 15 (sed non
Lyon 1910)
(Sp. Vir.) (Not Val. Pub.: Rule 12a2)
Phytamoeba sacchari, McWhorter 1922, 110, q.v.,
type species of genus Phytamoeba, McWhorter 1922,
109.
Marmor sacchari, Holmes 1939a, 435.
Marmor sacchari, Holmes 1939b, 60.
Saccharumvirus maculans, Roland 1959, 130.
Comment: Type species of genus Northiella, Likhite
1929, 15.

NOTHOSCORDUMVIRUS

Nothoscordumvirus maculans, Roland 1959, 129.
   (Sp. Vir.) (Not Val. Pub.: Rule 12a2)
   Marmor angustum, McKinney 1950, 705, q. v.

OCHROSTICTA, McKinney 1944a, 149.
   (Gen. Vir.) (Val. Pub., Leg.)
   Type sp. (orig. des.): Ochrosticta bemisiae, (Holmes)
   McKinney 1944a, 149.

Ochrosticta bemisiae, (Holmes) McKinney 1944a, 149.
   (Sp. Vir.) (Val. Pub., Leg.)
   Ruga bemisiae, Holmes 1939a, 435.
   Ruga bemisiae, Holmes 1939b, 117, q. v.
   Dalevirus manihot, Hansen 1945, 130.
   Jatrophavirus maculans, Roland 1959, 128.
   Comment: Type species of genus Ochrosticta,
   McKinney 1944a, 149.

OCHROVENA, Capoor and Varma 1950, 229.
   (Gen. Vir.) (Val. Pub., Leg.)
   Type sp. (monotype): Ochrovena hibiscae, Capoor and
   Varma 1950, 229.

Ochrovena hibiscae, Capoor and Varma 1950, 229.
   (Sp. Vir.) (Val. Pub., Leg.)
   Hibiscusvirus nervimaculans, Roland 1959, 128.
   Comment: Type species of genus Ochrovena, Capoor
   and Varma 1950, 229.

ORNITHOGALUMVIRUS

Ornithogalumvirus maculans, Roland 1959, 129.
   (Sp. Vir.) (Not Val. Pub.: Rule 12a2)
   Marmor scillearum, Smith and Brierley 1944, 503,
                              q. v.

ORYZAVIRUS

Oryzavirus limitifaciens, Roland 1959, 130.
   (Sp. Vir.) (Not Val. Pub.: Rule 12a2)

Oryzavirus nanescens, Roland 1959, 130.
   (Sp. Vir.) (Not Val. Pub.: Rule 12a2)
   Marmor oryzae, Holmes 1939b, 64, q. v.
   Fractilinea oryzae, (Holmes) Holmes 1948, 1160, q. v.

PELARGONIUMVIRUS

Pelargoniumvirus crispans, Roland 1959, 129.
   (Sp. Vir.) (Not Val. Pub.: Rule 12a2)
   Marmor pelargonii, Holmes 1948, 1199, q. v.

PERSICAVIRUS

Persicavirus anulosum, Roland 1959, 129.
   (Sp. Vir.) (Not Val. Pub.: Rule 12a2)
   Annulus cerasi, Hildebrand 1944, 1003, q. v.

Persicavirus flavescens, Roland 1959, 129.
   (Sp. Vir.) (Not Val. Pub.: Rule 12a2)
   Chlorogenus persicae, Holmes 1939b, 5, q. v.

Persicavirus gemmidecolorans, Roland 1959, 129.
   (Sp. Vir.) (Not Val. Pub.: Rule 12a2)

Persicavirus lacerans, (Holmes) Roland 1959, 129.
   (Sp. Vir.) (Not Val. Pub.: Rule 12a2)
   Carpophthora lacerans, (Holmes) McKinney 1944a, 152,
   q. v., type species of genus Carpophthora, McKinney
   1944a, 152.
   Marmor lacerans, Holmes 1939b, 82, q. v.

Persicavirus maculans, Roland 1959, 129.
   (Sp. Vir.) (Not Val. Pub.: Rule 12a2)
   Marmor persicae, Holmes 1939b, 81, q. v.
   Flavimacula persicae, (Holmes) McKinney 1944a, 149,
   q. v., type species of genus Flavimacula, McKinney
   1944a, 149.

Persicavirus mirabile, Roland 1959, 129.
   (Sp. Vir.) (Not Val. Pub.: Rule 12a2)
   Nanus mirabilis, Holmes 1939b, 126, q. v.

Persicavirus nanescens, Roland 1959, 129.
   (Sp. Vir.) (Not Val. Pub.: Rule 12a2)

Persicavirus nudans, Roland 1959, 129.
   (Sp. Vir.) (Not Val. Pub.: Rule 12a2)
   Chlorogenus persicae var. vulgare, Holmes 1939b, 5,
                             q. v.

Persicavirus occidentale, Roland 1959, 129.
   (Sp. Vir.) (Not Val. Pub.: Rule 12a2)

Persicavirus reticulosum, Roland 1959, 129.
   (Sp. Vir.) (Not Val. Pub.: Rule 12a2)

Persicavirus rosettans, Roland 1959, 129.
   (Sp. Vir.) (Not Val. Pub.: Rule 12a2)
   Nanus rosettae, Holmes 1939b, 125, q. v.
   Carpophthora rosettae, (Holmes) Holmes 1948, 1152,
                             q. v.

Persicavirus rubescens, Roland 1959, 129.
   (Sp. Vir.) (Not Val. Pub.: Rule 12a2)

Persicavirus variegans, Roland 1959, 129.
   (Sp. Vir.) (Not Val. Pub.: Rule 12a2)

Persicavirus verrucans, Roland 1959, 129.
   (Sp. Vir.) (Not Val. Pub.: Rule 12a2)
   Galla verrucae, Blodgett 1943, 30, q. v.

PHASEOLUSVIRUS

Phaseolusvirus flavescens, Roland 1959, 128.
   (Sp. Vir.) (Not Val. Pub.: Rule 12a2)

Phaseolusvirus laedens, Roland 1959, 128.
   (Sp. Vir.) (Not Val. Pub.: Rule 12a2)
   Marmor laesiofaciens, Zaumeyer and Harter 1943b,
                            305, q. v.

Phaseolusvirus maculans, Roland 1959, 128.
   (Sp. Vir.) (Not Val. Pub.: Rule 12a2)
   Marmor phaseoli, Holmes 1939b, 87, q. v.

PHORMIUMVIRUS

Phormiumvirus flavofaciens, Roland 1959, 129.
   (Sp. Vir.) (Not Val. Pub.: Rule 12a2)

PHOTOPHILUS, Ryzhkov 1952, 467.
   (Gen. Vir.) (Val. Pub., Leg.)
   Type sp. (monotype): Photophilus elegans, Ryzhkov
   1952, 467.

Photophilus elegans, Ryzhkov 1952, 467.
   (Sp. Vir.) (Val. Pub., Illeg.: Rule 24a)
   Marmor abutilon, Holmes 1939b, 50, q. v.

PHYLLOSPILUM, Hildebrand 1960, 756.
   (Gen. Vir.) (Val. Pub., Leg.)
   Type sp. (monotype): Phyllospilum ipomoeae,
   Hildebrand 1960, 756.

Phyllospilum ipomoeae, Hildebrand 1960, 756.
   (Sp. Vir.) (Val. Pub., Leg.)

PHYTAMOEBA, McWhorter 1922, 109.
   (Gen. Vir.) (Val. Pub., Illeg.: Prin. 1, Rule 24f)
   Northiella, McWhorter 1922, 103.
   Northiella, Likhite 1929, 15.
   Type sp. (monotype): Phytamoeba sacchari, McWhorter
   1922, 110.
   Comment: Described as a protozoan genus resembling
   the genus Entamoeba. The author failed to show causal
   relationship to the Fiji disease of sugar cane, caused by
   Galla fijiensis, Holmes, q. v.

Phytamoeba sacchari, McWhorter 1922, 110.
   (Sp. Vir.) (Val. Pub., Leg.)
   Northiella sacchari, "Lyon" in Likhite 1929, 15,
   type species of genus Northiella, Likhite 1929, 15.
   Marmor sacchari, Holmes 1939a, 435.
   Marmor sacchari, Holmes 1939b, 60.
   Saccharumvirus maculans, Roland 1959, 130.
   Comment: Type species of genus Phytamoeba,
   McWhorter 1922, 109.

PHYTOPHAGI, Holmes 1939a, 433.
  (Division, Vira) (Val. Pub., Leg.)

PHYTOPHAGI, McKinney 1944a, 146.
  (Calss Vir.) (Val. Pub., Illeg.: Rule 24a)
  Spermatophytophagi, Holmes 1939a, 434.

PHYTOPHAGINEAE, Holmes 1948, 1145.
  (Sub order Vir.) (Val. Pub., Leg.)

PHYTOVIRUS, Thornberry 1941, 23.
  (Gen. Vir.) (Not Val. Pub.: Rules 12a2, 12c2, 13a)
  Marmor, Holmes 1939b, 16.
  Type sp. (monotype): Phytovirus nicomosaicum,
  Thornberry 1941, 25.

PHYTOVIRUS, Bawden 1953, 543.
  (Gen. Vir.) (Not Val. Pub.: Rule 12a)
  Marmor, Holmes 1939b, 16.
  Type sp. (monotype): Phytovirus paracrystalis,
  Bawden 1953, 543.

Phytovirus nicomosaicum, Thornberry 1941, 23.
  (Sp. Vir.) (Not Val. Pub.: Rule 12a2)
  Protobios mosaicus, d'Herelle 1924, 343, q.v.
  Type sp. of genus Phytovirus, Thornberry 1941, 25.
  Marmor tabaci, Holmes 1939, 17.

Phytovirus nicomosaicum var. vulgare, (Holmes)
  Thornberry 1941, 23.
  (Var. Vir.) (Not Val. Pub., Rule 12a)
  Protobios mosaicum var. tabaci, d'Herelle 1924, 343,
                                                    q.v.

Phytovirus paracrystalis, Bawden 1953, 543.
  (Sp. Vir.) (Not Val. Pub.: Rule 12a2)
  Protobios mosaicus, d'Herelle 1924, 343.
  Type sp. of genus Phytovirus, Bawden 1953, 543.

Phytovirus paracrystalis var. aucuba, Bawden 1953, 543.
  (Var. Vir.) (Not Val. Pub.: Rule 12a)
  Marmor aucuba, Holmes 1939b, 49, q.v.

Phytovirus paracrystalis var. cucumis, Bawden 1953, 543.
  (Var. Vir.) (Not Val. Pub.: Rule 12a1)
  Marmor cucumeris, Holmes 1939b, 31, q.v.
  Murialba cucumeris, (Holmes) Valleau 1940, 823, q.v.

Phytovirus paracrystalis var. vulgare, (Holmes) Bawden
  1953, 543.
  (Var. Vir.) (Not Val. Pub.: Rule 12a)
  Protobios mosaicus var. tabaci, d'Herelle 1924, 343,
                                                    q.v.

PHYTOVECTALES, Krieg 1961, 142.
  (Subord. Vir.) (Val. Pub., Illeg.: Rule 4)

PIESMAPHILUS, Ryzhkov 1952, 466.
  (Gen. Vir.) (Val. Pub., Illeg.: Rule 24a)
  Savoia, Holmes 1939b, 131, q.v.
  Type sp. (subs. des. Barkley 1960, 70): Piesmaphilus
  europeus, Ryzhkov 1952, 466.

Piesmaphilus americanus, Ryzhkov 1952, 466.
  (Sp. Vir.) (Not Val. Pub.: Rule 14a2)

Piesmaphilus europaeus, Ryzhkov 1953, 161.
  (Sp. Vir.) (Not Val. Pub.: Rule 12a2)
  Savoia betae, Holmes 1939b, 132, q.v.,
  type species of genus Savoia, Holmes 1939b, 131.

Piesmaphilus europeus, Ryzhkov 1952, 466.
  (Sp. Vir.) (Val. Pub., Illeg.: Rule 24a)
  Savoia betae, Holmes 1939b, 131, q.v.,
  type species of genus Savoia, Holmes 1939b, 131.
  Comment: Type species of genus Piesmaphilus,
  Ryzhkov 1952, 466.

PISUMVIRUS

Pisumvirus maculosum, Roland 1959, 129.
  (Sp. Vir.) (Not Val. Pub.: Rule 12a2)
  Marmor efficiens, Johnson 1942, 115, q.v.

Pisumvirus verrucans, Roland 1959, 129.
  (Sp. Vir.) (Not Val. Pub.: Rule 12a2)
  Marmor pisi, Holmes 1939b, 90, q.v.

Pisumvirus virgatum, Roland 1959, 129.
  (Sp. Vir.) (Not Val. Pub.: Rule 12a2)

POAEVIR, Fawcett 1940, 560.
  (Gen. Vir.) (Not Val. Pub.: Rules 12a2, 13e)

POECILE, McKinney 1944a, 148.
  (Gen. Vir.) (Val. Pub., Leg.)
  Type sp. (monotype): Poecile rubi, (Holmes) McKinney
                                                1944a, 148.
Poecile rubi, (Holmes) McKinney 1944a, 148.
  (Sp. Vir.) (Val. Pub., Leg.)
  Marmor rubi, Holmes 1939b, 80, q.v.
  Comment: Type species of genus Poecile, McKinney
                                                1944a, 148.
POLYCLADUS, McKinney 1944a, 151.
  (Gen. Vir.) (Val. Pub., Leg.)
  Type sp. (orig. des.): Polycladus robiniae, (Holmes)
  McKinney 1944a, 151.

Polycladus robiniae, (Holmes) McKinney 1944a, 151.
  (Sp. Vir.) (Val. Pub., Leg.)
  Chlorogenus robiniae, Holmes 1939b, 13, q.v.
  Robiniavirus everriculosum, Roland 1959, 130.
  Chlorogenus robiniae, Holmes 1939a, 434.
  Comment: Type species of genus Polycladus, McKinney
                                                1944a, 151.
PRIMULAVIRUS

Primulavirus maculans, Roland 1959, 129.
  (Sp. Vir.) (Not Val. Pub.: Rule 12a2)
  Marmor primular, Holmes 1948, 1210, q.v.

PROTOBIOS, d'Herelle 1924, 342.
  (Gen. Vir.) (Val. Pub., Illeg.: Rule 24a)
  Bacteriophagum, d'Herelle 1918, 1161.
  Type sp. (orig. des.): Protobios bacteriophagus,
  d'Herelle 1924, 343.

Protobios bacteriophagus, d'Herelle 1924, 343.
  (Sp. Vir.) (Val. Pub., Illeg.: Rule 24a)
  Bacteriophagum intestinale, d'Herelle 1918, 1161.
  Type sp. of genus Protobios, d'Herelle 1924, 342.

Protobios bacteriophagus, d'Herelle 1924, 343, 345.
  (Sp. Vir.) (Val. Pub., Illeg.: Rule 24a)
  Bacteriophagum intestinale, d'Herelle 1918, 1161.

Protobios bacteriophagus var. pestis, Compton 1930, 152.
  (Var. Vir.) (Val. Pub., Illeg.: Rule 24b)

Protobios lyssae, d'Herelle 1924, 343.
  (Sp. Vir.) (Val. Pub., Illeg.: Rule 24a)
  Neuroryctes hydrophobiae, Calkins 1907, 560, q.v.

Protobios mosaicus var. tabaci, d'Herelle 1924, 343.
  (Var. Vir.) (Val. Pub., Illeg.: Rules 7 and 24b)
  Marmor tabaci var. vulgare, Holmes 1939a, 434.
  Marmor tabaci var. vulgare, Holmes 1939b, 17.
  Phytovirus nicomosaicum var. vulgare, (Holmes)
  Thornberry 1941, 25.
  Phytovirus paracrystalis var. vulgare, (Holmes)
  Bawden 1953, 543.

Protobios pestiavis, d'Herelle 1924, 343.
  (Sp. Vir.) (Val. Pub., Illeg.: Rule 24b)
  Protobios pestiavis var. gallinae, d'Herelle 1924, 343.
  Tortor balli, Holmes 1948, 1279.
  Pestigenes pullorum, Zhdanov and Korenblut 1950, 44.
  Pantropus avium, Ryzhkov 1950, 17.
  Gamaleia pullorum, Zhdanov 1953, 107.
  Myxovirus pestis-galli, Andrewes 1956, 621; Andrewes,
  Bang and Burnet 1955, 181.

Protobios pestiavis var. gallinae, d'Herelle 1924, 343.
  (Var. Vir.) (Val. Pub., Illeg.: Rules 7, 24b)
  Protobios pestiavis, d'Herelle 1924, 343, q.v.

Protobios portobios, d'Herelle 1924, 345.
  (Sp. Vir.) (Not Val. Pub.: Rule 12c2)

Protobios variabilis, d'Herelle 1924, 343.
  (Sp. Vir.) (Val. Pub., Illeg.: Rule 24b)

Protobios variabilis var. herpeti, d'Herelle 1924, 343.
  (Var. Vir.) (Val. Pub., Illeg.: Rule 24b)
  Neurocystis herpetii, Levaditi and Schoen 1927, 961,
                                                    q.v.
Protobios variabilis var. influenzae, d'Herelle 1924, 343.
  (Var. Vir.) (Val. Pub., Illeg.: Rule 24b)
  Tarpeia, Holmes 1948, 1268.

Protobios variabilis var. varicella, d'Herelle 1924, 343.
  (Var. Vir.) (Val. Pub., Illeg.: Rule 24b)
  Cytoryctes varicellae, (d'Herelle) Muchkovski 1945,
  33, q.v.
  Briareus varicellae, (d'Herelle) Holmes 1948, 1233, q.v.
  Strongyloplasm varicellae, (d'Herelle) Zhdanov 1953,
                                                204, q.v.
Protobios variolae, d'Herelle 1924, 343.
  (Sp. Vir.) Val. Pub., Illeg.: Rule 24b)
  Cytoryctes variolae, Guarnieri 1892, 422, q.v.

Protobios variolae var. bovis, d'Herelle 1924, 343.
  (Var. Vir.) (Val. Pub., Illeg.: Rule 24b)
  Strongyloplasma vacciniae var. bovis, (d'Herelle)
  Zhdanov 1953, 199, q.v.

Protobios variolae var. equi, d'Herelle 1924, 343.
  (Var. Vir.) (Val. Pub., Illeg.: Rule 24b)
  Strongyloplasma vacciniae var. equi, Zhdanov 1953,
  200, q.v.

Protobios variolae var. hominis, d'Herelle 1924, 343.
  (Var. Vir.) (Val. Pub., Illeg.: Rule 24b)
  Cytoryctes variolae, Guarnieri 1892, 422, q.v.

Protobios variolae var. ovis, d'Herelle 1924, 343.
  (Var. Vir.) (Val. Pub., Illeg.: Rule 24b)
  Strongyloplasma vacciniae var. ovis, (d'Herelle)
  Zhdanov 1953, 199, q.v.

Protobios variolae var. suis, d'Herelle 1924, 343.
  (Var. Vir.) (Val. Pub., Illeg.: Rule 24b) as Protobios
  variolae var. sui.
  Borreliota suis, (d'Herelle) Holmes 1948, 1232, q.v.
  Strongyloplasma (Zoovariola) suis, Zhdanov 1953, 203,
                                                    q.v.
PRUNIVIR, Fawcett 1940, 560.
  (Gen. Vir.) (Not Val. Pub.: Rule 12a2)
  Type sp. (monotype): Prunivir rosettae, Fawcett 1940,
                                                    560.
Prunivir cerasi, McLarty, Lott, Milbrath, Reeves and
  Zeller 1951, 106.
  (Sp. Vir.) (Not Val. Pub., Rule 12c1)
  Marmor cerasi, Zeller and Evans 1941, 467.

Prunivir circummaculatum, Cochran, Hutchins, Milbrath,
  Stout and Zeller 1951, 71.
  (Sp. Vir.) (Not Val. Pub.: Rule 12c1)
  Annulus cerasi, Hildebrand 1944, 1003, q.v.

Prunivir circummaculatum, "Fawcett" in Smith 1957,
  342 in syn.
  (Sp. Vir.) (Not Val. Pub.: Rule 12d)
  Annulus cerasi, Hildebrand 1944, 1003, q.v.

Prunivir flavimacula, Hutchins, Bodine, Cochran and
  Stout 1951, 26.
  (Sp. Vir.) (Not Val. Pub.: Rule 12c, 12d)
  Marmor persicae, Holmes 1939b, 81, q.v.
  Flavimacula persicae, (Holmes) McKinney 1944a, 149,
                                                    q.v.
Prunivir mirabilis, Hutchins, Cochran and Turner 1951,
  (Sp. Vir.) (Not Val. Pub.: Rule 12c1)   17.
  Nanus mirabilis, Holmes 1939b, 126, q.v.

Prunivir rosettae, Fawcett 1940, 560.
  (Sp. Vir.) (Not Val. Pub.: Rule 12a2)
  Carpophthora rosettae, (Holmes) Holmes 1948, 1152,
  Nanus rosettae, Holmes 1939b, 129, q.v.   q.v.
  Comment: Type species of genus Prunivir, Fawcett
  1940, 560.

Prunivir rubiginosum, Fawcett 1940, 560.
  (Sp. Vir.) (Val. Pub., Illeg.: Rule 24a)
  Marmor rubiginosum, Reeves 1940, 789, q.v.

Prunivir verruca, Blodgett, Milbrath, Reeves and
  Zeller 1951, 56.
  (Sp. Vir.) (Not Val. Pub.: Rule 12c1)
  Galla verrucae, Blodgett 1943, 30, q.v.

Prunivir verruca, "Fawcett" in Smith 1957, 346.
  Galla verrucae, Blodgett 1943, 30, q.v.

PRUNUSVIRUS

Prunusvirus nanescens, Roland 1959, 129.
  (Sp. Vir.) (Not Val. Pub.: Rule 12a2)
  Nanus pruni, Holmes 1939b, 128, q.v.

PSEUDOMARMOR, Limasset 1948, 293.
  (Gen. Vir.) (Not Val. Pub.: Rule 12a2)
  Type sp. (monotype): Pseudomarmor angliae, Limasset
                                                1948, 293.
Pseudomarmor angliae, Limasset 1948, 293.
  (Sp. Vir.) (Not Val. Pub.: Rule 12a2)
  Marmor angliae, Holmes 1939b, 48, q.v.

PTERIDOVIRUS, Thornberry 1941, 25.
  (Gen. Vir.) (Not Val. Pub.: Rules 12a2, 12c2, 13a)

PYRUSVIRUS

Pyrusvirus lignifaciens, Roland 1959, 129.
  (Sp. Vir.) (Not Val. Pub.: Rule 12a2)
  Marmor pyri, Holmes 1939b, 76, q.v.
  Rimocortius pyri, (Holmes) Holmes 1948, 1211, q.v.
  Dinvirus pyri, (Holmes) Hansen 1956, 126, q.v.

Pyrusvirus maculans, Roland 1959, 127.
  (Sp. Vir.) (Not Val. Pub.: Rule 12a2)
  Marmor mali, Holmes 1939b, 75, q.v.

Pyrusvirus molliens, Roland 1959, 127.
  (Sp. Vir.) (Not Val. Pub.: Rule 12a2)

Pyrusvirus rosettans, Roland 1959, 127.
  (Sp. Vir.) (Not Val. Pub.: Rule 12a2)
  Acrogenus rosettae, Baumann 1958, 119, q.v.

Pyrusvirus variegans, Roland 1959, 129.
  (Sp. Vir.) (Not Val. Pub.: Rule 12a2)

QUANJERIACEAE, Ryzhkov 1952, 465.
  (Fam. Vir.) (Val. Pub., Leg.)
  Type genus: Quanjeria, Ryzhkov 1952, 466.

QUANJERIA, Ryzhkov 1952, 466.
  (Gen. Vir.) (Not Val. Pub.: Rule 13a)
  Corium, Holmes 1939b, 119, q.v.
  Type sp. (subs. des.) Barkley 1958, 128): Quanjeria
  ruberosi, Ryzhkov 1952, 466.

Quanjeria tuberosi, Ryzhkov 1952, 466.
  (Sp. Vir.) (Not Val. Pub.: Rule 14a2)
  Corium solani, Holmes 1939b, 120, q.v.,
  type species of genus Corium, Holmes 1939a, 119.
  Comment: Type species of genus Quanjeria, Ryzhkov
                                                1952, 466.
Quanjeria wordereawskiana, Ryzhkov in Kohler and
  Klinkowski 1954, 519,
  see Quanjeria verelevskiana.

Quanjeria verdelevskiana, Ryzhkov 1952, 466.
  (Sp. Vir.) (Not Val. Pub.: Rule 14a2 as Quanjeria
  verdelevskiana.

RAPHANUSVIRUS

Raphanusvirus maculans, Roland 1959, 130.
  (Sp. Vir.) (Not Val. Pub.: Rule 12a2)
  Marmor raphani, Holmes 1948, 1200, q.v.
  Maphichorda raphani, (Holmes) Hansen 1956, 123, q.v.,
  type species of genus Maphichorda, Hansen 1956, 123.

RIBESVIRUS

Ribesvirus senticosum, Roland 1959, 128.
(Sp. Vir.) (Not Val. Pub.: Rule 12a2)
Acrogenus ribis, Holmes 1939b, 112, q.v.

RIMOCORTIODES, Bitancourt 1953, 453.
(Gen. Vir.) (Not Val. Pub.: Rule 12c2)
Rimocortius, Milbrath and Zeller 1942, 430. q.v.

RIMOCORTIUM

Rimocortium psorosis, (Fawcett) Holmes 1948, 1210.
(Sp. Vir.) (Val. Pub., Leg.)
Citrivir psorosis, Fawcett 1941, 357.
Source: RUTACEAE - Citrus sinensis, Osbeck,
orange; C. limonia, Osbeck, lemon; C. maxima, Merr.,
grapefruit.

RIMOCORTIUS, Milbrath and Zeller 1942, 430.
(Gen. Vir.) (Val. Pub., Leg.)
Rimocortiodes, Bitancourt 1953, 453.
Type sp. (orig. des.): Rimocortius kwanzani, Milbrath
and Zeller 1942, 430.

Rimocortius kwanzani, Milbrath and Zeller 1942, 430.
(Sp. Vir.) (Val. Pub., Leg.)
Source: Prunus serrulata, Lindl., var. kwanzan,
Flowering cherry; P. avium, L., Mazzard cherry.

Rimocortius kwanzani, Milbrath and Zeller 1942, 430.
(Sp. Vir.) (Val. Pub., Leg.)
Dinvirus pruni, Hansen 1956, 126.
Cerasusvirus asperans, Roland 1959, 128.
Comment: Type species of genus Rimocortius,
Milbrath and Zeller 1942, 430.

Rimocortius psorosis, (Fawcett) Holmes 1948, 1210.
(Sp. Vir.) (Val. Pub., Leg.)
Citrivir psorosis, Fawcett 1941, 357.
Dinvirus citri, Hansen 1956, 126.
Citrivirus acabiosum, Roland 1959, 128.
Type var. (orig. des.): Rimocortius psorosis var.
vulgare, (Fawcett) Holmes 1948, 1210.

Rimocortius psorosis, (Fawcett) Holmes 1948, 1210.
(Sp. Vir.) (Val. Pub., Leg.)
Citrivir psorosis, Fawcett 1941, 357,
type species of genus Citrivir, Fawcett 1941, 357.
Dinvirus citri, Hansen 1956, 126, q.v.,
type species of genus Dinvirus, Hansen 1956, 126.
Citrivirus scabiosum, Roland 1959, 128.
Type var. (orig. des.): Rimocortius psorosis var.
vulgare, (Fawcett) Holmes 1948, 1210.

Rimocortius psorosis var. alveatum, (Fawcett and
Bitancourt) Holmes 1948, 1211.
(Var. Vir.) (Val. Pub., Leg.)
Citrivir psorosis var. alveatum, Fawcett and Bitancourt
1943, 854.
Rimocortius psorosis var. anulatum, (Fawcett) Holmes
1948, 1210.
(Var. Vir.) (Val. Pub., Leg.)
Citrivir psorosis var. anulatum, Fawcett 1941, 561.

Rimocortius psorosis var. concavum, (Fawcett and
Bitancourt) Holmes 1948, 1210.
(Var. Vir.) (Val. Pub., Leg.)
Citrivir psorosis var. concavum, Fawcett and
Bitancourt 1943, 850.

Rimocortius psorosis var. vulgare, (Fawcett) Holmes
1948, 1210.
(Var. Vir.) (Val. Pub., Illeg.: Rule 7)
Citrivir psorosis var. vulgare, Fawcett 1940, 561;
1941, 357.
Comment: Type variety of species Rimocortius
psorosis, (Fawcett) Holmes 1948, 1210.

Rimocortius pyri, (Holmes) Holmes 1948, 1211.
(Sp. Vir.) (Val. Pub., Leg.)
Marmor pyri, Holmes 1939b, 76, q.v.
Dinvirus pyri, (Holmes) Hansen 1956, 126, q.v.
Pyrusvirus lignifaciens, Roland 1959, 129.
Pear stony pit virus
Source: ROSACEAE - Pyrus communis, L., pear.

ROBINIAVIRUS

Robiniavirus everriculosum, Roland 1959, 130.
(Sp. Vir.) (Not Val. Pub.: Rule 12a2)
Chlorogenus robiniae, Holmes 1939b, 13, q.v.
Polycladus robiniae, (Holmes) McKinney 1944a, 151,
q.v., type species of genus Polycladus, McKinney
1944a, 151.

RUBUSVIRUS

Rubusvirus crispans, Roland 1959, 130.
(Sp. Vir.) (Not Val. Pub.: Rule 12a2)
Corium rubi, Holmes 1939b, 121, q.v.

Rubusvirus deformans, Roland 1959, 128.
(Sp. Vir.) (Not Val. Pub.: Rule 12a2)
Nanus loganobacci, Holmes 1939b, 124, q.v.,
type species of genus Nanus, Holmes 1939b, 123.

Rubusvirus letale, Roland 1959, 130.
(Sp. Vir.) (Not Val. Pub.: Rule 12a2)

Rubusvirus nanescens, Roland 1959, 130.
(Sp. Vir.) (Not Val. Pub.: Rule 12a2)

Rubusvirus retinens, Roland 1959, 130.
(Sp. Vir.) (Not Val. Pub.: Rule 12a2)

Rubusvirus virgatum, Roland 1959, 130.
(Sp. Vir.) (Not Val. Pub.: Rule 12a2)
Nanus orientalis, Holmes 1939b, 124, q.v.

RUGA, Holmes 1939a, 435.
(Gen. Vir.) (Not Val. Pub.: Rule 12a2)
Ruga, Holmes 1939b, 114, q.v.
Type sp. (orig. des.): Ruga tabaci, Holmes 1939a,
435.
RUGA, Holmes 1939b, 114.
(Gen. Vir.) (Val. Pub., Leg.)
non Rugavirus, Krieg 1961, 151.
Ruga, Holmes 1939a, 435.
Type sp. (orig. des.): Ruga tabaci, Holmes 1939b, 115.

Ruga bemisiae, Holmes 1939a, 435.
(Sp. Vir.) (Not Val. Pub.: Rule 12a2)
Ruga bemisiae, Holmes 1939b, 117, q.v.
Ochrosticta bemisiae, (Holmes) McKinney 1944a, 149,
q.v., type species of genus Ochrosticta, McKinney
1944a, 149.
Ruga bemisiae, Holmes 1939b, 117.
(Sp. Vir.) (Val. Pub., Leg.)
Ruga bemisiae, Holmes 1939a, 435.
Ochrosticta bemisiae, (Holmes) McKinney 1944a, 149,
q.v., type species of genus Ochrosticta, McKinney
1944a, 149.
Dalevirus manihot, Hansen 1956, 130.
Jatrophavirus maculans, Roland 1959, 128.

Ruga gossypii, Holmes 1939a, 435.
(Sp. Vir.) (Not Val. Pub.: Rule 12a2)
Ruga gossypii, Holmes 1939b, 116, q.v.

Ruga gossypii, Holmes 1939b, 116.
(Sp. Vir.) (Val. Pub., Leg.)
Ruga gossypii, Holmes 1939a, 435.
Gossypiumvirus crispans, Roland 1959, 128.

Ruga tabaci, Holmes 1939b, 115.
(Sp. Vir.) (Val. Pub., Leg.)
Ruga tabaci, Holmes 1939a, 435, type
species of genus Ruga, Holmes 1939a, 435.
Dalevirus nicotianae, Hansen 1956, 130, type
species of genus Dalevirus, Hansen 1956, 130.
Nicotianavirus crispans, Roland 1959, 130.
Comment: Type species of genus Ruga, Holmes 1939b,
114.

Ruga verrucosans, Carsner and Bennett 1943, 386.
(Sp. Vir.) (Val. Pub., Illeg.: Rule 24a)
Chlorogenus eutettigicola, Holmes 1939b, 11, q.v.

Ruga verrucosans var. brasiliensis, Bennett and Costa
1949, 692.
(Var. Vir.) (Val. Pub., Illeg.: Rule 24b)

Ruga verrucosans var. distans, Bennett, Carsner, Coons
and Brandes 1946, 44.
(Var. Vir.) (Val. Pub., Illeg.: Rule 24b)

Ruga verrucosans var. solanacearum, Costa 1952, 402.
(Var. Vir.) (Val. Pub., Illeg.: Rule 24b)

RUGACEAE, Holmes 1939b, 114.
(Fam. Vir.) (Val. Pub., Leg.)
Type genus Ruga, Holmes 1939, 114.

RUGAVIRUS, Krieg 1961, 151.
(Gen. Vir.) (Val. Pub., Leg.)
non Ruga, Holmes 1939b, 114.
Betavir, Fawcett 1940, 560.
Type sp. (monotype): Rugavirus verrucosans, Krieg
1961, 151.
Rugavirus verrucosans, (Carsner and Bennett) Krieg 1961,
(Sp. Vir.) (Val. Pub., Illeg.: Rule 24a)   151.
Chlorogenus eutettigicola, Holmes 1939b, 11, q.v.

RUMEXVIRUS

Rumexvirus maculans, Roland 1959, 128.
(Sp. Vir.) (Not Val. Pub.: Rule 12a2)

SACCHARUMVIRUS

Saccharumvirus fijense, Roland 1959, 130.
(Sp. Vir.) (Not Val. Pub.: Rule 12a2)
Galla fijiensis, Holmes 1939b, 106,
type species of genus Galla, Holmes 1939b, 105.

Saccharumvirus maculans, Roland 1959, 130.
(Sp. Vir.) (Not Val. Pub.: Rule 12a2)
Phytamoeba sacchari, McWhorter 1922, 110, q.v.,
type species of genus Phytamoeba, McWhorter 1922,
109.

Saccharumvirus nanescens, Roland 1959, 130.
(Sp. Vir.) (Not Val. Pub.: Rule 12a2)
Galla queenslandiensis, Holmes 1939b, 109, q.v.

Saccharumvirus virgatum, Roland 1959, 130.
(Sp. Vir.) (Not Val. Pub.: Rule 12a2)

SANTALUMVIRUS

Santalumvirus crispans, Roland 1959, 130.
(Sp. Vir.) (Not Val. Pub.: Rule 12a2)
Marmor santali, Holmes 1939b, 94, q.v.

Santalumvirus spicans, Roland 1959, 130.
(Sp. Vir.) (Not Val. Pub.: Rule 12a2)
Chlorogenus santali, Holmes 1939b, 8, q.v.

SAVOIA, Holmes 1939b, 131.
(Gen. Vir.) (Val. Pub., Leg.)
Dahetvirus, Hansen 1956, 130.
Piesmaphilus, Ryzhkov 1952, 466.
Type sp. (orig. des.): Savoia betae, Holmes 1939b,
132.
Savoia betae, Holmes 1939b, 132.
(Sp. Vir.) (Val. Pub., Leg.)
Piesmaphilus europeus, Ryzhkov 1952, 466,
type species of genus Piesmaphilus, Ryzhkov 1952,
466.
Piesmaphilus europaeus, Ryzhkov 1953, 161.
Dahetvirus betae, (Holmes) Hansen 1956, 130,
type species of genus Dahetvirus, Hansen 1956, 130.
Betavirus crispans, Roland 1959, 128.
Comment: Type species of genus Savoia, Holmes 1939b,
131.
Beet Krauselkrankheit virus.
Sugar beet leaf-curl virus.
Sugar beet leaf-crinkle virus.
Kopfsalat virus.
Source: CHENOPODIACEAE - Beta vulgaris, L., beet.

Savoia napi, Holmes 1939b, 133.
(Sp. Vir.) (Val. Pub., Leg.)
Mehetvirus brassicae, Hansen 1956, 130,
type species of genus Mehetvirus, Hansen 1945, 130.
Brassicavirus crispans, Roland 1959, 130.

Savoia piesmae, Holmes 1939b, 132.
(Sp. Vir.) (Val. Pub., Leg.)

SAVOIACEAE, Holmes 1939b, 131.
(Fam. Vir.) (Val. Pub., Leg.)
Type genus Savoia, Holmes 1939b, 131.

SENECIOVIRUS

Seneciovirus maculans, Roland 1959, 128.
(Sp. Vir.) (Not Val. Pub.: Rule 12a2)
Marmor senecionis, Klinkowski 1954, 698.

SOLANIVIR, Fawcett 1940, 560.
(Gen. Vir.) (Not Val. Pub.: Rule 12a2)
Aureogenus, Black 1944, 141, q.v.
Type sp. (monotype): Solanivir vestans, Fawcett 1940,
560.
Solanivir vestans, Fawcett 1940, 560.
(Sp. Vir.) (Not Val. Pub.: Rule 12a2)
Marmor vastans, Holmes 1939b, 94, q.v.
Aureogenus vastans, Black 1944, 141, q.v.,
type species of genus Aureogenus, Black 1944, 141.
Comment: Type species of genus Solanivir, Fawcett
1940, 560.
SOLANOPHILUS, Ryzhkov 1952, 465.
(Gen. Vir.) (Val. Pub., Leg.)
Solanumvirus, Kohler 1952b, 51.
Solanum-virus, Kohler 1952a, 294.
Minflexus, Hansen 1956, 127.
Type sp. (subs. des. Barkley 1958, 128): Solanophilus
tuberosi, Ryzhkov 1952, 465.

Solanophilus tuberosi, Ryzhkov 1952, 465.
(Sp. Vir.) (Val. Pub., Illeg.: Rule 24a)
Marmor dubium, Holmes 1939b, 42, q.v.
Annulus dubius, (Holmes) Holmes 1948, 1214, q.v.
Comment: Type species of genus Solanophilus,
Ryzhkov 1952, 465.

SOLANUM-VIRUS, Kohler 1952a, 294.
(Gen. Vir.) (Val. Pub., Illeg.: Rule 24a)
Solanophilus, Ryzhkov 1952, 465, q.v.
Type sp. (monotype): Solanum-virus deformans,
Kohler 1952, 294.

SOLANUMVIRUS, Kohler 1952b, 51.
(Gen. Vir.) (Not Val. Pub.: Rule 12a2)
Solanophilus, Ryzhkov 1952, 465, q.v.

Solanumvirus aceratagalliatranslatum, (sic) Roland 1952,
(Sp. Vir.) (Not Val. Pub.: Rule 12a2)   53.
Marmor vastans, Holmes 1939b, 94, q.v.
Aureogenus vastans, (Holmes) Black 1944, 141, q.v.,
type species of genus Aureogenus, Black 1944, 141.

Solanumvirus alphaicum, Kohler 1952b, 52.
(Sp. Vir.) (Not Val. Pub.: Rule 12a2)
Marmor solani, Holmes 1939b, 47, q.v.

Solanumvirus altathermus, Roland 1952, 53.
(Sp. Vir.) (Not Val. Pub.: Rule 12a2)
Corium solani, Holmes 1939b, 120, q.v.,
type species of genus Corium, Holmes 1939b, 119.

Solanumvirus A-nominatum, Roland 1959, 129.
(Sp. Vir.) (Not Val. Pub.: Rule 12a2)

Solanumvirus anulosum, Kohler 1952b, 51.
(Sp. Vir.) (Not Val. Pub.: Rule 12a2)
Marmor dubium var. annulus, Holmes 1939b, 44, q.v.
Annulus dubius var. annulus, (Holmes) Holmes 1948,
1215, q.v.
Solanumvirus aucubamarmor, Roland 1952, 53.
(Sp. Vir.) (Not Val. Pub.: Rule 12a2)
Marmor aucuba, Holmes 1939b, 49, q.v.

Solanumvirus aucubamarmor var. F, Roland 1952, 55.
(Var. Vir.) (Not Val. Pub.: Rules 12a2, 7)

Solanumvirus aucubamarmor var. G, Roland 1952, 55.
(Var. Vir.) (Not Val. Pub.: Rules 12a2, 7)

Solanumvirus aucuboides, Kohler 1952b, 51.
(Sp. Vir.) (Not Val. Pub.: Rule 12a2)
Marmor aucuba, Holmes 1939b, 49, q.v.

Solanumvirus coleopterotranslatum, Roland 1952b, 53.
(Sp. Vir.) (Not Val. Pub.: Rule 12a2)
Acrogenus solani, Holmes 1939b, 111, q.v.

Solanumvirus contactutranslatum, Roland 1952, 53.
(Sp. Vir.) (Not Val. Pub.: Rule 12a2)
Marmor dubium var. annulus, Holmes 1939b, 44, q.v.
Annulus dubius var. annulus, (Holmes) Holmes 1948,
1215, q.v.
Solanumvirus contactutranslatum var. B, Roland 1952, 55.
(Var. Vir.) (Not Val. Pub.: Rules 12a2, 7)
Marmor dubium var. annulus, Holmes 1939b, 44, q.v.
Annulus dubius var. annulus, (Holmes) Holmes 1948,
1215, q.v.
Solanumvirus cuscutotranslatum, Roland 1952, 53.
(Sp. Vir.) (Not Val. Pub.: Rule 12a2)
Chlorogenus solani, Holmes 1939b, 7, q.v.
Chlorophthora solani, (Holmes) McKinney 1944a, 151,
q.v., type species of genus Chlorophthora, McKinney
1944a, 151.

Solanumvirus deformans, Kohler 1952a, 294.
(Sp. Vir.) (Val. Pub.: Illeg., Rule 24a)
Marmor dubium, Holmes 1939b, 42, q.v.
Annulus dubius, (Holmes) Holmes 1948, 1214, q.v.
Comment: Type species of genus Solanum-virus,
Kholer 1952a, 294.

Solanumvirus everriculosum, Roland 1959, 129.
(Sp. Vir.) (Not Val. Pub.: Rule 12a2)
Chlorogenus solani, Holmes 1939b, 7, q.v.
Chlorophthora solani, (Holmes) McKinney 1944a, 151,
q.v., type species of genus Chlorophthora, McKinney
1944a, 151.

Solanumvirus experimentotranslatum, Roland 1952, 53.
(Sp. Vir.) (Not Val. Pub.: Rule 12a2)
Marmor angliae, Holmes 1939b, 48, q.v.

Solanumvirus flavomaculans, Kohler 1952b, 51.
(Sp. Vir.) (Not Val. Pub.: Rule 12a2)

Solanumvirus fusifaciens, Kohler 1952b, 51.
(Sp. Vir.) (Not Val. Pub.: Rule 12a2)
Acrogenus solani, Holmes 1939b, 111, q.v.

Solanumvirus fusiformis, Roland 1959, 129.
(Sp. Vir.) (Not Val. Pub.: Rule 12a2)
Acrogenus solani, Holmes 1939b, 111, q.v.

Solanum virus inpermanens, Roland 1952, 53.
(Sp. Vir.) (Not Val. Pub.: Rule 12a)
Marmor upsilon, Holmes 1948, 1172, q.v.

Solanum virus inpersistens var. C, Roland 1952, 55.
(Var. Vir.) (Not Val. Pub.: Rule 12a2, 7)

Solanum virus inpersistens var. S, Roland 1952, 55.
(Var. Vir.) (Not Val. Pub.: Rules 12a2, 7)

Solanum virus librimatiferum, (sic) Klinkowski 1958, 2.
Solanum virus librimortiferum, Roland 1952, 53, q.v.

Solanum virus librimortiferum, Roland 1952, 53.
(Sp. Vir.) (Not Val. Pub.: Rule 12a2)
Corium solani, Holmes 1939b, 120, q.v.,
type species of genus Corium, Holmes 1939b, 119.

Solanum virus macrostelotranslatum, Roland 1952, 53.
(Sp. Vir.) (Not Val. Pub.: Rule 12a2)

Solanumvirus maculans, Roland 1959, 129.
(Sp. Vir.) (Not Val. Pub.: Rule 12a2)
Ginchorda nico-caulis, Hansen 1956, 127, q.v., type
species of genus Ginchorda, Hansen 1956, 127.

Solanumvirus mirum, Kohler 1952b, 51.
(Sp. Vir.) (Not Val. Pub.: Rule 12a2)
Marmor angliae, Holmes 1939b, 48, q.v.

Solanumvirus nanescens, Roland 1959, 129.
(Sp. Vir.) (Not Val. Pub.: Rule 12a2)

Solanum virus parvathermis, Roland 1952, 53.
(Sp. Vir.) (Not Val. Pub.: Rule 12a2)
Marmor solani, Holmes 1939b, 47, q.v.

Solanumvirus perniciosum, Roland 1959, 129.
(Sp. Vir.) (Not Val. Pub.: Rule 12a2)
Corium solani, Holmes 1939b, 120, q.v.,
type species of genus Corium, Holmes 1939b, 119.

Solanum virus psyllidotranslatum, Roland 1952, 53.
(Sp. Vir.) (Not Val. Pub.: Rule 12a2)

Solanumvirus rigidiformans, Kohler 1952b, 51.
(Sp. Vir.) (Not Val. Pub.: Rule 12a2)
Corium solani, Holmes 1939b, 120, q.v.,
type species of genus Corium, Holmes 1939b, 119.

Solanumvirus singulare, Kohler 1952b, 51.
(Sp. Vir.) (Not Val. Pub.: Rule 12a2)
Ginchorda nico-caulis, Hansen 1956, 127, q.v.,
type species of genus Ginchorda, Hansen 1956, 127.

Solanumvirus varians, Kohler 1952b, 51.
(Sp. Vir.) (Not Val. Pub.: Rule 12a2)
Corium solani, Holmes 1939b, 120, q.v.,
type species of genus Corium, Holmes 1939b, 119.

Solanumvirus vastans, (Holmes) Kohler 1952b, 51.
(Sp. Vir.) (Not Val. Pub.: Rule 12a2)
Marmor vastans, Holmes 1939b, 94, q.v.
Aureogenus vastans, (Holmes) Black 1944, 141, q.v.,
type species of genus Aureogenus, Black 1944, 141.

Solanumvirus X-nominatum, Roland 1959, 129.
(Sp. Vir.) (Not Val. Pub.: Rule 12a2)
Marmor upsilon, (Holmes) Holmes 1948, 1172, q.v.
Marmor dubium var. annulus, Holmes 1939b, 44, q.v.
Annulus dubius var. annulus, (Holmes) Holmes 1948,
1215, q.v.
Solanum virus ypsilonicum, Kohler 1952b, 51.
(Sp. Vir.) (Not Val. Pub.: Rule 12a)
Marmor upsilon, (Holmes) Holmes 1948, 1172, q.v.

SPERMATOPHYTOPHAGI, Holmes 1939a, 434.
(Class Vir.) (Val. Pub., Leg.)
Phytophagi, McKinney 1944a, 146.
Eucrystallinae, Ryzhkov 1952, 463, 465.

TARAXACUMVIRUS

Taraxacumvirus flavescens, Roland 1959, 128.
(Sp. Vir.) (Not Val. Pub.: Rule 12a2)
Marmor taraxaci, Klinkowski 1954, 702, q.v.

THALLOVIRUS, Thornberry 1941, 25.
(Gen. Vir.) (Not Val. Pub.: Rules 12a2, 12c2, 13a)

THRIPSOPHILACEAE, Ryzhkov 1952, 466.
(Fam. Vir.) (Val. Pub., Leg.)
Type genus: Thripsophilus, Ryzhkov 1952, 466.

THRIPSOPHILUS, Ryzhkov 1952, 466.
(Gen. Vir.) (Not Val. Pub.: Rule 13a)
Lethum, Holmes 1939b, 135, q.v.
Type sp. (monotype): Thripsophilus lycopersici,
Ryzhkov 1952, 466.

Thripsophilus lycopersici, Ryzhkov 1952, 466.
(Sp. Vir.) (Not Val. Pub.: Rule 14a2)
Lethum australiense, Holmes 1939b, 136, q.v.
Comment: Type species of genus Thripsophilus,
Ryzhkov 1952, 466.

THYVIRACEAE, Hansen 1956, 128.
(Fam. Vir.) (Val. Pub.: Illeg., Rule 3) collective
genus.
Comment: Includes Methyvirus, Hansen 1956, 129.

TRACTUS, Valleau 1940, 826.
  (Gen. Vir.) (Val. Pub., Leg.)
  Type sp. (monotype): Tractus orae, (Holmes) Valleau
                             1940, 826.

Tractus orae, (Holmes) Valleau 1940, 826.
  (Sp. Vir.) (Val. Pub., Leg.)
  Annulus orae, Holmes 1939, 103, q.v.
  Nicotianavirus vulnerans, Roland 1959, 130.
  Comment: Type species of genus Tractus, Valleau
                             1940, 826.

TRIFOLIUMVIRUS

Trifoliumvirus clavifoliatum, Roland 1959, 128.
  (Sp. Vir.) (Not Val. Pub.: Rule 12a2)
  Aureogenus clavifolium, Balck 1944, 141, q.v.

Trifoliumvirus maculans, Roland 1959, 128.
  (Sp. Vir.) (Not Val. Pub.: Rule 12a2)

Trifoliumvirus nervicrassans, Roland 1959, 128.
  (Sp. Vir.) (Not Val. Pub.: Rule 12a2)
  Aureogenus magnivena, Black 1944, 144, q.v.

Trifoliumvirus nervimaculans, Roland 1959, 128.
  (Sp. Vir.) (Not Val. Pub.: Rule 12a2)
  Marmor trifolii, Holmes 1939b, 93, q.v.

TRITICUMVIRUS, Klinkowski and Kreutzberg 1958, 2.
  (Gen. Vir.) (Val. Pub., Illeg.: Rule 24a)
  Graminevorus, Ryzhkov 1952, 466, q.v.
  Type sp. (monotype): Triticumvirus retardans,
  Klinkowski and Kreutzberg 1958, 2.

Triticumvirus maculans, Roland 1959, 130.
  (Sp. Vir.) (Not Val. Pub.: Rule 12a2)
  Marmor tritici, Holmes 1939b, 61; McKinney 1944b,
                           323, q.v.

Triticumvirus retardans, Klinkowski and Kreutzberg
  1958, 2.
  (Sp. Vir.) (Val. Pub., Illeg.: Rule 24a)
  Fractilinea tritici, McKinney 1944b, 327, q.v.
  Comment: Type species of genus Triticumvirus,
  Klinkowski and Kreutzberg 1958, 2.

Tulipavirus vulgare, Roland 1959, 130.
  (Sp. Vir.) (Not Val. Pub.: Rule 12a2)
  Marmor tulipae, Holmes 1939b, 52, q.v.

ULMUSVIRUS

Ulmusvirus librinecans, Roland 1959, 128.
  (Sp. Vir.) (Not Val. Pub.: Rule 12a2)
  Morsus ulmi, Holmes 1948, 1154, q.v.

VACCINIUMVIRUS

Vacciniumvirus nanescens, Roland 1959, 130.
  (Sp. Vir.) (Not Val. Pub.: Rule 12a2)

Vacciniumvirus sterilefaciens, Roland 1959, 130.
  (Sp. Vir.) (Not Val. Pub.: Rule 12a2)
  Chlorogenus vaccinii, Holmes 1939b, 10, q.v.

VACUOLARIUM, Likhite 1929, 16.
  (Gen. Vir.) (Val. Pub., Illeg.: Rule 24d)
  non Vacuolaria, Cienkowsky 1870, 426.
  Marmor, Holmes 1939a, 434.
  Marmor, Holmes 1939b, 16.
  Musivum, Valleau 1940, 822.
  Phytovirus, Thornberry 1941, 23.
  Virothrix, Ryzhkov 1952, 465 non Ryzhkov 1950, 16.
  Crystallobiotus, Ryzhkov 1952, 472.
  Phytovirus, Bawden 1953, 543.
  Minchorda, Hansen 1956, 126.
  Minvirus, Hansen 1956, 126.
  Type sp. (monotype): Vacuolarium iwanowski,
  Likhite 1929, 16.
  Comment: Vacuolarium, Likhite 1929, 16, is an
  orthographic variant of Vacuolaria, Cienkowsky 1870,
                             426.

Vacuolarium iwanowhki, Likhite 1929, 16.
  (Sp. Vir.) (Val. Pub., Illeg.: Rule 24a)
  Protobios mosaicus, d'Herelle 1924, 343, q.v.
  Type sp. of genus Vacuolarium, Likhite 1929, 16.

VECTOMARMOR, Limasset 1948, 293.
  (Gen. Vir.) (Not Val. Pub.: Rule 12a2)
  Maphiflexus, Hansen 1956, 123, q.v.
  Type sp. (orig. des.): Vactomarmor upsilon,
  Limasset 1948, 293.

Vectomarmor upsilon, Limasset 1948, 293.
  (Sp. Vir.) (Not Val. Pub.: Rule 12a2)
  Marmor upsilon, (Holmes) Holmes 1948, 1172, q.v.
  Comment: Type species of genus Vectomarmor,
  Limasset 1948, 273.

VICIAVIRUS, Quantz 1953, 421.
  (Gen. Vir.) (Val. Pub., Leg.)
  Type sp. (monotype): Viciavirus varians, Quantz
                         1953, 421.

Viciavirus chlorogenum, Quantz and Volk in Quantz
  1958, 48.
  (Sp. Vir.) (Val. Pub., Leg.)

Viciavirus maculans, Roland 1959, 128.
  (Sp. Vir.) (Not Val. Pub.: Rule 12a2)
  Viciavirus varians, Quantz 1953, 446.

Viciavirus varians, Quantz 1953, 446.
  (Sp. Vir.) (Val. Pub., Leg.)
  Viciavirus maculans, Roland 1959, 128.

VIGNAVIRUS

Vignavirus maculans, Roland 1959, 128.
  (Sp. Vir.) (Not Val. Pub.: Rule 12a2)
  Marmor vignae, Holmes 1948, 1188, q.v.

VIRALES, Breed, Murray and Hitchens 1944, 421.
  (Order sch.)

VIRALIA, Zhdanov and Korenblut 1950, 42.
  (Class Vir.) (Not Val. Pub., Rules 12a2, 12e)
  Microtatobiotes, Philip 1957, 933.

VIREAE, Barkley 1949, 88.
  (Class Vir.) (Not Val. Pub.: Rule 12a2)
  Microtatobiotes, Philip.

VIROCOCCACEAE, Ryzhkov 1952, 465.
  (Fam. Vir.) (Val. Pub., Leg.)
  Type genus: Virococcus, Ryzhkov 1952, 465.

VIROCOCCUS, Ryzhkov 1952, 465.
  (Gen. Vir.) (Val. Pub., Illeg.: Rule 24a)
  Murialba, Valleau 1940, 823, q.v.
  Type sp. (subs. des.: Barkley 1958, 129): Virococcus
  cucurbitae, Ryzhkov 1952, 465.

Virococcus cucurbitae, Ryzhkov 1952, 465; 1953, 160.
  (Sp. Vir.) (Not Val. Pub.: Rule 13d)
  Marmor cucumeris, Holmes 1939b, 31, q.v.
  Murialba cucumeris, (Holmes) Valleau 1940, 823, q.v.
  Type sp. of genus Virococcus, Ryzhkov 1952, 465.

VITISVIRUS

Vitisvirus vastans, Roland 1959, 130.
  (Sp. Vir.) (Not Val. Pub.: Rule 12a2)

VULNUS, Thomas and Rawlins 1951b, 185.
  (Gen. Vir.) (Val. Pub., Illeg.: Prin. 1 (2)).
  Type sp. (monotype): Vulnus immedicabile, Thomas
  and Rawlins 1951b, 185.
  Comment: Authors have stated intent to ridicule
  nomenclature as currently applied to the viruses.

Vulnus immedicabile, Thomas and Rawlins 1951b, 185.
  (Sp. Vir.) (Val. Pub., Illeg.: Prin. 1 (2)).
  Comment: Type species of genus Vulnus, Thomas and
  Rawlins 1951b, 185.

XENOVIRACEAE, Hansen 1956, 128.
  (Fam. Vir.) (Val. Pub., Illeg., Rule 3)
  Comment: Includes the genera Mexevirus, Hansen
  1956, 128 and Daxevirus, Hansen 1956, 128.

XENOVIRALES, Hansen 1956, 127.
  (Ord. Vir.) (Val. Pub., Leg.)
  Comment: Includes 6 families:
  Acaviraceae, Hansen 1956, 130.
  Aleviraceae, Hansen 1956, 129.
  Cocviraceae, Hansen 1956, 129.
  Hetviraceae, Hansen 1956, 130.
  Thyviraceae, Hansen 1956, 128.
  Xenoviraceae, Hansen 1956, 128.

ZEAVIRUS

Zeavirus maculans, Roland 1959, 129.
  (Sp. Vir.) (Not Val. Pub.: Rule 12a2)
  Marmor zeae, Holmes 1939b, 59, q.v.
  Fractilinea zeae, (Holmes) Holmes 1948, 1161, q.v.

Zeavirus variegans, Roland 1959, 129.
  (Sp. Vir.) (Not Val. Pub.: Rule 12a2)
  Corium zeae, Stoner 1952, 688, q.v.

Zeavirus verrucans, Roland 1959, 129.
  (Sp. Vir.) (Not Val. Pub.: Rule 12a2)
  Galla zeae, McKinney 1944b, 328, q.v.

Zeavirus virgatum, Roland 1959, 129.
  (Sp. Vir.) Not Val. Pub.: Rule 12a2)
  Marmor maidis, Holmes 1939b, 56, q.v.
  Fractilinea maidis, (Holmes) McKinney 1944a, 149,
  q.v., type species of genus Fractilinea, McKinney
  1944a, 148.

ACANTHACEAE
ACERACEAE
AIZOACEAE
ALISMACEAE
AMARANTHACEAE
AMARYLLIDACEAE
ANACARDIACEAE
APOCYNACEAE
ARACEAE
ARALIACEAE
ASCLEPIADACEAE
BALSAMINACEAE
BEGONIACEAE
BERBERIDACEAE
BIGNONIACEAE
BIXACEAE
BOMBACACEAE
BORAGINACEAE
BROMELIACEAE
CACTACEAE
CALYCANTHACEAE
CAMPANULACEAE
CANNACEAE
CAPPARIDACEAE
CAPRIFOLIACEAE
CARICACEAE
CARYOPHYLLACEAE
CELASTRACEAE
CHENOPODIACEAE
COCHLOSPERMACEAE
COMMELINACEAE
COMPOSITAE
CONVOLVULACEAE
CRASSULACEAE
CRUCIFERAE
CUCURBITACEAE
CYPERACEAE
DIOSCOREACEAE
DIPSACEAE
EQUISETACEAE
ERICACEAE
EUPHORBIACEAE
FRANKENIACEAE
FUMARIACEAE
GERANIACEAE
GESNERIACEAE
GOODENIACEAE
GRAMINEAE
HIPPOCASTANACEAE
HYDROPHYLLACEAE
HYPERICACEAE
IRIDACEAE
JUGLANDACEAE
LABIATAE
LAURACEAE
LEGUMINOSAE

LILIACEAE
LINACEAE
LOASCACEAE
LOBELIACEAE
LOGANIACEAE
LYTHRACEAE
MALVACEAE
MARANTACEAE
MARTYNIACEAE
MORACEAE
MUSACEAE
MYRICACEAE
MYRISTICACEAE
MYRTACEAE
NOLANACEAE
NYCTAGINACEAE
OLEACEAE
ONAGRACEAE
ORCHIDACEAE
OXALIDACEAE
PALMACEAE
PAPAVERACEAE
PASSIFLORACEAE
PEDALIACEAE
PHYTOLACCACEAE
PINACEAE
PIPERACEAE
PITTOSPORACEAE
PLANTAGINACEAE
PLUMBAGINACEAE
POLEMONIACEAE
POLYGONACEAE
POLYPODIACEAE
PONTEDERIACEAE
PORTULACACEAE
PRIMULACEAE
PUNICACEAE
RANUNCULACEAE
RESEDACEAE
RHAMNACEAE
ROSACEAE
RUBIACEAE
RUTACEAE
SALICACEAE
SANTALACEAE
SAPINDACEAE
SAPOTACEAE
SAURURACEAE
SAXIFRAGACEAE
SCROPHULARIACEAE
SCYTOPETALACEAE
SOLANACEAE
STERCULIACEAE
THEACEAE
THYMELEACEAE
TILIACEAE

TROPAEOLACEAE
TYPHACEAE
ULMACEAE
UMBELLIFERAE
URTICACEAE
VALERIANACEAE
VERBENACEAE
VIOLACEAE
VITACEAE
ZINGIBERACEAE
ZYGOPHYLLACEAE

Abelmoschus Medic. 1787

Abroma Jacq. 1776

Abutilon Tourn. ex Adans. 1763

Acacia ((Tourn.)) L. 1737

Acalypha L. 1737

Acanthospermum Schrank 1819

Acer ((Tourn.)) L. 1735

Achillea L. 1735

Achyranthes L. 1737

Adansonia L. 1753

Adenia Forsk. 1775

Adenoropium Pohl. 1827

Adiantum ((Tourn.)) L. 1753

Adlumia Rafin. 1808

Adonis Dill. ex L. 1735

Aegilops L. 1737

Aegle Correa 1800

Aeglopsis Swingle 1911

Aegopodium Knaut. ex L. 1735

Aeschynomene L. 1737

Aesculus L. 1740

Afraegle Stapf 1906

Agapanthus L'Herit. 1788

Ageratum L. 1737

Agropyron J. Gaert. 1770

Agrostis L. 1735

Aizoon L. 1737

Ajuga L. 1737

Aleurites Forst. 1776

Allium ((Tourn.)) L. 1735

Aloe Tourn. ex L. 1735

Alonsoa Ruiz & Pav. 1798

Alopecurus L. 1735

Alsine Scop. 1772

Alstonia R. Br. 1809

Alternanthera Forsk. 1775

Althaea ((Tourn.)) L. 1735

Alyssum Tourn. ex L. 1735

Amaranthus L. 1735

Amaryllis L. 1735

Ambrosia L. 1737

Amelanchier Medic. 1789

Ammannia ((Houst.)) L. 1737

Ammobium R. Br. 1824

Amsinckia Lehm. 1831

Amygdalus (See Prunus) ((Tourn.)) L. 1735

Anagallis ((Tourn.)) L. 1735

Ananas Tourn. ex L. 1735

Anchusa L. 1735

Androcera Nutt. 1818

Andropogon L. 1753

Anemone L. 1735

Anemopsis Hook. & Arn. *

Anethum Tourn. ex L. 1737

Anagraecum Bory 1804

Anthemis Mich. ex L. 1735

Anthoxanthum L. 1737

Anthriscus Bernh. 1800

Anthurium Schott 1829

Antirrhinum Tourn. ex L. 1735

Apeiba Aubl. 1775

Apios Moench 1794

Apium ((Tourn.)) L. 1735

Apocynum ((Tourn.)) L. 1735

Aquilegia ((Tourn.)) L. 1735

Arabis L. 1737

Arachis L. 1735

Aranda *

Arctium L. 1735

Arctotis L. 1737

Arenaria Rupp. ex L. 1735

Aristida L. 1753

Armeria L. 1735

Armoracia Gaertn. Mey. & Scherb. 1800

Arracacia Bancroft. 1826

(Arracacha) DC. 1829

Arrhenatherum Beauv. 1812

Artemesia L. 1735

Artocarpus Forst. 1776

Arum ((Tourn.)) L. 1735

Asclepias L. 1737

Asparagus Tourn. ex L. 1735

Asperula L. 1735

Asphodeline Reichb. 1830

Aster Tourn. ex L. 1735

Astragulus Tourn. ex L. 1737

Atalantia Correa 1805

Atriplex ((Tourn.)) L. 1735

Atropa L. 1737

Avena L. 1735

Babiana Ker-Gawl. 1802

Baccharis L. 1737

Baeria Fisch. & Mey. 1835

Baphia Afzel. ex Lodd. 1825

Baptisia Vent. 1808

Barbarea R. Br. 1812

Bassia All. 1766

Beckmannia Host 1805

Begonia ((Tourn.)) L. 1742

Belamcanda Adans. 1763

Bellis ((Tourn.)) L. 1737

Benincasa Savi 1818

Berberis ((Tourn.)) L. 1737

Berrya DC. 1824

Berteroa DC. 1821

Beta ((Tourn.)) L. 1735

Bidens ((Tourn.)) L. 1737

Bignonia ((Tourn.)) L. 1735

Bixa L. 1737

Boehmeria Jacq. 1760

Boltonia L'Herit. 1788

Bombax L. 1753

Borago L. 1753

Bouteloua Lag. 1805

Brachiaria Griseb. 1853

Brachycombe *

(Brachycome) Cass. 1825

Brachystegia Benth. 1865

Brassica ((Tourn.)) L. 1735

Brassocattleya X, Rolfe 1889

Brickellia Ell. 1824

Brodiaea Sm. 1811

Bromus Dill. ex L. 1735

Browallia L. 1737

Bryonia L. 1735

Bryonopsis Arn. 1841

Bryophyllum (See Kalanchoe) Salisb. 1805

Buchloe Engelm. 1859

Buddleia Houst. ex L. 1737

Buettneria Loefl. 1758

(Byttneria) Loefl. 1758

Bursa (See Capsella) Weber 1780

Caesalpinia L. 1753

Cajanus DC. 1813

Calandrinia H. B. & K. 1823

Calceolaria L. 1771

Calendula L. 1735

Callistephus Cass. 1825

Calochortus Pursh 1814

Calonyction Choisy 1833

Calycanthus L. 1759

Calystegia R. Br. 1810

Camassia Lindl. 1832

Camelina Crantz 1762

Camellia L. 1735

Campanula ((Tourn.)) L. 1735

Canavalia DC. 1825

Canna L. 1735

Canthium Lam. 1783

Capsella Medic. 1792

Capsicum ((Tourn.)) L. 1735

Cardamine ((Tourn.)) L. 1735

Cardiospermum L. 1735

Carduus ((Tourn.)) L. 1735

Carica L. 1737

Carthamus ((Tourn.)) L. 1735

Carum Rupp. ex L. 1735

Carya Nutt. 1818

Casimiroa La Llave 1825

Cassia Tourn. ex L. 1735

Catananche L. 1735

Catharanthus G. Don 1836

Cattleya Lindl. 1824

Ceanothus L. 1741

Ceiba Gaertn. 1791

Celeri Adans. 1763

Celosia L. 1737

Centaurea L. 1737

Cerastium ((Dill.)) L. 1735

Chaerefolium Haller 1768

(Chaetochloa) Scribn. 1897

Chamaesyce S.F. Gray 1821

Chapmannia Torr. & Gray 1839

Charieis Cass. 1817

Chayota Jacq. 1780

Cheiranthus L. 1737

Chelidonium Tourn. ex L. 1735

Chelone L. 1735

Chenopodium ((Tourn.)) L. 1735

Chloris Sw. 1788

Chorisia H. B. & K. 1821

Christiana DC. 1824

Chrysanthemum ((Tourn.)) L. 1735

Chrysopsis Ell. 1824

Cicer ((Tourn.)) L. 1735

Cichorium ((Tourn.)) L. 1735

Cineraria L. p.p. 1763

Circaea Tourn. ex L. 1735

Cirsium ((Tourn.)) Adans. 1763

Cistanthera K. Schum. 1897

Citropsis Swingle & Kellerman 1913

Citrullus Forsk. 1775

Citrus L. 1735

Clappertonia Meissn. 1837

Clarkia Pursh 1814

Clausena Burm. f. 1768

Claytonia Gronov. ex L. 1737

Cleome L. 1735

Clerodendron L. 1737

Clitoria L. 1737

Cobaea Cav. 1791

Cochlearia Tourn. ex L. 1735

Cochlospermum Kunth 1822

Cocos L. 1753

Codiaeum Rumph. ex A. Juss. 1824

Coffea L. 1735

Coix L. 1737

Cola Schott & Endl. 1832

Colchicum L. 1735

Coleus Lour. 1790

Collinsia Nutt. 1817

Colocynthis ((Tourn.)) L. 1735

Commelina Plum. ex L. 1735

Conium L. 1735

Conringia Heist. ex L. 1735

Convallaria L. 1735

Convolvulus ((Tourn.)) L. 1735

Cooperia Herb. 1836

Coprosma Forst. 1776

Corchorus ((Tourn.)) L. 1735

Coreopsis L. 1737

Coriandrum ((Tourn.)) L. 1735

Cortaderia Stapf 1897

Corydalis Vent. Choix, 19 1803, in nota

Cosmidium Nutt. 1841

Cosmos Cav. 1791

Cotoneaster Rupp. 1745

Cotula ((Tourn.)) L. 1735

Crambe Tourn. ex L. 1735

Crassina Scepin 1758

Crocus ((Tourn.)) L. 1735

Crotalaria Dill. ex L. 1737

Cryptostemma R. Br. 1813

Cucumis ((Tourn.)) L. 1735

Cucurbita ((Tourn.)) L. 1735

Cuscuta ((Tourn.)) L. 1735

Cyamopsis DC. 1825

Cyclamen ((Tourn.)) L. 1735

Cyclanthera Schrad. 1831

Cycloloma Moq. 1840

Cydonia Tourn. ex Mill. 1752

Cymbalaria Medic. 1791

Cymbidium Sw. 1799

Cymbopogon Spreng. 1815

Cynara Vaill. ex L. 1737

Cynodon Rich. 1805

Cynoglossum ((Tourn.)) L. 1735

Cynosurus L. 1737

Cyperus ((Mich.)) L. 1735

Cyphomandra Mart. ex Sendtn. 1845

Cypripedium L. 1735

Cytisus L. 1735

Dactylis L. 1742

Dactyloctenium Willd. 1809

Dahlia Cav. 1791

Dalbergia L. f. 1781

Daphne Tourn. ex L. 1735

Datura L. 1735

Daucus ((Tourn.)) L. 1735

Delphinium Tourn. ex L. 1735

Dendrobium Sw. 1799

Dendropogon Rafin. 1825

Deschampsia Beauv. 1812

Desmodium Desv. 1813

Desplatzia Bocquill. 1866-67

Dianthus L. 1735

Dichrostachys Wight & Arn. 1834

Didiscus DC. 1828

Digitalis ((Tourn.)) L. 1735

Digitaria Heist. ex Adans. 1763

Dimorphotheca Vaill. ex L. 1735

Dioscorea Plum ex L. 1737

Diplacus Nutt. 1838

Diplotaxis DC. 1821

Dipsacus L. 1735

Dithyrea Harv. 1845

Dodonaea L. 1737

Dolichos L. 1737

Dombeya Cav. 1787

Doronicum Tourn. ex L. 1735

Dracaena Vand. 1762

Duchesnea Smith 1811

Ecballium A. Rich. 1824

Echinacea Moench 1794

Echinochloa Beauv. 1812

Echinocystis Torr. & Gray 1840

Echinops L. 1737

Echium Tourn. ex L. 1737

Eclipta L. 1771

Elaeis Jacq. 1763

Elaeophorbia Stapf 1906

Elettaria Maton 1811

Eleusine Gaertn. 1788

Elymus L. 1748

Emilia Cass. 1817

Emmenanthe Benth. 1835

Ensete Bruce 1862

Epidendrum L. 1737

Epilobium Dill. ex L. 1735

Equisetum ((Tourn.)) L. 1753

Eragrostis Host 1809

Eremocarpus Benth. 1844

Erigeron L. 1737

Eriobotrya Lindl. 1822

Eriochloa H. B. & K. 1815

Eriogonum Michx. 1803

Erodium L'Herit. 1787

Eryngium ((Tourn.)) L. 1735

Erysimum ((Tourn.)) L. 1735

Erythronium L. 1735

Erythropsis Endl. *

Escallonia Mutis, ex L. f. 1781

Eschscholtzia Cham. 1820

(Eschscholzia) Cham. 1820

Euchlaena Schrad. 1832

Eucomis L'Herit. 1788

Eugenia Mich. ex L. 1735

Euonymus L. 1737

Eupatorium ((Tourn.)) L. 1735

Euphorbia L. 1737

Evodia Forst. 1776

Fagopyrum Tourn. ex Hall. 1742

Feijoa Berg 1858

Ferula Tourn. ex L. 1737

Festuca ((Tourn.)) L. 1735

Ficus Tourn. ex L. 1735

Foeniculum Tourn. ex L. 1735

Forsythia Vahl 1805

Fortunella Swingle 1915

Fragaria ((Tourn.)) L. 1735

Frankenia L. 1737

Franseria Cav. 1793

Fraxinus Tourn. ex L. 1735

Freesia Klatt 1865-66

Fritillaria ((Tourn.)) L. 1735

Fuchsia ((Plum.)) L. 1735

Fumaria Tourn. ex L. 1735

Funtumia Stapf 1901

Gaillardia Fouger. 1788

Galeopsis L. 1735

Galinsoga Ruiz & Pav. 1794

Galium L. 1737

Galtonia Decne. 1880

Gamolepis Less. 1832

Gastridium Beauv. 1812

Gaura L. 1751

Gazania Gaertn. 1791

Geranium ((Tourn.)) L. 1735

Gerardia L. 1737

Gerbera Bronov. 1737

Gesneria L. 1737

Geum L. 1735

Gilia Ruiz & Pav. 1794

Gladiolus ((Tourn.)) L. 1735

Gleditsia L. 1742

Gloriosa L. 1735

Gloxinia L'Herit. 1785

Glycine L. 1737

Glyphaea Hook. f. 1848

Gnaphalium L. 1737

Godetia Spach 1835

Gomphrena L. 1737

Gossypium L. 1735

Grewia L. 1735

Grindelia Willd. 1807

Guazuma Plum. ex Adans. 1763

Gutierrezia Lag. 1816

Gycosmis Correa 1805

Gynerium Humb. & Bonpl. 1809

Gypsophila L. 1751

Haplopappus Endl. 1838

Harpullia Roxb. 1814

Haworthia Duval 1809

Haynaldia Kanitz 1877

Hedeoma Pers. 1807

Hedera Tourn. ex L. 1737

Hedychium Koen. 1783

Hedysarum ((Tourn.)) L. 1735

Helenium L. 1753

Helianthus L. 1735

Helichrysum Vaill. ex L. 1737

Heliocarpus L. 1740

Heliophila Burm f. ex L. 1763

Heliopsis Pers. 1807

Heliotropium ((Tourn.)) L. 1735

Helipterum DC. 1837

Hemerocallis L. 1735

Hemizonia DC. 1836

Heracleum L. 1735

Hermannia L. 1735

Herrania Goudot 1844

Hesperis L. 1735

Hevea Aubl. 1775

Hibiscus L. 1737

Hicoria (See Carya) Rafin. 1838

Hieracium ((Tourn.)) L. 1735

Hildegardia Schott & Endl. 1832

Hippeastrum (See Amaryllis) Herb. 1821

Holcus L. 1735

Holodiscus Maxim. 1879

Hordeum ((Tourn.)) L. 1735

Hosta Tratt. 1812

Hoya R. Br. 1809

Humulus L. 1735

Hunnemannia Sweet 1828

Hyacinthus ((Tourn.)) L. 1735

Hydrangea Gronov. ex L. 1737

Hymenocallis Salisb. 1812

Hyoscyamus ((Tourn.)) L. 1735

Hypericum Tourn. ex L. 1737

Hypochoeris L. 1737

Hypoxis L. 1759

Iberis Dill. ex L. 1735

Ilysanthes Rafin. 1820

Impatiens Riv. ex L. 1735

Incarvillea Juss. 1789

Indigofera L. 1737

Iodanthus Torr. & Gray 1838

Ionoxalis Small 1903

Ipomoea L. 1735

Iris Tourn. ex L. 1735

Isatis Tourn. ex L. 1735

Ischaemum L. 1742

Isomeris Nutt. ex Torr. & Gray 1838

Isotoma Lindl. 1826

Ixia L. 1737

Jatropha L. 1735

Juglans L. 1737

Jussiaea L. 1747

Kalanchoe Adans. 1763

Kerria DC. 1817

Kickxia Blume 1828

Kleinhovia L. 1763

Kniphofia Moench 1794

Kochia Roth 1801

Koeleria Pers. 1805

Laburnum L. 1735

Lactuca ((Tourn.)) L. 1735

Laelia Lindl. 1831

Laeliocattleya X, Rolfe 1887

Lagenaria Ser. 1825

Lamium ((Tourn.)) L. 1735

Lantana L. 1737

Lapsana L. 1737

Lathyrus ((Tourn.)) L. 1735

Launea Endl. 1841

Lavandula Tourn. ex L. 1740

Lavatera L. 1737

Layia Hook. & Arn. 1833

Lens ((Tourn.)) L. 1735

Leonotis R. Br. in Ait. 1811

Leonurus L. 1735

Lepidium L. 1735

Lepidospartum A. Gray 1883

Leptochloa Beauv. 1812

Leptonychia Turcz. 1858

Leptosyne DC. 1836

Lespedeza Michx. 1803

Lessingia Cham. 1829

Liatris Schreb. 1791

Ligularia Cass. 1816

Ligusticum L. 1737

Ligustrum ((Tourn.)) L. 1735

Lilium Tourn. ex L. 1737

Limonium Tourn. ex Mill. 1752

Linaria Tourn. ex Mill. 1752

Linum Tourn. ex L. 1735

Lobelia Plum. ex L. 1737

Lobularia Desv. 1814

Lolium L. 1735

Lonicera L. 1737

Lotononis Eckl. & Zeyh. 1836

Lotus ((Tourn.)) L. 1735

Luffa ((Tourn.)) L. 1735

Lunaria Tourn. ex L. 1735

Lupinus ((Tourn.)) L. 1735

Lychnis ((Tourn.)) L. 1735

Lycium L. 1735

Lycopersicon Tourn. ex Rupp. 1745

(Lycopersicum) Hill. 1765

Lycopsis L. 1735

Lycopus Tourn. ex L. 1735

Lythrum L. 1735

Madia Molina 1782

Majorana ((Tourn.)) Rupp. 1745

Malachra L. 1767

Malcomia ((R. Br. in)) Ait. Hort. Kew. 1812

(Malcolmia) Spreng. 1818

Malope L. 1735

Malus Tourn. ex L. 1737

Malva ((Tourn.)) L. 1735

Malvastrum A. Gray 1849

Manihot Tourn. ex Adans. 1763

Mansonia J.R. Drumm. 1905

Maranta Plum. ex L. 1737

Marrubium Tourn. ex L. 1735

Martynia Houst. ex L. 1735

Matricaria ((Tourn.)) L. 1735

Matthiola R. Br. 1812

Medeola Gronov. ex L. 1735

Medicago Tourn. ex L. 1737

Melandryum Reichb. 1837

Melilotus Tourn. ex Hall. 1742

Melissa Tourn. ex L. 1737

Melochia Dill. ex L. 1735

Melothria L. 1737

Mentha ((Tourn.)) L. 1735

Mentzelia Plum. ex L. 1737

Merremia Dennst. 1818

Mertensia Roth 1797

Mesembryanthemum Dill. ex L. 1735

Micrampelis (See Echinocystis) Rafin. 1808

Microseris D. Don 1832

Millettia Wight & Arn. 1834

Mimulus L. 1741

Mirabilis Riv. ex L. 1735

Miscanthus Anderss. 1855

Modiola Moench 1794

Mollugo L. 1737

Momordica ((Tourn.)) L. 1735

Monolepis Schrad. 1830

Moraea Mill. ex L. 1762

Mucuna Adans. 1763

Muhlenbergia Schreb. 1789

Murraya Koen. ex L. 1771

Musa L. 1736

Muscari Tourn. ex Mill. 1752

Myosotis ((Tourn.)) Dill. ex L. 1735

Myrica L. 1735

Narcissus ((Tourn.)) L. 1735

Nasturtium L. 1735

Nemesia Vent. 1803

Nemophila Nutt. ex Barton 1882

Neomarica Sprague 1928

Nepeta Riv. ex L. 1737

Nerium L. 1735

Neslia Desv. 1814

Nesogordonia Baill. 1886

Nicandra Adans. 1763

Nicotiana L. 1735

Nierembergia Ruiz & Pav. 1794

Nigella ((Tourn.)) L. 1735

Nitrophila S. Wats. 1871

Nolana L. 1762

Nothopanax Miq., Seem. 1866

Ochroma Sw. 1788

Ocimum L. 1737

Octolobus Welw. 1869

Odontoglossum H. B. & K. 1815

Oenanthe ((Tourn.)) L. 1735

Oenothera L. 1735

Omphalocarpum Beauv. 1805

Oncidium Sw. 1800

Onobrychis L. 1735

Ophiopogon Ker-Gawl. 1807

Orchis ((Tourn.)) L. 1735

Ornithogalum ((Tourn.)) L. 1735

Oryza L. 1735

Oryzopsis Michx. 1803

Oxalis L. 1737

Pachira Aubl. 1775

Pachyrhizus Rich. ex DC. 1825

Paeonia ((Tourn.)) L. 1735

Pamburus Swingle 1916

Pancratium Dill. ex L. 1735

Panicum L. 1735

Papaver Tourn. ex L. 1735

Parthenium L. 1735

Parthenocissus Planch. in DC. 1887

Paspalum L. 1759

Passiflora L. 1735

Pastinaca L. 1737

Pectocarya DC. ex Meissn. 1840

Pedilanthus Neck. 1790

Pelargonium L'Herit. 1787

Pennisetum Rich. 1805

Penstemon Mitch. 1748

(Pentstemon) Mitch. 1748

Peperomia Ruiz & Pav. 1794

Pepo (See Cucurbita) ((Tourn.)) L. 1735

Persea Plum. ex L. 1737

Persicaria ((Tourn.)) L. 1735

Petroselinum Hoffm. 1814

Petunia Juss. 1803

Phacelia Juss. 1789

Phalaris L. 1735

Pharbitis Choisy 1833

Phaseolus ((Tourn.)) L. 1735

Phenax Wedd. 1854

Philadelphus ((Riv.)) L. 1735

Philodendron Schott 1829

Phleum L. 1735

Phlox L. 1737

Phormium Forst. 1776

Photinia Lindl. 1821

Phyllanthus L. 1737

Phyllostachys Sieb. & Zucc. 1843

Physalis L. 1735

Physostegia Benth. 1829

Phytolacca Tourn. ex L. 1735

Piaropus Rafin. 1836

Picris L. 1735

Pimpinella ((Riv.)) L. 1735

Pisum ((Tourn.)) L. 1735

Pittosporum Banks, ex Gaertn. 1788

Plantago Tourn. L. 1735

Platycodon A. DC. 1830

Pluchea Cass. 1817

Poa L. 1737

Polanisia Rafin. 1818

Polemonium ((Tourn.)) L. 1735

Polyanthus Auct. ex Benth. & Hook. 1883

Polygonatum ((Tourn.)) Adans. 1763

Polygonum ((Tourn.)) L. 1735

Polypodium ((Tourn.)) L. 1753

Polypogon Desf. 1798

Pontederia L. 1735

Populus L. 1735

Portulaca L. 1735

Potentilla L. 1735

Primula L. 1735

Proboscidea Schmid. 1747

Prunella L. 1753

Prunus ((Tourn.)) L. 1735

Pseudotsuga Carr. 1867

Psidium L. 1737

Psophocarpus Neck. 1790

Psoralea L. 1742

Ptelea L. 1735

Pterygota Schott & Endl. 1832

Pueraria DC. 1825

Punica ((Tourn.)) L. 1735

Pycnanthus Warb. 1895

Pyracantha M. Roem. 1847

Pyrethrum Hall. 1742

Pyrus ((Tourn.)) L. 1735

Quamoclit Tourn. ex Moench 1794

Radicula Dill. ex Moench 1794

Ranunculus ((Tourn.)) L. 1735

Raphanus ((Tourn.)) L. 1735

Reseda Tourn. ex L. 1735

Rhagodia R. Br. 1810

Rheum L. 1735

Rhoeo Hance 1853

Rhus ((Tourn.)) L. 1737

Rhynchosia Lour. 1790

(Rynchosia) MacFad. 1837

Ribes L. 1737

Ricinodendron Muell. 1864-1865

Ricinus ((Tourn.)) L. 1735

Rivinia Plum. ex L. 1735

Robinia L. 1737

Rorippa Scop. 1760

(Roripa) Scop. 1760

Rosa Tourn. ex L. 1735

Rosmarinus ((Tourn.)) L. 1735

Rottbeollia L. f. 1779

Rubus ((Tourn.)) L. 1735

Rudbeckia L. 1735

Ruellia . Plum. ex L. 1735

Rumex L. 1735

Ruta ((Tourn.)) L. 1735

Saccharum L. 1737

Sagittaria Rupp. ex L. 1735

Saintpaulia H. Wendl. 1893

Salix ((Tourn.)) L. 1735

Salpiglossis Ruiz & Pav. 1794

Salsola L. 1735

Salvia ((Tourn.)) L. 1735

Sambucus Tourn. ex L. 1735

Samolus ((Tourn.)) L. 1735

Sanguisorba Rupp. ex L. 1735

Sanicula ((Tourn.)) L. 1735
Sansevieria Thunb. 1794
Santalum L. 1742
Sanvitalia Gualt. in Lam. 1792
Saponaria L. 1735
Saracha Ruiz & Pav. 1794
Satureia L. 1737
Scabiosa ((Tourn.)) L. 1735
Scaevola L. 1771
Scaphopetalum Mast. 1869
Schizanthus Ruiz & Pav. 1794
Scilla L. 1735
Scoparia L. 1748
Scorzonera ((Tourn.)) L. 1735
Scrophularia Tourn. ex L. 1735
Scytopetalum Pierre 1897
Secale ((Tourn.)) L. 1735
Sechium P. Br. 1756
Sedum Tourn. ex L. 1735
Senecio ((Tourn.)) L. 1735
Sesamum L. 1737
Sesbania Scop. 1777
Setaria Beauv. 1807
Severinia Tenore 1840
Sicana Naud. 1862
Sicyos L. 1735
Sida L. 1735
Silene L. 1735
Silybum Vaill. ex Adans. 1763
Sinapis (See Brassica) L. 1735
Sinningia Nees 1825
Sisymbrium ((Tourn.)) L. 1735
Sitanion Rafin. 1819
Smilacina Desf. 1807
Smilax ((Tourn.)) L. 1735
Soja (See Glycine) Moench 1794
(Soya) Benth. 1838
Solanum ((Tourn.)) L. 1735
Solidago ((Vaill.)) L. 1735
Sonchus ((Tourn.)) L. 1735
Sorbus ((Tourn.)) L. 1735
Sorghastrum Nash 1901
Sorghum L. 1735
Sparaxis Ker-Gawl. 1804
Spathoglottis Blume 1825
Spergula L. 1735
Spinacia ((Tourn.)) L. 1735
Sprekelia Heist. 1748
Stachys ((Tourn.)) L. 1735
Stachytarpheta Vahl 1805
Stanleya Nutt. 1818
Statice Tourn. ex L. 1735
Stellaria L. 1753
Stenotaphrum Trin. 1820
Sterculia L. 1747
Stipa L. 1753

Stizolobium (See Mucuna) P. Br. 1756
Stokesia L'Herit. 1788
Streptanthera Sweet 1827
Streptosolen Miers 1850
Strychnos L. 1735
Stylosanthes Sw. 1788
Suaeda Forsk. 1775
Swainsona Salisb. 1805
Swinglea Merrill 1927
Symphoricarpos Dill. ex Juss. 1789
Symplocarpus Salisb. ex Nutt. 1818
Synedrella Gaertn. 1791
Syntherisma Walt. 1788
Syringa L. 1735
Tabebuia Gomez 1803
Tacsonia Juss. 1789
Tagetes L. 1737
Talinum Adans. 1763
Tanacetum Tourn. ex L. 1735
Taraxacum L. 1735
Tarrietia Blume 1825
Tephrosia Pers. 1807
Tetragonia L. 1735
Thea L. 1735
Thelesperma Less. 1831
Thelypodium Endl. 1839
Theobroma L. 1737
Thespesia Soland. ex Correa 1807
Thlaspi ((Tourn.)) L. 1737
Thunbergia Retz. 1776
Tigridia Juss. 1789
Tilia ((Tourn.)) L. 1735
Tillandsia L. 1735
Tithonia Desf. ex Juss. 1789
Torenia L. 1751
Trachelium Tourn. ex L. 1735
Trachymene Rudge 1811
Tradescantia Rupp. ex L. 1735
Tragopogon ((Tourn.)) L. 1735
Trema Lour. 1790
Trianthema L. 1753
Tribulus Tourn. ex L. 1735
Tricholaena Schrad. 1824
Trichosanthes L. 1737
Tricyrtis Wall. 1826
Trifolium ((Tourn.)) L. 1735
Trigonella L. 1737
Trillium L. 1753
Triphasia Lour. 1790
Triplochiton K. Schum. *
Tripsacum L. 1759
Triticum L. 1735
Tritonia Ker-Gawl. 1802
Triumfetta Plum, ex L. 1737
Tropaeolum L. 1737
Tulipa L. 1735

Tunica Hall. 1742

Tussilago ((Tourn.)) L. 1735

Typha L. 1735

Ulmus ((Tourn.)) L. 1735

Urena Dill. ex L. 1735

Urochloa Beauv. 1812

Urtica ((Tourn.)) L. 1735

Uvularia L. 1737

Vaccinium L. 1735

Valeriana Tourn. ex L. 1735

Valerianella Tourn. ex Hall. 1742

Valerianoides Medic. 1789

Vallota Herb. 1821

Vanda Jones 1795

Venidium Less. 1831

Verbascum Tourn. ex L. 1737

Verbena L. 1737

Verbesina L. 1735

Vernonia Schreb. 1791

Veronica ((Tourn.)) L. 1735

Vicia Tourn. ex L. 1735

Vigna Savi 1826 ?

Vinca L. 1735

Viola Tourn. ex L. 1735

Vitis ((Tourn.)) L. 1735

Waltheria L. 1737

Watsonia Mill. 1759

Wistaria Nutt. 1818

(Wisteria) Nutt. 1818

Withania Pauq. 1824

Xanthium ((Tourn.)) L. 1735

Xanthosoma Schott 1832

Xanthoxalis Small 1903

Xeranthemum Tourn. ex L. 1735

Yucca Dill. ex L. 1737

Zaluzianskya F.W. Schmidt 1793

Zantedeschia Spreng. 1826

Zea L. 1737

Zebrina Schnizl. 1849

Zephyranthes Herb. 1821

Zinnia L. 1759

Zizyphus Tourn. ex L. 1735

Zygadenus Michx. 1803

Zygocactus K. Schum. *

Zygopetalum Hook. 1827